Applied Calculus

Sixth Edition

HUGHES-HALLETT

NORTHEASTERN UNIVERSITY

Applied Calculus
MATH 1241

Wiley Custom Learning Solutions

CONTENTS

1   A Library of Functions   1

2   Key Concept: The Derivative   75

3   Short-Cuts to Differentiation   123

4   Using the Derivative   185

5   Key Concept: The Definite Integral   271

6   Constructing Antiderivatives   319

7   Integration   353

11   Differential Equations   585

Appendices   665

Ready Reference   691

Answers to Odd-Numbered Problems   697

Index   743

From *Functions Modeling Change: A Preparation for Calculus*, by Eric Connally et al

Appendices   491

Appendix Answers   538

CALCULUS

Sixth Edition

We dedicate this book to Andrew M. Gleason.

His brilliance and the extraordinary kindness and dignity with which he treated others made an enormous difference to us, and to many, many people. Andy brought out the best in everyone.

Deb Hughes Hallett
for the Calculus Consortium

CALCULUS

Sixth Edition

Produced by the Calculus Consortium and initially funded by a National Science Foundation Grant.

Deborah Hughes-Hallett
University of Arizona

William G. McCallum
University of Arizona

Andrew M. Gleason
Harvard University

Eric Connally
Harvard University Extension

David O. Lomen
University of Arizona

Douglas Quinney
University of Keele

Daniel E. Flath
Macalester College

David Lovelock
University of Arizona

Karen Rhea
University of Michigan

Selin Kalaycıoğlu
New York University

Guadalupe I. Lozano
University of Arizona

Adam H. Spiegler
Loyola University Chicago

Brigitte Lahme
Sonoma State University

Brad G. Osgood
Stanford University

Jeff Tecosky-Feldman
Haverford College

Patti Frazer Lock
St. Lawrence University

Cody L. Patterson
University of Arizona

Thomas W. Tucker
Colgate University

with the assistance of

Otto K. Bretscher
Colby College

David E. Sloane, MD
Harvard Medical School

Coordinated by
Elliot J. Marks

ACQUISITIONS EDITOR	Shannon Corliss
PUBLISHER	Laurie Rosatone
SENIOR EDITORIAL ASSISTANT	Jacqueline Sinacori
DEVELOPMENTAL EDITOR	Anne Scanlan-Rohrer/Two Ravens Editorial
MARKETING MANAGER	Melanie Kurkjian
SENIOR PRODUCT DESIGNER	Tom Kulesa
OPERATIONS MANAGER	Melissa Edwards
ASSOCIATE CONTENT EDITOR	Beth Pearson
SENIOR PRODUCTION EDITOR	Ken Santor
COVER DESIGNER	Madelyn Lesure
COVER AND CHAPTER OPENING PHOTO	©Patrick Zephyr/Patrick Zephyr Nature Photography

Problems from Calculus: The Analysis of Functions, by Peter D. Taylor (Toronto: Wall & Emerson, Inc., 1992). Reprinted with permission of the publisher.

This book was set in Times Roman by the Consortium using TEX, Mathematica, and the package ASTEX, which was written by Alex Kasman. It was printed and bound by R.R. Donnelley / Jefferson City. The cover was printed by R.R. Donnelley.

This book is printed on acid-free paper.

Founded in 1807, John Wiley & Sons, Inc. has been a valued source of knowledge and understanding for more than 200 years, helping people around the world meet their needs and fulfill their aspirations. Our company is built on a foundation of principles that include responsibility to the communities we serve and where we live and work. In 2008, we launched a Corporate Citizenship Initiative, a global effort to address the environmental, social, economic, and ethical challenges we face in our business. Among the issues we are addressing are carbon impact, paper specifications and procurement, ethical conduct within our business and among our vendors, and community and charitable support. For more information, please visit our website: www.wiley.com/go/citizenship.

This material is based upon work supported by the National Science Foundation under Grant No. DUE-9352905. Opinions expressed are those of the authors and not necessarily those of the Foundation.

ISBN-13 cloth 978-0470-88853-7
ISBN-13 paper 978-0470-88864-3
ISBN-13 binder-ready 978-1118-23377-1

Printed in the United States of America

PREFACE

Calculus is one of the greatest achievements of the human intellect. Inspired by problems in astronomy, Newton and Leibniz developed the ideas of calculus 300 years ago. Since then, each century has demonstrated the power of calculus to illuminate questions in mathematics, the physical sciences, engineering, and the social and biological sciences.

Calculus has been so successful both because its central theme—change—is pivotal to an analysis of the natural world and because of its extraordinary power to reduce complicated problems to simple procedures. Therein lies the danger in teaching calculus: it is possible to teach the subject as nothing but procedures—thereby losing sight of both the mathematics and of its practical value. This edition of *Calculus* continues our effort to promote courses in which understanding and computation reinforce each other.

Mathematical Thinking Supported by Theory and Modeling

The first stage in the development of mathematical thinking is the acquisition of a clear intuitive picture of the central ideas. In the next stage, the student learns to reason with the intuitive ideas in plain English. After this foundation has been laid, there is a choice of direction. All students benefit from both theory and modeling, but the balance may differ for different groups. Some students, such as mathematics majors, may prefer more theory, while others may prefer more modeling. For instructors wishing to emphasize the connection between calculus and other fields, the text includes:

- A variety of problems from the **physical sciences** and **engineering**.
- Examples from the **biological sciences** and **economics**.
- Models from the **health sciences** and of **population growth**.
- New problems on **sustainability**.
- New case studies on **medicine** by David E. Sloane, MD.

Origin of the Text

From the beginning, this textbook grew out of a community of mathematics instructors eager to find effective ways for students to learn calculus. This Sixth Edition of *Calculus* reflects the many voices of users at research universities, four-year colleges, community colleges, and secondary schools. Their input and that of our partner disciplines, engineering and the natural and social sciences, continue to shape our work.

Active Learning: Good Problems

As instructors ourselves, we know that interactive classrooms and well-crafted problems promote student learning. Since its inception, the hallmark of our text has been its innovative and engaging problems. These problems probe student understanding in ways often taken for granted. Praised for their creativity and variety, the influence of these problems has extended far beyond the users of our textbook.

The Sixth Edition continues this tradition. Under our approach, which we called the "Rule of Four," ideas are presented graphically, numerically, symbolically, and verbally, thereby encouraging students with a variety of learning styles to expand their knowledge. This edition expands the types of problems available:

- New **Strengthen Your Understanding** problems at the end of every section. These problems ask students to reflect on what they have learned by deciding "What is wrong?" with a statement and to "Give an example" of an idea.
- **ConcepTests** promote active learning in the classroom. These can be used with or without clickers (personal response systems), and have been shown to dramatically improve student learning. Available in a book or on the web at www.wiley.com/college/hughes-hallett.

- **Class Worksheets** allow instructors to engage students in individual or group class-work. Samples are available in the Instructor's Manual, and all are on the web at www.wiley.com/college/hughes-hallett.

- Updated **Data and Models**. For example, Section 11.7 follows the current debate on *Peak Oil Production*, underscoring the importance of mathematics in understanding the world's economic and social problems.

- **Projects** at the end of each chapter provide opportunities for a sustained investigation, often using skills from different parts of the course.

- **Drill Exercises** build student skill and confidence.

- **Online Problems** available in WileyPLUS or WeBWorK, for example. Many problems are randomized, providing students with expanded opportunities for practice with immediate feedback.

Symbolic Manipulation and Technology

To use calculus effectively, students need skill in both symbolic manipulation and the use of technology. The balance between the two may vary, depending on the needs of the students and the wishes of the instructor. The book is adaptable to many different combinations.

The book does not require any specific software or technology. It has been used with graphing calculators, graphing software, and computer algebra systems. Any technology with the ability to graph functions and perform numerical integration will suffice. Students are expected to use their own judgment to determine where technology is useful.

Content

This content represents our vision of how calculus can be taught. It is flexible enough to accommodate individual course needs and requirements. Topics can easily be added or deleted, or the order changed.

Changes to the text in the Sixth Edition are in italics. In all chapters, many new problems were added and others were updated.

Chapter 1: A Library of Functions

This chapter introduces all the elementary functions to be used in the book. Although the functions are probably familiar, the graphical, numerical, verbal, and modeling approach to them may be new. We introduce exponential functions at the earliest possible stage, since they are fundamental to the understanding of real-world processes. The chapter concludes with a section on limits, allowing for a discussion of continuity at a point and on an interval. The section on limits is flexible enough to allow for a brief introduction before derivatives or for a more extensive treatment.

Chapter 2: Key Concept: The Derivative

The purpose of this chapter is to give the student a practical understanding of the definition of the derivative and its interpretation as an instantaneous rate of change. The power rule is introduced; other rules are introduced in Chapter 3.

Chapter 3: Short-Cuts to Differentiation

The derivatives of all the functions in Chapter 1 are introduced, as well as the rules for differentiating products; quotients; and composite, inverse, hyperbolic, and implicitly defined functions.

Chapter 4: Using the Derivative

The aim of this chapter is to enable the student to use the derivative in solving problems, including optimization, graphing, rates, parametric equations, and indeterminate forms. It is not necessary to cover all the sections in this chapter.

To increase access to optimization, many sections of this chapter have been streamlined. Optimization and Modeling are now in Section 4.3, followed by Families of Functions and Modeling in Section 4.4. Upper and lower bounds have been moved to Section 4.2, and geometric optimization is now combined with Optimization and Modeling. Section 4.8 on Parametric Equations is linked to Appendix D, allowing discussion of velocity as a vector.

Chapter 5: Key Concept: The Definite Integral

The purpose of this chapter is to give the student a practical understanding of the definite integral as a limit of Riemann sums and to bring out the connection between the derivative and the definite integral in the Fundamental Theorem of Calculus.

Section 5.3 now includes the application of the Fundamental Theorem of Calculus to the computation of definite integrals. The use of integrals to find averages is now in Section 5.4.

Chapter 6: Constructing Antiderivatives

This chapter focuses on going backward from a derivative to the original function, first graphically and numerically, then analytically. It introduces the Second Fundamental Theorem of Calculus and the concept of a differential equation.

Section 6.3 on Differential Equations and Motion contains the material from the former Section 6.5.

Chapter 7: Integration

This chapter includes several techniques of integration, including substitution, parts, partial fractions, and trigonometric substitutions; others are included in the table of integrals. There are discussions of numerical methods and of improper integrals.

Section 7.4 now includes the use of triangles to help students visualize a trigonometric substitution. The two former sections on numerical methods have been combined into Section 7.5.

Chapter 8: Using the Definite Integral

This chapter emphasizes the idea of subdividing a quantity to produce Riemann sums which, in the limit, yield a definite integral. It shows how the integral is used in geometry, physics, economics, and probability; polar coordinates are introduced. It is not necessary to cover all the sections in this chapter.

Chapter 9: Sequences and Series

This chapter focuses on sequences, series of constants, and convergence. It includes the integral, ratio, comparison, limit comparison, and alternating series tests. It also introduces geometric series and general power series, including their intervals of convergence.

Chapter 10: Approximating Functions

This chapter introduces Taylor Series and Fourier Series using the idea of approximating functions by simpler functions.

Chapter 11: Differential Equations

This chapter introduces differential equations. The emphasis is on qualitative solutions, modeling, and interpretation.

Section 11.7 on Logistic Models (formerly on population models) has been rewritten around the thought-provoking predictions of peak oil production. This section encourages students to use the skills learned earlier in the course to analyze a problem of global importance. Sections 11.10 and 11.11 on Second Order Differential Equations are now on the web at www.wiley.com/college/hughes-hallett.

Appendices

There are appendices on roots, accuracy, and bounds; complex numbers; Newton's method; and vectors in the plane. The appendix on vectors can be covered at any time, but may be particularly useful in the conjunction with Section 4.8 on parametric equations.

Choice of Paths: Lean or Expanded

For those who prefer the lean topic list of earlier editions, we have kept clear the main conceptual paths. For example,

- The Key Concept chapters on the derivative and the definite integral (Chapters 2 and 5) can be covered at the outset of the course, right after Chapter 1.
- Limits and Continuity (Sections 1.7 and 1.8) can be covered in depth before the introduction of the derivative (Sections 2.1 and 2.2), or after.
- Approximating Functions Using Series (Chapter 10) can be covered before, or without, Chapter 9.
- In Chapter 4 (Using the Derivative), instructors can select freely from Sections 4.3–4.8.
- Chapter 8 (Using the Definite Integral) contains a wide range of applications. Instructors can select one or two to do in detail.

Supplementary Materials and Additional Resources

Supplements for the instructor can be obtained online at the book companion site or by contacting your Wiley representative. The following supplementary materials are available for this edition:

- **Instructor's Manual** containing teaching tips, calculator programs, overhead transparency masters, sample worksheets, and sample syllabi.
- **Computerized Test Bank**, comprised of nearly 7,000 questions, mostly algorithmically-generated, which allows for multiple versions of a single test or quiz.
- **Instructor's Solution Manual** with complete solutions to all problems.
- **Student Solution Manual** with complete solutions to half the odd-numbered problems.
- **Additional Material**, elaborating specially marked points in the text and password-protected electronic versions of the instructor ancillaries, can be found on the web at www.wiley.com/college/hughes-hallett.

ConcepTests

ConcepTests, modeled on the pioneering work of Harvard physicist Eric Mazur, are questions designed to promote active learning during class, particularly (but not exclusively) in large lectures. Our evaluation data show students taught with ConcepTests outperformed students taught by traditional lecture methods 73% versus 17% on conceptual questions, and 63% versus 54% on computational problems.

Faculty Resource Network

A peer-to-peer network of academic faculty dedicated to the effective use of technology in the classroom, this group can help you apply innovative classroom techniques and implement specific software packages. Visit www.facultyresourcenetwork.com or speak to your Wiley representative.

WileyPLUS

WileyPLUS, Wiley's digital learning environment, is loaded with all of the supplements above, and also features:

- Online version of the text, featuring hyperlinks to referenced content, applets, and supplements.
- Homework management tools, which enable the instructor to assign questions easily and grade them automatically, using a rich set of options and controls.
- QuickStart pre-designed reading and homework assignments. Use them as-is or customize them to fit the needs of your classroom.
- Guided Online (GO) Exercises, which prompt students to build solutions step by step. Rather than simply grading an exercise answer as wrong, GO problems show students precisely where they are making a mistake.

- Animated applets, which can be used in class to present and explore key ideas graphically and dynamically—especially useful for display of three-dimensional graphs in multivariable calculus.

- Algebra & Trigonometry Refresher material, which provide students with an opportunity to brush up on material necessary to master Calculus, as well as to determine areas that require further review.

- Graphing Calculator Manual, to help students get the most out of their graphing calculators, and to show how they can apply the numerical and graphing functions of their calculators to their study of calculus.

AP Teacher's Guide

The AP Guide, written by experienced AP teachers, provides day-by-day syllabi for AB and BC Calculus, sample multiple choice questions, a listing of the past 25 years of AP free-response questions by chapter of the text, teaching tips, and labs to encourage student exploration of concepts.

Acknowledgements

First and foremost, we want to express our appreciation to the National Science Foundation for their faith in our ability to produce a revitalized calculus curriculum and, in particular, to our program officers, Louise Raphael, John Kenelly, John Bradley, and James Lightbourne. We also want to thank the members of our Advisory Board, Benita Albert, Lida Barrett, Simon Bernau, Robert Davis, M. Lavinia DeConge-Watson, John Dossey, Ron Douglas, Eli Fromm, William Haver, Seymour Parter, John Prados, and Stephen Rodi.

In addition, a host of other people around the country and abroad deserve our thanks for their contributions to shaping this edition. They include: Huriye Arikan, Ruth Baruth, Paul Blanchard, Lewis Blake, David Bressoud, Stephen Boyd, Lucille Buonocore, Jo Cannon, Ray Cannon, Phil Cheifetz, Scott Clark, Jailing Dai, Ann Davidian, Tom Dick, Srdjan Divac, Tevian Dray, Steven Dunbar, David Durlach, John Eggers, Wade Ellis, Johann Engelbrecht, Brad Ernst, Sunny Fawcett, Paul Feehan, Sol Friedberg, Melanie Fulton, Tom Gearhart, David Glickenstein, Chris Goff, Sheldon P. Gordon, Salim Haïdar, Elizabeth Hentges, Rob Indik, Adrian Iovita, David Jackson, Sue Jensen, Alex Kasman, Matthias Kawski, Mike Klucznik, Donna Krawczyk, Stephane Lafortune, Andrew Lawrence, Carl Leinert, Andrew Looms, Bin Lu, Alex Mallozzi, Corinne Manogue, Jay Martin, Eric Mazur, Abby McCallum, Dan McGee, Ansie Meiring, Lang Moore, Jerry Morris, Hideo Nagahashi, Kartikeya Nagendra, Alan Newell, Steve Olson, John Orr, Arnie Ostebee, Andrew Pasquale, Wayne Raskind, Maria Robinson, Laurie Rosatone, Ayse Sahin, Nataliya Sandler, Ken Santor, Anne Scanlan-Rohrer, Ellen Schmierer, Michael Sherman, Pat Shure, Scott Pilzer, David Smith, Ernie Solheid, Misha Stepanov, Steve Strogatz, Peter Taylor, Dinesh Thakur, Sally Thomas, Joe Thrash, Alan Tucker, Doug Ulmer, Ignatios Vakalis, Bill Vélez, Joe Vignolini, Stan Wagon, Hannah Winkler, Debra Wood, Aaron Wootton, Deane Yang, Bruce Yoshiwara, Kathy Yoshiwara, and Paul Zorn.

Reports from the following reviewers were most helpful for the fifth edition:

Lewis Blake, Patrice Conrath, Christopher Ennis, John Eggers, Paul DeLand, Dana Fine, Dave Folk, Elizabeth Hodes, Richard Jenson, Emelie Kenney, Michael Kinter, Douglas Lapp, Glenn Ledder, Eric Marland, Cindy Moss, Michael Naylor, Genevra Neumann, Dennis Piontkowski, Robert Reed, Laurence Small, Ed Soares, Diana Staats, Kurt Verdeber, Elizabeth Wilcox, and Deborah Yoklic.

Reports from the following reviewers were most helpful for the sixth edition:

Barbara Armenta, James Baglama, Jon Clauss, Ann Darke, Marcel Finan, Dana Fine, Michael Huber, Greg Marks, Wes Ostertag, Ben Smith, Mark Turner, Aaron Weinberg, and Jianying Zhang.

Deborah Hughes-Hallett	Brigitte Lahme	Cody L. Patterson
Andrew M. Gleason	Patti Frazer Lock	Douglas Quinney
William G. McCallum	David O. Lomen	Karen Rhea
Eric Connally	David Lovelock	Adam Spiegler
Daniel E. Flath	Guadalupe I. Lozano	Jeff Tecosky-Feldman
Selin Kalaycıoğlu	Brad G. Osgood	Thomas W. Tucker

To Students: How to Learn from this Book

- This book may be different from other math textbooks that you have used, so it may be helpful to know about some of the differences in advance. This book emphasizes at every stage the *meaning* (in practical, graphical or numerical terms) of the symbols you are using. There is much less emphasis on "plug-and-chug" and using formulas, and much more emphasis on the interpretation of these formulas than you may expect. You will often be asked to explain your ideas in words or to explain an answer using graphs.

- The book contains the main ideas of calculus in plain English. Your success in using this book will depend on your reading, questioning, and thinking hard about the ideas presented. Although you may not have done this with other books, you should plan on reading the text in detail, not just the worked examples.

- There are very few examples in the text that are exactly like the homework problems. This means that you can't just look at a homework problem and search for a similar–looking "worked out" example. Success with the homework will come by grappling with the ideas of calculus.

- Many of the problems that we have included in the book are open-ended. This means that there may be more than one approach and more than one solution, depending on your analysis. Many times, solving a problem relies on common-sense ideas that are not stated in the problem but which you will know from everyday life.

- Some problems in this book assume that you have access to a graphing calculator or computer. There are many situations where you may not be able to find an exact solution to a problem, but you can use a calculator or computer to get a reasonable approximation.

- This book attempts to give equal weight to four methods for describing functions: graphical (a picture), numerical (a table of values), algebraic (a formula), and verbal. Sometimes you may find it easier to translate a problem given in one form into another. The best idea is to be flexible about your approach: if one way of looking at a problem doesn't work, try another.

- Students using this book have found discussing these problems in small groups very helpful. There are a great many problems which are not cut-and-dried; it can help to attack them with the other perspectives your colleagues can provide. If group work is not feasible, see if your instructor can organize a discussion session in which additional problems can be worked on.

- You are probably wondering what you'll get from the book. The answer is, if you put in a solid effort, you will get a real understanding of one of the most important accomplishments of the last millennium—calculus—as well as a real sense of the power of mathematics in the age of technology.

Table of Contents

1 A LIBRARY OF FUNCTIONS   1

1.1 FUNCTIONS AND CHANGE   2
1.2 EXPONENTIAL FUNCTIONS   12
1.3 NEW FUNCTIONS FROM OLD   21
1.4 LOGARITHMIC FUNCTIONS   29
1.5 TRIGONOMETRIC FUNCTIONS   36
1.6 POWERS, POLYNOMIALS, AND RATIONAL FUNCTIONS   45
1.7 INTRODUCTION TO CONTINUITY   53
1.8 LIMITS   57
   REVIEW PROBLEMS   68
   PROJECTS   73

2   KEY CONCEPT: THE DERIVATIVE   75

2.1 HOW DO WE MEASURE SPEED?   76
2.2 THE DERIVATIVE AT A POINT   83
2.3 THE DERIVATIVE FUNCTION   90
2.4 INTERPRETATIONS OF THE DERIVATIVE   98
2.5 THE SECOND DERIVATIVE   104
2.6 DIFFERENTIABILITY   111
   REVIEW PROBLEMS   116
   PROJECTS   122

3 SHORT-CUTS TO DIFFERENTIATION   123

3.1 POWERS AND POLYNOMIALS   124
3.2 THE EXPONENTIAL FUNCTION   132
3.3 THE PRODUCT AND QUOTIENT RULES   136
3.4 THE CHAIN RULE   142
3.5 THE TRIGONOMETRIC FUNCTIONS   149
3.6 THE CHAIN RULE AND INVERSE FUNCTIONS   156
3.7 IMPLICIT FUNCTIONS   162

3.8 HYPERBOLIC FUNCTIONS   165
3.9 LINEAR APPROXIMATION AND THE DERIVATIVE   169
3.10 THEOREMS ABOUT DIFFERENTIABLE FUNCTIONS   175
REVIEW PROBLEMS   180
PROJECTS   184

4 USING THE DERIVATIVE   185

4.1 USING FIRST AND SECOND DERIVATIVES   186
4.2 OPTIMIZATION   196
4.3 OPTIMIZATION AND MODELING   205
4.4 FAMILIES OF FUNCTIONS AND MODELING   216
4.5 APPLICATIONS TO MARGINALITY   224
4.6 RATES AND RELATED RATES   233
4.7 L'HOPITAL'S RULE, GROWTH, AND DOMINANCE   242
4.8 PARAMETRIC EQUATIONS   249
REVIEW PROBLEMS   260
PROJECTS   267

5 KEY CONCEPT: THE DEFINITE INTEGRAL   271

5.1 HOW DO WE MEASURE DISTANCE TRAVELED?   272
5.2 THE DEFINITE INTEGRAL   281
5.3 THE FUNDAMENTAL THEOREM AND INTERPRETATIONS   289
5.4 THEOREMS ABOUT DEFINITE INTEGRALS   298
REVIEW PROBLEMS   309
PROJECTS   316

6 CONSTRUCTING ANTIDERIVATIVES   319

6.1 ANTIDERIVATIVES GRAPHICALLY AND NUMERICALLY   320
6.2 CONSTRUCTING ANTIDERIVATIVES ANALYTICALLY   326
6.3 DIFFERENTIAL EQUATIONS AND MOTION   332
6.4 SECOND FUNDAMENTAL THEOREM OF CALCULUS   340
REVIEW PROBLEMS   345
PROJECTS   350

7 INTEGRATION   353

7.1 INTEGRATION BY SUBSTITUTION   354
7.2 INTEGRATION BY PARTS   364
7.3 TABLES OF INTEGRALS   371
7.4 ALGEBRAIC IDENTITIES AND TRIGONOMETRIC SUBSTITUTIONS   376
7.5 NUMERICAL METHODS FOR DEFINITE INTEGRALS   387
7.6 IMPROPER INTEGRALS   395
7.7 COMPARISON OF IMPROPER INTEGRALS   403
     REVIEW PROBLEMS   408
     PROJECTS   412

8 USING THE DEFINITE INTEGRAL   413

8.1 AREAS AND VOLUMES   414
8.2 APPLICATIONS TO GEOMETRY   422
8.3 AREA AND ARC LENGTH IN POLAR COORDINATES   431
8.4 DENSITY AND CENTER OF MASS   439
8.5 APPLICATIONS TO PHYSICS   449
8.6 APPLICATIONS TO ECONOMICS   459
8.7 DISTRIBUTION FUNCTIONS   466
8.8 PROBABILITY, MEAN, AND MEDIAN   473
     REVIEW PROBLEMS   481
     PROJECTS   486

9 SEQUENCES AND SERIES   491

9.1 SEQUENCES   492
9.2 GEOMETRIC SERIES   498
9.3 CONVERGENCE OF SERIES   505
9.4 TESTS FOR CONVERGENCE   512
9.5 POWER SERIES AND INTERVAL OF CONVERGENCE   521
     REVIEW PROBLEMS   529
     PROJECTS   533

10 APPROXIMATING FUNCTIONS USING SERIES   537

10.1 TAYLOR POLYNOMIALS   538
10.2 TAYLOR SERIES   546
10.3 FINDING AND USING TAYLOR SERIES   552

10.4 THE ERROR IN TAYLOR POLYNOMIAL APPROXIMATIONS   560
10.5 FOURIER SERIES   565
      REVIEW PROBLEMS   578
      PROJECTS   582

11 DIFFERENTIAL EQUATIONS   585

11.1 WHAT IS A DIFFERENTIAL EQUATION?   586
11.2 SLOPE FIELDS   591
11.3 EULER'S METHOD   599
11.4 SEPARATION OF VARIABLES   604
11.5 GROWTH AND DECAY   609
11.6 APPLICATIONS AND MODELING   620
11.7 THE LOGISTIC MODEL   629
11.8 SYSTEMS OF DIFFERENTIAL EQUATIONS   639
11.9 ANALYZING THE PHASE PLANE   649
      REVIEW PROBLEMS   655
      PROJECTS   661

APPENDICES   665

A ROOTS, ACCURACY, AND BOUNDS   666
B COMPLEX NUMBERS   674
C NEWTON'S METHOD   681
D VECTORS IN THE PLANE   684

READY REFERENCE   691

ANSWERS TO ODD-NUMBERED PROBLEMS   697

INDEX   743

Chapter One

A LIBRARY OF FUNCTIONS

Contents

1.1 Functions and Change 2
   The Rule of Four 2
   Examples of Domain and Range 3
   Linear Functions 4
   Families of Linear Functions 5
   Increasing versus Decreasing Functions 6
   Proportionality 6

1.2 Exponential Functions 12
   Concavity 12
   Elimination of a Drug from the Body 13
   The General Exponential Function 13
   Half-Life and Doubling Time 14
   The Family of Exponential Functions 15
   Exponential Functions with Base e 15

1.3 New Functions from Old 21
   Shifts and Stretches 21
   Composite Functions 21
   Odd and Even Functions: Symmetry 22
   Inverse Functions 23

1.4 Logarithmic Functions 29
   Logarithms to Base 10 and to Base e 29
   Solving Equations Using Logarithms 31

1.5 Trigonometric Functions 36
   Radians 36
   The Sine and Cosine Functions 37
   The Tangent Function 40
   The Inverse Trigonometric Functions 40

1.6 Powers, Polynomials, and Rational Functions   45
   Power Functions 45
   Dominance 46
   Polynomials 46
   Rational Functions 49

1.7 Introduction to Continuity 53
   Graphical Viewpoint 53
   The Intermediate Value Theorem 54
   Numerical Viewpoint 55

1.8 Limits 57
   The Idea of a Limit 58
   Definition of Limit 58
   Definition of Continuity 63

REVIEW PROBLEMS 68
PROJECTS 73

1.1 FUNCTIONS AND CHANGE

In mathematics, a *function* is used to represent the dependence of one quantity upon another.

Let's look at an example. Syracuse, New York has the highest annual snowfall of any US city because of the "lake effect" snow coming from cold Northwest winds blowing over nearby Lake Erie. Lake effect snowfall has been heavier over the last few decades; some have suggested this is due to the warming of Lake Erie by climate change. In December 2010, Syracuse got 66.9 inches of snow in one 12 day period, all of it from lake effect snow. See Table 1.1.

Table 1.1   *Daily snowfall in Syracuse, December 5–16, 2010*

Date (December 2010)	5	6	7	8	9	10	11	12	13	14	15	16
Snowfall in inches	6.8	12.2	9.3	14.9	1.9	0.1	0.0	0.0	1.4	5.0	11.9	3.4

You may not have thought of something so unpredictable as daily snowfall as being a function, but it *is* a function of date, because each day gives rise to one snowfall total. There is no formula for the daily snowfall (otherwise we would not need a weather bureau), but nevertheless the daily snowfall in Syracuse does satisfy the definition of a function: Each date, t, has a unique snowfall, S, associated with it.

We define a function as follows:

> A **function** is a rule that takes certain numbers as inputs and assigns to each a definite output number. The set of all input numbers is called the **domain** of the function and the set of resulting output numbers is called the **range** of the function.

The input is called the *independent variable* and the output is called the *dependent variable*. In the snowfall example, the domain is the set of December dates $\{5, 6, 7, 8, 9, 10, 11, 12, 13, 14, 15, 16\}$ and the range is the set of daily snowfalls $\{0.0, 0.1, 1.4, 1.9, 3.4, 5.0, 6.8, 9.3, 11.9, 12.2, 14.9\}$. We call the function f and write $S = f(t)$. Notice that a function may have identical outputs for different inputs (December 11 and 12, for example).

Some quantities, such as date, are *discrete*, meaning they take only certain isolated values (dates must be integers). Other quantities, such as time, are *continuous* as they can be any number. For a continuous variable, domains and ranges are often written using interval notation:

The set of numbers t such that $a \leq t \leq b$ is called a *closed interval* and written $[a, b]$.

The set of numbers t such that $a < t < b$ is called an *open interval* and written (a, b).

The Rule of Four: Tables, Graphs, Formulas, and Words

Functions can be represented by tables, graphs, formulas, and descriptions in words. For example, the function giving the daily snowfall in Syracuse can be represented by the graph in Figure 1.1, as well as by Table 1.1.

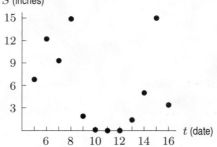

Figure 1.1: Syracuse snowfall, December, 2010

As another example of a function, consider the snow tree cricket. Surprisingly enough, all such crickets chirp at essentially the same rate if they are at the same temperature. That means that the chirp rate is a function of temperature. In other words, if we know the temperature, we can determine the chirp rate. Even more surprisingly, the chirp rate, C, in chirps per minute, increases steadily with the temperature, T, in degrees Fahrenheit, and can be computed by the formula

$$C = 4T - 160$$

to a fair degree of accuracy. We write $C = f(T)$ to express the fact that we think of C as a function of T and that we have named this function f. The graph of this function is in Figure 1.2.

Figure 1.2: Cricket chirp rate versus temperature

Examples of Domain and Range

If the domain of a function is not specified, we usually take it to be the largest possible set of real numbers. For example, we usually think of the domain of the function $f(x) = x^2$ as all real numbers. However, the domain of the function $g(x) = 1/x$ is all real numbers except zero, since we cannot divide by zero.

Sometimes we restrict the domain to be smaller than the largest possible set of real numbers. For example, if the function $f(x) = x^2$ is used to represent the area of a square of side x, we restrict the domain to nonnegative values of x.

Example 1   The function $C = f(T)$ gives chirp rate as a function of temperature. We restrict this function to temperatures for which the predicted chirp rate is positive, and up to the highest temperature ever recorded at a weather station, $136°F$. What is the domain of this function f?

Solution   If we consider the equation

$$C = 4T - 160$$

simply as a mathematical relationship between two variables C and T, any T value is possible. However, if we think of it as a relationship between cricket chirps and temperature, then C cannot be less than 0. Since $C = 0$ leads to $0 = 4T - 160$, and so $T = 40°F$, we see that T cannot be less than $40°F$. (See Figure 1.2.) In addition, we are told that the function is not defined for temperatures above $136°$. Thus, for the function $C = f(T)$ we have

$$\text{Domain} = \text{All } T \text{ values between } 40°F \text{ and } 136°F$$
$$= \text{All } T \text{ values with } 40 \le T \le 136$$
$$= [40, 136].$$

Example 2   Find the range of the function f, given the domain from Example 1. In other words, find all possible values of the chirp rate, C, in the equation $C = f(T)$.

Solution   Again, if we consider $C = 4T - 160$ simply as a mathematical relationship, its range is all real C values. However, when thinking of the meaning of $C = f(T)$ for crickets, we see that the function predicts cricket chirps per minute between 0 (at $T = 40°F$) and 384 (at $T = 136°F$). Hence,

$$\text{Range} = \text{All } C \text{ values from 0 to 384}$$
$$= \text{All } C \text{ values with } 0 \le C \le 384$$
$$= [0, 384].$$

In using the temperature to predict the chirp rate, we thought of the temperature as the *independent variable* and the chirp rate as the *dependent variable*. However, we could do this backward, and calculate the temperature from the chirp rate. From this point of view, the temperature is dependent on the chirp rate. Thus, which variable is dependent and which is independent may depend on your viewpoint.

Linear Functions

The chirp-rate function, $C = f(T)$, is an example of a *linear function*. A function is linear if its slope, or rate of change, is the same at every point. The rate of change of a function that is not linear may vary from point to point.

Olympic and World Records

During the early years of the Olympics, the height of the men's winning pole vault increased approximately 8 inches every four years. Table 1.2 shows that the height started at 130 inches in 1900, and increased by the equivalent of 2 inches a year. So the height was a linear function of time from 1900 to 1912. If y is the winning height in inches and t is the number of years since 1900, we can write

$$y = f(t) = 130 + 2t.$$

Since $y = f(t)$ increases with t, we say that f is an *increasing function*. The coefficient 2 tells us the rate, in inches per year, at which the height increases.

Table 1.2   *Men's Olympic pole vault winning height (approximate)*

Year	1900	1904	1908	1912
Height (inches)	130	138	146	154

This rate of increase is the *slope* of the line in Figure 1.3. The slope is given by the ratio

$$\text{Slope} = \frac{\text{Rise}}{\text{Run}} = \frac{146 - 138}{8 - 4} = \frac{8}{4} = 2 \text{ inches/year.}$$

Calculating the slope (rise/run) using any other two points on the line gives the same value.

What about the constant 130? This represents the initial height in 1900, when $t = 0$. Geometrically, 130 is the *intercept* on the vertical axis.

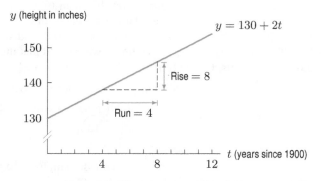

Figure 1.3: Olympic pole vault records

You may wonder whether the linear trend continues beyond 1912. Not surprisingly, it doesn't exactly. The formula $y = 130 + 2t$ predicts that the height in the 2008 Olympics would be 346 inches or 28 feet 10 inches, which is considerably higher than the actual value of 19 feet 6.65 inches. There is clearly a danger in *extrapolating* too far from the given data. You should also observe that the data in Table 1.2 is discrete, because it is given only at specific points (every four years). However, we have treated the variable t as though it were continuous, because the function $y = 130 + 2t$ makes sense for all values of t. The graph in Figure 1.3 is of the continuous function because it is a solid line, rather than four separate points representing the years in which the Olympics were held.

As the pole vault heights have increased over the years, the time to run the mile has decreased. If y is the world record time to run the mile, in seconds, and t is the number of years since 1900, then records show that, approximately,

$$y = g(t) = 260 - 0.39t.$$

The 260 tells us that the world record was 260 seconds in 1900 (at $t = 0$). The slope, -0.39, tells us that the world record decreased by about 0.39 seconds per year. We say that g is a *decreasing function*.

Difference Quotients and Delta Notation

We use the symbol Δ (the Greek letter capital delta) to mean "change in," so Δx means change in x and Δy means change in y.

The slope of a linear function $y = f(x)$ can be calculated from values of the function at two points, given by x_1 and x_2, using the formula

$$m = \frac{\text{Rise}}{\text{Run}} = \frac{\Delta y}{\Delta x} = \frac{f(x_2) - f(x_1)}{x_2 - x_1}.$$

The quantity $(f(x_2) - f(x_1))/(x_2 - x_1)$ is called a *difference quotient* because it is the quotient of two differences. (See Figure 1.4.) Since $m = \Delta y/\Delta x$, the units of m are y-units over x-units.

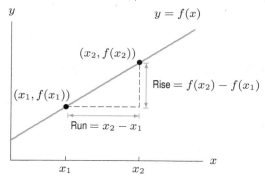

Figure 1.4: Difference quotient $= \dfrac{f(x_2) - f(x_1)}{x_2 - x_1}$

Families of Linear Functions

A **linear function** has the form

$$y = f(x) = b + mx.$$

Its graph is a line such that
- m is the **slope**, or rate of change of y with respect to x.
- b is the **vertical intercept**, or value of y when x is zero.

Notice that if the slope, m, is zero, we have $y = b$, a horizontal line.

To recognize that a table of x and y values comes from a linear function, $y = b + mx$, look for differences in y-values that are constant for equally spaced x-values.

Formulas such as $f(x) = b + mx$, in which the constants m and b can take on various values, give a *family of functions*. All the functions in a family share certain properties—in this case, all the graphs are straight lines. The constants m and b are called *parameters*; their meaning is shown in Figures 1.5 and 1.6. Notice that the greater the magnitude of m, the steeper the line.

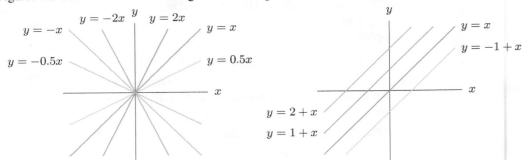

Figure 1.5: The family $y = mx$
(with $b = 0$)

Figure 1.6: The family $y = b + x$
(with $m = 1$)

Increasing versus Decreasing Functions

The terms increasing and decreasing can be applied to other functions, not just linear ones. See Figure 1.7. In general,

> A function f is **increasing** if the values of $f(x)$ increase as x increases.
> A function f is **decreasing** if the values of $f(x)$ decrease as x increases.
>
> The graph of an *increasing* function *climbs* as we move from left to right.
> The graph of a *decreasing* function *falls* as we move from left to right.
>
> A function $f(x)$ is **monotonic** if it increases for all x or decreases for all x.

Figure 1.7: Increasing and decreasing functions

Proportionality

A common functional relationship occurs when one quantity is *proportional* to another. For example, the area, A, of a circle is proportional to the square of the radius, r, because

$$A = f(r) = \pi r^2.$$

> We say y is (directly) **proportional** to x if there is a nonzero constant k such that
>
> $$y = kx.$$
>
> This k is called the constant of proportionality.

We also say that one quantity is *inversely proportional* to another if one is proportional to the reciprocal of the other. For example, the speed, v, at which you make a 50-mile trip is inversely proportional to the time, t, taken, because v is proportional to $1/t$:

$$v = 50\left(\frac{1}{t}\right) = \frac{50}{t}.$$

Exercises and Problems for Section 1.1

Exercises

1. The population of a city, P, in millions, is a function of t, the number of years since 1970, so $P = f(t)$. Explain the meaning of the statement $f(35) = 12$ in terms of the population of this city.

2. The pollutant PCB (polychlorinated biphenyl) affects the thickness of pelican eggs. Thinking of the thickness, T, of the eggs, in mm, as a function of the concentration, P, of PCBs in ppm (parts per million), we have $T = f(P)$. Explain the meaning of $f(200)$ in terms of thickness of pelican eggs and concentration of PCBs.

3. Describe what Figure 1.8 tells you about an assembly line whose productivity is represented as a function of the number of workers on the line.

Figure 1.8

For Exercises 4–7, find an equation for the line that passes through the given points.

4. $(0, 0)$ and $(1, 1)$ **5.** $(0, 2)$ and $(2, 3)$

6. $(-2, 1)$ and $(2, 3)$ **7.** $(-1, 0)$ and $(2, 6)$

For Exercises 8–11, determine the slope and the y-intercept of the line whose equation is given.

8. $2y + 5x - 8 = 0$ **9.** $7y + 12x - 2 = 0$

10. $-4y + 2x + 8 = 0$ **11.** $12x = 6y + 4$

12. Match the graphs in Figure 1.9 with the following equations. (Note that the x and y scales may be unequal.)

(a) $y = x - 5$ (b) $-3x + 4 = y$
(c) $5 = y$ (d) $y = -4x - 5$
(e) $y = x + 6$ (f) $y = x/2$

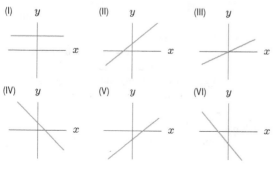

Figure 1.9

13. Match the graphs in Figure 1.10 with the following equations. (Note that the x and y scales may be unequal.)

(a) $y = -2.72x$ (b) $y = 0.01 + 0.001x$
(c) $y = 27.9 - 0.1x$ (d) $y = 0.1x - 27.9$
(e) $y = -5.7 - 200x$ (f) $y = x/3.14$

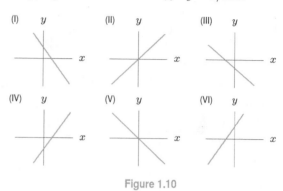

Figure 1.10

14. Estimate the slope and the equation of the line in Figure 1.11.

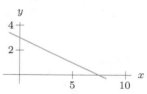

Figure 1.11

15. Find an equation for the line with slope m through the point (a, c).

16. Find a linear function that generates the values in Table 1.3.

Table 1.3

x	5.2	5.3	5.4	5.5	5.6
y	27.8	29.2	30.6	32.0	33.4

For Exercises 17–19, use the facts that parallel lines have equal slopes and that the slopes of perpendicular lines are negative reciprocals of one another.

17. Find an equation for the line through the point $(2, 1)$ which is perpendicular to the line $y = 5x - 3$.

18. Find equations for the lines through the point $(1, 5)$ that are parallel to and perpendicular to the line with equation $y + 4x = 7$.

19. Find equations for the lines through the point (a, b) that are parallel and perpendicular to the line $y = mx + c$, assuming $m \neq 0$.

For Exercises 20–23, give the approximate domain and range of each function. Assume the entire graph is shown.

20.

21.

22.

23.

Find domain and range in Exercises 24–25.

24. $y = x^2 + 2$

25. $y = \dfrac{1}{x^2 + 2}$

26. If $f(t) = \sqrt{t^2 - 16}$, find all values of t for which $f(t)$ is a real number. Solve $f(t) = 3$.

In Exercises 27–31, write a formula representing the function.

27. The volume of a sphere is proportional to the cube of its radius, r.

28. The average velocity, v, for a trip over a fixed distance, d, is inversely proportional to the time of travel, t.

29. The strength, S, of a beam is proportional to the square of its thickness, h.

30. The energy, E, expended by a swimming dolphin is proportional to the cube of the speed, v, of the dolphin.

31. The number of animal species, N, of a certain body length, l, is inversely proportional to the square of l.

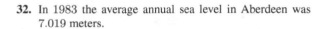

Problems

In Problems 32–35 the function $S = f(t)$ gives the average annual sea level, S, in meters, in Aberdeen, Scotland,[1] as a function of t, the number of years before 2008. Write a mathematical expression that represents the given statement.

32. In 1983 the average annual sea level in Aberdeen was 7.019 meters.

33. The average annual sea level in Aberdeen in 2008.

34. The average annual sea level in Aberdeen was the same in 1865 and 1911.

35. The average annual sea level in Aberdeen increased by 1 millimeter from 2007 to 2008.

36. In December 2010, the snowfall in Minneapolis was unusually high,[2] leading to the collapse of the roof of the Metrodome. Figure 1.12 gives the snowfall, S, in Minneapolis for December 6–15, 2010.

   (a) How do you know that the snowfall data represents a function of date?
   (b) Estimate the snowfall on December 12.
   (c) On which day was the snowfall more than 10 inches?
   (d) During which consecutive two-day interval was the increase in snowfall largest?

Figure 1.12

37. The value of a car, $V = f(a)$, in thousands of dollars, is a function of the age of the car, a, in years.

   (a) Interpret the statement $f(5) = 6$
   (b) Sketch a possible graph of V against a. Is f an increasing or decreasing function? Explain.
   (c) Explain the significance of the horizontal and vertical intercepts in terms of the value of the car.

38. Which graph in Figure 1.13 best matches each of the following stories?[3] Write a story for the remaining graph.

   (a) I had just left home when I realized I had forgotten my books, and so I went back to pick them up.
   (b) Things went fine until I had a flat tire.
   (c) I started out calmly but sped up when I realized I was going to be late.

[1] www.decc.gov.uk, accessed June 2011
[2] http://www.crh.noaa.gov/mpx/Climate/DisplayRecords.php
[3] Adapted from Jan Terwel, "Real Math in Cooperative Groups in Secondary Education." *Cooperative Learning in Mathematics*, ed. Neal Davidson, p. 234 (Reading: Addison Wesley, 1990).

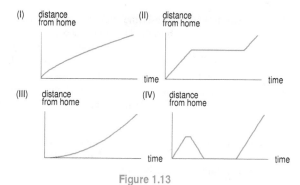

Figure 1.13

39. An object is put outside on a cold day at time $t = 0$. Its temperature, $H = f(t)$, in °C, is graphed in Figure 1.14.

(a) What does the statement $f(30) = 10$ mean in terms of temperature? Include units for 30 and for 10 in your answer.

(b) Explain what the vertical intercept, a, and the horizontal intercept, b, represent in terms of temperature of the object and time outside.

Figure 1.14

40. A rock is dropped from a window and falls to the ground below. The height, s (in meters), of the rock above ground is a function of the time, t (in seconds), since the rock was dropped, so $s = f(t)$.

(a) Sketch a possible graph of s as a function of t.

(b) Explain what the statement $f(7) = 12$ tells us about the rock's fall.

(c) The graph drawn as the answer for part (a) should have a horizontal and vertical intercept. Interpret each intercept in terms of the rock's fall.

41. In a California town, the monthly charge for waste collection is $8 for 32 gallons of waste and $12.32 for 68 gallons of waste.

(a) Find a linear formula for the cost, C, of waste collection as a function of the number of gallons of waste, w.

(b) What is the slope of the line found in part (a)? Give units and interpret your answer in terms of the cost of waste collection.

(c) What is the vertical intercept of the line found in part (a)? Give units and interpret your answer in terms of the cost of waste collection.

42. For tax purposes, you may have to report the value of your assets, such as cars or refrigerators. The value you report drops with time. "Straight-line depreciation" assumes that the value is a linear function of time. If a $950 refrigerator depreciates completely in seven years, find a formula for its value as a function of time.

43. A company rents cars at $40 a day and 15 cents a mile. Its competitor's cars are $50 a day and 10 cents a mile.

(a) For each company, give a formula for the cost of renting a car for a day as a function of the distance traveled.

(b) On the same axes, graph both functions.

(c) How should you decide which company is cheaper?

44. Residents of the town of Maple Grove who are connected to the municipal water supply are billed a fixed amount monthly plus a charge for each cubic foot of water used. A household using 1000 cubic feet was billed $40, while one using 1600 cubic feet was billed $55.

(a) What is the charge per cubic foot?

(b) Write an equation for the total cost of a resident's water as a function of cubic feet of water used.

(c) How many cubic feet of water used would lead to a bill of $100?

Problems 45–48 ask you to plot graphs based on the following story: "As I drove down the highway this morning, at first traffic was fast and uncongested, then it crept nearly bumper-to-bumper until we passed an accident, after which traffic flow went back to normal until I exited."

45. Driving speed against time on the highway

46. Distance driven against time on the highway

47. Distance from my exit vs time on the highway

48. Distance between cars vs distance driven on the highway

49. Let $f(t)$ be the number of US billionaires in the US in year t.

(a) Express the following statements[4] in terms of f.

(i) In 1985 there were 13 US billionaires.

(ii) In 1990 there were 99 US billionaires.

(b) Find the average yearly increase in the number of US billionaires between 1985 and 1990. Express this using f.

(c) Assuming the yearly increase remains constant, find a formula predicting the number of US billionaires in year t.

[4]//hypertextbook.com/facts/2005/MichelleLee.shtml

50. An alternative to petroleum-based diesel fuel, biodiesel, is derived from renewable resources such as food crops, algae, and animal oils. The table shows the recent annual percent growth in US biodiesel consumption.[5]

Year	2005	2006	2007	2008	2009
% growth over previous yr	237	186.6	37.2	−11.7	7.3

(a) Find the largest time interval over which the percentage growth in the US consumption of biodiesel was an increasing function of time. Interpret what increasing means, practically speaking, in this case.

(b) Find the largest time interval over which the actual US consumption of biodiesel was an increasing function of time. Interpret what increasing means, practically speaking, in this case.

51. Hydroelectric power is electric power generated by the force of moving water. Figure 1.15 shows[6] the annual percent growth in hydroelectric power consumption by the US industrial sector between 2004 and 2009.

(a) Find the largest time interval over which the percentage growth in the US consumption of hydroelectric power was a decreasing function of time. Interpret what decreasing means, practically speaking, in this case.

(b) Find the largest time interval over which the actual US consumption of hydroelectric power was a decreasing function of time. Interpret what decreasing means, practically speaking, in this case.

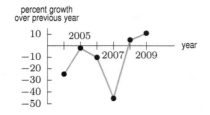

Figure 1.15

52. Solar panels are arrays of photovoltaic cells that convert solar radiation into electricity. The table shows the annual percent change in the US price per watt of a solar panel.[7]

Year	2004	2005	2006	2007	2008
% growth over previous yr	−5.7	6.7	9.7	−3.7	3.6

(a) Find the largest time interval over which the percentage growth in the US price per watt of a solar panel was an increasing function of time. Interpret what increasing means, practically speaking, in this case.

(b) Find the largest time interval over which the actual price per watt of a solar panel was an increasing function of time. Interpret what increasing means, practically speaking, in this case.

53. Table 1.4 shows the average annual sea level, S, in meters, in Aberdeen, Scotland,[8] as a function of time, t, measured in years before 2008.

Table 1.4

t	0	25	50	75	100	125
S	7.094	7.019	6.992	6.965	6.938	6.957

(a) What was the average sea level in Aberdeen in 2008?

(b) In what year was the average sea level 7.019 meters? 6.957 meters?

(c) Table 1.5 gives the average sea level, S, in Aberdeen as a function of the year, x. Complete the missing values.

Table 1.5

x	1883	?	1933	1958	1983	2008
S	?	6.938	?	6.992	?	?

54. A controversial 1992 Danish study[9] reported that men's average sperm count has decreased from 113 million per milliliter in 1940 to 66 million per milliliter in 1990.

(a) Express the average sperm count, S, as a linear function of the number of years, t, since 1940.

(b) A man's fertility is affected if his sperm count drops below about 20 million per milliliter. If the linear model found in part (a) is accurate, in what year will the average male sperm count fall below this level?

55. The table gives the average weight, w, in pounds, of American men in their sixties for height, h, in inches.[10]

(a) How do you know that the data in this table could represent a linear function?

(b) Find weight, w, as a linear function of height, h. What is the slope of the line? What are the units for the slope?

[5] http://www.eia.doe.gov/aer/renew.html. Accessed February 2011.

[6] Yearly values have been joined with segments to highlight trends in the data, however values in between years should not be inferred from the segments. From http://www.eia.doe.gov/aer/renew.html. Accessed February 2011.

[7] We use the official price per peak watt, which uses the maximum number of watts a solar panel can produce under ideal conditions. From http://www.eia.doe.gov/aer/renew.html. Accessed February 2011.

[8] www.decc.gov.uk, accessed June 2011.

[9] "Investigating the Next Silent Spring," *US News and World Report*, pp. 50–52 (March 11, 1996).

[10] Adapted from "Average Weight of Americans by Height and Age," *The World Almanac* (New Jersey: Funk and Wagnalls, 1992), p. 956.

(c) Find height, h, as a linear function of weight, w. What is the slope of the line? What are the units for the slope?

h (inches)	68	69	70	71	72	73	74	75
w (pounds)	166	171	176	181	186	191	196	201

56. An airplane uses a fixed amount of fuel for takeoff, a (different) fixed amount for landing, and a third fixed amount per mile when it is in the air. How does the total quantity of fuel required depend on the length of the trip? Write a formula for the function involved. Explain the meaning of the constants in your formula.

57. The cost of planting seed is usually a function of the number of acres sown. The cost of the equipment is a *fixed cost* because it must be paid regardless of the number of acres planted. The costs of supplies and labor vary with the number of acres planted and are called *variable costs*. Suppose the fixed costs are $10,000 and the variable costs are $200 per acre. Let C be the total cost, measured in thousands of dollars, and let x be the number of acres planted.

(a) Find a formula for C as a function of x.
(b) Graph C against x.
(c) Which feature of the graph represents the fixed costs? Which represents the variable costs?

58. You drive at a constant speed from Chicago to Detroit, a distance of 275 miles. About 120 miles from Chicago you pass through Kalamazoo, Michigan. Sketch a graph of your distance from Kalamazoo as a function of time.

59. (a) Consider the functions graphed in Figure 1.16(a). Find the coordinates of C.

(b) Consider the functions in Figure 1.16(b). Find the coordinates of C in terms of b.

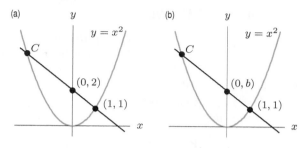

Figure 1.16

60. When Galileo was formulating the laws of motion, he considered the motion of a body starting from rest and falling under gravity. He originally thought that the velocity of such a falling body was proportional to the distance it had fallen. What do the experimental data in Table 1.6 tell you about Galileo's hypothesis? What alternative hypothesis is suggested by the two sets of data in Table 1.6 and Table 1.7?

Table 1.6

Distance (ft)	0	1	2	3	4
Velocity (ft/sec)	0	8	11.3	13.9	16

Table 1.7

Time (sec)	0	1	2	3	4
Velocity (ft/sec)	0	32	64	96	128

Strengthen Your Understanding

In Problems 61–62, explain what is wrong with the statement.

61. Values of y on the graph of $y = 0.5x - 3$ increase more slowly than values of y on the graph of $y = 0.5 - 3x$.

62. The equation $y = 2x + 1$ indicates that y is directly proportional to x with a constant of proportionality 2.

In Problems 63–64, give an example of:

63. A linear function with a positive slope and a negative x-intercept.

64. A formula representing the statement "q is inversely proportional to the cube root of p and has a positive constant of proportionality."

Are the statements in Problems 65–68 true or false? Give an explanation for your answer.

65. For any two points in the plane, there is a linear function whose graph passes through them.

66. If $y = f(x)$ is a linear function, then increasing x by 1 unit changes the corresponding y by m units, where m is the slope.

67. If y is a linear function of x, then the ratio y/x is constant for all points on the graph at which $x \neq 0$.

68. If $y = f(x)$ is a linear function, then increasing x by 2 units adds $m + 2$ units to the corresponding y, where m is the slope.

69. Which of the following functions has its domain identical with its range?

(a) $f(x) = x^2$ **(b)** $g(x) = \sqrt{x}$
(c) $h(x) = x^3$ **(d)** $i(x) = |x|$

1.2 EXPONENTIAL FUNCTIONS

Population Growth

The population of Burkina Faso, a sub-Saharan African country,[11] from 2003 to 2009 is given in Table 1.8. To see how the population is growing, we look at the increase in population in the third column. If the population had been growing linearly, all the numbers in the third column would be the same.

Table 1.8 *Population of Burkina Faso (estimated), 2003–2009*

Year	Population (millions)	Change in population (millions)
2003	12.853	
		0.437
2004	13.290	
		0.457
2005	13.747	
		0.478
2006	14.225	
		0.496
2007	14.721	
		0.513
2008	15.234	
		0.523
2009	15.757	

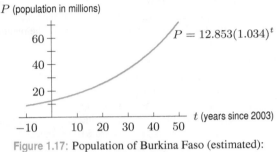

P (population in millions)

$P = 12.853(1.034)^t$

Figure 1.17: Population of Burkina Faso (estimated): Exponential growth

Suppose we divide each year's population by the previous year's population. For example,

$$\frac{\text{Population in 2004}}{\text{Population in 2003}} = \frac{13.290 \text{ million}}{12.853 \text{ million}} = 1.034$$

$$\frac{\text{Population in 2005}}{\text{Population in 2004}} = \frac{13.747 \text{ million}}{13.290 \text{ million}} = 1.034.$$

The fact that both calculations give 1.034 shows the population grew by about 3.4% between 2003 and 2004 *and* between 2004 and 2005. Similar calculations for other years show that the population grew by a factor of about 1.034, or 3.4%, every year. Whenever we have a constant growth factor (here 1.034), we have exponential growth. The population t years after 2003 is given by the *exponential* function

$$P = 12.853(1.034)^t.$$

If we assume that the formula holds for 50 years, the population graph has the shape shown in Figure 1.17. Since the population is growing faster and faster as time goes on, the graph is bending upward; we say it is *concave up*. Even exponential functions which climb slowly at first, such as this one, eventually climb extremely quickly.

> To recognize that a table of t and P values comes from an exponential function, look for ratios of P values that are constant for equally spaced t values.

Concavity

We have used the term concave up[12] to describe the graph in Figure 1.17. In words:

> The graph of a function is **concave up** if it bends upward as we move left to right; it is **concave down** if it bends downward. (See Figure 1.18 for four possible shapes.) A line is neither concave up nor concave down.

---

[11] dataworldbank.org, accessed January 12, 2011.
[12] In Chapter 2 we consider concavity in more depth.

Figure 1.18: Concavity of a graph

Elimination of a Drug from the Body

Now we look at a quantity which is decreasing exponentially instead of increasing. When a patient is given medication, the drug enters the bloodstream. As the drug passes through the liver and kidneys, it is metabolized and eliminated at a rate that depends on the particular drug. For the antibiotic ampicillin, approximately 40% of the drug is eliminated every hour. A typical dose of ampicillin is 250 mg. Suppose $Q = f(t)$, where Q is the quantity of ampicillin, in mg, in the bloodstream at time t hours since the drug was given. At $t = 0$, we have $Q = 250$. Since every hour the amount remaining is 60% of the previous amount, we have

$$f(0) = 250$$
$$f(1) = 250(0.6)$$
$$f(2) = (250(0.6))(0.6) = 250(0.6)^2,$$

and after t hours,

$$Q = f(t) = 250(0.6)^t.$$

This is an *exponential decay function*. Some values of the function are in Table 1.9; its graph is in Figure 1.19.

Notice the way in which the function in Figure 1.19 is decreasing. Each hour a smaller quantity of the drug is removed than in the previous hour. This is because as time passes, there is less of the drug in the body to be removed. Compare this to the exponential growth in Figure 1.17, where each step upward is larger than the previous one. Notice, however, that both graphs are concave up.

Table 1.9 *Drug elimination*

t (hours)	Q (mg)
0	250
1	150
2	90
3	54
4	32.4
5	19.4

Figure 1.19: Drug elimination: Exponential decay

The General Exponential Function

We say P is an **exponential function** of t with base a if

$$P = P_0 a^t,$$

where P_0 is the initial quantity (when $t = 0$) and a is the factor by which P changes when t increases by 1.

If $a > 1$, we have exponential growth; if $0 < a < 1$, we have exponential decay.

Provided $a > 0$, the largest possible domain for the exponential function is all real numbers. The reason we do not want $a \leq 0$ is that, for example, we cannot define $a^{1/2}$ if $a < 0$. Also, we do not usually have $a = 1$, since $P = P_0 1^t = P_0$ is then a constant function.

The value of a is closely related to the percent growth (or decay) rate. For example, if $a = 1.03$, then P is growing at 3%; if $a = 0.94$, then P is decaying at 6%.

Example 1   Suppose that $Q = f(t)$ is an exponential function of t. If $f(20) = 88.2$ and $f(23) = 91.4$:

(a)   Find the base.   (b)   Find the growth rate.   (c)   Evaluate $f(25)$.

Solution   (a) Let

$$Q = Q_0 a^t.$$

Substituting $t = 20, Q = 88.2$ and $t = 23, Q = 91.4$ gives two equations for Q_0 and a:

$$88.2 = Q_0 a^{20} \quad \text{and} \quad 91.4 = Q_0 a^{23}.$$

Dividing the two equations enables us to eliminate Q_0:

$$\frac{91.4}{88.2} = \frac{Q_0 a^{23}}{Q_0 a^{20}} = a^3.$$

Solving for the base, a, gives

$$a = \left(\frac{91.4}{88.2}\right)^{1/3} = 1.012.$$

(b) Since $a = 1.012$, the growth rate is $0.012 = 1.2\%$.

(c) We want to evaluate $f(25) = Q_0 a^{25} = Q_0(1.012)^{25}$. First we find Q_0 from the equation

$$88.2 = Q_0(1.012)^{20}.$$

Solving gives $Q_0 = 69.5$. Thus,

$$f(25) = 69.5(1.012)^{25} = 93.6.$$

Half-Life and Doubling Time

Radioactive substances, such as uranium, decay exponentially. A certain percentage of the mass disintegrates in a given unit of time; the time it takes for half the mass to decay is called the *half-life* of the substance.

A well-known radioactive substance is carbon-14, which is used to date organic objects. When a piece of wood or bone was part of a living organism, it accumulated small amounts of radioactive carbon-14. Once the organism dies, it no longer picks up carbon-14. Using the half-life of carbon-14 (about 5730 years), we can estimate the age of the object. We use the following definitions:

The **half-life** of an exponentially decaying quantity is the time required for the quantity to be reduced by a factor of one half.

The **doubling time** of an exponentially increasing quantity is the time required for the quantity to double.

The Family of Exponential Functions

The formula $P = P_0 a^t$ gives a family of exponential functions with positive parameters P_0 (the initial quantity) and a (the base, or growth/decay factor). The base tells us whether the function is increasing ($a > 1$) or decreasing ($0 < a < 1$). Since a is the factor by which P changes when t is increased by 1, large values of a mean fast growth; values of a near 0 mean fast decay. (See Figures 1.20 and 1.21.) All members of the family $P = P_0 a^t$ are concave up.

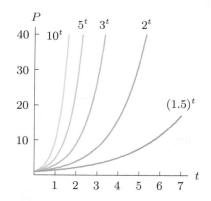

Figure 1.20: Exponential growth: $P = a^t$, for $a > 1$

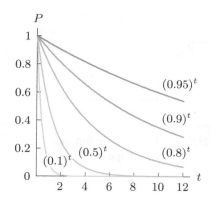

Figure 1.21: Exponential decay: $P = a^t$, for $0 < a < 1$

Example 2   Figure 1.22 is the graph of three exponential functions. What can you say about the values of the six constants, a, b, c, d, p, q?

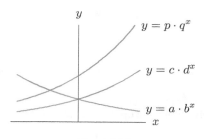

Figure 1.22

Solution   All the constants are positive. Since a, c, p represent y-intercepts, we see that $a = c$ because these graphs intersect on the y-axis. In addition, $a = c < p$, since $y = p \cdot q^x$ crosses the y-axis above the other two.

Since $y = a \cdot b^x$ is decreasing, we have $0 < b < 1$. The other functions are increasing, so $1 < d$ and $1 < q$.

Exponential Functions with Base e

The most frequently used base for an exponential function is the famous number $e = 2.71828\ldots$. This base is used so often that you will find an e^x button on most scientific calculators. At first glance, this is all somewhat mysterious. Why is it convenient to use the base $2.71828\ldots$? The full answer to that question must wait until Chapter 3, where we show that many calculus formulas come out neatly when e is used as the base. We often use the following result:

Any **exponential growth** function can be written, for some $a > 1$ and $k > 0$, in the form

$$P = P_0 a^t \quad \text{or} \quad P = P_0 e^{kt}$$

and any **exponential decay** function can be written, for some $0 < a < 1$ and $-k < 0$, as

$$Q = Q_0 a^t \quad \text{or} \quad Q = Q_0 e^{-kt},$$

where P_0 and Q_0 are the initial quantities.

We say that P and Q are growing or decaying at a *continuous*[13] *rate* of k. (For example, $k = 0.02$ corresponds to a continuous rate of 2%.)

Example 3   Convert the functions $P = e^{0.5t}$ and $Q = 5e^{-0.2t}$ into the form $y = y_0 a^t$. Use the results to explain the shape of the graphs in Figures 1.23 and 1.24.

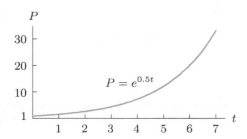

Figure 1.23: An exponential growth function

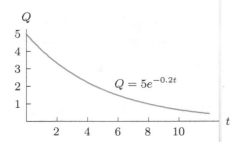

Figure 1.24: An exponential decay function

Solution   We have

$$P = e^{0.5t} = (e^{0.5})^t = (1.65)^t.$$

Thus, P is an exponential growth function with $P_0 = 1$ and $a = 1.65$. The function is increasing and its graph is concave up, similar to those in Figure 1.20. Also,

$$Q = 5e^{-0.2t} = 5(e^{-0.2})^t = 5(0.819)^t,$$

so Q is an exponential decay function with $Q_0 = 5$ and $a = 0.819$. The function is decreasing and its graph is concave up, similar to those in Figure 1.21.

Example 4   The quantity, Q, of a drug in a patient's body at time t is represented for positive constants S and k by the function $Q = S(1 - e^{-kt})$. For $t \geq 0$, describe how Q changes with time. What does S represent?

Solution   The graph of Q is shown in Figure 1.25. Initially none of the drug is present, but the quantity increases with time. Since the graph is concave down, the quantity increases at a decreasing rate. This is realistic because as the quantity of the drug in the body increases, so does the rate at which the body excretes the drug. Thus, we expect the quantity to level off. Figure 1.25 shows that S is the saturation level. The line $Q = S$ is called a *horizontal asymptote*.

---

[13]The reason that k is called the continuous rate is explored in detail in Chapter 11.

Figure 1.25: Buildup of the quantity of a drug in body

Exercises and Problems for Section 1.2

Exercises

In Exercises 1–4, decide whether the graph is concave up, concave down, or neither.

1.

2.

3.

4.

The functions in Exercises 5–8 represent exponential growth or decay. What is the initial quantity? What is the growth rate? State if the growth rate is continuous.

5. $P = 5(1.07)^t$

6. $P = 7.7(0.92)^t$

7. $P = 3.2e^{0.03t}$

8. $P = 15e^{-0.06t}$

Write the functions in Exercises 9–12 in the form $P = P_0 a^t$. Which represent exponential growth and which represent exponential decay?

9. $P = 15e^{0.25t}$

10. $P = 2e^{-0.5t}$

11. $P = P_0 e^{0.2t}$

12. $P = 7e^{-\pi t}$

In Exercises 13–14, let $f(t) = Q_0 a^t = Q_0(1 + r)^t$.
(a) Find the base, a.
(b) Find the percentage growth rate, r.

13. $f(5) = 75.94$ and $f(7) = 170.86$

14. $f(0.02) = 25.02$ and $f(0.05) = 25.06$

15. A town has a population of 1000 people at time $t = 0$. In each of the following cases, write a formula for the population, P, of the town as a function of year t.

(a) The population increases by 50 people a year.
(b) The population increases by 5% a year.

16. An air-freshener starts with 30 grams and evaporates. In each of the following cases, write a formula for the quantity, Q grams, of air-freshener remaining t days after the start and sketch a graph of the function. The decrease is:

(a) 2 grams a day   (b) 12% a day

17. For which pairs of consecutive points in Figure 1.26 is the function graphed:

(a) Increasing and concave up?
(b) Increasing and concave down?
(c) Decreasing and concave up?
(d) Decreasing and concave down?

Figure 1.26

18. The table gives the average temperature in Wallingford, Connecticut, for the first 10 days in March.

(a) Over which intervals was the average temperature increasing? Decreasing?
(b) Find a pair of consecutive intervals over which the average temperature was increasing at a decreasing rate. Find another pair of consecutive intervals over which the average temperature was increasing at an increasing rate.

Day	1	2	3	4	5	6	7	8	9	10
°F	42°	42°	34°	25°	22°	34°	38°	40°	49°	49°

Problems

19. (a) Which (if any) of the functions in the following table could be linear? Find formulas for those functions.

(b) Which (if any) of these functions could be exponential? Find formulas for those functions.

x	$f(x)$	$g(x)$	$h(x)$
-2	12	16	37
-1	17	24	34
0	20	36	31
1	21	54	28
2	18	81	25

In Problems 20–21, find all the tables that have the given characteristic.

(A)
x	0	40	80	160
y	2.2	2.2	2.2	2.2

(B)
x	-8	-4	0	8
y	51	62	73	95

(C)
x	-4	-3	4	6
y	18	0	4.5	-2.25

(D)
x	3	4	5	6
y	18	9	4.5	2.25

20. y could be a linear function of x.

21. y could be an exponential function of x.

22. In 2010, the world's population reached 6.91 billion and was increasing at a rate of 1.1% per year. Assume that this growth rate remains constant. (In fact, the growth rate has decreased since 1987.)

(a) Write a formula for the world population (in billions) as a function of the number of years since 2010.

(b) Estimate the population of the world in the year 2020.

(c) Sketch world population as a function of years since 2010. Use the graph to estimate the doubling time of the population of the world.

23. (a) A population, P, grows at a continuous rate of 2% a year and starts at 1 million. Write P in the form $P = P_0 e^{kt}$, with P_0, k constants.

(b) Plot the population in part (a) against time.

24. A certain region has a population of 10,000,000 and an annual growth rate of 2%. Estimate the doubling time by guessing and checking.

25. A photocopy machine can reduce copies to 80% of their original size. By copying an already reduced copy, further reductions can be made.

(a) If a page is reduced to 80%, what percent enlargement is needed to return it to its original size?

(b) Estimate the number of times in succession that a page must be copied to make the final copy less than 15% of the size of the original.

26. When a new product is advertised, more and more people try it. However, the rate at which new people try it slows as time goes on.

(a) Graph the total number of people who have tried such a product against time.

(b) What do you know about the concavity of the graph?

27. Sketch reasonable graphs for the following. Pay particular attention to the concavity of the graphs.

(a) The total revenue generated by a car rental business, plotted against the amount spent on advertising.

(b) The temperature of a cup of hot coffee standing in a room, plotted as a function of time.

28. Each of the functions g, h, k in Table 1.10 is increasing, but each increases in a different way. Which of the graphs in Figure 1.27 best fits each function?

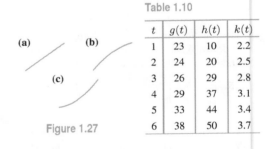

Figure 1.27

Table 1.10

t	$g(t)$	$h(t)$	$k(t)$
1	23	10	2.2
2	24	20	2.5
3	26	29	2.8
4	29	37	3.1
5	33	44	3.4
6	38	50	3.7

29. Each of the functions in Table 1.11 decreases, but each decreases in a different way. Which of the graphs in Figure 1.28 best fits each function?

Figure 1.28

Table 1.11

x	$f(x)$	$g(x)$	$h(x)$
1	100	22.0	9.3
2	90	21.4	9.1
3	81	20.8	8.8
4	73	20.2	8.4
5	66	19.6	7.9
6	60	19.0	7.3

30. One of the main contaminants of a nuclear accident, such as that at Chernobyl, is strontium-90, which decays exponentially at a continuous rate of approximately 2.47% per year. After the Chernobyl disaster, it was suggested that it would be about 100 years before the region would again be safe for human habitation. What percent of the original strontium-90 would still remain then?

Give a possible formula for the functions in Problems 31–34.

31.

32.

33.

34.

35. Table 1.12 shows some values of a linear function f and an exponential function g. Find exact values (not decimal approximations) for each of the missing entries.

Table 1.12

x	0	1	2	3	4
$f(x)$	10	?	20	?	?
$g(x)$	10	?	20	?	?

36. Match the functions $h(s)$, $f(s)$, and $g(s)$, whose values are in Table 1.13, with the formulas

$$y = a(1.1)^s , \quad y = b(1.05)^s , \quad y = c(1.03)^s,$$

assuming a, b, and c are constants. Note that the function values have been rounded to two decimal places.

Table 1.13

s	$h(s)$	s	$f(s)$	s	$g(s)$
2	1.06	1	2.20	3	3.47
3	1.09	2	2.42	4	3.65
4	1.13	3	2.66	5	3.83
5	1.16	4	2.93	6	4.02
6	1.19	5	3.22	7	4.22

37. **(a)** Estimate graphically the doubling time of the exponentially growing population shown in Figure 1.29. Check that the doubling time is independent of where you start on the graph.
(b) Show algebraically that if $P = P_0 a^t$ doubles between time t and time $t + d$, then d is the same number for any t.

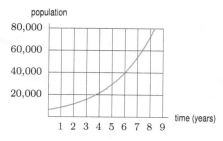

Figure 1.29

38. A deposit of P_0 into a bank account has a doubling time of 50 years. No other deposits or withdrawals are made.

(a) How much money is in the bank account after 50 years? 100 years? 150 years? (Your answer will involve P_0.)
(b) How many times does the amount of money double in t years? Use this to write a formula for P, the amount of money in the account after t years.

39. A 325 mg aspirin has a half-life of H hours in a patient's body.

(a) How long does it take for the quantity of aspirin in the patient's body to be reduced to 162.5 mg? To 81.25 mg? To 40.625 mg? (Note that $162.5 = 325/2$, etc. Your answers will involve H.)
(b) How many times does the quantity of aspirin, A mg, in the body halve in t hours? Use this to give a formula for A after t hours.

40. **(a)** The half-life of radium-226 is 1620 years. If the initial quantity of radium is Q_0, explain why the quantity, Q, of radium left after t years, is given by

$$Q = Q_0 \left(\frac{1}{2}\right)^{t/1620} .$$

(b) What percentage of the original amount of radium is left after 500 years?

41. In the early 1960s, radioactive strontium-90 was released during atmospheric testing of nuclear weapons and got into the bones of people alive at the time. If the half-life of strontium-90 is 29 years, what fraction of the strontium-90 absorbed in 1960 remained in people's bones in 2010? [Hint: Write the function in the form $Q = Q_0(1/2)^{t/29}$.]

42. Aircraft require longer takeoff distances, called takeoff rolls, at high altitude airports because of diminished air density. The table shows how the takeoff roll for a certain light airplane depends on the airport elevation. (Takeoff rolls are also strongly influenced by air temperature; the data shown assume a temperature of $0°$ C.) Determine a formula for this particular aircraft that gives the takeoff roll as an exponential function of airport elevation.

Elevation (ft)	Sea level	1000	2000	3000	4000
Takeoff roll (ft)	670	734	805	882	967

Problems 43–44 concern biodiesel, a fuel derived from renewable resources such as food crops, algae, and animal oils. The table shows the percent growth over the previous year in US biodiesel consumption.[14]

Year	2003	2004	2005	2006	2007	2008	2009
% growth	−12.5	92.9	237	186.6	37.2	−11.7	7.3

43. (a) According to the US Department of Energy, the US consumed 91 million gallons of biodiesel in 2005. Approximately how much biodiesel (in millions of gallons) did the US consume in 2006? In 2007?

(b) Graph the points showing the annual US consumption of biodiesel, in millions of gallons of biodiesel, for the years 2005 to 2009. Label the scales on the horizontal and vertical axes.

44. (a) True or false: The annual US consumption of biodiesel grew exponentially from 2003 to 2005. Justify your answer without doing any calculations.

(b) According to this data, during what single year(s), if any, did the US consumption of biodiesel at least double?

(c) According to this data, during what single year(s), if any, did the US consumption of biodiesel at least triple?

45. Hydroelectric power is electric power generated by the force of moving water. The table shows the annual percent change in hydroelectric power consumption by the US industrial sector.[15]

Year	2005	2006	2007	2008	2009
% growth over previous yr	−1.9	−10	−45.4	5.1	11

(a) According to the US Department of Energy, the US industrial sector consumed about 29 trillion BTUs of hydroelectric power in 2006. Approximately how much hydroelectric power (in trillion BTUs) did the US consume in 2007? In 2005?

(b) Graph the points showing the annual US consumption of hydroelectric power, in trillion BTUs, for the years 2004 to 2009. Label the scales on the horizontal and vertical axes.

(c) According to this data, when did the largest yearly decrease, in trillion BTUs, in the US consumption of hydroelectric power occur? What was this decrease?

Problems 46–47 concern wind power, which has been used for centuries to propel ships and mill grain. Modern wind power is obtained from windmills which convert wind energy into electricity. Figure 1.30 shows the annual percent growth in US wind power consumption[16] between 2005 and 2009.

Figure 1.30

46. (a) According to the US Department of Energy, the US consumption of wind power was 341 trillion BTUs in 2007. How much wind power did the US consume in 2006? In 2008?

(b) Graph the points showing the annual US consumption of wind power, in trillion BTUs, for the years 2005 to 2009. Label the scales on the horizontal and vertical axes.

(c) Based on this data, in what year did the largest yearly increase, in trillion BTUs, in the US consumption of wind power occur? What was this increase?

47. (a) According to Figure 1.30, during what single year(s), if any, did the US consumption of wind power energy increase by at least 40%? Decrease by at least 40%?

(b) Did the US consumption of wind power energy double from 2006 to 2008?

Strengthen Your Understanding

In Problems 48–49, explain what is wrong with the statement.

48. The function $y = e^{-0.25x}$ is decreasing and its graph is concave down.

49. The function $y = 2x$ is increasing, and its graph is concave up.

In Problems 50–52, give an example of:

50. A formula representing the statement "q decreases at a constant percent rate, and $q = 2.2$ when $t = 0$."

51. A function that is increasing at a constant percent rate and that has the same vertical intercept as $f(x) = 0.3x + 2$.

52. A function with a horizontal asymptote at $y = -5$ and range $y > -5$.

[14]http://www.eia.doe.gov/aer/renew.html. Accessed February 2011.

[15]From http://www.eia.doe.gov/aer/renew.html. Accessed February 2011.

[16]Yearly values have been joined with segments to highlight trends in the data. Actual values in between years should not be inferred from the segments. From http://www.eia.doe.gov/aer/renew.html. Accessed February 2011.

Are the statements in Problems 53–59 true or false? Give an explanation for your answer.

53. The function $y = 2 + 3e^{-t}$ has a y-intercept of $y = 3$.

54. The function $y = 5 - 3e^{-4t}$ has a horizontal asymptote of $y = 5$.

55. If $y = f(x)$ is an exponential function and if increasing x by 1 increases y by a factor of 5, then increasing x by 2 increases y by a factor of 10.

56. If $y = Ab^x$ and increasing x by 1 increases y by a factor of 3, then increasing x by 2 increases y by a factor of 9.

57. An exponential function can be decreasing.

58. If a and b are positive constants, $b \neq 1$, then $y = a + ab^x$ has a horizontal asymptote.

59. The function $y = 20/(1 + 2e^{-kt})$ with $k > 0$, has a horizontal asymptote at $y = 20$.

1.3 NEW FUNCTIONS FROM OLD

Shifts and Stretches

The graph of a constant multiple of a given function is easy to visualize: each y-value is stretched or shrunk by that multiple. For example, consider the function $f(x)$ and its multiples $y = 3f(x)$ and $y = -2f(x)$. Their graphs are shown in Figure 1.31. The factor 3 in the function $y = 3f(x)$ stretches each $f(x)$ value by multiplying it by 3; the factor -2 in the function $y = -2f(x)$ stretches $f(x)$ by multiplying by 2 and reflects it about the x-axis. You can think of the multiples of a given function as a family of functions.

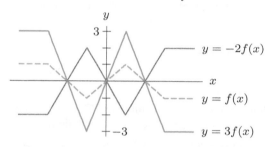

Figure 1.31: Multiples of the function $f(x)$

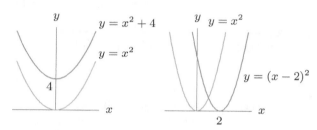

Figure 1.32: Graphs of $y = x^2$ with $y = x^2 + 4$ and $y = (x - 2)^2$

It is also easy to create families of functions by shifting graphs. For example, $y - 4 = x^2$ is the same as $y = x^2 + 4$, which is the graph of $y = x^2$ shifted up by 4. Similarly, $y = (x - 2)^2$ is the graph of $y = x^2$ shifted right by 2. (See Figure 1.32.)

- Multiplying a function by a constant, c, stretches the graph vertically (if $c > 1$) or shrinks the graph vertically (if $0 < c < 1$). A negative sign (if $c < 0$) reflects the graph about the x-axis, in addition to shrinking or stretching.
- Replacing y by $(y - k)$ moves a graph up by k (down if k is negative).
- Replacing x by $(x - h)$ moves a graph to the right by h (to the left if h is negative).

Composite Functions

If oil is spilled from a tanker, the area of the oil slick grows with time. Suppose that the oil slick is always a perfect circle. Then the area, A, of the oil slick is a function of its radius, r:

$$A = f(r) = \pi r^2.$$

The radius is also a function of time, because the radius increases as more oil spills. Thus, the area, being a function of the radius, is also a function of time. If, for example, the radius is given by

$$r = g(t) = 1 + t,$$

then the area is given as a function of time by substitution:

$$A = \pi r^2 = \pi(1+t)^2.$$

We are thinking of A as a *composite function* or a "function of a function," which is written

$$A = \underbrace{f(g(t))} = \pi(g(t))^2 = \pi(1+t)^2.$$

Composite function;
f is outside function,
g is inside function

To calculate A using the formula $\pi(1+t)^2$, the first step is to find $1+t$, and the second step is to square and multiply by π. The first step corresponds to the inside function $g(t) = 1+t$, and the second step corresponds to the outside function $f(r) = \pi r^2$.

Example 1   If $f(x) = x^2$ and $g(x) = x - 2$, find each of the following:
(a) $f(g(3))$ (b) $g(f(3))$ (c) $f(g(x))$ (d) $g(f(x))$

Solution   (a) Since $g(3) = 1$, we have $f(g(3)) = f(1) = 1$.
(b) Since $f(3) = 9$, we have $g(f(3)) = g(9) = 7$. Notice that $f(g(3)) \neq g(f(3))$.
(c) $f(g(x)) = f(x-2) = (x-2)^2$.
(d) $g(f(x)) = g(x^2) = x^2 - 2$. Again, notice that $f(g(x)) \neq g(f(x))$.
Notice that the horizontal shift in Figure 1.32 can be thought of as a composition $f(g(x)) = (x-2)^2$.

Example 2   Express each of the following functions as a composition:

(a) $h(t) = (1+t^3)^{27}$ (b) $k(y) = e^{-y^2}$ (c) $l(y) = -(e^y)^2$

Solution   In each case think about how you would calculate a value of the function. The first stage of the calculation gives you the inside function, and the second stage gives you the outside function.

(a) For $(1+t^3)^{27}$, the first stage is cubing and adding 1, so an inside function is $g(t) = 1+t^3$. The second stage is taking the 27th power, so an outside function is $f(y) = y^{27}$. Then

$$f(g(t)) = f(1+t^3) = (1+t^3)^{27}.$$

In fact, there are lots of different answers: $g(t) = t^3$ and $f(y) = (1+y)^{27}$ is another possibility.

(b) To calculate e^{-y^2} we square y, take its negative, and then take e to that power. So if $g(y) = -y^2$ and $f(z) = e^z$, then we have

$$f(g(y)) = e^{-y^2}.$$

(c) To calculate $-(e^y)^2$, we find e^y, square it, and take the negative. Using the same definitions of f and g as in part (b), the composition is

$$g(f(y)) = -(e^y)^2.$$

Since parts (b) and (c) give different answers, we see the order in which functions are composed is important.

Odd and Even Functions: Symmetry

There is a certain symmetry apparent in the graphs of $f(x) = x^2$ and $g(x) = x^3$ in Figure 1.33. For each point (x, x^2) on the graph of f, the point $(-x, x^2)$ is also on the graph; for each point (x, x^3) on the graph of g, the point $(-x, -x^3)$ is also on the graph. The graph of $f(x) = x^2$ is symmetric about the y-axis, whereas the graph of $g(x) = x^3$ is symmetric about the origin. The graph of any polynomial involving only even powers of x has symmetry about the y-axis, while polynomials with only odd powers of x are symmetric about the origin. Consequently, any functions with these symmetry properties are called *even* and *odd*, respectively.

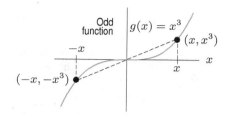

Figure 1.33: Symmetry of even and odd functions

> For any function f,
> f is an **even** function if $f(-x) = f(x)$ for all x.
> f is an **odd** function if $f(-x) = -f(x)$ for all x.

For example, $g(x) = e^{x^2}$ is even and $h(x) = x^{1/3}$ is odd. However, many functions do not have any symmetry and are neither even nor odd.

Inverse Functions

On August 26, 2005, the runner Kenenisa Bekele[17] of Ethiopia set a world record for the 10,000-meter race. His times, in seconds, at 2000-meter intervals are recorded in Table 1.14, where $t = f(d)$ is the number of seconds Bekele took to complete the first d meters of the race. For example, Bekele ran the first 4000 meters in 629.98 seconds, so $f(4000) = 629.98$. The function f was useful to athletes planning to compete with Bekele.

Let us now change our point of view and ask for distances rather than times. If we ask how far Bekele ran during the first 629.98 seconds of his race, the answer is clearly 4000 meters. Going backward in this way from numbers of seconds to numbers of meters gives f^{-1}, the *inverse function*[18] of f. We write $f^{-1}(629.98) = 4000$. Thus, $f^{-1}(t)$ is the number of meters that Bekele ran during the first t seconds of his race. See Table 1.15, which contains values of f^{-1}.

The independent variable for f is the dependent variable for f^{-1}, and vice versa. The domains and ranges of f and f^{-1} are also interchanged. The domain of f is all distances d such that $0 \leq d \leq 10000$, which is the range of f^{-1}. The range of f is all times t, such that $0 \leq t \leq 1577.53$, which is the domain of f^{-1}.

Table 1.14   *Bekele's running time*

d (meters)	$t = f(d)$ (seconds)
0	0.00
2000	315.63
4000	629.98
6000	944.66
8000	1264.63
10000	1577.53

Table 1.15   *Distance run by Bekele*

t (seconds)	$d = f^{-1}(t)$ (meters)
0.00	0
315.63	2000
629.98	4000
944.66	6000
1264.63	8000
1577.53	10000

Which Functions Have Inverses?

If a function has an inverse, we say it is *invertible*. Let's look at a function which is not invertible. Consider the flight of the Mercury spacecraft *Freedom 7*, which carried Alan Shepard, Jr. into space

---

[17]kenenisabekelle.com/, accessed January 11, 2011.
[18]The notation f^{-1} represents the inverse function, which is not the same as the reciprocal, $1/f$.

in May 1961. Shepard was the first American to journey into space. After launch, his spacecraft rose to an altitude of 116 miles, and then came down into the sea. The function $f(t)$ giving the altitude in miles t minutes after lift-off does not have an inverse. To see why not, try to decide on a value for $f^{-1}(100)$, which should be the time when the altitude of the spacecraft was 100 miles. However, there are two such times, one when the spacecraft was ascending and one when it was descending. (See Figure 1.34.)

The reason the altitude function does not have an inverse is that the altitude has the same value for two different times. The reason the Bekele time function did have an inverse is that each running time, t, corresponds to a unique distance, d.

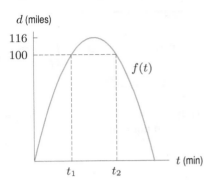

Figure 1.34: Two times, t_1 and t_2, at which altitude of spacecraft is 100 miles

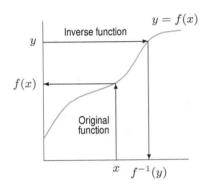

Figure 1.35: A function which has an inverse

Figure 1.35 suggests when an inverse exists. The original function, f, takes us from an x-value to a y-value, as shown in Figure 1.35. Since having an inverse means there is a function going from a y-value to an x-value, the crucial question is whether we can get back. In other words, does each y-value correspond to a unique x-value? If so, there's an inverse; if not, there is not. This principle may be stated geometrically, as follows:

A function has an inverse if (and only if) its graph intersects any horizontal line at most once.

For example, the function $f(x) = x^2$ does not have an inverse because many horizontal lines intersect the parabola twice.

Definition of an Inverse Function

If the function f is invertible, its inverse is defined as follows:

$$f^{-1}(y) = x \quad \text{means} \quad y = f(x).$$

Formulas for Inverse Functions

If a function is defined by a formula, it is sometimes possible to find a formula for the inverse function. In Section 1.1, we looked at the snow tree cricket, whose chirp rate, C, in chirps per minute, is approximated at the temperature, T, in degrees Fahrenheit, by the formula

$$C = f(T) = 4T - 160.$$

So far we have used this formula to predict the chirp rate from the temperature. But it is also possible to use this formula backward to calculate the temperature from the chirp rate.

Example 3   Find the formula for the function giving temperature in terms of the number of cricket chirps per minute; that is, find the inverse function f^{-1} such that

$$T = f^{-1}(C).$$

Solution   Since C is an increasing function, f is invertible. We know $C = 4T - 160$. We solve for T, giving

$$T = \frac{C}{4} + 40,$$

so

$$f^{-1}(C) = \frac{C}{4} + 40.$$

Graphs of Inverse Functions

The function $f(x) = x^3$ is increasing everywhere and so has an inverse. To find the inverse, we solve

$$y = x^3$$

for x, giving

$$x = y^{1/3}.$$

The inverse function is

$$f^{-1}(y) = y^{1/3}$$

or, if we want to call the independent variable x,

$$f^{-1}(x) = x^{1/3}.$$

The graphs of $y = x^3$ and $y = x^{1/3}$ are shown in Figure 1.36. Notice that these graphs are the reflections of one another about the line $y = x$. For example, $(8, 2)$ is on the graph of $y = x^{1/3}$ because $2 = 8^{1/3}$, and $(2, 8)$ is on the graph of $y = x^3$ because $8 = 2^3$. The points $(8, 2)$ and $(2, 8)$ are reflections of one another about the line $y = x$.

In general, we have the following result.

> If the x- and y-axes have the same scales, the graph of f^{-1} is the reflection of the graph of f about the line $y = x$.

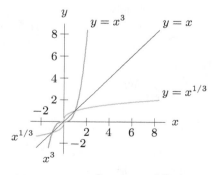

Figure 1.36: Graphs of inverse functions, $y = x^3$ and $y = x^{1/3}$, are reflections about the line $y = x$

Exercises and Problems for Section 1.3

Exercises

For the functions f in Exercises 1–3, graph:

(a) $f(x+2)$ (b) $f(x-1)$ (c) $f(x)-4$
(d) $f(x+1)+3$ (e) $3f(x)$ (f) $-f(x)+1$

1.

2.

3.

In Exercises 4–7, use Figure 1.37 to graph the functions.

Figure 1.37

4. $n(t) = m(t) + 2$ **5.** $p(t) = m(t-1)$

6. $k(t) = m(t+1.5)$

7. $w(t) = m(t-0.5) - 2.5$

For the functions f and g in Exercises 8–11, find

(a) $f(g(1))$ (b) $g(f(1))$ (c) $f(g(x))$
(d) $g(f(x))$ (e) $f(t)g(t)$

8. $f(x) = x^2, g(x) = x+1$

9. $f(x) = \sqrt{x+4}, g(x) = x^2$

10. $f(x) = e^x, g(x) = x^2$

11. $f(x) = 1/x, g(x) = 3x+4$

12. For $g(x) = x^2 + 2x + 3$, find and simplify:

(a) $g(2+h)$ (b) $g(2)$
(c) $g(2+h) - g(2)$

13. If $f(x) = x^2 + 1$, find and simplify:

(a) $f(t+1)$ (b) $f(t^2+1)$ (c) $f(2)$
(d) $2f(t)$ (e) $(f(t))^2 + 1$

Simplify the quantities in Exercises 14–17 using $m(z) = z^2$.

14. $m(z+1) - m(z)$ **15.** $m(z+h) - m(z)$

16. $m(z) - m(z-h)$ **17.** $m(z+h) - m(z-h)$

18. Let p be the price of an item and q be the number of items sold at that price, where $q = f(p)$. What do the following quantities mean in terms of prices and quantities sold?

(a) $f(25)$ (b) $f^{-1}(30)$

19. Let $C = f(A)$ be the cost, in dollars, of building a store of area A square feet. In terms of cost and square feet, what do the following quantities represent?

(a) $f(10,000)$ (b) $f^{-1}(20,000)$

20. Let $f(x)$ be the temperature (°F) when the column of mercury in a particular thermometer is x inches long. What is the meaning of $f^{-1}(75)$ in practical terms?

21. (a) Write an equation for a graph obtained by vertically stretching the graph of $y = x^2$ by a factor of 2, followed by a vertical upward shift of 1 unit. Sketch it.
(b) What is the equation if the order of the transformations (stretching and shifting) in part (a) is interchanged?
(c) Are the two graphs the same? Explain the effect of reversing the order of transformations.

22. Use Figure 1.38 to graph each of the following. Label any intercepts or asymptotes that can be determined.

(a) $y = f(x) + 3$ (b) $y = 2f(x)$
(c) $y = f(x+4)$ (d) $y = 4 - f(x)$

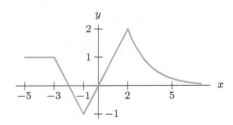

Figure 1.38

For Exercises 23–24, decide if the function $y = f(x)$ is invertible.

23.

24.

For Exercises 25–27, use a graph of the function to decide whether or not it is invertible.

25. $f(x) = x^2 + 3x + 2$ **26.** $f(x) = x^3 - 5x + 10$

27. $f(x) = x^3 + 5x + 10$

Are the functions in Exercises 28–35 even, odd, or neither?

28. $f(x) = x^6 + x^3 + 1$ **29.** $f(x) = x^3 + x^2 + x$

30. $f(x) = x^4 - x^2 + 3$ **31.** $f(x) = x^3 + 1$

32. $f(x) = 2x$ **33.** $f(x) = e^{x^2 - 1}$

34. $f(x) = x(x^2 - 1)$ **35.** $f(x) = e^x - x$

Problems

For Problems 36–39, determine functions f and g such that $h(x) = f(g(x))$. [Note: There is more than one correct answer. Do not choose $f(x) = x$ or $g(x) = x$.]

36. $h(x) = (x + 1)^3$ **37.** $h(x) = x^3 + 1$

38. $h(x) = \sqrt{x^2 + 4}$ **39.** $h(x) = e^{2x}$

Find possible formulas for the graphs in Problems 40–41 using shifts of x^2 or x^3.

40.

41.

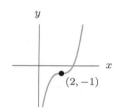

42. (a) Use Figure 1.39 to estimate $f^{-1}(2)$.
(b) Sketch a graph of f^{-1} on the same axes.

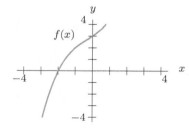

Figure 1.39

43. Write a table of values for f^{-1}, where f is as given below. The domain of f is the integers from 1 to 7. State the domain of f^{-1}.

x	1	2	3	4	5	6	7
$f(x)$	3	-7	19	4	178	2	1

For Problems 44–47, decide if the function f is invertible.

44. $f(d)$ is the total number of gallons of fuel an airplane has used by the end of d minutes of a particular flight.

45. $f(t)$ is the number of customers in Macy's department store at t minutes past noon on December 18, 2008.

46. $f(n)$ is the number of students in your calculus class whose birthday is on the nth day of the year.

47. $f(w)$ is the cost of mailing a letter weighing w grams.

In Problems 48–51 the functions $r = f(t)$ and $V = g(r)$ give the radius and the volume of a commercial hot air balloon being inflated for testing. The variable t is in minutes, r is in feet, and V is in cubic feet. The inflation begins at $t = 0$. In each case, give a mathematical expression that represents the given statement.

48. The volume of the balloon t minutes after inflation began.

49. The volume of the balloon if its radius were twice as big.

50. The time that has elapsed when the radius of the balloon is 30 feet.

51. The time that has elapsed when the volume of the balloon is 10,000 cubic feet.

In Problems 52–55, use Figure 1.40 to estimate the function value or explain why it cannot be done.

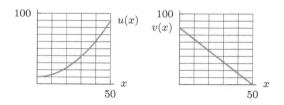

Figure 1.40

52. $u(v(10))$ **53.** $u(v(40))$

54. $v(u(10))$ **55.** $v(u(40))$

56. Figure 1.41 shows $f(t)$, the number (in millions) of motor vehicles registered[19] in the world in the year t.

  (a) Is f invertible? Explain.
  (b) What is the meaning of $f^{-1}(400)$ in practical terms? Evaluate $f^{-1}(400)$.
  (c) Sketch the graph of f^{-1}.

(millions)

Figure 1.41

For Problems 57–62, use the graphs in Figure 1.42.

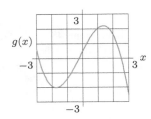

Figure 1.42

57. Estimate $f(g(1))$.

58. Estimate $g(f(2))$.

59. Estimate $f(f(1))$.

60. Graph $f(g(x))$.

61. Graph $g(f(x))$.

62. Graph $f(f(x))$.

63. Figure 1.43 is a graph of the function $f(t)$. Here $f(t)$ is the depth in meters below the Atlantic Ocean floor where t million-year-old rock can be found.[20]

  (a) Evaluate $f(15)$, and say what it means in practical terms.
  (b) Is f invertible? Explain.
  (c) Evaluate $f^{-1}(120)$, and say what it means in practical terms.
  (d) Sketch a graph of f^{-1}.

Time (millions of years)

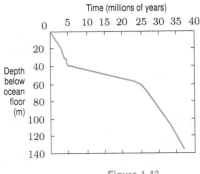

Figure 1.43

64. A tree of height y meters has, on average, B branches, where $B = y - 1$. Each branch has, on average, n leaves, where $n = 2B^2 - B$. Find the average number of leaves of a tree as a function of height.

65. A spherical balloon is growing with radius $r = 3t + 1$, in centimeters, for time t in seconds. Find the volume of the balloon at 3 seconds.

66. The cost of producing q articles is given by the function $C = f(q) = 100 + 2q$.

  (a) Find a formula for the inverse function.
  (b) Explain in practical terms what the inverse function tells you.

67. How does the graph of $Q = S(1 - e^{-kt})$ in Example 4 on page 16 relate to the graph of the exponential decay function, $y = Se^{-kt}$?

68. Complete the following table with values for the functions f, g, and h, given that:

  (a) f is an even function.
  (b) g is an odd function.
  (c) h is the composition $h(x) = g(f(x))$.

x	$f(x)$	$g(x)$	$h(x)$
-3	0	0	
-2	2	2	
-1	2	2	
0	0	0	
1			
2			
3			

---

[19]www.earth-policy.org, accessed June 5, 2011. In 2000, about 30% of the registered vehicles were in the US.
[20]Data of Dr. Murlene Clark based on core samples drilled by the research ship *Glomar Challenger*, taken from *Initial Reports of the Deep Sea Drilling Project*.

Strengthen Your Understanding

In Problems 69–71, explain what is wrong with the statement.

69. The graph of $f(x) = -(x + 1)^3$ is the graph of $g(x) = -x^3$ shifted right by 1 unit.

70. $f(x) = 3x + 5$ and $g(x) = -3x - 5$ are inverse functions of each other.

71. The inverse of $f(x) = x$ is $f^{-1}(x) = 1/x$.

In Problems 72–75, give an example of:

72. An invertible function whose graph contains the point $(0, 3)$.

73. An even function whose graph does not contain the point $(0, 0)$.

74. An increasing function $f(x)$ whose values are greater than those of its inverse function $f^{-1}(x)$ for $x > 0$.

75. Two functions $f(x)$ and $g(x)$ such that moving the graph of f to the left 2 units gives the graph of g and moving the graph of f up 3 also gives the graph of g.

Are the statements in Problems 76–83 true or false? Give an explanation for your answer.

76. The graph of $f(x) = 100(10^x)$ is a horizontal shift of the graph of $g(x) = 10^x$.

77. If f is an increasing function, then f^{-1} is an increasing function.

78. If a function is even, then it does not have an inverse.

79. If a function is odd, then it does not have an inverse.

80. The function $f(x) = e^{-x^2}$ is decreasing for all x.

81. If $g(x)$ is an even function then $f(g(x))$ is even for every function $f(x)$.

82. If $f(x)$ is an even function then $f(g(x))$ is even for every function $g(x)$.

83. There is a function which is both even and odd.

Suppose f is an increasing function and g is a decreasing function. In Problems 84–87, give an example for f and g for which the statement is true, or say why such an example is impossible.

84. $f(x) + g(x)$ is decreasing for all x.

85. $f(x) - g(x)$ is decreasing for all x.

86. $f(x)g(x)$ is decreasing for all x.

87. $f(g(x))$ is increasing for all x.

1.4 LOGARITHMIC FUNCTIONS

In Section 1.2, we approximated the population of Burkina Faso (in millions) by the function

$$P = f(t) = 12.853(1.034)^t,$$

where t is the number of years since 2003. Now suppose that instead of calculating the population at time t, we ask when the population will reach 20 million. We want to find the value of t for which

$$20 = f(t) = 12.853(1.034)^t.$$

We use logarithms to solve for a variable in an exponent.

Logarithms to Base 10 and to Base e

We define the *logarithm* function, $\log_{10} x$, to be the inverse of the exponential function, 10^x, as follows:

> The **logarithm** to base 10 of x, written **$\log_{10} x$**, is the power of 10 we need to get x. In other words,
>
> $$\log_{10} x = c \quad \text{means} \quad 10^c = x.$$
>
> We often write $\log x$ in place of $\log_{10} x$.

The other frequently used base is e. The logarithm to base e is called the *natural logarithm* of x, written $\ln x$ and defined to be the inverse function of e^x, as follows:

> The **natural logarithm** of x, written $\ln x$, is the power of e needed to get x. In other words,
>
> $$\ln x = c \quad \text{means} \quad e^c = x.$$

Values of $\log x$ are in Table 1.16. Because no power of 10 gives 0, $\log 0$ is undefined. The graph of $y = \log x$ is shown in Figure 1.44. The domain of $y = \log x$ is positive real numbers; the range is all real numbers. In contrast, the inverse function $y = 10^x$ has domain all real numbers and range all positive real numbers. The graph of $y = \log x$ has a vertical asymptote at $x = 0$, whereas $y = 10^x$ has a horizontal asymptote at $y = 0$.

One big difference between $y = 10^x$ and $y = \log x$ is that the exponential function grows extremely quickly whereas the log function grows extremely slowly. However, $\log x$ does go to infinity, albeit slowly, as x increases. Since $y = \log x$ and $y = 10^x$ are inverse functions, the graphs of the two functions are reflections of one another about the line $y = x$, provided the scales along the x- and y-axes are equal.

Table 1.16   *Values for* $\log x$ *and* 10^x

x	$\log x$	x	10^x
0	undefined	0	1
1	0	1	10
2	0.3	2	100
3	0.5	3	10^3
4	0.6	4	10^4
$\vdots$	$\vdots$	$\vdots$	$\vdots$
10	1	10	10^{10}

Figure 1.44: Graphs of $\log x$ and 10^x

The graph of $y = \ln x$ in Figure 1.45 has roughly the same shape as the graph of $y = \log x$. The x-intercept is $x = 1$, since $\ln 1 = 0$. The graph of $y = \ln x$ also climbs very slowly as x increases. Both graphs, $y = \log x$ and $y = \ln x$, have *vertical asymptotes* at $x = 0$.

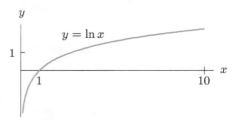

Figure 1.45: Graph of the natural logarithm

The following properties of logarithms may be deduced from the properties of exponents:

Properties of Logarithms

Note that $\log x$ and $\ln x$ are not defined when x is negative or 0.

1. $\log(AB) = \log A + \log B$
2. $\log\left(\dfrac{A}{B}\right) = \log A - \log B$
3. $\log\left(A^p\right) = p \log A$
4. $\log\left(10^x\right) = x$
5. $10^{\log x} = x$

1. $\ln(AB) = \ln A + \ln B$
2. $\ln\left(\dfrac{A}{B}\right) = \ln A - \ln B$
3. $\ln\left(A^p\right) = p \ln A$
4. $\ln e^x = x$
5. $e^{\ln x} = x$

In addition, $\log 1 = 0$ because $10^0 = 1$, and $\ln 1 = 0$ because $e^0 = 1$.

Solving Equations Using Logarithms

Logs are frequently useful when we have to solve for unknown exponents, as in the next examples.

Example 1   Find t such that $2^t = 7$.

Solution   First, notice that we expect t to be between 2 and 3 (because $2^2 = 4$ and $2^3 = 8$). To calculate t, we take logs to base 10 of both sides. (Natural logs could also be used.)

$$\log(2^t) = \log 7.$$

Then use the third property of logs, which says $\log(2^t) = t \log 2$, and get:

$$t \log 2 = \log 7.$$

Using a calculator to find the logs gives

$$t = \frac{\log 7}{\log 2} \approx 2.81.$$

Example 2   Find when the population of Burkina Faso reaches 20 million by solving $20 = 12.853(1.034)^t$.

Solution   Dividing both sides of the equation by 12.853, we get

$$\frac{20}{12.853} = (1.034)^t.$$

Now take logs of both sides:

$$\log\left(\frac{20}{12.853}\right) = \log(1.034^t).$$

Using the fact that $\log(A^t) = t \log A$, we get

$$\log\left(\frac{20}{12.853}\right) = t \log(1.034).$$

Solving this equation using a calculator to find the logs, we get

$$t = \frac{\log(20/12.853)}{\log(1.034)} = 13.22 \text{ years}$$

which is between $t = 13$ and $t = 14$. This value of t corresponds to the year 2016.

Example 3   Traffic pollution is harmful to school-age children. The concentration of carbon monoxide, CO, in the air near a busy road is a function of distance from the road. The concentration decays exponentially at a continuous rate of 3.3% per meter.[21] At what distance from the road is the concentration of CO half what it is on the road?

Solution   If C_0 is the concentration of CO on the road, then the concentration x meters from the road is

$$C = C_0 e^{-0.033x}.$$

We want to find the value of x making $C = C_0/2$, that is,

$$C_0 e^{-0.033x} = \frac{C_0}{2}.$$

Dividing by C_0 and then taking natural logs yields

$$\ln\left(e^{-0.033x}\right) = -0.033x = \ln\left(\frac{1}{2}\right) = -0.6931,$$

so

$$x = 21 \text{ meters.}$$

At 21 meters from the road the concentration of CO in the air is half the concentration on the road.

---

[21] Rickwood, P. and Knight, D. (2009). "The health impacts of local traffic pollution on primary school age children." *State of Australian Cities 2009 Conference Proceedings*.

In Example 3 the decay rate was given. However, in many situations where we expect to find exponential growth or decay, the rate is not given. To find it, we must know the quantity at two different times and then solve for the growth or decay rate, as in the next example.

Example 4 The population of Mexico was 99.9 million in 2000 and 113.4 million in 2010.[22] Assuming it increases exponentially, find a formula for the population of Mexico as a function of time.

Solution If we measure the population, P, in millions and time, t, in years since 2000, we can say

$$P = P_0 e^{kt} = 99.9 e^{kt},$$

where $P_0 = 99.9$ is the initial value of P. We find k by using the fact that $P = 113.4$ when $t = 10$, so

$$113.4 = 99.9 e^{k \cdot 10}.$$

To find k, we divide both sides by 99.9, giving

$$\frac{113.4}{99.9} = 1.135 = e^{10k}.$$

Now take natural logs of both sides:

$$\ln(1.135) = \ln(e^{10k}).$$

Using a calculator and the fact that $\ln(e^{10k}) = 10k$, this becomes

$$0.127 = 10k.$$

So

$$k = 0.0127,$$

and therefore

$$P = 99.9 e^{0.0127t}.$$

Since $k = 0.0127 = 1.27\%$, the population of Mexico was growing at a continuous rate of 1.27% per year.

In Example 4 we chose to use e for the base of the exponential function representing Mexico's population, making clear that the continuous growth rate was 1.27%. If we had wanted to emphasize the annual growth rate, we could have expressed the exponential function in the form $P = P_0 a^t$.

Example 5 Give a formula for the inverse of the following function (that is, solve for t in terms of P):

$$P = f(t) = 12.853(1.034)^t.$$

Solution We want a formula expressing t as a function of P. Take logs:

$$\log P = \log(12.853(1.034)^t).$$

Since $\log(AB) = \log A + \log B$, we have

$$\log P = \log 12.853 + \log((1.034)^t).$$

Now use $\log(A^t) = t \log A$:

$$\log P = \log 12.853 + t \log 1.034.$$

Solve for t in two steps, using a calculator at the final stage:

$$t \log 1.034 = \log P - \log 12.853$$

$$t = \frac{\log P}{\log 1.034} - \frac{\log 12.853}{\log 1.034} = 68.868 \log P - 76.375.$$

---

[22]http://data.worldbank.org/country/mexico. Accessed January 14, 2012.

Thus,

$$f^{-1}(P) = 68.868 \log P - 76.375.$$

Note that

$$f^{-1}(20) = 68.868(\log 20) - 76.375 = 13.22,$$

which agrees with the result of Example 2.

Exercises and Problems for Section 1.4

Exercises

Simplify the expressions in Exercises 1–6 completely.

1. $e^{\ln(1/2)}$

2. $10^{\log(AB)}$

3. $5e^{\ln(A^2)}$

4. $\ln(e^{2AB})$

5. $\ln(1/e) + \ln(AB)$

6. $2\ln\left(e^A\right) + 3\ln B^e$

For Exercises 7–18, solve for x using logs.

7. $3^x = 11$

8. $17^x = 2$

9. $20 = 50(1.04)^x$

10. $4 \cdot 3^x = 7 \cdot 5^x$

11. $7 = 5e^{0.2x}$

12. $2^x = e^{x+1}$

13. $50 = 600e^{-0.4x}$

14. $2e^{3x} = 4e^{5x}$

15. $7^{x+2} = e^{17x}$

16. $10^{x+3} = 5e^{7-x}$

17. $2x - 1 = e^{\ln x^2}$

18. $4e^{2x-3} - 5 = e$

For Exercises 19–24, solve for t. Assume a and b are positive constants and k is nonzero.

19. $a = b^t$

20. $P = P_0 a^t$

21. $Q = Q_0 a^{nt}$

22. $P_0 a^t = Q_0 b^t$

23. $a = be^t$

24. $P = P_0 e^{kt}$

In Exercises 25–28, put the functions in the form $P = P_0 e^{kt}$.

25. $P = 15(1.5)^t$

26. $P = 10(1.7)^t$

27. $P = 174(0.9)^t$

28. $P = 4(0.55)^t$

Find the inverse function in Exercises 29–31.

29. $p(t) = (1.04)^t$

30. $f(t) = 50e^{0.1t}$

31. $f(t) = 1 + \ln t$

Problems

32. The population of a region is growing exponentially. There were 40,000,000 people in 2000 ($t = 0$) and 48,000,000 in 2010. Find an expression for the population at any time t, in years. What population would you predict for the year 2020? What is the doubling time?

33. One hundred kilograms of a radioactive substance decay to 40 kg in 10 years. How much remains after 20 years?

34. A culture of bacteria originally numbers 500. After 2 hours there are 1500 bacteria in the culture. Assuming exponential growth, how many are there after 6 hours?

35. The population of the US was 281.4 million in 2000 and 308.7 million in 2010.[23] Assuming exponential growth,

    (a) In what year is the population expected to go over 350 million?
    (b) What population is predicted for the 2020 census?

36. The concentration of the car exhaust fume nitrous oxide, NO_2, in the air near a busy road is a function of distance from the road. The concentration decays exponentially at a continuous rate of 2.54% per meter.[24] At what distance from the road is the concentration of NO_2 half what it is on the road?

37. For children and adults with diseases such as asthma, the number of respiratory deaths per year increases by 0.33% when pollution particles increase by a microgram per cubic meter of air.[25]

    (a) Write a formula for the number of respiratory deaths per year as a function of quantity of pollution in the air. (Let Q_0 be the number of deaths per year with no pollution.)
    (b) What quantity of air pollution results in twice as many respiratory deaths per year as there would be without pollution?

---

[23] http://2010.census.gov/2010census/. Accessed April 17, 2011.

[24] Rickwood, P. and Knight, D. (2009). "The health impacts of local traffic pollution on primary school age children." *State of Australian Cities 2009 Conference Proceedings.*

[25] Brook, R. D., Franklin, B., Cascio, W., Hong, Y., Howard, G., Lipsett, M., Luepker, R., Mittleman, M., Samet, J., and Smith, S. C. (2004). "Air pollution and cardiovascular disease." *Circulation,* 109(21):2655267.

38. The number of alternative fuel vehicles[26] running on E85, fuel that is up to 85% plant-derived ethanol, increased exponentially in the US between 2003 and 2008.

    (a) Use this information to complete the missing table values.

    (b) How many E85-powered vehicles were there in the US in 2003?

    (c) By what percent did the number of E85-powered vehicles grow from 2004 to 2008?

Year	2004	2005	2006	2007	2008
Number of E85 vehicles	211,800	?	?	?	450,327

39. At time t hours after taking the cough suppressant hydrocodone bitartrate, the amount, A, in mg, remaining in the body is given by $A = 10(0.82)^t$.

    (a) What was the initial amount taken?

    (b) What percent of the drug leaves the body each hour?

    (c) How much of the drug is left in the body 6 hours after the dose is administered?

    (d) How long is it until only 1 mg of the drug remains in the body?

40. A cup of coffee contains 100 mg of caffeine, which leaves the body at a continuous rate of 17% per hour.

    (a) Write a formula for the amount, A mg, of caffeine in the body t hours after drinking a cup of coffee.

    (b) Graph the function from part (a). Use the graph to estimate the half-life of caffeine.

    (c) Use logarithms to find the half-life of caffeine.

41. The exponential function $y(x) = Ce^{\alpha x}$ satisfies the conditions $y(0) = 2$ and $y(1) = 1$. Find the constants C and α. What is $y(2)$?

42. Without a calculator or computer, match the functions e^x, $\ln x$, x^2, and $x^{1/2}$ to their graphs in Figure 1.46.

A B

C
D

x

Figure 1.46

43. With time, t, in years since the start of 1980, textbook prices have increased at 6.7% per year while inflation has been 3.3% per year.[27] Assume both rates are continuous growth rates.

    (a) Find a formula for $B(t)$, the price of a textbook in year t if it cost $\$B_0$ in 1980.

    (b) Find a formula for $P(t)$, the price of an item in year t if it cost $\$P_0$ in 1980 and its price rose according to inflation.

    (c) A textbook cost $50 in 1980. When is its price predicted to be double the price that would have resulted from inflation alone?

44. In November 2010, a "tiger summit" was held in St. Petersburg, Russia.[28] In 1900, there were 100,000 wild tigers worldwide; in 2010 the number was 3200.

    (a) Assuming the tiger population has decreased exponentially, find a formula for $f(t)$, the number of wild tigers t years since 1900.

    (b) Between 2000 and 2010, the number of wild tigers decreased by 40%. Is this percentage larger or smaller than the decrease in the tiger population predicted by your answer to part (a)?

45. In 2011, the populations of China and India were approximately 1.34 and 1.19 billion people[29], respectively. However, due to central control the annual population growth rate of China was 0.4% while the population of India was growing by 1.37% each year. If these growth rates remain constant, when will the population of India exceed that of China?

46. The third-quarter revenue of Apple® went from $3.68 billion[30] in 2005 to $15.68 billion[31] in 2010. Find an exponential function to model the revenue as a function of years since 2005. What is the continuous percent growth rate, per year, of sales?

47. The world population was 6.9 billion at the end of 2010 and is predicted to reach 9 billion by the end of 2050.[32]

    (a) Assuming the population is growing exponentially, what is the continuous growth rate per year?

    (b) The United Nations celebrated the "Day of 5 Billion" on July 11, 1987, and the "Day of 6 Billion" on October 12, 1999. Using the growth rate in part (a), when is the "Day of 7 Billion" predicted to be?

[26] http://www.eia.doe.gov/aer/renew.html
[27] Data from "Textbooks headed for ash heap of history", http://educationtechnews.com, Vol 5, 2010.
[28] "Tigers would be extinct in Russia if unprotected," Yahoo! News, Nov. 21, 2010.
[29] http://www.indexmundi.com/. Accessed April 17, 2011.
[30] http://www.apple.com/pr/library/2005/oct/11results.html. Accessed April 27, 2011.
[31] http://www.apple.com/pr/library/2010/01/25results.html. Accessed April 27, 2011.
[32] "Reviewing the Bidding on the Climate Files", in About Dot Earth, *New York Times*, Nov. 19, 2010.

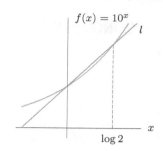

Figure 1.47

48. In the early 1920s, Germany had tremendously high inflation, called hyperinflation. Photographs of the time show people going to the store with wheelbarrows full of money. If a loaf of bread cost 1/4 marks in 1919 and 2,400,000 marks in 1922, what was the average yearly inflation rate between 1919 and 1922?

49. Different isotopes (versions) of the same element can have very different half-lives. With t in years, the decay of plutonium-240 is described by the formula

$$Q = Q_0 e^{-0.00011t},$$

whereas the decay of plutonium-242 is described by

$$Q = Q_0 e^{-0.0000018t}.$$

Find the half-lives of plutonium-240 and plutonium-242.

50. The size of an exponentially growing bacteria colony doubles in 5 hours. How long will it take for the number of bacteria to triple?

51. Air pressure, P, decreases exponentially with height, h, above sea level. If P_0 is the air pressure at sea level and h is in meters, then

$$P = P_0 e^{-0.00012h}.$$

(a) At the top of Mount McKinley, height 6194 meters (about 20,320 feet), what is the air pressure, as a percent of the pressure at sea level?

(b) The maximum cruising altitude of an ordinary commercial jet is around 12,000 meters (about 39,000 feet). At that height, what is the air pressure, as a percent of the sea level value?

52. Find the equation of the line l in Figure 1.47.

53. In 2010, there were about 246 million vehicles (cars and trucks) and about 308.7 million people in the US.[33] The number of vehicles grew 15.5% over the previous decade, while the population has been growing at 9.7% per decade. If the growth rates remain constant, when will there be, on average, one vehicle per person?

54. A picture supposedly painted by Vermeer (1632–1675) contains 99.5% of its carbon-14 (half-life 5730 years). From this information decide whether the picture is a fake. Explain your reasoning.

55. Is there a difference between $\ln[\ln(x)]$ and $\ln^2(x)$? [Note: $\ln^2(x)$ is another way of writing $(\ln x)^2$.]

56. If $h(x) = \ln(x + a)$, where $a > 0$, what is the effect of increasing a on

(a) The y-intercept?   (b) The x-intercept?

57. If $h(x) = \ln(x + a)$, where $a > 0$, what is the effect of increasing a on the vertical asymptote?

58. If $g(x) = \ln(ax + 2)$, where $a \neq 0$, what is the effect of increasing a on

(a) The y-intercept?   (b) The x-intercept?

59. If $f(x) = a\ln(x + 2)$, what is the effect of increasing a on the vertical asymptote?

60. If $g(x) = \ln(ax + 2)$, where $a \neq 0$, what is the effect of increasing a on the vertical asymptote?

Strengthen Your Understanding

In Problems 61–62, explain what is wrong with the statement.

61. The function $-\log|x|$ is odd.

62. For all $x > 0$, the value of $\ln(100x)$ is 100 times larger than $\ln x$.

In Problems 63–64, give an example of:

63. A function $f(x)$ such that $\ln(f(x))$ is only defined for $x < 0$.

64. A function with a vertical asymptote at $x = 3$ and defined only for $x > 3$.

Are the statements in Problems 65–68 true or false? Give an explanation for your answer.

65. The graph of $f(x) = \ln x$ is concave down.

66. The graph of $g(x) = \log(x - 1)$ crosses the x-axis at $x = 1$.

67. The inverse function of $y = \log x$ is $y = 1/\log x$.

68. If a and b are positive constants, then $y = \ln(ax + b)$ has no vertical asymptote.

[33]http://www.autoblog.com/2010/01/04/report-number-of-cars-in-the-u-s-dropped-by-four-million-in-20/   and
http://2010.census.gov/news/releases/operations/cb10-cn93.html. Accessed February 2012.

1.5 TRIGONOMETRIC FUNCTIONS

Trigonometry originated as part of the study of triangles. The name *tri-gon-o-metry* means the measurement of three-cornered figures, and the first definitions of the trigonometric functions were in terms of triangles. However, the trigonometric functions can also be defined using the unit circle, a definition that makes them periodic, or repeating. Many naturally occurring processes are also periodic. The water level in a tidal basin, the blood pressure in a heart, an alternating current, and the position of the air molecules transmitting a musical note all fluctuate regularly. Such phenomena can be represented by trigonometric functions.

Radians

There are two commonly used ways to represent the input of the trigonometric functions: radians and degrees. The formulas of calculus, as you will see, are neater in radians than in degrees.

> An angle of 1 **radian** is defined to be the angle at the center of a unit circle which cuts off an arc of length 1, measured counterclockwise. (See Figure 1.48(a).) A unit circle has radius 1.

An angle of 2 radians cuts off an arc of length 2 on a unit circle. A negative angle, such as $-1/2$ radians, cuts off an arc of length $1/2$, but measured clockwise. (See Figure 1.48(b).)

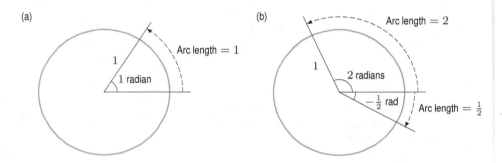

Figure 1.48: Radians defined using unit circle

It is useful to think of angles as rotations, since then we can make sense of angles larger than 360°; for example, an angle of 720° represents two complete rotations counterclockwise. Since one full rotation of 360° cuts off an arc of length 2π, the circumference of the unit circle, it follows that

$$360° = 2\pi \text{ radians}, \quad \text{so} \quad 180° = \pi \text{ radians}.$$

In other words, 1 radian = $180°/\pi$, so one radian is about 60°. The word radians is often dropped, so if an angle or rotation is referred to without units, it is understood to be in radians.

Radians are useful for computing the length of an arc in any circle. If the circle has radius r and the arc cuts off an angle θ, as in Figure 1.49, then we have the following relation:

> Arc length $= s = r\theta$.

Figure 1.49: Arc length of a sector of a circle

The Sine and Cosine Functions

The two basic trigonometric functions—the sine and cosine—are defined using a unit circle. In Figure 1.50, an angle of t radians is measured counterclockwise around the circle from the point $(1, 0)$. If P has coordinates (x, y), we define

$$\cos t = x \quad \text{and} \quad \sin t = y.$$

We assume that the angles are *always* in radians unless specified otherwise.

Since the equation of the unit circle is $x^2 + y^2 = 1$, writing $\cos^2 t$ for $(\cos t)^2$, we have the identity

$$\cos^2 t + \sin^2 t = 1.$$

As t increases and P moves around the circle, the values of $\sin t$ and $\cos t$ oscillate between 1 and -1, and eventually repeat as P moves through points where it has been before. If t is negative, the angle is measured clockwise around the circle.

Amplitude, Period, and Phase

The graphs of sine and cosine are shown in Figure 1.51. Notice that sine is an odd function, and cosine is even. The maximum and minimum values of sine and cosine are $+1$ and -1, because those are the maximum and minimum values of y and x on the unit circle. After the point P has moved around the complete circle once, the values of $\cos t$ and $\sin t$ start to repeat; we say the functions are *periodic*.

For any periodic function of time, the
- **Amplitude** is half the distance between the maximum and minimum values (if it exists).
- **Period** is the smallest time needed for the function to execute one complete cycle.

The amplitude of $\cos t$ and $\sin t$ is 1, and the period is 2π. Why 2π? Because that's the value of t when the point P has gone exactly once around the circle. (Remember that $360° = 2\pi$ radians.)

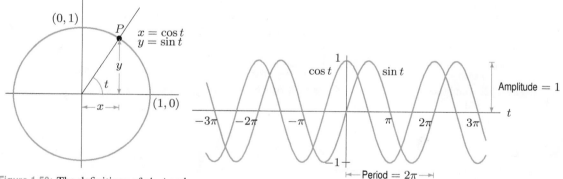

Figure 1.50: The definitions of $\sin t$ and $\cos t$

Figure 1.51: Graphs of $\cos t$ and $\sin t$

In Figure 1.51, we see that the sine and cosine graphs are exactly the same shape, only shifted horizontally. Since the cosine graph is the sine graph shifted $\pi/2$ to the left,

$$\cos t = \sin(t + \pi/2).$$

Equivalently, the sine graph is the cosine graph shifted $\pi/2$ to the right, so

$$\sin t = \cos(t - \pi/2).$$

We say that the *phase difference* or *phase shift* between $\sin t$ and $\cos t$ is $\pi/2$.

Functions whose graphs are the shape of a sine or cosine curve are called *sinusoidal* functions.

> To describe arbitrary amplitudes and periods of sinusoidal functions, we use functions of the form
>
> $$f(t) = A\sin(Bt) \qquad \text{and} \qquad g(t) = A\cos(Bt),$$
>
> where $|A|$ is the amplitude and $2\pi/|B|$ is the period.
>
> The graph of a sinusoidal function is shifted horizontally by a distance $|h|$ when t is replaced by $t - h$ or $t + h$.
>
> Functions of the form $f(t) = A\sin(Bt) + C$ and $g(t) = A\cos(Bt) + C$ have graphs which are shifted vertically by C and oscillate about this value.

Example 1   Find and show on a graph the amplitude and period of the functions

(a) $y = 5\sin(2t)$ (b) $y = -5\sin\left(\dfrac{t}{2}\right)$ (c) $y = 1 + 2\sin t$

Solution

(a) From Figure 1.52, you can see that the amplitude of $y = 5\sin(2t)$ is 5 because the factor of 5 stretches the oscillations up to 5 and down to -5. The period of $y = \sin(2t)$ is π, because when t changes from 0 to π, the quantity $2t$ changes from 0 to 2π, so the sine function goes through one complete oscillation.

(b) Figure 1.53 shows that the amplitude of $y = -5\sin(t/2)$ is again 5, because the negative sign reflects the oscillations in the t-axis, but does not change how far up or down they go. The period of $y = -5\sin(t/2)$ is 4π because when t changes from 0 to 4π, the quantity $t/2$ changes from 0 to 2π, so the sine function goes through one complete oscillation.

(c) The 1 shifts the graph $y = 2\sin t$ up by 1. Since $y = 2\sin t$ has an amplitude of 2 and a period of 2π, the graph of $y = 1 + 2\sin t$ goes up to 3 and down to -1, and has a period of 2π. (See Figure 1.54.) Thus, $y = 1 + 2\sin t$ also has amplitude 2.

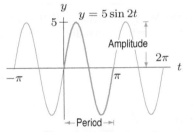

Figure 1.52: Amplitude = 5, period = π

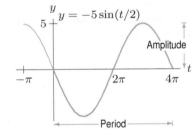

Figure 1.53: Amplitude = 5, period = 4π

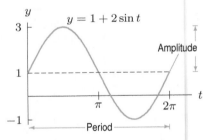

Figure 1.54: Amplitude = 2, period = 2π

Example 2   Find possible formulas for the following sinusoidal functions.

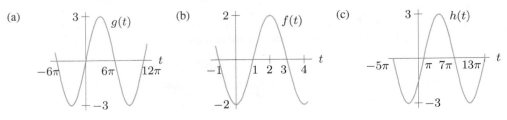

Solution

(a) This function looks like a sine function with amplitude 3, so $g(t) = 3\sin(Bt)$. Since the function executes one full oscillation between $t = 0$ and $t = 12\pi$, when t changes by 12π, the quantity Bt changes by 2π. This means $B \cdot 12\pi = 2\pi$, so $B = 1/6$. Therefore, $g(t) = 3\sin(t/6)$ has the graph shown.

(b) This function looks like an upside-down cosine function with amplitude 2, so $f(t) = -2\cos(Bt)$. The function completes one oscillation between $t = 0$ and $t = 4$. Thus, when t changes by 4, the quantity Bt changes by 2π, so $B \cdot 4 = 2\pi$, or $B = \pi/2$. Therefore, $f(t) = -2\cos(\pi t/2)$ has the graph shown.

(c) This function looks like the function $g(t)$ in part (a), but shifted a distance of π to the right. Since $g(t) = 3\sin(t/6)$, we replace t by $(t - \pi)$ to obtain $h(t) = 3\sin[(t - \pi)/6]$.

Example 3   On July 1, 2007, high tide in Boston was at midnight. The water level at high tide was 9.9 feet; later, at low tide, it was 0.1 feet. Assuming the next high tide is at exactly 12 noon and that the height of the water is given by a sine or cosine curve, find a formula for the water level in Boston as a function of time.

Solution   Let y be the water level in feet, and let t be the time measured in hours from midnight. The oscillations have amplitude 4.9 feet ($= (9.9 - 0.1)/2$) and period 12, so $12B = 2\pi$ and $B = \pi/6$. Since the water is highest at midnight, when $t = 0$, the oscillations are best represented by a cosine function. (See Figure 1.55.) We can say

$$\text{Height above average} = 4.9\cos\left(\frac{\pi}{6}t\right).$$

Since the average water level was 5 feet ($= (9.9 + 0.1)/2$), we shift the cosine up by adding 5:

$$y = 5 + 4.9\cos\left(\frac{\pi}{6}t\right).$$

Figure 1.55: Function approximating the tide in Boston on July 1, 2007

Example 4   Of course, there's something wrong with the assumption in Example 3 that the next high tide is at noon. If so, the high tide would always be at noon or midnight, instead of progressing slowly through the day, as in fact it does. The interval between successive high tides actually averages about 12 hours 24 minutes. Using this, give a more accurate formula for the height of the water as a function of time.

Solution   The period is 12 hours 24 minutes $= 12.4$ hours, so $B = 2\pi/12.4$, giving

$$y = 5 + 4.9\cos\left(\frac{2\pi}{12.4}t\right) = 5 + 4.9\cos(0.507t).$$

Example 5   Use the information from Example 4 to write a formula for the water level in Boston on a day when the high tide is at 2 pm.

Solution   When the high tide is at midnight,

$$y = 5 + 4.9\cos(0.507t).$$

Since 2 pm is 14 hours after midnight, we replace t by $(t - 14)$. Therefore, on a day when the high tide is at 2 pm,

$$y = 5 + 4.9\cos(0.507(t - 14)).$$

The Tangent Function

If t is any number with $\cos t \neq 0$, we define the tangent function as follows

$$\tan t = \frac{\sin t}{\cos t}.$$

Figure 1.50 on page 37 shows the geometrical meaning of the tangent function: $\tan t$ is the slope of the line through the origin $(0, 0)$ and the point $P = (\cos t, \sin t)$ on the unit circle.

The tangent function is undefined wherever $\cos t = 0$, namely, at $t = \pm\pi/2, \pm3\pi/2, \ldots$, and it has a vertical asymptote at each of these points. The function $\tan t$ is positive where $\sin t$ and $\cos t$ have the same sign. The graph of the tangent is shown in Figure 1.56.

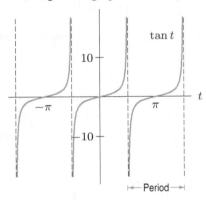

Figure 1.56: The tangent function

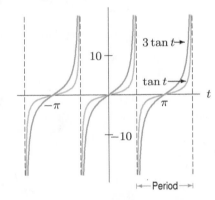

Figure 1.57: Multiple of tangent

The tangent function has period π, because it repeats every π units. Does it make sense to talk about the amplitude of the tangent function? Not if we're thinking of the amplitude as a measure of the size of the oscillation, because the tangent becomes infinitely large near each vertical asymptote. We can still multiply the tangent by a constant, but that constant no longer represents an amplitude. (See Figure 1.57.)

The Inverse Trigonometric Functions

On occasion, you may need to find a number with a given sine. For example, you might want to find x such that

$$\sin x = 0$$

or such that

$$\sin x = 0.3.$$

The first of these equations has solutions $x = 0, \pm\pi, \pm2\pi, \ldots$. The second equation also has infinitely many solutions. Using a calculator and a graph, we get

$$x \approx 0.305, 2.84, 0.305 \pm 2\pi, 2.84 \pm 2\pi, \ldots.$$

For each equation, we pick out the solution between $-\pi/2$ and $\pi/2$ as the preferred solution. For example, the preferred solution to $\sin x = 0$ is $x = 0$, and the preferred solution to $\sin x = 0.3$ is $x = 0.305$. We define the inverse sine, written "arcsin" or "$\sin^{-1}$," as the function which gives the preferred solution.

> For $-1 \leq y \leq 1$,
>
> $$\arcsin y = x$$
>
> means
>
> $$\sin x = y \quad \text{with} \quad -\frac{\pi}{2} \leq x \leq \frac{\pi}{2}.$$

Thus the arcsine is the inverse function to the piece of the sine function having domain $[-\pi/2, \pi/2]$. (See Table 1.17 and Figure 1.58.) On a calculator, the arcsine function[34] is usually denoted by $\boxed{\sin^{-1}}$.

Table 1.17   *Values of $\sin x$ and $\sin^{-1} x$*

x	$\sin x$	x	$\sin^{-1} x$
$-\frac{\pi}{2}$	-1.000	-1.000	$-\frac{\pi}{2}$
-1.0	-0.841	-0.841	-1.0
-0.5	-0.479	-0.479	-0.5
0.0	0.000	0.000	0.0
0.5	0.479	0.479	0.5
1.0	0.841	0.841	1.0
$\frac{\pi}{2}$	1.000	1.000	$\frac{\pi}{2}$

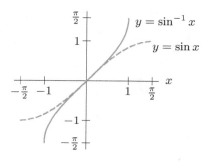

Figure 1.58: The arcsine function

The inverse tangent, written "arctan" or "$\tan^{-1}$," is the inverse function for the piece of the tangent function having the domain $-\pi/2 < x < \pi/2$. On a calculator, the inverse tangent is usually denoted by $\boxed{\tan^{-1}}$. The graph of the arctangent is shown in Figure 1.60.

> For any y,
>
> $$\arctan y = x$$
>
> means
>
> $$\tan x = y \quad \text{with} \quad -\frac{\pi}{2} < x < \frac{\pi}{2}.$$

The inverse cosine function, written "arccos" or "$\cos^{-1}$," is discussed in Problem 55. The range of the arccosine function is $0 \leq x \leq \pi$.

Figure 1.59: The tangent function

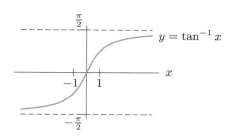

Figure 1.60: The arctangent function

---

[34]Note that $\sin^{-1} x = \arcsin x$ is not the same as $(\sin x)^{-1} = 1/\sin x$.

Exercises and Problems for Section 1.5

Exercises

For Exercises 1–9, draw the angle using a ray through the origin, and determine whether the sine, cosine, and tangent of that angle are positive, negative, zero, or undefined.

1. $\frac{3\pi}{2}$ **2.** 2π **3.** $\frac{\pi}{4}$

4. 3π **5.** $\frac{\pi}{6}$ **6.** $\frac{4\pi}{3}$

7. $\frac{-4\pi}{3}$ **8.** 4 **9.** -1

Find the period and amplitude in Exercises 10–13.

10. $y = 7\sin(3t)$ **11.** $z = 3\cos(u/4) + 5$

12. $w = 8 - 4\sin(2x + \pi)$ **13.** $r = 0.1\sin(\pi t) + 2$

For Exercises 14–23, find a possible formula for each graph.

14.

15.

16.

17.

18.

19.

20.

21.

22.

23.

In Exercises 24–26, calculate the quantity without using the the trigonometric functions on your calculator. You are given that $\sin(\pi/12) = 0.259$ and $\cos(\pi/5) = 0.809$. You may want to draw a picture showing the angles involved and check your answer on a calculator.

24. $\cos\left(-\frac{\pi}{5}\right)$ **25.** $\sin\frac{\pi}{5}$ **26.** $\cos\frac{\pi}{12}$

In Exercises 27–31, find a solution to the equation if possible. Give the answer in exact form and in decimal form.

27. $2 = 5\sin(3x)$ **28.** $1 = 8\cos(2x + 1) - 3$

29. $8 = 4\tan(5x)$ **30.** $1 = 8\tan(2x + 1) - 3$

31. $8 = 4\sin(5x)$

Problems

32. Without a calculator or computer, match the formulas with the graphs in Figure 1.61.

(a) $y = 2\cos(t - \pi/2)$ (b) $y = 2\cos t$
(c) $y = 2\cos(t + \pi/2)$

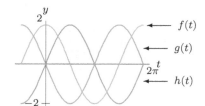

Figure 1.61

33. What is the difference between $\sin x^2$, $\sin^2 x$, and $\sin(\sin x)$? Express each of the three as a composition. (Note: $\sin^2 x$ is another way of writing $(\sin x)^2$.)

34. On the graph of $y = \sin x$, points P and Q are at consecutive lowest and highest points. Find the slope of the line through P and Q.

35. A population of animals oscillates sinusoidally between a low of 700 on January 1 and a high of 900 on July 1.

(a) Graph the population against time.
(b) Find a formula for the population as a function of time, t, in months since the start of the year.

36. The desert temperature, H, oscillates daily between $40°F$ at 5 am and $80°F$ at 5 pm. Write a possible formula for H in terms of t, measured in hours from 5 am.

37. **(a)** Match the functions $\omega = f(t), \omega = g(t), \omega = h(t)$, $\omega = k(t)$, whose values are in the table, with the functions with formulas:

    (i) $\omega = 1.5 + \sin t$ (ii) $\omega = 0.5 + \sin t$
    (iii) $\omega = -0.5 + \sin t$ (iv) $\omega = -1.5 + \sin t$

(b) Based on the table, what is the relationship between the values of $g(t)$ and $k(t)$? Explain this relationship using the formulas you chose for g and k.

(c) Using the formulas you chose for g and h, explain why all the values of g are positive, whereas all the values of h are negative.

t	$f(t)$	t	$g(t)$	t	$h(t)$	t	$k(t)$
6.0	−0.78	3.0	1.64	5.0	−2.46	3.0	0.64
6.5	−0.28	3.5	1.15	5.1	−2.43	3.5	0.15
7.0	0.16	4.0	0.74	5.2	−2.38	4.0	−0.26
7.5	0.44	4.5	0.52	5.3	−2.33	4.5	−0.48
8.0	0.49	5.0	0.54	5.4	−2.27	5.0	−0.46

38. The depth of water in a tank oscillates sinusoidally once every 6 hours. If the smallest depth is 5.5 feet and the largest depth is 8.5 feet, find a possible formula for the depth in terms of time in hours.

39. The voltage, V, of an electrical outlet in a home as a function of time, t (in seconds), is $V = V_0 \cos(120\pi t)$.

(a) What is the period of the oscillation?
(b) What does V_0 represent?
(c) Sketch the graph of V against t. Label the axes.

40. The power output, P, of a solar panel varies with the position of the sun. Let $P = 10 \sin \theta$ watts, where θ is the angle between the sun's rays and the panel, $0 \leq \theta \leq \pi$. On a typical summer day in Ann Arbor, Michigan, the sun rises at 6 am and sets at 8 pm and the angle is $\theta = \pi t/14$, where t is time in hours since 6 am and $0 \leq t \leq 14$.

(a) Write a formula for a function, $f(t)$, giving the power output of the solar panel (in watts) t hours after 6 am on a typical summer day in Ann Arbor.
(b) Graph the function $f(t)$ in part (a) for $0 \leq t \leq 14$.
(c) At what time is the power output greatest? What is the power output at this time?
(d) On a typical winter day in Ann Arbor, the sun rises at 8 am and sets at 5 pm. Write a formula for a function, $g(t)$, giving the power output of the solar panel (in watts) t hours after 8 am on a typical winter day.

41. A baseball hit at an angle of θ to the horizontal with initial velocity v_0 has horizontal range, R, given by

$$R = \frac{v_0^2}{g} \sin(2\theta).$$

Here g is the acceleration due to gravity. Sketch R as a function of θ for $0 \leq \theta \leq \pi/2$. What angle gives the maximum range? What is the maximum range?

42. The visitors' guide to St. Petersburg, Florida, contains the chart shown in Figure 1.62 to advertise their good weather. Fit a trigonometric function approximately to the data, where H is temperature in degrees Fahrenheit, and the independent variable is time in months. In order to do this, you will need to estimate the amplitude and period of the data, and when the maximum occurs. (There are many possible answers to this problem, depending on how you read the graph.)

H (°F)	Jan	Feb	Mar	Apr	May	June	July	Aug	Sept	Oct	Nov	Dec
100°												
90°												
80°												
70°												
60°												
50°												

Figure 1.62: "St. Petersburg...where we're famous for our wonderful weather and year-round sunshine." (Reprinted with permission)

43. The Bay of Fundy in Canada has the largest tides in the world. The difference between low and high water levels is 15 meters (nearly 50 feet). At a particular point the depth of the water, y meters, is given as a function of time, t, in hours since midnight by

$$y = D + A \cos(B(t - C)).$$

(a) What is the physical meaning of D?
(b) What is the value of A?
(c) What is the value of B? Assume the time between successive high tides is 12.4 hours.
(d) What is the physical meaning of C?

44. A compact disc spins at a rate of 200 to 500 revolutions per minute. What are the equivalent rates measured in radians per second?

45. When a car's engine makes less than about 200 revolutions per minute, it stalls. What is the period of the rotation of the engine when it is about to stall?

46. What is the period of the earth's revolution around the sun?

47. What is the approximate period of the moon's revolution around the earth?

48. For a boat to float in a tidal bay, the water must be at least 2.5 meters deep. The depth of water around the boat, $d(t)$, in meters, where t is measured in hours since midnight, is

$$d(t) = 5 + 4.6 \sin(0.5t).$$

(a) What is the period of the tides in hours?
(b) If the boat leaves the bay at midday, what is the latest time it can return before the water becomes too shallow?

49. Match graphs A-D in Figure 1.63 with the functions below. Assume a, b, c and d are positive constants.

$$f(t) = \sin t + b \qquad\qquad h(t) = \sin t + e^{ct} + d$$
$$g(t) = \sin t + at + b \qquad\quad r(t) = \sin t - e^{ct} + b$$

Figure 1.63

50. In Figure 1.64, the blue curve shows monthly mean carbon dioxide (CO_2) concentration, in parts per million (ppm) at Mauna Loa Observatory, Hawaii, as a function of t, in months, since December 2005. The black curve shows the monthly mean concentration adjusted for seasonal CO_2 variation.[35]

   (a) Approximately how much did the monthly mean CO_2 increase between December 2005 and December 2010?

   (b) Find the average monthly rate of increase of the monthly mean CO_2 between December 2005 and December 2010. Use this information to find a linear function that approximates the black curve.

   (c) The seasonal CO_2 variation between December 2005 and December 2010 can be approximated by a sinusoidal function. What is the approximate period of the function? What is its amplitude? Give a formula for the function.

   (d) The blue curve may be approximated by a function of the form $h(t) = f(t) + g(t)$, where $f(t)$ is sinusoidal and $g(t)$ is linear. Using your work in parts (b) and (c), find a possible formula for $h(t)$. Graph $h(t)$ using the scale in Figure 1.64.

Figure 1.64

51. (a) Use a graphing calculator or computer to estimate the period of $2 \sin \theta + 3 \cos(2\theta)$.

   (b) Explain your answer, given that the period of $\sin \theta$ is 2π and the period of $\cos(2\theta)$ is π.

52. Find the area of the trapezoidal cross-section of the irrigation canal shown in Figure 1.65.

Figure 1.65

53. Graph $y = \sin x$, $y = 0.4$, and $y = -0.4$.

   (a) From the graph, estimate to one decimal place all the solutions of $\sin x = 0.4$ with $-\pi \le x \le \pi$.

   (b) Use a calculator to find $\arcsin(0.4)$. What is the relation between $\arcsin(0.4)$ and each of the solutions you found in part (a)?

   (c) Estimate all the solutions to $\sin x = -0.4$ with $-\pi \le x \le \pi$ (again, to one decimal place).

   (d) What is the relation between $\arcsin(0.4)$ and each of the solutions you found in part (c)?

54. Find the angle, in degrees, that a wheelchair ramp makes with the ground if the ramp rises 1 foot over a horizontal distance of

   (a) 12 ft, the normal requirement[36]

   (b) 8 ft, the steepest ramp legally permitted

   (c) 20 ft, the recommendation if snow can be expected on the ramp

55. This problem introduces the arccosine function, or inverse cosine, denoted by $\boxed{\cos^{-1}}$ on most calculators.

   (a) Using a calculator set in radians, make a table of values, to two decimal places, of $g(x) = \arccos x$, for $x = -1, -0.8, -0.6, \ldots, 0, \ldots, 0.6, 0.8, 1$.

   (b) Sketch the graph of $g(x) = \arccos x$.

   (c) Why is the domain of the arccosine the same as the domain of the arcsine?

   (d) What is the range of the arccosine?

   (e) Why is the range of the arccosine *not* the same as the range of the arcsine?

---

[35]http://www.esrl.noaa.gov/gmd/ccgg/trends/. Accessed March 2011. Monthly means joined by segments to highlight trends.

[36]http://www.access-board.gov/adaag/html/adaag.htm#4.1.6(3)a, accessed June 6, 2011.

Strengthen Your Understanding

In Problems 56–57, explain what is wrong with the statement.

56. For the function $f(x) = \sin(Bx)$ with $B > 0$, increasing the value of B increases the period.

57. For positive A, B, C, the maximum value of the function $y = A\sin(Bx) + C$ is $y = A$.

In Problems 58–59, give an example of:

58. A sine function with period 23.

59. A cosine function which oscillates between values of 1200 and 2000.

Are the statements in Problems 60–72 true or false? Give an explanation for your answer.

60. The function $f(\theta) = \cos\theta - \sin\theta$ is increasing on $0 \leq \theta \leq \pi/2$.

61. The function $f(t) = \sin(0.05\pi t)$ has period 0.05.

62. If t is in seconds, $g(t) = \cos(200\pi t)$ executes 100 cycles in one second.

63. The function $f(\theta) = \tan(\theta - \pi/2)$ is not defined at $\theta = \pi/2, 3\pi/2, 5\pi/2 \ldots$.

64. $\sin|x| = \sin x$ for $-2\pi < x < 2\pi$

65. $\sin|x| = |\sin x|$ for $-2\pi < x < 2\pi$

66. $\cos|x| = |\cos x|$ for $-2\pi < x < 2\pi$

67. $\cos|x| = \cos x$ for $-2\pi < x < 2\pi$

68. The function $f(x) = \sin(x^2)$ is periodic, with period 2π.

69. The function $g(\theta) = e^{\sin\theta}$ is periodic.

70. If $f(x)$ is a periodic function with period k, then $f(g(x))$ is periodic with period k for every function $g(x)$.

71. If $g(x)$ is a periodic function, then $f(g(x))$ is periodic for every function $f(x)$.

72. The function $f(x) = |\sin x|$ is even.

1.6 POWERS, POLYNOMIALS, AND RATIONAL FUNCTIONS

Power Functions

A *power function* is a function in which the dependent variable is proportional to a power of the independent variable:

> A **power function** has the form
>
> $$f(x) = kx^p, \qquad \text{where } k \text{ and } p \text{ are constant.}$$

For example, the volume, V, of a sphere of radius r is given by

$$V = g(r) = \frac{4}{3}\pi r^3.$$

As another example, the gravitational force, F, on a unit mass at a distance r from the center of the earth is given by Newton's Law of Gravitation, which says that, for some positive constant k,

$$F = \frac{k}{r^2} \qquad \text{or} \qquad F = kr^{-2}.$$

We consider the graphs of the power functions x^n, with n a positive integer. Figures 1.66 and 1.67 show that the graphs fall into two groups: odd and even powers. For n greater than 1, the odd powers have a "seat" at the origin and are increasing everywhere else. The even powers are first decreasing and then increasing. For large x, the higher the power of x, the faster the function climbs.

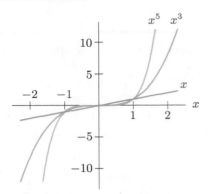

Figure 1.66: Odd powers of x: "Seat" shaped for $n > 1$

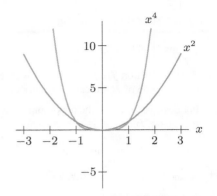

Figure 1.67: Even powers of x: $\bigcup$-shaped

Exponentials and Power Functions: Which Dominate?

In everyday language, the word exponential is often used to imply very fast growth. But do exponential functions always grow faster than power functions? To determine what happens "in the long run," we often want to know which functions *dominate* as x gets arbitrarily large.

Let's consider $y = 2^x$ and $y = x^3$. The close-up view in Figure 1.68(a) shows that between $x = 2$ and $x = 4$, the graph of $y = 2^x$ lies below the graph of $y = x^3$. The far-away view in Figure 1.68(b) shows that the exponential function $y = 2^x$ eventually overtakes $y = x^3$. Figure 1.68(c), which gives a very far-away view, shows that, for large x, the value of x^3 is insignificant compared to 2^x. Indeed, 2^x is growing so much faster than x^3 that the graph of 2^x appears almost vertical in comparison to the more leisurely climb of x^3.

We say that Figure 1.68(a) gives a *local* view of the functions' behavior, whereas Figure 1.68(c) gives a *global* view.

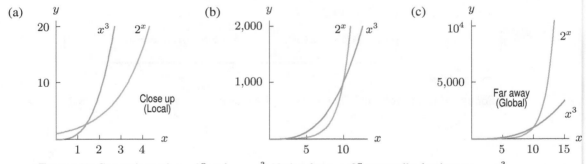

Figure 1.68: Comparison of $y = 2^x$ and $y = x^3$: Notice that $y = 2^x$ eventually dominates $y = x^3$

In fact, *every* exponential growth function eventually dominates *every* power function. Although an exponential function may be below a power function for some values of x, if we look at large enough x-values, a^x (with $a > 1$) will eventually dominate x^n, no matter what n is.

Polynomials

Polynomials are the sums of power functions with nonnegative integer exponents:

$$y = p(x) = a_n x^n + a_{n-1} x^{n-1} + \cdots + a_1 x + a_0.$$

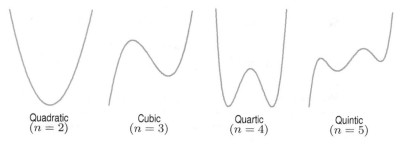

Quadratic
$(n = 2)$

Cubic
$(n = 3)$

Quartic
$(n = 4)$

Quintic
$(n = 5)$

Figure 1.69: Graphs of typical polynomials of degree n

Here n is a nonnegative integer called the *degree* of the polynomial, and $a_n, a_{n-1}, \ldots, a_1, a_0$ are constants, with leading coefficient $a_n \neq 0$. An example of a polynomial of degree $n = 3$ is

$$y = p(x) = 2x^3 - x^2 - 5x - 7.$$

In this case $a_3 = 2, a_2 = -1, a_1 = -5$, and $a_0 = -7$. The shape of the graph of a polynomial depends on its degree; typical graphs are shown in Figure 1.69. These graphs correspond to a positive coefficient for x^n; a negative leading coefficient turns the graph upside down. Notice that the quadratic "turns around" once, the cubic "turns around" twice, and the quartic (fourth degree) "turns around" three times. An nth degree polynomial "turns around" at most $n - 1$ times (where n is a positive integer), but there may be fewer turns.

Example 1   Find possible formulas for the polynomials whose graphs are in Figure 1.70.

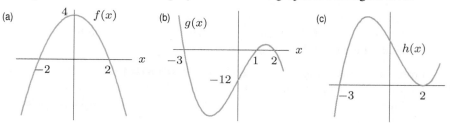

(a)

$f(x)$

(b)

$g(x)$

(c)

$h(x)$

Figure 1.70: Graphs of polynomials

Solution   (a) This graph appears to be a parabola, turned upside down, and moved up by 4, so

$$f(x) = -x^2 + 4.$$

The negative sign turns the parabola upside down and the $+4$ moves it up by 4. Notice that this formula does give the correct x-intercepts since $0 = -x^2 + 4$ has solutions $x = \pm 2$. These values of x are called *zeros* of f.

We can also solve this problem by looking at the x-intercepts first, which tell us that $f(x)$ has factors of $(x + 2)$ and $(x - 2)$. So

$$f(x) = k(x + 2)(x - 2).$$

To find k, use the fact that the graph has a y-intercept of 4, so $f(0) = 4$, giving

$$4 = k(0 + 2)(0 - 2),$$

or $k = -1$. Therefore, $f(x) = -(x + 2)(x - 2)$, which multiplies out to $-x^2 + 4$.

Note that $f(x) = 4 - x^4/4$ also has the same basic shape, but is flatter near $x = 0$. There are many possible answers to these questions.

(b) This looks like a cubic with factors $(x + 3)$, $(x - 1)$, and $(x - 2)$, one for each intercept:

$$g(x) = k(x + 3)(x - 1)(x - 2).$$

Since the y-intercept is -12, we have

$$-12 = k(0 + 3)(0 - 1)(0 - 2).$$

So $k = -2$, and we get the cubic polynomial

$$g(x) = -2(x+3)(x-1)(x-2).$$

(c) This also looks like a cubic with zeros at $x = 2$ and $x = -3$. Notice that at $x = 2$ the graph of $h(x)$ touches the x-axis but does not cross it, whereas at $x = -3$ the graph crosses the x-axis. We say that $x = 2$ is a *double zero*, but that $x = -3$ is a single zero.

To find a formula for $h(x)$, imagine the graph of $h(x)$ to be slightly lower down, so that the graph has one x-intercept near $x = -3$ and two near $x = 2$, say at $x = 1.9$ and $x = 2.1$. Then a formula would be

$$h(x) \approx k(x+3)(x-1.9)(x-2.1).$$

Now move the graph back to its original position. The zeros at $x = 1.9$ and $x = 2.1$ move toward $x = 2$, giving

$$h(x) = k(x+3)(x-2)(x-2) = k(x+3)(x-2)^2.$$

The double zero leads to a repeated factor, $(x-2)^2$. Notice that when $x > 2$, the factor $(x-2)^2$ is positive, and when $x < 2$, the factor $(x-2)^2$ is still positive. This reflects the fact that $h(x)$ does not change sign near $x = 2$. Compare this with the behavior near the single zero at $x = -3$, where h does change sign.

We cannot find k, as no coordinates are given for points off of the x-axis. Any positive value of k stretches the graph vertically but does not change the zeros, so any positive k works.

Example 2   Using a calculator or computer, graph $y = x^4$ and $y = x^4 - 15x^2 - 15x$ for $-4 \le x \le 4$ and for $-20 \le x \le 20$. Set the y range to $-100 \le y \le 100$ for the first domain, and to $-100 \le y \le 200{,}000$ for the second. What do you observe?

Solution   From the graphs in Figure 1.71 we see that close up ($-4 \le x \le 4$) the graphs look different; from far away, however, they are almost indistinguishable. The reason is that the leading terms (those with the highest power of x) are the same, namely x^4, and for large values of x, the leading term dominates the other terms.

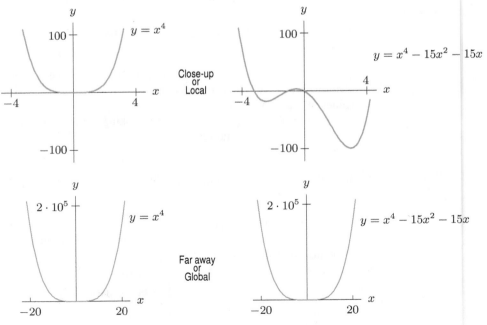

Figure 1.71: Local and global views of $y = x^4$ and $y = x^4 - 15x^2 - 15x$

Rational Functions

Rational functions are ratios of polynomials, p and q:

$$f(x) = \frac{p(x)}{q(x)}.$$

Example 3   Look at a graph and explain the behavior of $y = \dfrac{1}{x^2 + 4}$.

Solution   The function is even, so the graph is symmetric about the y-axis. As x gets larger, the denominator gets larger, making the value of the function closer to 0. Thus the graph gets arbitrarily close to the x-axis as x increases without bound. See Figure 1.72.

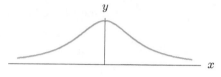

Figure 1.72: Graph of $y = \frac{1}{x^2+4}$

In the previous example, we say that $y = 0$ (i.e. the x-axis) is a *horizontal asymptote*. Writing "$\to$" to mean "tends to," we have $y \to 0$ as $x \to \infty$ and $y \to 0$ as $x \to -\infty$.

If the graph of $y = f(x)$ approaches a horizontal line $y = L$ as $x \to \infty$ or $x \to -\infty$, then the line $y = L$ is called a **horizontal asymptote**.[37] This occurs when

$$f(x) \to L \quad \text{as} \quad x \to \infty \qquad \text{or} \qquad f(x) \to L \quad \text{as} \quad x \to -\infty.$$

If the graph of $y = f(x)$ approaches the vertical line $x = K$ as $x \to K$ from one side or the other, that is, if

$$y \to \infty \quad \text{or} \quad y \to -\infty \quad \text{when} \quad x \to K,$$

then the line $x = K$ is called a **vertical asymptote**.

The graphs of rational functions may have vertical asymptotes where the denominator is zero. For example, the function in Example 3 has no vertical asymptotes as the denominator is never zero. The function in Example 4 has two vertical asymptotes corresponding to the two zeros in the denominator.

Rational functions have horizontal asymptotes if $f(x)$ approaches a finite number as $x \to \infty$ or $x \to -\infty$. We call the behavior of a function as $x \to \pm\infty$ its *end behavior*.

Example 4   Look at a graph and explain the behavior of $y = \dfrac{3x^2 - 12}{x^2 - 1}$, including end behavior.

Solution   Factoring gives

$$y = \frac{3x^2 - 12}{x^2 - 1} = \frac{3(x + 2)(x - 2)}{(x + 1)(x - 1)}$$

so $x = \pm 1$ are vertical asymptotes. If $y = 0$, then $3(x + 2)(x - 2) = 0$ or $x = \pm 2$; these are the x-intercepts. Note that zeros of the denominator give rise to the vertical asymptotes, whereas zeros of the numerator give rise to x-intercepts. Substituting $x = 0$ gives $y = 12$; this is the y-intercept. The function is even, so the graph is symmetric about the y-axis.

---

[37] We are assuming that $f(x)$ gets arbitrarily close to L as $x \to \infty$.

Table 1.18   *Values of* $y = \frac{3x^2 - 12}{x^2 - 1}$

x	$y = \frac{3x^2 - 12}{x^2 - 1}$
± 10	2.909091
± 100	2.999100
± 1000	2.999991

Figure 1.73: Graph of the function $y = \frac{3x^2 - 12}{x^2 - 1}$

To see what happens as $x \to \pm\infty$, look at the y-values in Table 1.18. Clearly y is getting closer to 3 as x gets large positively or negatively. Alternatively, realize that as $x \to \pm\infty$, only the highest powers of x matter. For large x, the 12 and the 1 are insignificant compared to x^2, so

$$y = \frac{3x^2 - 12}{x^2 - 1} \approx \frac{3x^2}{x^2} = 3 \quad \text{for large } x.$$

So $y \to 3$ as $x \to \pm\infty$, and therefore the horizontal asymptote is $y = 3$. See Figure 1.73. Since, for $x > 1$, the value of $(3x^2 - 12)/(x^2 - 1)$ is less than 3, the graph lies *below* its asymptote. (Why doesn't the graph lie below $y = 3$ when $-1 < x < 1$?)

Exercises and Problems for Section 1.6

Exercises

For Exercises 1–2, what happens to the value of the function as $x \to \infty$ and as $x \to -\infty$?

1. $y = 0.25x^3 + 3$ **2.** $y = 2 \cdot 10^{4x}$

In Exercises 3–10, determine the end behavior of each function as $x \to +\infty$ and as $x \to -\infty$.

3. $f(x) = -10x^4$

4. $f(x) = 3x^5$

5. $f(x) = 5x^4 - 25x^3 - 62x^2 + 5x + 300$

6. $f(x) = 1000 - 38x + 50x^2 - 5x^3$

7. $f(x) = \dfrac{3x^2 + 5x + 6}{x^2 - 4}$

8. $f(x) = \dfrac{10 + 5x^2 - 3x^3}{2x^3 - 4x + 12}$

9. $f(x) = 3x^{-4}$

10. $f(x) = e^x$

In Exercises 11–16, which function dominates as $x \to \infty$?

11. $1000x^4$ or $0.2x^5$

12. $10e^{0.1x}$ or $5000x^2$

13. $100x^5$ or 1.05^x

14. $2x^4$ or $10x^3 + 25x^2 + 50x + 100$

15. $20x^4 + 100x^2 + 5x$ or $25 - 40x^2 + x^3 + 3x^5$

16. $\sqrt{x}$ or $\ln x$

17. Each of the graphs in Figure 1.74 is of a polynomial. The windows are large enough to show end behavior.

(a) What is the minimum possible degree of the polynomial?

(b) Is the leading coefficient of the polynomial positive or negative?

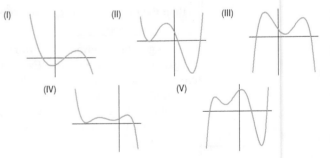

Figure 1.74

Find cubic polynomials for the graphs in Exercises 18–19.

18.

19.

Find possible formulas for the graphs in Exercises 20–23.

20.

21.

22.

23.

In Exercises 24–26, choose the functions that are in the given family, assuming a, b, and c are constants.

$$f(x) = \sqrt{x^4 + 16} \qquad g(x) = ax^{23}$$

$$h(x) = -\frac{1}{5^{x-2}} \qquad p(x) = \frac{a^3 b^x}{c}$$

$$q(x) = \frac{ab^2}{c} \qquad r(x) = -x + b - \sqrt{cx^4}$$

24. Exponential   **25.** Quadratic   **26.** Linear

Problems

27. How many distinct roots can a polynomial of degree 5 have? (List all possibilities.) Sketch a possible graph for each case.

28. A rational function $y = f(x)$ is graphed in Figure 1.75. If $f(x) = g(x)/h(x)$ with $g(x)$ and $h(x)$ both quadratic functions, give possible formulas for $g(x)$ and $h(x)$.

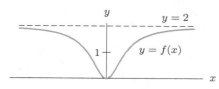

Figure 1.75

29. Find a calculator window in which the graphs of $f(x) = x^3 + 1000x^2 + 1000$ and $g(x) = x^3 - 1000x^2 - 1000$ appear indistinguishable.

30. For each function, fill in the blanks in the statements:

$$f(x) \to \underline{\hspace{2cm}} \text{ as } x \to -\infty,$$
$$f(x) \to \underline{\hspace{2cm}} \text{ as } x \to +\infty.$$

    (a) $f(x) = 17 + 5x^2 - 12x^3 - 5x^4$

    (b) $f(x) = \dfrac{3x^2 - 5x + 2}{2x^2 - 8}$

    (c) $f(x) = e^x$

31. The DuBois formula relates a person's surface area s, in m^2, to weight w, in kg, and height h, in cm, by

$$s = 0.01w^{0.25}h^{0.75}.$$

    (a) What is the surface area of a person who weighs 65 kg and is 160 cm tall?

    (b) What is the weight of a person whose height is 180 cm and who has a surface area of 1.5 m^2?

    (c) For people of fixed weight 70 kg, solve for h as a function of s. Simplify your answer.

32. According to *Car and Driver*, an Alfa Romeo going at 70 mph requires 177 feet to stop. Assuming that the stopping distance is proportional to the square of velocity, find the stopping distances required by an Alfa Romeo going at 35 mph and at 140 mph (its top speed).

33. Poiseuille's Law gives the rate of flow, R, of a gas through a cylindrical pipe in terms of the radius of the pipe, r, for a fixed drop in pressure between the two ends of the pipe.

    (a) Find a formula for Poiseuille's Law, given that the rate of flow is proportional to the fourth power of the radius.

    (b) If $R = 400$ cm^3/sec in a pipe of radius 3 cm for a certain gas, find a formula for the rate of flow of that gas through a pipe of radius r cm.

    (c) What is the rate of flow of the same gas through a pipe with a 5 cm radius?

34. A box of fixed volume V has a square base with side length x. Write a formula for the height, h, of the box in terms of x and V. Sketch a graph of h versus x.

35. A closed cylindrical can of fixed volume V has radius r.

    (a) Find the surface area, S, as a function of r.

    (b) What happens to the value of S as $r \to \infty$?

    (c) Sketch a graph of S against r, if $V = 10$ cm^3.

In Problems 36–38, find all horizontal and vertical asymptotes for each rational function.

36. $f(x) = \dfrac{5x - 2}{2x + 3}$ **37.** $f(x) = \dfrac{x^2 + 5x + 4}{x^2 - 4}$

38. $f(x) = \dfrac{5x^3 + 7x - 1}{x^3 - 27}$

39. The height of an object above the ground at time t is given by

$$s = v_0 t - \frac{g}{2}t^2,$$

where v_0 is the initial velocity and g is the acceleration due to gravity.

(a) At what height is the object initially?
(b) How long is the object in the air before it hits the ground?
(c) When will the object reach its maximum height?
(d) What is that maximum height?

40. A pomegranate is thrown from ground level straight up into the air at time $t = 0$ with velocity 64 feet per second. Its height at time t seconds is $f(t) = -16t^2 + 64t$. Find the time it hits the ground and the time it reaches its highest point. What is the maximum height?

41. (a) If $f(x) = ax^2 + bx + c$, what can you say about the values of a, b, and c if:

  (i) $(1, 1)$ is on the graph of $f(x)$?
  (ii) $(1, 1)$ is the vertex of the graph of $f(x)$? [Hint: The axis of symmetry is $x = -b/(2a)$.]
  (iii) The y-intercept of the graph is $(0, 6)$?

(b) Find a quadratic function satisfying all three conditions.

42. A cubic polynomial with positive leading coefficient is shown in Figure 1.76 for $-10 \le x \le 10$ and $-10 \le y \le 10$. What can be concluded about the total number of zeros of this function? What can you say about the location of each of the zeros? Explain.

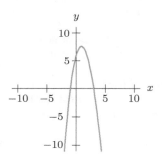

Figure 1.76

43. After running 3 miles at a speed of x mph, a man walked the next 6 miles at a speed that was 2 mph slower. Express the total time spent on the trip as a function of x. What horizontal and vertical asymptotes does the graph of this function have?

44. Which of the functions I–III meet each of the following descriptions? There may be more than one function for each description, or none at all.

(a) Horizontal asymptote of $y = 1$.
(b) The x-axis is a horizontal asymptote.

(c) Symmetric about the y-axis.
(d) An odd function.
(e) Vertical asymptotes at $x = \pm 1$.

I. $\quad y = \dfrac{x - 1}{x^2 + 1}$ II. $\quad y = \dfrac{x^2 - 1}{x^2 + 1}$ III. $\quad y = \dfrac{x^2 + 1}{x^2 - 1}$

45. Values of three functions are given in Table 1.19, rounded to two decimal places. One function is of the form $y = ab^t$, one is of the form $y = ct^2$, and one is of the form $y = kt^3$. Which function is which?

Table 1.19

t	$f(t)$	t	$g(t)$	t	$h(t)$
2.0	4.40	1.0	3.00	0.0	2.04
2.2	5.32	1.2	5.18	1.0	3.06
2.4	6.34	1.4	8.23	2.0	4.59
2.6	7.44	1.6	12.29	3.0	6.89
2.8	8.62	1.8	17.50	4.0	10.33
3.0	9.90	2.0	24.00	5.0	15.49

46. Use a graphing calculator or a computer to graph $y = x^4$ and $y = 3^x$. Determine approximate domains and ranges that give each of the graphs in Figure 1.77.

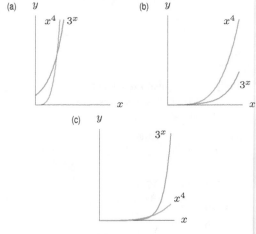

Figure 1.77

47. The rate, R, at which a population in a confined space increases is proportional to the product of the current population, P, and the difference between the carrying capacity, L, and the current population. (The carrying capacity is the maximum population the environment can sustain.)

(a) Write R as a function of P.
(b) Sketch R as a function of P.

48. Consider the point P at the intersection of the circle $x^2 + y^2 = 2a^2$ and the parabola $y = x^2/a$ in Figure 1.78. If a is increased, the point P traces out a curve. For $a > 0$, find the equation of this curve.

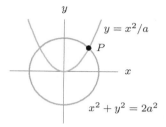

Figure 1.78

49. When an object of mass m moves with a velocity v that is small compared to the velocity of light, c, its energy is given approximately by

$$E \approx \frac{1}{2} mv^2.$$

If v is comparable in size to c, then the energy must be computed by the exact formula

$$E = mc^2 \left(\frac{1}{\sqrt{1 - v^2/c^2}} - 1 \right).$$

(a) Plot a graph of both functions for E against v for $0 \leq v \leq 5 \cdot 10^8$ and $0 \leq E \leq 5 \cdot 10^{17}$. Take $m = 1$ kg and $c = 3 \cdot 10^8$ m/sec. Explain how you can predict from the exact formula the position of the vertical asymptote.
(b) What do the graphs tell you about the approximation? For what values of v does the first formula give a good approximation to E?

Strengthen Your Understanding

In Problems 50–51, explain what is wrong with the statement.

50. The graph of a polynomial of degree 5 cuts the horizontal axis five times.

51. Every rational function has a horizontal asymptote.

In Problems 52–57, give an example of:

52. A polynomial of degree 3 whose graph cuts the horizontal axis three times to the right of the origin.

53. A rational function with horizontal asymptote $y = 3$.

54. A rational function that is not a polynomial and that has no vertical asymptote.

55. A function that has a vertical asymptote at $x = -7\pi$.

56. A function that has exactly 17 vertical asymptotes.

57. A function that has a vertical asymptote which is crossed by a horizontal asymptote.

Are the statements in Problems 58–59 true or false? Give an explanation for your answer.

58. Every polynomial of even degree has a least one real zero.

59. Every polynomial of odd degree has a least one real zero.

60. List the following functions in order from smallest to largest as $x \to \infty$ (that is, as x increases without bound).

(a) $f(x) = -5x$ **(b)** $g(x) = 10^x$
(c) $h(x) = 0.9^x$ **(d)** $k(x) = x^5$
(e) $l(x) = \pi^x$

1.7 INTRODUCTION TO CONTINUITY

This section gives an intuitive introduction to the idea of *continuity*. This leads to the concept of limit and a definition of continuity in Section 1.8.

Continuity of a Function on an Interval: Graphical Viewpoint

Roughly speaking, a function is said to be *continuous* on an interval if its graph has no breaks, jumps, or holes in that interval. Continuity is important because, as we shall see, continuous functions have many desirable properties.

For example, to locate the zeros of a function, we often look for intervals where the function changes sign. In the case of the function $f(x) = 3x^3 - x^2 + 2x - 1$, for instance, we expect[38] to find a zero between 0 and 1 because $f(0) = -1$ and $f(1) = 3$. (See Figure 1.79.) To be sure that $f(x)$ has a zero there, we need to know that the graph of the function has no breaks or jumps in it. Otherwise the graph could jump across the x-axis, changing sign but not creating a zero. For example, $f(x) = 1/x$ has opposite signs at $x = -1$ and $x = 1$, but no zeros for $-1 \leq x \leq 1$

---

[38]This is due to the Intermediate Value Theorem, which is discussed on page 55.

because of the break at $x = 0$. (See Figure 1.80.) To be certain that a function has a zero in an interval on which it changes sign, we need to know that the function is defined and continuous in that interval.

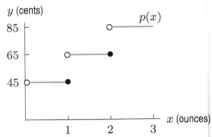

Figure 1.79: The graph of $f(x) = 3x^3 - x^2 + 2x - 1$

Figure 1.80: No zero although $f(-1)$ and $f(1)$ have opposite signs

Figure 1.81: Cost of mailing a letter

A continuous function has a graph which can be drawn without lifting the pencil from the paper.

Example: The function $f(x) = 3x^3 - x^2 + 2x - 1$ is continuous on any interval. (See Figure 1.79.)

Example: The function $f(x) = 1/x$ is not defined at $x = 0$. It is continuous on any interval not containing the origin. (See Figure 1.80.)

Example: Suppose $p(x)$ is the price of mailing a first-class letter weighing x ounces. It costs 45¢ for one ounce or less, 65¢ between one and two ounces, and so on. So the graph (in Figure 1.81) is a series of steps. This function is not continuous on any open interval containing a positive integer because the graph jumps at these points.

Which Functions Are Continuous?

Requiring a function to be continuous on an interval is not asking very much, as any function whose graph is an unbroken curve over the interval is continuous. For example, exponential functions, polynomials, and the sine and cosine are continuous on every interval. Rational functions are continuous on any interval in which their denominators are not zero. Functions created by adding, multiplying, or composing continuous functions are also continuous.

The Intermediate Value Theorem

Continuity tells us about the values taken by a function. In particular, a continuous function cannot skip values. For example, the function in the next example must have a zero because its graph cannot skip over the x-axis.

Example 1   What do the values in Table 1.20 tell you about the zeros of $f(x) = \cos x - 2x^2$?

Table 1.20

x	$f(x)$
0	1.00
0.2	0.90
0.4	0.60
0.6	0.11
0.8	−0.58
1.0	−1.46

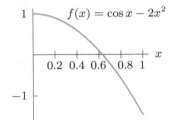

Figure 1.82: Zeros occur where the graph of a continuous function crosses the horizontal axis

Solution   Since $f(x)$ is the difference of two continuous functions, it is continuous. We conclude that $f(x)$ has at least one zero in the interval $0.6 < x < 0.8$, since $f(x)$ changes from positive to negative on that interval. The graph of $f(x)$ in Figure 1.82 suggests that there is only one zero in the interval $0 \le x \le 1$, but we cannot be sure of this from the graph or the table of values.

In the previous example, we concluded that $f(x) = \cos x - 2x^2$ has a zero between $x = 0$ and $x = 1$ because $f(x)$ is positive at $x = 0$ and negative at $x = 1$. More generally, an intuitive notion of continuity tells us that, as we follow the graph of a continuous function f from some point $(a, f(a))$ to another point $(b, f(b))$, then f takes on all intermediate values between $f(a)$ and $f(b)$. (See Figure 1.83.) This is:

Theorem 1.1: Intermediate Value Theorem

Suppose f is continuous on a closed interval $[a, b]$. If k is any number between $f(a)$ and $f(b)$, then there is at least one number c in $[a, b]$ such that $f(c) = k$.

The Intermediate Value Theorem depends on the formal definition of continuity given in Section 1.8. See also www.wiley.com/college/hughes-hallett. The key idea is to find successively smaller subintervals of $[a, b]$ on which f changes from less than k to more than k. These subintervals converge on the number c.

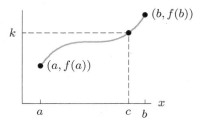

Figure 1.83: The Intermediate Value Theorem

Continuity of a Function at a Point: Numerical Viewpoint

A function is continuous if nearby values of the independent variable give nearby values of the function. In practical work, continuity is important because it means that small errors in the independent variable lead to small errors in the value of the function.

Example: Suppose that $f(x) = x^2$ and that we want to compute $f(\pi)$. Knowing f is continuous tells us that taking $x = 3.14$ should give a good approximation to $f(\pi)$, and that we can get as accurate an approximation to $f(\pi)$ as we want by using enough decimals of π.

Example: If $p(x)$ is the cost of mailing a letter weighing x ounces, then $p(0.99) = p(1) = 45¢$, whereas $p(1.01) = 65¢$, because as soon as we get over 1 ounce, the price jumps up to 65¢. So a small difference in the weight of a letter can lead to a significant difference in its mailing cost. Hence p is not continuous at $x = 1$.

In other words, if $f(x)$ is continuous at $x = c$, the values of $f(x)$ approach $f(c)$ as x approaches c. Using the concept of a limit introduced in Section 1.8, we can define more precisely what it means for the values of $f(x)$ to approach $f(c)$ as x approaches c.

Example 2   Investigate the continuity of $f(x) = x^2$ at $x = 2$.

Solution   From Table 1.21, it appears that the values of $f(x) = x^2$ approach $f(2) = 4$ as x approaches 2. Thus f appears to be continuous at $x = 2$. Continuity at a point describes behavior of a function *near* a point, as well as *at* the point.

Table 1.21   *Values of x^2 near $x = 2$*

x	1.9	1.99	1.999	2.001	2.01	2.1
x^2	3.61	3.96	3.996	4.004	4.04	4.41

Exercises and Problems for Section 1.7

Exercises

In Exercises 1–10, is the function continuous on the interval?

1. $\dfrac{1}{x-2}$ on $[-1,1]$

2. $\dfrac{1}{x-2}$ on $[0,3]$

3. $\dfrac{1}{\sqrt{2x-5}}$ on $[3,4]$

4. $\dfrac{x}{x^2+2}$ on $[-2,2]$

5. $2x + x^{2/3}$ on $[-1,1]$

6. $2x + x^{-1}$ on $[-1,1]$

7. $\dfrac{1}{\cos x}$ on $[0,\pi]$

8. $\dfrac{1}{\sin x}$ on $[-\frac{\pi}{2}, \frac{\pi}{2}]$

9. $\dfrac{e^x}{e^x - 1}$ on $[-1,1]$

10. $\dfrac{e^{\sin\theta}}{\cos\theta}$ on $[-\frac{\pi}{4}, \frac{\pi}{4}]$

In Exercises 11–14, show that there is a number c, with $0 \le c \le 1$, such that $f(c) = 0$.

11. $f(x) = x^3 + x^2 - 1$

12. $f(x) = e^x - 3x$

13. $f(x) = x - \cos x$

14. $f(x) = 2^x - 1/x$

15. Are the following functions continuous? Explain.

(a) $f(x) = \begin{cases} x & x \le 1 \\ x^2 & 1 < x \end{cases}$

(b) $g(x) = \begin{cases} x & x \le 3 \\ x^2 & 3 < x \end{cases}$

Problems

16. Which of the following are continuous functions of time?

(a) The quantity of gas in the tank of a car on a journey between New York and Boston.

(b) The number of students enrolled in a class during a semester.

(c) The age of the oldest person alive.

17. A car is coasting down a hill at a constant speed. A truck collides with the rear of the car, causing it to lurch ahead. Graph the car's speed from a time shortly before impact to a time shortly after impact. Graph the distance from the top of the hill for this time period. What can you say about the continuity of each of these functions?

18. An electrical circuit switches instantaneously from a 6 volt battery to a 12 volt battery 7 seconds after being turned on. Graph the battery voltage against time. Give formulas for the function represented by your graph. What can you say about the continuity of this function?

In Problems 19–22 find k so that the function is continuous on any interval.

19. $f(x) = \begin{cases} kx & x \le 3 \\ 5 & 3 < x \end{cases}$

20. $f(x) = \begin{cases} kx & 0 \le x < 2 \\ 3x^2 & 2 \le x \end{cases}$

21. $g(t) = \begin{cases} t + k & t \le 5 \\ kt & 5 < t \end{cases}$

22. $h(x) = \begin{cases} k \cos x & 0 \le x \le \pi \\ 12 - x & \pi < x \end{cases}$

23. (a) For $k = 1$, sketch

$$f(x) = \begin{cases} kx & 0 \le x \le 2 \\ (x-2)^2 + 3 & 2 < x \le 4. \end{cases}$$

(b) Find the value of k so that $f(x)$ is continuous at $x = 2$.

(c) Sketch $f(x)$ using the value of k you found in part (a).

In Problems 24–29, find a value of k making $h(x)$ continuous on $[0,5]$.

24. $h(x) = \begin{cases} kx & 0 \le x < 1 \\ x + 3 & 1 \le x \le 5. \end{cases}$

25. $h(x) = \begin{cases} kx & 0 \le x \le 1 \\ 2kx + 3 & 1 < x \le 5. \end{cases}$

26. $h(x) = \begin{cases} k \sin x & 0 \le x \le \pi \\ x + 4 & \pi < x \le 5. \end{cases}$

27. $h(x) = \begin{cases} e^{kx} & 0 \le x < 2 \\ x + 1 & 2 \le x \le 5. \end{cases}$

28. $h(x) = \begin{cases} 0.5x & 0 \le x < 1 \\ \sin(kx) & 1 \le x \le 5. \end{cases}$

29. $h(x) = \begin{cases} \ln(kx + 1) & 0 \le x \le 2 \\ x + 4 & 2 < x \le 5. \end{cases}$

30. For t in months, a population, in thousands, is approximated by a continuous function

$$P(t) = \begin{cases} e^{kt} & 0 \le t \le 12 \\ 100 & t > 12. \end{cases}$$

(a) What is the initial value of the population?

(b) What must be the value of k?

(c) Describe in words how the population is changing.

31. Is the following function continuous on $[-1,1]$?

$$f(x) = \begin{cases} \dfrac{x}{|x|} & x \ne 0 \\ 0 & x = 0 \end{cases}$$

32. Discuss the continuity of the function g graphed in Figure 1.84 and defined as follows:

$$g(\theta) = \begin{cases} \dfrac{\sin\theta}{\theta} & \text{for } \theta \neq 0 \\ 1/2 & \text{for } \theta = 0. \end{cases}$$

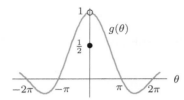

Figure 1.84

33. A 0.6 ml dose of a drug is injected into a patient steadily for half a second. At the end of this time, the quantity, Q, of the drug in the body starts to decay exponentially at a continuous rate of 0.2% per second. Using formulas, express Q as a continuous function of time, t in seconds.

34. Sketch the graphs of three different functions that are continuous on $0 \leq x \leq 1$ and that have the values given in the table. The first function is to have exactly one zero in $[0, 1]$, the second is to have at least two zeros in the interval $[0.6, 0.8]$, and the third is to have at least two zeros in the interval $[0, 0.6]$.

x	0	0.2	0.4	0.6	0.8	1.0
$f(x)$	1.00	0.90	0.60	0.11	-0.58	-1.46

35. Let $p(x)$ be a cubic polynomial with $p(5) < 0$, $p(10) > 0$, and $p(12) < 0$. What can you say about the number and location of zeros of $p(x)$?

36. **(a)** What does a graph of $y = e^x$ and $y = 4 - x^2$ tell you about the solutions to the equation $e^x = 4 - x^2$?
   (b) Evaluate $f(x) = e^x + x^2 - 4$ at $x = -4, -3, -2, -1, 0, 1, 2, 3, 4$. In which intervals do the solutions to $e^x = 4 - x^2$ lie?

37. **(a)** Sketch the graph of a continuous function f with *all* of the following properties:

   (i) $f(0) = 2$

   (ii) $f(x)$ is decreasing for $0 \leq x \leq 3$

   (iii) $f(x)$ is increasing for $3 < x \leq 5$

   (iv) $f(x)$ is decreasing for $x > 5$

   (v) $f(x) \to 9$ as $x \to \infty$

   (b) Is it possible that the graph of f is concave down for all $x > 6$? Explain.

38. **(a)** Does $f(x)$ satisfy the conditions for the Intermediate Value Theorem on $0 \leq x \leq 2$ if

$$f(x) = \begin{cases} e^x & 0 \leq x \leq 1 \\ 4 + (x-1)^2 & 1 < x \leq 2? \end{cases}$$

   (b) What are $f(0)$ and $f(2)$? Can you find a value of k between $f(0)$ and $f(2)$ such that the equation $f(x) = k$ has no solution? If so, what is it?

Strengthen Your Understanding

In Problems 39–40, explain what is wrong with the statement.

39. For any function $f(x)$, if $f(a) = 2$ and $f(b) = 4$, the Intermediate Value Theorem says that f takes on the value 3 for some x between a and b.

40. If $f(x)$ is continuous on $0 \leq x \leq 2$ and if $f(0) = 0$ and $f(2) = 10$, the Intermediate Value Theorem says that $f(1) = 5$.

In Problems 41–44, give an example of:

41. A function which is defined for all x and continuous everywhere except at $x = 15$.

42. A function to which the Intermediate Value Theorem does not apply on the interval $-1 \leq x \leq 1$.

43. A function that is continuous on $[0, 1]$ but not continuous on $[1, 3]$.

44. A function that is increasing but not continuous on $[0, 10]$.

Are the statements in Problems 45–47 true or false? Give an explanation for your answer.

45. If a function is not continuous at a point, then it is not defined at that point.

46. If f is continuous on the interval $[0, 10]$ and $f(0) = 0$ and $f(10) = 100$, then $f(c)$ cannot be negative for c in $[0, 10]$.

47. If $f(x)$ is not continuous on the interval $[a, b]$, then $f(x)$ must omit at least one value between $f(a)$ and $f(b)$.

1.8 LIMITS

The concept of *limit* is the underpinning of calculus. In Section 1.7, we said that a function f is continuous at $x = c$ if the values of $f(x)$ approach $f(c)$ as x approaches c. In this section, we define a limit, which makes precise what we mean by approaching.

The Idea of a Limit

We first introduce some notation:

> We write $\lim_{x \to c} f(x) = L$ if the values of $f(x)$ approach L as x approaches c.

How should we find L, or even know whether such a number exists? We will look for trends in the values of $f(x)$ as x gets closer to c, but $x \neq c$. A graph from a calculator or computer often helps.

Example 1   Use a graph to estimate $\lim_{\theta \to 0} \left(\dfrac{\sin \theta}{\theta} \right)$. (Use radians.)

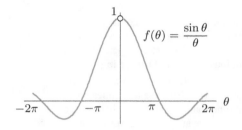

Figure 1.85: Find the limit as $\theta \to 0$

Solution   Figure 1.85 shows that as θ approaches 0 from either side, the value of $\sin \theta / \theta$ appears to approach 1, suggesting that $\lim_{\theta \to 0} (\sin \theta / \theta) = 1$. Zooming in on the graph near $\theta = 0$ provides further support for this conclusion. Notice that $\sin \theta / \theta$ is undefined at $\theta = 0$.

Figure 1.85 strongly suggests that $\lim_{\theta \to 0} (\sin \theta / \theta) = 1$, but to be sure we need to be more precise about words like "approach" and "close."

Definition of Limit

By the beginning of the 19th century, calculus had proved its worth, and there was no doubt about the correctness of its answers. However, it was not until the work of the French mathematician Augustin Cauchy (1789–1857) that calculus was put on a rigorous footing. Cauchy gave a formal definition of the limit, similar to the following:

> A function f is defined on an interval around c, except perhaps at the point $x = c$. We define the **limit** of the function $f(x)$ as x approaches c, written $\lim_{x \to c} f(x)$, to be a number L (if one exists) such that $f(x)$ is as close to L as we want whenever x is sufficiently close to c (but $x \neq c$). If L exists, we write
> $$\lim_{x \to c} f(x) = L.$$

Shortly, we see how "as close as we want" and "sufficiently close" are expressed using inequalities. First, we look at $\lim_{\theta \to 0} (\sin \theta / \theta)$ more closely (see Example 1).

Example 2   By graphing $y = (\sin\theta)/\theta$ in an appropriate window, find how close θ should be to 0 in order to make $(\sin\theta)/\theta$ within 0.01 of 1.

Solution   Since we want $(\sin\theta)/\theta$ to be within 0.01 of 1, we set the y-range on the graphing window to go from 0.99 to 1.01. Our first attempt with $-0.5 \le \theta \le 0.5$ yields the graph in Figure 1.86. Since we want the y-values to stay within the range $0.99 < y < 1.01$, we do not want the graph to leave the window through the top or bottom. By trial and error, we find that changing the θ-range to $-0.2 \le \theta \le 0.2$ gives the graph in Figure 1.87. Thus, the graph suggests that $(\sin\theta)/\theta$ is within 0.01 of 1 whenever θ is within 0.2 of 0. Proving this requires an analytical argument, not just graphs from a calculator.

Figure 1.86: $(\sin\theta)/\theta$ with $-0.5 \le \theta \le 0.5$

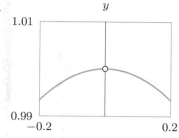

Figure 1.87: $(\sin\theta)/\theta$ with $-0.2 \le \theta \le 0.2$

When we say "$f(x)$ is close to L," we measure closeness by the distance between $f(x)$ and L, expressed using absolute values:

$$|f(x) - L| = \text{Distance between } f(x) \text{ and } L.$$

When we say "as close to L as we want," we use ϵ (the Greek letter epsilon) to specify how close. We write

$$|f(x) - L| < \epsilon$$

to indicate that we want the distance between $f(x)$ and L to be less than ϵ. In Example 2 we used $\epsilon = 0.01$. Similarly, we interpret "x is sufficiently close to c" as specifying a distance between x and c:

$$|x - c| < \delta,$$

where δ (the Greek letter delta) tells us how close x should be to c. In Example 2 we found $\delta = 0.2$.

If $\lim\limits_{x \to c} f(x) = L$, we know that no matter how narrow the horizontal band determined by ϵ in Figure 1.88, there is always a δ which makes the graph stay within that band, for $c - \delta < x < c + \delta$.

Thus we restate the definition of a limit, using symbols:

Definition of Limit

We define $\lim\limits_{x \to c} f(x)$ to be the number L (if one exists) such that for every $\epsilon > 0$ (as small as we want), there is a $\delta > 0$ (sufficiently small) such that if $|x - c| < \delta$ and $x \ne c$, then $|f(x) - L| < \epsilon$.

We have arrived at a formal definition of limit. Let's see if it agrees with our intuition.

Figure 1.88: What the definition of the limit means graphically

Example 3   Use the definition of limit to show that $\lim_{x \to 3} 2x = 6$.

Solution   We must show how, given any $\epsilon > 0$, we can find a $\delta > 0$ such that

$$\text{If } |x - 3| < \delta \text{ and } x \neq 3, \text{ then } |2x - 6| < \epsilon.$$

Since $|2x - 6| = 2|x - 3|$, to get $|2x - 6| < \epsilon$ we require that $|x - 3| < \epsilon/2$. Thus we take $\delta = \epsilon/2$.

It is important to understand that the ϵ, δ definition does not make it easier to calculate limits; rather, the ϵ, δ definition makes it possible to put calculus on a rigorous foundation. From this foundation, we can prove the following properties. See Problems 78–80.

Theorem 1.2: Properties of Limits

Assuming all the limits on the right-hand side exist:
1. If b is a constant, then $\lim_{x \to c} (bf(x)) = b \left(\lim_{x \to c} f(x) \right)$.
2. $\lim_{x \to c} (f(x) + g(x)) = \lim_{x \to c} f(x) + \lim_{x \to c} g(x)$.
3. $\lim_{x \to c} (f(x)g(x)) = \left(\lim_{x \to c} f(x) \right) \left(\lim_{x \to c} g(x) \right)$.
4. $\lim_{x \to c} \dfrac{f(x)}{g(x)} = \dfrac{\lim_{x \to c} f(x)}{\lim_{x \to c} g(x)}$, provided $\lim_{x \to c} g(x) \neq 0$.
5. For any constant k, $\lim_{x \to c} k = k$.
6. $\lim_{x \to c} x = c$.

These properties underlie many limit calculations, though we may not acknowledge them explicitly.

Example 4   Explain how the limit properties are used in the following calculation:

$$\lim_{x \to 3} \frac{x^2 + 5x}{x + 9} = \frac{3^2 + 5 \cdot 3}{3 + 9} = 2.$$

Solution We calculate this limit in stages, using the limit properties to justify each step:

$$\lim_{x \to 3} \frac{x^2 + 5x}{x + 9} = \frac{\lim\limits_{x \to 3}(x^2 + 5x)}{\lim\limits_{x \to 3}(x + 9)} \qquad \text{(Property 4, since } \lim_{x \to 3}(x + 9) \neq 0\text{)}$$

$$= \frac{\lim\limits_{x \to 3}(x^2) + \lim\limits_{x \to 3}(5x)}{\lim\limits_{x \to 3} x + \lim\limits_{x \to 3} 9} \qquad \text{(Property 2)}$$

$$= \frac{\left(\lim\limits_{x \to 3} x\right)^2 + 5\left(\lim\limits_{x \to 3} x\right)}{\lim\limits_{x \to 3} x + \lim\limits_{x \to 3} 9} \qquad \text{(Properties 1 and 3)}$$

$$= \frac{3^2 + 5 \cdot 3}{3 + 9} = 2. \qquad \text{(Properties 5 and 6)}$$

One- and Two-Sided Limits

When we write

$$\lim_{x \to 2} f(x),$$

we mean the number that $f(x)$ approaches as x approaches 2 *from both sides*. We examine values of $f(x)$ as x approaches 2 through values greater than 2 (such as 2.1, 2.01, 2.003) and values less than 2 (such as 1.9, 1.99, 1.994). If we want x to approach 2 only through values greater than 2, we write

$$\lim_{x \to 2^+} f(x)$$

for the number that $f(x)$ approaches (assuming such a number exists). Similarly,

$$\lim_{x \to 2^-} f(x)$$

denotes the number (if it exists) obtained by letting x approach 2 through values less than 2. We call $\lim\limits_{x \to 2^+} f(x)$ a *right-hand limit* and $\lim\limits_{x \to 2^-} f(x)$ a *left-hand limit*. Problems 43 and 44 ask for formal definitions of left- and right-hand limits.

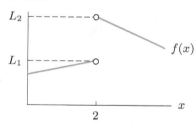

Figure 1.89: Left- and right-hand limits at $x = 2$

For the function graphed in Figure 1.89, we have

$$\lim_{x \to 2^-} f(x) = L_1 \qquad \lim_{x \to 2^+} f(x) = L_2.$$

If the left- and right-hand limits were equal, that is, if $L_1 = L_2$, then it can be proved that $\lim\limits_{x \to 2} f(x)$ exists and $\lim\limits_{x \to 2} f(x) = L_1 = L_2$. Since $L_1 \neq L_2$ in Figure 1.89, we see that $\lim\limits_{x \to 2} f(x)$ does not exist in this case.

When Limits Do Not Exist

Whenever there is no number L such that $\lim\limits_{x \to c} f(x) = L$, we say $\lim\limits_{x \to c} f(x)$ does not exist. Here are three examples in which limits fail to exist.

Example 5   Explain why $\lim\limits_{x \to 2} \dfrac{|x-2|}{x-2}$ does not exist.

Solution   Figure 1.90 shows the problem: The right-hand limit and the left-hand limit are different. For $x > 2$, we have $|x-2| = x-2$, so as x approaches 2 from the right,

$$\lim_{x \to 2^+} \frac{|x-2|}{x-2} = \lim_{x \to 2^+} \frac{x-2}{x-2} = \lim_{x \to 2^+} 1 = 1.$$

Similarly, if $x < 2$, then $|x-2| = 2-x$ so

$$\lim_{x \to 2^-} \frac{|x-2|}{x-2} = \lim_{x \to 2^-} \frac{2-x}{x-2} = \lim_{x \to 2^-} (-1) = -1.$$

So if $\lim\limits_{x \to 2} \dfrac{|x-2|}{x-2} = L$ then L would have to be both 1 and -1. Since L cannot have two different values, the limit does not exist.

Figure 1.90: Graph of
$|x-2|/(x-2)$

Figure 1.91: Graph of $1/x^2$

Figure 1.92: Graph of $\sin(1/x)$

Example 6   Explain why $\lim\limits_{x \to 0} \dfrac{1}{x^2}$ does not exist.

Solution   As x approaches zero, $1/x^2$ becomes arbitrarily large, so it cannot approach any finite number L. See Figure 1.91. Therefore we say $1/x^2$ has no limit as $x \to 0$.

If $\lim\limits_{x \to a} f(x)$ does not exist because $f(x)$ gets arbitrarily large on both sides of a, we also say $\lim\limits_{x \to a} f(x) = \infty$. So in Example 6 we could say $\lim\limits_{x \to 0} 1/x^2 = \infty$. This behavior may also be described as "diverging to infinity."

Example 7   Explain why $\lim\limits_{x \to 0} \sin\left(\dfrac{1}{x}\right)$ does not exist.

Solution   The sine function has values between -1 and 1. The graph in Figure 1.92 oscillates more and more rapidly as $x \to 0$. There are x-values approaching 0 where $\sin(1/x) = -1$. There are also x-values approaching 0 where $\sin(1/x) = 1$. So if the limit existed, it would have to be both -1 and 1. Thus, the limit does not exist.

Limits at Infinity

Sometimes we want to know what happens to $f(x)$ as x gets large, that is, the end behavior of f.

> If $f(x)$ gets as close to a number L as we please when x gets sufficiently large, then we write
>
> $$\lim_{x \to \infty} f(x) = L.$$
>
> Similarly, if $f(x)$ approaches L when x is negative and has a sufficiently large absolute value, then we write
>
> $$\lim_{x \to -\infty} f(x) = L.$$

The symbol ∞ does not represent a number. Writing $x \to \infty$ means that we consider arbitrarily large values of x. If the limit of $f(x)$ as $x \to \infty$ or $x \to -\infty$ is L, we say that the graph of f has $y = L$ as a *horizontal asymptote*. Problem 45 asks for a formal definition of $\lim_{x \to \infty} f(x)$.

Example 8   Investigate $\displaystyle\lim_{x \to \infty} \frac{1}{x}$ and $\displaystyle\lim_{x \to -\infty} \frac{1}{x}$.

Solution   A graph of $f(x) = 1/x$ in a large window shows $1/x$ approaching zero as x increases in either the positive or the negative direction (see Figure 1.93). This is as we would expect, since dividing 1 by larger and larger numbers yields answers which are closer and closer to zero. This suggests that

$$\lim_{x \to \infty} \frac{1}{x} = \lim_{x \to -\infty} \frac{1}{x} = 0,$$

and that $f(x) = 1/x$ has $y = 0$ as a horizontal asymptote as $x \to \pm\infty$.

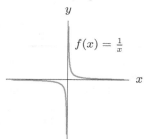

Figure 1.93: The end behavior of $f(x) = 1/x$

Definition of Continuity

We can now give a precise definition of continuity using limits.

> The function f is **continuous** at $x = c$ if f is defined at $x = c$ and if
>
> $$\lim_{x \to c} f(x) = f(c).$$
>
> In other words, $f(x)$ is as close as we want to $f(c)$ provided x is close enough to c. The function is **continuous on an interval** $[a, b]$ if it is continuous at every point in the interval.[39]

Constant functions and $f(x) = x$ are continuous for all x. Using the continuity of sums and products, we can show that any polynomial is continuous. Proving that $\sin x$, $\cos x$, and e^x are

---

[39]If c is an endpoint of the interval, we define continuity at $x = c$ using one-sided limits at c.

continuous is more difficult. The following theorem, based on the properties of limits on page 60, makes it easier to decide whether certain combinations of functions are continuous.

Theorem 1.3: Continuity of Sums, Products, and Quotients of Functions

Suppose that f and g are continuous on an interval and that b is a constant. Then, on that same interval,

1. $bf(x)$ is continuous.
2. $f(x) + g(x)$ is continuous.
3. $f(x)g(x)$ is continuous.
4. $f(x)/g(x)$ is continuous, provided $g(x) \neq 0$ on the interval.

We prove the third of these properties.

Proof Let c be any point in the interval. We must show that $\lim_{x \to c}(f(x)g(x)) = f(c)g(c)$. Since $f(x)$ and $g(x)$ are continuous, we know that $\lim_{x \to c} f(x) = f(c)$ and $\lim_{x \to c} g(x) = g(c)$. So, by the third property of limits in Theorem 1.2,

$$\lim_{x \to c}(f(x)g(x)) = \left(\lim_{x \to c} f(x)\right)\left(\lim_{x \to c} g(x)\right) = f(c)g(c).$$

Since c was chosen arbitrarily, we have shown that $f(x)g(x)$ is continuous at every point in the interval.

Theorem 1.4: Continuity of Composite Functions

If f and g are continuous, and if the composite function $f(g(x))$ is defined on an interval, then $f(g(x))$ is continuous on that interval.

Assuming the continuity of $\sin x$ and e^x, Theorem 1.4 shows us, for example, that $\sin(e^x)$ and $e^{\sin x}$ are both continuous.

Although we now have a formal definition of continuity, some properties of continuous functions, such as the Intermediate Value Theorem, can be difficult to prove. For a further treatment of limits and continuity, see www.wiley.com/college/hughes-hallett.

Exercises and Problems for Section 1.8

Exercises

1. Use Figure 1.94 to give approximate values for the following limits (if they exist).

   (a) $\lim_{x \to -2} f(x)$
   (b) $\lim_{x \to 0} f(x)$
   (c) $\lim_{x \to 2} f(x)$
   (d) $\lim_{x \to 4} f(x)$

2. Use Figure 1.95 to estimate the following limits, if they exist.

   (a) $\lim_{x \to 1^-} f(x)$
   (b) $\lim_{x \to 1^+} f(x)$
   (c) $\lim_{x \to 1} f(x)$
   (d) $\lim_{x \to 2^-} f(x)$
   (e) $\lim_{x \to 2^+} f(x)$
   (f) $\lim_{x \to 2} f(x)$

Figure 1.94

Figure 1.95

3. Using Figures 1.96 and 1.97, estimate

(a) $\lim\limits_{x \to 1^-} (f(x) + g(x))$ (b) $\lim\limits_{x \to 1^+} (f(x) + 2g(x))$

(c) $\lim\limits_{x \to 1^-} f(x)g(x)$ (d) $\lim\limits_{x \to 1^+} \dfrac{f(x)}{g(x)}$

Figure 1.96

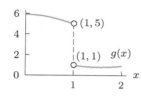

Figure 1.97

In Exercises 4–9, draw a possible graph of $f(x)$. Assume $f(x)$ is defined and continuous for all real x.

4. $\lim\limits_{x \to \infty} f(x) = -\infty$ and $\lim\limits_{x \to -\infty} f(x) = -\infty$

5. $\lim\limits_{x \to \infty} f(x) = -\infty$ and $\lim\limits_{x \to -\infty} f(x) = +\infty$

6. $\lim\limits_{x \to \infty} f(x) = 1$ and $\lim\limits_{x \to -\infty} f(x) = +\infty$

7. $\lim\limits_{x \to \infty} f(x) = -\infty$ and $\lim\limits_{x \to -\infty} f(x) = 3$

8. $\lim\limits_{x \to \infty} f(x) = +\infty$ and $\lim\limits_{x \to -1} f(x) = 2$

9. $\lim\limits_{x \to 3} f(x) = 5$ and $\lim\limits_{x \to -\infty} f(x) = +\infty$

In Exercises 10–15, give $\lim\limits_{x \to -\infty} f(x)$ and $\lim\limits_{x \to +\infty} f(x)$.

10. $f(x) = -x^4$

11. $f(x) = 5 + 21x - 2x^3$

12. $f(x) = x^5 + 25x^4 - 37x^3 - 200x^2 + 48x + 10$

13. $f(x) = \dfrac{3x^3 + 6x^2 + 45}{5x^3 + 25x + 12}$

14. $f(x) = 8x^{-3}$

15. $f(x) = 25e^{0.08x}$

Estimate the limits in Exercises 16–17 graphically.

16. $\lim\limits_{x \to 0} \dfrac{|x|}{x}$

17. $\lim\limits_{x \to 0} x \ln|x|$

18. Does $f(x) = \dfrac{|x|}{x}$ have right or left limits at 0? Is $f(x)$ continuous?

Use a graph to estimate each of the limits in Exercises 19–28. Use radians unless degrees are indicated by $\theta°$.

19. $\lim\limits_{\theta \to 0} \dfrac{\sin(2\theta)}{\theta}$ **20.** $\lim\limits_{\theta \to 0} \dfrac{\cos\theta - 1}{\theta}$

21. $\lim\limits_{\theta \to 0} \dfrac{\sin\theta°}{\theta°}$ **22.** $\lim\limits_{\theta \to 0} \dfrac{\theta}{\tan(3\theta)}$

23. $\lim\limits_{h \to 0} \dfrac{e^h - 1}{h}$ **24.** $\lim\limits_{h \to 0} \dfrac{e^{5h} - 1}{h}$

25. $\lim\limits_{h \to 0} \dfrac{2^h - 1}{h}$ **26.** $\lim\limits_{h \to 0} \dfrac{3^h - 1}{h}$

27. $\lim\limits_{h \to 0} \dfrac{\cos(3h) - 1}{h}$ **28.** $\lim\limits_{h \to 0} \dfrac{\sin(3h)}{h}$

For the functions in Exercises 29–31, use algebra to evaluate the limits $\lim\limits_{x \to a+} f(x)$, $\lim\limits_{x \to a-} f(x)$, and $\lim\limits_{x \to a} f(x)$ if they exist. Sketch a graph to confirm your answers.

29. $a = 4$, $f(x) = \dfrac{|x - 4|}{x - 4}$

30. $a = 2$, $f(x) = \dfrac{|x - 2|}{x}$

31. $a = 3$, $f(x) = \begin{cases} x^2 - 2, & 0 < x < 3 \\ 2, & x = 3 \\ 2x + 1, & 3 < x \end{cases}$

32. Estimate how close θ should be to 0 to make $(\sin\theta)/\theta$ stay within 0.001 of 1.

33. Write the definition of the following statement both in words and in symbols:

$$\lim\limits_{h \to a} g(h) = K.$$

Problems

In Problems 34–37, is the function continuous for all x? If not, say where it is not continuous and explain in what way the definition of continuity is not satisfied.

34. $f(x) = 1/x$

35. $f(x) = \begin{cases} |x|/x & x \neq 0 \\ 0 & x = 0 \end{cases}$

36. $f(x) = \begin{cases} x/x & x \neq 0 \\ 1 & x = 0 \end{cases}$

37. $f(x) = \begin{cases} 2x/x & x \neq 0 \\ 3 & x = 0 \end{cases}$

38. By graphing $y = (1 + x)^{1/x}$, estimate $\lim\limits_{x \to 0} (1 + x)^{1/x}$. You should recognize the answer you get. What does the limit appear to be?

39. Investigate $\lim\limits_{h \to 0} (1 + h)^{1/h}$ numerically.

40. What does a calculator suggest about $\lim\limits_{x \to 0+} xe^{1/x}$? Does the limit appear to exist? Explain.

41. If $p(x)$ is the function on page 54 giving the price of mailing a first-class letter, explain why $\lim_{x \to 1} p(x)$ does not exist.

42. The notation $\lim_{x \to 0^+}$ means that we only consider values of x greater than 0. Estimate the limit

$$\lim_{x \to 0^+} x^x,$$

either by evaluating x^x for smaller and smaller positive values of x (say $x = 0.1, 0.01, 0.001, \ldots$) or by zooming in on the graph of $y = x^x$ near $x = 0$.

In Problems 43–45, modify the definition of limit on page 59 to give a definition of each of the following.

43. A right-hand limit   **44.** A left-hand limit

45. $\lim_{x \to \infty} f(x) = L$

For the functions in Problems 46–53, do the following:
(a) Make a table of values of $f(x)$ for $x = 0.1, 0.01, 0.001, 0.0001, -0.1, -0.01, -0.001,$ and -0.0001.
(b) Make a conjecture about the value of $\lim_{x \to 0} f(x)$.
(c) Graph the function to see if it is consistent with your answers to parts (a) and (b).
(d) Find an interval for x near 0 such that the difference between your conjectured limit and the value of the function is less than 0.01. (In other words, find a window of height 0.02 such that the graph exits the sides of the window and not the top or bottom of the window.)

46. $f(x) = 3x + 1$ **47.** $f(x) = x^2 - 1$

48. $f(x) = \sin 2x$ **49.** $f(x) = \sin 3x$

50. $f(x) = \dfrac{\sin 2x}{x}$ **51.** $f(x) = \dfrac{\sin 3x}{x}$

52. $f(x) = \dfrac{e^x - 1}{x}$ **53.** $f(x) = \dfrac{e^{2x} - 1}{x}$

Assuming that limits as $x \to \infty$ have the properties listed for limits as $x \to c$ on page 60, use algebraic manipulations to evaluate $\lim_{x \to \infty}$ for the functions in Problems 54–63.

54. $f(x) = \dfrac{x + 3}{2 - x}$ **55.** $f(x) = \dfrac{\pi + 3x}{\pi x - 3}$

56. $f(x) = \dfrac{x - 5}{5 + 2x^2}$ **57.** $f(x) = \dfrac{x^2 + 2x - 1}{3 + 3x^2}$

58. $f(x) = \dfrac{x^2 + 4}{x + 3}$ **59.** $f(x) = \dfrac{2x^3 - 16x^2}{4x^2 + 3x^3}$

60. $f(x) = \dfrac{x^4 + 3x}{x^4 + 2x^5}$ **61.** $f(x) = \dfrac{3e^x + 2}{2e^x + 3}$

62. $f(x) = \dfrac{2^{-x} + 5}{3^{-x} + 7}$ **63.** $f(x) = \dfrac{2e^{-x} + 3}{3e^{-x} + 2}$

In Problems 64–71, find a value of the constant k such that the limit exists.

64. $\lim_{x \to 4} \dfrac{x^2 - k^2}{x - 4}$ **65.** $\lim_{x \to 1} \dfrac{x^2 - kx + 4}{x - 1}$

66. $\lim_{x \to -2} \dfrac{x^2 + 4x + k}{x + 2}$ **67.** $\lim_{x \to \infty} \dfrac{x^2 + 3x + 5}{4x + 1 + x^k}$

68. $\lim_{x \to -\infty} \dfrac{e^{2x} - 5}{e^{kx} + 3}$ **69.** $\lim_{x \to \infty} \dfrac{x^3 - 6}{x^k + 3}$

70. $\lim_{x \to \infty} \dfrac{3^{kx} + 6}{3^{2x} + 4}$ **71.** $\lim_{x \to -\infty} \dfrac{3^{kx} + 6}{3^{2x} + 4}$

For each value of ϵ in Problems 72–73, find a positive value of δ such that the graph of the function leaves the window $a - \delta < x < a + \delta, b - \epsilon < y < b + \epsilon$ by the sides and not through the top or bottom.

72. $f(x) = -2x + 3$; $a = 0$; $b = 3$; $\epsilon = 0.2, 0.1, 0.02, 0.01, 0.002, 0.001$.

73. $g(x) = -x^3 + 2$; $a = 0$; $b = 2$; $\epsilon = 0.1, 0.01, 0.001$.

74. Show that $\lim_{x \to 0} (-2x + 3) = 3$. [Hint: Use Problem 72.]

75. Consider the function $f(x) = \sin(1/x)$.

(a) Find a sequence of x-values that approach 0 such that $\sin(1/x) = 0$.
[Hint: Use the fact that $\sin(\pi) = \sin(2\pi) = \sin(3\pi) = \ldots = \sin(n\pi) = 0$.]
(b) Find a sequence of x-values that approach 0 such that $\sin(1/x) = 1$.
[Hint: Use the fact that $\sin(n\pi/2) = 1$ if $n = 1, 5, 9, \ldots$.]
(c) Find a sequence of x-values that approach 0 such that $\sin(1/x) = -1$.
(d) Explain why your answers to any two of parts (a)–(c) show that $\lim_{x \to 0} \sin(1/x)$ does not exist.

For the functions in Problems 76–77, do the following:
(a) Make a table of values of $f(x)$ for $x = a+0.1, a+0.01, a + 0.001, a + 0.0001, a - 0.1, a - 0.01, a - 0.001,$ and $a - 0.0001$.
(b) Make a conjecture about the value of $\lim_{x \to a} f(x)$.
(c) Graph the function to see if it is consistent with your answers to parts (a) and (b).
(d) Find an interval for x containing a such that the difference between your conjectured limit and the value of the function is less than 0.01 on that interval. (In other words, find a window of height 0.02 such that the graph exits the sides of the window and not the top or bottom of the window.)

76. $f(x) = \dfrac{\cos 2x - 1 + 2x^2}{x^3}, \quad a = 0$

77. $f(x) = \dfrac{\cos 3x - 1 + 4.5x^2}{x^3}, \quad a = 0$

78. This problem suggests a proof of the first property of limits on page 60: $\lim_{x \to c} bf(x) = b \lim_{x \to c} f(x)$.

    (a) First, prove the property in the case $b = 0$.

    (b) Now suppose that $b \neq 0$. Let $\epsilon > 0$. Show that if $|f(x) - L| < \epsilon/|b|$, then $|bf(x) - bL| < \epsilon$.

    (c) Finally, prove that if $\lim_{x \to c} f(x) = L$ then $\lim_{x \to c} bf(x) = bL$. [Hint: Choose δ so that if $|x - c| < \delta$, then $|f(x) - L| < \epsilon/|b|$.]

79. Prove the second property of limits: $\lim_{x \to c} (f(x) + g(x)) = \lim_{x \to c} f(x) + \lim_{x \to c} g(x)$. Assume that the limits on the right exist.

80. This problem suggests a proof of the third property of limits (assuming the limits on the right exist):

$$\lim_{x \to c} (f(x)g(x)) = \left(\lim_{x \to c} f(x) \right) \left(\lim_{x \to c} g(x) \right)$$

Let $L_1 = \lim_{x \to c} f(x)$ and $L_2 = \lim_{x \to c} g(x)$.

    (a) First, show that if $\lim_{x \to c} f(x) = \lim_{x \to c} g(x) = 0$, then $\lim_{x \to c} (f(x)g(x)) = 0$.

    (b) Show algebraically that $f(x)g(x) = (f(x) - L_1)(g(x) - L_2) + L_1 g(x) + L_2 f(x) - L_1 L_2$.

    (c) Use the second limit property (see Problem 79) to explain why $\lim_{x \to c} (f(x) - L_1) = \lim_{x \to c} (g(x) - L_2) = 0$.

    (d) Use parts (a) and (c) to explain why $\lim_{x \to c} (f(x) - L_1)(g(x) - L_2) = 0$.

    (e) Finally, use parts (b) and (d) and the first and second limit properties to show that $\lim_{x \to c} (f(x)g(x)) = \left(\lim_{x \to c} f(x) \right) \left(\lim_{x \to c} g(x) \right)$.

81. Show $f(x) = x$ is continuous everywhere.

82. Use Problem 81 to show that for any positive integer n, the function x^n is continuous everywhere.

83. Use Theorem 1.2 on page 60 to explain why if f and g are continuous on an interval, then so are $f + g$, fg, and f/g (assuming $g(x) \neq 0$ on the interval).

Strengthen Your Understanding

In Problems 84–86, explain what is wrong with the statement.

84. If $P(x)$ and $Q(x)$ are polynomials, $P(x)/Q(x)$ must be continuous for all x.

85. $\lim_{x \to 1} \dfrac{x - 1}{|x - 1|} = 1$.

86. If $\lim_{x \to c} f(x)$ exists, then $f(x)$ is continuous at $x = c$.

In Problems 87–88, give an example of:

87. A rational function that has a limit at $x = 1$ but is not continuous at $x = 1$.

88. A function $f(x)$ where $\lim_{x \to \infty} f(x) = 2$ and $\lim_{x \to -\infty} f(x) = -2$.

Suppose that $\lim_{x \to 3} f(x) = 7$. Are the statements in Problems 89–95 true or false? If a statement is true, explain how you know. If a statement is false, give a counterexample.

89. $\lim_{x \to 3} (xf(x)) = 21$.

90. If $g(3) = 4$, then $\lim_{x \to 3} (f(x)g(x)) = 28$.

91. If $\lim_{x \to 3} g(x) = 5$, then $\lim_{x \to 3} (f(x) + g(x)) = 12$.

92. If $\lim_{x \to 3} (f(x) + g(x)) = 12$, then $\lim_{x \to 3} g(x) = 5$.

93. $f(2.99)$ is closer to 7 than $f(2.9)$ is.

94. If $f(3.1) > 0$, then $f(3.01) > 0$.

95. If $\lim_{x \to 3} g(x)$ does not exist, then $\lim_{x \to 3} (f(x)g(x))$ does not exist.

Which of the statements in Problems 96–100 are true about every function $f(x)$ such that $\lim_{x \to c} f(x) = L$? Give a reason for your answer.

96. If $f(x)$ is within 10^{-3} of L, then x is within 10^{-3} of c.

97. There is a positive ϵ such that, provided x is within 10^{-3} of c, and $x \neq c$, we can be sure $f(x)$ is within ϵ of L.

98. For any positive ϵ, we can find a positive δ such that, provided x is within δ of c, and $x \neq c$, we can be sure that $f(x)$ is within ϵ of L.

99. For each $\epsilon > 0$, there is a $\delta > 0$ such that if x is not within δ of c, then $f(x)$ is not within ϵ of L.

100. For each $\epsilon > 0$, there is some $\delta > 0$ such that if $f(x)$ is within ϵ of L, then we can be sure that x is within δ of c.

101. Which of the following statements is a direct consequence of the statement: "If f and g are continuous at $x = a$ and $g(a) \neq 0$ then f/g is continuous at $x = a$?"

    (a) If f and g are continuous at $x = a$ and $f(a) \neq 0$ then g/f is continuous at $x = a$.

    (b) If f and g are continuous at $x = a$ and $g(a) = 0$, then f/g is not continuous at $x = a$.

    (c) If f, g, are continuous at $x = a$, but f/g is not continuous at $x = a$, then $g(a) = 0$.

    (d) If f and f/g are continuous at $x = a$ and $g(a) \neq 0$, then g is continuous at $x = a$.

CHAPTER SUMMARY (see also Ready Reference at the end of the book)

- **Function terminology**
  Domain/range, increasing/decreasing, concavity, zeros (roots), even/odd, end behavior, asymptotes.

- **Linear functions**
  Slope, vertical intercept. Grow by equal amounts in equal times.

- **Exponential functions**
  Exponential growth and decay, with base e, growth rate, continuous growth rate, doubling time, half life. Grow by equal percentages in equal times.

- **Logarithmic functions**
  Log base 10, natural logarithm.

- **Trigonometric functions**
  Sine and cosine, tangent, amplitude, period, arcsine, arctangent.

- **Power functions**

- **Polynomials and rational functions**

- **New functions from old**
  Inverse functions, composition of functions, shifting, stretching, shrinking.

- **Working with functions**
  Find a formula for a linear, exponential, power, logarithmic, or trigonometric function, given graph, table of values, or verbal description. Find vertical and horizontal asymptotes. End behavior. Proportional relationships.

- **Comparisons between functions**
  Exponential functions dominate power and linear functions.

- **Continuity**
  Interpret graphically and numerically. Intermediate Value Theorem.

- **Limits**
  Graphical interpretation, ϵ-δ definition, properties, one-sided limits, limits to infinity.

REVIEW EXERCISES AND PROBLEMS FOR CHAPTER ONE

Exercises

Find formulas for the functions described in Exercises 1–8.

1. A line with slope 2 and x-intercept 5.

2. A parabola opening downward with its vertex at $(2,5)$.

3. A parabola with x-intercepts ± 1 and y-intercept 3.

4. The bottom half of a circle centered at the origin and with radius $\sqrt{2}$.

5. The top half of a circle with center $(-1, 2)$ and radius 3.

6. A cubic polynomial having x-intercepts at $1, 5, 7$.

7. A rational function of the form $y = ax/(x + b)$ with a vertical asymptote at $x = 2$ and a horizontal asymptote of $y = -5$.

8. A cosine curve with a maximum at $(0, 5)$, a minimum at $(\pi, -5)$, and no maxima or minima in between.

9. When a patient with a rapid heart rate takes a drug, the heart rate plunges dramatically and then slowly rises again as the drug wears off. Sketch the heart rate against time from the moment the drug is administered.

10. If $g(x) = (4 - x^2)/(x^2 + x)$, find the domain of $g(x)$. Solve $g(x) = 0$.

11. The entire graph of $f(x)$ is shown in Figure 1.98.

    (a) What is the domain of $f(x)$?
    (b) What is the range of $f(x)$?
    (c) List all zeros of $f(x)$.
    (d) List all intervals on which $f(x)$ is decreasing.

(e) Is $f(x)$ concave up or concave down at $x = 6$?
(f) What is $f(4)$?
(g) Is this function invertible? Explain.

Figure 1.98

12. For $f(n) = 3n^2 - 2$ and $g(n) = n + 1$, find and simplify:

    (a) $f(n) + g(n)$
    (b) $f(n)g(n)$
    (c) The domain of $f(n)/g(n)$
    (d) $f(g(n))$
    (e) $g(f(n))$

13. Let $m = f(A)$ be the minimum annual gross income, in thousands of dollars, needed to obtain a 30-year home mortgage loan of A thousand dollars at an interest rate of 6%. What do the following quantities represent in terms of the income needed for a loan?

    (a) $f(100)$ **(b)** $f^{-1}(75)$

For Exercises 14–17, solve for t using logs.

14. $5^t = 7$ **15.** $2 = (1.02)^t$ **16.** $7 \cdot 3^t = 5 \cdot 2^t$

17. $5.02(1.04)^t = 12.01(1.03)^t$

In Exercises 18–19, put the functions in the form $P = P_0 e^{kt}$.

18. $P = P_0 2^t$ **19.** $P = 5.23(0.2)^t$

For Exercises 20–21, find functions f and g such that $h(x) = f(g(x))$. [Note: Do not choose $f(x) = x$ or $g(x) = x$.]

20. $h(x) = \ln(x^3)$ **21.** $h(x) = (\ln x)^3$

Find the amplitudes and periods in Exercises 22–23.

22. $y = 5\sin(x/3)$ **23.** $y = 4 - 2\cos(5x)$

24. Consider the function $y = 5 + \cos(3x)$.

   (a) What is its amplitude?
   (b) What is its period?
   (c) Sketch its graph.

25. Determine the end behavior of each function as $x \to +\infty$ and as $x \to -\infty$.

   (a) $f(x) = x^7$ **(b)** $f(x) = 3x + 7x^3 - 12x^4$
   (c) $f(x) = x^{-4}$ **(d)** $f(x) = \dfrac{6x^3 - 5x^2 + 2}{x^3 - 8}$

In Exercises 26–27, which function dominates as $x \to \infty$?

26. $10 \cdot 2^x$ or $72{,}000x^{12}$ **27.** $0.25\sqrt{x}$ or $25{,}000x^{-3}$

Find possible formulas for the graphs in Exercises 28–41.

28.

29.

30.

31.

32.

33.

34.

35.

36.

37.

38.

39.

40.

41.

Are the functions in Exercises 42–43 continuous on $[-1, 1]$?

42. $g(x) = \dfrac{1}{x^2 + 1}$ **43.** $h(x) = \dfrac{1}{1 - x^2}$

44. Use Figure 1.99 to estimate the limits if they exist:

   (a) $\lim_{x \to 0} f(x)$ **(b)** $\lim_{x \to 1} f(x)$
   (c) $\lim_{x \to 2} f(x)$ **(d)** $\lim_{x \to 3^-} f(x)$

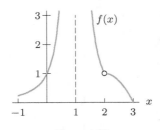

Figure 1.99

For the functions in Exercises 45–46, use algebra to evaluate the limits $\lim_{x \to a+} f(x)$, $\lim_{x \to a-} f(x)$, and $\lim_{x \to a} f(x)$ if they exist. Sketch a graph to confirm your answers.

45. $a = 3$, $f(x) = \dfrac{x^3 |2x - 6|}{x - 3}$

46. $a = 0$, $f(x) = \begin{cases} e^x & -1 < x < 0 \\ 1 & x = 0 \\ \cos x & 0 < x < 1 \end{cases}$

Problems

47. The yield, Y, of an apple orchard (in bushels) as a function of the amount, a, of fertilizer (in pounds) used on the orchard is shown in Figure 1.100.

(a) Describe the effect of the amount of fertilizer on the yield of the orchard.
(b) What is the vertical intercept? Explain what it means in terms of apples and fertilizer.
(c) What is the horizontal intercept? Explain what it means in terms of apples and fertilizer.
(d) What is the range of this function for $0 \le a \le 80$?
(e) Is the function increasing or decreasing at $a = 60$?
(f) Is the graph concave up or down near $a = 40$?

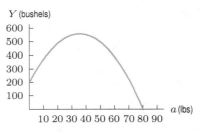

Figure 1.100

48. The graph of Fahrenheit temperature, °F, as a function of Celsius temperature, °C, is a line. You know that 212°F and 100°C both represent the temperature at which water boils. Similarly, 32°F and 0°C both represent water's freezing point.

(a) What is the slope of the graph?
(b) What is the equation of the line?
(c) Use the equation to find what Fahrenheit temperature corresponds to 20°C.
(d) What temperature is the same number of degrees in both Celsius and Fahrenheit?

49. The demand function for a certain product, $q = D(p)$, is linear, where p is the price per item in dollars and q is the quantity demanded. If p increases by \$5, market research

shows that q drops by two items. In addition, 100 items are purchased if the price is \$550.

(a) Find a formula for
   (i) q as a linear function of p
   (ii) p as a linear function of q
(b) Draw a graph with q on the horizontal axis.

50. A flight from Dulles Airport in Washington, DC, to LaGuardia Airport in New York City has to circle LaGuardia several times before being allowed to land. Plot a graph of the distance of the plane from Washington, DC, against time, from the moment of takeoff until landing.

51. The force, F, between two atoms depends on the distance r separating them. See Figure 1.101. A positive F represents a repulsive force; a negative F represents an attractive force.

(a) What happens to the force if the atoms start with $r = a$ and are
   (i) Pulled slightly further apart?
   (ii) Pushed slightly closer together?
(b) The atoms are said to be in *stable equilibrium* if the force between them is zero and the atoms tend to return to the equilibrium after a minor disturbance. Does $r = a$ represent a stable equilibrium? Explain.

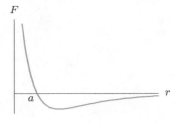

Figure 1.101

52. When the Olympic Games were held outside Mexico City in 1968, there was much discussion about the effect the high altitude (7340 feet) would have on the athletes. Assuming air pressure decays exponentially by 0.4% every 100 feet, by what percentage is air pressure reduced by moving from sea level to Mexico City?

[40]http://www.indexmundi.com/ukraine/population.html. Accessed April 17, 2011.

53. The population of the Ukraine fell from 45.7 million in 2009 to 45.42 million in 2010.[40] Assuming exponential decline, in what year is the population predicted to be 45 million?

54. During April 2006, Zimbabwe's inflation rate averaged 0.67% a day. This means that, on average, prices went up by 0.67% from one day to the next.

   (a) By what percentage did prices in Zimbabwe increase in April of 2006?

   (b) Assuming the same rate all year, what was Zimbabwe's annual inflation rate during 2006?

55. Hydroelectric power is electric power generated by the force of moving water. The table shows the annual percent change in hydroelectric power consumption by the US industrial sector.[41]

   (a) According to the table, during what single year(s), if any, did the US consumption of hydroelectric power energy increase by at least 10%? Decrease by 10% or more?

   (b) True or False: The hydroelectric power consumption nearly doubled from 2008 to 2009.

   (c) True or False: The hydroelectric power consumption decreased by about 36% from 2006 to 2009.

Year	2005	2006	2007	2008	2009
% growth over previous yr	−1.9	−10	−45.4	5.1	11

56. A kilogram weighs about 2.2 pounds.

   (a) Write a formula for the function, f, which gives an object's mass in kilograms, k, as a function of its weight in pounds, p.

   (b) Find a formula for the inverse function of f. What does this inverse function tell you, in practical terms?

57. The graph of $f(x)$ is a parabola that opens upward and the graph of $g(x)$ is a line with negative slope. Describe the graph of $g(f(x))$ in words.

58. Each of the functions in the table is increasing over its domain, but each increases in a different way. Match the functions f, g, h to the graphs in Figure 1.102.

x	$f(x)$	x	$g(x)$	x	$h(x)$
1	1	3.0	1	10	1
2	2	3.2	2	20	2
4	3	3.4	3	28	3
7	4	3.6	4	34	4
11	5	3.8	5	39	5
16	6	4.0	6	43	6
22	7	4.2	7	46.5	7
29	8	4.4	8	49	8
37	9	4.6	9	51	9
47	10	4.8	10	52	10

Figure 1.102

59. A culture of 100 bacteria doubles after 2 hours. How long will it take for the number of bacteria to reach 3,200?

60. If $f(x) = a \ln(x + 2)$, how does increasing a affect

   (a) The y-intercept?   **(b)** The x-intercept?

61. What is the doubling time of prices which are increasing by 5% a year?

62. Find the half-life of a radioactive substance that is reduced by 30% in 20 hours.

63. The air in a factory is being filtered so that the quantity of a pollutant, P (in mg/liter), is decreasing according to the function $P = P_0 e^{-kt}$, where t is time in hours. If 10% of the pollution is removed in the first five hours:

   (a) What percentage of the pollution is left after 10 hours?

   (b) How long is it before the pollution is reduced by 50%?

   (c) Plot a graph of pollution against time. Show the results of your calculations on the graph.

   (d) Explain why the quantity of pollutant might decrease in this way.

64. The half-life of radioactive strontium-90 is 29 years. In 1960, radioactive strontium-90 was released into the atmosphere during testing of nuclear weapons, and was absorbed into people's bones. How many years does it take until only 10% of the original amount absorbed remains?

65. What is the period of the motion of the minute hand of a clock?

66. In an electrical outlet, the voltage, V, in volts, is given as a function of time, t, in seconds, by the formula

$$V = V_0 \sin(120\pi t).$$

   (a) What does V_0 represent in terms of voltage?

   (b) What is the period of this function?

   (c) How many oscillations are completed in 1 second?

[41]http://www.eia.doe.gov/aer/renew.html. Accessed February 2011.

67. In a US household, the voltage in volts in an electric outlet is given by

$$V = 156\sin(120\pi t),$$

where t is in seconds. However, in a European house, the voltage is given (in the same units) by

$$V = 339\sin(100\pi t).$$

Compare the voltages in the two regions, considering the maximum voltage and number of cycles (oscillations) per second.

68. **(a)** How does the parameter A affect the graph of $y = A\sin(Bx)$? (Plot for $A = 1, 2, 3$ with $B = 1$.)
   (b) How does the parameter B affect the graph of $y = A\sin(Bx)$? (Plot for $B = 1, 2, 3$ with $A = 1$.)

69. Water is flowing down a cylindrical pipe of radius r.

   (a) Write a formula for the volume, V, of water that emerges from the end of the pipe in one second if the water is flowing at a rate of

   (i) 3 cm/sec   (ii) k cm/sec

   (b) Graph your answer to part (a)(ii) as a function of

   (i) r, assuming k is constant

   (ii) k, assuming r is constant

70. Values of three functions are given in Table 1.22, rounded to two decimal places. Two are power functions and one is an exponential. One of the power functions is a quadratic and one a cubic. Which one is exponential? Which one is quadratic? Which one is cubic?

Table 1.22

x	$f(x)$	x	$g(x)$	x	$k(x)$
8.4	5.93	5.0	3.12	0.6	3.24
9.0	7.29	5.5	3.74	1.0	9.01
9.6	8.85	6.0	4.49	1.4	17.66
10.2	10.61	6.5	5.39	1.8	29.19
10.8	12.60	7.0	6.47	2.2	43.61
11.4	14.82	7.5	7.76	2.6	60.91

71. Figure 1.103 shows the *hat function*

$$h_N(x) = \begin{cases} 0 & \text{if } x < N-1 \\ 1+x-N & \text{if } N-1 \le x < N \\ 1+N-x & \text{if } N \le x < N+1 \\ 0 & \text{if } N+1 \le x \end{cases}.$$

   (a) Graph the function $f(x) = 3h_1(x) + 2h_2(x) + 4h_3(x)$.
   (b) Describe the graph of $g(x) = ah_1(x) + bh_2(x) + ch_3(x)$.

Figure 1.103: Graph of $h_N(x)$

72. The point P moves around the circle of radius 5 shown in Figure 1.104. The angle θ, in radians, is given as a function of time, t, by the graph in Figure 1.105.

   (a) Estimate the coordinates of P when $t = 1.5$.
   (b) Describe in words the motion of the point P on the circle.

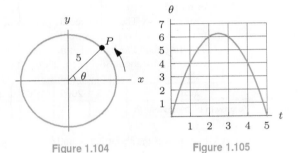

Figure 1.104   Figure 1.105

73. Match the following functions with the graphs in Figure 1.106. Assume $0 < b < a$.

   (a) $y = \dfrac{a}{x} - x$ **(b)** $y = \dfrac{(x-a)(x+a)}{x}$

   (c) $y = \dfrac{(x-a)(x^2+a)}{x^2}$ **(d)** $y = \dfrac{(x-a)(x+a)}{(x-b)(x+b)}$

Figure 1.106

74. Use a computer or calculator to sketch the functions

$$y(x) = \sin x \quad \text{and} \quad z_k(x) = ke^{-x}$$

for $k = 1, 2, 4, 6, 8, 10$. In each case find the smallest positive solution of the equation $y(x) = z_k(x)$. Now define a new function f by

$$f(k) = \{\text{Smallest positive solution of } y(x) = z_k(x)\}.$$

Explain why the function $f(k)$ is not continuous on the interval $0 \leq k \leq 10$.

For each value of ϵ in Problems 75–76, find a positive value of δ such that the graph of the function leaves the window $a - \delta < x < a + \delta, b - \epsilon < y < b + \epsilon$ by the sides and not through the top or bottom.

75. $h(x) = \sin x, a = b = 0, \epsilon = 0.1, 0.05, 0.0007$.

76. $k(x) = \cos x, a = 0, b = 1, \epsilon = 0.1, 0.001, 0.00001$.

77. If possible, choose k so that the following function is continuous on any interval:

$$f(x) = \begin{cases} \dfrac{5x^3 - 10x^2}{x - 2} & x \neq 2 \\ k & x = 2 \end{cases}$$

78. Find k so that the following function is continuous on any interval:

$$j(x) = \begin{cases} k \cos x & x \leq 0 \\ e^x - k & x > 0 \end{cases}$$

CAS Challenge Problems

79. **(a)** Factor $f(x) = x^4 + bx^3 - cx^3 - a^2x^2 - bcx^2 - a^2bx + a^2cx + a^2bc$ using a computer algebra system.
  (b) Assuming a, b, c are constants with $0 < a < b < c$, use your answer to part (a) to make a hand sketch of the graph of f. Explain how you know its shape.

80. **(a)** Using a computer algebra system, factor $f(x) = -x^5 + 11x^4 - 46x^3 + 90x^2 - 81x + 27$.
  (b) Use your answer to part (a) to make a hand sketch of the graph of f. Explain how you know its shape.

81. Let $f(x) = e^{6x} + e^{5x} - 2e^{4x} - 10e^{3x} - 8e^{2x} + 16e^x + 16$.

  (a) What happens to the value of $f(x)$ as $x \to \infty$? As $x \to -\infty$? Explain your answer.
  (b) Using a computer algebra system, factor $f(x)$ and predict the number of zeros of the function $f(x)$.
  (c) What are the exact values of the zeros? What is the relationship between successive zeros?

82. Let $f(x) = x^2 - x$.

  (a) Find the polynomials $f(f(x))$ and $f(f(f(x)))$ in expanded form.
  (b) What do you expect to be the degree of the polynomial $f(f(f(f(f(f(x))))))$? Explain.

83. **(a)** Use a computer algebra system to rewrite the rational function

$$f(x) = \frac{x^3 - 30}{x - 3}$$

in the form

$$f(x) = p(x) + \frac{r(x)}{q(x)},$$

where $p(x), q(x), r(x)$ are polynomials and the degree of $r(x)$ is less than the degree of $q(x)$.
  (b) What is the vertical asymptote of f? Use your answer to part (a) to write the formula for a function whose graph looks like the graph of f for x near the vertical asymptote.
  (c) Use your answer to part (a) to write the formula for a function whose graph looks like the graph of f for $x \to \infty$ and $x \to -\infty$.
  (d) Using graphs, confirm the asymptote you found in part (b) and the formula you found in part (c).

For Problems 84–85, we note that a function can be written as a polynomial in $\sin x$ (or $\cos x$) if it is of the form $p(\sin x)$ (or $p(\cos x)$) for some polynomial $p(x)$. For example, $\cos 2x$ can be written as a polynomial in $\sin x$ because $\cos(2x) = 1 - 2\sin^2 x = p(\sin x)$, where $p(x) = 1 - 2x^2$.

84. Use the trigonometric capabilities of your computer algebra system to express $\sin(5x)$ as a polynomial in $\sin x$.

85. Use the trigonometric capabilities of your computer algebra system to express $\cos(4x)$ as a polynomial in

  (a) $\sin x$
  (b) $\cos x$.

PROJECTS FOR CHAPTER ONE

1. Matching Functions to Data

From the data in Table 1.23, determine a possible formula for each function.[42] Write an explanation of your reasoning.

---

[42]Based on a problem by Lee Zia.

Table 1.23

x	$f(x)$	$g(x)$	$h(x)$	$F(x)$	$G(x)$	$H(x)$
−5	−10	20	25	0.958924	0.544021	2.958924
−4.5	−9	19	20.25	0.97753	−0.412118	2.97753
−4	−8	18	16	0.756802	−0.989358	2.756802
−3.5	−7	17	12.25	0.350783	−0.656987	2.350783
−3	−6	16	9	−0.14112	0.279415	1.85888
−2.5	−5	15	6.25	−0.598472	0.958924	1.401528
−2	−4	14	4	−0.909297	0.756802	1.090703
−1.5	−3	13	2.25	−0.997495	−0.14112	1.002505
−1	−2	12	1	−0.841471	−0.909297	1.158529
−0.5	−1	11	0.25	−0.479426	−0.841471	1.520574
0	0	10	0	0	0	2
0.5	1	9	0.25	0.479426	0.841471	2.479426
1	2	8	1	0.841471	0.909297	2.841471
1.5	3	7	2.25	0.997495	0.14112	2.997495
2	4	6	4	0.909297	−0.756802	2.909297
2.5	5	5	6.25	0.598472	−0.958924	2.598472
3	6	4	9	0.14112	−0.279415	2.14112
3.5	7	3	12.25	−0.350783	0.656987	1.649217
4	8	2	16	−0.756802	0.989358	1.243198
4.5	9	1	20.25	−0.97753	0.412118	1.02247
5	10	0	25	−0.958924	−0.544021	1.041076

2. Which Way is the Wind Blowing?

Mathematicians name a wind by giving the angle *toward* which it is blowing measured counterclockwise from east. Meteorologists give the angle *from* which it is blowing measured clockwise from north. Both use values from 0° to 360°. Figure 1.107 shows the two angles for a wind blowing from the northeast.

(a) Graph the mathematicians' angle θ_{math} as a function of the meteorologists' angle θ_{met}.

(b) Find a piecewise formula that gives θ_{math} in terms of θ_{met}.

Figure 1.107

Chapter Two

KEY CONCEPT: THE DERIVATIVE

Contents

2.1 How Do We Measure Speed? 76

    Average and Instantaneous Velocity 76

        Velocity versus Speed 76

    Defining Instantaneous Velocity 78

    Visualizing Velocity: Slope of Curve 78

    Computing the Instantaneous Velocity 80

2.2 The Derivative at a Point 83

    Average Rate of Change 83

    Instantaneous Rate of Change: The Derivative . . . 83

    Visualizing the Derivative: Slope of Curve and

        Slope of Tangent 84

        Estimating the Derivative 85

    Computing the Derivative Algebraically 86

2.3 The Derivative Function 90

    The Derivative Function: Graphically 91

    What Does the Derivative Tell Us Graphically? . . 92

    The Derivative Function: Numerically 92

        Improving Numerical Estimates 93

    Derivative Function: From a Formula 93

        Derivative of a Constant Function 94

        Derivative of a Linear Function 94

        Derivative of a Power Function 94

2.4 Interpretations of the Derivative 98

    An Alternative Notation for the Derivative . . . 99

    Using Units to Interpret the Derivative 99

2.5 The Second Derivative 104

    What Do Derivatives Tell Us? 104

    Interpretation of the Second Derivative as a

        Rate of Change 106

    Velocity and Acceleration 107

2.6 Differentiability 111

    What Does It Mean for a Function to Be

        Differentiable? 111

        Some Nondifferentiable Functions . . . 112

    Differentiability and Continuity 113

REVIEW PROBLEMS 116

PROJECTS 122

2.1   HOW DO WE MEASURE SPEED?

The speed of an object at an instant in time is surprisingly difficult to define precisely. Consider the statement: "At the instant it crossed the finish line, the horse was traveling at 42 mph." How can such a claim be substantiated? A photograph taken at that instant will show the horse motionless—it is no help at all. There is some paradox in trying to study the horse's motion at a particular instant in time, since by focusing on a single instant we stop the motion!

Problems of motion were of central concern to Zeno and other philosophers as early as the fifth century B.C. The modern approach, made famous by Newton's calculus, is to stop looking for a simple notion of speed at an instant, and instead to look at speed over small time intervals containing the instant. This method sidesteps the philosophical problems mentioned earlier but introduces new ones of its own.

We illustrate the ideas discussed above by an idealized example, called a thought experiment. It is idealized in the sense that we assume that we can make measurements of distance and time as accurately as we wish.

A Thought Experiment: Average and Instantaneous Velocity

We look at the speed of a small object (say, a grapefruit) that is thrown straight upward into the air at $t = 0$ seconds. The grapefruit leaves the thrower's hand at high speed, slows down until it reaches its maximum height, and then speeds up in the downward direction and finally, "Splat!" (See Figure 2.1.)

Suppose that we want to determine the speed, say, at $t = 1$ second. Table 2.1 gives the height, y, of the grapefruit above the ground as a function of time. During the first second the grapefruit travels $90 - 6 = 84$ feet, and during the second second it travels only $142 - 90 = 52$ feet. Hence the grapefruit traveled faster over the first interval, $0 \leq t \leq 1$, than the second interval, $1 \leq t \leq 2$.

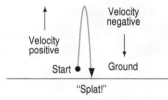

Figure 2.1: The grapefruit's path is straight up and down

Table 2.1   *Height of the grapefruit above the ground*

t (sec)	0	1	2	3	4	5	6
y (feet)	6	90	142	162	150	106	30

Velocity versus Speed

From now on, we will distinguish between velocity and speed. Suppose an object moves along a line. We pick one direction to be positive and say that the *velocity* is positive if it is in the same direction, and negative if it is in the opposite direction. For the grapefruit, upward is positive and downward is negative. (See Figure 2.1.) *Speed* is the magnitude of the velocity and so is always positive or zero.

> If $s(t)$ is the position of an object at time t, then the **average velocity** of the object over the interval $a \leq t \leq b$ is
>
> $$\text{Average velocity} = \frac{\text{Change in position}}{\text{Change in time}} = \frac{s(b) - s(a)}{b - a}.$$
>
> In words, the **average velocity** of an object over an interval is the net change in position during the interval divided by the change in time.

Example 1   Compute the average velocity of the grapefruit over the interval $4 \leq t \leq 5$. What is the significance of the sign of your answer?

Solution   During this one-second interval, the grapefruit moves $(106 - 150) = -44$ feet. Therefore the average velocity is $-44/(5 - 4) = -44$ ft/sec. The negative sign means the height is decreasing and the grapefruit is moving downward.

Example 2   Compute the average velocity of the grapefruit over the interval $1 \leq t \leq 3$.

Solution   Average velocity $= (162 - 90)/(3 - 1) = 72/2 = 36$ ft/sec.

The average velocity is a useful concept since it gives a rough idea of the behavior of the grapefruit: If two grapefruits are hurled into the air, and one has an average velocity of 10 ft/sec over the interval $0 \leq t \leq 1$ while the second has an average velocity of 100 ft/sec over the same interval, the second one is moving faster.

But average velocity over an interval does not solve the problem of measuring the velocity of the grapefruit at *exactly* $t = 1$ second. To get closer to an answer to that question, we have to look at what happens near $t = 1$ in more detail. The data[1] in Figure 2.2 shows the average velocity over small intervals on either side of $t = 1$.

Notice that the average velocity before $t = 1$ is slightly more than the average velocity after $t = 1$. We expect to define the velocity *at* $t = 1$ to be between these two average velocities. As the size of the interval shrinks, the values of the velocity before $t = 1$ and the velocity after $t = 1$ get closer together. In the smallest interval in Figure 2.2, both velocities are 68.0 ft/sec (to one decimal place), so we define the velocity at $t = 1$ to be 68.0 ft/sec (to one decimal place).

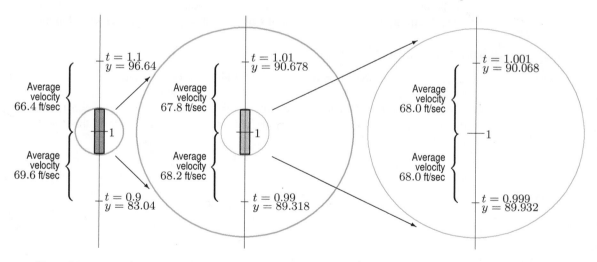

Figure 2.2: Average velocities over intervals on either side of $t = 1$: showing successively smaller intervals

Of course, if we calculate to more decimal places, the average velocities before and after $t = 1$ would no longer agree. To calculate the velocity at $t = 1$ to more decimal places of accuracy, we take smaller and smaller intervals on either side of $t = 1$ until the average velocities agree to the number of decimal places we want. In this way, we can estimate the velocity at $t = 1$ to any accuracy.

[1]The data is in fact calculated from the formula $y = 6 + 100t - 16t^2$.

Defining Instantaneous Velocity Using Limit Notation

When we take smaller and smaller intervals, it turns out that the average velocities get closer and closer to 68 ft/sec. It seems natural, then, to define *instantaneous velocity* at the instant $t = 1$ to be 68 ft/sec. Its definition depends on our being convinced that smaller and smaller intervals give averages that come arbitrarily close to 68; that is, the average speed approaches 68 ft/sec as a limit.

Notice how we have replaced the original difficulty of computing velocity at a point by a search for an argument to convince ourselves that the average velocities approach a limit as the time intervals shrink in size. Showing that the limit is exactly 68 requires the precise definition of limit given in Section 1.8.

To define instantaneous velocity at an arbitrary point $t = a$, we use the same method as for $t = 1$. On small intervals of size h around $t = a$, we calculate

$$\text{Average velocity} = \frac{s(a + h) - s(a)}{h}.$$

The instantaneous velocity is the number that the average velocities approach as the intervals decrease in size, that is, as h becomes smaller. So we make the following definition:

Let $s(t)$ be the position at time t. Then the **instantaneous velocity** at $t = a$ is defined as

$$\begin{array}{c}\text{Instantaneous velocity} \\ \text{at } t = a\end{array} = \lim_{h \to 0} \frac{s(a + h) - s(a)}{h}.$$

In words, the **instantaneous velocity** of an object at time $t = a$ is given by the limit of the average velocity over an interval, as the interval shrinks around a.

This limit refers to the number that the average velocities approach as the intervals shrink. To estimate the limit, we look at intervals of smaller and smaller, but never zero, length.

Visualizing Velocity: Slope of Curve

Now we visualize velocity using a graph of height. The cornerstone of the idea is the fact that, on a very small scale, most functions look almost like straight lines. Imagine taking the graph of a function near a point and "zooming in" to get a close-up view. (See Figure 2.3.) The more we zoom in, the more the curve appears to be a straight line. We call the slope of this line the *slope of the curve* at the point.

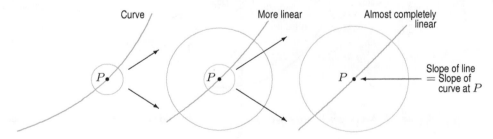

Figure 2.3: Estimating the slope of the curve at the point by "zooming in"

To visualize the instantaneous velocity, we think about how we calculated it. We took average velocities over small intervals containing $t = 1$. Two such velocities are represented by the slopes of the lines in Figure 2.4. As the length of the interval shrinks, the slope of the line gets closer to the slope of the curve at $t = 1$.

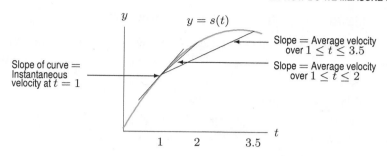

Figure 2.4: Average velocities over small intervals

> The **instantaneous velocity** is the slope of the curve at a point.

Let's go back to the grapefruit. Figure 2.5 shows the height of the grapefruit plotted against time. (Note that this is not a picture of the grapefruit's path, which is straight up and down.)

How can we visualize the average velocity on this graph? Suppose $y = s(t)$. We consider the interval $1 \leq t \leq 2$ and the expression

$$\text{Average velocity} = \frac{\text{Change in position}}{\text{Change in time}} = \frac{s(2) - s(1)}{2 - 1} = \frac{142 - 90}{1} = 52 \text{ ft/sec}.$$

Now $s(2) - s(1)$ is the change in position over the interval, and it is marked vertically in Figure 2.5. The 1 in the denominator is the time elapsed and is marked horizontally in Figure 2.5. Therefore,

$$\text{Average velocity} = \frac{\text{Change in position}}{\text{Change in time}} = \text{Slope of line joining } B \text{ and } C.$$

(See Figure 2.5.) A similar argument shows the following:

> The **average velocity** over any time interval $a \leq t \leq b$ is the slope of the line joining the points on the graph of $s(t)$ corresponding to $t = a$ and $t = b$.

Figure 2.5 shows how the grapefruit's velocity varies during its journey. At points A and B the curve has a large positive slope, indicating that the grapefruit is traveling up rapidly. Point D is almost at the top: the grapefruit is slowing down. At the peak, the slope of the curve is zero: the fruit has slowed to zero velocity for an instant in preparation for its return to earth. At point E the curve has a small negative slope, indicating a slow velocity of descent. Finally, the slope of the curve at point G is large and negative, indicating a large downward velocity that is responsible for the "Splat."

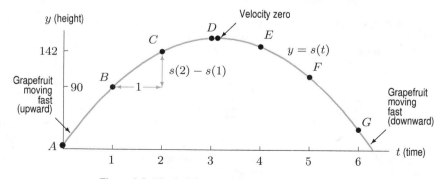

Figure 2.5: The height, y, of the grapefruit at time t

Using Limits to Compute the Instantaneous Velocity

Suppose we want to calculate the instantaneous velocity for $s(t) = t^2$ at $t = 3$. We must find:

$$\lim_{h \to 0} \frac{s(3+h) - s(3)}{h} = \lim_{h \to 0} \frac{(3+h)^2 - 9}{h}.$$

We show two possible approaches.

Example 3 Estimate $\lim\limits_{h \to 0} \dfrac{(3+h)^2 - 9}{h}$ numerically.

Solution The limit is the value approached by this expression as h approaches 0. The values in Table 2.2 seem to be converging to 6 as $h \to 0$. So it is a reasonable guess that

$$\lim_{h \to 0} \frac{(3+h)^2 - 9}{h} = 6.$$

However, we cannot be sure that the limit is *exactly* 6 by looking at the table. To calculate the limit exactly requires algebra.

Table 2.2 *Values of* $\left((3+h)^2 - 9\right)/h$ *near* $h = 0$

h	−0.1	−0.01	−0.001	0.001	0.01	0.1
$\left((3+h)^2 - 9\right)/h$	5.9	5.99	5.999	6.001	6.01	6.1

Example 4 Use algebra to find $\lim\limits_{h \to 0} \dfrac{(3+h)^2 - 9}{h}$.

Solution Expanding the numerator gives

$$\frac{(3+h)^2 - 9}{h} = \frac{9 + 6h + h^2 - 9}{h} = \frac{6h + h^2}{h}.$$

Since taking the limit as $h \to 0$ means looking at values of h near, but not equal, to 0, we can cancel h, giving

$$\lim_{h \to 0} \frac{(3+h)^2 - 9}{h} = \lim_{h \to 0}(6 + h).$$

As h approaches 0, the values of $(6 + h)$ approach 6, so

$$\lim_{h \to 0} \frac{(3+h)^2 - 9}{h} = \lim_{h \to 0}(6 + h) = 6.$$

Exercises and Problems for Section 2.1

Exercises

1. The distance, s, a car has traveled on a trip is shown in the table as a function of the time, t, since the trip started. Find the average velocity between $t = 2$ and $t = 5$.

t (hours)	0	1	2	3	4	5
s (km)	0	45	135	220	300	400

2. The table gives the position of a particle moving along the x-axis as a function of time in seconds, where x is in

meters. What is the average velocity of the particle from $t = 0$ to $t = 4$?

t	0	2	4	6	8
$x(t)$	−2	4	−6	−18	−14

3. The table gives the position of a particle moving along the x-axis as a function of time in seconds, where x is in angstroms. What is the average velocity of the particle from $t = 2$ to $t = 8$?

t	0	2	4	6	8
$x(t)$	0	14	−6	−18	−4

4. Figure 2.6 shows a particle's distance from a point. What is the particle's average velocity from $t = 0$ to $t = 3$?

Figure 2.6

5. Figure 2.7 shows a particle's distance from a point. What is the particle's average velocity from $t = 1$ to $t = 3$?

Figure 2.7

6. At time t in seconds, a particle's distance $s(t)$, in micrometers (μm), from a point is given by $s(t) = e^t - 1$. What is the average velocity of the particle from $t = 2$ to $t = 4$?

7. At time t in seconds, a particle's distance $s(t)$, in centimeters, from a point is given by $s(t) = 4 + 3\sin t$. What is the average velocity of the particle from $t = \pi/3$ to $t = 7\pi/3$?

8. In a time of t seconds, a particle moves a distance of s meters from its starting point, where $s = 3t^2$.

   (a) Find the average velocity between $t = 1$ and $t = 1 + h$ if:

   (i) $h = 0.1$,   (ii) $h = 0.01$,   (iii) $h = 0.001$.

   (b) Use your answers to part (a) to estimate the instantaneous velocity of the particle at time $t = 1$.

9. In a time of t seconds, a particle moves a distance of s meters from its starting point, where $s = 4t^3$.

   (a) Find the average velocity between $t = 0$ and $t = h$ if:

   (i) $h = 0.1$,   (ii) $h = 0.01$,   (iii) $h = 0.001$.

   (b) Use your answers to part (a) to estimate the instantaneous velocity of the particle at time $t = 0$.

10. In a time of t seconds, a particle moves a distance of s meters from its starting point, where $s = \sin(2t)$.

    (a) Find the average velocity between $t = 1$ and $t = 1 + h$ if:

    (i) $h = 0.1$,   (ii) $h = 0.01$,   (iii) $h = 0.001$.

    (b) Use your answers to part (a) to estimate the instantaneous velocity of the particle at time $t = 1$.

11. A car is driven at a constant speed. Sketch a graph of the distance the car has traveled as a function of time.

12. A car is driven at an increasing speed. Sketch a graph of the distance the car has traveled as a function of time.

13. A car starts at a high speed, and its speed then decreases slowly. Sketch a graph of the distance the car has traveled as a function of time.

Problems

Estimate the limits in Problems 14–17 by substituting smaller and smaller values of h. For trigonometric functions, use radians. Give answers to one decimal place.

14. $\lim\limits_{h \to 0} \dfrac{(3+h)^3 - 27}{h}$

15. $\lim\limits_{h \to 0} \dfrac{\cos h - 1}{h}$

16. $\lim\limits_{h \to 0} \dfrac{7^h - 1}{h}$

17. $\lim\limits_{h \to 0} \dfrac{e^{1+h} - e}{h}$

18. Match the points labeled on the curve in Figure 2.8 with the given slopes.

Slope	Point
-3	
-1	
0	
$1/2$	
1	
2	

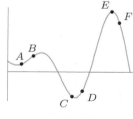

Figure 2.8

19. For the function shown in Figure 2.9, at what labeled points is the slope of the graph positive? Negative? At which labeled point does the graph have the greatest (i.e., most positive) slope? The least slope (i.e., negative and with the largest magnitude)?

Figure 2.9

20. For the graph $y = f(x)$ in Figure 2.10, arrange the following numbers from smallest to largest:

    • The slope of the graph at A.
    • The slope of the graph at B.
    • The slope of the graph at C.
    • The slope of the line AB.
    • The number 0.
    • The number 1.

Figure 2.10

21. The graph of $f(t)$ in Figure 2.11 gives the position of a particle at time t. List the following quantities in order, smallest to largest.

- A, average velocity between $t = 1$ and $t = 3$,
- B, average velocity between $t = 5$ and $t = 6$,
- C, instantaneous velocity at $t = 1$,
- D, instantaneous velocity at $t = 3$,
- E, instantaneous velocity at $t = 5$,
- F, instantaneous velocity at $t = 6$.

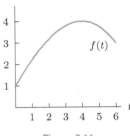

Figure 2.11

22. Find the average velocity over the interval $0 \le t \le 0.2$, and estimate the velocity at $t = 0.2$ of a car whose position, s, is given by the following table.

t (sec)	0	0.2	0.4	0.6	0.8	1.0
s (ft)	0	0.5	1.8	3.8	6.5	9.6

23. A particle moves at varying velocity along a line and $s = f(t)$ represents the particle's distance from a point as a function of time, t. Sketch a possible graph for f if the average velocity of the particle between $t = 2$ and $t = 6$ is the same as the instantaneous velocity at $t = 5$.

24. A ball is tossed into the air from a bridge, and its height, y (in feet), above the ground t seconds after it is thrown is given by

$$y = f(t) = -16t^2 + 50t + 36.$$

- **(a)** How high above the ground is the bridge?
- **(b)** What is the average velocity of the ball for the first second?
- **(c)** Approximate the velocity of the ball at $t = 1$ second.
- **(d)** Graph f, and determine the maximum height the ball reaches. What is the velocity at the time the ball is at the peak?
- **(e)** Use the graph to decide at what time, t, the ball reaches its maximum height.

Use algebra to evaluate the limits in Problems 25–28.

25. $\lim\limits_{h \to 0} \dfrac{(2 + h)^2 - 4}{h}$

26. $\lim\limits_{h \to 0} \dfrac{(1 + h)^3 - 1}{h}$

27. $\lim\limits_{h \to 0} \dfrac{3(2 + h)^2 - 12}{h}$

28. $\lim\limits_{h \to 0} \dfrac{(3 + h)^2 - (3 - h)^2}{2h}$

Strengthen Your Understanding

In Problems 29–31, explain what is wrong with the statement.

29. Velocity and speed are the same.

30. Since $\lim_{h \to 0}(2 + h)^2 = 4$, we have

$$\lim\limits_{h \to 0} \dfrac{(2 + h)^2 - 2^2}{h} = 0.$$

31. The particle whose position is shown in Figure 2.11 has velocity at time $t = 4$ greater than the velocity at $t = 2$.

In Problems 32–33, give an example of:

32. A function which has a negative instantaneous velocity for $t < 0$ and a positive instantaneous velocity for $t > 0$.

33. A function giving the position of a particle that has the same speed at $t = -1$ and $t = 1$ but different velocities.

Are the statements in Problems 34–39 true or false? Give an explanation for your answer.

34. If a car is going 50 miles per hour at 2 pm and 60 miles per hour at 3 pm then it travels between 50 and 60 miles during the hour between 2 pm and 3 pm.

35. If a car travels 80 miles between 2 and 4 pm, then its velocity is close to 40 mph at 2 pm.

36. If the time interval is short enough, then the average velocity of a car over the time interval and the instantaneous velocity at a time in the interval can be expected to be close.

37. If an object moves with the same average velocity over every time interval, then its average velocity equals its instantaneous velocity at any time.

38. The formula Distance traveled = Average velocity × Time is valid for every moving object for every time interval.

39. By definition, the instantaneous velocity of an object equals a difference quotient.

2.2 THE DERIVATIVE AT A POINT

Average Rate of Change

In Section 2.1, we looked at the change in height divided by the change in time; this ratio is called the *difference quotient*. Now we define the rate of change of a function f that depends on a variable other than time. We say:

$$\text{Average rate of change of } f \text{ over the interval from } a \text{ to } a + h = \frac{f(a+h) - f(a)}{h}.$$

The numerator, $f(a+h) - f(a)$, measures the change in the value of f over the interval from a to $a + h$. The difference quotient is the change in f divided by the change in the independent variable, which we call x. Although the interval is no longer necessarily a time interval, we still talk about the *average rate of change* of f over the interval. If we want to emphasize the independent variable, we talk about the average rate of change of f *with respect to x*.

Instantaneous Rate of Change: The Derivative

We define the *instantaneous rate of change* of a function at a point in the same way that we defined instantaneous velocity: we look at the average rate of change over smaller and smaller intervals. This instantaneous rate of change is called the *derivative of f at a*, denoted by $f'(a)$.

The **derivative of f at a**, written $f'(a)$, is defined as

$$\text{Rate of change of } f \text{ at } a = f'(a) = \lim_{h \to 0} \frac{f(a+h) - f(a)}{h}.$$

If the limit exists, then f is said to be **differentiable at a**.

To emphasize that $f'(a)$ is the rate of change of $f(x)$ as the variable x changes, we call $f'(a)$ the derivative of f *with respect to x* at $x = a$. When the function $y = s(t)$ represents the position of an object, the derivative $s'(t)$ is the velocity.

Example 1   Eucalyptus trees, common in California and the Pacific Northwest, grow better with more water. Scientists in North Africa, analyzing where to plant trees, found that the volume of wood that grows on a square kilometer, in meters^3, is approximated by[2]

$$V(r) = 0.2r^2 - 20r + 600,$$

where r is rainfall in cm per year, and $60 \leq r \leq 120$.

(a) Calculate the average rate of change of V with respect to r over the intervals $90 \leq r \leq 100$ and $100 \leq r \leq 110$.

(b) By choosing small values for h, estimate the instantaneous rate of change of V with respect to r at $r = 100$ cm.

Solution   (a) Using the formula for the average rate of change gives

$$\text{Average rate of change of volume for } 90 \leq r \leq 100 = \frac{V(100) - V(90)}{10} = \frac{600 - 420}{10} = 18 \text{ meter}^3/\text{cm}.$$

---

[2]"Is urban forestry a solution to the energy crises of Sahelian cities?" by Cornelia Sepp, www.nzdl.org, accessed Feb 11, 2012.

$$\text{Average rate of change of volume} \atop \text{for } 100 \le r \le 110 \quad = \frac{V(110) - V(100)}{10} = \frac{820 - 600}{10} = 22 \text{ meter}^3/\text{cm}.$$

So we see that the average rate of change of the volume of wood grown on a square kilometer increases as the rainfall increases.

(b) With $h = 0.1$ and $h = -0.1$, we have the difference quotients

$$\frac{V(100.1) - V(100)}{0.1} = 20.02 \text{ m}^3/\text{cm} \quad \text{and} \quad \frac{V(99.9) - V(100)}{-0.1} = 19.98 \text{ m}^3/\text{cm}.$$

With $h = 0.01$ and $h = -0.01$,

$$\frac{V(100.01) - V(100)}{0.01} = 20.002 \text{ m}^3/\text{cm} \quad \text{and} \quad \frac{V(99.99) - V(100)}{-0.01} = 19.998 \text{ m}^3/\text{cm}.$$

These difference quotients suggest that when the yearly rainfall is 100 cm, the instantaneous rate of change of the volume of wood grown on a square kilometer is about 20 meter^3 per cm of rainfall. To confirm that the instantaneous rate of change of the function is exactly 20, that is, $V'(100) = 20$, we would need to take the limit as $h \to 0$.

Visualizing the Derivative: Slope of Curve and Slope of Tangent

As with velocity, we can visualize the derivative $f'(a)$ as the slope of the graph of f at $x = a$. In addition, there is another way to think of $f'(a)$. Consider the difference quotient $(f(a + h) - f(a))/h$. The numerator, $f(a + h) - f(a)$, is the vertical distance marked in Figure 2.12 and h is the horizontal distance, so

$$\text{Average rate of change of } f = \frac{f(a + h) - f(a)}{h} = \text{Slope of line } AB.$$

As h becomes smaller, the line AB approaches the tangent line to the curve at A. (See Figure 2.13.) We say

$$\text{Instantaneous rate of change} \atop \text{of } f \text{ at } a \quad = \lim_{h \to 0} \frac{f(a + h) - f(a)}{h} = \text{Slope of tangent at } A.$$

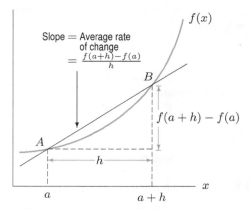

Figure 2.12: Visualizing the average rate of change of f

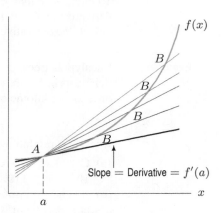

Figure 2.13: Visualizing the instantaneous rate of change of f

The derivative at point A can be interpreted as:
- The slope of the curve at A.
- The slope of the tangent line to the curve at A.

The slope interpretation is often useful in gaining rough information about the derivative, as the following examples show.

Example 2   Is the derivative of $\sin x$ at $x = \pi$ positive or negative?

Solution   Looking at a graph of $\sin x$ in Figure 2.14 (remember, x is in radians), we see that a tangent line drawn at $x = \pi$ has negative slope. So the derivative at this point is negative.

Figure 2.14: Tangent line to $\sin x$ at $x = \pi$

Recall that if we zoom in on the graph of a function $y = f(x)$ at the point $x = a$, we usually find that the graph looks like a straight line with slope $f'(a)$.

Example 3   By zooming in on the point $(0, 0)$ on the graph of the sine function, estimate the value of the derivative of $\sin x$ at $x = 0$, with x in radians.

Solution   Figure 2.15 shows graphs of $\sin x$ with smaller and smaller scales. On the interval $-0.1 \leq x \leq 0.1$, the graph looks like a straight line of slope 1. Thus, the derivative of $\sin x$ at $x = 0$ is about 1.

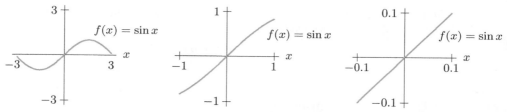

Figure 2.15: Zooming in on the graph of $\sin x$ near $x = 0$ shows the derivative is about 1 at $x = 0$

Later we will show that the derivative of $\sin x$ at $x = 0$ is exactly 1. (See page 152 in Section 3.5.) From now on we will assume that this is so. This simple result is one of the reasons we choose to use radians when doing calculus with trigonometric functions. If we had done Example 3 in degrees, the derivative of $\sin x$ would have turned out to be a much messier number. (See Problem 24, page 89.)

Estimating the Derivative

Example 4   Estimate the value of the derivative of $f(x) = 2^x$ at $x = 0$ graphically and numerically.

Solution   Graphically: Figure 2.16 indicates that the graph is concave up. Assuming this, the slope at A is between the slope of BA and the slope of AC. Since

$$\text{Slope of line } BA = \frac{(2^0 - 2^{-1})}{(0 - (-1))} = \frac{1}{2} \quad \text{and} \quad \text{Slope of line } AC = \frac{(2^1 - 2^0)}{(1 - 0)} = 1,$$

we know that at $x = 0$ the derivative of 2^x is between $1/2$ and 1.

Numerically: To estimate the derivative at $x = 0$, we look at values of the difference quotient

$$\frac{f(0 + h) - f(0)}{h} = \frac{2^h - 2^0}{h} = \frac{2^h - 1}{h}$$

for small h. Table 2.3 shows some values of 2^h together with values of the difference quotients. (See Problem 33 on page 89 for what happens for very small values of h.)

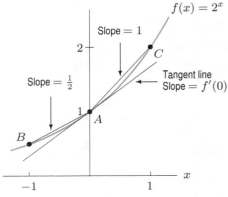

Figure 2.16: Graph of $y = 2^x$ showing the derivative at $x = 0$

Table 2.3   *Numerical values for difference quotient of 2^x at $x = 0$*

h	2^h	Difference quotient: $\frac{2^h - 1}{h}$
-0.0003	0.999792078	0.693075
-0.0002	0.999861380	0.693099
-0.0001	0.999930688	0.693123
0	1	
0.0001	1.00006932	0.693171
0.0002	1.00013864	0.693195
0.0003	1.00020797	0.693219

The concavity of the curve tells us that difference quotients calculated with negative h's are smaller than the derivative, and those calculated with positive h's are larger. From Table 2.3 we see that the derivative is between 0.693123 and 0.693171. To three decimal places, $f'(0) = 0.693$.

Example 5   Find an approximate equation for the tangent line to $f(x) = 2^x$ at $x = 0$.

Solution   From the previous example, we know the slope of the tangent line is about 0.693. Since the tangent line has y-intercept 1, its equation is

$$y = 0.693x + 1.$$

Computing the Derivative Algebraically

The graph of $f(x) = 1/x$ in Figure 2.17 leads us to expect that $f'(2)$ is negative. To compute $f'(2)$ exactly, we use algebra.

Figure 2.17: Tangent line to $f(x) = 1/x$ at $x = 2$

Example 6   Find the derivative of $f(x) = 1/x$ at the point $x = 2$.

Solution   The derivative is the limit of the difference quotient, so we look at

$$f'(2) = \lim_{h \to 0} \frac{f(2 + h) - f(2)}{h}.$$

Using the formula for f and simplifying gives

$$f'(2) = \lim_{h \to 0} \frac{1}{h}\left(\frac{1}{2 + h} - \frac{1}{2}\right) = \lim_{h \to 0} \left(\frac{2 - (2 + h)}{2h(2 + h)}\right) = \lim_{h \to 0} \frac{-h}{2h(2 + h)}.$$

Since the limit only examines values of h close to, but not equal to, zero, we can cancel h. We get

$$f'(2) = \lim_{h \to 0} \frac{-1}{2(2+h)} = -\frac{1}{4}.$$

Thus, $f'(2) = -1/4$. The slope of the tangent line in Figure 2.17 is $-1/4$.

Exercises and Problems for Section 2.2

Exercises

1. The table shows values of $f(x) = x^3$ near $x = 2$ (to three decimal places). Use it to estimate $f'(2)$.

x	1.998	1.999	2.000	2.001	2.002
x^3	7.976	7.988	8.000	8.012	8.024

2. By choosing small values for h, estimate the instantaneous rate of change of the function $f(x) = x^3$ with respect to x at $x = 1$.

3. The income that a company receives from selling an item is called the revenue. Production decisions are based, in part, on how revenue changes if the quantity sold changes; that is, on the rate of change of revenue with respect to quantity sold. Suppose a company's revenue, in dollars, is given by $R(q) = 100q - 10q^2$, where q is the quantity sold in kilograms.

    (a) Calculate the average rate of change of R with respect to q over the intervals $1 \le q \le 2$ and $2 \le q \le 3$.

    (b) By choosing small values for h, estimate the instantaneous rate of change of revenue with respect to change in quantity at $q = 2$ kilograms.

4. **(a)** Make a table of values rounded to two decimal places for the function $f(x) = e^x$ for $x = 1, 1.5, 2, 2.5,$ and 3. Then use the table to answer parts (b) and (c).

    (b) Find the average rate of change of $f(x)$ between $x = 1$ and $x = 3$.

    (c) Use average rates of change to approximate the instantaneous rate of change of $f(x)$ at $x = 2$.

5. **(a)** Make a table of values, rounded to two decimal places, for $f(x) = \log x$ (that is, log base 10) with $x = 1, 1.5, 2, 2.5, 3$. Then use this table to answer parts (b) and (c).

    (b) Find the average rate of change of $f(x)$ between $x = 1$ and $x = 3$.

    (c) Use average rates of change to approximate the instantaneous rate of change of $f(x)$ at $x = 2$.

6. If $f(x) = x^3 + 4x$, estimate $f'(3)$ using a table with values of x near 3, spaced by 0.001.

7. Graph $f(x) = \sin x$, and use the graph to decide whether the derivative of $f(x)$ at $x = 3\pi$ is positive or negative.

8. For the function $f(x) = \log x$, estimate $f'(1)$. From the graph of $f(x)$, would you expect your estimate to be greater than or less than $f'(1)$?

9. Estimate $f'(2)$ for $f(x) = 3^x$. Explain your reasoning.

10. The graph of $y = f(x)$ is shown in Figure 2.18. Which is larger in each of the following pairs?

    (a) Average rate of change: Between $x = 1$ and $x = 3$? Or between $x = 3$ and $x = 5$?

    (b) $f(2)$ or $f(5)$?

    (c) $f'(1)$ or $f'(4)$?

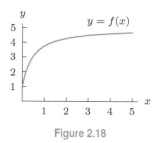

Figure 2.18

11. Figure 2.19 shows the graph of f. Match the derivatives in the table with the points a, b, c, d, e.

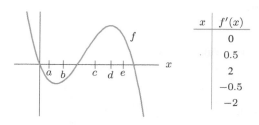

Figure 2.19

x	$f'(x)$
	0
	0.5
	2
	-0.5
	-2

12. Label points $A, B, C, D, E,$ and F on the graph of $y = f(x)$ in Figure 2.20.

   (a) Point A is a point on the curve where the derivative is negative.

   (b) Point B is a point on the curve where the value of the function is negative.

   (c) Point C is a point on the curve where the derivative is largest.

   (d) Point D is a point on the curve where the derivative is zero.

   (e) Points E and F are different points on the curve where the derivative is about the same.

Figure 2.20

Problems

13. Suppose that $f(x)$ is a function with $f(100) = 35$ and $f'(100) = 3$. Estimate $f(102)$.

14. Show how to represent the following on Figure 2.21.

   (a) $f(4)$ **(b)** $f(4) - f(2)$

   (c) $\dfrac{f(5) - f(2)}{5 - 2}$ **(d)** $f'(3)$

Figure 2.21

15. For each of the following pairs of numbers, use Figure 2.21 to decide which is larger. Explain your answer.

   (a) $f(3)$ or $f(4)$?

   (b) $f(3) - f(2)$ or $f(2) - f(1)$?

   (c) $\dfrac{f(2) - f(1)}{2 - 1}$ or $\dfrac{f(3) - f(1)}{3 - 1}$?

   (d) $f'(1)$ or $f'(4)$?

16. With the function f given by Figure 2.21, arrange the following quantities in ascending order:

$$0, \quad f'(2), \quad f'(3), \quad f(3) - f(2)$$

17. The function in Figure 2.22 has $f(4) = 25$ and $f'(4) = 1.5$. Find the coordinates of the points A, B, C.

Figure 2.22

18. Use Figure 2.23 to fill in the blanks in the following statements about the function g at point B.

   (a) $g(\underline{}) = \underline{}$ **(b)** $g'(\underline{}) = \underline{}$

Figure 2.23

19. On a copy of Figure 2.24, mark lengths that represent the quantities in parts (a)–(d). (Pick any positive x and h.)

   (a) $f(x)$ **(b)** $f(x + h)$

   (c) $f(x + h) - f(x)$ **(d)** h

   (e) Using your answers to parts (a)–(d), show how the quantity $\dfrac{f(x + h) - f(x)}{h}$ can be represented as the slope of a line in Figure 2.24.

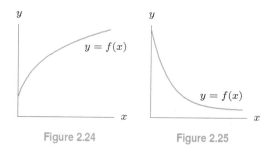

Figure 2.24   Figure 2.25

20. On a copy of Figure 2.25, mark lengths that represent the quantities in parts (a)–(d). (Pick any convenient x, and assume $h > 0$.)
  (a) $f(x)$ **(b)** $f(x+h)$ **(c)** $f(x+h) - f(x)$ **(d)** h
  (e) Using your answers to parts (a)–(d), show how the quantity $\dfrac{f(x+h) - f(x)}{h}$ can be represented as the slope of a line on the graph.

21. Consider the function shown in Figure 2.26.

  (a) Write an expression involving f for the slope of the line joining A and B.
  (b) Draw the tangent line at C. Compare its slope to the slope of the line in part (a).
  (c) Are there any other points on the curve at which the slope of the tangent line is the same as the slope of the tangent line at C? If so, mark them on the graph. If not, why not?

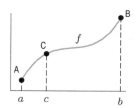

Figure 2.26

22. (a) If f is even and $f'(10) = 6$, what is $f'(-10)$?
  (b) If f is any even function and $f'(0)$ exists, what is $f'(0)$?

23. If g is an odd function and $g'(4) = 5$, what is $g'(-4)$?

24. (a) Estimate $f'(0)$ if $f(x) = \sin x$, with x in degrees.
  (b) In Example 3 on page 85, we found that the derivative of $\sin x$ at $x = 0$ was 1. Why do we get a different result here? (This problem shows why radians are almost always used in calculus.)

25. Find the equation of the tangent line to $f(x) = x^2 + x$ at $x = 3$. Sketch the function and this tangent line.

26. Estimate the instantaneous rate of change of the function $f(x) = x \ln x$ at $x = 1$ and at $x = 2$. What do these values suggest about the concavity of the graph between 1 and 2?

27. Estimate the derivative of $f(x) = x^x$ at $x = 2$.

28. For $y = f(x) = 3x^{3/2} - x$, use your calculator to construct a graph of $y = f(x)$, for $0 \le x \le 2$. From your graph, estimate $f'(0)$ and $f'(1)$.

29. Let $f(x) = \ln(\cos x)$. Use your calculator to approximate the instantaneous rate of change of f at the point $x = 1$. Do the same thing for $x = \pi/4$. (Note: Be sure that your calculator is set in radians.)

30. On October 17, 2006, in an article called "US Population Reaches 300 Million," the BBC reported that the US gains 1 person every 11 seconds. If $f(t)$ is the US population in millions t years after October 17, 2006, find $f(0)$ and $f'(0)$.

31. The population, $P(t)$, of China,[3] in billions, can be approximated by

$$P(t) = 1.267(1.007)^t,$$

where t is the number of years since the start of 2000. According to this model, how fast was the population growing at the start of 2000 and at the start of 2007? Give your answers in millions of people per year.

32. (a) Graph $f(x) = \frac{1}{2}x^2$ and $g(x) = f(x) + 3$ on the same set of axes. What can you say about the slopes of the tangent lines to the two graphs at the point $x = 0$? $x = 2$? Any point $x = x_0$?
  (b) Explain why adding a constant value, C, to any function does not change the value of the slope of its graph at any point. [Hint: Let $g(x) = f(x) + C$, and calculate the difference quotients for f and g.]

33. Suppose Table 2.3 on page 86 is continued with smaller values of h. A particular calculator gives the results in Table 2.4. (Your calculator may give slightly different results.) Comment on the values of the difference quotient in Table 2.4. In particular, why is the last value of $(2^h - 1)/h$ zero? What do you expect the calculated value of $(2^h - 1)/h$ to be when $h = 10^{-20}$?

Table 2.4 *Questionable values of difference quotients of 2^x near $x = 0$*

h	Difference quotient: $(2^h - 1)/h$
10^{-4}	0.6931712
10^{-6}	0.693147
10^{-8}	0.6931
10^{-10}	0.69
10^{-12}	0

---

[3] www.unescap.org/stat/data/apif/index.asp, accessed May 1, 2007.

34. (a) Let $f(x) = x^2$. Explain what Table 2.5 tells us about $f'(1)$.

(b) Find $f'(1)$ exactly.

(c) If x changes by 0.1 near $x = 1$, what does $f'(1)$ tell us about how $f(x)$ changes? Illustrate your answer with a sketch.

Table 2.5

x	x^2	Difference in successive x^2 values
0.998	0.996004	
		0.001997
0.999	0.998001	
		0.001999
1.000	1.000000	
		0.002001
1.001	1.002001	
		0.002003
1.002	1.004004	

Use algebra to evaluate the limits in Problems 35–40.

35. $\lim_{h \to 0} \dfrac{(-3 + h)^2 - 9}{h}$

36. $\lim_{h \to 0} \dfrac{(2 - h)^3 - 8}{h}$

37. $\lim_{h \to 0} \dfrac{1/(1 + h) - 1}{h}$

38. $\lim_{h \to 0} \dfrac{1/(1 + h)^2 - 1}{h}$

39. $\lim_{h \to 0} \dfrac{\sqrt{4 + h} - 2}{h}$ [Hint: Multiply by $\sqrt{4 + h} + 2$ in numerator and denominator.]

40. $\lim_{h \to 0} \dfrac{1/\sqrt{4 + h} - 1/2}{h}$

Find the derivatives in Problems 41–46 algebraically.

41. $f(x) = 5x^2$ at $x = 10$

42. $f(x) = x^3$ at $x = -2$

43. $g(t) = t^2 + t$ at $t = -1$

44. $f(x) = x^3 + 5$ at $x = 1$

45. $g(x) = 1/x$ at $x = 2$

46. $g(z) = z^{-2}$, find $g'(2)$

For Problems 47–50, find the equation of the line tangent to the function at the given point.

47. $f(x) = 5x^2$ at $x = 10$

48. $f(x) = x^3$ at $x = -2$

49. $f(x) = x$ at $x = 20$

50. $f(x) = 1/x^2$ at $(1, 1)$

Strengthen Your Understanding

In Problems 51–52, explain what is wrong with the statement.

51. For the function $f(x) = \log x$ we have $f'(0.5) < 0$.

52. The derivative of a function $f(x)$ at $x = a$ is the tangent line to the graph of $f(x)$ at $x = a$.

In Problems 53–54, give an example of:

53. A continuous function which is always increasing and positive.

54. A linear function with derivative 2 at $x = 0$.

Are the statements in Problems 55–57 true or false? Give an explanation for your answer.

55. You cannot be sure of the exact value of a derivative of a function at a point using only the information in a table of values of the function. The best you can do is find an approximation.

56. If you zoom in (with your calculator) on the graph of $y = f(x)$ in a small interval around $x = 10$ and see a straight line, then the slope of that line equals the derivative $f'(10)$.

57. If $f(x)$ is concave up, then $f'(a) < (f(b) - f(a))/(b - a)$ for $a < b$.

58. Assume that f is an odd function and that $f'(2) = 3$, then $f'(-2) =$

(a) 3   **(b)** -3

(c) 1/3   **(d)** $-1/3$

2.3 THE DERIVATIVE FUNCTION

In the previous section we looked at the derivative of a function at a fixed point. Now we consider what happens at a variety of points. The derivative generally takes on different values at different points and is itself a function.

First, remember that the derivative of a function at a point tells us the rate at which the value of the function is changing at that point. Geometrically, we can think of the derivative as the slope of the curve or of the tangent line at the point.

Example 1   Estimate the derivative of the function $f(x)$ graphed in Figure 2.27 at $x = -2, -1, 0, 1, 2, 3, 4, 5$.

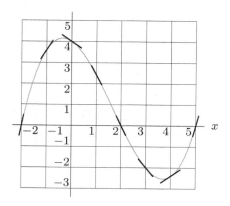

Figure 2.27: Estimating the derivative graphically as the slope of the tangent line

Solution   From the graph we estimate the derivative at any point by placing a straightedge so that it forms the tangent line at that point, and then using the grid squares to estimate the slope of the straightedge. For example, the tangent at $x = -1$ is drawn in Figure 2.27, and has a slope of about 2, so $f'(-1) \approx 2$. Notice that the slope at $x = -2$ is positive and fairly large; the slope at $x = -1$ is positive but smaller. At $x = 0$, the slope is negative, by $x = 1$ it has become more negative, and so on. Some estimates of the derivative are listed in Table 2.6. You should check these values. Are they reasonable? Is the derivative positive where you expect? Negative?

Table 2.6   *Estimated values of derivative of function in Figure 2.27*

x	-2	-1	0	1	2	3	4	5
$f'(x)$	6	2	-1	-2	-2	-1	1	4

Notice that for every x-value, there's a corresponding value of the derivative. Therefore, the derivative is itself a function of x.

For any function f, we define the **derivative function**, f', by

$$f'(x) = \text{Rate of change of } f \text{ at } x = \lim_{h \to 0} \frac{f(x+h) - f(x)}{h}.$$

For every x-value for which this limit exists, we say f is *differentiable at* that x-value. If the limit exists for all x in the domain of f, we say f is *differentiable everywhere*. Most functions we meet are differentiable at every point in their domain, except perhaps for a few isolated points.

The Derivative Function: Graphically

Example 2   Sketch the graph of the derivative of the function shown in Figure 2.27.

Solution   We plot the values of the derivative in Table 2.6 and connect them with a smooth curve to obtain the estimate of the derivative function in Figure 2.28. Values of the derivative function give slopes of the original graph.

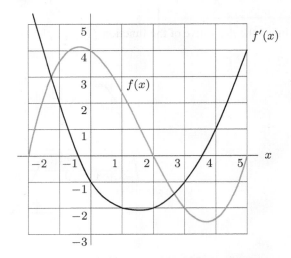

Figure 2.28: Function (colored) and derivative (black) from Example 1

Check that this graph of f' makes sense: Where the values of f' are positive, f is increasing ($x < -0.3$ or $x > 3.8$) and where f' is negative, f is decreasing. Notice that at the points where f has large positive slope, such as $x = -2$, the graph of the derivative is far above the x-axis, as it should be, since the value of the derivative is large there. At points where the slope is gentler, such as $x = -1$, the graph of f' is closer to the x-axis, since the derivative is smaller.

What Does the Derivative Tell Us Graphically?

Where f' is positive, the tangent line to f is sloping up; where f' is negative, the tangent line to f is sloping down. If $f' = 0$ everywhere, then the tangent line to f is horizontal everywhere, and f is constant. We see that the sign of f' tells us whether f is increasing or decreasing.

> If $f' > 0$ on an interval, then f is *increasing* over that interval.
> If $f' < 0$ on an interval, then f is *decreasing* over that interval.

Moreover, the magnitude of the derivative gives us the magnitude of the rate of change; so if f' is large (positive or negative), then the graph of f is steep (up or down), whereas if f' is small the graph of f slopes gently. With this in mind, we can learn about the behavior of a function from the behavior of its derivative.

The Derivative Function: Numerically

If we are given values of a function instead of its graph, we can estimate values of the derivative.

Example 3   Table 2.7 gives values of $c(t)$, the concentration (μg/cm^3) of a drug in the bloodstream at time t (min). Construct a table of estimated values for $c'(t)$, the rate of change of $c(t)$ with respect to time.

Table 2.7   *Concentration as a function of time*

t (min)	0	0.1	0.2	0.3	0.4	0.5	0.6	0.7	0.8	0.9	1.0
$c(t)$ (μg/cm^3)	0.84	0.89	0.94	0.98	1.00	1.00	0.97	0.90	0.79	0.63	0.41

Solution   We estimate values of c' using the values in the table. To do this, we have to assume that the data points are close enough together that the concentration does not change wildly between them. From the table, we see that the concentration is increasing between $t = 0$ and $t = 0.4$, so we expect a positive derivative there. However, the increase is quite slow, so we expect the derivative to be small. The concentration does not change between 0.4 and 0.5, so we expect the derivative to be roughly 0 there. From $t = 0.5$ to $t = 1.0$, the concentration starts to decrease, and the rate of decrease gets larger and larger, so we expect the derivative to be negative and of greater and greater magnitude.

Using the data in the table, we estimate the derivative using the difference quotient:

$$c'(t) \approx \frac{c(t + h) - c(t)}{h}.$$

Since the data points are 0.1 apart, we use $h = 0.1$, giving, for example,

$$c'(0) \approx \frac{c(0.1) - c(0)}{0.1} = \frac{0.89 - 0.84}{0.1} = 0.5 \ \mu\text{g/cm}^3/\text{min}$$

$$c'(0.1) \approx \frac{c(0.2) - c(0.1)}{0.1} = \frac{0.94 - 0.89}{0.1} = 0.5 \ \mu\text{g/cm}^3/\text{min}.$$

See Table 2.8. Notice that the derivative has small positive values until $t = 0.4$, where it is roughly 0, and then it gets more and more negative, as we expected. The slopes are graphed in Figure 2.29.

Table 2.8   *Estimated derivative of concentration*

t	$c'(t)$
0	0.5
0.1	0.5
0.2	0.4
0.3	0.2
0.4	0.0
0.5	−0.3
0.6	−0.7
0.7	−1.1
0.8	−1.6
0.9	−2.2

Figure 2.29: Graph of concentration as a function of time

Improving Numerical Estimates for the Derivative

In the previous example, the estimate for the derivative at 0.2 used the interval to the right; we found the average rate of change between $t = 0.2$ and $t = 0.3$. However, we could equally well have gone to the left and used the rate of change between $t = 0.1$ and $t = 0.2$ to approximate the derivative at 0.2. For a more accurate result, we could average these slopes and say

$$c'(0.2) \approx \frac{1}{2} \left(\begin{array}{c} \text{Slope to left} \\ \text{of } 0.2 \end{array} + \begin{array}{c} \text{Slope to right} \\ \text{of } 0.2 \end{array} \right) = \frac{0.5 + 0.4}{2} = 0.45.$$

In general, averaging the slopes leads to a more accurate answer.

Derivative Function: From a Formula

If we are given a formula for f, can we come up with a formula for f'? We often can, as shown in the next example. Indeed, much of the power of calculus depends on our ability to find formulas for the derivatives of all the functions we described earlier. This is done systematically in Chapter 3.

Derivative of a Constant Function

The graph of a constant function $f(x) = k$ is a horizontal line, with a slope of 0 everywhere. Therefore, its derivative is 0 everywhere. (See Figure 2.30.)

If $f(x) = k$, then $f'(x) = 0$.

Figure 2.30: A constant function

Derivative of a Linear Function

We already know that the slope of a straight line is constant. This tells us that the derivative of a linear function is constant.

If $f(x) = b + mx$, then $f'(x) = \text{Slope} = m$.

Derivative of a Power Function

Example 4   Find a formula for the derivative of $f(x) = x^2$.

Solution   Before computing the formula for $f'(x)$ algebraically, let's try to guess the formula by looking for a pattern in the values of $f'(x)$. Table 2.9 contains values of $f(x) = x^2$ (rounded to three decimals), which we can use to estimate the values of $f'(1)$, $f'(2)$, and $f'(3)$.

Table 2.9   *Values of $f(x) = x^2$ near $x = 1$, $x = 2$, $x = 3$ (rounded to three decimals)*

x	x^2	x	x^2	x	x^2
0.999	0.998	1.999	3.996	2.999	8.994
1.000	1.000	2.000	4.000	3.000	9.000
1.001	1.002	2.001	4.004	3.001	9.006
1.002	1.004	2.002	4.008	3.002	9.012

Near $x = 1$, the value of x^2 increases by about 0.002 each time x increases by 0.001, so

$$f'(1) \approx \frac{0.002}{0.001} = 2.$$

Similarly, near $x = 2$ and $x = 3$, the value of x^2 increases by about 0.004 and 0.006, respectively, when x increases by 0.001. So

$$f'(2) \approx \frac{0.004}{0.001} = 4 \quad \text{and} \quad f'(3) \approx \frac{0.006}{0.001} = 6.$$

Knowing the value of f' at specific points can never tell us the formula for f', but it certainly can be suggestive: Knowing $f'(1) \approx 2$, $f'(2) \approx 4$, $f'(3) \approx 6$ suggests that $f'(x) = 2x$.

The derivative is calculated by forming the difference quotient and taking the limit as h goes to zero. The difference quotient is

$$\frac{f(x+h) - f(x)}{h} = \frac{(x+h)^2 - x^2}{h} = \frac{x^2 + 2xh + h^2 - x^2}{h} = \frac{2xh + h^2}{h}.$$

Since h never actually reaches zero, we can cancel it in the last expression to get $2x + h$. The limit of this as h goes to zero is $2x$, so

$$f'(x) = \lim_{h \to 0} (2x + h) = 2x.$$

Example 5   Calculate $f'(x)$ if $f(x) = x^3$.

Solution   We look at the difference quotient

$$\frac{f(x+h) - f(x)}{h} = \frac{(x+h)^3 - x^3}{h}.$$

Multiplying out gives $(x+h)^3 = x^3 + 3x^2h + 3xh^2 + h^3$, so

$$f'(x) = \lim_{h \to 0} \frac{x^3 + 3x^2h + 3xh^2 + h^3 - x^3}{h} = \lim_{h \to 0} \frac{3x^2h + 3xh^2 + h^3}{h}.$$

Since in taking the limit as $h \to 0$, we consider values of h near, but not equal to, zero, we can cancel h, giving

$$f'(x) = \lim_{h \to 0} \frac{3x^2h + 3xh^2 + h^3}{h} = \lim_{h \to 0} (3x^2 + 3xh + h^2).$$

As $h \to 0$, the value of $(3xh + h^2) \to 0$, so

$$f'(x) = \lim_{h \to 0} (3x^2 + 3xh + h^2) = 3x^2.$$

The previous two examples show how to compute the derivatives of power functions of the form $f(x) = x^n$, when n is 2 or 3. We can use the Binomial Theorem to show the *power rule* for a positive integer n:

$$\boxed{\text{If } f(x) = x^n \text{ then } f'(x) = nx^{n-1}.}$$

This result is in fact valid for any real value of n.

Exercises and Problems for Section 2.3

Exercises

1. (a) Estimate $f'(2)$ using the values of f in the table.
(b) For what values of x does $f'(x)$ appear to be positive? Negative?

x	0	2	4	6	8	10	12
$f(x)$	10	18	24	21	20	18	15

2. Find approximate values for $f'(x)$ at each of the x-values given in the following table.

x	0	5	10	15	20
$f(x)$	100	70	55	46	40

For Exercises 3–12, graph the derivative of the given functions.

3.

4.

5.

6.

7.

8.

9.

10.

11.

12.

For Exercises 13–18, sketch the graph of $f(x)$, and use this graph to sketch the graph of $f'(x)$.

13. $f(x) = 5x$ **14.** $f(x) = x^2$

15. $f(x) = x(x - 1)$ **16.** $f(x) = e^x$

17. $f(x) = \cos x$ **18.** $f(x) = \ln x$

In Exercises 19–20, find a formula for the derivative using the power rule. Confirm it using difference quotients.

19. $k(x) = 1/x$ **20.** $l(x) = 1/x^2$

Find a formula for the derivatives of the functions in Exercises 21–22 using difference quotients.

21. $g(x) = 2x^2 - 3$ **22.** $m(x) = 1/(x + 1)$

Problems

23. In each case, graph a smooth curve whose slope meets the condition.

(a) Everywhere positive and increasing gradually.
(b) Everywhere positive and decreasing gradually.
(c) Everywhere negative and increasing gradually (becoming less negative).
(d) Everywhere negative and decreasing gradually (becoming more negative).

24. Draw a possible graph of $y = f(x)$ given the following information about its derivative.

- $f'(x) > 0$ for $x < -1$
- $f'(x) < 0$ for $x > -1$
- $f'(x) = 0$ at $x = -1$

25. For $f(x) = \ln x$, construct tables, rounded to four decimals, near $x = 1$, $x = 2$, $x = 5$, and $x = 10$. Use the tables to estimate $f'(1)$, $f'(2)$, $f'(5)$, and $f'(10)$. Then guess a general formula for $f'(x)$.

26. Given the numerical values shown, find approximate values for the derivative of $f(x)$ at each of the x-values given. Where is the rate of change of $f(x)$ positive? Where is it negative? Where does the rate of change of $f(x)$ seem to be greatest?

x	0	1	2	3	4	5	6	7	8
$f(x)$	18	13	10	9	9	11	15	21	30

27. Values of x and $g(x)$ are given in the table. For what value of x does $g'(x)$ appear to be closest to 3?

x	2.7	3.2	3.7	4.2	4.7	5.2	5.7	6.2
$g(x)$	3.4	4.4	5.0	5.4	6.0	7.4	9.0	11.0

28. In the graph of f in Figure 2.31, at which of the labeled x-values is

(a) $f(x)$ greatest?   (b) $f(x)$ least?
(c) $f'(x)$ greatest?   (d) $f'(x)$ least?

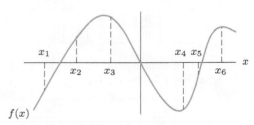

Figure 2.31

For Problems 29–38, sketch the graph of $f'(x)$.

29.

30.

31.

32.

33.

34.

35.

36.

37.

38.

Figure 2.32

41. A child inflates a balloon, admires it for a while and then lets the air out at a constant rate. If $V(t)$ gives the volume of the balloon at time t, then Figure 2.33 shows $V'(t)$ as a function of t. At what time does the child:

  (a) Begin to inflate the balloon?
  (b) Finish inflating the balloon?
  (c) Begin to let the air out?
  (d) What would the graph of $V'(t)$ look like if the child had alternated between pinching and releasing the open end of the balloon, instead of letting the air out at a constant rate?

Figure 2.33

42. Figure 2.34 shows a graph of voltage across an electrical capacitor as a function of time. The current is proportional to the derivative of the voltage; the constant of proportionality is positive. Sketch a graph of the current as a function of time.

Figure 2.34

39. Roughly sketch the shape of the graph of a quadratic polynomial, f, if it is known that:

  • $(1, 3)$ is on the graph of f.
  • $f'(0) = 3$, $f'(2) = 1$, $f'(3) = 0$.

40. A vehicle moving along a straight road has distance $f(t)$ from its starting point at time t. Which of the graphs in Figure 2.32 could be $f'(t)$ for the following scenarios? (Assume the scales on the vertical axes are all the same.)

  (a) A bus on a popular route, with no traffic
  (b) A car with no traffic and all green lights
  (c) A car in heavy traffic conditions

43. Figure 2.35 is the graph of f', the derivative of a function f. On what interval(s) is the function f

  (a) Increasing?   **(b)** Decreasing?

Figure 2.35: Graph of f', not f

44. The derivative of f is the spike function in Figure 2.36. What can you say about the graph of f?

Figure 2.36

45. The population of a herd of deer is modeled by

$$P(t) = 4000 + 500 \sin\left(2\pi t - \frac{\pi}{2}\right)$$

where t is measured in years from January 1.

(a) How does this population vary with time? Sketch a graph of $P(t)$ for one year.
(b) Use the graph to decide when in the year the population is a maximum. What is that maximum? Is there a minimum? If so, when?
(c) Use the graph to decide when the population is growing fastest. When is it decreasing fastest?
(d) Estimate roughly how fast the population is changing on the first of July.

46. The graph in Figure 2.37 shows the accumulated federal debt since 1970. Sketch the derivative of this function. What does it represent?

Figure 2.37

47. Draw the graph of a continuous function $y = f(x)$ that satisfies the following three conditions:

- $f'(x) > 0$ for $x < -2$,
- $f'(x) < 0$ for $-2 < x < 2$,
- $f'(x) = 0$ for $x > 2$.

48. Draw the graph of a continuous function $y = f(x)$ that satisfies the following three conditions:

- $f'(x) > 0$ for $1 < x < 3$
- $f'(x) < 0$ for $x < 1$ and $x > 3$
- $f'(x) = 0$ at $x = 1$ and $x = 3$

49. If $\lim_{x \to \infty} f(x) = 50$ and $f'(x)$ is positive for all x, what is $\lim_{x \to \infty} f'(x)$? (Assume this limit exists.) Explain your answer with a picture.

50. Using a graph, explain why if $f(x)$ is an even function, then $f'(x)$ is odd.

51. Using a graph, explain why if $g(x)$ is an odd function, then $g'(x)$ is even.

Strengthen Your Understanding

In Problems 52–54, explain what is wrong with the statement.

52. The graph of the derivative of the function $f(x) = \cos x$ is always above the x-axis.

53. A function, f, whose graph is above the x-axis for all x has a positive derivative for all x.

54. If $f'(x) = g'(x)$ then $f(x) = g(x)$.

In Problems 55–56, give an example of:

55. A function representing the position of a particle which has positive velocity for $0 < t < 0.5$ and negative velocity for $0.5 < t < 1$.

56. A family of linear functions all with the same derivative.

Are the statements in Problems 57–60 true or false? Give an explanation for your answer.

57. The derivative of a linear function is constant.

58. If $g(x)$ is a vertical shift of $f(x)$, then $f'(x) = g'(x)$.

59. If $f'(x)$ is increasing, then $f(x)$ is also increasing.

60. If $f(a) \neq g(a)$, then $f'(a) \neq g'(a)$.

2.4   INTERPRETATIONS OF THE DERIVATIVE

We have seen the derivative interpreted as a slope and as a rate of change. In this section, we see other interpretations. The purpose of these examples is not to make a catalog of interpretations but to illustrate the process of obtaining them.

An Alternative Notation for the Derivative

So far we have used the notation f' to stand for the derivative of the function f. An alternative notation for derivatives was introduced by the German mathematician Wilhelm Gottfried Leibniz (1646–1716). If the variable y depends on the variable x, that is, if

$$y = f(x),$$

then he wrote dy/dx for the derivative, so

$$\frac{dy}{dx} = f'(x).$$

Leibniz's notation is quite suggestive if we think of the letter d in dy/dx as standing for "small difference in . . . ." The notation dy/dx reminds us that the derivative is a limit of ratios of the form

$$\frac{\text{Difference in } y\text{-values}}{\text{Difference in } x\text{-values}}.$$

The notation dy/dx suggests the units for the derivative: the units for y divided by the units for x. The separate entities dy and dx officially have no independent meaning: they are all part of one notation. In fact, a good way to view the notation dy/dx is to think of d/dx as a single symbol meaning "the derivative with respect to x of . . . ." So dy/dx can be viewed as

$$\frac{d}{dx}(y), \quad \text{meaning "the derivative with respect to } x \text{ of } y\text{."}$$

On the other hand, many scientists and mathematicians think of dy and dx as separate entities representing "infinitesimally" small differences in y and x, even though it is difficult to say exactly how small "infinitesimal" is. Although not formally correct, it can be helpful to think of dy/dx as a small change in y divided by a small change in x.

For example, recall that if $s = f(t)$ is the position of a moving object at time t, then $v = f'(t)$ is the velocity of the object at time t. Writing

$$v = \frac{ds}{dt}$$

reminds us that v is a velocity, since the notation suggests a distance, ds, over a time, dt, and we know that distance over time is velocity. Similarly, we recognize

$$\frac{dy}{dx} = f'(x)$$

as the slope of the graph of $y = f(x)$ since slope is vertical rise, dy, over horizontal run, dx.

The disadvantage of Leibniz's notation is that it is awkward to specify the x-value at which we are evaluating the derivative. To specify $f'(2)$, for example, we have to write

$$\left.\frac{dy}{dx}\right|_{x=2}.$$

Using Units to Interpret the Derivative

The following examples illustrate how useful units can be in suggesting interpretations of the derivative. We use the fact that the units of the instantaneous and the average rate of change are the same.

For example, suppose $s = f(t)$ gives the distance, in meters, of a body from a fixed point as a function of time, t, in seconds. Then knowing that

$$\left.\frac{ds}{dt}\right|_{t=2} = f'(2) = 10 \text{ meters/sec}$$

tells us that when $t = 2$ seconds, the body is moving at an instantaneous velocity of 10 meters/sec. This means that if the body continued to move at this speed for a whole second, it would move 10 meters. In practice, however, the velocity of the body may not remain 10 meters/sec for long. Notice that the units of instantaneous velocity and of average velocity are the same.

Example 1   The cost C (in dollars) of building a house A square feet in area is given by the function $C = f(A)$. What is the practical interpretation of the function $f'(A)$?

Solution   In the alternative notation,

$$f'(A) = \frac{dC}{dA}.$$

This is a cost divided by an area, so it is measured in dollars per square foot. You can think of dC as the extra cost of building an extra dA square feet of house. Then you can think of dC/dA as the additional cost per square foot. So if you are planning to build a house roughly A square feet in area, $f'(A)$ is the cost per square foot of the *extra* area involved in building a slightly larger house, and is called the *marginal cost*. The marginal cost is probably smaller than the average cost per square foot for the entire house, since once you are already set up to build a large house, the cost of adding a few square feet is likely to be small.

Example 2   The cost of extracting T tons of ore from a copper mine is $C = f(T)$ dollars. What does it mean to say that $f'(2000) = 100$?

Solution   In the alternative notation,

$$f'(2000) = \left.\frac{dC}{dT}\right|_{T=2000} = 100.$$

Since C is measured in dollars and T is measured in tons, dC/dT must be measured in dollars per ton. So the statement $f'(2000) = 100$ says that when 2000 tons of ore have already been extracted from the mine, the cost of extracting the next ton is approximately \$100.

Example 3   If $q = f(p)$ gives the number of pounds of sugar produced when the price per pound is p dollars, then what are the units and the meaning of the statement $f'(3) = 50$?

Solution   Since $f'(3)$ is the limit as $h \to 0$ of the difference quotient

$$\frac{f(3+h) - f(3)}{h},$$

the units of $f'(3)$ and the difference quotient are the same. Since $f(3+h) - f(3)$ is in pounds and h is in dollars, the units of the difference quotient and $f'(3)$ are pounds/dollar. The statement

$$f'(3) = 50 \text{ pounds/dollar}$$

tells us that the instantaneous rate of change of q with respect to p is 50 when $p = 3$. In other words, when the price is \$3, the quantity produced is increasing at 50 pounds/dollar. Thus, if the price increased by a dollar, the quantity produced would increase by approximately 50 pounds.

Example 4   Water is flowing through a pipe at a constant rate of 10 cubic feet per second. Interpret this rate as the derivative of some function.

Solution   You might think at first that the statement has something to do with the velocity of the water, but in fact a flow rate of 10 cubic feet per second could be achieved either with very slowly moving water through a large pipe, or with very rapidly moving water through a narrow pipe. If we look at the units—cubic feet per second—we realize that we are being given the rate of change of a quantity measured in cubic feet. But a cubic foot is a measure of volume, so we are being told the rate of change of a volume. One way to visualize this is to imagine all the water that is flowing through the pipe ending up in a tank somewhere. Let $V(t)$ be the volume of water in the tank at time t. Then we are being told that the rate of change of $V(t)$ is 10, or

$$V'(t) = \frac{dV}{dt} = 10.$$

Example 5   Let $N = g(t)$ be the estimated number of alternative-fueled vehicles[4] in use in the US, in thousands, where t is the number of years since 1995. Explain the meaning of the statements:

(a) $g'(6) = 38$ (b) $g^{-1}(696) = 12$ (c) $(g^{-1})'(696) = 0.0145$

Solution   (a) The units of N are thousands of vehicles, the units of t are years, so the units of $g'(t)$ are thousand vehicles per year. Thus, the statement $g'(6) = 38$ tells us that in the year 2001, the use of alternative-fueled vehicles was increasing at 38,000 per year. Thus, in the year between 2001 and 2002, we would have expected the number of alternative-fueled vehicles in use in the US to increase by about 38,000 vehicles.

(b) The statement $g^{-1}(696) = 12$, which is equivalent to $g(12) = 696$, tells us that the year in which the number of alternative-fueled vehicles was 696,000 was 2007.

(c) The units of $(g^{-1})'(V)$ are years per thousand vehicles. The statement $(g^{-1})'(696) = 0.0145$ tells us that when the number of alternative-fueled vehicles was 696,000, it took about 0.0145 years, or between 5 and 6 days, for the number of alternative-fueled vehicles to grow by a thousand vehicles.

Exercises and Problems for Section 2.4

Exercises

1. The cost, C (in dollars), to produce g gallons of a chemical can be expressed as $C = f(g)$. Using units, explain the meaning of the following statements in terms of the chemical:

(a) $f(200) = 1300$ (b) $f'(200) = 6$

2. The time for a chemical reaction, T (in minutes), is a function of the amount of catalyst present, a (in milliliters), so $T = f(a)$.

(a) If $f(5) = 18$, what are the units of 5? What are the units of 18? What does this statement tell us about the reaction?

(b) If $f'(5) = -3$, what are the units of 5? What are the units of -3? What does this statement tell us?

3. The temperature, T, in degrees Fahrenheit, of a cold yam placed in a hot oven is given by $T = f(t)$, where t is the time in minutes since the yam was put in the oven.

(a) What is the sign of $f'(t)$? Why?

(b) What are the units of $f'(20)$? What is the practical meaning of the statement $f'(20) = 2$?

4. The temperature, H, in degrees Celsius, of a cup of coffee placed on the kitchen counter is given by $H = f(t)$, where t is in minutes since the coffee was put on the counter.

(a) Is $f'(t)$ positive or negative? Give a reason for your answer.

(b) What are the units of $f'(20)$? What is its practical meaning in terms of the temperature of the coffee?

5. The cost, C (in dollars), to produce q quarts of ice cream is $C = f(q)$. In each of the following statements, what are the units of the two numbers? In words, what does each statement tell us?

(a) $f(200) = 600$ (b) $f'(200) = 2$

6. An economist is interested in how the price of a certain item affects its sales. At a price of $\$p$, a quantity, q, of the item is sold. If $q = f(p)$, explain the meaning of each of the following statements:

(a) $f(150) = 2000$ (b) $f'(150) = -25$

7. Suppose $C(r)$ is the total cost of paying off a car loan borrowed at an annual interest rate of $r\%$. What are the units of $C'(r)$? What is the practical meaning of $C'(r)$? What is its sign?

8. Let $f(x)$ be the elevation in feet of the Mississippi River x miles from its source. What are the units of $f'(x)$? What can you say about the sign of $f'(x)$?

9. Suppose $P(t)$ is the monthly payment, in dollars, on a mortgage which will take t years to pay off. What are the units of $P'(t)$? What is the practical meaning of $P'(t)$? What is its sign?

10. After investing $\$1000$ at an annual interest rate of 7% compounded continuously for t years, your balance is $\$B$, where $B = f(t)$. What are the units of dB/dt? What is the financial interpretation of dB/dt?

[4]http://www.eia.doe.gov/aer/renew.html, accessed January 12, 2011.

11. Investing $1000 at an annual interest rate of $r\%$, compounded continuously, for 10 years gives you a balance of $\$B$, where $B = g(r)$. Give a financial interpretation of the statements:

(a) $g(5) \approx 1649$.

(b) $g'(5) \approx 165$. What are the units of $g'(5)$?

12. Meteorologists define the temperature lapse rate to be $-dT/dz$ where T is the air temperature in Celsius at altitude z kilometers above the ground.

(a) What are the units of the lapse rate?

(b) What is the practical meaning of a lapse rate of 6.5?

Problems

13. A laboratory study investigating the relationship between diet and weight in adult humans found that the weight of a subject, W, in pounds, was a function, $W = f(c)$, of the average number of Calories per day, c, consumed by the subject.

(a) In terms of diet and weight, interpret the statements $f(1800) = 155$, $f'(2000) = 0$, and $f^{-1}(162) = 2200$.

(b) What are the units of $f'(c) = dW/dc$?

14. In 2011, the Greenland Ice Sheet was melting at a rate between 82 and 224 cubic km per year.[5]

(a) What derivative does this tell us about? Define the function and give units for each variable.

(b) What numerical statement can you make about the derivative? Give units.

15. A city grew in population throughout the 1980s and into the early 1990s. The population was at its largest in 1995, and then shrank until 2010. Let $P = f(t)$ represent the population of the city t years since 1980. Sketch graphs of $f(t)$ and $f'(t)$, labeling the units on the axes.

16. If t is the number of years since 2011, the population, P, of China, in billions, can be approximated by the function

$$P = f(t) = 1.34(1.004)^t.$$

Estimate $f(9)$ and $f'(9)$, giving units. What do these two numbers tell you about the population of China?

17. An economist is interested in how the price of a certain commodity affects its sales. Suppose that at a price of $\$p$, a quantity q of the commodity is sold. If $q = f(p)$, explain in economic terms the meaning of the statements $f(10) = 240,000$ and $f'(10) = -29,000$.

18. On May 9, 2007, CBS Evening News had a 4.3 point rating. (Ratings measure the number of viewers.) News executives estimated that a 0.1 drop in the ratings for the CBS Evening News corresponds to a $5.5 million drop in revenue.[6] Express this information as a derivative. Specify the function, the variables, the units, and the point at which the derivative is evaluated.

19. The population of Mexico in millions is $P = f(t)$, where t is the number of years since 1980. Explain the meaning of the statements:

(a) $f'(6) = 2$

(b) $f^{-1}(95.5) = 16$

(c) $(f^{-1})'(95.5) = 0.46$

20. Let $f(t)$ be the number of centimeters of rainfall that has fallen since midnight, where t is the time in hours. Interpret the following in practical terms, giving units.

(a) $f(10) = 3.1$

(b) $f^{-1}(5) = 16$

(c) $f'(10) = 0.4$

(d) $(f^{-1})'(5) = 2$

21. Water is flowing into a tank; the depth, in feet, of the water at time t in hours is $h(t)$. Interpret, with units, the following statements.

(a) $h(5) = 3$

(b) $h'(5) = 0.7$

(c) $h^{-1}(5) = 7$

(d) $(h^{-1})'(5) = 1.2$

22. Let $p(h)$ be the pressure in dynes per cm^2 on a diver at a depth of h meters below the surface of the ocean. What do each of the following quantities mean to the diver? Give units for the quantities.

(a) $p(100)$

(b) h such that $p(h) = 1.2 \cdot 10^6$

(c) $p(h) + 20$

(d) $p(h + 20)$

(e) $p'(100)$

(f) h such that $p'(h) = 100,000$

23. Let $g(t)$ be the height, in inches, of Amelia Earhart (one of the first woman airplane pilots) t years after her birth. What are the units of $g'(t)$? What can you say about the signs of $g'(10)$ and $g'(30)$? (Assume that $0 \leq t < 39$, the age at which Amelia Earhart's plane disappeared.)

24. If $g(v)$ is the fuel efficiency, in miles per gallon, of a car going at v miles per hour, what are the units of $g'(90)$? What is the practical meaning of the statement $g'(55) = -0.54$?

25. Let P be the total petroleum reservoir on Earth in the year t. (In other words, P represents the total quantity of petroleum, including what's not yet discovered, on Earth at time t.) Assume that no new petroleum is being made and that P is measured in barrels. What are the units of dP/dt? What is the meaning of dP/dt? What is its sign? How would you set about estimating this derivative in practice? What would you need to know to make such an estimate?

26. (a) If you jump out of an airplane without a parachute, you fall faster and faster until air resistance causes you to approach a steady velocity, called the *terminal* velocity. Sketch a graph of your velocity against time.

(b) Explain the concavity of your graph.

(c) Assuming air resistance to be negligible at $t = 0$, what natural phenomenon is represented by the slope of the graph at $t = 0$?

---

[5]www.climate.org/topics/sea-level, accessed June 5, 2011.

[6]OC Register, May 9, 2007; *The New York Times*, May 14, 2007.

27. Let W be the amount of water, in gallons, in a bathtub at time t, in minutes.

   (a) What are the meaning and units of dW/dt?

   (b) Suppose the bathtub is full of water at time t_0, so that $W(t_0) > 0$. Subsequently, at time $t_p > t_0$, the plug is pulled. Is dW/dt positive, negative, or zero:

      (i) For $t_0 < t < t_p$?

      (ii) After the plug is pulled, but before the tub is empty?

      (iii) When all the water has drained from the tub?

28. A company's revenue from car sales, C (in thousands of dollars), is a function of advertising expenditure, a, in thousands of dollars, so $C = f(a)$.

   (a) What does the company hope is true about the sign of f'?

   (b) What does the statement $f'(100) = 2$ mean in practical terms? How about $f'(100) = 0.5$?

   (c) Suppose the company plans to spend about $100,000 on advertising. If $f'(100) = 2$, should the company spend more or less than $100,000 on advertising? What if $f'(100) = 0.5$?

29. In May 2007 in the US, there was one birth every 8 seconds, one death every 13 seconds, and one new international migrant every 27 seconds.[7]

   (a) Let $f(t)$ be the population of the US, where t is time in seconds measured from the start of May 2007. Find $f'(0)$. Give units.

   (b) To the nearest second, how long did it take for the US population to add one person in May 2007?

30. During the 1970s and 1980s, the build up of chlorofluorocarbons (CFCs) created a hole in the ozone layer over Antarctica. After the 1987 Montreal Protocol, an agreement to phase out CFC production, the ozone hole has shrunk. The ODGI (ozone depleting gas index) shows the level of CFCs present.[8] Let $O(t)$ be the ODGI for Antarctica in year t; then $O(2000) = 95$ and $O'(2000) = -1.25$. Assuming that the ODGI decreases at a constant rate, estimate when the ozone hole will have recovered, which occurs when ODGI $= 0$.

31. Let $P(x)$ be the number of people of height $\leq x$ inches in the US. What is the meaning of $P'(66)$? What are its units? Estimate $P'(66)$ (using common sense). Is $P'(x)$ ever negative? [Hint: You may want to approximate $P'(66)$ by a difference quotient, using $h = 1$. Also, you may assume the US population is about 300 million, and note that 66 inches = 5 feet 6 inches.]

32. When you breathe, a muscle (called the diaphragm) reduces the pressure around your lungs and they expand to fill with air. The table shows the volume of a lung as a function of the reduction in pressure from the diaphragm.

Pulmonologists (lung doctors) define the *compliance* of the lung as the derivative of this function.[9]

   (a) What are the units of compliance?

   (b) Estimate the maximum compliance of the lung.

   (c) Explain why the compliance gets small when the lung is nearly full (around 1 liter).

Pressure reduction (cm of water)	Volume (liters)
0	0.20
5	0.29
10	0.49
15	0.70
20	0.86
25	0.95
30	1.00

33. The compressibility index, γ, of cold matter (in a neutron star or black hole) is given by

$$\gamma = \frac{\delta + (p/c^2)}{p} \frac{dp}{d\delta},$$

where p is the pressure (in dynes/cm^2), δ is the density (in g/cm^3), and $c \approx 3 \cdot 10^{10}$ is the speed of light (in cm/sec). Figure 2.38 shows the relationship between δ, γ, and p. Values of $\log p$ are marked along the graph.[10]

   (a) Estimate $dp/d\delta$ for cold iron, which has a density of about 10 g/cm^3. What does the magnitude of your answer tell you about cold iron?

   (b) Estimate $dp/d\delta$ for the matter inside a white dwarf star, which has a density of about 10^6 g/cm^3. What does your answer tell you about matter inside a white dwarf?

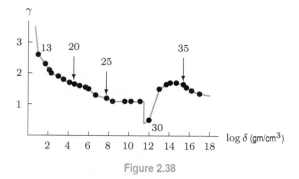

Figure 2.38

[7]www.census.gov, accessed May 14, 2007.

[8]www.esrl.noaa.gov/gmd/odgi

[9]Adapted from John B. West, *Respiratory Physiology*, 4th Ed. (New York: Williams and Wilkins, 1990).

[10]From C. W. Misner, K. S. Thorne, and J. A. Wheeler, *Gravitation* (San Francisco: W. H. Freeman and Company, 1973).

In Problems 34–36, explain what is wrong with the statement.

34. If the position of a car at time t is given by $s(t)$ then the velocity of the car is $s'(t)$ and the units of s' are meters per second.

35. A spherical balloon originally contains 3 liters of air and it is leaking 1% of its volume per hour. If $r(t)$ is the radius of the balloon at time t then $r'(t) > 0$.

36. A laser printer takes $T(P)$ minutes to produce P pages, so the derivative $\dfrac{dT}{dP}$ is measured in pages per minute.

In Problems 37–38, give an example of:

37. A function whose derivative is measured in years/dollar.

38. A function whose derivative is measured in miles/day.

Are the statements in Problems 39–41 true or false? Give an explanation for your answer.

39. If $y = f(x)$, then $\left.\dfrac{dy}{dx}\right|_{x=a} = f'(a)$.

40. If $f(t)$ is the quantity in grams of a chemical produced after t minutes and $g(t)$ is the same quantity in kilograms, then $f'(t) = 1000g'(t)$.

41. If $f(t)$ is the quantity in kilograms of a chemical produced after t minutes and $g(t)$ is the quantity in kilograms produced after t seconds, then $f'(t) = 60g'(t)$.

For Problems 42–43, assume $g(v)$ is the fuel efficiency, in miles per gallon, of a car going at a speed of v miles per hour.

42. What are the units of $g'(v) = \dfrac{dg}{dv}$? There may be more than one option.

   (a) $(\text{miles})^2/(\text{gal})(\text{hour})$
   (b) hour/gal
   (c) gal/hour
   (d) $(\text{gal})(\text{hour})/(\text{miles})^2$
   (e) (miles/gallon)/(miles/hour)

43. What is the practical meaning of $g'(55) = -0.54$? There may be more than one option.

   (a) When the car is going 55 mph, the rate of change of the fuel efficiency decreases *to* approximately 0.54 miles/gal.
   (b) When the car is going 55 mph, the rate of change of the fuel efficiency decreases *by* approximately 0.54 miles/gal.
   (c) If the car speeds up from 55 mph to 56 mph, then the fuel efficiency is approximately -0.54 miles per gallon.
   (d) If the car speeds up from 55 mph to 56 mph, then the car becomes less fuel efficient by approximately 0.54 miles per gallon.

2.5 THE SECOND DERIVATIVE

Since the derivative is itself a function, we can consider its derivative. For a function f, the derivative of its derivative is called the *second derivative*, and written f'' (read "f double-prime"). If $y = f(x)$, the second derivative can also be written as $\dfrac{d^2y}{dx^2}$, which means $\dfrac{d}{dx}\left(\dfrac{dy}{dx}\right)$, the derivative of $\dfrac{dy}{dx}$.

What Do Derivatives Tell Us?

Recall that the derivative of a function tells you whether a function is increasing or decreasing:

- If $f' > 0$ on an interval, then f is *increasing* over that interval.
- If $f' < 0$ on an interval, then f is *decreasing* over that interval.

If f' is always positive on an interval or always negative on an interval, then f is monotonic over that interval.

Since f'' is the derivative of f',

- If $f'' > 0$ on an interval, then f' is *increasing* over that interval.
- If $f'' < 0$ on an interval, then f' is *decreasing* over that interval.

What does it mean for f' to be increasing or decreasing? An example in which f' is increasing is shown in Figure 2.39, where the curve is bending upward, or is *concave up*. In the example shown in Figure 2.40, in which f' is decreasing, the graph is bending downward, or is *concave down*. These figures suggest the following result:

> If $f'' > 0$ on an interval, then f' is increasing, so the graph of f is concave up there.
> If $f'' < 0$ on an interval, then f' is decreasing, so the graph of f is concave down there.

Figure 2.39: Meaning of f'': The slope of f increases from left to right, f'' is positive, and f is concave up

Figure 2.40: Meaning of f'': The slope of f decreases from left to right, f'' is negative, and f is concave down

Warning! The graph of a function f can be concave up everywhere and yet have $f'' = 0$ at some point. For instance, the graph of $f(x) = x^4$ in Figure 2.41 is concave up, but it can be shown that $f''(0) = 0$. If we are told that the graph of a function f is concave up, we can be sure that f'' is not negative, that is $f'' \geq 0$, but not that f'' is positive, $f'' > 0$.

Figure 2.41: Graph of $f(x) = x^4$

> If the graph of f is concave up and f'' exists on an interval, then $f'' \geq 0$ there.
> If the graph of f is concave down and f'' exists on an interval, then $f'' \leq 0$ there.

Example 1   For the functions graphed in Figure 2.42, what can be said about the sign of the second derivative?

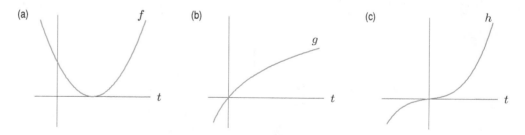

Figure 2.42: What signs do the second derivatives have?

Solution   (a) The graph of f is concave up everywhere, so $f'' \geq 0$ everywhere.
(b) The graph of g is concave down everywhere, so $g'' \leq 0$ everywhere.
(c) For $t < 0$, the graph of h is concave down, so $h'' \leq 0$ there. For $t > 0$, the graph of h is concave up, so $h'' \geq 0$ there.

Example 2   Sketch the second derivative f'' for the function f of Example 1 on page 91, graphed with its derivative, f', in Figure 2.43. Relate the resulting graph of f'' to the graphs of f and f'.

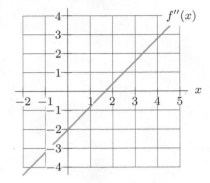

Figure 2.43: Function, f in color; derivative, f', in black   Figure 2.44: Graph of f''

Solution   We want to sketch the derivative of f'. We do this by estimating the slopes of f' and plotting them, obtaining Figure 2.44.

We observe that where $f'' > 0$, the graph of f is concave up and f' is increasing, and that where $f'' < 0$, the graph of f is concave down and f' is decreasing. Where $f''(x) = 0$, the graph of f changes from concave up to concave down, and f' changes from decreasing to increasing.

Interpretation of the Second Derivative as a Rate of Change

If we think of the derivative as a rate of change, then the second derivative is a rate of change of a rate of change. If the second derivative is positive, the rate of change of f is increasing; if the second derivative is negative, the rate of change of f is decreasing.

The second derivative can be a matter of practical concern. A 2009 article[11] reported that although the US economy was shrinking, the rate of decrease had slowed. (The derivative of the size of the economy was negative and the second derivative was positive). The article continued "although the economy is spiralling down, it is doing so more slowly."

Example 3   A population, P, growing in a confined environment often follows a *logistic* growth curve, like that shown in Figure 2.45. Relate the sign of d^2P/dt^2 to how the rate of growth, dP/dt, changes over time. What are practical interpretations of t_0 and L?

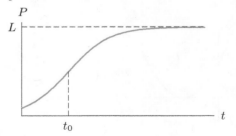

Figure 2.45: Logistic growth curve

Solution   For $t < t_0$, the rate of growth, dP/dt, is increasing and $d^2P/dt^2 \geq 0$. At t_0, the rate dP/dt is a maximum. In other words, at time t_0 the population is growing fastest. For $t > t_0$, the rate of growth, dP/dt, is decreasing and $dP^2/dt^2 \leq 0$. At t_0, the curve changes from concave up to concave down, and $d^2P/dt^2 = 0$ there.

---

[11]*The Economist,*   February 19, 2009, Washington, DC, "The second derivative may be turning positive," www.economist.com/node/13145616

The quantity L represents the limiting value of the population as $t \to \infty$. Biologists call L the *carrying capacity* of the environment.

Example 4   Tests on the 2011 Chevy Corvette ZR1 sports car gave the results[12] in Table 2.10.

(a) Estimate dv/dt for the time intervals shown.

(b) What can you say about the sign of d^2v/dt^2 over the period shown?

Table 2.10   *Velocity of 2011 Chevy Corvette ZR1*

Time, t (sec)	0	3	6	9	12
Velocity, v (meters/sec)	0	23	42	59	72

Solution   (a) For each time interval we can calculate the average rate of change of velocity. For example, from $t = 0$ to $t = 3$ we have

$$\frac{dv}{dt} \approx \text{Average rate of change of velocity} = \frac{23 - 0}{3 - 0} = 7.67 \; \frac{\text{m/sec}}{\text{sec}}.$$

Estimated values of dv/dt are in Table 2.11.

(b) Since the values of dv/dt are decreasing between the points shown, we expect $d^2v/dt^2 \leq 0$. The graph of v against t in Figure 2.46 supports this; it is concave down. The fact that $dv/dt > 0$ tells us that the car is speeding up; the fact that $d^2v/dt^2 \leq 0$ tells us that the rate of increase decreased (actually, did not increase) over this time period.

Table 2.11   *Estimates for dv/dt (meters/sec/sec)*

Time interval (sec)	$0 - 3$	$3 - 6$	$6 - 9$	$9 - 12$
Average rate of change (dv/dt)	7.67	6.33	5.67	4.33

Figure 2.46: Velocity of 2011 Chevy Corvette ZR1

Velocity and Acceleration

When a car is speeding up, we say that it is accelerating. We define *acceleration* as the rate of change of velocity with respect to time. If $v(t)$ is the velocity of an object at time t, we have

$$\begin{array}{c} \text{Average acceleration} \\ \text{from } t \text{ to } t + h \end{array} = \frac{v(t + h) - v(t)}{h},$$

$$\text{Instantaneous acceleration} = v'(t) = \lim_{h \to 0} \frac{v(t + h) - v(t)}{h}.$$

If the term velocity or acceleration is used alone, it is assumed to be instantaneous. Since velocity is the derivative of position, acceleration is the second derivative of position. Summarizing:

[12] Adapted from data in http://www.corvette-web-central.com/Corvettetopspeed.html

If $y = s(t)$ is the position of an object at time t, then

- Velocity: $v(t) = \dfrac{dy}{dt} = s'(t)$.

- Acceleration: $a(t) = \dfrac{d^2y}{dt^2} = s''(t) = v'(t)$.

Example 5   A particle is moving along a straight line; its acceleration is zero only once. Its distance, s, to the right of a fixed point is given by Figure 2.47. Estimate:

(a) When the particle is moving to the right and when it is moving to the left.
(b) When the acceleration of the particle is zero, when it is negative, and when it is positive.

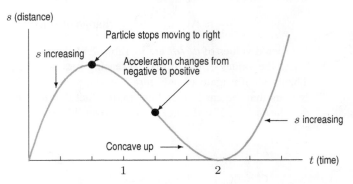

Figure 2.47: Distance of particle to right of a fixed point

Solution   (a) The particle is moving to the right whenever s is increasing. From the graph, this appears to be for $0 < t < \frac{2}{3}$ and for $t > 2$. For $\frac{2}{3} < t < 2$, the value of s is decreasing, so the particle is moving to the left.

(b) Since the acceleration is zero only once, this must be when the curve changes concavity, at about $t = \frac{4}{3}$. Then the acceleration is negative for $t < \frac{4}{3}$, since the graph is concave down there, and the acceleration is positive for $t > \frac{4}{3}$, since the graph is concave up there.

Exercises and Problems for Section 2.5

Exercises

1. Fill in the blanks:

   (a) If f'' is positive on an interval, then f' is _____ on that interval, and f is _____ on that interval.

   (b) If f'' is negative on an interval, then f' is _____ on that interval, and f is _____ on that interval.

2. For the function graphed in Figure 2.48, are the following nonzero quantities positive or negative?

   (a) $f(2)$ (b) $f'(2)$ (c) $f''(2)$

Figure 2.48

3. At one of the labeled points on the graph in Figure 2.49 both dy/dx and d^2y/dx^2 are positive. Which is it?

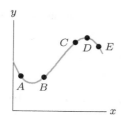

Figure 2.49

4. At exactly two of the labeled points in Figure 2.50, the derivative f' is 0; the second derivative f'' is not zero at any of the labeled points. On a copy of the table, give the signs of f, f', f'' at each marked point.

Point	f	f'	f''
A			
B			
C			
D			

Figure 2.50

5. Graph the functions described in parts (a)–(d).

   (a) First and second derivatives everywhere positive.
   (b) Second derivative everywhere negative; first derivative everywhere positive.
   (c) Second derivative everywhere positive; first derivative everywhere negative.
   (d) First and second derivatives everywhere negative.

6. Sketch the graph of a function whose first derivative is everywhere negative and whose second derivative is positive for some x-values and negative for other x-values.

7. Sketch the graph of the height of a particle against time if velocity is positive and acceleration is negative.

For Exercises 8–13, give the signs of the first and second derivatives for the following functions. Each derivative is either positive everywhere, zero everywhere, or negative everywhere.

8.

9.

10.

11.

12.

13.

14. The position of a particle moving along the x-axis is given by $s(t) = 5t^2 + 3$. Use difference quotients to find the velocity $v(t)$ and acceleration $a(t)$.

Problems

15. The table gives the number of passenger cars, $C = f(t)$, in millions,[13] in the US in the year t.

   (a) Do $f'(t)$ and $f''(t)$ appear to be positive or negative during the period 1975–1990?
   (b) Do $f'(t)$ and $f''(t)$ appear to be positive or negative during the period 1990–2000?
   (c) Estimate $f'(2005)$. Using units, interpret your answer in terms of passenger cars.

t	1975	1980	1985	1990	1995	2000	2005
C	106.7	121.6	127.9	133.7	128.4	133.6	136.6

16. An accelerating sports car goes from 0 mph to 60 mph in five seconds. Its velocity is given in the following table, converted from miles per hour to feet per second, so that all time measurements are in seconds. (Note: 1 mph is 22/15 ft/sec.) Find the average acceleration of the car over each of the first two seconds.

Time, t (sec)	0	1	2	3	4	5
Velocity, $v(t)$ (ft/sec)	0	30	52	68	80	88

17. Sketch the curves described in (a)–(c):

   (a) Slope is positive and increasing at first but then is positive and decreasing.
   (b) The first derivative of the function whose graph is in part (a).
   (c) The second derivative of the function whose graph is in part (a).

---

[13]www.bts.gov/publications/national_transportation_statistics/html/table_01_11.html. Accessed April 27, 2011.

In Problems 18–23, graph the second derivative of the function.

18.

19.

20.

21.

22.

23.

24. Let $P(t)$ represent the price of a share of stock of a corporation at time t. What does each of the following statements tell us about the signs of the first and second derivatives of $P(t)$?

(a) "The price of the stock is rising faster and faster."
(b) "The price of the stock is close to bottoming out."

25. In economics, *total utility* refers to the total satisfaction from consuming some commodity. According to the economist Samuelson:[14]

> As you consume more of the same good, the total (psychological) utility increases. However, ...with successive new units of the good, your total utility will grow at a slower and slower rate because of a fundamental tendency for your psychological ability to appreciate more of the good to become less keen.

(a) Sketch the total utility as a function of the number of units consumed.
(b) In terms of derivatives, what is Samuelson saying?

26. "Winning the war on poverty" has been described cynically as slowing the rate at which people are slipping below the poverty line. Assuming that this is happening:

(a) Graph the total number of people in poverty against time.
(b) If N is the number of people below the poverty line at time t, what are the signs of dN/dt and d^2N/dt^2? Explain.

27. An industry is being charged by the Environmental Protection Agency (EPA) with dumping unacceptable levels of toxic pollutants in a lake. Over a period of several months, an engineering firm makes daily measurements of the rate at which pollutants are being discharged into the lake. The engineers produce a graph similar to either Figure 2.51(a) or Figure 2.51(b). For each case, give an idea of what argument the EPA might make in court against the industry and of the industry's defense.

(a)

(b)

Figure 2.51

28. At which of the marked x-values in Figure 2.52 can the following statements be true?

(a) $f(x) < 0$
(b) $f'(x) < 0$
(c) $f(x)$ is decreasing
(d) $f'(x)$ is decreasing
(e) Slope of $f(x)$ is positive
(f) Slope of $f(x)$ is increasing

Figure 2.52

29. Figure 2.53 gives the position, $f(t)$, of a particle at time t. At which of the marked values of t can the following statements be true?

(a) The position is positive
(b) The velocity is positive
(c) The acceleration is positive
(d) The position is decreasing
(e) The velocity is decreasing

[14]From Paul A. Samuelson, *Economics*, 11th edition (New York: McGraw-Hill, 1981).

Figure 2.53

30. The graph of f' (not f) is given in Figure 2.54. At which of the marked values of x is

(a) $f(x)$ greatest?   (b) $f(x)$ least?
(c) $f'(x)$ greatest?   (d) $f'(x)$ least?
(e) $f''(x)$ greatest?   (f) $f''(x)$ least?

Figure 2.54: Graph of f', not f

31. A function f has $f(5) = 20$, $f'(5) = 2$, and $f''(x) < 0$, for $x \geq 5$. Which of the following are possible values for $f(7)$ and which are impossible?

(a) 26   (b) 24   (c) 22

32. Chlorofluorocarbons (CFCs) were used as propellants in spray cans until their build up in the atmosphere started destroying the ozone, which protects us from ultraviolet rays. Since the 1987 Montreal Protocol (an agreement to curb CFCs), the CFCs in the atmosphere above the US have been reduced from a high of 3200 parts per trillion (ppt) in 1994 to 2750 ppt in 2010.[15] The reduction has been approximately linear. Let $C(t)$ be the concentration of CFCs in ppt in year t.

(a) Find $C(1994)$ and $C(2010)$.
(b) Estimate $C'(1994)$ and $C'(2010)$.
(c) Assuming $C(t)$ is linear, find a formula for $C(t)$.
(d) When is $C(t)$ expected to reach 1850 ppt, the level before CFCs were introduced?
(e) If you were told that in the future, $C(t)$ would not be exactly linear, and that $C''(t) > 0$, would your answer to part (d) be too early or too late?

Strengthen Your Understanding

In Problems 33–34, explain what is wrong with the statement.

33. A function that is not concave up is concave down.

34. When the acceleration of a car is zero, the car is not moving.

In Problems 35–36, give an example of:

35. A function that has a non-zero first derivative but zero second derivative.

36. A function for which $f'(0) = 0$ but $f''(0) \neq 0$.

Are the statements in Problems 37–41 true or false? Give an explanation for your answer.

37. If $f''(x) > 0$ then $f'(x)$ is increasing.

38. The instantaneous acceleration of a moving particle at time t is the limit of difference quotients.

39. A function which is monotonic on an interval is either increasing or decreasing on the interval.

40. The function $f(x) = x^3$ is monotonic on any interval.

41. The function $f(x) = x^2$ is monotonic on any interval.

2.6 DIFFERENTIABILITY

What Does It Mean for a Function to Be Differentiable?

A function is differentiable at a point if it has a derivative there. In other words:

The function f is **differentiable** at x if

$$\lim_{h \to 0} \frac{f(x+h) - f(x)}{h} \qquad \text{exists.}$$

Thus, the graph of f has a nonvertical tangent line at x. The value of the limit and the slope of the tangent line are the derivative of f at x.

[15]www.esrl.noaa.gov/gmd/odgi

Occasionally we meet a function which fails to have a derivative at a few points. A function fails to be differentiable at a point if:

- The function is not continuous at the point.

- The graph has a sharp corner at that point.

- The graph has a vertical tangent line.

Figure 2.55 shows a function which appears to be differentiable at all points except $x = a$ and $x = b$. There is no tangent at A because the graph has a corner there. As x approaches a from the left, the slope of the line joining P to A converges to some positive number. As x approaches a from the right, the slope of the line joining P to A converges to some negative number. Thus the slopes approach different numbers as we approach $x = a$ from different sides. Therefore the function is not differentiable at $x = a$. At B, the graph has a vertical tangent. As x approaches b, the slope of the line joining B to Q does not approach a limit; it just keeps growing larger and larger. Again, the limit defining the derivative does not exist and the function is not differentiable at $x = b$.

Figure 2.55: A function which is not differentiable at A or B

Figure 2.56: Graph of absolute value function, showing point of non-differentiability at $x = 0$

Examples of Nondifferentiable Functions

An example of a function whose graph has a corner is the *absolute value* function defined as follows:

$$f(x) = |x| = \begin{cases} x & \text{if } x \geq 0, \\ -x & \text{if } x < 0. \end{cases}$$

This function is called *piecewise linear* because each part of it is linear. Its graph is in Figure 2.56. Near $x = 0$, even close-up views of the graph of $f(x)$ look the same, so this is a corner which can't be straightened out by zooming in.

Example 1   Try to compute the derivative of the function $f(x) = |x|$ at $x = 0$. Is f differentiable there?

Solution   To find the derivative at $x = 0$, we want to look at

$$\lim_{h \to 0} \frac{f(h) - f(0)}{h} = \lim_{h \to 0} \frac{|h| - 0}{h} = \lim_{h \to 0} \frac{|h|}{h}.$$

As h approaches 0 from the right, h is positive, so $|h| = h$, and the ratio is always 1. As h approaches 0 from the left, h is negative, so $|h| = -h$, and the ratio is -1. Since the limits are different from each side, the limit of the difference quotient does not exist. Thus, the absolute value function is not differentiable at $x = 0$. The limits of 1 and -1 correspond to the fact that the slope of the right-hand part of the graph is 1, and the slope of the left-hand part is -1.

Example 2   Investigate the differentiability of $f(x) = x^{1/3}$ at $x = 0$.

Solution   This function is smooth at $x = 0$ (no sharp corners) but appears to have a vertical tangent there. (See Figure 2.57.) Looking at the difference quotient at $x = 0$, we see

$$\lim_{h \to 0} \frac{(0 + h)^{1/3} - 0^{1/3}}{h} = \lim_{h \to 0} \frac{h^{1/3}}{h} = \lim_{h \to 0} \frac{1}{h^{2/3}}.$$

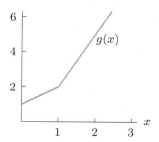

Figure 2.57: Continuous function not differentiable at $x = 0$: Vertical tangent

Figure 2.58: Continuous function not differentiable at $x = 1$

As $h \to 0$ the denominator becomes small, so the fraction grows without bound. Hence, the function fails to have a derivative at $x = 0$.

Example 3 Consider the function given by the formulas

$$g(x) = \begin{cases} x + 1 & \text{if } x \leq 1 \\ 3x - 1 & \text{if } x > 1. \end{cases}$$

Draw the graph of g. Is g continuous? Is g differentiable at $x = 1$?

Solution The graph in Figure 2.58 has no breaks in it, so the function is continuous. However, the graph has a corner at $x = 1$ which no amount of magnification will remove. To the left of $x = 1$, the slope is 1; to the right of $x = 1$, the slope is 3. Thus, the difference quotient at $x = 1$ has no limit, so the function g is not differentiable at $x = 1$.

The Relationship Between Differentiability and Continuity

The fact that a function which is differentiable at a point has a tangent line suggests that the function is continuous there, as the next theorem shows.

> ### Theorem 2.1: A Differentiable Function Is Continuous
>
> If $f(x)$ is differentiable at a point $x = a$, then $f(x)$ is continuous at $x = a$.

Proof We assume f is differentiable at $x = a$. Then we know that $f'(a)$ exists where

$$f'(a) = \lim_{x \to a} \frac{f(x) - f(a)}{x - a}.$$

To show that f is continuous at $x = a$, we want to show that $\lim_{x \to a} f(x) = f(a)$. We calculate $\lim_{x \to a}(f(x) - f(a))$, hoping to get 0. By algebra, we know that for $x \neq a$,

$$f(x) - f(a) = (x - a) \cdot \frac{f(x) - f(a)}{x - a}.$$

Taking the limits, we have

$$\lim_{x \to a}(f(x) - f(a)) = \lim_{x \to a}\left((x - a)\frac{f(x) - f(a)}{x - a}\right)$$

$$= \left(\lim_{x \to a}(x - a)\right) \cdot \left(\lim_{x \to a}\frac{f(x) - f(a)}{x - a}\right) \quad \text{(By Theorem 1.2, Property 3)}$$

$$= 0 \cdot f'(a) = 0. \quad \text{(Since } f'(a) \text{ exists)}$$

Thus we know that $\lim_{x \to a} f(x) = f(a)$, which means $f(x)$ is continuous at $x = a$.

Exercises and Problems for Section 2.6

Exercises

For the graphs in Exercises 1–2, list the x-values for which the function appears to be

(a) Not continuous.　　**(b)** Not differentiable.

1.

2.

In Exercises 3–4, does the function appear to be differentiable on the interval of x-values shown?

3.

4.

Problems

Decide if the functions in Problems 5–7 are differentiable at $x = 0$. Try zooming in on a graphing calculator, or calculating the derivative $f'(0)$ from the definition.

5. $f(x) = (x + |x|)^2 + 1$

6. $f(x) = \begin{cases} x \sin(1/x) + x & \text{for } x \neq 0 \\ 0 & \text{for } x = 0 \end{cases}$

7. $f(x) = \begin{cases} x^2 \sin(1/x) & \text{for } x \neq 0 \\ 0 & \text{for } x = 0 \end{cases}$

8. In each of the following cases, sketch the graph of a continuous function $f(x)$ with the given properties.

(a) $f''(x) > 0$ for $x < 2$ and for $x > 2$ and $f'(2)$ is undefined.

(b) $f''(x) > 0$ for $x < 2$ and $f''(x) < 0$ for $x > 2$ and $f'(2)$ is undefined.

9. Look at the graph of $f(x) = (x^2 + 0.0001)^{1/2}$ shown in Figure 2.59. The graph of f appears to have a sharp corner at $x = 0$. Do you think f has a derivative at $x = 0$?

Figure 2.59

10. The acceleration due to gravity, g, varies with height above the surface of the earth, in a certain way. If you go down below the surface of the earth, g varies in a different way. It can be shown that g is given by

$$g = \begin{cases} \dfrac{GMr}{R^3} & \text{for } r < R \\[2mm] \dfrac{GM}{r^2} & \text{for } r \geq R \end{cases}$$

where R is the radius of the earth, M is the mass of the earth, G is the gravitational constant, and r is the distance to the center of the earth.

(a) Sketch a graph of g against r.
(b) Is g a continuous function of r? Explain your answer.
(c) Is g a differentiable function of r? Explain your answer.

11. An electric charge, Q, in a circuit is given as a function of time, t, by

$$Q = \begin{cases} C & \text{for } t \leq 0 \\ Ce^{-t/RC} & \text{for } t > 0, \end{cases}$$

where C and R are positive constants. The electric current, I, is the rate of change of charge, so

$$I = \frac{dQ}{dt}.$$

(a) Is the charge, Q, a continuous function of time?
(b) Do you think the current, I, is defined for all times, t? [Hint: To graph this function, take, for example, $C = 1$ and $R = 1$.]

12. A magnetic field, B, is given as a function of the distance, r, from the center of a wire as follows:

$$B = \begin{cases} \dfrac{r}{r_0} B_0 & \text{for } r \leq r_0 \\[3mm] \dfrac{r_0}{r} B_0 & \text{for } r > r_0. \end{cases}$$

(a) Sketch a graph of B against r. What is the meaning of the constant B_0?
(b) Is B continuous at $r = r_0$? Give reasons.
(c) Is B differentiable at $r = r_0$? Give reasons.

13. A cable is made of an insulating material in the shape of a long, thin cylinder of radius r_0. It has electric charge distributed evenly throughout it. The electric field, E, at a distance r from the center of the cable is given by

$$E = \begin{cases} kr & \text{for } r \leq r_0 \\[3mm] k\dfrac{r_0^2}{r} & \text{for } r > r_0. \end{cases}$$

(a) Is E continuous at $r = r_0$?
(b) Is E differentiable at $r = r_0$?
(c) Sketch a graph of E as a function of r.

14. Graph the function defined by

$$g(r) = \begin{cases} 1 + \cos(\pi r/2) & \text{for } -2 \leq r \leq 2 \\ 0 & \text{for } r < -2 \quad \text{or} \quad r > 2. \end{cases}$$

(a) Is g continuous at $r = 2$? Explain your answer.
(b) Do you think g is differentiable at $r = 2$? Explain your answer.

15. The potential, ϕ, of a charge distribution at a point on the y-axis is given by

$$\phi = \begin{cases} 2\pi\sigma \left(\sqrt{y^2 + a^2} - y \right) & \text{for } y \geq 0 \\[3mm] 2\pi\sigma \left(\sqrt{y^2 + a^2} + y \right) & \text{for } y < 0 \end{cases}$$

where σ and a are positive constants. [Hint: To graph this function, take, for example, $2\pi\sigma = 1$ and $a = 1$.]

(a) Is ϕ continuous at $y = 0$?
(b) Do you think ϕ is differentiable at $y = 0$?

16. Sometimes, odd behavior can be hidden beneath the surface of a rather normal-looking function. Consider the following function:

$$f(x) = \begin{cases} 0 & \text{if } x < 0 \\ x^2 & \text{if } x \geq 0. \end{cases}$$

(a) Sketch a graph of this function. Does it have any vertical segments or corners? Is it differentiable everywhere? If so, sketch the derivative f' of this function. [Hint: You may want to use the result of Example 4 on page 94.]
(b) Is the derivative function, $f'(x)$, differentiable everywhere? If not, at what point(s) is it not differentiable? Draw the second derivative of $f(x)$ wherever it exists. Is the second derivative function, $f''(x)$, differentiable? Continuous?

Strengthen Your Understanding

In Problems 17–18, explain what is wrong with the statement.

17. A function f that is not differentiable at $x = 0$ has a graph with a sharp corner at $x = 0$.

18. If f is not differentiable at a point then it is not continuous at that point.

In Problems 19–21, give an example of:

19. A continuous function that is not differentiable at $x = 2$.

20. An invertible function that is not differentiable at $x = 0$.

21. A rational function that has zeros at $x = \pm 1$ and is not differentiable at $x = \pm 2$.

Are the statements in Problems 22–26 true or false? If a statement is true, give an example illustrating it. If a statement is false, give a counterexample.

22. There is a function which is continuous on $[1, 5]$ but not differentiable at $x = 3$.

23. If a function is differentiable, then it is continuous.

24. If a function is continuous, then it is differentiable.

25. If a function is not continuous, then it is not differentiable.

26. If a function is not differentiable, then it is not continuous.

27. Which of the following would be a counterexample to the statement: "If f is differentiable at $x = a$ then f is continuous at $x = a$"?

(a) A function which is not differentiable at $x = a$ but is continuous at $x = a$.
(b) A function which is not continuous at $x = a$ but is differentiable at $x = a$.
(c) A function which is both continuous and differentiable at $x = a$.
(d) A function which is neither continuous nor differentiable at $x = a$.

CHAPTER SUMMARY (see also Ready Reference at the end of the book)

- **Rate of change**
  Average, instantaneous.
- **Definition of derivative**
  Difference quotient, limit.
- **Estimating and computing derivatives**
  Estimate derivatives from a graph, table of values, or formula. Use definition to find derivatives of simple functions algebraically. Know derivatives of constant, linear, and power functions.

- **Interpretation of derivatives**
  Rate of change, instantaneous velocity, slope, using units.
- **Second derivative**
  Concavity, acceleration.
- **Working with derivatives**
  Understand relation between sign of f' and whether f is increasing or decreasing. Sketch graph of f' from graph of f.
- **Differentiability**

REVIEW EXERCISES AND PROBLEMS FOR CHAPTER TWO

Exercises

1. At time t in seconds, a particle's distance $s(t)$, in cm, from a point is given in the table. What is the average velocity of the particle from $t = 3$ to $t = 10$?

t	0	3	6	10	13
$s(t)$	0	72	92	144	180

In Exercises 2–7, find the average velocity for the position function $s(t)$, in mm, over the interval $1 \leq t \leq 3$, where t is in seconds.

2. $s(t) = 12t - t^2$

3. $s(t) = \ln(t)$

4.

t	0	1	2	3
$s(t)$	7	3	7	11

5.

t	0	1	2	3
$s(t)$	8	4	2	4

6.

7.

8. In a time of t seconds, a particle moves a distance of s meters from its starting point, where $s = 4t^2 + 3$.

  (a) Find the average velocity between $t = 1$ and $t = 1 + h$ if:

    (i) $h = 0.1$,   (ii) $h = 0.01$, (iii) $h = 0.001$.

  (b) Use your answers to part (a) to estimate the instantaneous velocity of the particle at time $t = 1$.

9. A bicyclist pedals at a fairly constant rate, with evenly spaced intervals of coasting. Sketch a graph of the distance she has traveled as a function of time.

10. As you drive away from home, your speed is fast, then slow, then fast again. Draw a graph of your distance from home as a function of time.

11. **(a)** Graph $f(x) = x \sin x$ for $-10 \leq x \leq 10$.
    (b) How many zeros does $f(x)$ have on this interval?
    (c) Is f increasing or decreasing at $x = 1$? At $x = 4$?
    (d) On which interval is the average rate of change greater: $0 \leq x \leq 2$ or $6 \leq x \leq 8$?
    (e) Is the instantaneous rate of change greater at $x = -9$ or $x = 1$?

12. **(a)** Using the data in the table, estimate an equation for the tangent line to the graph of $f(x)$ at $x = 0.6$.
    (b) Using this equation, estimate $f(0.7)$, $f(1.2)$, and $f(1.4)$. Which of these estimates is most likely to be reliable? Why?

x	0	0.2	0.4	0.6	0.8	1.0
$f(x)$	3.7	3.5	3.5	3.9	4.0	3.9

Sketch the graphs of the derivatives of the functions shown in Exercises 13–18. Be sure your sketches are consistent with the important features of the graphs of the original functions.

13.

14.

15.

16.

17.

18.

19. Roughly sketch the shape of the graph of a cubic polynomial, f, if it is known that:

- $(0,3)$ is on the graph of f.
- $f'(0) = 4$, $f'(1) = 0$, $f'(2) = -\frac{4}{3}$, $f'(4) = 4$.

In Exercises 20–21, graph the second derivative of the function.

20.

21.

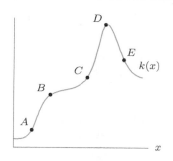

Figure 2.60

In Exercises 26–30, use the difference quotient definition of the derivative to find a formula for the derivative of the function.

26. $f(x) = 3x - 1$ **27.** $f(x) = 5x^2$

28. $f(x) = x^2 + 4$ **29.** $f(x) = 3x^2 - 7$

30. $f(x) = x^3$

In Exercises 22–23, find a formula for the derivative of the function algebraically.

22. $f(x) = 5x^2 + x$ **23.** $n(x) = (1/x) + 1$

In Exercises 31–35, evaluate the limit algebraically for $a > 0$.

31. $\lim_{h \to 0} \dfrac{(a+h)^2 - a^2}{h}$ **32.** $\lim_{h \to 0} \dfrac{1/(a+h) - 1/a}{h}$

24. Find the derivative of $f(x) = x^2 + 1$ at $x = 3$ algebraically. Find the equation of the tangent line to f at $x = 3$.

33. $\lim_{h \to 0} \dfrac{1/(a+h)^2 - 1/a^2}{h}$

25. **(a)** Between which pair of consecutive points in Figure 2.60 is the average rate of change of k

  (a) Greatest?   **(b)** Closest to zero?

(b) Between which two pairs of consecutive points are the average rates of change of k closest?

34. $\lim_{h \to 0} \dfrac{\sqrt{a+h} - \sqrt{a}}{h}$ [Hint: Multiply by $\sqrt{a+h} + \sqrt{a}$ in numerator and denominator.]

35. $\lim_{h \to 0} \dfrac{1/\sqrt{a+h} - 1/\sqrt{a}}{h}$

Problems

36. Sketch the graph of a function whose first and second derivatives are everywhere positive.

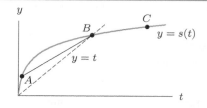

Figure 2.61

37. Figure 2.61 gives the position, $y = s(t)$, of a particle at time t. Arrange the following numbers from smallest to largest:

- The instantaneous velocity at A.
- The instantaneous velocity at B.
- The instantaneous velocity at C.
- The average velocity between A and B.
- The number 0.
- The number 1.

38. Match each property (a)–(d) with one or more of graphs (I)–(IV) of functions.

  (a) $f'(x) = 1$ for all $0 \le x \le 4$.
  (b) $f'(x) > 0$ for all $0 \le x \le 4$
  (c) $f'(2) = 1$
  (d) $f'(1) = 2$

39. (a) In Figure 2.62, if $f(t)$ gives the position of a particle at time t, list the labeled points at which the particle has zero velocity.
    (b) If we now suppose instead that $f(t)$ is the *velocity* of a particle at time t, what is the significance of the points listed in your answer to part (a)?

Figure 2.62

40. The table[16] gives the number of passenger cars, $C = f(t)$, in millions, in the US in the year t.

    (a) During the period 2003–2007, when is $f'(t)$ positive? Negative?
    (b) Estimate $f'(2006)$. Using units, interpret your answer in terms of passenger cars.

t (year)	2003	2004	2005	2006	2007
C (cars, in millions)	135.7	136.4	136.6	135.4	135.9

41. Let $f(t)$ be the depth, in centimeters, of water in a tank at time t, in minutes.

    (a) What does the sign of $f'(t)$ tell us?
    (b) Explain the meaning of $f'(30) = 20$. Include units.
    (c) Using the information in part (b), at time $t = 30$ minutes, find the rate of change of depth, in meters, with respect to time in hours. Give units.

42. If t is the number of years since 2009, the population, P, of Ukraine,[17] in millions, can be approximated by the function
    $$P = f(t) = 45.7e^{-0.0061t}$$
    Estimate $f(6)$ and $f'(6)$, giving units. What do these two numbers tell you about the population of Ukraine?

43. The revenue, in thousands of dollars, earned by a gas station when the price of gas is $\$p$ per gallon is $R(p)$.

    (a) What are the units of $R'(3)$? Interpret this quantity.
    (b) What are the units of $(R^{-1})'(5)$? Interpret this quantity.

44. (a) Give an example of a function with $\lim_{x \to 2} f(x) = \infty$.
    (b) Give an example of a function with $\lim_{x \to 2} f(x) = -\infty$.

45. Draw a possible graph of $y = f(x)$ given the following information about its derivative:

    • For $x < -2$, $f'(x) > 0$ and the derivative is increasing.
    • For $-2 < x < 1$, $f'(x) > 0$ and the derivative is decreasing.
    • At $x = 1$, $f'(x) = 0$.
    • For $x > 1$, $f'(x) < 0$ and the derivative is decreasing (getting more and more negative).

46. Suppose $f(2) = 3$ and $f'(2) = 1$. Find $f(-2)$ and $f'(-2)$, assuming that $f(x)$ is

    (a) Even   (b) Odd.

47. Do the values for the function $y = k(x)$ in the table suggest that the graph of $k(x)$ is concave up or concave down for $1 \le x \le 3.3$? Write a sentence in support of your conclusion.

x	1.0	1.2	1.5	1.9	2.5	3.3
$k(x)$	4.0	3.8	3.6	3.4	3.2	3.0

48. Suppose that $f(x)$ is a function with $f(20) = 345$ and $f'(20) = 6$. Estimate $f(22)$.

49. Students were asked to evaluate $f'(4)$ from the following table which shows values of the function f:

x	1	2	3	4	5	6
$f(x)$	4.2	4.1	4.2	4.5	5.0	5.7

    • Student A estimated the derivative as $f'(4) \approx \dfrac{f(5) - f(4)}{5 - 4} = 0.5$.
    • Student B estimated the derivative as $f'(4) \approx \dfrac{f(4) - f(3)}{4 - 3} = 0.3$.
    • Student C suggested that they should split the difference and estimate the average of these two results, that is, $f'(4) \approx \frac{1}{2}(0.5 + 0.3) = 0.4$.

[16]www.bts.gov. Accessed April 27, 2011.
[17]http://www.indexmundi.com/ukraine/population.html. Accessed April 27, 2011.

(a) Sketch the graph of f, and indicate how the three estimates are represented on the graph.
(b) Explain which answer is likely to be best.
(c) Use Student C's method to find an algebraic formula to approximate $f'(x)$ using increments of size h.

50. Use Figure 2.63 to fill in the blanks in the following statements about the function f at point A.
  (a) $f(\_\_) = \_\_$ (b) $f'(\_\_) = \_\_$

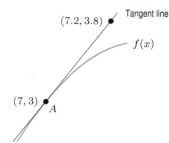

Figure 2.63

51. Use Figure 2.64. At point A, we are told that $x = 1$. In addition, $f(1) = 3$, $f'(1) = 2$, and $h = 0.1$. What are the values of $x_1, x_2, x_3, y_1, y_2, y_3$?

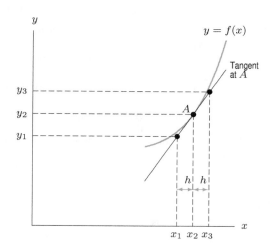

Figure 2.64

52. Given all of the following information about a function f, sketch its graph.

  • $f(x) = 0$ at $x = -5, x = 0$, and $x = 5$
  • $\lim\limits_{x \to -\infty} f(x) = \infty$
  • $\lim\limits_{x \to \infty} f(x) = -3$
  • $f'(x) = 0$ at $x = -3, x = 2.5$, and $x = 7$

53. Suppose w is the weight of a stack of papers in an open container, and t is time. A lighted match is thrown into the stack at time $t = 0$.

  (a) What is the sign of dw/dt for t while the stack of paper is burning?
  (b) What behavior of dw/dt indicates that the fire is no longer burning?
  (c) If the fire starts small but increases in vigor over a certain time interval, then does dw/dt increase or decrease over that interval? What about $|dw/dt|$?

54. A yam has just been taken out of the oven and is cooling off before being eaten. The temperature, T, of the yam (measured in degrees Fahrenheit) is a function of how long it has been out of the oven, t (measured in minutes). Thus, we have $T = f(t)$.

  (a) Is $f'(t)$ positive or negative? Why?
  (b) What are the units for $f'(t)$?

55. For some painkillers, the size of the dose, D, given depends on the weight of the patient, W. Thus, $D = f(W)$, where D is in milligrams and W is in pounds.

  (a) Interpret the statements $f(140) = 120$ and $f'(140) = 3$ in terms of this painkiller.
  (b) Use the information in the statements in part (a) to estimate $f(145)$.

56. In April 1991, the *Economist* carried an article[18] which said:

> Suddenly, everywhere, it is not the rate of change of things that matters, it is the rate of change of rates of change. Nobody cares much about inflation; only whether it is going up or down. Or rather, whether it is going up fast or down fast. "Inflation drops by disappointing two points," cries the billboard. Which roughly translated means that prices are still rising, but less fast than they were, though not quite as much less fast as everybody had hoped.

In the last sentence, there are three statements about prices. Rewrite these as statements about derivatives.

57. At time, t, in years, the US population is growing at 0.8% per year times its size, $P(t)$, at that moment. Using the derivative, write an equation representing this statement.

---

[18]From "The Tyranny of Differential Calculus: $d^2P/dt^2 > 0 =$ misery." *The Economist* (London: April 6, 1991).

58. A continuous function defined for all x has the following properties:

- f is increasing
- f is concave down
- $f(5) = 2$
- $f'(5) = \frac{1}{2}$

(a) Sketch a possible graph for f.
(b) How many zeros does f have?
(c) What can you say about the location of the zeros?
(d) What is $\lim_{x \to -\infty} f(x)$?
(e) Is it possible that $f'(1) = 1$?
(f) Is it possible that $f'(1) = \frac{1}{4}$?

59. (a) Using the table, estimate $f'(0.6)$ and $f'(0.5)$.
(b) Estimate $f''(0.6)$.
(c) Where do you think the maximum and minimum values of f occur in the interval $0 \le x \le 1$?

x	0	0.2	0.4	0.6	0.8	1.0
$f(x)$	3.7	3.5	3.5	3.9	4.0	3.9

60. Let $g(x) = \sqrt{x}$ and $f(x) = kx^2$, where k is a constant.

(a) Find the slope of the tangent line to the graph of g at the point $(4, 2)$.
(b) Find the equation of this tangent line.
(c) If the graph of f contains the point $(4, 2)$, find k.
(d) Where does the graph of f intersect the tangent line found in part (b)?

61. A circle with center at the origin and radius of length $\sqrt{19}$ has equation $x^2 + y^2 = 19$. Graph the circle.

(a) Just from looking at the graph, what can you say about the slope of the line tangent to the circle at the point $(0, \sqrt{19})$? What about the slope of the tangent at $(\sqrt{19}, 0)$?
(b) Estimate the slope of the tangent to the circle at the point $(2, -\sqrt{15})$ by graphing the tangent carefully at that point.
(c) Use the result of part (b) and the symmetry of the circle to find slopes of the tangents drawn to the circle at $(-2, \sqrt{15})$, $(-2, -\sqrt{15})$, and $(2, \sqrt{15})$.

62. Each of the graphs in Figure 2.65 shows the position of a particle moving along the x-axis as a function of time, $0 \le t \le 5$. The vertical scales of the graphs are the same. During this time interval, which particle has

(a) Constant velocity?
(b) The greatest initial velocity?
(c) The greatest average velocity?
(d) Zero average velocity?
(e) Zero acceleration?
(f) Positive acceleration throughout?

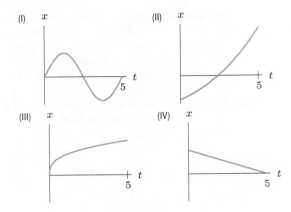

Figure 2.65

63. The population of a herd of deer is modeled by

$$P(t) = 4000 + 400 \sin\left(\frac{\pi}{6}t\right) + 180 \sin\left(\frac{\pi}{3}t\right)$$

where t is measured in months from the first of April.

(a) Use a calculator or computer to sketch a graph showing how this population varies with time.

Use the graph to answer the following questions.

(b) When is the herd largest? How many deer are in it at that time?
(c) When is the herd smallest? How many deer are in it then?
(d) When is the herd growing the fastest? When is it shrinking the fastest?
(e) How fast is the herd growing on April 1?

64. The number of hours, H, of daylight in Madrid is a function of t, the number of days since the start of the year. Figure 2.66 shows a one-month portion of the graph of H.

Figure 2.66

(a) Comment on the shape of the graph. Why does it look like a straight line?
(b) What month does this graph show? How do you know?
(c) What is the approximate slope of this line? What does the slope represent in practical terms?

65. You put a yam in a hot oven, maintained at a constant temperature of 200°C. As the yam picks up heat from the oven, its temperature rises.[19]

   (a) Draw a possible graph of the temperature T of the yam against time t (minutes) since it is put into the oven. Explain any interesting features of the graph, and in particular explain its concavity.

   (b) At $t = 30$, the temperature T of the yam is 120° and increasing at the (instantaneous) rate of 2°/min. Using this information and the shape of the graph, estimate the temperature at time $t = 40$.

   (c) In addition, you are told that at $t = 60$, the temperature of the yam is 165°. Can you improve your estimate of the temperature at $t = 40$?

   (d) Assuming all the data given so far, estimate the time at which the temperature of the yam is 150°.

66. You are given the following values for the error function, $\text{erf}(x)$.

$$\text{erf}(0) = 0 \quad \text{erf}(1) = 0.84270079$$

$$\text{erf}(0.1) = 0.11246292 \quad \text{erf}(0.01) = 0.01128342.$$

   (a) Use all this information to determine your best estimate for $\text{erf}'(0)$. (Give only those digits of which you feel reasonably certain.)

   (b) You find that $\text{erf}(0.001) = 0.00112838$. How does this extra information change your answer to part (a)?

67. **(a)** Use your calculator to approximate the derivative of the hyperbolic sine function (written $\sinh x$) at the points 0, 0.3, 0.7, and 1.

   (b) Can you find a relation between the values of this derivative and the values of the hyperbolic cosine (written $\cosh x$)?

68. In 2009, a study was done on the impact of sea level rise in the mid-Atlantic states.[20] Let $a(t)$ be the depth of the sea in millimeters (mm) at a typical point on the Atlantic Coast, and let $m(t)$ be the depth of the sea in mm at a typical point on the Gulf of Mexico, with time t in years since data collection started.

   (a) The study reports "Sea level is rising and there is evidence that the rate is accelerating." What does this statement tell us about $a(t)$ and $m(t)$?

   (b) The study also reports "The Atlantic Coast and the Gulf of Mexico experience higher rates of sea-level rise (2 to 4 mm per year and 2 to 10 mm per year, respectively) than the current global average (1.7 mm per year)." What does this tell us about $a(t)$ and $m(t)$?

   (c) Assume the rate at which the sea level rises on the Atlantic Coast and the Gulf of Mexico are constant for a century and within the ranges given in the report.

     (i) What is the largest amount the sea could rise on the Atlantic Coast during a century? Your answer should be a range of values.

     (ii) What is the shortest amount of time in which the sea level in the Gulf of Mexico could rise 1 meter?

CAS Challenge Problems

69. Use a computer algebra system to find the derivative of $f(x) = \sin^2 x + \cos^2 x$ and simplify your answer. Explain your result.

70. **(a)** Use a computer algebra system to find the derivative of $f(x) = 2 \sin x \cos x$.

   (b) Simplify $f(x)$ and $f'(x)$ using double angle formulas. Write down the derivative formula that you get after doing this simplification.

71. **(a)** Use a computer algebra system to find the second derivative of $g(x) = e^{-ax^2}$ with respect to x.

   (b) Graph $g(x)$ and $g''(x)$ on the same axes for $a = 1, 2, 3$ and describe the relation between the two graphs.

   (c) Explain your answer to part (b) in terms of concavity.

72. **(a)** Use a computer algebra system to find the derivative of $f(x) = \ln(x)$, $g(x) = \ln(2x)$, and $h(x) = \ln(3x)$. What is the relationship between the answers?

   (b) Use the properties of logarithms to explain what you see in part (a).

73. **(a)** Use a computer algebra system to find the derivative of $(x^2 + 1)^2$, $(x^2 + 1)^3$, and $(x^2 + 1)^4$.

   (b) Conjecture a formula for the derivative of $(x^2 + 1)^n$ that works for any integer n. Check your formula using the computer algebra system.

74. **(a)** Use a computer algebra system to find the derivatives of $\sin x$, $\cos x$ and $\sin x \cos x$.

   (b) Is the derivative of a product of two functions always equal to the product of their derivatives?

---

[19]From Peter D. Taylor, *Calculus: The Analysis of Functions* (Toronto: Wall & Emerson, Inc., 1992).

[20]www.epa.gov/climatechange/effects/coastal/sap4-1.html, *Coastal Sensitivity to Sea-Level Rise: A Focus on the Mid-Atlantic Region*, US Climate Change Science Program, January 2009.

PROJECTS FOR CHAPTER TWO

1. **Hours of Daylight as a Function of Latitude**

   Let $S(x)$ be the number of sunlight hours on a cloudless June 21, as a function of latitude, x, measured in degrees.

   (a) What is $S(0)$?

   (b) Let x_0 be the latitude of the Arctic Circle ($x_0 \approx 66°30'$). In the northern hemisphere, $S(x)$ is given, for some constants a and b, by the formula:

   $$S(x) = \begin{cases} a + b \arcsin\left(\dfrac{\tan x}{\tan x_0}\right) & \text{for } 0 \le x < x_0 \\ 24 & \text{for } x_0 \le x \le 90. \end{cases}$$

   Find a and b so that $S(x)$ is continuous.

   (c) Calculate $S(x)$ for Tucson, Arizona ($x = 32°13'$) and Walla Walla, Washington ($46°4'$).

   (d) Graph $S(x)$, for $0 \le x \le 90$.

   (e) Does $S(x)$ appear to be differentiable?

2. **US Population**

   Census figures for the US population (in millions) are listed in Table 2.12. Let f be the function such that $P = f(t)$ is the population (in millions) in year t.

   Table 2.12   *US population (in millions), 1790–2000*

Year	Population	Year	Population	Year	Population	Year	Population
1790	3.9	1850	23.1	1910	92.0	1970	205.0
1800	5.3	1860	31.4	1920	105.7	1980	226.5
1810	7.2	1870	38.6	1930	122.8	1990	248.7
1820	9.6	1880	50.2	1940	131.7	2000	281.4
1830	12.9	1890	62.9	1950	150.7		
1840	17.1	1900	76.0	1960	179.0		

   (a) (i) Estimate the rate of change of the population for the years 1900, 1945, and 2000.

   (ii) When, approximately, was the rate of change of the population greatest?

   (iii) Estimate the US population in 1956.

   (iv) Based on the data from the table, what would you predict for the census in the year 2010?

   (b) Assume that f is increasing (as the values in the table suggest). Then f is invertible.

   (i) What is the meaning of $f^{-1}(100)$?

   (ii) What does the derivative of $f^{-1}(P)$ at $P = 100$ represent? What are its units?

   (iii) Estimate $f^{-1}(100)$.

   (iv) Estimate the derivative of $f^{-1}(P)$ at $P = 100$.

   (c) (i) Usually we think the US population $P = f(t)$ as a smooth function of time. To what extent is this justified? What happens if we zoom in at a point of the graph? What about events such as the Louisiana Purchase? Or the moment of your birth?

   (ii) What do we in fact mean by the rate of change of the population at a particular time t?

   (iii) Give another example of a real-world function which is not smooth but is usually treated as such.

Chapter Three

SHORT-CUTS TO DIFFERENTIATION

Contents

3.1 Powers and Polynomials **124**

    Derivative of a Constant Times a Function . . . 124

    Derivatives of Sums and Differences 124

    Powers of x 125

    Derivatives of Polynomials 127

3.2 The Exponential Function **132**

    Derivatives of Exponential Functions and e . . 132

    A Formula for the Derivative of a^x 134

3.3 The Product and Quotient Rules **136**

    The Product Rule 136

    The Quotient Rule 138

3.4 The Chain Rule **142**

    Intuition Behind the Chain Rule 142

    The Derivative of a Composition of Functions . . 142

3.5 The Trigonometric Functions **149**

    Derivatives of the Sine and Cosine 149

    Derivative of the Tangent Function 151

    Informal Justification of $\frac{d}{dx}(\sin x) = \cos x$ 152

3.6 The Chain Rule and Inverse Functions **156**

    Finding the Derivative of an Inverse Function . . 156

    Derivative of $\ln x$ 156

    Derivative of a^x 157

    Derivatives of Inverse Trigonometric Functions . 157

    Derivative of a General Inverse Function 158

3.7 Implicit Functions **162**

3.8 Hyperbolic Functions **165**

    Properties of Hyperbolic Functions 165

    Identities Involving $\cosh x$ and $\sinh x$ 166

    The Hyperbolic Tangent 167

    Derivatives of Hyperbolic Functions 167

3.9 Linear Approximation and the Derivative . . . **169**

    The Tangent Line Approximation 169

    Estimating the Error in the Approximation . . . 170

    Why Differentiability Makes a Graph
        Look Straight 171

3.10 Theorems About Differentiable Functions . . . **175**

    The Mean Value Theorem 175

    The Increasing Function Theorem 176

    The Constant Function Theorem 176

    The Racetrack Principle 177

REVIEW PROBLEMS **180**

PROJECTS **184**

3.1 POWERS AND POLYNOMIALS

Derivative of a Constant Times a Function

Figure 3.1 shows the graph of $y = f(x)$ and of three multiples: $y = 3f(x)$, $y = \frac{1}{2}f(x)$, and $y = -2f(x)$. What is the relationship between the derivatives of these functions? In other words, for a particular x-value, how are the slopes of these graphs related?

Figure 3.1: A function and its multiples: Derivative of multiple is multiple of derivative

Multiplying the value of a function by a constant stretches or shrinks the original graph (and reflects it across the x-axis if the constant is negative). This changes the slope of the curve at each point. If the graph has been stretched, the "rises" have all been increased by the same factor, whereas the "runs" remain the same. Thus, the slopes are all steeper by the same factor. If the graph has been shrunk, the slopes are all smaller by the same factor. If the graph has been reflected across the x-axis, the slopes will all have their signs reversed. In other words, if a function is multiplied by a constant, c, so is its derivative:

Theorem 3.1: Derivative of a Constant Multiple

If f is differentiable and c is a constant, then

$$\frac{d}{dx}\left[cf(x)\right] = cf'(x).$$

Proof Although the graphical argument makes the theorem plausible, to prove it we must use the definition of the derivative:

$$\frac{d}{dx}\left[cf(x)\right] = \lim_{h \to 0} \frac{cf(x+h) - cf(x)}{h} = \lim_{h \to 0} c\,\frac{f(x+h) - f(x)}{h}$$

$$= c \lim_{h \to 0} \frac{f(x+h) - f(x)}{h} = cf'(x).$$

We can take c across the limit sign by the properties of limits (part 1 of Theorem 1.2 on page 60).

Derivatives of Sums and Differences

Suppose we have two functions, $f(x)$ and $g(x)$, with the values listed in Table 3.1. Values of the sum $f(x) + g(x)$ are given in the same table.

Table 3.1   *Sum of Functions*

x	$f(x)$	$g(x)$	$f(x) + g(x)$
0	100	0	100
1	110	0.2	110.2
2	130	0.4	130.4
3	160	0.6	160.6
4	200	0.8	200.8

We see that adding the increments of $f(x)$ and the increments of $g(x)$ gives the increments of $f(x) + g(x)$. For example, as x increases from 0 to 1, $f(x)$ increases by 10 and $g(x)$ increases by 0.2, while $f(x) + g(x)$ increases by $110.2 - 100 = 10.2$. Similarly, as x increases from 3 to 4, $f(x)$ increases by 40 and $g(x)$ by 0.2, while $f(x) + g(x)$ increases by $200.8 - 160.6 = 40.2$.

From this example, we see that the rate at which $f(x) + g(x)$ is increasing is the sum of the rates at which $f(x)$ and $g(x)$ are increasing. Similar reasoning applies to the difference, $f(x) - g(x)$. In terms of derivatives:

Theorem 3.2: Derivative of Sum and Difference

If f and g are differentiable, then

$$\frac{d}{dx}[f(x) + g(x)] = f'(x) + g'(x) \quad \text{and} \quad \frac{d}{dx}[f(x) - g(x)] = f'(x) - g'(x).$$

Proof Using the definition of the derivative:

$$\frac{d}{dx}[f(x) + g(x)] = \lim_{h \to 0} \frac{[f(x+h) + g(x+h)] - [f(x) + g(x)]}{h}$$

$$= \lim_{h \to 0} \left[\underbrace{\frac{f(x+h) - f(x)}{h}}_{\text{Limit of this is } f'(x)} + \underbrace{\frac{g(x+h) - g(x)}{h}}_{\text{Limit of this is } g'(x)} \right]$$

$$= f'(x) + g'(x).$$

We have used the fact that the limit of a sum is the sum of the limits, part 2 of Theorem 1.2 on page 60. The proof for $f(x) - g(x)$ is similar.

Powers of x

In Chapter 2 we showed that

$$f'(x) = \frac{d}{dx}(x^2) = 2x \quad \text{and} \quad g'(x) = \frac{d}{dx}(x^3) = 3x^2.$$

The graphs of $f(x) = x^2$ and $g(x) = x^3$ and their derivatives are shown in Figures 3.2 and 3.3. Notice $f'(x) = 2x$ has the behavior we expect. It is negative for $x < 0$ (when f is decreasing), zero for $x = 0$, and positive for $x > 0$ (when f is increasing). Similarly, $g'(x) = 3x^2$ is zero when $x = 0$, but positive everywhere else, as g is increasing everywhere else.

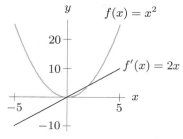

Figure 3.2: Graphs of $f(x) = x^2$ and its derivative $f'(x) = 2x$

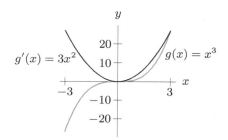

Figure 3.3: Graphs of $g(x) = x^3$ and its derivative $g'(x) = 3x^2$

These examples are special cases of the power rule, which we justify for any positive integer n on page 127:

The Power Rule

For any constant real number n,

$$\frac{d}{dx}(x^n) = nx^{n-1}.$$

Problem 80 asks you to show that this rule holds for negative integral powers; such powers can also be differentiated using the quotient rule (Section 3.3). In Section 3.6 we indicate how to justify the power rule for powers of the form $1/n$.

Example 1   Use the power rule to differentiate (a) $\dfrac{1}{x^3}$,   (b) $x^{1/2}$,   (c) $\dfrac{1}{\sqrt[3]{x}}$.

Solution   (a) For $n = -3$: $\dfrac{d}{dx}\left(\dfrac{1}{x^3}\right) = \dfrac{d}{dx}(x^{-3}) = -3x^{-3-1} = -3x^{-4} = -\dfrac{3}{x^4}.$

(b) For $n = 1/2$: $\dfrac{d}{dx}\left(x^{1/2}\right) = \dfrac{1}{2}x^{(1/2)-1} = \dfrac{1}{2}x^{-1/2} = \dfrac{1}{2\sqrt{x}}.$

(c) For $n = -1/3$: $\dfrac{d}{dx}\left(\dfrac{1}{\sqrt[3]{x}}\right) = \dfrac{d}{dx}\left(x^{-1/3}\right) = -\dfrac{1}{3}x^{(-1/3)-1} = -\dfrac{1}{3}x^{-4/3} = -\dfrac{1}{3x^{4/3}}.$

Example 2   Use the definition of the derivative to justify the power rule for $n = -2$: Show $\dfrac{d}{dx}(x^{-2}) = -2x^{-3}$.

Solution   Provided $x \neq 0$, we have

$$\frac{d}{dx}(x^{-2}) = \frac{d}{dx}\left(\frac{1}{x^2}\right) = \lim_{h \to 0}\left(\frac{\frac{1}{(x+h)^2} - \frac{1}{x^2}}{h}\right) = \lim_{h \to 0}\frac{1}{h}\left[\frac{x^2 - (x+h)^2}{(x+h)^2 x^2}\right] \quad \text{(Combining fractions over a common denominator)}$$

$$= \lim_{h \to 0}\frac{1}{h}\left[\frac{x^2 - (x^2 + 2xh + h^2)}{(x+h)^2 x^2}\right] \quad \text{(Multiplying out)}$$

$$= \lim_{h \to 0}\frac{-2xh - h^2}{h(x+h)^2 x^2} \quad \text{(Simplifying numerator)}$$

$$= \lim_{h \to 0}\frac{-2x - h}{(x+h)^2 x^2} \quad \text{(Dividing numerator and denominator by } h\text{)}$$

$$= \frac{-2x}{x^4} \quad \text{(Letting } h \to 0\text{)}$$

$$= -2x^{-3}.$$

The graphs of x^{-2} and its derivative, $-2x^{-3}$, are shown in Figure 3.4. Does the graph of the derivative have the features you expect?

Figure 3.4: Graphs of x^{-2} and its derivative, $-2x^{-3}$

Justification of $\frac{d}{dx}(x^n) = nx^{n-1}$, for n a Positive Integer

To calculate the derivatives of x^2 and x^3, we had to expand $(x+h)^2$ and $(x+h)^3$. To calculate the derivative of x^n, we must expand $(x+h)^n$. Let's look back at the previous expansions:

$$(x+h)^2 = x^2 + 2xh + h^2, \qquad (x+h)^3 = x^3 + 3x^2h + 3xh^2 + h^3,$$

and multiply out a few more examples:

$$(x+h)^4 = x^4 + 4x^3h + 6x^2h^2 + 4xh^3 + h^4,$$
$$(x+h)^5 = x^5 + 5x^4h + \underbrace{10x^3h^2 + 10x^2h^3 + 5xh^4 + h^5}.$$

Terms involving h^2 and higher powers of h

In general, we can say

$$(x+h)^n = x^n + nx^{n-1}h + \underbrace{\cdots + h^n}.$$

Terms involving h^2 and higher powers of h

We have just seen this is true for $n = 2, 3, 4, 5$. It can be proved in general using the Binomial Theorem (see www.wiley.com/college/hughes-hallett). Now to find the derivative,

$$\frac{d}{dx}(x^n) = \lim_{h \to 0} \frac{(x+h)^n - x^n}{h}$$
$$= \lim_{h \to 0} \frac{(x^n + nx^{n-1}h + \cdots + h^n) - x^n}{h}$$

Terms involving h^2 and higher powers of h

$$= \lim_{h \to 0} \frac{nx^{n-1}h + \overbrace{\cdots + h^n}}{h}.$$

When we factor out h from terms involving h^2 and higher powers of h, each term will still have an h in it. Factoring and dividing, we get:

Terms involving h and higher powers of h

$$\frac{d}{dx}(x^n) = \lim_{h \to 0} \frac{h(nx^{n-1} + \cdots + h^{n-1})}{h} = \lim_{h \to 0} (nx^{n-1} + \overbrace{\cdots + h^{n-1}}).$$

But as $h \to 0$, all terms involving an h will go to 0, so

$$\frac{d}{dx}(x^n) = \lim_{h \to 0} (nx^{n-1} + \underbrace{\cdots + h^{n-1}}) = nx^{n-1}.$$

These terms go to 0

Derivatives of Polynomials

Now that we know how to differentiate powers, constant multiples, and sums, we can differentiate any polynomial.

Example 3 Find the derivatives of (a) $5x^2 + 3x + 2$, (b) $\sqrt{3}x^7 - \dfrac{x^5}{5} + \pi$.

Solution (a)
$$\frac{d}{dx}(5x^2 + 3x + 2) = 5\frac{d}{dx}(x^2) + 3\frac{d}{dx}(x) + \frac{d}{dx}(2)$$
$$= 5 \cdot 2x + 3 \cdot 1 + 0 \qquad \text{(Since the derivative of a constant, } \frac{d}{dx}(2)\text{, is zero.)}$$
$$= 10x + 3.$$

(b)

$$\frac{d}{dx}\left(\sqrt{3}x^7 - \frac{x^5}{5} + \pi\right) = \sqrt{3}\frac{d}{dx}(x^7) - \frac{1}{5}\frac{d}{dx}(x^5) + \frac{d}{dx}(\pi)$$

$$= \sqrt{3}\cdot 7x^6 - \frac{1}{5}\cdot 5x^4 + 0 \qquad \text{(Since π is a constant, $d\pi/dx = 0$.)}$$

$$= 7\sqrt{3}x^6 - x^4.$$

We can also use the rules we have seen so far to differentiate expressions that are not polynomials.

Example 4   Differentiate (a) $5\sqrt{x} - \dfrac{10}{x^2} + \dfrac{1}{2\sqrt{x}}$.   (b) $0.1x^3 + 2x^{\sqrt{2}}$.

Solution   (a) $\dfrac{d}{dx}\left(5\sqrt{x} - \dfrac{10}{x^2} + \dfrac{1}{2\sqrt{x}}\right) = \dfrac{d}{dx}\left(5x^{1/2} - 10x^{-2} + \dfrac{1}{2}x^{-1/2}\right)$

$$= 5\cdot\frac{1}{2}x^{-1/2} - 10(-2)x^{-3} + \frac{1}{2}\left(-\frac{1}{2}\right)x^{-3/2}$$

$$= \frac{5}{2\sqrt{x}} + \frac{20}{x^3} - \frac{1}{4x^{3/2}}.$$

(b) $\dfrac{d}{dx}(0.1x^3 + 2x^{\sqrt{2}}) = 0.1\dfrac{d}{dx}(x^3) + 2\dfrac{d}{dx}(x^{\sqrt{2}}) = 0.3x^2 + 2\sqrt{2}x^{\sqrt{2}-1}.$

Example 5   Find the second derivative and interpret its sign for
(a) $f(x) = x^2$,   (b) $g(x) = x^3$,   (c) $k(x) = x^{1/2}$.

Solution   (a) If $f(x) = x^2$, then $f'(x) = 2x$, so $f''(x) = \dfrac{d}{dx}(2x) = 2$. Since f'' is always positive, f is concave up, as expected for a parabola opening upward. (See Figure 3.5.)

(b) If $g(x) = x^3$, then $g'(x) = 3x^2$, so $g''(x) = \dfrac{d}{dx}(3x^2) = 3\dfrac{d}{dx}(x^2) = 3\cdot 2x = 6x$. This is positive for $x > 0$ and negative for $x < 0$, which means x^3 is concave up for $x > 0$ and concave down for $x < 0$. (See Figure 3.6.)

(c) If $k(x) = x^{1/2}$, then $k'(x) = \frac{1}{2}x^{(1/2)-1} = \frac{1}{2}x^{-1/2}$, so

$$k''(x) = \frac{d}{dx}\left(\frac{1}{2}x^{-1/2}\right) = \frac{1}{2}\cdot(-\frac{1}{2})x^{-(1/2)-1} = -\frac{1}{4}x^{-3/2}.$$

Now k' and k'' are only defined on the domain of k, that is, $x \geq 0$. When $x > 0$, we see that $k''(x)$ is negative, so k is concave down. (See Figure 3.7.)

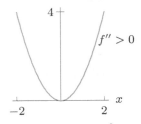

Figure 3.5: $f(x) = x^2$ has
$f''(x) = 2$

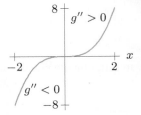

Figure 3.6: $g(x) = x^3$ has
$g''(x) = 6x$

Figure 3.7: $k(x) = x^{1/2}$ has
$k''(x) = -\frac{1}{4}x^{-3/2}$

Example 6   If the position of a body, in meters, is given as a function of time t, in seconds, by

$$s = -4.9t^2 + 5t + 6,$$

find the velocity and acceleration of the body at time t.

Solution   The velocity, v, is the derivative of the position:

$$v = \frac{ds}{dt} = \frac{d}{dt}(-4.9t^2 + 5t + 6) = -9.8t + 5,$$

and the acceleration, a, is the derivative of the velocity:

$$a = \frac{dv}{dt} = \frac{d}{dt}(-9.8t + 5) = -9.8.$$

Note that v is in meters/second and a is in meters/second^2.

Example 7   Figure 3.8 shows the graph of a cubic polynomial. Both graphically and algebraically, describe the behavior of the derivative of this cubic.

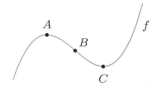

Figure 3.8: The cubic of Example 7   Figure 3.9: Derivative of the cubic of Example 7

Solution   Graphical approach: Suppose we move along the curve from left to right. To the left of A, the slope is positive; it starts very positive and decreases until the curve reaches A, where the slope is 0. Between A and C the slope is negative. Between A and B the slope is decreasing (getting more negative); it is most negative at B. Between B and C the slope is negative but increasing; at C the slope is zero. From C to the right, the slope is positive and increasing. The graph of the derivative function is shown in Figure 3.9.

Algebraic approach: f is a cubic that goes to $+\infty$ as $x \to +\infty$, so

$$f(x) = ax^3 + bx^2 + cx + d$$

with $a > 0$. Hence,

$$f'(x) = 3ax^2 + 2bx + c,$$

whose graph is a parabola opening upward, as in Figure 3.9.

Exercises and Problems for Section 3.1

Exercises

1. Let $f(x) = 7$. Using the definition of the derivative, show that $f'(x) = 0$ for all values of x.

2. Let $f(x) = 17x + 11$. Use the definition of the derivative to calculate $f'(x)$.

For Exercises 3–5, determine if the derivative rules from this section apply. If they do, find the derivative. If they don't apply, indicate why.

3. $y = 3^x$

4. $y = x^3$

5. $y = x^\pi$

For Exercises 6–49, find the derivatives of the given functions. Assume that a, b, c, and k are constants.

6. $y = x^{12}$

7. $y = x^{11}$

8. $y = -x^{-11}$

9. $y = x^{-12}$

10. $y = x^{3.2}$

11. $y = x^{-3/4}$

12. $y = x^{4/3}$

13. $y = x^{3/4}$

14. $y = x^2 + 5x + 7$

15. $f(t) = t^3 - 3t^2 + 8t - 4$

16. $f(x) = \dfrac{1}{x^4}$

17. $g(t) = \dfrac{1}{t^5}$

18. $f(z) = -\dfrac{1}{z^{6.1}}$

19. $y = \dfrac{1}{r^{7/2}}$

20. $y = \sqrt{x}$

21. $f(x) = \sqrt[4]{x}$

22. $h(\theta) = \dfrac{1}{\sqrt[3]{\theta}}$

23. $f(x) = \sqrt{\dfrac{1}{x^3}}$

24. $h(x) = \ln e^{ax}$

25. $y = 4x^{3/2} - 5x^{1/2}$

26. $f(t) = 3t^2 - 4t + 1$

27. $y = 17x + 24x^{1/2}$

28. $y = z^2 + \dfrac{1}{2z}$

29. $f(x) = 5x^4 + \dfrac{1}{x^2}$

30. $h(w) = -2w^{-3} + 3\sqrt{w}$

31. $y = -3x^4 - 4x^3 - 6x$

32. $y = 3t^5 - 5\sqrt{t} + \dfrac{7}{t}$

33. $y = 3t^2 + \dfrac{12}{\sqrt{t}} - \dfrac{1}{t^2}$

34. $y = \sqrt{x}(x + 1)$

35. $y = t^{3/2}(2 + \sqrt{t})$

36. $h(t) = \dfrac{3}{t} + \dfrac{4}{t^2}$

37. $h(\theta) = \theta(\theta^{-1/2} - \theta^{-2})$

38. $y = \dfrac{x^2 + 1}{x}$

39. $f(z) = \dfrac{z^2 + 1}{3z}$

40. $g(x) = \dfrac{x^2 + \sqrt{x} + 1}{x^{3/2}}$

41. $y = \dfrac{\theta - 1}{\sqrt{\theta}}$

42. $g(t) = \dfrac{\sqrt{t}(1 + t)}{t^2}$

43. $j(x) = \dfrac{x^3}{a} + \dfrac{a}{b}x^2 - cx$

44. $f(x) = \dfrac{ax + b}{x}$

45. $h(x) = \dfrac{ax + b}{c}$

46. $V = \frac{4}{3}\pi r^2 b$

47. $w = 3ab^2 q$

48. $y = ax^2 + bx + c$

49. $P = a + b\sqrt{t}$

Problems

For Problems 50–55, determine if the derivative rules from this section apply. If they do, find the derivative. If they don't apply, indicate why.

50. $y = (x + 3)^{1/2}$

51. $y = \pi^x$

52. $g(x) = x^\pi - x^{-\pi}$

53. $y = 3x^2 + 4$

54. $y = \dfrac{1}{3x^2 + 4}$

55. $y = \dfrac{1}{3z^2} + \dfrac{1}{4}$

56. The graph of $y = x^3 - 9x^2 - 16x + 1$ has a slope of 5 at two points. Find the coordinates of the points.

57. Find the equation of the line tangent to the graph of f at $(1, 1)$, where f is given by $f(x) = 2x^3 - 2x^2 + 1$.

58. **(a)** Find the equation of the tangent line to $f(x) = x^3$ at the point where $x = 2$.
(b) Graph the tangent line and the function on the same axes. If the tangent line is used to estimate values of the function, will the estimates be overestimates or underestimates?

59. Find the equation of the line tangent to $y = x^2 + 3x - 5$ at $x = 2$.

60. Find the equation of the line tangent to $f(x)$ at $x = 2$, if

$$f(x) = \dfrac{x^3}{2} - \dfrac{4}{3x}.$$

61. Using a graph to help you, find the equations of all lines through the origin tangent to the parabola

$$y = x^2 - 2x + 4.$$

Sketch the lines on the graph.

62. On what intervals is the graph of $f(x) = x^4 - 4x^3$ both decreasing and concave up?

63. For what values of x is the function $y = x^5 - 5x$ both increasing and concave up?

64. If $f(x) = 4x^3 + 6x^2 - 23x + 7$, find the intervals on which $f'(x) \geq 1$.

65. If $f(x) = (3x + 8)(2x - 5)$, find $f'(x)$ and $f''(x)$.

66. Given $p(x) = x^n - x$, find the intervals over which p is a decreasing function when:
  (a) $n = 2$ **(b)** $n = \frac{1}{2}$ **(c)** $n = -1$

67. Suppose W is proportional to r^3. The derivative dW/dr is proportional to what power of r?

68. The height of a sand dune (in centimeters) is represented by $f(t) = 700 - 3t^2$, where t is measured in years since 2005. Find $f(5)$ and $f'(5)$. Using units, explain what each means in terms of the sand dune.

69. A ball is dropped from the top of the Empire State building to the ground below. The height, y, of the ball above the ground (in feet) is given as a function of time, t, (in seconds) by

$$y = 1250 - 16t^2.$$

  (a) Find the velocity of the ball at time t. What is the sign of the velocity? Why is this to be expected?
  (b) Show that the acceleration of the ball is a constant. What are the value and sign of this constant?
  (c) When does the ball hit the ground, and how fast is it going at that time? Give your answer in feet per second and in miles per hour (1 ft/sec = 15/22 mph).

70. At a time t seconds after it is thrown up in the air, a tomato is at a height of $f(t) = -4.9t^2 + 25t + 3$ meters.

  (a) What is the average velocity of the tomato during the first 2 seconds? Give units.
  (b) Find (exactly) the instantaneous velocity of the tomato at $t = 2$. Give units.
  (c) What is the acceleration at $t = 2$?
  (d) How high does the tomato go?
  (e) How long is the tomato in the air?

71. A particle is moving on the x-axis, where x is in centimeters. Its velocity, v, in cm/sec, when it is at the point with coordinate x is given by

$$v = x^2 + 3x - 2.$$

Find the acceleration of the particle when it is at the point $x = 2$. Give units in your answer.

72. Let $f(t)$ and $g(t)$ give, respectively, the amount of water (in acre-feet) in two different reservoirs on day t. Suppose that $f(0) = 2000, g(0) = 1500$ and that $f'(0) = 11, g'(0) = 13.5$. Let $h(t) = f(t) - g(t)$.

   (a) Evaluate $h(0)$ and $h'(0)$. What do these quantities tell you about the reservoir?
   (b) Assume h' is constant for $0 \leq t \leq 250$. Does h have any zeros? What does this tell you about the reservoirs?

73. If M is the mass of the earth and G is a constant, the acceleration due to gravity, g, at a distance r from the center of the earth is given by

$$g = \frac{GM}{r^2}.$$

   (a) Find dg/dr.
   (b) What is the practical interpretation (in terms of acceleration) of dg/dr? Why would you expect it to be negative?
   (c) You are told that $M = 6 \cdot 10^{24}$ and $G = 6.67 \cdot 10^{-20}$ where M is in kilograms and r in kilometers. What is the value of dg/dr at the surface of the earth ($r = 6400$ km)?
   (d) What does this tell you about whether or not it is reasonable to assume g is constant near the surface of the earth?

74. The period, T, of a pendulum is given in terms of its length, l, by

$$T = 2\pi \sqrt{\frac{l}{g}},$$

where g is the acceleration due to gravity (a constant).

   (a) Find dT/dl.
   (b) What is the sign of dT/dl? What does this tell you about the period of pendulums?

75. **(a)** Use the formula for the area of a circle of radius r, $A = \pi r^2$, to find dA/dr.
   (b) The result from part (a) should look familiar. What does dA/dr represent geometrically?
   (c) Use the difference quotient to explain the observation you made in part (b).

76. What is the formula for V, the volume of a sphere of radius r? Find dV/dr. What is the geometrical meaning of dV/dr?

77. Show that for any power function $f(x) = x^n$, we have $f'(1) = n$.

78. Given a power function of the form $f(x) = ax^n$, with $f'(2) = 3$ and $f'(4) = 24$, find n and a.

79. Is there a value of n which makes $y = x^n$ a solution to the equation $13x(dy/dx) = y$? If so, what value?

80. Using the definition of derivative, justify the formula $d(x^n)/dx = nx^{n-1}$.

   (a) For $n = -1$; for $n = -3$.
   (b) For any negative integer n.

81. **(a)** Find the value of a making $f(x)$ continuous at $x = 1$:

$$f(x) = \begin{cases} ax & 0 \leq x \leq 1 \\ x^2 + 3 & 1 < x \leq 2. \end{cases}$$

   (b) With the value of a you found in part (a), does $f(x)$ have a derivative at every point in $0 \leq x \leq 2$? Explain.

82. Find values of a and b making $f(x)$ continuous and differentiable on $0 < x < 2$:

$$f(x) = \begin{cases} ax + b & 0 \leq x \leq 1 \\ x^2 + 3 & 1 < x \leq 2. \end{cases}$$

Strengthen Your Understanding

In Problems 83–84, explain what is wrong with the statement.

83. The only function that has derivative $2x$ is x^2.

84. The derivative of $f(x) = 1/x^2$ is $f'(x) = 1/(2x)$.

In Problems 85–87, give an example of:

85. Two functions $f(x)$ and $g(x)$ such that

$$\frac{d}{dx}(f(x) + g(x)) = 2x + 3.$$

86. A function whose derivative is $g'(x) = 2x$ and whose graph has no x-intercepts.

87. A function which has second derivative equal to 6 everywhere.

Are the statements in Problems 88–90 true or false? Give an explanation for your answer.

88. The derivative of a polynomial is always a polynomial.

89. The derivative of π/x^2 is $-\pi/x$.

90. If $f'(2) = 3.1$ and $g'(2) = 7.3$, then the graph of $f(x) + g(x)$ has slope 10.4 at $x = 2$.

Suppose that f'' and g'' exist and that f and g are concave up for all x. Are the statements in Problems 91–92 true or false for all such f and g? If a statement is true, explain how you know. If a statement is false, give a counterexample.

91. $f(x) + g(x)$ is concave up for all x.

92. $f(x) - g(x)$ cannot be concave up for all x.

3.2   THE EXPONENTIAL FUNCTION

What do we expect the graph of the derivative of the exponential function $f(x) = a^x$ to look like? The exponential function in Figure 3.10 increases slowly for $x < 0$ and more rapidly for $x > 0$, so the values of f' are small for $x < 0$ and larger for $x > 0$. Since the function is increasing for all values of x, the graph of the derivative must lie above the x-axis. It appears that the graph of f' may resemble the graph of f itself.

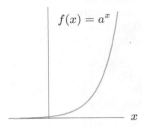

Figure 3.10: $f(x) = a^x$, with $a > 1$

In this section we see that $f'(x) = k \cdot a^x$, where k is a constant, so in fact $f'(x)$ is proportional to $f(x)$. This property of exponential functions makes them particularly useful in modeling because many quantities have rates of change which are proportional to themselves. For example, the simplest model of population growth has this property.

Derivatives of Exponential Functions and the Number e

We start by calculating the derivative of $g(x) = 2^x$, which is given by

$$g'(x) = \lim_{h \to 0} \left(\frac{2^{x+h} - 2^x}{h} \right) = \lim_{h \to 0} \left(\frac{2^x 2^h - 2^x}{h} \right) = \lim_{h \to 0} 2^x \left(\frac{2^h - 1}{h} \right)$$

$$= \lim_{h \to 0} \left(\frac{2^h - 1}{h} \right) \cdot 2^x. \qquad \text{(Since x and 2^x are fixed during this calculation).}$$

To find $\lim_{h \to 0} (2^h - 1)/h$, see Table 3.2 where we have substituted values of h near 0. The table suggests that the limit exists and has value 0.693. Let us call the limit k, so $k = 0.693$. Then

$$\frac{d}{dx}(2^x) = k \cdot 2^x = 0.693 \cdot 2^x.$$

So the derivative of 2^x is proportional to 2^x with constant of proportionality 0.693. A similar calculation shows that the derivative of $f(x) = a^x$ is

$$f'(x) = \lim_{h \to 0} \left(\frac{a^{x+h} - a^x}{h} \right) = \lim_{h \to 0} \left(\frac{a^h - 1}{h} \right) \cdot a^x.$$

Table 3.2

h	$(2^h - 1)/h$
-0.1	0.6697
-0.01	0.6908
-0.001	0.6929
0.001	0.6934
0.01	0.6956
0.1	0.7177

Table 3.3

a	$k = \lim_{h \to 0} \frac{a^h - 1}{h}$
2	0.693
3	1.099
4	1.386
5	1.609
6	1.792
7	1.946

Table 3.4

h	$(1 + h)^{1/h}$
-0.001	2.7196422
-0.0001	2.7184178
-0.00001	2.7182954
0.00001	2.7182682
0.0001	2.7181459
0.001	2.7169239

The quantity $\lim_{h \to 0}(a^h - 1)/h$ is also a constant, although the value of the constant depends on a. Writing $k = \lim_{h \to 0}(a^h - 1)/h$, we see that the derivative of $f(x) = a^x$ is proportional to a^x:

$$\frac{d}{dx}(a^x) = k \cdot a^x.$$

For particular values of a, we can estimate k by substituting values of h near 0 into the expression $(a^h - 1)/h$. Table 3.3 shows the results. Notice that for $a = 2$, the value of k is less than 1, while for $a = 3, 4, 5, \ldots$, the values of k are greater than 1. The values of k appear to be increasing, so we guess that there is a value of a between 2 and 3 for which $k = 1$. If so, we have found a value of a with the remarkable property that the function a^x is equal to its own derivative.

So let us look for such an a. This means we want to find a such that

$$\lim_{h \to 0} \frac{a^h - 1}{h} = 1, \qquad \text{or, for small } h, \qquad \frac{a^h - 1}{h} \approx 1.$$

Solving for a, we can estimate a as follows:

$$a^h - 1 \approx h, \qquad \text{or} \qquad a^h \approx 1 + h, \qquad \text{so} \qquad a \approx (1 + h)^{1/h}.$$

Taking small values of h, as in Table 3.4, we see $a \approx 2.718 \ldots$. This is the number e introduced in Chapter 1. In fact, it can be shown that if

$$e = \lim_{h \to 0}(1 + h)^{1/h} = 2.718 \ldots \qquad \text{then} \qquad \lim_{h \to 0} \frac{e^h - 1}{h} = 1.$$

This means that e^x is its own derivative:

$$\boxed{\frac{d}{dx}(e^x) = e^x.}$$

Figure 3.11 shows the graphs 2^x, 3^x, and e^x together with their derivatives. Notice that the derivative of 2^x is below the graph of 2^x, since $k < 1$ there, and the graph of the derivative of 3^x is above the graph of 3^x, since $k > 1$ there. With $e \approx 2.718$, the function e^x and its derivative are identical.

Note on Round-Off Error and Limits

If we try to evaluate $(1 + h)^{1/h}$ on a calculator by taking smaller and smaller values of h, the values of $(1 + h)^{1/h}$ at first get closer to $2.718 \ldots$. However, they will eventually move away again because of the *round-off error* (that is, errors introduced by the fact that the calculator can only hold a certain number of digits).

As we try smaller and smaller values of h, how do we know when to stop? Unfortunately, there is no fixed rule. A calculator can only suggest the value of a limit, but can never confirm that this value is correct. In this case, it looks like the limit is $2.718 \ldots$ because the values of $(1 + h)^{1/h}$ approach this number for a while. To be sure this is correct, we have to find the limit analytically.

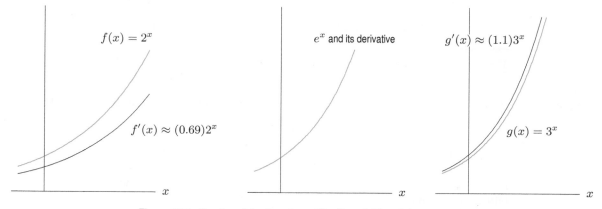

Figure 3.11: Graphs of the functions 2^x, e^x, and 3^x and their derivatives

A Formula for the Derivative of a^x

To get a formula for the derivative of a^x, we must calculate

$$f'(x) = \lim_{h \to 0} \frac{a^{x+h} - a^x}{h} = \underbrace{\left(\lim_{h \to 0} \frac{a^h - 1}{h} \right)}_{k} a^x.$$

However, without knowing the value of a, we can't use a calculator to estimate k. We take a different approach, rewriting $a = e^{\ln a}$, so

$$\lim_{h \to 0} \frac{a^h - 1}{h} = \lim_{h \to 0} \frac{(e^{\ln a})^h - 1}{h} = \lim_{h \to 0} \frac{e^{(\ln a)h} - 1}{h}.$$

To evaluate this limit, we use a limit that we already know:

$$\lim_{h \to 0} \frac{e^h - 1}{h} = 1.$$

In order to use this limit, we substitute $t = (\ln a)h$. Since t approaches 0 as h approaches 0, we have

$$\lim_{h \to 0} \frac{e^{(\ln a)h} - 1}{h} = \lim_{t \to 0} \frac{e^t - 1}{(t/\ln a)} = \lim_{t \to 0} \left(\ln a \cdot \frac{e^t - 1}{t} \right) = \ln a \left(\lim_{t \to 0} \frac{e^t - 1}{t} \right) = (\ln a) \cdot 1 = \ln a.$$

Thus, we have

$$f'(x) = \lim_{h \to 0} \frac{a^{x+h} - a^x}{h} = \left(\lim_{h \to 0} \frac{a^h - 1}{h} \right) a^x = (\ln a)a^x.$$

In Section 3.6 we obtain the same result by another method. We conclude that:

$$\boxed{\frac{d}{dx}(a^x) = (\ln a)a^x.}$$

Thus, for any a, the derivative of a^x is proportional to a^x. The constant of proportionality is $\ln a$. The derivative of a^x is equal to a^x if the constant of proportionality is 1, that is, if $\ln a = 1$, then $a = e$. The fact that the constant of proportionality is 1 when $a = e$ makes e a particularly convenient base for exponential functions.

Example 1   Differentiate $2 \cdot 3^x + 5e^x$.

Solution

$$\frac{d}{dx}(2 \cdot 3^x + 5e^x) = 2\frac{d}{dx}(3^x) + 5\frac{d}{dx}(e^x) = 2\ln 3 \cdot 3^x + 5e^x \approx (2.1972)3^x + 5e^x.$$

We can now use the new differentiation formula to compute rates.

Example 2   The population of the world in billions can be modeled by the function $f(t) = 6.91(1.011)^t$, where t is years since 2010. Find and interpret $f(0)$ and $f'(0)$.

Solution   We have $f(t) = 6.91(1.011)^t$ so $f'(t) = 6.91(\ln 1.011)(1.011)^t = 0.0756(1.011)^t$. Therefore,

$$f(0) = 6.91 \text{ billion people}$$

and

$$f'(0) = 0.0756 \text{ billion people per year.}$$

In 2010, the population of the world was 6.91 billion people and was increasing at a rate of 0.0756 billion, or 75.6 million, people per year.

Exercises and Problems for Section 3.2

Exercises

In Exercises 1–26, find the derivatives of the functions . Assume that a, b, c, and k are constants.

1. $f(x) = 2e^x + x^2$

2. $y = 5t^2 + 4e^t$

3. $f(x) = a^{5x}$

4. $f(x) = 12e^x + 11^x$

5. $y = 5x^2 + 2^x + 3$

6. $f(x) = 2^x + 2 \cdot 3^x$

7. $y = 4 \cdot 10^x - x^3$

8. $z = (\ln 4)e^x$

9. $y = \dfrac{3^x}{3} + \dfrac{33}{\sqrt{x}}$

10. $y = 2^x + \dfrac{2}{x^3}$

11. $z = (\ln 4)4^x$

12. $f(t) = (\ln 3)^t$

13. $y = 5 \cdot 5^t + 6 \cdot 6^t$

14. $h(z) = (\ln 2)^z$

15. $f(x) = e^2 + x^e$

16. $y = \pi^2 + \pi^x$

17. $f(x) = e^\pi + \pi^x$

18. $f(x) = \pi^x + x^\pi$

19. $f(x) = e^k + k^x$

20. $f(x) = e^{1+x}$

21. $f(t) = e^{t+2}$

22. $f(\theta) = e^{k\theta} - 1$

23. $y(x) = a^x + x^a$

24. $f(x) = x^{\pi^2} + (\pi^2)^x$

25. $g(x) = 2x - \dfrac{1}{\sqrt[3]{x}} + 3^x - e$

26. $f(x) = (3x^2 + \pi)(e^x - 4)$

Problems

In Problems 27–37, can the functions be differentiated using the rules developed so far? Differentiate if you can; otherwise, indicate why the rules discussed so far do not apply.

27. $y = x^2 + 2^x$

28. $y = \sqrt{x} - (\frac{1}{2})^x$

29. $y = x^2 \cdot 2^x$

30. $f(s) = 5^s e^s$

31. $y = e^{x+5}$

32. $y = e^{5x}$

33. $y = 4^{(x^2)}$

34. $f(z) = (\sqrt{4})^z$

35. $f(\theta) = 4^{\sqrt{\theta}}$

36. $f(x) = 4^{(3^x)}$

37. $y = \dfrac{2^x}{x}$

38. An animal population is given by $P(t) = 300(1.044)^t$ where t is the number of years since the study of the population began. Find $P'(5)$ and interpret your result.

39. With a yearly inflation rate of 5%, prices are given by

$$P = P_0(1.05)^t,$$

where P_0 is the price in dollars when $t = 0$ and t is time in years. Suppose $P_0 = 1$. How fast (in cents/year) are prices rising when $t = 10$?

40. The value of an automobile purchased in 2009 can be approximated by the function $V(t) = 25(0.85)^t$, where t is the time, in years, from the date of purchase, and $V(t)$ is the value, in thousands of dollars.

   (a) Evaluate and interpret $V(4)$, including units.
   (b) Find an expression for $V'(t)$, including units.
   (c) Evaluate and interpret $V'(4)$, including units.
   (d) Use $V(t)$, $V'(t)$, and any other considerations you think are relevant to write a paragraph in support of or in opposition to the following statement: "From a monetary point of view, it is best to keep this vehicle as long as possible."

41. In 2009, the population of Mexico was 111 million and growing 1.13% annually, while the population of the US was 307 million and growing 0.975% annually.[1] If we measure growth rates in people/year, which population was growing faster in 2009?

42. Some antique furniture increased very rapidly in price over the past decade. For example, the price of a particular rocking chair is well approximated by

$$V = 75(1.35)^t,$$

where V is in dollars and t is in years since 2000. Find the rate, in dollars per year, at which the price is increasing at time t.

43. **(a)** Find the slope of the graph of $f(x) = 1 - e^x$ at the point where it crosses the x-axis.
   (b) Find the equation of the tangent line to the curve at this point.
   (c) Find the equation of the line perpendicular to the tangent line at this point. (This is the *normal* line.)

44. Find the value of c in Figure 3.12, where the line l tangent to the graph of $y = 2^x$ at $(0, 1)$ intersects the x-axis.

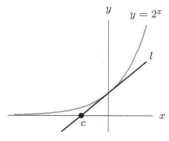

Figure 3.12

[1] https://www.cia.gov/library/publications/the-world-factbook/print/ms.html and https://www.cia.gov/library/publications/the-world-factbook/print/us.html, accessed 4/14/09.

45. Find the quadratic polynomial $g(x) = ax^2 + bx + c$ which best fits the function $f(x) = e^x$ at $x = 0$, in the sense that

$$g(0) = f(0), \quad \text{and} \quad g'(0) = f'(0), \quad \text{and} \quad g''(0) = f''(0).$$

Using a computer or calculator, sketch graphs of f and g on the same axes. What do you notice?

46. Using the equation of the tangent line to the graph of e^x at $x = 0$, show that

$$e^x \geq 1 + x$$

for all values of x. A sketch may be helpful.

47. For what value(s) of a are $y = a^x$ and $y = 1 + x$ tangent at $x = 0$? Explain.

48. Explain for which values of a the function a^x is increasing and for which values it is decreasing. Use the fact that, for $a > 0$,

$$\frac{d}{dx}(a^x) = (\ln a)a^x.$$

Strengthen Your Understanding

In Problems 49–50, explain what is wrong with the statement.

49. The derivative of $f(x) = 2^x$ is $f'(x) = x2^{x-1}$.

50. The derivative of $f(x) = \pi^e$ is $f'(x) = e\pi^{e-1}$.

In Problems 51–52, give an example of:

51. An exponential function for which the derivative is always negative.

52. A function f such that $f'''(x) = f(x)$.

Are the statements in Problems 53–55 true or false? Give an explanation for your answer.

53. If $f(x)$ is increasing, then $f'(x)$ is increasing.

54. There is no function such that $f'(x) = f(x)$ for all x.

55. If $f(x)$ is defined for all x, then $f'(x)$ is defined for all x.

3.3   THE PRODUCT AND QUOTIENT RULES

We now know how to find derivatives of powers and exponentials, and of sums and constant multiples of functions. This section shows how to find the derivatives of products and quotients.

Using Δ Notation

To express the difference quotients of general functions, some additional notation is helpful. We write Δf, read "delta f," for a small change in the value of f at the point x,

$$\Delta f = f(x + h) - f(x).$$

In this notation, the derivative is the limit of the ratio $\Delta f / h$:

$$f'(x) = \lim_{h \to 0} \frac{\Delta f}{h}.$$

The Product Rule

Suppose we know the derivatives of $f(x)$ and $g(x)$ and want to calculate the derivative of the product, $f(x)g(x)$. The derivative of the product is calculated by taking the limit, namely,

$$\frac{d[f(x)g(x)]}{dx} = \lim_{h \to 0} \frac{f(x + h)g(x + h) - f(x)g(x)}{h}.$$

To picture the quantity $f(x + h)g(x + h) - f(x)g(x)$, imagine the rectangle with sides $f(x + h)$ and $g(x + h)$ in Figure 3.13, where $\Delta f = f(x + h) - f(x)$ and $\Delta g = g(x + h) - g(x)$. Then

$$f(x + h)g(x + h) - f(x)g(x) = (\text{Area of whole rectangle}) - (\text{Unshaded area})$$
$$= \text{Area of the three shaded rectangles}$$
$$= \Delta f \cdot g(x) + f(x) \cdot \Delta g + \Delta f \cdot \Delta g.$$

Now divide by h:

$$\frac{f(x+h)g(x+h) - f(x)g(x)}{h} = \frac{\Delta f}{h} \cdot g(x) + f(x) \cdot \frac{\Delta g}{h} + \frac{\Delta f \cdot \Delta g}{h}.$$

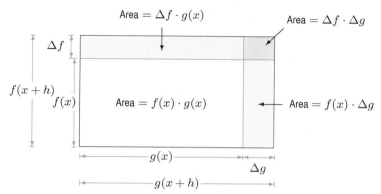

Figure 3.13: Illustration for the product rule (with Δf, Δg positive)

To evaluate the limit as $h \to 0$, we examine the three terms on the right separately. Notice that

$$\lim_{h \to 0} \frac{\Delta f}{h} \cdot g(x) = f'(x)g(x) \quad \text{and} \quad \lim_{h \to 0} f(x) \cdot \frac{\Delta g}{h} = f(x)g'(x).$$

In the third term we multiply the top and bottom by h to get $\dfrac{\Delta f}{h} \cdot \dfrac{\Delta g}{h} \cdot h$. Then,

$$\lim_{h \to 0} \frac{\Delta f \cdot \Delta g}{h} = \lim_{h \to 0} \frac{\Delta f}{h} \cdot \frac{\Delta g}{h} \cdot h = \lim_{h \to 0} \frac{\Delta f}{h} \cdot \lim_{h \to 0} \frac{\Delta g}{h} \cdot \lim_{h \to 0} h = f'(x) \cdot g'(x) \cdot 0 = 0.$$

Therefore, we conclude that

$$\lim_{h \to 0} \frac{f(x+h)g(x+h) - f(x)g(x)}{h} = \lim_{h \to 0} \left(\frac{\Delta f}{h} \cdot g(x) + f(x) \cdot \frac{\Delta g}{h} + \frac{\Delta f \cdot \Delta g}{h} \right)$$

$$= \lim_{h \to 0} \frac{\Delta f}{h} \cdot g(x) + \lim_{h \to 0} f(x) \cdot \frac{\Delta g}{h} + \lim_{h \to 0} \frac{\Delta f \cdot \Delta g}{h}$$

$$= f'(x)g(x) + f(x)g'(x).$$

Thus we have proved the following rule:

Theorem 3.3: The Product Rule

If $u = f(x)$ and $v = g(x)$ are differentiable, then

$$(fg)' = f'g + fg'.$$

The product rule can also be written

$$\frac{d(uv)}{dx} = \frac{du}{dx} \cdot v + u \cdot \frac{dv}{dx}.$$

In words:

> The derivative of a product is the derivative of the first times the second plus the first times the derivative of the second.

Another justification of the product rule is given in Problem 41 on page 174.

Example 1   Differentiate (a) $x^2 e^x$,   (b) $(3x^2 + 5x)e^x$,   (c) $\dfrac{e^x}{x^2}$.

Solution   (a)

$$\frac{d(x^2 e^x)}{dx} = \left(\frac{d(x^2)}{dx}\right)e^x + x^2\frac{d(e^x)}{dx} = 2xe^x + x^2 e^x = (2x + x^2)e^x.$$

(b)

$$\frac{d((3x^2 + 5x)e^x)}{dx} = \left(\frac{d(3x^2 + 5x)}{dx}\right)e^x + (3x^2 + 5x)\frac{d(e^x)}{dx}$$
$$= (6x + 5)e^x + (3x^2 + 5x)e^x = (3x^2 + 11x + 5)e^x.$$

(c) First we must write $\dfrac{e^x}{x^2}$ as the product $x^{-2}e^x$:

$$\frac{d}{dx}\left(\frac{e^x}{x^2}\right) = \frac{d(x^{-2}e^x)}{dx} = \left(\frac{d(x^{-2})}{dx}\right)e^x + x^{-2}\frac{d(e^x)}{dx}$$
$$= -2x^{-3}e^x + x^{-2}e^x = (-2x^{-3} + x^{-2})e^x.$$

The Quotient Rule

Suppose we want to differentiate a function of the form $Q(x) = f(x)/g(x)$. (Of course, we have to avoid points where $g(x) = 0$.) We want a formula for Q' in terms of f' and g'.

Assuming that $Q(x)$ is differentiable, we can use the product rule on $f(x) = Q(x)g(x)$:

$$f'(x) = Q'(x)g(x) + Q(x)g'(x)$$
$$= Q'(x)g(x) + \frac{f(x)}{g(x)}g'(x).$$

Solving for $Q'(x)$ gives

$$Q'(x) = \frac{f'(x) - \dfrac{f(x)}{g(x)}g'(x)}{g(x)}.$$

Multiplying the top and bottom by $g(x)$ to simplify gives

$$\frac{d}{dx}\left(\frac{f(x)}{g(x)}\right) = \frac{f'(x)g(x) - f(x)g'(x)}{(g(x))^2}.$$

So we have the following rule:

Theorem 3.4: The Quotient Rule

If $u = f(x)$ and $v = g(x)$ are differentiable, then

$$\left(\frac{f}{g}\right)' = \frac{f'g - fg'}{g^2},$$

or equivalently,

$$\frac{d}{dx}\left(\frac{u}{v}\right) = \frac{\dfrac{du}{dx}\cdot v - u\cdot\dfrac{dv}{dx}}{v^2}.$$

In words:

The derivative of a quotient is the derivative of the numerator times the denominator minus the numerator times the derivative of the denominator, all over the denominator squared.

Example 2   Differentiate (a) $\dfrac{5x^2}{x^3+1}$,   (b) $\dfrac{1}{1+e^x}$,   (c) $\dfrac{e^x}{x^2}$.

Solution   (a)

$$\frac{d}{dx}\left(\frac{5x^2}{x^3+1}\right) = \frac{\left(\frac{d}{dx}(5x^2)\right)(x^3+1) - 5x^2\frac{d}{dx}(x^3+1)}{(x^3+1)^2} = \frac{10x(x^3+1) - 5x^2(3x^2)}{(x^3+1)^2}$$

$$= \frac{-5x^4+10x}{(x^3+1)^2}.$$

(b)

$$\frac{d}{dx}\left(\frac{1}{1+e^x}\right) = \frac{\left(\frac{d}{dx}(1)\right)(1+e^x) - 1\frac{d}{dx}(1+e^x)}{(1+e^x)^2} = \frac{0(1+e^x) - 1(0+e^x)}{(1+e^x)^2}$$

$$= \frac{-e^x}{(1+e^x)^2}.$$

(c) This is the same as part (c) of Example 1, but this time we do it by the quotient rule.

$$\frac{d}{dx}\left(\frac{e^x}{x^2}\right) = \frac{\left(\frac{d(e^x)}{dx}\right)x^2 - e^x\left(\frac{d(x^2)}{dx}\right)}{(x^2)^2} = \frac{e^x x^2 - e^x(2x)}{x^4}$$

$$= e^x\left(\frac{x^2-2x}{x^4}\right) = e^x\left(\frac{x-2}{x^3}\right).$$

This is, in fact, the same answer as before, although it looks different. Can you show that it is the same?

Exercises and Problems for Section 3.3

Exercises

1. If $f(x) = x^2(x^3+5)$, find $f'(x)$ two ways: by using the product rule and by multiplying out before taking the derivative. Do you get the same result? Should you?

2. If $f(x) = 2^x \cdot 3^x$, find $f'(x)$ two ways: by using the product rule and by using the fact that $2^x \cdot 3^x = 6^x$. Do you get the same result?

For Exercises 3–30, find the derivative. It may be to your advantage to simplify first. Assume that a, b, c, and k are constants.

3. $f(x) = xe^x$

4. $y = x \cdot 2^x$

5. $y = \sqrt{x} \cdot 2^x$

6. $y = (t^2+3)e^t$

7. $f(x) = (x^2 - \sqrt{x})3^x$

8. $y = (t^3 - 7t^2 + 1)e^t$

9. $f(x) = \dfrac{x}{e^x}$

10. $g(x) = \dfrac{25x^2}{e^x}$

11. $y = \dfrac{t+1}{2^t}$

12. $g(w) = \dfrac{w^{3.2}}{5^w}$

13. $q(r) = \dfrac{3r}{5r+2}$

14. $g(t) = \dfrac{t-4}{t+4}$

15. $z = \dfrac{3t+1}{5t+2}$

16. $z = \dfrac{t^2+5t+2}{t+3}$

17. $f(t) = 2te^t - \dfrac{1}{\sqrt{t}}$

18. $f(x) = \dfrac{x^2+3}{x}$

19. $w = \dfrac{y^3 - 6y^2 + 7y}{y}$

20. $g(t) = \dfrac{4}{3+\sqrt{t}}$

21. $f(z) = \dfrac{z^2+1}{\sqrt{z}}$

22. $w = \dfrac{5-3z}{5+3z}$

23. $h(r) = \dfrac{r^2}{2r+1}$

24. $f(z) = \dfrac{3z^2}{5z^2+7z}$

25. $w(x) = \dfrac{17e^x}{2^x}$

26. $h(p) = \dfrac{1+p^2}{3+2p^2}$

27. $f(x) = \dfrac{x^2+3x+2}{x+1}$

28. $f(x) = \dfrac{ax+b}{cx+k}$

29. $y = \left(x^2+5\right)^3 \left(3x^3-2\right)^2$

30. $f(x) = (2-4x-3x^2)(6x^e - 3\pi)$

Problems

In Problems 31–33, use Figure 3.14 and the product or quotient rule to estimate the derivative, or state why the rules of this section do not apply. The graph of $f(x)$ has a sharp corner at $x = 2$.

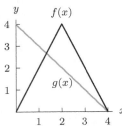

Figure 3.14

31. Let $h(x) = f(x) \cdot g(x)$. Find:

(a) $h'(1)$ (b) $h'(2)$ (c) $h'(3)$

32. Let $k(x) = (f(x))/(g(x))$. Find:

(a) $k'(1)$ (b) $k'(2)$ (c) $k'(3)$

33. Let $j(x) = (g(x))/(f(x))$. Find:

(a) $j'(1)$ (b) $j'(2)$ (c) $j'(3)$

For Problems 34–39, let $h(x) = f(x) \cdot g(x)$, and $k(x) = f(x)/g(x)$, and $l(x) = g(x)/f(x)$. Use Figure 3.15 to estimate the derivatives.

  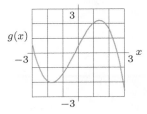

Figure 3.15

34. $h'(1)$ **35.** $k'(1)$ **36.** $h'(2)$

37. $k'(2)$ **38.** $l'(1)$ **39.** $l'(2)$

40. Differentiate $f(t) = e^{-t}$ by writing it as $f(t) = \dfrac{1}{e^t}$.

41. Differentiate $f(x) = e^{2x}$ by writing it as $f(x) = e^x \cdot e^x$.

42. Differentiate $f(x) = e^{3x}$ by writing it as $f(x) = e^x \cdot e^{2x}$ and using the result of Problem 41.

43. For what intervals is $f(x) = xe^x$ concave up?

44. For what intervals is $g(x) = \dfrac{1}{x^2 + 1}$ concave down?

45. Find the equation of the tangent line to the graph of $f(x) = \dfrac{2x - 5}{x + 1}$ at the point at which $x = 0$.

46. Find the equation of the tangent line at $x = 1$ to $y = f(x)$ where $f(x) = \dfrac{3x^2}{5x^2 + 7x}$.

47. (a) Differentiate $y = \dfrac{e^x}{x}$, $y = \dfrac{e^x}{x^2}$, and $y = \dfrac{e^x}{x^3}$.

(b) What do you anticipate the derivative of $y = \dfrac{e^x}{x^n}$ will be? Confirm your guess.

In Problems 48–51, the functions $f(x)$, $g(x)$, and $h(x)$ are differentiable for all values of x. Find the derivative of each of the following functions, using symbols such as $f(x)$ and $f'(x)$ in your answers as necessary.

48. $x^2 f(x)$ **49.** $4^x(f(x) + g(x))$

50. $\dfrac{f(x)}{g(x) + 1}$ **51.** $\dfrac{f(x)g(x)}{h(x)}$

52. Suppose f and g are differentiable functions with the values shown in the following table. For each of the following functions h, find $h'(2)$.

(a) $h(x) = f(x) + g(x)$ (b) $h(x) = f(x)g(x)$

(c) $h(x) = \dfrac{f(x)}{g(x)}$

x	$f(x)$	$g(x)$	$f'(x)$	$g'(x)$
2	3	4	5	-2

53. If $H(3) = 1, H'(3) = 3, F(3) = 5, F'(3) = 4$, find:

(a) $G'(3)$ if $G(z) = F(z) \cdot H(z)$
(b) $G'(3)$ if $G(w) = F(w)/H(w)$

54. Let $f(3) = 6, g(3) = 12, f'(3) = \frac{1}{2}$, and $g'(3) = \frac{4}{3}$. Evaluate the following when $x = 3$.

$$(f(x)g(x))' - (g(x) - 4f'(x))$$

55. Find a possible formula for a function $y = f(x)$ such that $f'(x) = 10x^9 e^x + x^{10}e^x$.

56. The quantity, q, of a certain skateboard sold depends on the selling price, p, in dollars, so we write $q = f(p)$. You are given that $f(140) = 15{,}000$ and $f'(140) = -100$.

(a) What do $f(140) = 15{,}000$ and $f'(140) = -100$ tell you about the sales of skateboards?

(b) The total revenue, R, earned by the sale of skateboards is given by $R = pq$. Find $\left.\dfrac{dR}{dp}\right|_{p=140}$.

(c) What is the sign of $\left.\dfrac{dR}{dp}\right|_{p=140}$? If the skateboards are currently selling for $140, what happens to revenue if the price is increased to $141?

57. When an electric current passes through two resistors with resistance r_1 and r_2, connected in parallel, the combined resistance, R, can be calculated from the equation

$$\frac{1}{R} = \frac{1}{r_1} + \frac{1}{r_2}.$$

Find the rate at which the combined resistance changes with respect to changes in r_1. Assume that r_2 is constant.

58. A museum has decided to sell one of its paintings and to invest the proceeds. If the picture is sold between the years 2000 and 2020 and the money from the sale is invested in a bank account earning 5% interest per year compounded annually, then $B(t)$, the balance in the year 2020, depends on the year, t, in which the painting is sold and the sale price $P(t)$. If t is measured from the year 2000 so that $0 < t < 20$ then

$$B(t) = P(t)(1.05)^{20-t}.$$

(a) Explain why $B(t)$ is given by this formula.
(b) Show that the formula for $B(t)$ is equivalent to

$$B(t) = (1.05)^{20}\frac{P(t)}{(1.05)^t}.$$

(c) Find $B'(10)$, given that $P(10) = 150{,}000$ and $P'(10) = 5000$.

59. Let $f(v)$ be the gas consumption (in liters/km) of a car going at velocity v (in km/hr). In other words, $f(v)$ tells you how many liters of gas the car uses to go one kilometer, if it is going at velocity v. You are told that

$$f(80) = 0.05 \text{ and } f'(80) = 0.0005.$$

(a) Let $g(v)$ be the distance the same car goes on one liter of gas at velocity v. What is the relationship between $f(v)$ and $g(v)$? Find $g(80)$ and $g'(80)$.
(b) Let $h(v)$ be the gas consumption in liters per hour. In other words, $h(v)$ tells you how many liters of gas the car uses in one hour if it is going at velocity v. What is the relationship between $h(v)$ and $f(v)$? Find $h(80)$ and $h'(80)$.
(c) How would you explain the practical meaning of the values of these functions and their derivatives to a driver who knows no calculus?

60. The function $f(x) = e^x$ has the properties

$$f'(x) = f(x) \text{ and } f(0) = 1.$$

Explain why $f(x)$ is the only function with both these properties. [Hint: Assume $g'(x) = g(x)$, and $g(0) = 1$, for some function $g(x)$. Define $h(x) = g(x)/e^x$, and compute $h'(x)$. Then use the fact that a function with a derivative of 0 must be a constant function.]

61. Find $f'(x)$ for the following functions with the product rule, rather than by multiplying out.

(a) $f(x) = (x-1)(x-2)$.
(b) $f(x) = (x-1)(x-2)(x-3)$.
(c) $f(x) = (x-1)(x-2)(x-3)(x-4)$.

62. Use the answer from Problem 61 to guess $f'(x)$ for the following function:

$$f(x) = (x-r_1)(x-r_2)(x-r_3)\cdots(x-r_n)$$

where $r_1, r_2, \ldots, r_n$ are any real numbers.

63. **(a)** Provide a three-dimensional analogue for the geometrical demonstration of the formula for the derivative of a product, given in Figure 3.13 on page 137. In other words, find a formula for the derivative of $F(x) \cdot G(x) \cdot H(x)$ using Figure 3.16.
(b) Confirm your results by writing $F(x) \cdot G(x) \cdot H(x)$ as $[F(x) \cdot G(x)] \cdot H(x)$ and using the product rule twice.
(c) Generalize your result to n functions: what is the derivative of

$$f_1(x) \cdot f_2(x) \cdot f_3(x) \cdots f_n(x)?$$

Figure 3.16: A graphical representation of the three-dimensional product rule

64. If $P(x) = (x-a)^2 Q(x)$, where $Q(x)$ is a polynomial and $Q(a) \neq 0$, we call $x = a$ a double zero of the polynomial $P(x)$.

(a) If $x = a$ is a double zero of a polynomial $P(x)$, show that $P(a) = P'(a) = 0$.
(b) If $P(x)$ is a polynomial and $P(a) = P'(a) = 0$, show that $x = a$ is a double zero of $P(x)$.

65. Find and simplify $\dfrac{d^2}{dx^2}(f(x)g(x))$.

Strengthen Your Understanding

In Problems 66–68, explain what is wrong with the statement.

66. The derivative of $f(x) = x^2 e^x$ is $f'(x) = 2xe^x$.

67. Differentiating $f(x) = x/(x+1)$ by the quotient rule

gives

$$f'(x) = \frac{x\frac{d}{dx}(x+1) - (x+1)\frac{d}{dx}(x)}{(x+1)^2}.$$

68. The quotient $f(x) = (x+1)/e^{-x}$ cannot be differentiated using the product rule.

In Problems 69–70, give an example of:

69. A function involving a sine and an exponential that can be differentiated using the product rule or the quotient rule.

70. A function $f(x)$ that can be differentiated both using the product rule and in some other way.

Are the statements in Problems 71–73 true or false? Give an explanation for your answer.

71. Let f and g be two functions whose second derivatives are defined. Then

$$(fg)'' = fg'' + f''g.$$

72. If the function $f(x)/g(x)$ is defined but not differentiable at $x = 1$, then either $f(x)$ or $g(x)$ is not differentiable at $x = 1$.

73. Suppose that f'' and g'' exist and f and g are concave up for all x, then $f(x)g(x)$ is concave up for all x.

74. Which of the following would be a counterexample to the product rule?

(a) Two differentiable functions f and g satisfying $(fg)' = f'g'$.

(b) A differentiable function f such that $(xf(x))' = xf'(x) + f(x)$.

(c) A differentiable function f such that $(f(x)^2)' = 2f(x)$.

(d) Two differentiable functions f and g such that $f'(a) = 0$ and $g'(a) = 0$ and fg has positive slope at $x = a$.

3.4 THE CHAIN RULE

The chain rule enables us to differentiate composite functions such as $\sqrt{x^2 + 1}$ or e^{-x^2}. Before seeing a formula, let's think about the derivative of a composite function in a practical situation.

Intuition Behind the Chain Rule

Imagine we are moving straight upward in a hot air balloon. Let y be our distance from the ground. The temperature, H, is changing as a function of altitude, so $H = f(y)$. How does our temperature change with time?

The rate of change of our temperature is affected both by how fast the temperature is changing with altitude (about $16°F$ per mile), and by how fast we are climbing (say 2 mph). Then our temperature changes by $16°$ for every mile we climb, and since we move 2 miles in an hour, our temperature changes by $16 \cdot 2 = 32$ degrees in an hour.

Since temperature is a function of height, $H = f(y)$, and height is a function of time, $y = g(t)$, we can think of temperature as a composite function of time, $H = f(g(t))$, with f as the outside function and g as the inside function. The example suggests the following result, which turns out to be true:

Rate of change of composite function	=	Rate of change of outside function	×	Rate of change of inside function

The Derivative of a Composition of Functions

We now obtain a formula for the chain rule. Suppose $f(g(x))$ is a composite function, with f being the outside function and g being the inside. Let us write

$$z = g(x) \quad \text{and} \quad y = f(z), \quad \text{so} \quad y = f(g(x)).$$

Then a small change in x, called Δx, generates a small change in z, called Δz. In turn, Δz generates a small change in y called Δy. Provided Δx and Δz are not zero, we can say:

$$\frac{\Delta y}{\Delta x} = \frac{\Delta y}{\Delta z} \cdot \frac{\Delta z}{\Delta x}.$$

Since $\dfrac{dy}{dx} = \lim\limits_{\Delta x \to 0} \dfrac{\Delta y}{\Delta x}$, this suggests that in the limit as Δx, Δy, and Δz get smaller and smaller, we have:

The Chain Rule

$$\frac{dy}{dx} = \frac{dy}{dz} \cdot \frac{dz}{dx}.$$

In other words:

The rate of change of a composite function is the product of the rates of change of the outside and inside functions.

Since $\dfrac{dy}{dz} = f'(z)$ and $\dfrac{dz}{dx} = g'(x)$, we can also write

$$\frac{d}{dx} f(g(x)) = f'(z) \cdot g'(x).$$

Substituting $z = g(x)$, we can rewrite this as follows:

Theorem 3.5: The Chain Rule

If f and g are differentiable functions, then

$$\frac{d}{dx} f(g(x)) = f'(g(x)) \cdot g'(x).$$

In words:

The derivative of a composite function is the product of the derivatives of the outside and inside functions. The derivative of the outside function must be evaluated at the inside function.

A justification of the chain rule is given in Problem 42 on page 175. The following example shows how units confirm that the rate of change of a composite function is the product of the rates of change of the outside and inside functions.

Example 1   The length, L, in micrometers (μm), of steel depends on the air temperature, $H°C$, and the temperature H depends on time, t, measured in hours. If the length of a steel bridge increases by 0.2 μm for every degree increase in temperature, and the temperature is increasing at 3°C per hour, how fast is the length of the bridge increasing? What are the units for your answer?

Solution   We want to know how much the length of the bridge changes in one hour; this rate is in μm/hr. We are told that the length of the bridge changes by 0.2 μm for each degree that the temperature changes, and that the temperature changes by 3°C each hour. Thus, in one hour, the length of the bridge changes by $0.2 \cdot 3 = 0.6$ μm.

Now we do the same calculation using derivative notation and the chain rule. We know that

$$\text{Rate length increasing with respect to temperature} = \frac{dL}{dH} = 0.2 \ \mu\text{m}/°\text{C}$$

$$\text{Rate temperature increasing with respect to time} = \frac{dH}{dt} = 3°\text{C/hr}.$$

We want to calculate the rate at which the length is increasing with respect to time, or dL/dt. We think of L as a function of H, and H as a function of t. The chain rule tells us that

$$\frac{dL}{dt} = \frac{dL}{dH} \cdot \frac{dH}{dt} = \left(0.2 \frac{\mu\text{m}}{°\text{C}}\right) \cdot \left(3 \frac{°\text{C}}{\text{hr}}\right) = 0.6 \ \mu\text{m/hr}.$$

Thus, the length is increasing at 0.6 μm/hr. Notice that the units work out as we expect.

Example 1 shows us how to interpret the chain rule in practical terms. The next examples show how the chain rule is used to compute derivatives of functions given by formulas.

Example 2　Find the derivatives of the following functions:

(a)　$(x^2 + 1)^{100}$　　(b)　$\sqrt{3x^2 + 5x - 2}$　　(c)　$\dfrac{1}{x^2 + x^4}$　　(d)　e^{3x}　　(e)　e^{x^2}

Solution　(a) Here $z = g(x) = x^2 + 1$ is the inside function; $f(z) = z^{100}$ is the outside function. Now $g'(x) = 2x$ and $f'(z) = 100z^{99}$, so

$$\frac{d}{dx}((x^2 + 1)^{100}) = 100z^{99} \cdot 2x = 100(x^2 + 1)^{99} \cdot 2x = 200x(x^2 + 1)^{99}.$$

(b) Here $z = g(x) = 3x^2 + 5x - 2$ and $f(z) = \sqrt{z}$, so $g'(x) = 6x + 5$ and $f'(z) = \dfrac{1}{2\sqrt{z}}$. Hence

$$\frac{d}{dx}(\sqrt{3x^2 + 5x - 2}) = \frac{1}{2\sqrt{z}} \cdot (6x + 5) = \frac{1}{2\sqrt{3x^2 + 5x - 2}} \cdot (6x + 5).$$

(c) Let $z = g(x) = x^2 + x^4$ and $f(z) = 1/z$, so $g'(x) = 2x + 4x^3$ and $f'(z) = -z^{-2} = -\dfrac{1}{z^2}$. Then

$$\frac{d}{dx}\left(\frac{1}{x^2 + x^4}\right) = -\frac{1}{z^2}(2x + 4x^3) = -\frac{2x + 4x^3}{(x^2 + x^4)^2}.$$

We could have done this problem using the quotient rule. Try it and see that you get the same answer!

(d) Let $z = g(x) = 3x$ and $f(z) = e^z$. Then $g'(x) = 3$ and $f'(z) = e^z$, so

$$\frac{d}{dx}\left(e^{3x}\right) = e^z \cdot 3 = 3e^{3x}.$$

(e) To figure out which is the inside function and which is the outside, notice that to evaluate e^{x^2} we first evaluate x^2 and then take e to that power. This tells us that the inside function is $z = g(x) = x^2$ and the outside function is $f(z) = e^z$. Therefore, $g'(x) = 2x$, and $f'(z) = e^z$, giving

$$\frac{d}{dx}(e^{x^2}) = e^z \cdot 2x = e^{x^2} \cdot 2x = 2xe^{x^2}.$$

To differentiate a complicated function, we may have to use the chain rule more than once, as in the following example.

Example 3　Differentiate: (a)　$\sqrt{e^{-x/7} + 5}$　　(b)　$(1 - e^{2\sqrt{t}})^{19}$

Solution　(a) Let $z = g(x) = e^{-x/7} + 5$ be the inside function; let $f(z) = \sqrt{z}$ be the outside function. Now $f'(z) = \dfrac{1}{2\sqrt{z}}$, but we need the chain rule to find $g'(x)$.

We choose inside and outside functions whose composition is $g(x)$. Let $u = h(x) = -x/7$ and $k(u) = e^u + 5$ so $g(x) = k(h(x)) = e^{-x/7} + 5$. Then $h'(x) = -1/7$ and $k'(u) = e^u$, so

$$g'(x) = e^u \cdot \left(-\frac{1}{7}\right) = -\frac{1}{7}e^{-x/7}.$$

Using the chain rule to combine the derivatives of $f(z)$ and $g(x)$, we have

$$\frac{d}{dx}(\sqrt{e^{-x/7} + 5}) = \frac{1}{2\sqrt{z}}\left(-\frac{1}{7}e^{-x/7}\right) = -\frac{e^{-x/7}}{14\sqrt{e^{-x/7} + 5}}.$$

(b) Let $z = g(t) = 1 - e^{2\sqrt{t}}$ be the inside function and $f(z) = z^{19}$ be the outside function. Then $f'(z) = 19z^{18}$ but we need the chain rule to differentiate $g(t)$.

Now we choose $u = h(t) = 2\sqrt{t}$ and $k(u) = 1 - e^u$, so $g(t) = k(h(t))$. Then $h'(t) = 2 \cdot \dfrac{1}{2} t^{-1/2} = \dfrac{1}{\sqrt{t}}$ and $k'(u) = -e^u$, so

$$g'(t) = -e^u \cdot \frac{1}{\sqrt{t}} = -\frac{e^{2\sqrt{t}}}{\sqrt{t}}.$$

Using the chain rule to combine the derivatives of $f(z)$ and $g(t)$, we have

$$\frac{d}{dx}(1 - e^{2\sqrt{t}})^{19} = 19z^{18}\left(-\frac{e^{2\sqrt{t}}}{\sqrt{t}}\right) = -19\frac{e^{2\sqrt{t}}}{\sqrt{t}}\left(1 - e^{2\sqrt{t}}\right)^{18}.$$

It is often faster to use the chain rule without introducing new variables, as in the following examples.

Example 4   Differentiate $\sqrt{1 + e^{\sqrt{3+x^2}}}$.

Solution   The chain rule is needed four times:

$$\frac{d}{dx}\left(\sqrt{1 + e^{\sqrt{3+x^2}}}\right) = \frac{1}{2}\left(1 + e^{\sqrt{3+x^2}}\right)^{-1/2} \cdot \frac{d}{dx}\left(1 + e^{\sqrt{3+x^2}}\right)$$

$$= \frac{1}{2}\left(1 + e^{\sqrt{3+x^2}}\right)^{-1/2} \cdot e^{\sqrt{3+x^2}} \cdot \frac{d}{dx}\left(\sqrt{3 + x^2}\right)$$

$$= \frac{1}{2}\left(1 + e^{\sqrt{3+x^2}}\right)^{-1/2} \cdot e^{\sqrt{3+x^2}} \cdot \frac{1}{2}\left(3 + x^2\right)^{-1/2} \cdot \frac{d}{dx}\left(3 + x^2\right)$$

$$= \frac{1}{2}\left(1 + e^{\sqrt{3+x^2}}\right)^{-1/2} \cdot e^{\sqrt{3+x^2}} \cdot \frac{1}{2}\left(3 + x^2\right)^{-1/2} \cdot 2x.$$

Example 5   Find the derivative of e^{2x} by the chain rule and by the product rule.

Solution   Using the chain rule, we have

$$\frac{d}{dx}(e^{2x}) = e^{2x} \cdot \frac{d}{dx}(2x) = e^{2x} \cdot 2 = 2e^{2x}.$$

Using the product rule, we write $e^{2x} = e^x \cdot e^x$. Then

$$\frac{d}{dx}(e^{2x}) = \frac{d}{dx}(e^x e^x) = \left(\frac{d}{dx}(e^x)\right)e^x + e^x\left(\frac{d}{dx}(e^x)\right) = e^x \cdot e^x + e^x \cdot e^x = 2e^{2x}.$$

Using the Product and Chain Rules to Differentiate a Quotient

If you prefer, you can differentiate a quotient by the product and chain rules, instead of by the quotient rule. The resulting formulas may look different, but they will be equivalent.

Example 6   Find $k'(x)$ if $k(x) = \dfrac{x}{x^2 + 1}$.

Solution   One way is to use the quotient rule:

$$k'(x) = \frac{1 \cdot (x^2 + 1) - x \cdot (2x)}{(x^2 + 1)^2}$$

$$= \frac{1 - x^2}{(x^2 + 1)^2}.$$

Alternatively, we can write the original function as a product,

$$k(x) = x\frac{1}{x^2+1} = x \cdot (x^2+1)^{-1},$$

and use the product rule:

$$k'(x) = 1 \cdot (x^2+1)^{-1} + x \cdot \frac{d}{dx}\left[(x^2+1)^{-1}\right].$$

Now use the chain rule to differentiate $(x^2+1)^{-1}$, giving

$$\frac{d}{dx}\left[(x^2+1)^{-1}\right] = -(x^2+1)^{-2} \cdot 2x = \frac{-2x}{(x^2+1)^2}.$$

Therefore,

$$k'(x) = \frac{1}{x^2+1} + x \cdot \frac{-2x}{(x^2+1)^2} = \frac{1}{x^2+1} - \frac{2x^2}{(x^2+1)^2}.$$

Putting these two fractions over a common denominator gives the same answer as the quotient rule.

Exercises and Problems for Section 3.4

Exercises

In Exercises 1–56, find the derivatives. Assume that a and b are constants.

1. $f(x) = (x+1)^{99}$

2. $w = (t^3+1)^{100}$

3. $g(x) = (4x^2+1)^7$

4. $f(x) = \sqrt{1-x^2}$

5. $y = \sqrt{e^x+1}$

6. $w = (\sqrt{t}+1)^{100}$

7. $h(w) = (w^4-2w)^5$

8. $s(t) = (3t^2+4t+1)^3$

9. $w(r) = \sqrt{r^4+1}$

10. $k(x) = (x^3+e^x)^4$

11. $f(x) = e^{2x}\left(x^2+5^x\right)$

12. $y = e^{3w/2}$

13. $g(x) = e^{\pi x}$

14. $B = 15e^{0.20t}$

15. $w = 100e^{-x^2}$

16. $f(\theta) = 2^{-\theta}$

17. $y = \pi^{(x+2)}$

18. $g(x) = 3^{(2x+7)}$

19. $f(t) = te^{5-2t}$

20. $p(t) = e^{4t+2}$

21. $v(t) = t^2 e^{-ct}$

22. $g(t) = e^{(1+3t)^2}$

23. $w = e^{\sqrt{s}}$

24. $y = e^{-4t}$

25. $y = \sqrt{s^3+1}$

26. $y = te^{-t^2}$

27. $f(z) = \sqrt{z}e^{-z}$

28. $z(x) = \sqrt[3]{2^x+5}$

29. $z = 2^{5t-3}$

30. $w = \sqrt{(x^2 \cdot 5^x)^3}$

31. $f(y) = \sqrt{10^{(5-y)}}$

32. $f(z) = \dfrac{\sqrt{z}}{e^z}$

33. $y = \dfrac{\sqrt{z}}{2^z}$

34. $y = \left(\dfrac{x^2+2}{3}\right)^2$

35. $h(x) = \sqrt{\dfrac{x^2+9}{x+3}}$

36. $y = \dfrac{e^x-e^{-x}}{e^x+e^{-x}}$

37. $y = \dfrac{1}{e^{3x}+x^2}$

38. $h(z) = \left(\dfrac{b}{a+z^2}\right)^4$

39. $f(x) = \dfrac{1}{\sqrt{x^3+1}}$

40. $f(z) = \dfrac{1}{(e^z+1)^2}$

41. $w = (t^2+3t)(1-e^{-2t})$

42. $h(x) = 2e^{e^{3x}}$

43. $f(x) = 6e^{5x}+e^{-x^2}$

44. $f(x) = e^{-(x-1)^2}$

45. $f(w) = (5w^2+3)e^{w^2}$

46. $f(\theta) = (e^\theta+e^{-\theta})^{-1}$

47. $y = \sqrt{e^{-3t^2}+5}$

48. $z = (te^{3t}+e^{5t})^9$

49. $f(y) = e^{e^{(y^2)}}$

50. $f(t) = 2e^{-2e^{2t}}$

51. $f(x) = (ax^2+b)^3$

52. $f(t) = ae^{bt}$

53. $f(x) = axe^{-bx}$

54. $g(\alpha) = e^{\alpha e^{-2\alpha}}$

55. $y = ae^{-be^{-cx}}$

56. $y = \left(e^x-e^{-x}\right)^2$

Problems

In Problems 57–60, use Figure 3.17 and the chain rule to estimate the derivative, or state why the chain rule does not apply. The graph of $f(x)$ has a sharp corner at $x = 2$.

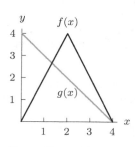

Figure 3.17

57. Let $h(x) = f(g(x))$. Find:

    (a) $h'(1)$ **(b)** $h'(2)$ **(c)** $h'(3)$

58. Let $u(x) = g(f(x))$. Find:

    (a) $u'(1)$ **(b)** $u'(2)$ **(c)** $u'(3)$

59. Let $v(x) = f(f(x))$. Find:

    (a) $v'(1)$ **(b)** $v'(2)$ **(c)** $v'(3)$

60. Let $w(x) = g(g(x))$. Find:

    (a) $w'(1)$ **(b)** $w'(2)$ **(c)** $w'(3)$

In Problems 61–64, use Figure 3.18 to evaluate the derivative.

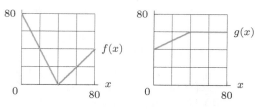

Figure 3.18

61. $\frac{d}{dx} f(g(x))\big|_{x=30}$ **62.** $\frac{d}{dx} f(g(x))\big|_{x=70}$

63. $\frac{d}{dx} g(f(x))\big|_{x=30}$ **64.** $\frac{d}{dx} g(f(x))\big|_{x=70}$

65. Find the equation of the tangent line to $f(x) = (x-1)^3$ at the point where $x = 2$.

66. Find the equation of the line tangent to $y = f(x)$ at $x = 1$, where $f(x)$ is the function in Exercise 43.

67. Find the equation of the line tangent to $f(t) = 100e^{-0.3t}$ at $t = 2$.

68. For what values of x is the graph of $y = e^{-x^2}$ concave down?

69. For what intervals is $f(x) = xe^{-x}$ concave down?

70. Suppose $f(x) = (2x + 1)^{10}(3x - 1)^7$. Find a formula for $f'(x)$. Decide on a reasonable way to simplify your result, and find a formula for $f''(x)$.

71. A fish population is approximated by $P(t) = 10e^{0.6t}$, where t is in months. Calculate and use units to explain what each of the following tells us about the population:

    (a) $P(12)$ **(b)** $P'(12)$

72. Find the mean and variance of the normal distribution of statistics using parts (a) and (b) with $m(t) = e^{\mu t + \sigma^2 t^2 / 2}$.

    (a) Mean $= m'(0)$

    (b) Variance $= m''(0) - (m'(0))^2$

73. If the derivative of $y = k(x)$ equals 2 when $x = 1$, what is the derivative of

    (a) $k(2x)$ when $x = \frac{1}{2}$?

    (b) $k(x + 1)$ when $x = 0$?

    (c) $k\left(\frac{1}{4}x\right)$ when $x = 4$?

74. Is $x = \sqrt[3]{2t + 5}$ a solution to the equation $3x^2 \dfrac{dx}{dt} = 2$? Why or why not?

75. Find a possible formula for a function $m(x)$ such that $m'(x) = x^5 \cdot e^{(x^6)}$.

76. Given $F(2) = 1, F'(2) = 5, F(4) = 3, F'(4) = 7$ and $G(4) = 2, G'(4) = 6, G(3) = 4, G'(3) = 8$, find:

    (a) $H(4)$ if $H(x) = F(G(x))$

    (b) $H'(4)$ if $H(x) = F(G(x))$

    (c) $H(4)$ if $H(x) = G(F(x))$

    (d) $H'(4)$ if $H(x) = G(F(x))$

    (e) $H'(4)$ if $H(x) = F(x)/G(x)$

77. Given $y = f(x)$ with $f(1) = 4$ and $f'(1) = 3$, find

    (a) $g'(1)$ if $g(x) = \sqrt{f(x)}$.

    (b) $h'(1)$ if $h(x) = f(\sqrt{x})$.

78. Figure 3.19 is the graph of $f(x)$. Let $h(x) = e^{f(x)}$ and $p(x) = f(e^x)$. Estimate the solution(s) to the equations

    (a) $h'(x) = 0$ **(b)** $p'(x) = 0$

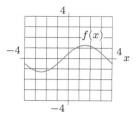

Figure 3.19

In Problems 79–83, use Figures 3.20 and 3.21 and $h(x) = f(g(x))$.

Figure 3.20

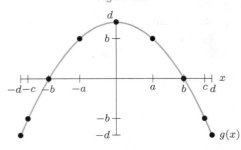

Figure 3.21

79. Evaluate $h(0)$ and $h'(0)$.

80. At $x = -c$, is h positive, negative, or zero? Increasing or decreasing?

81. At $x = a$, is h increasing or decreasing?

82. What are the signs of $h(d)$ and $h'(d)$?

83. How does the value of $h(x)$ change on the interval $-d < x < -b$?

84. The world's population[2] is about $f(t) = 6.91e^{0.011t}$ billion, where t is time in years since 2010. Find $f(0)$, $f'(0)$, $f(10)$, and $f'(10)$. Using units, interpret your answers in terms of population.

85. The 2010 Census[3] determined the population of the US was 308.75 million on April 1, 2010. If the population was increasing exponentially at a rate of 2.85 million per year on that date, find a formula for the population as a function of time, t, in years since that date.

86. Since the 1950s, the carbon dioxide concentration in the air has been recorded at the Mauna Loa Observatory in Hawaii.[4] A graph of this data is called the Keeling Curve, after Charles Keeling, who started recording the data. With t in years since 1950, fitting functions to the data gives three models for the carbon dioxide concentration in parts per million (ppm):

$$f(t) = 303 + 1.3t$$
$$g(t) = 304e^{0.0038t}$$
$$h(t) = 0.0135t^2 + 0.5133t + 310.5.$$

(a) What family of function is used in each model?
(b) Find the rate of change of carbon dioxide in 2010 in each of the three models. Give units.
(c) Arrange the three models in increasing order of the rates of change they give for 2010. (Which model predicts the largest rate of change in 2010? Which predicts the smallest?)
(d) Consider the same three models for all positive time t. Will the ordering in part (c) remain the same for all t? If not, how will it change?

87. Annual net sales for the Hershey Company, in billion dollars, in t years from 2008 can be approximated by $f(t) = 5.1e^{0.043t}$. Find $f(5)$ and $f'(5)$. Give units and interpret in terms of Hershey sales.

88. A yam is put in a hot oven, maintained at a constant temperature 200°C. At time $t = 30$ minutes, the temperature T of the yam is 120° and is increasing at an (instantaneous) rate of 2°/min. Newton's law of cooling (or, in our case, warming) implies that the temperature at time t is given by

$$T(t) = 200 - ae^{-bt}.$$

Find a and b.

89. If you invest P dollars in a bank account at an annual interest rate of $r\%$, then after t years you will have B dollars, where

$$B = P\left(1 + \frac{r}{100}\right)^t.$$

(a) Find dB/dt, assuming P and r are constant. In terms of money, what does dB/dt represent?
(b) Find dB/dr, assuming P and t are constant. In terms of money, what does dB/dr represent?

90. The balance in a bank account t years after money is deposited is given by $f(t) = 1000e^{0.08t}$ dollars.

(a) How much money was deposited? What is the interest rate earned by the account?
(b) Find $f(10)$ and $f'(10)$. Give units and interpret in terms of balance in the account.

91. The theory of relativity predicts that an object whose mass is m_0 when it is at rest will appear heavier when moving at speeds near the speed of light. When the object is moving at speed v, its mass m is given by

$$m = \frac{m_0}{\sqrt{1 - (v^2/c^2)}}, \qquad \text{where } c \text{ is the speed of light.}$$

(a) Find dm/dv.
(b) In terms of physics, what does dm/dv tell you?

---

[2]http://www.indexmundi.com/world/. Accessed April 27, 2011.
[3]http://2010.census.gov/2010census/
[4]www.esrl.hoaa.gov/gmd/ccgg

92. The charge, Q, on a capacitor which starts discharging at time $t = 0$ is given by

$$Q = \begin{cases} Q_0 & \text{for } t \leq 0 \\ Q_0 e^{-t/RC} & \text{for } t > 0, \end{cases}$$

where R and C are positive constants depending on the circuit and Q_0 is the charge at $t = 0$, where $Q_0 \neq 0$. The current, I, flowing in the circuit is given by $I = dQ/dt$.

(a) Find the current I for $t < 0$ and for $t > 0$.
(b) Is it possible to define I at $t = 0$?
(c) Is the function Q differentiable at $t = 0$?

93. A polynomial f is said to have a *zero of multiplicity* m at $x = a$ if

$$f(x) = (x - a)^m h(x),$$

with h a polynomial such that $h(a) \neq 0$. Explain why a polynomial having a zero of multiplicity m at $x = a$ satisfies $f^{(p)}(a) = 0$, for $p = 1, 2, \ldots m - 1$. [Note: $f^{(p)}$ is the pth derivative.]

94. Find and simplify $\dfrac{d^2}{dx^2}\left(f(g(x))\right)$.

95. Find and simplify $\dfrac{d^2}{dx^2}\left(\dfrac{f(x)}{g(x)}\right)$ using the product and chain rules.

Strengthen Your Understanding

In Problems 96–97, explain what is wrong with the statement.

96. The derivative of $g(x) = (e^x + 2)^5$ is $g'(x) = 5(e^x + 2)^4$.

97. The derivative of $w(x) = e^{x^2}$ is $w'(x) = e^{x^2}$.

In Problems 98–99, give an example of:

98. A function involving a sine and an exponential that requires the chain rule to differentite.

99. A function that can be differentiated both using the chain rule and by another method.

Are the statements in Problems 100–102 true or false? If a statement is true, explain how you know. If a statement is false, give a counterexample.

100. $(fg)'(x)$ is never equal to $f'(x)g'(x)$.

101. If the derivative of $f(g(x))$ is equal to the derivative of $f(x)$ for all x, then $g(x) = x$ for all x.

102. Suppose that f'' and g'' exist and that f and g are concave up for all x, then $f(g(x))$ is concave up for all x.

3.5 THE TRIGONOMETRIC FUNCTIONS

Derivatives of the Sine and Cosine

Since the sine and cosine functions are periodic, their derivatives must be periodic also. (Why?) Let's look at the graph of $f(x) = \sin x$ in Figure 3.22 and estimate the derivative function graphically.

$f(x) = \sin x$

Figure 3.22: The sine function

First we might ask where the derivative is zero. (At $x = \pm\pi/2, \pm 3\pi/2, \pm 5\pi/2$, etc.) Then ask where the derivative is positive and where it is negative. (Positive for $-\pi/2 < x < \pi/2$; negative for $\pi/2 < x < 3\pi/2$, etc.) Since the largest positive slopes are at $x = 0, 2\pi$, and so on, and the largest negative slopes are at $x = \pi, 3\pi$, and so on, we get something like the graph in Figure 3.23.

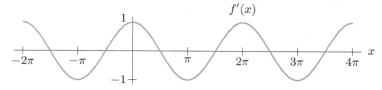

$f'(x)$

Figure 3.23: Derivative of $f(x) = \sin x$

The graph of the derivative in Figure 3.23 looks suspiciously like the graph of the cosine function. This might lead us to conjecture, quite correctly, that the derivative of the sine is the cosine.

Of course, we cannot be sure, just from the graphs, that the derivative of the sine really is the cosine. However, for now we'll assume that the derivative of the sine *is* the cosine and confirm the result at the end of the section.

One thing we can do now is to check that the derivative function in Figure 3.23 has amplitude 1 (as it ought to if it is the cosine). That means we have to convince ourselves that the derivative of $f(x) = \sin x$ is 1 when $x = 0$. The next example suggests that this is true when x is in radians.

Example 1   Using a calculator set in radians, estimate the derivative of $f(x) = \sin x$ at $x = 0$.

Solution   Since $f(x) = \sin x$,
$$f'(0) = \lim_{h \to 0} \frac{\sin(0 + h) - \sin 0}{h} = \lim_{h \to 0} \frac{\sin h}{h}.$$
Table 3.5 contains values of $(\sin h)/h$ which suggest that this limit is 1, so we estimate
$$f'(0) = \lim_{h \to 0} \frac{\sin h}{h} = 1.$$

Table 3.5

h (radians)	-0.1	-0.01	-0.001	-0.0001	0.0001	0.001	0.01	0.1
$(\sin h)/h$	0.99833	0.99998	1.0000	1.0000	1.0000	1.0000	0.99998	0.99833

Warning: It is important to notice that in the previous example h was in *radians*; any conclusions we have drawn about the derivative of $\sin x$ are valid *only* when x is in radians. If you find the derivative with h in degrees, you get a different result.

Example 2   Starting with the graph of the cosine function, sketch a graph of its derivative.

Solution   The graph of $g(x) = \cos x$ is in Figure 3.24(a). Its derivative is 0 at $x = 0, \pm\pi, \pm 2\pi$, and so on; it is positive for $-\pi < x < 0$, $\pi < x < 2\pi$, and so on; and it is negative for $0 < x < \pi$, $2\pi < x < 3\pi$, and so on. The derivative is in Figure 3.24(b).

(a)

(b)

Figure 3.24: $g(x) = \cos x$ and its derivative, $g'(x)$

As we did with the sine, we use the graphs to make a conjecture. The derivative of the cosine in Figure 3.24(b) looks exactly like the graph of sine, except reflected across the x-axis. But how can we be sure that the derivative is $-\sin x$?

Example 3   Use the relation $\dfrac{d}{dx}(\sin x) = \cos x$ to show that $\dfrac{d}{dx}(\cos x) = -\sin x$.

Solution   Since the cosine function is the sine function shifted to the left by $\pi/2$ (that is, $\cos x = \sin(x + \pi/2)$), we expect the derivative of the cosine to be the derivative of the sine, shifted to the left by $\pi/2$. Differentiating using the chain rule:
$$\frac{d}{dx}(\cos x) = \frac{d}{dx}\left(\sin\left(x + \frac{\pi}{2}\right)\right) = \cos\left(x + \frac{\pi}{2}\right).$$

But $\cos(x + \pi/2)$ is the cosine shifted to the left by $\pi/2$, which gives a sine curve reflected across the x-axis. So we have

$$\frac{d}{dx}(\cos x) = \cos\left(x + \frac{\pi}{2}\right) = -\sin x.$$

At the end of this section and in Problems 66 and 67, we show that our conjectures for the derivatives of $\sin x$ and $\cos x$ are correct. Thus, we have:

For x in radians, $\dfrac{d}{dx}(\sin x) = \cos x$ and $\dfrac{d}{dx}(\cos x) = -\sin x.$

Example 4   Differentiate   (a) $2\sin(3\theta)$,   (b) $\cos^2 x$,   (c) $\cos(x^2)$,   (d) $e^{-\sin t}$.

Solution   Use the chain rule:

(a) $\dfrac{d}{d\theta}(2\sin(3\theta)) = 2\dfrac{d}{d\theta}(\sin(3\theta)) = 2(\cos(3\theta))\dfrac{d}{d\theta}(3\theta) = 2(\cos(3\theta))3 = 6\cos(3\theta).$

(b) $\dfrac{d}{dx}(\cos^2 x) = \dfrac{d}{dx}\left((\cos x)^2\right) = 2(\cos x)\cdot\dfrac{d}{dx}(\cos x) = 2(\cos x)(-\sin x) = -2\cos x \sin x.$

(c) $\dfrac{d}{dx}\left(\cos(x^2)\right) = -\sin(x^2)\cdot\dfrac{d}{dx}(x^2) = -2x\sin(x^2).$

(d) $\dfrac{d}{dt}(e^{-\sin t}) = e^{-\sin t}\dfrac{d}{dt}(-\sin t) = -(\cos t)e^{-\sin t}.$

Derivative of the Tangent Function

Since $\tan x = \sin x/\cos x$, we differentiate $\tan x$ using the quotient rule. Writing $(\sin x)'$ for $d(\sin x)/dx$, we have:

$$\frac{d}{dx}(\tan x) = \frac{d}{dx}\left(\frac{\sin x}{\cos x}\right) = \frac{(\sin x)'(\cos x) - (\sin x)(\cos x)'}{\cos^2 x} = \frac{\cos^2 x + \sin^2 x}{\cos^2 x} = \frac{1}{\cos^2 x}.$$

For x in radians, $\dfrac{d}{dx}(\tan x) = \dfrac{1}{\cos^2 x}.$

The graphs of $f(x) = \tan x$ and $f'(x) = 1/\cos^2 x$ are in Figure 3.25. Is it reasonable that f' is always positive? Are the asymptotes of f' where we expect?

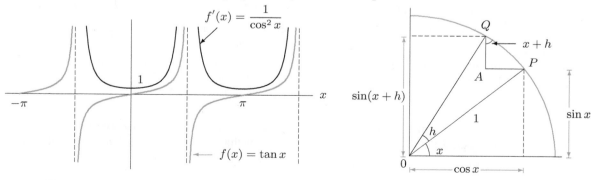

Figure 3.25: The function $\tan x$ and its derivative

Figure 3.26: Unit circle showing $\sin(x + h)$ and $\sin x$

Example 5   Differentiate (a) $2\tan(3t)$,   (b) $\tan(1-\theta)$,   (c) $\dfrac{1+\tan t}{1-\tan t}$.

Solution   (a) Use the chain rule:

$$\frac{d}{dt}(2\tan(3t)) = 2\frac{1}{\cos^2(3t)}\frac{d}{dt}(3t) = \frac{6}{\cos^2(3t)}.$$

(b) Use the chain rule:

$$\frac{d}{d\theta}(\tan(1-\theta)) = \frac{1}{\cos^2(1-\theta)} \cdot \frac{d}{d\theta}(1-\theta) = -\frac{1}{\cos^2(1-\theta)}.$$

(c) Use the quotient rule:

$$\frac{d}{dt}\left(\frac{1+\tan t}{1-\tan t}\right) = \frac{\frac{d}{dt}(1+\tan t)(1-\tan t) - (1+\tan t)\frac{d}{dt}(1-\tan t)}{(1-\tan t)^2}$$

$$= \frac{\frac{1}{\cos^2 t}(1-\tan t) - (1+\tan t)\left(-\frac{1}{\cos^2 t}\right)}{(1-\tan t)^2}$$

$$= \frac{2}{\cos^2 t \cdot (1-\tan t)^2}.$$

Example 6   The Bay of Fundy in Canada is known for extreme tides. The depth of the water, y, in meters can be modeled as a function of time, t, in hours after midnight, by

$$y = 10 + 7.5\cos(0.507t).$$

How quickly is the depth of the water rising or falling at 6:00 am and at 9:00 am?

Solution   To find how fast the water depth is changing, we compute the derivative of y, using the chain rule:

$$\frac{dy}{dt} = -7.5(0.507)\sin(0.507t) = -3.8025\sin(0.507t).$$

When $t = 6$, we have $\dfrac{dy}{dt} = -3.8025\sin(0.507 \cdot 6) = -0.378$ meters/hour. So the tide is falling at 0.378 meters/hour.

When $t = 9$, we have $\dfrac{dy}{dt} = -3.8025\sin(0.507 \cdot 9) = 3.760$ meters/hour. So the tide is rising at 3.760 meters/hour.

Informal Justification of $\frac{d}{dx}(\sin x) = \cos x$

Consider the unit circle in Figure 3.26. To find the derivative of $\sin x$, we need to estimate

$$\frac{\sin(x+h) - \sin x}{h}.$$

In Figure 3.26, the quantity $\sin(x+h) - \sin x$ is represented by the length QA. The arc QP is of length h, so

$$\frac{\sin(x+h) - \sin x}{h} = \frac{QA}{\text{Arc } QP}.$$

Now, if h is small, QAP is approximately a right triangle because the arc QP is almost a straight line. Furthermore, using geometry, we can show that angle $AQP = x + h$. For small h, we have

$$\frac{\sin(x+h) - \sin x}{h} = \frac{QA}{\text{Arc } QP} \approx \cos(x+h).$$

As $h \to 0$, the approximation gets better, so

$$\frac{d}{dx}(\sin x) = \lim_{h \to 0} \frac{\sin(x+h) - \sin x}{h} = \cos x.$$

Other derivations of this result are given in Problems 66 and 67 on pages 154–155.

Exercises and Problems for Section 3.5

Exercises

1. Construct a table of values for $\cos x$, $x = 0, 0.1, 0.2, \ldots, 0.6$. Using the difference quotient, estimate the derivative at these points (use $h = 0.001$), and compare it with $-\sin x$.

In Exercises 2–47, find the derivatives of the functions. Assume $a, b,$ and c are constants.

2. $r(\theta) = \sin\theta + \cos\theta$

3. $s(\theta) = \cos\theta \sin\theta$

4. $z = \cos(4\theta)$

5. $f(x) = \sin(3x)$

6. $y = 5\sin(3t)$

7. $P = 4\cos(2t)$

8. $g(x) = \sin(2 - 3x)$

9. $R(x) = 10 - 3\cos(\pi x)$

10. $g(\theta) = \sin^2(2\theta) - \pi\theta$

11. $g(t) = (2 + \sin(\pi t))^3$

12. $f(x) = x^2 \cos x$

13. $w = \sin(e^t)$

14. $f(x) = e^{\cos x}$

15. $f(y) = e^{\sin y}$

16. $z = \theta e^{\cos\theta}$

17. $R(\theta) = e^{\sin(3\theta)}$

18. $g(\theta) = \sin(\tan\theta)$

19. $w(x) = \tan(x^2)$

20. $f(x) = \sqrt{1 - \cos x}$

21. $f(x) = \sqrt{3 + \sin(8x)}$

22. $f(x) = \cos(\sin x)$

23. $f(x) = \tan(\sin x)$

24. $k(x) = \sqrt{(\sin(2x))^3}$

25. $f(x) = 2x\sin(3x)$

26. $y = e^\theta \sin(2\theta)$

27. $f(x) = e^{-2x} \cdot \sin x$

28. $z = \sqrt{\sin t}$

29. $y = \sin^5\theta$

30. $g(z) = \tan(e^z)$

31. $z = \tan(e^{-3\theta})$

32. $w = e^{-\sin\theta}$

33. $Q = \cos(e^{2x})$

34. $h(t) = t\cos t + \tan t$

35. $f(\alpha) = \cos\alpha + 3\sin\alpha$

36. $k(\alpha) = \sin^5\alpha \cos^3\alpha$

37. $f(\theta) = \theta^3\cos\theta$

38. $y = \cos^2 w + \cos(w^2)$

39. $y = \sin(\sin x + \cos x)$

40. $y = \sin(2x) \cdot \sin(3x)$

41. $P = \dfrac{\cos t}{t^3}$

42. $t(\theta) = \dfrac{\cos\theta}{\sin\theta}$

43. $f(x) = \sqrt{\dfrac{1 - \sin x}{1 - \cos x}}$

44. $r(y) = \dfrac{y}{\cos y + a}$

45. $G(x) = \dfrac{\sin^2 x + 1}{\cos^2 x + 1}$

46. $y = a\sin(bt) + c$

47. $P = a\cos(bt + c)$

Problems

48. Is the graph of $y = \sin(x^4)$ increasing or decreasing when $x = 10$? Is it concave up or concave down?

49. Find the line tangent to $f(t) = 3\sin(2t) + 5$ at the point where $t = \pi$.

50. Find the 50th derivative of $y = \cos x$.

51. Find d^2x/dt^2 as a function of x if $dx/dt = x\sin x$.

52. Find a possible formula for the function $q(x)$ such that

$$q'(x) = \frac{e^x \cdot \sin x - e^x \cdot \cos x}{(\sin x)^2}.$$

53. Find a function $F(x)$ satisfying $F'(x) = \sin(4x)$.

54. Let $f(x) = \sin^2 x + \cos^2 x$.

    (a) Find $f'(x)$ using the formula for $f(x)$ and derivative formulas from this section. Simplify your answer.

    (b) Use a trigonometric identity to check your answer to part (a). Explain.

55. Let $f'(x) = \sin\left(x^2\right)$, Find $h''(x)$ if $h(x) = f\left(x^2\right)$.

56. On page 39 the depth, y, in feet, of water in Boston harbor is given in terms of t, the number of hours since midnight, by

$$y = 5 + 4.9\cos\left(\frac{\pi}{6}t\right).$$

    (a) Find dy/dt. What does dy/dt represent, in terms of water level?

    (b) For $0 \le t \le 24$, when is dy/dt zero? (Figure 1.55 on page 39 may be helpful.) Explain what it means (in terms of water level) for dy/dt to be zero.

57. A boat at anchor is bobbing up and down in the sea. The vertical distance, y, in feet, between the sea floor and the boat is given as a function of time, t, in minutes, by

$$y = 15 + \sin(2\pi t).$$

(a) Find the vertical velocity, v, of the boat at time t.
(b) Make rough sketches of y and v against t.

58. The voltage, V, in volts, in an electrical outlet is given as a function of time, t, in seconds, by the function $V = 156 \cos(120\pi t)$.

(a) Give an expression for the rate of change of voltage with respect to time.
(b) Is the rate of change ever zero? Explain.
(c) What is the maximum value of the rate of change?

59. An oscillating mass at the end of a spring is at a distance y from its equilibrium position given by

$$y = A \sin\left(\left(\sqrt{\frac{k}{m}}\right) t\right).$$

The constant k measures the stiffness of the spring.

(a) Find a time at which the mass is farthest from its equilibrium position. Find a time at which the mass is moving fastest. Find a time at which the mass is accelerating fastest.
(b) What is the period, T, of the oscillation?
(c) Find dT/dm. What does the sign of dT/dm tell you?

60. With t in years, the population of a herd of deer is represented by

$$P(t) = 4000 + 500 \sin\left(2\pi t - \frac{\pi}{2}\right).$$

(a) How does this population vary with time? Graph $P(t)$ for one year.
(b) When in the year the population is a maximum? What is that maximum? Is there a minimum? If so, when?
(c) When is the population growing fastest? When is it decreasing fastest?
(d) How fast is the population changing on July 1?

61. An environmentalist reports that the depth of the water in a new reservoir is approximated by

$$h = d(t) = \begin{cases} kt & 0 \le t \le 2 \\ 50 + \sin(0.1t) & t > 2, \end{cases}$$

where t is in weeks since the date the reservoir was completed and h is in meters.

(a) During what period was the reservoir filling at a constant rate? What was that rate?
(b) In this model, is the rate at which the water level is changing defined for all times $t > 0$? Explain.

62. The metal bar of length l in Figure 3.27 has one end attached at the point P to a circle of radius a. Point Q at the other end can slide back and forth along the x-axis.

(a) Find x as a function of θ.
(b) Assume lengths are in centimeters and the angular speed $(d\theta/dt)$ is 2 radians/second counterclockwise. Find the speed at which the point Q is moving when

(i) $\theta = \pi/2$,   (ii) $\theta = \pi/4$.

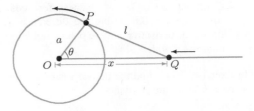

Figure 3.27

63. Find the equations of the tangent lines to the graph of $f(x) = \sin x$ at $x = 0$ and at $x = \pi/3$. Use each tangent line to approximate $\sin(\pi/6)$. Would you expect these results to be equally accurate, since they are taken equally far away from $x = \pi/6$ but on opposite sides? If the accuracy is different, can you account for the difference?

64. If $k \ge 1$, the graphs of $y = \sin x$ and $y = ke^{-x}$ intersect for $x \ge 0$. Find the smallest value of k for which the graphs are tangent. What are the coordinates of the point of tangency?

65. A wave travels along a string that is joined to a thicker rope. The wave both reflects back along the string and is transmitted to the rope. For positive constants k_1, k_2, w and time t, the wave along the string, given by $x < 0$, is

$$f(x) = \cos(k_1 x - wt) + R \cos(-k_1 x - wt)$$

and the wave along the rope, given by $x > 0$, is

$$g(x) = T \cos(k_2 x - wt).$$

For every value of t, the two waves have the same tangent line at $x = 0$, so they have the same value and same slope at $x = 0$. Use this fact to show that

$$R = \frac{k_1 - k_2}{k_1 + k_2} \quad \text{and} \quad T = \frac{2k_1}{k_1 + k_2}.$$

These amplitudes are called the *reflection coefficient*, R, and the *transmission coefficient*, T.

66. We will use the following identities to calculate the derivatives of $\sin x$ and $\cos x$:

$$\sin(a + b) = \sin a \cos b + \cos a \sin b$$
$$\cos(a + b) = \cos a \cos b - \sin a \sin b.$$

(a) Use the definition of the derivative to show that if $f(x) = \sin x$,

$$f'(x) = \sin x \lim_{h \to 0} \frac{\cos h - 1}{h} + \cos x \lim_{h \to 0} \frac{\sin h}{h}.$$

(b) Estimate the limits in part (a) with your calculator to explain why $f'(x) = \cos x$.

(c) If $g(x) = \cos x$, use the definition of the derivative to show that $g'(x) = -\sin x$.

67. In this problem you will calculate the derivative of $\tan \theta$ rigorously (and without using the derivatives of $\sin \theta$ or $\cos \theta$). You will then use your result for $\tan \theta$ to calculate the derivatives of $\sin \theta$ and $\cos \theta$. Figure 3.28 shows $\tan \theta$ and $\Delta(\tan \theta)$, which is the change in $\tan \theta$, namely $\tan(\theta + \Delta\theta) - \tan \theta$.

(a) By paying particular attention to how the two figures relate and using the fact that

$$\begin{array}{ccc} \text{Area of} & \leq & \text{Area of} & \leq & \text{Area of} \\ \text{Sector OAQ} & & \text{Triangle OQR} & & \text{Sector OBR} \end{array}$$

explain why

$$\frac{\Delta\theta}{2\pi} \cdot \frac{\pi}{(\cos \theta)^2} \leq \frac{\Delta(\tan \theta)}{2} \leq \frac{\Delta\theta}{2\pi} \cdot \frac{\pi}{(\cos(\theta + \Delta\theta))^2}.$$

[Hint: A sector of a circle with angle α at the center has area $\alpha/(2\pi)$ times the area of the whole circle.]

(b) Use part (a) to show as $\Delta\theta \to 0$ that

$$\frac{\Delta \tan \theta}{\Delta\theta} \to \left(\frac{1}{\cos \theta}\right)^2,$$

and hence that $\dfrac{d(\tan \theta)}{d\theta} = \left(\dfrac{1}{\cos \theta}\right)^2.$

(c) Derive the identity $(\tan \theta)^2 + 1 = \left(\dfrac{1}{\cos \theta}\right)^2$. Then differentiate both sides of this identity with respect to θ, using the chain rule and the result of part (b) to show that $\dfrac{d}{d\theta}(\cos \theta) = -\sin \theta.$

(d) Differentiate both sides of the identity $(\sin \theta)^2 + (\cos \theta)^2 = 1$ and use the result of part (c) to show that $\dfrac{d}{d\theta}(\sin \theta) = \cos \theta.$

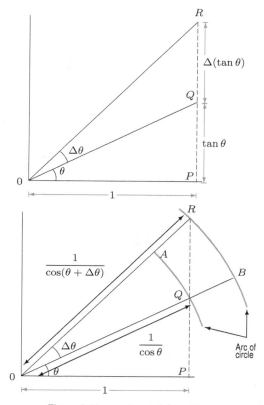

Figure 3.28: $\tan \theta$ and $\Delta(\tan \theta)$

Strengthen Your Understanding

In Problems 68–69, explain what is wrong with the statement.

68. The derivative of $n(x) = \sin(\cos x)$ is $n'(x) = \cos(-\sin x)$.

69. The derivative of $f(x) = \sin(\sin x)$ is $f'(x) = (\cos x)(\sin x) + (\sin x)(\cos x)$.

In Problems 70–71, give an example of:

70. A trigonometric function whose derivative must be calculated using the chain rule.

71. A function $f(x)$ such that $f''(x) = -f(x)$.

Are the statements in Problems 72–74 true or false? Give an explanation for your answer.

72. The derivative of $\tan \theta$ is periodic.

73. If a function is periodic, with period c, then so is its derivative.

74. The only functions whose fourth derivatives are equal to $\cos t$ are of the form $\cos t + C$, where C is any constant.

3.6 THE CHAIN RULE AND INVERSE FUNCTIONS

In this section we will use the chain rule to calculate the derivatives of fractional powers, logarithms, exponentials, and the inverse trigonometric functions.[5] The same method is used to obtain a formula for the derivative of a general inverse function.

Finding the Derivative of an Inverse Function: Derivative of $x^{1/2}$

Earlier we calculated the derivative of x^n with n an integer, but we have been using the result for non-integer values of n as well. We now confirm that the power rule holds for $n = 1/2$ by calculating the derivative of $f(x) = x^{1/2}$ using the chain rule. Since

$$(f(x))^2 = x,$$

the derivative of $(f(x))^2$ and the derivative of x must be equal, so

$$\frac{d}{dx}(f(x))^2 = \frac{d}{dx}(x).$$

We can use the chain rule with $f(x)$ as the inside function to obtain:

$$\frac{d}{dx}(f(x))^2 = 2f(x) \cdot f'(x) = 1.$$

Solving for $f'(x)$ gives

$$f'(x) = \frac{1}{2f(x)} = \frac{1}{2x^{1/2}},$$

or

$$\frac{d}{dx}(x^{1/2}) = \frac{1}{2x^{1/2}} = \frac{1}{2}x^{-1/2}.$$

A similar calculation can be used to obtain the derivative of $x^{1/n}$ where n is a positive integer.

Derivative of $\ln x$

We use the chain rule to differentiate an identity involving $\ln x$. Since $e^{\ln x} = x$, we have

$$\frac{d}{dx}(e^{\ln x}) = \frac{d}{dx}(x),$$

$$e^{\ln x} \cdot \frac{d}{dx}(\ln x) = 1. \qquad \text{(Since } e^x \text{ is outside function and } \ln x \text{ is inside function)}$$

Solving for $d(\ln x)/dx$ gives

$$\frac{d}{dx}(\ln x) = \frac{1}{e^{\ln x}} = \frac{1}{x},$$

so

$$\boxed{\frac{d}{dx}(\ln x) = \frac{1}{x}.}$$

Example 1   Differentiate (a) $\ln(x^2 + 1)$ (b) $t^2 \ln t$ (c) $\sqrt{1 + \ln(1 - y)}$.

Solution   (a) Using the chain rule:

$$\frac{d}{dx}\left(\ln(x^2 + 1)\right) = \frac{1}{x^2 + 1}\frac{d}{dx}(x^2 + 1) = \frac{2x}{x^2 + 1}.$$

(b) Using the product rule:

$$\frac{d}{dt}(t^2 \ln t) = \frac{d}{dt}(t^2) \cdot \ln t + t^2 \frac{d}{dt}(\ln t) = 2t \ln t + t^2 \cdot \frac{1}{t} = 2t \ln t + t.$$

---

[5]It requires a separate justification, not given here, that these functions are differentiable.

(c) Using the chain rule:

$$\frac{d}{dy}\left(\sqrt{1+\ln(1-y)}\right) = \frac{d}{dy}(1+\ln(1-y))^{1/2}$$

$$= \frac{1}{2}(1+\ln(1-y))^{-1/2}\cdot\frac{d}{dy}(1+\ln(1-y)) \qquad \text{(Using the chain rule)}$$

$$= \frac{1}{2\sqrt{1+\ln(1-y)}}\cdot\frac{1}{1-y}\cdot\frac{d}{dy}(1-y) \qquad \text{(Using the chain rule again)}$$

$$= \frac{-1}{2(1-y)\sqrt{1+\ln(1-y)}}.$$

Derivative of a^x

In Section 3.2, we saw that the derivative of a^x is proportional to a^x. Now we see another way of calculating the constant of proportionality. We use the identity

$$\ln(a^x) = x\ln a.$$

Differentiating both sides, using $\frac{d}{dx}(\ln x) = \frac{1}{x}$ and the chain rule, and remembering that $\ln a$ is a constant, we obtain:

$$\frac{d}{dx}(\ln a^x) = \frac{1}{a^x}\cdot\frac{d}{dx}(a^x) = \ln a.$$

Solving gives the result we obtained earlier:

$$\boxed{\frac{d}{dx}(a^x) = (\ln a)a^x.}$$

Derivatives of Inverse Trigonometric Functions

In Section 1.5 we defined $\arcsin x$ as the angle between $-\pi/2$ and $\pi/2$ (inclusive) whose sine is x. Similarly, $\arctan x$ as the angle strictly between $-\pi/2$ and $\pi/2$ whose tangent is x. To find $\frac{d}{dx}(\arctan x)$ we use the identity $\tan(\arctan x) = x$. Differentiating using the chain rule gives

$$\frac{1}{\cos^2(\arctan x)}\cdot\frac{d}{dx}(\arctan x) = 1,$$

so

$$\frac{d}{dx}(\arctan x) = \cos^2(\arctan x).$$

Using the identity $1+\tan^2\theta = \frac{1}{\cos^2\theta}$, and replacing θ by $\arctan x$, we have

$$\cos^2(\arctan x) = \frac{1}{1+\tan^2(\arctan x)} = \frac{1}{1+x^2}.$$

Thus we have

$$\boxed{\frac{d}{dx}(\arctan x) = \frac{1}{1+x^2}.}$$

By a similar argument, we obtain the result:

$$\frac{d}{dx}(\arcsin x) = \frac{1}{\sqrt{1-x^2}}.$$

Example 2   Differentiate   (a) $\arctan(t^2)$ (b) $\arcsin(\tan\theta)$.

Solution   Use the chain rule:

(a) $\dfrac{d}{dt}\left(\arctan(t^2)\right) = \dfrac{1}{1+(t^2)^2}\cdot\dfrac{d}{dt}(t^2) = \dfrac{2t}{1+t^4}.$

(b) $\dfrac{d}{dt}\left(\arcsin(\tan\theta)\right) = \dfrac{1}{\sqrt{1-(\tan\theta)^2}}\cdot\dfrac{d}{d\theta}(\tan\theta) = \dfrac{1}{\sqrt{1-\tan^2\theta}}\cdot\dfrac{1}{\cos^2\theta}.$

Derivative of a General Inverse Function

Each of the previous results gives the derivative of an inverse function. In general, if a function f has a differentiable inverse, f^{-1}, we find its derivative by differentiating $f(f^{-1}(x)) = x$ by the chain rule:

$$\frac{d}{dx}\left(f\left(f^{-1}(x)\right)\right) = 1$$

$$f'\left(f^{-1}(x)\right)\cdot\frac{d}{dx}\left(f^{-1}(x)\right) = 1$$

so

$$\frac{d}{dx}\left(f^{-1}(x)\right) = \frac{1}{f'(f^{-1}(x))}.$$

Thus, the derivative of the inverse is the reciprocal of the derivative of the original function, but evaluated at the point $f^{-1}(x)$ instead of the point x.

Example 3   Figure 3.29 shows $f(x)$ and $f^{-1}(x)$. Using Table 3.6, find

(a) (i) $f(2)$ (ii) $f^{-1}(2)$ (iii) $f'(2)$ (iv) $(f^{-1})'(2)$

(b) The equation of the tangent lines at the points P and Q.

(c) What is the relationship between the two tangent lines?

Table 3.6

x	$f(x)$	$f'(x)$
0	1	0.7
1	2	1.4
2	4	2.8
3	8	5.5

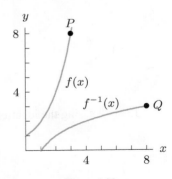

Figure 3.29

Solution   (a) Reading from the table, we have

(i) $f(2) = 4$.

(ii) $f^{-1}(2) = 1$.

(iii) $f'(2) = 2.8$.

(iv) To find the derivative of the inverse function, we use

$$(f^{-1})'(2) = \frac{1}{f'(f^{-1}(2))} = \frac{1}{f'(1)} = \frac{1}{1.4} = 0.714.$$

Notice that the derivative of f^{-1} is the reciprocal of the derivative of f. However, the derivative of f^{-1} is evaluated at 2, while the derivative of f is evaluated at 1, where $f^{-1}(2) = 1$ and $f(1) = 2$.

(b) At the point P, we have $f(3) = 8$ and $f'(3) = 5.5$, so the equation of the tangent line at P is

$$y - 8 = 5.5(x - 3).$$

At the point Q, we have $f^{-1}(8) = 3$, so the slope at Q is

$$(f^{-1})'(8) = \frac{1}{f'(f^{-1}(8))} = \frac{1}{f'(3)} = \frac{1}{5.5}.$$

Thus, the equation of the tangent line at Q is

$$y - 3 = \frac{1}{5.5}(x - 8).$$

(c) The two tangent lines have reciprocal slopes, and the points $(3, 8)$ and $(8, 3)$ are reflections of one another in the line $y = x$. Thus, the two tangent lines are reflections of one another in the line $y = x$.

Exercises and Problems for Section 3.6

Exercises

For Exercises 1–41, find the derivative. It may be to your advantage to simplify before differentiating. Assume a, b, c, and k are constants.

1. $f(t) = \ln(t^2 + 1)$

2. $f(x) = \ln(1 - x)$

3. $f(x) = \ln(5x^2 + 3)$

4. $y = 2x^2 + 3\ln x$

5. $y = \arcsin(x + 1)$

6. $f(x) = \arctan(3x)$

7. $P = 3\ln(x^2 + 5x + 3)$

8. $Q = a\ln(bx + c)$

9. $f(x) = \ln(e^{2x})$

10. $f(x) = e^{\ln(e^{2x^2 + 3})}$

11. $f(x) = \ln(1 - e^{-x})$

12. $f(\alpha) = \ln(\sin \alpha)$

13. $f(x) = \ln(e^x + 1)$

14. $y = x\ln x - x + 2$

15. $j(x) = \ln(e^{ax} + b)$

16. $y = x^3 \ln x$

17. $h(w) = w^3 \ln(10w)$

18. $f(x) = \ln(e^{7x})$

19. $f(x) = e^{(\ln x) + 1}$

20. $f(\theta) = \ln(\cos \theta)$

21. $f(t) = \ln(e^{\ln t})$

22. $f(y) = \arcsin(y^2)$

23. $s(x) = \arctan(2 - x)$

24. $g(\alpha) = \sin(\arcsin \alpha)$

25. $g(t) = e^{\arctan(3t^2)}$

26. $g(t) = \cos(\ln t)$

27. $h(z) = z^{\ln 2}$

28. $h(w) = w \arcsin w$

29. $f(x) = e^{\ln(kx)}$

30. $r(t) = \arcsin(2t)$

31. $j(x) = \cos(\sin^{-1} x)$

32. $f(x) = \cos(\arctan 3x)$

33. $f(z) = \dfrac{1}{\ln z}$

34. $g(t) = \dfrac{\ln(kt) + t}{\ln(kt) - t}$

35. $f(w) = 6\sqrt{w} + \dfrac{1}{w^2} + 5\ln w$

36. $y = 2x(\ln x + \ln 2) - 2x + e$

37. $f(x) = \ln(\sin x + \cos x)$

38. $f(t) = \ln(\ln t) + \ln(\ln 2)$

39. $T(u) = \arctan\left(\dfrac{u}{1 + u}\right)$

40. $a(t) = \ln\left(\dfrac{1 - \cos t}{1 + \cos t}\right)^4$

41. $f(x) = \cos(\arcsin(x + 1))$

Problems

42. Let $f(x) = \ln(3x)$.

    (a) Find $f'(x)$ and simplify your answer.
    (b) Use properties of logs to rewrite $f(x)$ as a sum of logs.
    (c) Differentiate the result of part (b). Compare with the result in part (a).

43. On what intervals is $\ln(x^2 + 1)$ concave up?

44. Use the chain rule to obtain the formula for $\dfrac{d}{dx}(\arcsin x)$.

45. Using the chain rule, find $\dfrac{d}{dx}(\log x)$.
    (Recall $\log x = \log_{10} x$.)

46. To compare the acidity of different solutions, chemists use the pH (which is a single number, not the product of p and H). The pH is defined in terms of the concentration, x, of hydrogen ions in the solution as

    $$pH = -\log x.$$

    Find the rate of change of pH with respect to hydrogen ion concentration when the pH is 2. [Hint: Use the result of Problem 45.]

47. The number of years, T, it takes an investment of $1000 to grow to F in an account which pays 5% interest compounded continuously is given by

    $$T = g(F) = 20 \ln(0.001F).$$

    Find $g(5000)$ and $g'(5000)$. Give units with your answers and interpret them in terms of money in the account.

48. A firm estimates that the total revenue, R, in dollars, received from the sale of q goods is given by

    $$R = \ln(1 + 1000q^2).$$

    The marginal revenue, MR, is the rate of change of the total revenue as a function of quantity. Calculate the marginal revenue when $q = 10$.

49. (a) Find the equation of the tangent line to $y = \ln x$ at $x = 1$.
    (b) Use it to calculate approximate values for $\ln(1.1)$ and $\ln(2)$.
    (c) Using a graph, explain whether the approximate values are smaller or larger than the true values. Would the same result have held if you had used the tangent line to estimate $\ln(0.9)$ and $\ln(0.5)$? Why?

50. (a) Find the equation of the best quadratic approximation to $y = \ln x$ at $x = 1$. The best quadratic approximation has the same first and second derivatives as $y = \ln x$ at $x = 1$.
    (b) Use a computer or calculator to graph the approximation and $y = \ln x$ on the same set of axes. What do you notice?
    (c) Use your quadratic approximation to calculate approximate values for $\ln(1.1)$ and $\ln(2)$.

51. (a) For $x > 0$, find and simplify the derivative of $f(x) = \arctan x + \arctan(1/x)$.
    (b) What does your result tell you about f?

52. Imagine you are zooming in on the graph of each of the following functions near the origin:

    $$y = x \qquad\qquad y = \sqrt{x}$$
    $$y = x^2 \qquad\qquad y = \sin x$$
    $$y = x \sin x \qquad\quad y = \tan x$$
    $$y = \sqrt{x/(x+1)} \quad y = x^3$$
    $$y = \ln(x+1) \quad y = \tfrac{1}{2}\ln(x^2+1)$$
    $$y = 1 - \cos x \quad y = \sqrt{2x - x^2}$$

    Which of them look the same? Group together those functions which become indistinguishable, and give the equations of the lines they look like.

In Problems 53–56, use Figure 3.30 to find a point x where $h(x) = n(m(x))$ has the given derivative.

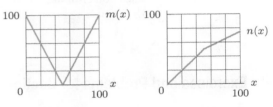

Figure 3.30

53. $h'(x) = -2$ 54. $h'(x) = 2$

55. $h'(x) = 1$ 56. $h'(x) = -1$

In Problems 57–59, use Figure 3.31 to estimate the derivatives.

Figure 3.31

57. $(f^{-1})'(5)$ 58. $(f^{-1})'(10)$ 59. $(f^{-1})'(15)$

In Problems 60–62, use Figure 3.32 to calculate the derivative.

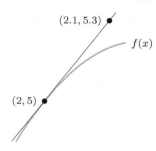

(2.1, 5.3)

$f(x)$

(2, 5)

Figure 3.32

60. $h'(2)$ if $h(x) = (f(x))^3$

61. $k'(2)$ if $k(x) = (f(x))^{-1}$

62. $g'(5)$ if $g(x) = f^{-1}(x)$

63. (a) Given that $f(x) = x^3$, find $f'(2)$.
   (b) Find $f^{-1}(x)$.
   (c) Use your answer from part (b) to find $(f^{-1})'(8)$.
   (d) How could you have used your answer from part (a) to find $(f^{-1})'(8)$?

64. (a) For $f(x) = 2x^5 + 3x^3 + x$, find $f'(x)$.
   (b) How can you use your answer to part (a) to determine if $f(x)$ is invertible?
   (c) Find $f(1)$.
   (d) Find $f'(1)$.
   (e) Find $(f^{-1})'(6)$.

65. Use the table and the fact that $f(x)$ is invertible and differentiable everywhere to find $(f^{-1})'(3)$.

x	$f(x)$	$f'(x)$
3	1	7
6	2	10
9	3	5

66. At a particular location, $f(p)$ is the number of gallons of gas sold when the price is p dollars per gallon.

   (a) What does the statement $f(2) = 4023$ tell you about gas sales?
   (b) Find and interpret $f^{-1}(4023)$.
   (c) What does the statement $f'(2) = -1250$ tell you about gas sales?
   (d) Find and interpret $(f^{-1})'(4023)$

67. Let $P = f(t)$ give the US population[6] in millions in year t.

   (a) What does the statement $f(2005) = 296$ tell you about the US population?
   (b) Find and interpret $f^{-1}(296)$. Give units.
   (c) What does the statement $f'(2005) = 2.65$ tell you about the population? Give units.
   (d) Evaluate and interpret $(f^{-1})'(296)$. Give units.

68. Figure 3.33 shows the number of motor vehicles,[7] $f(t)$, in millions, registered in the world t years after 1965. With units, estimate and interpret

   (a) $f(20)$ (b) $f'(20)$
   (c) $f^{-1}(500)$ (d) $(f^{-1})'(500)$

Figure 3.33

69. Using Figure 3.34, where $f'(2) = 2.1$, $f'(4) = 3.0$, $f'(6) = 3.7$, $f'(8) = 4.2$, find $(f^{-1})'(8)$.

Figure 3.34

70. If f is increasing and $f(20) = 10$, which of the two options, (a) or (b), must be wrong?

   (a) $f'(10)(f^{-1})'(20) = 1$.
   (b) $f'(20)(f^{-1})'(10) = 2$.

71. An invertible function $f(x)$ has values in the table. Evaluate

   (a) $f'(a) \cdot (f^{-1})'(A)$ (b) $f'(b) \cdot (f^{-1})'(B)$
   (c) $f'(c) \cdot (f^{-1})'(C)$

x	a	b	c	d
$f(x)$	A	B	C	D

72. If f is continuous, invertible, and defined for all x, why must at least one of the statements $(f^{-1})'(10) = 8$, $(f^{-1})'(20) = -6$ be wrong?

73. (a) Calculate $\lim_{h\to 0}(\ln(1+h)/h)$ by identifying the limit as the derivative of $\ln(1+x)$ at $x = 0$.
   (b) Use the result of part (a) to show that $\lim_{h\to 0}(1+h)^{1/h} = e$.
   (c) Use the result of part (b) to calculate the related limit, $\lim_{n\to\infty}(1+1/n)^n$.

---

[6]Data from www.census.gov/Press-Release/www/releases/archives/population/006142.html, accessed May 27, 2007.
[7]www.earth-policy.org, accessed May 18, 2007.

Strengthen Your Understanding

In Problems 74–76, explain what is wrong with the statement.

74. If $w(x) = \ln(1 + x^4)$ then $w'(x) = 1/(1 + x^4)$.

75. The derivative of $f(x) = \ln(\ln x)$ is

$$f'(x) = \frac{1}{x} \ln x + \ln x \frac{1}{x} = \frac{2 \ln x}{x}.$$

76. Given $f(2) = 6$, $f'(2) = 3$, and $f^{-1}(3) = 4$, we have

$$(f^{-1})'(2) = \frac{1}{f^{-1}(f'(2))} = \frac{1}{f^{-1}(3)} = \frac{1}{4}.$$

In Problems 77–80, give an example of:

77. A function that is equal to a constant multiple of its derivative but that is not equal to its derivative.

78. A function whose derivative is c/x, where c is a constant.

79. A function $f(x)$ for which $f'(x) = f'(cx)$, where c is a constant.

80. A function f such that $\dfrac{d}{dx}\left(f^{-1}(x)\right) = \dfrac{1}{f'(x)} = 1$.

Are the statements in Problems 81–82 true or false? Give an explanation for your answer.

81. The graph of $\ln(x^2)$ is concave up for $x > 0$.

82. If $f(x)$ has an inverse function, $g(x)$, then the derivative of $g(x)$ is $1/f'(x)$.

3.7 IMPLICIT FUNCTIONS

In earlier chapters, most functions were written in the form $y = f(x)$; here y is said to be an *explicit* function of x. An equation such as

$$x^2 + y^2 = 4$$

is said to give y as an *implicit* function of x. Its graph is the circle in Figure 3.35. Since there are x-values which correspond to two y-values, y is not a function of x on the whole circle. Solving gives

$$y = \pm\sqrt{4 - x^2},$$

where $y = \sqrt{4 - x^2}$ represents the top half of the circle and $y = -\sqrt{4 - x^2}$ represents the bottom half. So y is a function of x on the top half, and y is a different function of x on the bottom half.

But let's consider the circle as a whole. The equation does represent a curve which has a tangent line at each point. The slope of this tangent can be found by differentiating the equation of the circle with respect to x:

$$\frac{d}{dx}(x^2) + \frac{d}{dx}(y^2) = \frac{d}{dx}(4).$$

If we think of y as a function of x and use the chain rule, we get

$$2x + 2y\frac{dy}{dx} = 0.$$

Solving gives

$$\frac{dy}{dx} = -\frac{x}{y}.$$

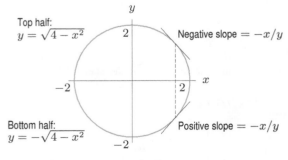

Figure 3.35: Graph of $x^2 + y^2 = 4$

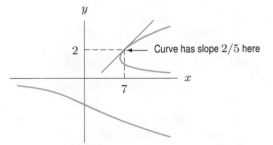

Figure 3.36: Graph of $y^3 - xy = -6$ and its tangent line at $(7, 2)$

The derivative here depends on both x and y (instead of just on x). This is because for many x-values there are two y-values, and the curve has a different slope at each one. Figure 3.35 shows that for x and y both positive, we are on the top right quarter of the curve and the slope is negative (as the formula predicts). For x positive and y negative, we are on the bottom right quarter of the curve and the slope is positive (as the formula predicts).

Differentiating the equation of the circle has given us the slope of the curve at all points except $(2, 0)$ and $(-2, 0)$, where the tangent is vertical. In general, this process of *implicit differentiation* leads to a derivative whenever the expression for the derivative does not have a zero in the denominator.

Example 1   Make a table of x and approximate y-values for the equation $y^3 - xy = -6$ near $x = 7, y = 2$. Your table should include the x-values $6.8, 6.9, 7.0, 7.1$, and 7.2.

Solution   We would like to solve for y in terms of x, but we cannot isolate y by factoring. There is a formula for solving cubics, somewhat like the quadratic formula, but it is too complicated to be useful here. Instead, first observe that $x = 7, y = 2$ does satisfy the equation. (Check this!) Now find dy/dx by implicit differentiation:

$$\frac{d}{dx}(y^3) - \frac{d}{dx}(xy) = \frac{d}{dx}(-6)$$

$$3y^2\frac{dy}{dx} - 1 \cdot y - x\frac{dy}{dx} = 0 \quad \text{(Differentiating with respect to } x\text{)}$$

$$3y^2\frac{dy}{dx} - x\frac{dy}{dx} = y$$

$$(3y^2 - x)\frac{dy}{dx} = y \quad \text{(Factoring out } \frac{dy}{dx}\text{)}$$

$$\frac{dy}{dx} = \frac{y}{3y^2 - x}.$$

When $x = 7$ and $y = 2$, we have

$$\frac{dy}{dx} = \frac{2}{12 - 7} = \frac{2}{5}.$$

(See Figure 3.36.) The equation of the tangent line at $(7, 2)$ is

$$y - 2 = \frac{2}{5}(x - 7)$$

or

$$y = 0.4x - 0.8.$$

Since the tangent lies very close to the curve near the point $(7, 2)$, we use the equation of the tangent line to calculate the following approximate y-values:

x	6.8	6.9	7.0	7.1	7.2
Approximate y	1.92	1.96	2.00	2.04	2.08

Notice that although the equation $y^3 - xy = -6$ leads to a curve which is difficult to deal with algebraically, it still looks like a straight line locally.

Example 2   Find all points where the tangent line to $y^3 - xy = -6$ is either horizontal or vertical.

Solution   From the previous example, $\dfrac{dy}{dx} = \dfrac{y}{3y^2 - x}$. The tangent is horizontal when the numerator of dy/dx equals 0, so $y = 0$. Since we also must satisfy $y^3 - xy = -6$, we get $0^3 - x \cdot 0 = -6$, which is impossible. We conclude that there are no points on the curve where the tangent line is horizontal.

The tangent is vertical when the denominator of dy/dx is 0, giving $3y^2 - x = 0$. Thus, $x = 3y^2$ at any point with a vertical tangent line. Again, we must also satisfy $y^3 - xy = -6$, so

$$y^3 - (3y^2)y = -6,$$

$$-2y^3 = -6,$$

$$y = \sqrt[3]{3} \approx 1.442.$$

We can then find x by substituting $y = \sqrt[3]{3}$ in $y^3 - xy = -6$. We get $3 - x(\sqrt[3]{3}) = -6$, so $x = 9/(\sqrt[3]{3}) \approx 6.240$. So the tangent line is vertical at $(6.240, 1.442)$.

Using implicit differentiation and the expression for dy/dx to locate the points where the tangent is vertical or horizontal, as in the previous example, is a first step in obtaining an overall picture of the curve $y^3 - xy = -6$. However, filling in the rest of the graph, even roughly, by using the sign of dy/dx to tell us where the curve is increasing or decreasing can be difficult.

Exercises and Problems for Section 3.7

Exercises

For Exercises 1–21, find dy/dx. Assume a, b, c are constants.

1. $x^2 + y^2 = \sqrt{7}$

2. $x^2 + y^3 = 8$

3. $x^2 + xy - y^3 = xy^2$

4. $x^2 + y^2 + 3x - 5y = 25$

5. $xy + x + y = 5$

6. $x^2 y - 2y + 5 = 0$

7. $x^2 y^3 - xy = 6$

8. $\sqrt{x} = 5\sqrt{y}$

9. $\sqrt{x} + \sqrt{y} = 25$

10. $xy - x - 3y - 4 = 0$

11. $6x^2 + 4y^2 = 36$

12. $ax^2 - by^2 = c^2$

13. $\ln x + \ln(y^2) = 3$

14. $x \ln y + y^3 = \ln x$

15. $\sin(xy) = 2x + 5$

16. $e^{\cos y} = x^3 \arctan y$

17. $\arctan(x^2 y) = xy^2$

18. $e^{x^2} + \ln y = 0$

19. $(x - a)^2 + y^2 = a^2$

20. $x^{2/3} + y^{2/3} = a^{2/3}$

21. $\sin(ay) + \cos(bx) = xy$

In Exercises 22–25, find the slope of the tangent to the curve at the point specified.

22. $x^2 + y^2 = 1$ at $(0, 1)$

23. $\sin(xy) = x$ at $(1, \pi/2)$

24. $x^3 + 2xy + y^2 = 4$ at $(1, 1)$

25. $x^3 + 5x^2 y + 2y^2 = 4y + 11$ at $(1, 2)$

For Exercises 26–30, find the equations of the tangent lines to the following curves at the indicated points.

26. $xy^2 = 1$ at $(1, -1)$

27. $\ln(xy) = 2x$ at $(1, e^2)$

28. $y^2 = \dfrac{x^2}{xy - 4}$ at $(4, 2)$

29. $y = \dfrac{x}{y + a}$ at $(0, 0)$

30. $x^{2/3} + y^{2/3} = a^{2/3}$ at $(a, 0)$

Problems

31. (a) Find dy/dx given that $x^2 + y^2 - 4x + 7y = 15$.
(b) Under what conditions on x and/or y is the tangent line to this curve horizontal? Vertical?

32. (a) Find the slope of the tangent line to the ellipse $\dfrac{x^2}{25} + \dfrac{y^2}{9} = 1$ at the point (x, y).
(b) Are there any points where the slope is not defined?

33. Find the equations of the tangent lines at $x = 2$ to the ellipse
$$\frac{(x - 2)^2}{16} + \frac{y^2}{4} = 1.$$

34. (a) Find the equations of the tangent lines to the circle $x^2 + y^2 = 25$ at the points where $x = 4$.
(b) Find the equations of the normal lines to this circle at the same points. (The normal line is perpendicular to the tangent line at that point.)
(c) At what point do the two normal lines intersect?

35. (a) If $x^3 + y^3 - xy^2 = 5$, find dy/dx.
(b) Using your answer to part (a), make a table of approximate y-values of points on the curve near $x =$

$1, y = 2$. Include $x = 0.96, 0.98, 1, 1.02, 1.04$.
(c) Find the y-value for $x = 0.96$ by substituting $x = 0.96$ in the original equation and solving for y using a computer or calculator. Compare with your answer in part (b).
(d) Find all points where the tangent line is horizontal or vertical.

36. Find the equation of the tangent line to the curve $y = x^2$ at $x = 1$. Show that this line is also a tangent to a circle centered at $(8, 0)$ and find the equation of this circle.

37. At pressure P atmospheres, a certain fraction f of a gas decomposes. The quantities P and f are related, for some positive constant K, by the equation
$$\frac{4f^2 P}{1 - f^2} = K.$$
(a) Find df/dP.
(b) Show that $df/dP < 0$ always. What does this mean in practical terms?

38. Sketch the circles $y^2 + x^2 = 1$ and $y^2 + (x-3)^2 = 4$. There is a line with positive slope that is tangent to both circles. Determine the points at which this tangent line touches each circle.

39. If $y = \arcsin x$ then $x = \sin y$. Use implicit differentiation on $x = \sin y$ to show that

$$\frac{d}{dx} \arcsin x = \frac{1}{\sqrt{1-x^2}}.$$

40. Show that the power rule for derivatives applies to rational powers of the form $y = x^{m/n}$ by raising both sides to the nth power and using implicit differentiation.

41. For constants a, b, n, R, Van der Waal's equation relates the pressure, P, to the volume, V, of a fixed quantity of a gas at constant temperature T:

$$\left(P + \frac{n^2 a}{V^2}\right)(V - nb) = nRT.$$

Find the rate of change of volume with pressure, dV/dP.

Strengthen Your Understanding

In Problems 42–43, explain what is wrong with the statement.

42. If $y = \sin(xy)$ then $dy/dx = y\cos(xy)$.

43. The formula $dy/dx = -x/y$ gives the slope of the circle $x^2 + y^2 = 10$ at every point in the plane except where $y = 0$.

In Problems 44–45, give an example of:

44. A formula for dy/dx leading to a vertical tangent at $y = 2$ and a horizontal tangent at $x = \pm 2$.

45. A curve that has two horizontal tangents at the same x-value, but no vertical tangents.

46. True or false? Explain your answer: If y satisfies the equation $y^2 + xy - 1 = 0$, then dy/dx exists everywhere.

3.8 HYPERBOLIC FUNCTIONS

There are two combinations of e^x and e^{-x} which are used so often in engineering that they are given their own name. They are the *hyperbolic sine*, abbreviated sinh, and the *hyperbolic cosine*, abbreviated cosh. They are defined as follows:

Hyperbolic Functions

$$\cosh x = \frac{e^x + e^{-x}}{2} \qquad \sinh x = \frac{e^x - e^{-x}}{2}$$

Properties of Hyperbolic Functions

The graphs of $\cosh x$ and $\sinh x$ are given in Figures 3.37 and 3.38 together with the graphs of multiples of e^x and e^{-x}. The graph of $\cosh x$ is called a *catenary*; it is the shape of a hanging cable.

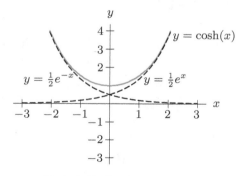

Figure 3.37: Graph of $y = \cosh x$

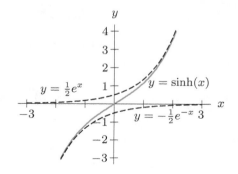

Figure 3.38: Graph of $y = \sinh x$

The graphs suggest that the following results hold:

$$\cosh 0 = 1 \qquad \sinh 0 = 0$$

$$\cosh(-x) = \cosh x \qquad \sinh(-x) = -\sinh x$$

To show that the hyperbolic functions really do have these properties, we use their formulas.

Example 1   Show that (a) $\cosh(0) = 1$ (b) $\cosh(-x) = \cosh x$

Solution   (a) Substituting $x = 0$ into the formula for $\cosh x$ gives

$$\cosh 0 = \frac{e^0 + e^{-0}}{2} = \frac{1 + 1}{2} = 1.$$

(b) Substituting $-x$ for x gives

$$\cosh(-x) = \frac{e^{-x} + e^{-(-x)}}{2} = \frac{e^{-x} + e^x}{2} = \cosh x.$$

Thus, we know that $\cosh x$ is an even function.

Example 2   Describe and explain the behavior of $\cosh x$ as $x \to \infty$ and $x \to -\infty$.

Solution   From Figure 3.37, it appears that as $x \to \infty$, the graph of $\cosh x$ resembles the graph of $\frac{1}{2}e^x$. Similarly, as $x \to -\infty$, the graph of $\cosh x$ resembles the graph of $\frac{1}{2}e^{-x}$. This behavior is explained by using the formula for $\cosh x$ and the facts that $e^{-x} \to 0$ as $x \to \infty$ and $e^x \to 0$ as $x \to -\infty$:

$$\text{As } x \to \infty, \qquad \cosh x = \frac{e^x + e^{-x}}{2} \to \frac{1}{2}e^x.$$

$$\text{As } x \to -\infty, \qquad \cosh x = \frac{e^x + e^{-x}}{2} \to \frac{1}{2}e^{-x}.$$

Identities Involving $\cosh x$ and $\sinh x$

The reason the hyperbolic functions have names that remind us of the trigonometric functions is that they share similar properties. A familiar identity for trigonometric functions is

$$(\cos x)^2 + (\sin x)^2 = 1.$$

To discover an analogous identity relating $(\cosh x)^2$ and $(\sinh x)^2$, we first calculate

$$(\cosh x)^2 = \left(\frac{e^x + e^{-x}}{2} \right)^2 = \frac{e^{2x} + 2e^x e^{-x} + e^{-2x}}{4} = \frac{e^{2x} + 2 + e^{-2x}}{4}$$

$$(\sinh x)^2 = \left(\frac{e^x - e^{-x}}{2} \right)^2 = \frac{e^{2x} - 2e^x e^{-x} + e^{-2x}}{4} = \frac{e^{2x} - 2 + e^{-2x}}{4}.$$

If we add these expressions, the resulting right-hand side contains terms involving both e^{2x} and e^{-2x}. If, however, we subtract the expressions for $(\cosh x)^2$ and $(\sinh x)^2$, we obtain a simple result:

$$(\cosh x)^2 - (\sinh x)^2 = \frac{e^{2x} + 2 + e^{-2x}}{4} - \frac{e^{2x} - 2 + e^{-2x}}{4} = \frac{4}{4} = 1.$$

Thus, writing $\cosh^2 x$ for $(\cosh x)^2$ and $\sinh^2 x$ for $(\sinh x)^2$, we have the identity

$$\cosh^2 x - \sinh^2 x = 1$$

This identity shows us how the hyperbolic functions got their name. Suppose (x, y) is a point in the plane and $x = \cosh t$ and $y = \sinh t$ for some t. Then the point (x, y) lies on the hyperbola $x^2 - y^2 = 1$.

The Hyperbolic Tangent

Extending the analogy to the trigonometric functions, we define

$$\tanh x = \frac{\sinh x}{\cosh x} = \frac{e^x - e^{-x}}{e^x + e^{-x}}$$

Derivatives of Hyperbolic Functions

We calculate the derivatives using the fact that $\frac{d}{dx}(e^x) = e^x$. The results are again reminiscent of the trigonometric functions. For example,

$$\frac{d}{dx}(\cosh x) = \frac{d}{dx}\left(\frac{e^x + e^{-x}}{2}\right) = \frac{e^x - e^{-x}}{2} = \sinh x.$$

We find $\frac{d}{dx}(\sinh x)$ similarly, giving the following results:

$$\frac{d}{dx}(\cosh x) = \sinh x \qquad \frac{d}{dx}(\sinh x) = \cosh x$$

Example 3   Compute the derivative of $\tanh x$.

Solution   Using the quotient rule gives

$$\frac{d}{dx}(\tanh x) = \frac{d}{dx}\left(\frac{\sinh x}{\cosh x}\right) = \frac{(\cosh x)^2 - (\sinh x)^2}{(\cosh x)^2} = \frac{1}{\cosh^2 x}.$$

Exercises and Problems for Section 3.8

Exercises

In Exercises 1–11, find the derivative of the function.

1. $y = \sinh(3z + 5)$ **2.** $y = \cosh(2x)$

3. $g(t) = \cosh^2 t$ **4.** $f(t) = \cosh(\sinh t)$

5. $f(t) = t^3 \sinh t$ **6.** $y = \cosh(3t)\sinh(4t)$

7. $y = \tanh(3 + \sinh x)$ **8.** $f(t) = \cosh(e^{t^2})$

9. $g(\theta) = \ln(\cosh(1 + \theta))$

10. $f(y) = \sinh(\sinh(3y))$

11. $f(t) = \cosh^2 t - \sinh^2 t$

12. Show that $d(\sinh x)/dx = \cosh x$.

13. Show that $\sinh 0 = 0$.

14. Show that $\sinh(-x) = -\sinh(x)$.

In Exercises 15–16, simplify the expressions.

15. $\cosh(\ln t)$ **16.** $\sinh(\ln t)$

Problems

17. Describe and explain the behavior of $\sinh x$ as $x \to \infty$ and as $x \to -\infty$.

18. If $x = \cosh t$ and $y = \sinh t$, explain why the point (x, y) always lies on the curve $x^2 - y^2 = 1$. (This curve is called a hyperbola and gave this family of functions its name.)

19. Is there an identity analogous to $\sin(2x) = 2\sin x \cos x$ for the hyperbolic functions? Explain.

20. Is there an identity analogous to $\cos(2x) = \cos^2 x - \sin^2 x$ for the hyperbolic functions? Explain.

Prove the identities in Problems 21–22.

21. $\cosh(A + B) = \cosh A \cosh B + \sinh A \sinh B$

22. $\sinh(A + B) = \sinh A \cosh B + \cosh A \sinh B$

In Problems 23–26, find the limit of the function as $x \to \infty$.

23. $\dfrac{\sinh(2x)}{\cosh(3x)}$

24. $\dfrac{e^{2x}}{\sinh(2x)}$

25. $\dfrac{\sinh(x^2)}{\cosh(x^2)}$

26. $\dfrac{\cosh(2x)}{\sinh(3x)}$

27. For what values of k is $\lim\limits_{x \to \infty} e^{-3x} \cosh kx$ finite?

28. For what values of k is $\lim\limits_{x \to \infty} \dfrac{\sinh kx}{\cosh 2x}$ finite?

29. The cable between the two towers of a power line hangs in the shape of the curve

$$y = \frac{T}{w} \cosh\left(\frac{wx}{T}\right),$$

where T is the tension in the cable at its lowest point and w is the weight of the cable per unit length. This curve is called a *catenary*.

(a) Suppose the cable stretches between the points $x = -T/w$ and $x = T/w$. Find an expression for the "sag" in the cable. (That is, find the difference between the height of the cable at the highest and lowest points.)

(b) Show that the shape of the cable satisfies the equation

$$\frac{d^2y}{dx^2} = \frac{w}{T}\sqrt{1 + \left(\frac{dy}{dx}\right)^2}.$$

30. The Saint Louis Arch can be approximated by using a function of the form $y = b - a\cosh(x/a)$. Putting the origin on the ground in the center of the arch and the y-axis upward, find an approximate equation for the arch given the dimensions shown in Figure 3.39. (In other words, find a and b.)

615 ft

530 ft

Figure 3.39

31. (a) Using a calculator or computer, sketch the graph of $y = 2e^x + 5e^{-x}$ for $-3 \le x \le 3$, $0 \le y \le 20$. Observe that it looks like the graph of $y = \cosh x$. Approximately where is its minimum?

(b) Show algebraically that $y = 2e^x + 5e^{-x}$ can be written in the form $y = A\cosh(x - c)$. Calculate the values of A and c. Explain what this tells you about the graph in part (a).

32. The following problem is a generalization of Problem 31. Show that any function of the form

$$y = Ae^x + Be^{-x}, \quad A > 0, \ B > 0,$$

can be written, for some K and c, in the form

$$y = K\cosh(x - c).$$

What does this tell you about the graph of $y = Ae^x + Be^{-x}$?

33. (a) Find $\tanh 0$.

(b) For what values of x is $\tanh x$ positive? Negative? Explain your answer algebraically.

(c) On what intervals is $\tanh x$ increasing? Decreasing? Use derivatives to explain your answer.

(d) Find $\lim_{x \to \infty} \tanh x$ and $\lim_{x \to -\infty} \tanh x$. Show this information on a graph.

(e) Does $\tanh x$ have an inverse? Justify your answer using derivatives.

Strengthen Your Understanding

In Problems 34–37, explain what is wrong with the statement.

34. The function $f(x) = \cosh x$ is periodic.

35. The derivative of the function $f(x) = \cosh x$ is $f'(x) = -\sinh x$.

36. $\cosh^2 x + \sinh^2 x = 1$.

37. $\tanh x \to \infty$ as $x \to \infty$.

In Problems 38–40, give an example of:

38. A hyperbolic function which is concave up.

39. A value of k such that $\lim\limits_{x \to \infty} e^{kx} \cosh x$ does not exist.

40. A function involving the hyperbolic cosine that passes through the point $(1, 3)$.

Are the statements in Problems 41–45 true or false? Give an explanation for your answer.

41. The function $\tanh x$ is odd, that is, $\tanh(-x) = -\tanh x$.

42. The 100th derivative of $\sinh x$ is $\cosh x$.

43. $\sinh x + \cosh x = e^x$.

44. The function $\sinh x$ is periodic.

45. The function $\sinh^2 x$ is concave down everywhere.

3.9   LINEAR APPROXIMATION AND THE DERIVATIVE

The Tangent Line Approximation

When we zoom in on the graph of a differentiable function, it looks like a straight line. In fact, the graph is not exactly a straight line when we zoom in; however, its deviation from straightness is so small that it can't be detected by the naked eye. Let's examine what this means. The straight line that we think we see when we zoom in on the graph of $f(x)$ at $x = a$ has slope equal to the derivative, $f'(a)$, so the equation is

$$y = f(a) + f'(a)(x - a).$$

The fact that the graph looks like a line means that y is a good approximation to $f(x)$. (See Figure 3.40.) This suggests the following definition:

The Tangent Line Approximation

Suppose f is differentiable at a. Then, for values of x near a, the tangent line approximation to $f(x)$ is

$$f(x) \approx f(a) + f'(a)(x - a).$$

The expression $f(a) + f'(a)(x - a)$ is called the *local linearization* of f near $x = a$. We are thinking of a as fixed, so that $f(a)$ and $f'(a)$ are constant.
The **error**, $E(x)$, in the approximation is defined by

$$E(x) = f(x) - f(a) - f'(a)(x - a).$$

It can be shown that the tangent line approximation is the best linear approximation to f near a. See Problem 43.

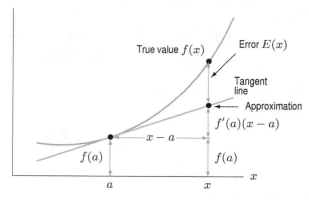

Figure 3.40: The tangent line approximation and its error

Example 1   What is the tangent line approximation for $f(x) = \sin x$ near $x = 0$?

Solution   The tangent line approximation of f near $x = 0$ is

$$f(x) \approx f(0) + f'(0)(x - 0).$$

If $f(x) = \sin x$, then $f'(x) = \cos x$, so $f(0) = \sin 0 = 0$ and $f'(0) = \cos 0 = 1$, and the approximation is

$$\sin x \approx x.$$

This means that, near $x = 0$, the function $f(x) = \sin x$ is well approximated by the function $y = x$. If we zoom in on the graphs of the functions $\sin x$ and x near the origin, we won't be able to tell them apart. (See Figure 3.41.)

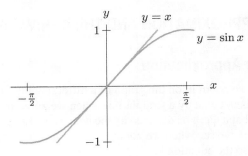

Figure 3.41: Tangent line approximation to $y = \sin x$

Example 2   What is the local linearization of e^{kx} near $x = 0$?

Solution   If $f(x) = e^{kx}$, then $f(0) = 1$ and, by the chain rule, $f'(x) = ke^{kx}$, so $f'(0) = ke^{k \cdot 0} = k$. Thus

$$f(x) \approx f(0) + f'(0)(x - 0)$$

becomes

$$e^{kx} \approx 1 + kx.$$

This is the tangent line approximation to e^{kx} near $x = 0$. In other words, if we zoom in on the functions $f(x) = e^{kx}$ and $y = 1 + kx$ near the origin, we won't be able to tell them apart.

Estimating the Error in the Approximation

Let us look at the error, $E(x)$, which is the difference between $f(x)$ and the local linearization. (Look back at Figure 3.40.) The fact that the graph of f looks like a line as we zoom in means that not only is $E(x)$ small for x near a, but also that $E(x)$ is small relative to $(x - a)$. To demonstrate this, we prove the following theorem about the ratio $E(x)/(x - a)$.

Theorem 3.6: Differentiability and Local Linearity

Suppose f is differentiable at $x = a$ and $E(x)$ is the error in the tangent line approximation, that is:

$$E(x) = f(x) - f(a) - f'(a)(x - a).$$

Then

$$\lim_{x \to a} \frac{E(x)}{x - a} = 0.$$

Proof   Using the definition of $E(x)$, we have

$$\frac{E(x)}{x - a} = \frac{f(x) - f(a) - f'(a)(x - a)}{x - a} = \frac{f(x) - f(a)}{x - a} - f'(a).$$

Taking the limit as $x \to a$ and using the definition of the derivative, we see that

$$\lim_{x \to a} \frac{E(x)}{x - a} = \lim_{x \to a} \left(\frac{f(x) - f(a)}{x - a} - f'(a) \right) = f'(a) - f'(a) = 0.$$

Theorem 3.6 says that $E(x)$ approaches 0 faster than $(x - a)$. For the function in Example 3, we see that $E(x) \approx k(x - a)^2$ for constant k if x is near a.

Example 3   Let $E(x)$ be the error in the tangent line approximation to $f(x) = x^3 - 5x + 3$ for x near 2.

(a) What does a table of values for $E(x)/(x - 2)$ suggest about $\lim_{x \to 2} E(x)/(x - 2)$?

(b) Make another table to see that $E(x) \approx k(x-2)^2$. Estimate the value of k. Check that a possible value is $k = f''(2)/2$.

Solution

(a) Since $f(x) = x^3 - 5x + 3$, we have $f'(x) = 3x^2 - 5$, and $f''(x) = 6x$. Thus, $f(2) = 1$ and $f'(2) = 3 \cdot 2^2 - 5 = 7$, so the tangent line approximation for x near 2 is

$$f(x) \approx f(2) + f'(2)(x - 2)$$
$$f(x) \approx 1 + 7(x - 2).$$

Thus,

$$E(x) = \text{True value} - \text{Approximation} = (x^3 - 5x + 3) - (1 + 7(x - 2)).$$

The values of $E(x)/(x - 2)$ in Table 3.7 suggest that $E(x)/(x - 2)$ approaches 0 as $x \to 2$.

(b) Notice that if $E(x) \approx k(x - 2)^2$, then $E(x)/(x - 2)^2 \approx k$. Thus we make Table 3.8 showing values of $E(x)/(x - 2)^2$. Since the values are all approximately 6, we guess that $k = 6$ and $E(x) \approx 6(x - 2)^2$.

Since $f''(2) = 12$, our value of k satisfies $k = f''(2)/2$.

Table 3.7

x	$E(x)/(x - 2)$
2.1	0.61
2.01	0.0601
2.001	0.006001
2.0001	0.00060001

Table 3.8

x	$E(x)/(x - 2)^2$
2.1	6.1
2.01	6.01
2.001	6.001
2.0001	6.0001

The relationship between $E(x)$ and $f''(x)$ that appears in Example 3 holds more generally. If $f(x)$ satisfies certain conditions, it can be shown that the error in the tangent line approximation behaves near $x = a$ as

$$E(x) \approx \frac{f''(a)}{2}(x - a)^2.$$

This is part of a general pattern for obtaining higher-order approximations called Taylor polynomials, which are studied in Chapter 10.

Why Differentiability Makes a Graph Look Straight

We use the properties of the error $E(x)$ to understand why differentiability makes a graph look straight when we zoom in.

Example 4

Consider the graph of $f(x) = \sin x$ near $x = 0$, and its linear approximation computed in Example 1. Show that there is an interval around 0 with the property that the distance from $f(x) = \sin x$ to the linear approximation is less than $0.1|x|$ for all x in the interval.

Solution

The linear approximation of $f(x) = \sin x$ near 0 is $y = x$, so we write

$$\sin x = x + E(x).$$

Since $\sin x$ is differentiable at $x = 0$, Theorem 3.6 tells us that

$$\lim_{x \to 0} \frac{E(x)}{x} = 0.$$

If we take $\epsilon = 1/10$, then the definition of limit guarantees that there is a $\delta > 0$ such that

$$\left| \frac{E(x)}{x} \right| < 0.1 \quad \text{for all} \quad |x| < \delta.$$

In other words, for x in the interval $(-\delta, \delta)$, we have $|x| < \delta$, so

$$|E(x)| < 0.1|x|.$$

(See Figure 3.42.)

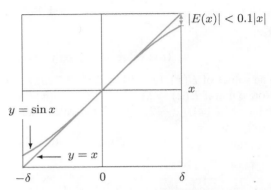

Figure 3.42: Graph of $y = \sin x$ and its linear approximation $y = x$, showing a window in which the magnitude of the error, $|E(x)|$, is less than $0.1|x|$ for all x in the window

We can generalize from this example to explain why differentiability makes the graph of f look straight when viewed over a small graphing window. Suppose f is differentiable at $x = a$. Then we know $\lim_{x \to a} \left| \frac{E(x)}{x - a} \right| = 0$. So, for any $\epsilon > 0$, we can find a δ small enough so that

$$\left| \frac{E(x)}{x - a} \right| < \epsilon, \qquad \text{for} \quad a - \delta < x < a + \delta.$$

So, for any x in the interval $(a - \delta, a + \delta)$, we have

$$|E(x)| < \epsilon|x - a|.$$

Thus, the error, $E(x)$, is less than ϵ times $|x - a|$, the distance between x and a. So, as we zoom in on the graph by choosing smaller ϵ, the deviation, $|E(x)|$, of f from its tangent line shrinks, even relative to the scale on the x-axis. So, zooming makes a differentiable function look straight.

Exercises and Problems for Section 3.9

Exercises

1. Find the tangent line approximation for $\sqrt{1+x}$ near $x = 0$.

2. What is the tangent line approximation to e^x near $x = 0$?

3. Find the tangent line approximation to $1/x$ near $x = 1$.

4. Find the local linearization of $f(x) = x^2$ near $x = 1$.

5. What is the local linearization of e^{x^2} near $x = 1$?

6. Show that $1 - x/2$ is the tangent line approximation to $1/\sqrt{1+x}$ near $x = 0$.

7. Show that $e^{-x} \approx 1 - x$ near $x = 0$.

8. Local linearization gives values too small for the function x^2 and too large for the function $\sqrt{x}$. Draw pictures

to explain why.

9. Using a graph like Figure 3.41, estimate to one decimal place the magnitude of the error in approximating $\sin x$ by x for $-1 \leq x \leq 1$. Is the approximation an over- or an underestimate?

10. For x near 0, local linearization gives

$$e^x \approx 1 + x.$$

Using a graph, decide if the approximation is an over- or underestimate, and estimate to one decimal place the magnitude of the error for $-1 \leq x \leq 1$.

Problems

11. **(a)** Find the best linear approximation, $L(x)$, to $f(x) = e^x$ near $x = 0$.
   (b) What is the sign of the error, $E(x) = f(x) - L(x)$ for x near 0?
   (c) Find the true value of the function at $x = 1$. What is the error? (Give decimal answers.) Illustrate with a graph.
   (d) Before doing any calculations, explain which you expect to be larger, $E(0.1)$ or $E(1)$, and why.
   (e) Find $E(0.1)$.

12. **(a)** Find the tangent line approximation to $\cos x$ at $x = \pi/4$.
   (b) Use a graph to explain how you know whether the tangent line approximation is an under- or overestimate for $0 \le x \le \pi/2$.
   (c) To one decimal place, estimate the error in the approximation for $0 \le x \le \pi/2$.

13. **(a)** Graph $f(x) = x^3 - 3x^2 + 3x + 1$.
   (b) Find and add to your sketch the local linearization to $f(x)$ at $x = 2$.
   (c) Mark on your sketch the true value of $f(1.5)$, the tangent line approximation to $f(1.5)$ and the error in the approximation.

14. **(a)** Show that $1+kx$ is the local linearization of $(1+x)^k$ near $x = 0$.
   (b) Someone claims that the square root of 1.1 is about 1.05. Without using a calculator, do you think that this estimate is about right?
   (c) Is the actual number above or below 1.05?

15. Figure 3.43 shows $f(x)$ and its local linearization at $x = a$. What is the value of a? Of $f(a)$? Is the approximation an under- or overestimate? Use the linearization to approximate the value of $f(1.2)$.

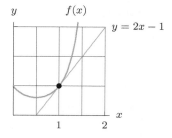

Figure 3.43

In Problems 16–17, the equation has a solution near $x = 0$. By replacing the left side of the equation by its linearization, find an approximate value for the solution.

16. $e^x + x = 2$
17. $x + \ln(1 + x) = 0.2$

18. **(a)** Given that $f(7) = 13$ and $f'(7) = -0.38$, estimate $f(7.1)$.
   (b) Suppose also $f''(x) < 0$ for all x. Does this make your answer to part (a) an under- or overestimate?

19. **(a)** Explain why the following equation has a solution near 0:
$$e^t = 0.02t + 1.098.$$
   (b) Replace e^t by its linearization near 0. Solve the new equation to get an approximate solution to the original equation.

20. The speed of sound in dry air is
$$f(T) = 331.3\sqrt{1 + \frac{T}{273.15}} \text{ meters/second}$$
where T is the temperature in degrees Celsius. Find a linear function that approximates the speed of sound for temperatures near $0°\text{C}$.

21. Air pressure at sea level is 30 inches of mercury. At an altitude of h feet above sea level, the air pressure, P, in inches of mercury, is given by
$$P = 30e^{-3.23 \times 10^{-5} h}$$
   (a) Sketch a graph of P against h.
   (b) Find the equation of the tangent line at $h = 0$.
   (c) A rule of thumb used by travelers is that air pressure drops about 1 inch for every 1000-foot increase in height above sea level. Write a formula for the air pressure given by this rule of thumb.
   (d) What is the relation between your answers to parts (b) and (c)? Explain why the rule of thumb works.
   (e) Are the predictions made by the rule of thumb too large or too small? Why?

22. On October 7, 2010, the *Wall Street Journal*[8] reported that Android cell phone users had increased to 10.9 million by the end of August 2010 from 866,000 a year earlier. During the same period, iPhone users increased to 13.5 million, up from 7.8 million a year earlier. Let $A(t)$ be the number of Android users, in millions, at time t in years since the end of August 2009. Let $P(t)$ be the number of iPhone users in millions.
   (a) Estimate $A'(0)$. Give units.
   (b) Estimate $P'(0)$. Give units.
   (c) Using the tangent line approximation, when are the numbers of Android and iPhone users predicted to be the same?
   (d) What assumptions did you make in part (c)?

---

[8]"Apple Readies Verizon iPhone", WSJ, Oct 7, 2010.

23. Writing g for the acceleration due to gravity, the period, T, of a pendulum of length l is given by

$$T = 2\pi \sqrt{\frac{l}{g}}.$$

(a) Show that if the length of the pendulum changes by Δl, the change in the period, ΔT, is given by

$$\Delta T \approx \frac{T}{2l} \Delta l.$$

(b) If the length of the pendulum increases by 2%, by what percent does the period change?

24. Suppose now the length of the pendulum in Problem 23 remains constant, but that the acceleration due to gravity changes.

(a) Use the method of the preceding problem to relate ΔT approximately to Δg, the change in g.
(b) If g increases by 1%, find the percent change in T.

25. Suppose f has a continuous positive second derivative for all x. Which is larger, $f(1+\Delta x)$ or $f(1)+f'(1)\Delta x$? Explain.

26. Suppose $f'(x)$ is a differentiable decreasing function for all x. In each of the following pairs, which number is the larger? Give a reason for your answer.

(a) $f'(5)$ and $f'(6)$
(b) $f''(5)$ and 0
(c) $f(5 + \Delta x)$ and $f(5) + f'(5)\Delta x$

Problems 27–29 investigate the motion of a projectile shot from a cannon. The fixed parameters are the acceleration of gravity, $g = 9.8$ m/sec^2, and the muzzle velocity, $v_0 = 500$ m/sec, at which the projectile leaves the cannon. The angle θ, in degrees, between the muzzle of the cannon and the ground can vary.

27. The range of the projectile is

$$f(\theta) = \frac{v_0^2}{g} \sin \frac{\pi\theta}{90} wq = 25510 \sin \frac{\pi\theta}{90} \text{ meters.}$$

(a) Find the range with $\theta = 20°$.
(b) Find a linear function of θ that approximates the range for angles near $20°$.
(c) Find the range and its approximation from part (b) for $21°$.

28. The time that the projectile stays in the air is

$$t(\theta) = \frac{2v_0}{g} \sin \frac{\pi\theta}{180} = 102 \sin \frac{\pi\theta}{180} \text{ seconds.}$$

(a) Find the time in the air for $\theta = 20°$.
(b) Find a linear function of θ that approximates the time in the air for angles near $20°$.
(c) Find the time in air and its approximation from part (b) for $21°$.

29. At its highest point the projectile reaches a peak altitude given by

$$h(\theta) = \frac{v_0^2}{2g} \sin^2 \frac{\pi\theta}{180} = 12755 \sin^2 \frac{\pi\theta}{180} \text{ meters.}$$

(a) Find the peak altitude for $\theta = 20°$.
(b) Find a linear function of θ that approximates the peak altitude for angles near $20°$.
(c) Find the peak altitude and its approximation from part (b) for $21°$.

In Problems 30–32, find the local linearization of $f(x)$ near 0 and use this to approximate the value of a.

30. $f(x) = (1+x)^r$, $\quad a = (1.2)^{3/5}$
31. $f(x) = e^{kx}$, $\quad a = e^{0.3}$
32. $f(x) = \sqrt{b^2 + x}$, $\quad a = \sqrt{26}$

In Problems 33–37, find a formula for the error $E(x)$ in the tangent line approximation to the function near $x = a$. Using a table of values for $E(x)/(x - a)$ near $x = a$, find a value of k such that $E(x)/(x - a) \approx k(x - a)$. Check that, approximately, $k = f''(a)/2$ and that $E(x) \approx (f''(a)/2)(x - a)^2$.

33. $f(x) = x^4$, $a = 1$ $\qquad$ **34.** $f(x) = \cos x$, $a = 0$

35. $f(x) = e^x$, $a = 0$ $\qquad$ **36.** $f(x) = \sqrt{x}$, $a = 1$

37. $f(x) = \ln x$, $a = 1$

38. Multiply the local linearization of e^x near $x = 0$ by itself to obtain an approximation for e^{2x}. Compare this with the actual local linearization of e^{2x}. Explain why these two approximations are consistent, and discuss which one is more accurate.

39. (a) Show that $1 - x$ is the local linearization of $\dfrac{1}{1+x}$ near $x = 0$.

(b) From your answer to part (a), show that near $x = 0$,

$$\frac{1}{1+x^2} \approx 1 - x^2.$$

(c) Without differentiating, what do you think the derivative of $\dfrac{1}{1+x^2}$ is at $x = 0$?

40. From the local linearizations of e^x and $\sin x$ near $x = 0$, write down the local linearization of the function $e^x \sin x$. From this result, write down the derivative of $e^x \sin x$ at $x = 0$. Using this technique, write down the derivative of $e^x \sin x/(1 + x)$ at $x = 0$.

41. Use local linearization to derive the product rule,

$$[f(x)g(x)]' = f'(x)g(x) + f(x)g'(x).$$

[Hint: Use the definition of the derivative and the local linearizations $f(x+h) \approx f(x)+f'(x)h$ and $g(x+h) \approx g(x) + g'(x)h$.]

42. Derive the chain rule using local linearization. [Hint: In other words, differentiate $f(g(x))$, using $g(x + h) \approx g(x) + g'(x)h$ and $f(z + k) \approx f(z) + f'(z)k$.]

43. Consider a function f and a point a. Suppose there is a number L such that the linear function g

$$g(x) = f(a) + L(x - a)$$

is a good approximation to f. By good approximation, we mean that

$$\lim_{x \to a} \frac{E_L(x)}{x - a} = 0,$$

where $E_L(x)$ is the approximation error defined by

$$f(x) = g(x) + E_L(x) = f(a) + L(x - a) + E_L(x).$$

Show that f is differentiable at $x = a$ and that $f'(a) = L$. Thus the tangent line approximation is the only good linear approximation.

44. Consider the graph of $f(x) = x^2$ near $x = 1$. Find an interval around $x = 1$ with the property that throughout any smaller interval, the graph of $f(x) = x^2$ never differs from its local linearization at $x = 1$ by more than $0.1|x - 1|$.

Strengthen Your Understanding

In Problems 45–46, explain what is wrong with the statement.

45. To approximate $f(x) = e^x$, we can always use the linear approximation $f(x) = e^x \approx x + 1$.

46. The linear approximation for $F(x) = x^3 + 1$ near $x = 0$ is an underestimate for the function F for all x, $x \neq 0$.

In Problems 47–49, give an example of:

47. Two different functions that have the same linear approximation near $x = 0$.

48. A non-polynomial function that has the tangent line approximation $f(x) \approx 1$ near $x = 0$.

49. A function that does not have a linear approximation at $x = -1$.

50. Let f be a differentiable function and let L be the linear function $L(x) = f(a) + k(x - a)$ for some constant a. Decide whether the following statements are true or false for all constants k. Explain your answer.

(a) L is the local linearization for f near $x = a$,
(b) If $\lim_{x \to a} (f(x) - L(x)) = 0$, then L is the local linearization for f near $x = a$.

3.10 THEOREMS ABOUT DIFFERENTIABLE FUNCTIONS

A Relationship Between Local and Global: The Mean Value Theorem

We often want to infer a global conclusion (for example, f is increasing on an interval) from local information (for example, f' is positive at each point on an interval). The following theorem relates the average rate of change of a function on an interval (global information) to the instantaneous rate of change at a point in the interval (local information).

Theorem 3.7: The Mean Value Theorem

If f is continuous on $a \leq x \leq b$ and differentiable on $a < x < b$, then there exists a number c, with $a < c < b$, such that

$$f'(c) = \frac{f(b) - f(a)}{b - a}.$$

In other words, $f(b) - f(a) = f'(c)(b - a)$.

To understand this theorem geometrically, look at Figure 3.44. Join the points on the curve where $x = a$ and $x = b$ with a secant line and observe that

$$\text{Slope of secant line} = \frac{f(b) - f(a)}{b - a}.$$

Now consider the tangent lines drawn to the curve at each point between $x = a$ and $x = b$. In general, these lines have different slopes. For the curve shown in Figure 3.44, the tangent line at

$x = a$ is flatter than the secant line. Similarly, the tangent line at $x = b$ is steeper than the secant line. However, there appears to be at least one point between a and b where the slope of the tangent line to the curve is precisely the same as the slope of the secant line. Suppose this occurs at $x = c$. Then

$$\text{Slope of tangent line } = f'(c) = \frac{f(b) - f(a)}{b - a}.$$

The Mean Value Theorem tells us that the point $x = c$ exists, but it does not tell us how to find c. Problems 44 and 45 in Section 4.2 show how the Mean Value Theorem can be derived.

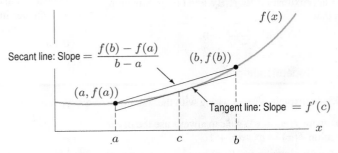

Figure 3.44: The point c with $f'(c) = \frac{f(b)-f(a)}{b-a}$

If f satisfies the conditions of the Mean Value Theorem on $a < x < b$ and $f(a) = f(b) = 0$, the Mean Value Theorem tells us that there is a point c, with $a < c < b$, such that $f'(c) = 0$. This result is called **Rolle's Theorem**.

The Increasing Function Theorem

We say that a function f is *increasing* on an interval if, for any two numbers x_1 and x_2 in the interval such that $x_1 < x_2$, we have $f(x_1) < f(x_2)$. If instead we have $f(x_1) \leq f(x_2)$, we say f is *nondecreasing*.

Theorem 3.8: The Increasing Function Theorem

Suppose that f is continuous on $a \leq x \leq b$ and differentiable on $a < x < b$.
- If $f'(x) > 0$ on $a < x < b$, then f is increasing on $a \leq x \leq b$.
- If $f'(x) \geq 0$ on $a < x < b$, then f is nondecreasing on $a \leq x \leq b$.

Proof   Suppose $a \leq x_1 < x_2 \leq b$. By the Mean Value Theorem, there is a number c, with $x_1 < c < x_2$, such that

$$f(x_2) - f(x_1) = f'(c)(x_2 - x_1).$$

If $f'(c) > 0$, this says $f(x_2) - f(x_1) > 0$, which means f is increasing. If $f'(c) \geq 0$, this says $f(x_2) - f(x_1) \geq 0$, which means f is nondecreasing.

It may seem that something as simple as the Increasing Function Theorem should follow immediately from the definition of the derivative, and you may be surprised that the Mean Value Theorem is needed.

The Constant Function Theorem

If f is constant on an interval, then we know that $f'(x) = 0$ on the interval. The following theorem is the converse.

Theorem 3.9: The Constant Function Theorem

Suppose that f is continuous on $a \leq x \leq b$ and differentiable on $a < x < b$. If $f'(x) = 0$ on $a < x < b$, then f is constant on $a \leq x \leq b$.

Proof The proof is the same as for the Increasing Function Theorem, only in this case $f'(c) = 0$ so $f(x_2) - f(x_1) = 0$. Thus $f(x_2) = f(x_1)$ for $a \leq x_1 < x_2 \leq b$, so f is constant.

A proof of the Constant Function Theorem using the Increasing Function Theorem is given in Problems 17 and 25.

The Racetrack Principle

Theorem 3.10: The Racetrack Principle[9]

Suppose that g and h are continuous on $a \leq x \leq b$ and differentiable on $a < x < b$, and that $g'(x) \leq h'(x)$ for $a < x < b$.

- If $g(a) = h(a)$, then $g(x) \leq h(x)$ for $a \leq x \leq b$.
- If $g(b) = h(b)$, then $g(x) \geq h(x)$ for $a \leq x \leq b$.

The Racetrack Principle has the following interpretation. We can think of $g(x)$ and $h(x)$ as the positions of two racehorses at time x, with horse h always moving faster than horse g. If they start together, horse h is ahead during the whole race. If they finish together, horse g was ahead during the whole race.

Proof Consider the function $f(x) = h(x) - g(x)$. Since $f'(x) = h'(x) - g'(x) \geq 0$, we know that f is nondecreasing by the Increasing Function Theorem. So $f(x) \geq f(a) = h(a) - g(a) = 0$. Thus $g(x) \leq h(x)$ for $a \leq x \leq b$. This proves the first part of the Racetrack Principle. Problem 24 asks for a proof of the second part.

Example 1 Explain graphically why $e^x \geq 1 + x$ for all values of x. Then use the Racetrack Principle to prove the inequality.

Solution The graph of the function $y = e^x$ is concave up everywhere and the equation of its tangent line at the point $(0, 1)$ is $y = x + 1$. (See Figure 3.45.) Since the graph always lies above its tangent, we have the inequality

$$e^x \geq 1 + x.$$

Figure 3.45: Graph showing that $e^x \geq 1 + x$

---

[9]Based on the Racetrack Principle in *Calculus & Mathematica*, by William Davis, Horacio Porta, Jerry Uhl (Reading: Addison Wesley, 1994).

Now we prove the inequality using the Racetrack Principle. Let $g(x) = 1 + x$ and $h(x) = e^x$. Then $g(0) = h(0) = 1$. Furthermore, $g'(x) = 1$ and $h'(x) = e^x$. Hence $g'(x) \leq h'(x)$ for $x \geq 0$. So by the Racetrack Principle, with $a = 0$, we have $g(x) \leq h(x)$, that is, $1 + x \leq e^x$.

For $x \leq 0$ we have $h'(x) \leq g'(x)$. So by the Racetrack Principle, with $b = 0$, we have $g(x) \leq h(x)$, that is, $1 + x \leq e^x$.

Exercises and Problems for Section 3.10

Exercises

In Exercises 1–5, decide if the statements are true or false. Give an explanation for your answer.

1. Let $f(x) = [x]$, the greatest integer less than or equal to x. Then $f'(x) = 0$, so $f(x)$ is constant by the Constant Function Theorem.

2. If $a < b$ and $f'(x)$ is positive on $[a, b]$ then $f(a) < f(b)$.

3. If $f(x)$ is increasing and differentiable on the interval $[a, b]$, then $f'(x) > 0$ on $[a, b]$.

4. The Racetrack Principle can be used to justify the statement that if two horses start a race at the same time, the horse that wins must have been moving faster than the other throughout the race.

5. Two horses start a race at the same time and one runs slower than the other throughout the race. The Racetrack Principle can be used to justify the fact that the slower horse loses the race.

Do the functions graphed in Exercises 6–9 appear to satisfy the hypotheses of the Mean Value Theorem on the interval $[a, b]$? Do they satisfy the conclusion?

6.

7.

8.

9.

Problems

10. Applying the Mean Value Theorem with $a = 2$, $b = 7$ to the function in Figure 3.46 leads to $c = 4$. What is the equation of the tangent line at 4?

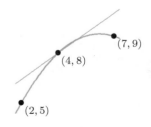

Figure 3.46

11. Applying the Mean Value Theorem with $a = 3$, $b = 13$ to the function in Figure 3.47 leads to the point c shown. What is the value of $f'(c)$? What can you say about the values of $f'(x_1)$ and $f'(x_2)$?

Figure 3.47

12. Let $p(x) = x^5 + 8x^4 - 30x^3 + 30x^2 - 31x + 22$. What is the relationship between $p(x)$ and $f(x) = 5x^4 + 32x^3 - 90x^2 + 60x - 31$? What do the values of $p(1)$ and $p(2)$ tell you about the values of $f(x)$?

13. Let $p(x)$ be a seventh-degree polynomial with 7 distinct zeros. How many zeros does $p'(x)$ have?

14. Use the Racetrack Principle and the fact that $\sin 0 = 0$ to show that $\sin x \leq x$ for all $x \geq 0$.

15. Use the Racetrack Principle to show that $\ln x \leq x - 1$.

16. Use the fact that $\ln x$ and e^x are inverse functions to show that the inequalities $e^x \geq 1 + x$ and $\ln x \leq x - 1$ are equivalent for $x > 0$.

17. State a Decreasing Function Theorem, analogous to the Increasing Function Theorem. Deduce your theorem from the Increasing Function Theorem. [Hint: Apply the Increasing Function Theorem to $-f$.]

18. Dominic drove from Phoenix to Tucson on Interstate 10, a distance of 116 miles. The speed limit on this highway varies between 55 and 75 miles per hour. He started his trip at 11:44 pm and arrived in Tucson at 1:12 am. Prove that Dominic was speeding at some point during his trip.

In Problems 19–22, use one of the theorems in this section to prove the statements .

19. If $f'(x) \leq 1$ for all x and $f(0) = 0$, then $f(x) \leq x$ for all $x \geq 0$.

20. If $f''(t) \leq 3$ for all t and $f(0) = f'(0) = 0$, then $f(t) \leq \frac{3}{2}t^2$ for all $t \geq 0$.

21. If $f'(x) = g'(x)$ for all x and $f(5) = g(5)$, then $f(x) = g(x)$ for all x.

22. If f is differentiable and $f(0) < f(1)$, then there is a number c, with $0 < c < 1$, such that $f'(c) > 0$.

23. The position of a particle on the x-axis is given by $s = f(t)$; its initial position and velocity are $f(0) = 3$ and

$f'(0) = 4$. The acceleration is bounded by $5 \leq f''(t) \leq 7$ for $0 \leq t \leq 2$. What can we say about the position $f(2)$ of the particle at $t = 2$?

24. Suppose that g and h are continuous on $[a, b]$ and differentiable on (a, b). Prove that if $g'(x) \leq h'(x)$ for $a < x < b$ and $g(b) = h(b)$, then $h(x) \leq g(x)$ for $a \leq x \leq b$.

25. Deduce the Constant Function Theorem from the Increasing Function Theorem and the Decreasing Function Theorem. (See Problem 17.)

26. Prove that if $f'(x) = g'(x)$ for all x in (a, b), then there is a constant C such that $f(x) = g(x) + C$ on (a, b). [Hint: Apply the Constant Function Theorem to $h(x) = f(x) - g(x)$.]

27. Suppose that $f'(x) = f(x)$ for all x. Prove that $f(x) = Ce^x$ for some constant C. [Hint: Consider $f(x)/e^x$.]

28. Suppose that f is continuous on $[a, b]$ and differentiable on (a, b) and that $m \leq f'(x) \leq M$ on (a, b). Use the Racetrack Principle to prove that $f(x) - f(a) \leq M(x - a)$ for all x in $[a, b]$, and that $m(x - a) \leq f(x) - f(a)$ for all x in $[a, b]$. Conclude that $m \leq (f(b) - f(a))/(b - a) \leq M$. This is called the Mean Value Inequality. In words: If the instantaneous rate of change of f is between m and M on an interval, so is the average rate of change of f over the interval.

29. Suppose that $f''(x) \geq 0$ for all x in (a, b). We will show the graph of f lies above the tangent line at $(c, f(c))$ for any c with $a < c < b$.

(a) Use the Increasing Function Theorem to prove that $f'(c) \leq f'(x)$ for $c \leq x < b$ and that $f'(x) \leq f'(c)$ for $a < x \leq c$.

(b) Use (a) and the Racetrack Principle to conclude that $f(c) + f'(c)(x - c) \leq f(x)$, for $a < x < b$.

Strengthen Your Understanding

In Problems 30–32, explain what is wrong with the statement.

30. The Mean Value Theorem applies to $f(x) = |x|$, for $-2 < x < 2$.

31. The following function satisfies the conditions of the Mean Value Theorem on the interval $[0, 1]$:

$$f(x) = \begin{cases} x & \text{if } 0 < x \leq 1 \\ 1 & \text{if } x = 0. \end{cases}$$

32. If $f'(x) = 0$ on $a < x < b$, then by the Constant Function Theorem f is constant on $a \leq x \leq b$.

In Problems 33–37, give an example of:

33. An interval where the Mean Value Theorem applies when $f(x) = \ln x$.

34. An interval where the Mean Value Theorem does not apply when $f(x) = 1/x$.

35. A continuous function f on the interval $[-1, 1]$ that does not satisfy the conclusion of the Mean Value Theorem.

36. A function f that is differentiable on the interval $(0, 2)$, but does not satisfy the conclusion of the Mean Value Theorem on the interval $[0, 2]$.

37. A function that is differentiable on $(0, 1)$ and not continuous on $[0, 1]$, but which satisfies the conclusion of the Mean Value Theorem.

Are the statements in Problems 38–41 true or false for a function f whose domain is all real numbers? If a statement is true, explain how you know. If a statement is false, give a counterexample.

38. If $f'(x) \geq 0$ for all x, then $f(a) \leq f(b)$ whenever $a \leq b$.

39. If $f'(x) \leq g'(x)$ for all x, then $f(x) \leq g(x)$ for all x.

40. If $f'(x) = g'(x)$ for all x, then $f(x) = g(x)$ for all x.

41. If $f'(x) \leq 1$ for all x and $f(0) = 0$, then $f(x) \leq x$ for all x.

CHAPTER SUMMARY (see also Ready Reference at the end of the book)

- **Derivatives of elementary functions**
  Power, polynomial, rational, exponential, logarithmic, trigonometric, inverse trigonometric, and hyperbolic functions.

- **Derivatives of sums, differences, and constant multiples**

- **Product and quotient rules**

- **Chain rule**

- **Differentiation of implicitly defined functions and inverse functions**

- **Hyperbolic functions**

- **Tangent line approximation, local linearity**

- **Theorems about differentiable functions**
  Mean value theorem, increasing function theorem, constant function theorem, Racetrack Principle.

REVIEW EXERCISES AND PROBLEMS FOR CHAPTER THREE

Exercises

Find derivatives for the functions in Exercises 1–73. Assume $a, b, c,$ and k are constants.

1. $w = (t^2 + 1)^{100}$

2. $f(t) = e^{3t}$

3. $z = \dfrac{t^2 + 3t + 1}{t + 1}$

4. $y = \dfrac{\sqrt{t}}{t^2 + 1}$

5. $h(t) = \dfrac{4 - t}{4 + t}$

6. $f(x) = x^e$

7. $f(x) = \dfrac{x^3}{9}(3 \ln x - 1)$

8. $f(x) = \dfrac{1 + x}{2 + 3x + 4x^2}$

9. $g(\theta) = e^{\sin \theta}$

10. $y = \sqrt{\theta}\left(\sqrt{\theta} + \dfrac{1}{\sqrt{\theta}}\right)$

11. $f(w) = \ln(\cos(w - 1))$

12. $f(y) = \ln\left(\ln(2y^3)\right)$

13. $g(x) = x^k + k^x$

14. $y = e^{-\pi} + \pi^{-e}$

15. $z = \sin^3 \theta$

16. $f(t) = \cos^2(3t + 5)$

17. $M(\alpha) = \tan^2(2 + 3\alpha)$

18. $s(\theta) = \sin^2(3\theta - \pi)$

19. $h(t) = \ln\left(e^{-t} - t\right)$

20. $p(\theta) = \dfrac{\sin(5 - \theta)}{\theta^2}$

21. $w(\theta) = \dfrac{\theta}{\sin^2 \theta}$

22. $f(\theta) = \dfrac{1}{1 + e^{-\theta}}$

23. $g(w) = \dfrac{1}{2^w + e^w}$

24. $f(t) = \dfrac{t^2 + t^3 - 1}{t^4}$

25. $h(z) = \sqrt{\dfrac{\sin(2z)}{\cos(2z)}}$

26. $q(\theta) = \sqrt{4\theta^2 - \sin^2(2\theta)}$

27. $w = 2^{-4z} \sin(\pi z)$

28. $g(t) = \arctan(3t - 4)$

29. $r(\theta) = e^{(e^\theta + e^{-\theta})}$

30. $m(n) = \sin(e^n)$

31. $G(\alpha) = e^{\tan(\sin \alpha)}$

32. $g(t) = t \cos(\sqrt{t} e^t)$

33. $f(r) = (\tan 2 + \tan r)^e$

34. $h(x) = x e^{\tan x}$

35. $y = e^{2x} \sin^2(3x)$

36. $g(x) = \tan^{-1}(3x^2 + 1)$

37. $y = 2^{\sin x} \cos x$

38. $F(x) = \ln(e^{ax}) + \ln b$

39. $y = e^{\theta - 1}$

40. $f(t) = e^{-4kt} \sin t$

41. $H(t) = (at^2 + b)e^{-ct}$

42. $g(\theta) = \sqrt{a^2 - \sin^2 \theta}$

43. $y = 5^x + 2$

44. $f(x) = \dfrac{a^2 - x^2}{a^2 + x^2}$

45. $w(r) = \dfrac{ar^2}{b + r^3}$

46. $f(s) = \dfrac{a^2 - s^2}{\sqrt{a^2 + s^2}}$

47. $y = \arctan\left(\dfrac{2}{x}\right)$

48. $r(t) = \ln\left(\sin\left(\dfrac{t}{k}\right)\right)$

49. $g(w) = \dfrac{5}{(a^2 - w^2)^2}$

50. $y = \dfrac{e^{2x}}{x^2 + 1}$

51. $g(u) = \dfrac{e^{au}}{a^2 + b^2}$

52. $y = \dfrac{e^{ax} - e^{-ax}}{e^{ax} + e^{-ax}}$

53. $f(x) = \dfrac{x}{1 + \ln x}$

54. $z = \dfrac{e^{t^2} + t}{\sin(2t)}$

55. $f(t) = \sin \sqrt{e^t + 1}$

56. $g(y) = e^{2e^{(y^3)}}$

57. $y = 6x^3 + 4x^2 - 2x$

58. $g(z) = \dfrac{z^7 + 5z^6 - z^3}{z^2}$

59. $f(z) = (\ln 3)z^2 + (\ln 4)e^z$

60. $y = 3x - 2 \cdot 4^x$

61. $f(x) = x^3 + 3^x$

62. $f(\theta) = \theta^2 \sin \theta + 2\theta \cos \theta - 2 \sin \theta$

63. $y = \sqrt{\cos(5\theta) + \sin^2(6\theta)}$

64. $r(\theta) = \sin\left((3\theta - \pi)^2\right)$

65. $z = (s^2 - \sqrt{s})(s^2 + \sqrt{s})$

66. $N(\theta) = \tan(\arctan(k\theta))$

67. $h(t) = e^{kt}(\sin at + \cos bt)$

68. $f(y) = 4^y(2 - y^2)$

69. $f(t) = (\sin(2t) - \cos(3t))^4$

70. $s(y) = \sqrt[3]{(\cos^2 y + 3 + \sin^2 y)}$

71. $f(x) = (4 - x^2 + 2x^3)(6 - 4x + x^7)$

72. $h(x) = \left(\dfrac{1}{x} - \dfrac{1}{x^2}\right)(2x^3 + 4)$

73. $f(z) = \sqrt{5z} + 5\sqrt{z} + \dfrac{5}{\sqrt{z}} - \sqrt{\dfrac{5}{z}} + \sqrt{5}$

For Exercises 74–75, assume that y is a differentiable function of x and find dy/dx.

74. $x^3 + y^3 - 4x^2 y = 0$

75. $\cos^2 y + \sin^2 y = y + 2$

76. Find the slope of the curve $x^2 + 3y^2 = 7$ at $(2, -1)$.

77. Assume y is a differentiable function of x and that $y + \sin y + x^2 = 9$. Find dy/dx at the point $x = 3, y = 0$.

78. Find the equations for the lines tangent to the graph of $xy + y^2 = 4$ where $x = 3$.

Problems

79. If $f(t) = 2t^3 - 4t^2 + 3t - 1$, find $f'(t)$ and $f''(t)$.

80. If $f(x) = 13 - 8x + \sqrt{2}x^2$ and $f'(r) = 4$, find r.

81. If $f(x) = x^3 - 6x^2 - 15x + 20$, find analytically all values of x for which $f'(x) = 0$. Show your answers on a graph of f.

82. (a) Find the *eighth* derivative of $f(x) = x^7 + 5x^5 - 4x^3 + 6x - 7$. Think ahead!
   (The nth derivative, $f^{(n)}(x)$, is the result of differentiating $f(x)$ n times.)
   (b) Find the seventh derivative of $f(x)$.

For Problems 83–88, use Figure 3.48.

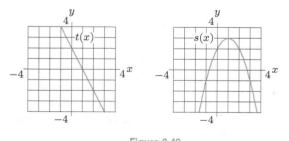

Figure 3.48

83. Let $h(x) = t(x)s(x)$ and $p(x) = t(x)/s(x)$. Estimate:
   (a) $h'(1)$ **(b)** $h'(0)$ **(c)** $p'(0)$

84. Let $r(x) = s(t(x))$. Estimate $r'(0)$.

85. Let $h(x) = s(s(x))$. Estimate:
   (a) $h'(1)$ **(b)** $h'(2)$

86. Estimate all values of x for which the tangent line to $y = s(s(x))$ is horizontal.

87. Let $h(x) = x^2 t(x)$ and $p(x) = t(x^2)$. Estimate:
   (a) $h'(-1)$ **(b)** $p'(-1)$

88. Find an approximate equation for the tangent line to $r(x) = s(t(x))$ at $x = 1$.

For Problems 89–92, let $h(x) = f(g(x))$ and $k(x) = g(f(x))$. Use Figure 3.49 to estimate the derivatives.

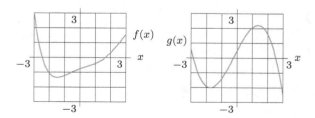

Figure 3.49

89. $h'(1)$ **90.** $k'(1)$ **91.** $h'(2)$ **92.** $k'(2)$

93. Using the information in the table about f and g, find:

(a) $h(4)$ if $h(x) = f(g(x))$
(b) $h'(4)$ if $h(x) = f(g(x))$
(c) $h(4)$ if $h(x) = g(f(x))$
(d) $h'(4)$ if $h(x) = g(f(x))$
(e) $h'(4)$ if $h(x) = g(x)/f(x)$
(f) $h'(4)$ if $h(x) = f(x)g(x)$

x	1	2	3	4
$f(x)$	3	2	1	4
$f'(x)$	1	4	2	3
$g(x)$	2	1	4	3
$g'(x)$	4	2	3	1

94. Given: $r(2) = 4$, $s(2) = 1$, $s(4) = 2$, $r'(2) = -1$, $s'(2) = 3$, $s'(4) = 3$. Compute the following derivatives, or state what additional information you would need to be able to do so.

(a) $H'(2)$ if $H(x) = r(x) \cdot s(x)$
(b) $H'(2)$ if $H(x) = \sqrt{r(x)}$
(c) $H'(2)$ if $H(x) = r(s(x))$
(d) $H'(2)$ if $H(x) = s(r(x))$

95. If $g(2) = 3$ and $g'(2) = -4$, find $f'(2)$ for the following:

(a) $f(x) = x^2 - 4g(x)$ (b) $f(x) = \dfrac{x}{g(x)}$
(c) $f(x) = x^2 g(x)$ (d) $f(x) = (g(x))^2$
(e) $f(x) = x\sin(g(x))$ (f) $f(x) = x^2 \ln(g(x))$

96. For parts (a)–(f) of Problem 95, determine the equation of the line tangent to f at $x = 2$.

97. Imagine you are zooming in on the graphs of the following functions near the origin:

$y = \arcsin x$ $y = \sin x - \tan x$ $y = x - \sin x$

$y = \arctan x$ $y = \dfrac{\sin x}{1 + \sin x}$ $y = \dfrac{x^2}{x^2 + 1}$

$y = \dfrac{1 - \cos x}{\cos x}$ $y = \dfrac{x}{x^2 + 1}$ $y = \dfrac{\sin x}{x} - 1$

$y = -x \ln x$ $y = e^x - 1$ $y = x^{10} + \sqrt[10]{x}$

$y = \dfrac{x}{x + 1}$

Which of them look the same? Group together those functions which become indistinguishable, and give the equation of the line they look like. [Note: $(\sin x)/x - 1$ and $-x\ln x$ never quite make it to the origin.]

[10] From data.giss.nasa.gov/gistemp/tabledate/GLB.Ts.txt

98. The graphs of $\sin x$ and $\cos x$ intersect once between 0 and $\pi/2$. What is the angle between the two curves at the point where they intersect? (You need to think about how the angle between two curves should be defined.)

In Problems 99–100, show that the curves meet at least once and determine whether the curves are perpendicular at the point of intersection.

99. $y = 1 + x - x^2$ and $y = 1 - x + x^2$
100. $y = 1 - x^3/3$ and $y = x - 1$
101. For some constant b and $x > 0$, let $y = x \ln x - bx$. Find the equation of the tangent line to this graph at the point at which the graph crosses the x-axis.

In Problems 102–104, find the limit as $x \to -\infty$.

102. $\dfrac{\cosh(2x)}{\sinh(3x)}$ **103.** $\dfrac{e^{-2x}}{\sinh(2x)}$ **104.** $\dfrac{\sinh(x^2)}{\cosh(x^2)}$

105. Consider the function $f(x) = \sqrt{x}$.

(a) Find and sketch $f(x)$ and the tangent line approximation to $f(x)$ near $x = 4$.
(b) Compare the true value of $f(4.1)$ with the value obtained by using the tangent line approximation.
(c) Compare the true and approximate values of $f(16)$.
(d) Using a graph, explain why the tangent line approximation is a good one when $x = 4.1$ but not when $x = 16$.

106. Figure 3.50 shows the tangent line approximation to $f(x)$ near $x = a$.

(a) Find a, $f(a)$, $f'(a)$.
(b) Estimate $f(2.1)$ and $f(1.98)$. Are these under- or overestimates? Which estimate would you expect to be more accurate and why?

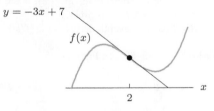

Figure 3.50

107. Global temperatures have been rising, on average, for more than a century, sparking concern that the polar ice will melt and sea levels will rise. With t in years since 1880, fitting functions to the data[10] gives three models for the average global temperature in Celsius:

$$f(t) = 13.625 + 0.006t$$
$$g(t) = 0.00006t^2 - 0.0017t + 13.788$$
$$h(t) = 13.63e^{0.0004t}.$$

(a) What family of functions is used in each model?

(b) Find the rate of change of temperature in 2010 in each of the three models. Give units.

(c) For each model, find the change in temperature over a 130-year period if the temperature had been changing at the rate you found in part (b) for that model.

(d) For each model, find the predicted change in temperature for the 130 years from 1880 to 2010.

(e) For which model, if any, are the answers equal in parts (c) and (d)?

(f) For which model is the discrepancy largest between the answers in parts (c) and (d)?

108. In 2009, the population of Hungary[11] was approximated by

$$P = 9.906(0.997)^t,$$

where P is in millions and t is in years since 2009. Assume the trend continues.

(a) What does this model predict for the population of Hungary in the year 2020?

(b) How fast (in people/year) does this model predict Hungary's population will be decreasing in 2020?

109. The gravitational attraction, F, between the earth and a satellite of mass m at a distance r from the center of the earth is given by

$$F = \frac{GMm}{r^2},$$

where M is the mass of the earth, and G is a constant. Find the rate of change of force with respect to distance.

110. The distance, s, of a moving body from a fixed point is given as a function of time, t, by $s = 20e^{t/2}$.

(a) Find the velocity, v, of the body as a function of t.

(b) Find a relationship between v and s, then show that s satisfies the differential equation $s' = \frac{1}{2}s$.

111. At any time, t, a population, $P(t)$, is growing at a rate proportional to the population at that moment.

(a) Using derivatives, write an equation representing the growth of the population. Let k be the constant of proportionality.

(b) Show that the function $P(t) = Ae^{kt}$ satisfies the equation in part (a) for any constant A.

112. An object is oscillating at the end of a spring. Its position, in centimeters, relative to a fixed point, is given as a function of time, t, in seconds, by

$$y = y_0 \cos(2\pi\omega t), \quad \text{with } \omega \text{ a constant.}$$

(a) Find an expression for the velocity and acceleration of the object.

(b) How do the amplitudes of the position, velocity, and acceleration functions compare? How do the periods of these functions compare?

(c) Show that the function y satisfies the differential equation

$$\frac{d^2y}{dt^2} + 4\pi^2\omega^2 y = 0.$$

113. The total number of people, N, who have contracted a disease by a time t days after its outbreak is given by

$$N = \frac{1{,}000{,}000}{1 + 5{,}000e^{-0.1t}}.$$

(a) In the long run, how many people get the disease?

(b) Is there any day on which more than a million people fall sick? Half a million? Quarter of a million? (Note: You do not have to find on what days these things happen.)

114. The world population was 6.7 billion at the beginning of 2008. An exponential model predicts the population to be $P(t) = 6.7e^{kt}$ billion t years after 2008, where k is the continuous annual growth rate.

(a) How long does the model predict it will take for the population to reach 10 billion, as a function $f(k)$?

(b) One current estimate is $k = 0.012 = 1.2\%$. How long will it take for the population to reach 10 billion if k has this value?

(c) For continuous growth rates near 1.2%, find a linear function of k that approximates the time for the world population to reach 10 billion.

(d) Find the time to reach 10 billion and its approximation from part (c) if the continuous growth rate is 1.0%.

115. The acceleration due to gravity, g, is given by

$$g = \frac{GM}{r^2},$$

where M is the mass of the earth, r is the distance from the center of the earth, and G is the universal gravitational constant.

(a) Show that when r changes by Δr, the change in the acceleration due to gravity, Δg, is given by

$$\Delta g \approx -2g\frac{\Delta r}{r}.$$

(b) What is the significance of the negative sign?

(c) What is the percent change in g when moving from sea level to the top of Pike's Peak (4.315 km)? Assume the radius of the earth is 6400 km.

116. Given that f and g are differentiable everywhere, g is the inverse of f, and that $f(3) = 4$, $f'(3) = 6$, $f'(4) = 7$, find $g'(4)$.

117. An increasing function $f(x)$ has the value $f(10) = 5$. Explain how you know that the calculations $f'(10) = 8$ and $(f^{-1})'(5) = 8$ cannot both be correct.

118. A particle is moving on the x-axis. It has velocity $v(x)$ when it is at the point with coordinate x. Show that its acceleration at that point is $v(x)v'(x)$.

---

[11]https://www.cia.gov/library/publications/the-world-factbook/print/hu.html, accessed 4/14/09.

119. If f is decreasing and $f(20) = 10$, which of the following must be incorrect?

(a) $(f^{-1})'(20) = -3$.   (b) $(f^{-1})'(10) = 12$.

120. Find the nth derivative of the following functions:

(a) $\ln x$ (b) xe^x (c) $e^x \cos x$

121. The derivative f' gives the (absolute) rate of change of a quantity f, and f'/f gives the relative rate of change of the quantity. In this problem, we show that the product rule is equivalent to an additive rule for relative rates of change. Assume $h = f \cdot g$ with $f \neq 0$ and $g \neq 0$.

(a) Show that the additive rule

$$\frac{f'}{f} + \frac{g'}{g} = \frac{h'}{h}$$

implies the product rule, by multiplying through by h and using the fact that $h = f \cdot g$.

(b) Show that the product rule implies the additive rule in part (a), by starting with the product rule and dividing through by $h = f \cdot g$.

122. The relative rate of change of a function f is defined to be f'/f. Find an expression for the relative rate of change of a quotient f/g in terms of the relative rates of change of the functions f and g.

CAS Challenge Problems

123. (a) Use a computer algebra system to differentiate $(x + 1)^x$ and $(\sin x)^x$.

(b) Conjecture a rule for differentiating $(f(x))^x$, where f is any differentiable function.

(c) Apply your rule to $g(x) = (\ln x)^x$. Does your answer agree with the answer given by the computer algebra system?

(d) Prove your conjecture by rewriting $(f(x))^x$ in the form $e^{h(x)}$.

For Problems 124–126,

(a) Use a computer algebra system to find and simplify the derivative of the given function.

(b) Without a computer algebra system, use differentiation rules to calculate the derivative. Make sure that the answer simplifies to the same answer as in part (a).

(c) Explain how you could have predicted the derivative by using algebra before taking the derivative.

124. $f(x) = \sin(\arcsin x)$

125. $g(r) = 2^{-2r} 4^r$

126. $h(t) = \ln(1 - 1/t) + \ln(t/(t - 1))$

PROJECTS FOR CHAPTER THREE

1. Rule of 70

The "Rule of 70" is a rule of thumb to estimate how long it takes money in a bank to double. Suppose the money is in an account earning $i\%$ annual interest, compounded yearly. The Rule of 70 says that the time it takes the amount of money to double is approximately $70/i$ years, assuming i is small. Find the local linearization of $\ln(1 + x)$ near $x = 0$, and use it to explain why this rule works.

2. Newton's Method

Read about how to find roots using bisection and Newton's method in Appendices A and C.

(a) What is the smallest positive zero of the function $f(x) = \sin x$? Apply Newton's method, with initial guess $x_0 = 3$, to see how fast it converges to $\pi = 3.1415926536\ldots$.

(i) Compute the first two approximations, x_1 and x_2; compare x_2 with π.

(ii) Newton's method works very well here. Explain why. To do this, you will have to outline the basic idea behind Newton's method.

(iii) Estimate the location of the zero using bisection, starting with the interval $[3, 4]$. How does bisection compare to Newton's method in terms of accuracy?

(b) Newton's method can be very sensitive to your initial estimate, x_0. For example, consider finding a zero of $f(x) = \sin x - \frac{2}{3}x$.

(i) Use Newton's method with the following initial estimates to find a zero:

$$x_0 = 0.904, \quad x_0 = 0.905, \quad x_0 = 0.906.$$

(ii) What happens?

Chapter Four

USING THE DERIVATIVE

Contents

4.1 Using First and Second Derivatives 186
What Derivatives Tell Us About a Function
and Its Graph 186
Local Maxima and Minima 187
How Do We Detect a Local Maximum or
Minimum? 187
Testing for Local Maxima and Minima at a
Critical Point 188
The Second-Derivative Test 189
Concavity and Inflection Points 190
How Do We Detect an Inflection Point? 190
Showing Local Extrema Are at Critical Points . . 192

4.2 Optimization 196
Global Maxima and Minima 196
Existence of Global Extrema 196
How Do We Find Global Extrema? . . . 197
Finding Upper and Lower Bounds 200

4.3 Optimization and Modeling 205
A Graphical Example 209

4.4 Families of Functions and Modeling 216
The Bell-Shaped Curve 216
Modeling with Families of Functions 217
Motion Under Gravity 217
Exponential Model with a Limit 218
The Logistic Model 219

4.5 Applications to Marginality 224
Marginal Analysis 225
Maximizing Profit 227

4.6 Rates and Related Rates 233
Related Rates 234

4.7 L'Hopital's Rule, Growth, and Dominance . . 242
Dominance 244
Recognizing the Form of a Limit 245
A Famous Limit 245

4.8 Parametric Equations 249
Representing Motion in the Plane 249
Speed and Velocity 252
Tangent Lines 253
Parametric Representations of Curves 254

REVIEW PROBLEMS 260
PROJECTS 267

4.1 USING FIRST AND SECOND DERIVATIVES

What Derivatives Tell Us About a Function and Its Graph

As we saw in Chapter 2, the connection between derivatives of a function and the function itself is given by the following:

- If $f' > 0$ on an interval, then f is increasing on that interval.
- If $f' < 0$ on an interval, then f is decreasing on that interval.

If f' is always positive on an interval or always negative on an interval, then f is monotonic over that interval.

- If $f'' > 0$ on an interval, then the graph of f is concave up on that interval.
- If $f'' < 0$ on an interval, then the graph of f is concave down on that interval.

We can do more with these principles now than we could in Chapter 2 because we now have formulas for the derivatives of the elementary functions.

When we graph a function on a computer or calculator, we often see only part of the picture, and we may miss some significant features. Information given by the first and second derivatives can help identify regions with interesting behavior.

Example 1   Use the first and second derivatives to analyze the function $f(x) = x^3 - 9x^2 - 48x + 52$.

Solution   Since f is a cubic polynomial, we expect a graph that is roughly S-shaped. We can use the derivative to determine where the function is increasing and where it is decreasing. The derivative of f is

$$f'(x) = 3x^2 - 18x - 48.$$

To find where $f' > 0$ or $f' < 0$, we first find where $f' = 0$, that is, where $3x^2 - 18x - 48 = 0$. Factoring, we get $3(x + 2)(x - 8) = 0$, so $x = -2$ or $x = 8$. Since $f' = 0$ *only* at $x = -2$ and $x = 8$, and since f' is continuous, f' cannot change sign on any of the three intervals $x < -2$, or $-2 < x < 8$, or $8 < x$. How can we tell the sign of f' on each of these intervals? One way is to pick a point and substitute into f'. For example, since $f'(-3) = 33 > 0$, we know f' is positive for $x < -2$, so f is increasing for $x < -2$. Similarly, since $f'(0) = -48$ and $f'(10) = 72$, we know that f decreases between $x = -2$ and $x = 8$ and increases for $x > 8$. Summarizing:

$$
\begin{array}{c|ccc|cc}
& x = -2 & & & x = 8 & \\
\text{f increasing } \nearrow & | & \text{f decreasing } \searrow & & | & \text{f increasing } \nearrow \\
\hline
f' > 0 & f' = 0 & f' < 0 & & f' = 0 & f' > 0
\end{array} \quad x
$$

We find that $f(-2) = 104$ and $f(8) = -396$. Hence on the interval $-2 < x < 8$ the function decreases from a high of 104 to a low of -396. One more point on the graph is easy to get: the y intercept, $f(0) = 52$. With just these three points we can get a graph. See Figure 4.1.

In Figure 4.1, we see that part of the graph is concave up and part is concave down. We can use the second derivative to analyze concavity. We have

$$f''(x) = 6x - 18.$$

Thus, $f''(x) < 0$ when $x < 3$ and $f''(x) > 0$ when $x > 3$, so the graph of f is concave down for $x < 3$ and concave up for $x > 3$. At $x = 3$, we have $f''(x) = 0$. See Figure 4.1. Summarizing:

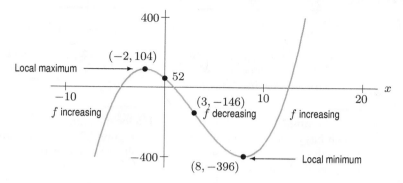

Figure 4.1: Useful graph of $f(x) = x^3 - 9x^2 - 48x + 52$

Local Maxima and Minima

We are often interested in points such as those marked local maximum and local minimum in Figure 4.1. We have the following definition:

> Suppose p is a point in the domain of f:
> - f has a **local minimum** at p if $f(p)$ is less than or equal to the values of f for points near p.
> - f has a **local maximum** at p if $f(p)$ is greater than or equal to the values of f for points near p.

We use the adjective "local" because we are describing only what happens near p. Local maxima and minima are sometimes called *local extrema*.

How Do We Detect a Local Maximum or Minimum?

In the preceding example, the points $x = -2$ and $x = 8$, where $f'(x) = 0$, played a key role in leading us to local maxima and minima. We give a name to such points:

> For any function f, a point p in the domain of f where $f'(p) = 0$ or $f'(p)$ is undefined is called a **critical point** of the function. In addition, the point $(p, f(p))$ on the graph of f is also called a critical point. A **critical value** of f is the value, $f(p)$, at a critical point, p.

Notice that "critical point of f" can refer either to points in the domain of f or to points on the graph of f. You will know which meaning is intended from the context.

Geometrically, at a critical point where $f'(p) = 0$, the line tangent to the graph of f at p is horizontal. At a critical point where $f'(p)$ is undefined, there is no horizontal tangent to the graph—there's either a vertical tangent or no tangent at all. (For example, $x = 0$ is a critical point for the absolute value function $f(x) = |x|$.) However, most of the functions we work with are differentiable everywhere, and therefore most of our critical points are of the $f'(p) = 0$ variety.

The critical points divide the domain of f into intervals within which the sign of the derivative remains the same, either positive or negative. Therefore, if f is defined on the interval between two successive critical points, its graph cannot change direction on that interval; it is either increasing or decreasing. The following result, which is proved on page 192, tells us that all local maxima and minima which are not at endpoints occur at critical points.

Theorem 4.1: Local Extrema and Critical Points

Suppose f is defined on an interval and has a local maximum or minimum at the point $x = a$, which is not an endpoint of the interval. If f is differentiable at $x = a$, then $f'(a) = 0$. Thus, a is a critical point.

Warning! Not every critical point is a local maximum or local minimum. Consider $f(x) = x^3$, which has a critical point at $x = 0$. (See Figure 4.2.) The derivative, $f'(x) = 3x^2$, is positive on both sides of $x = 0$, so f increases on both sides of $x = 0$, and there is neither a local maximum nor a local minimum at $x = 0$.

Figure 4.2: Critical point which is not a local maximum or minimum

Testing for Local Maxima and Minima at a Critical Point

If f' has different signs on either side of a critical point p, with $f'(p) = 0$, then the graph changes direction at p and looks like one of those in Figure 4.3. So we have the following criterion:

The First-Derivative Test for Local Maxima and Minima

Suppose p is a critical point of a continuous function f. Moving from left to right:
  • If f' changes from negative to positive at p, then f has a local minimum at p.
  • If f' changes from positive to negative at p, then f has a local maximum at p.

Figure 4.3: Changes in direction at a critical point, p: Local maxima and minima

Example 2   Use a graph of the function $f(x) = \dfrac{1}{x(x-1)}$ to observe its local maxima and minima. Confirm your observation analytically.

Solution   The graph in Figure 4.4 suggests that this function has no local minima but that there is a local maximum at about $x = \frac{1}{2}$. Confirming this analytically means using the formula for the derivative to show that what we expect is true. Since $f(x) = (x^2 - x)^{-1}$, we have

$$f'(x) = -1(x^2 - x)^{-2}(2x - 1) = -\frac{2x - 1}{(x^2 - x)^2}.$$

So $f'(x) = 0$ where $2x - 1 = 0$. Thus, the only critical point in the domain of f is $x = \frac{1}{2}$.

Furthermore, $f'(x) > 0$ where $0 < x < 1/2$, and $f'(x) < 0$ where $1/2 < x < 1$. Thus, f increases for $0 < x < 1/2$ and decreases for $1/2 < x < 1$. According to the first derivative test, the critical point $x = 1/2$ is a local maximum.

For $-\infty < x < 0$ or $1 < x < \infty$, there are no critical points and no local maxima or minima. Although $1/(x(x-1)) \to 0$ both as $x \to \infty$ and as $x \to -\infty$, we don't say 0 is a local minimum because $1/(x(x-1))$ never actually *equals* 0.

Notice that although $f' > 0$ everywhere that it is defined for $x < 1/2$, the function f is not increasing throughout this interval. The problem is that f and f' are not defined at $x = 0$, so we cannot conclude that f is increasing when $x < 1/2$.

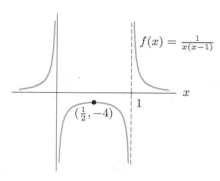

Figure 4.4: Find local maxima and minima

Figure 4.5: Explain the absence of local maxima and minima for $x \geq 0$

Example 3   The graph of $f(x) = \sin x + 2e^x$ is in Figure 4.5. Using the derivative, explain why there are no local maxima or minima for $x \geq 0$.

Solution   Local maxima and minima can occur only at critical points. Now $f'(x) = \cos x + 2e^x$, which is defined for all x. We know $\cos x$ is always between -1 and 1, and $2e^x \geq 2$ for $x \geq 0$, so $f'(x)$ cannot be 0 for any $x \geq 0$. Therefore there are no local maxima or minima there.

The Second-Derivative Test for Local Maxima and Minima

Knowing the concavity of a function can also be useful in testing if a critical point is a local maximum or a local minimum. Suppose p is a critical point of f, with $f'(p) = 0$, so that the graph of f has a horizontal tangent line at p. If the graph is concave up at p, then f has a local minimum at p. Likewise, if the graph is concave down, f has a local maximum. (See Figure 4.6.) This suggests:

The Second-Derivative Test for Local Maxima and Minima

- If $f'(p) = 0$ and $f''(p) > 0$ then f has a local minimum at p.
- If $f'(p) = 0$ and $f''(p) < 0$ then f has a local maximum at p.
- If $f'(p) = 0$ and $f''(p) = 0$ then   the test tells us nothing.

Figure 4.6: Local maxima and minima and concavity

Example 4 Classify as local maxima or local minima the critical points of $f(x) = x^3 - 9x^2 - 48x + 52$.

Solution As we saw in Example 1 on page 186,

$$f'(x) = 3x^2 - 18x - 48$$

and the critical points of f are $x = -2$ and $x = 8$. We have

$$f''(x) = 6x - 18.$$

Thus $f''(8) = 30 > 0$, so f has a local minimum at $x = 8$. Since $f''(-2) = -30 < 0$, f has a local maximum at $x = -2$.

Warning! The second-derivative test does not tell us anything if both $f'(p) = 0$ and $f''(p) = 0$. For example, if $f(x) = x^3$ and $g(x) = x^4$, both $f'(0) = f''(0) = 0$ and $g'(0) = g''(0) = 0$. The point $x = 0$ is a minimum for g but is neither a maximum nor a minimum for f. However, the first-derivative test is still useful. For example, g' changes sign from negative to positive at $x = 0$, so we know g has a local minimum there.

Concavity and Inflection Points

Investigating points where the slope changes sign led us to critical points. Now we look at points where the concavity changes.

> A point, p, at which the graph of a continuous function, f, changes concavity is called an **inflection point** of f.

The words "inflection point of f" can refer either to a point in the domain of f or to a point on the graph of f. The context of the problem will tell you which is meant.

How Do We Detect an Inflection Point?

To identify candidates for an inflection point of a continuous function, we often use the second derivative.

> Suppose f'' is defined on both sides of a point p:
> - If f'' is zero or undefined at p, then p is a possible inflection point.
> - To test whether p is an inflection point, check whether f'' changes sign at p.

The following example illustrates how local maxima and minima and inflection points are found.

Example 5 For $x \geq 0$, find the local maxima and minima and inflection points for $g(x) = xe^{-x}$ and sketch the graph of g.

Solution Taking derivatives and simplifying, we have

$$g'(x) = (1 - x)e^{-x} \quad \text{and} \quad g''(x) = (x - 2)e^{-x}.$$

So $x = 1$ is a critical point, and $g' > 0$ for $x < 1$ and $g' < 0$ for $x > 1$. Hence g increases to a local maximum at $x = 1$ and then decreases. Since $g(0) = 0$ and $g(x) > 0$ for $x > 0$, there is a local minimum at $x = 0$. Also, $g(x) \to 0$ as $x \to \infty$. There is an inflection point at $x = 2$ since $g'' < 0$ for $x < 2$ and $g'' > 0$ for $x > 2$. The graph is sketched in Figure 4.7.

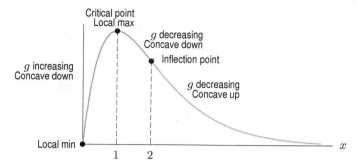

Figure 4.7: Graph of $g(x) = xe^{-x}$

Warning! Not every point x where $f''(x) = 0$ (or f'' is undefined) is an inflection point (just as not every point where $f' = 0$ is a local maximum or minimum). For instance $f(x) = x^4$ has $f''(x) = 12x^2$ so $f''(0) = 0$, but $f'' > 0$ when $x < 0$ and when $x > 0$, so there is *no* change in concavity at $x = 0$. See Figure 4.8.

Figure 4.8: Graph of $f(x) = x^4$

Inflection Points and Local Maxima and Minima of the Derivative

Inflection points can also be interpreted in terms of first derivatives. Applying the First Derivative Test for local maxima and minima to f', we obtain the following result:

> Suppose a function f has a continuous derivative. If f'' changes sign at p, then f has an inflection point at p, and f' has a local minimum or a local maximum at p.

Figure 4.9 shows two inflection points. Notice that the curve crosses the tangent line at these points and that the slope of the curve is a maximum or a minimum there.

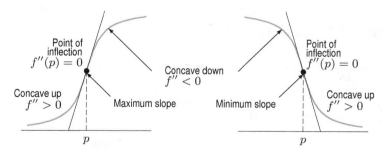

Figure 4.9: Change in concavity at p: Points of inflection

Example 6   Water is being poured into the vase in Figure 4.10 at a constant rate, measured in volume per unit time. Graph $y = f(t)$, the depth of the water against time, t. Explain the concavity and indicate the inflection points.

Solution   At first the water level, y, rises slowly because the base of the vase is wide, and it takes a lot of water to make the depth increase. However, as the vase narrows, the rate at which the water is rising increases. Thus, y is increasing at an increasing rate and the graph is concave up. The rate of increase in the water level is at a maximum when the water reaches the middle of the vase, where the diameter is smallest; this is an inflection point. After that, the rate at which y increases decreases again, so the graph is concave down. (See Figure 4.11.)

Figure 4.10: A vase

Figure 4.11: Graph of depth of water in the vase, y, against time, t

Showing Local Extrema Are at Critical Points

We now prove Theorem 4.1, which says that inside an interval, local maxima and minima can only occur at critical points. Suppose that f has a local maximum at $x = a$. Assuming that $f'(a)$ is defined, the definition of the derivative gives

$$f'(a) = \lim_{h \to 0} \frac{f(a+h) - f(a)}{h}.$$

Since this is a two-sided limit, we have

$$f'(a) = \lim_{h \to 0^-} \frac{f(a+h) - f(a)}{h} = \lim_{h \to 0^+} \frac{f(a+h) - f(a)}{h}.$$

By the definition of local maximum, $f(a+h) \le f(a)$ for all sufficiently small h. Thus $f(a+h) - f(a) \le 0$ for sufficiently small h. The denominator, h, is negative when we take the limit from the left and positive when we take the limit from the right. Thus

$$\lim_{h \to 0^-} \frac{f(a+h) - f(a)}{h} \ge 0 \quad \text{and} \quad \lim_{h \to 0^+} \frac{f(a+h) - f(a)}{h} \le 0.$$

Since both these limits are equal to $f'(a)$, we have $f'(a) \ge 0$ and $f'(a) \le 0$, so we must have $f'(a) = 0$. The proof for a local minimum at $x = a$ is similar.

Exercises and Problems for Section 4.1

Exercises

1. Indicate all critical points on the graph of f in Figure 4.12 and determine which correspond to local maxima of f, which to local minima, and which to neither.

Figure 4.12

2. Graph a function which has exactly one critical point, at $x = 2$, and exactly one inflection point, at $x = 4$.

3. Graph a function with exactly two critical points, one of which is a local minimum and the other is neither a local maximum nor a local minimum.

In Exercises 4–8, use derivatives to find the critical points and inflection points.

4. $f(x) = x^3 - 9x^2 + 24x + 5$

5. $f(x) = x^5 - 10x^3 - 8$

6. $f(x) = x^5 + 15x^4 + 25$

7. $f(x) = 5x - 3\ln x$

8. $f(x) = 4xe^{3x}$

In Exercises 9–12, find all critical points and then use the first-derivative test to determine local maxima and minima. Check your answer by graphing.

9. $f(x) = 3x^4 - 4x^3 + 6$ **10.** $f(x) = (x^2 - 4)^7$

11. $f(x) = (x^3 - 8)^4$ **12.** $f(x) = \dfrac{x}{x^2 + 1}$

In Exercises 13–14, find the critical points of the function and classify them as local maxima or local minima or neither.

13. $g(x) = xe^{-3x}$ **14.** $h(x) = x + 1/x$

15. (a) Use a graph to estimate the x-values of any critical points and inflection points of $f(x) = e^{-x^2}$.
   (b) Use derivatives to find the x-values of any critical points and inflection points exactly.

In Exercises 16–19, the function f is defined for all x. Use the graph of f' to decide:
 (a) Over what intervals is f increasing? Decreasing?
 (b) Does f have local maxima or minima? If so, which, and where?

16.   **17.**

18.   **19.**

Problems

20. (a) Show that if a is a positive constant, then $x = 0$ is the only critical point of $f(x) = x + a\sqrt{x}$.
   (b) Use derivatives to show that f is increasing and its graph is concave down for all $x > 0$.

21. (a) If b is a positive constant and $x > 0$, find all critical points of $f(x) = x - b\ln x$.
   (b) Use the second-derivative test to determine whether the function has a local maximum or local minimum at each critical point.

22. (a) If a is a nonzero constant, find all critical points of
$$f(x) = \frac{a}{x^2} + x.$$

   (b) Use the second-derivative test to show that if a is positive then the graph has a local minimum, and if a is negative then the graph has a local maximum.

23. If U and V are positive constants, find all critical points of
$$F(t) = Ue^t + Ve^{-t}.$$

24. Indicate on the graph of the derivative function f' in Figure 4.13 the x-values that are critical points of the function f itself. At which critical points does f have local maxima, local minima, or neither?

Figure 4.13

25. Indicate on the graph of the derivative f' in Figure 4.14 the x-values that are inflection points of the function f.

Figure 4.14

26. Indicate on the graph of the second derivative f'' in Figure 4.15 the x-values that are inflection points of the function f.

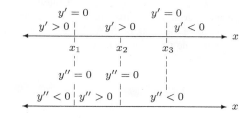

Figure 4.15

For Problems 27–30, sketch a possible graph of $y = f(x)$, using the given information about the derivatives $y' = f'(x)$ and $y'' = f''(x)$. Assume that the function is defined and continuous for all real x.

27.

28.

29.

30.

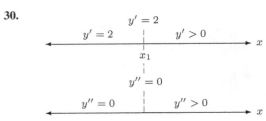

31. Suppose f has a continuous derivative whose values are given in the following table.

   (a) Estimate the x-coordinates of critical points of f for $0 \leq x \leq 10$.

   (b) For each critical point, indicate if it is a local maximum of f, local minimum, or neither.

x	0	1	2	3	4	5	6	7	8	9	10
$f'(x)$	5	2	1	-2	-5	-3	-1	2	3	1	-1

32. **(a)** The following table gives values of the differentiable function $y = f(x)$. Estimate the x-values of critical points of $f(x)$ on the interval $0 < x < 10$. Classify each critical point as a local maximum, local minimum, or neither.

   (b) Now assume that the table gives values of the continuous function $y = f'(x)$ (instead of $f(x)$). Estimate and classify critical points of the function $f(x)$.

x	0	1	2	3	4	5	6	7	8	9	10
y	1	2	1	-2	-5	-3	-1	2	3	1	-1

33. If water is flowing at a constant rate (i.e., constant volume per unit time) into the vase in Figure 4.16, sketch a graph of the depth of the water against time. Mark on the graph the time at which the water reaches the corner of the vase.

Figure 4.16   Figure 4.17

34. If water is flowing at a constant rate (i.e., constant volume per unit time) into the Grecian urn in Figure 4.17, sketch a graph of the depth of the water against time. Mark on the graph the time at which the water reaches the widest point of the urn.

35. Find and classify the critical points of $f(x) = x^3(1-x)^4$ as local maxima and minima.

36. If $m, n \geq 2$ are integers, find and classify the critical points of $f(x) = x^m(1 - x)^n$.

37. The rabbit population on a small Pacific island is approximated by

$$P = \frac{2000}{1 + e^{5.3 - 0.4t}}$$

with t measured in years since 1774, when Captain James Cook left 10 rabbits on the island.

   (a) Graph P. Does the population level off?

   (b) Estimate when the rabbit population grew most rapidly. How large was the population at that time?

   (c) What natural causes could lead to the shape of the graph of P?

38. Find values of a and b so that the function $f(x) = x^2 + ax + b$ has a local minimum at the point $(6, -5)$.

39. Find the value of a so that the function $f(x) = xe^{ax}$ has a critical point at $x = 3$.

40. Find constants a and b in the function $f(x) = axe^{bx}$ such that $f(\frac{1}{3}) = 1$ and the function has a local maximum at $x = \frac{1}{3}$.

41. Graph $f(x) = x + \sin x$, and determine where f is increasing most rapidly and least rapidly.

42. You might think the graph of $f(x) = x^2 + \cos x$ should look like a parabola with some waves on it. Sketch the actual graph of $f(x)$ using a calculator or computer. Explain what you see using $f''(x)$.

Problems 43–44 show graphs of the three functions f, f', f''. Identify which is which.

43.

44.

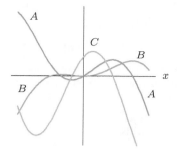

Problems 45–46 show graphs of f, f', f''. Each of these three functions is either odd or even. Decide which functions are odd and which are even. Use this information to identify which graph corresponds to f, which to f', and which to f''.

45.

46.

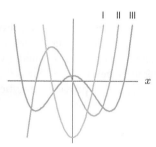

47. Use the derivative formulas and algebra to find the intervals where $f(x) = (x + 50)/(x^2 + 525)$ is increasing and the intervals where it is decreasing. It is possible, but difficult, to solve this problem by graphing f; describe the difficulty.

48. Let f be a function with $f(x) > 0$ for all x. Set $g = 1/f$.

  (a) If f is increasing in an interval around x_0, what about g?

  (b) If f has a local maximum at x_1, what about g?

  (c) If f is concave down at x_2, what about g?

In Problems 49–50, the differentiable function f has $x = 1$ as its only zero and $x = 2$ as its only critical point. For the given functions, find all

(a) Zeros   **(b)** Critical points.

49. $y = f\left(x^2 - 3\right)$ **50.** $y = (f(x))^2 + 3$

In Problems 51–52, the graph of f lies entirely above the x-axis and $f'(x) < 0$ for all x.

(a) Give the critical point(s) of the function, or explain how you know there are none.

(b) Say where the function increases and where it decreases.

51. $y = (f(x))^2$ **52.** $y = f\left(x^2\right)$

Strengthen Your Understanding

In Problems 53–54, explain what is wrong with the statement.

53. An increasing function has no inflection points.

54. For any function f, if $f''(0) = 0$, there is an inflection point at $x = 0$.

In Problems 55–57, give an example of:

55. A function which has no critical points on the interval between 0 and 1.

56. A function, f, which has a critical point at $x = 1$ but for which $f'(1) \neq 0$.

57. A function with local maxima and minima at an infinite number of points.

Are the statements in Problems 58–66 true or false for a function f whose domain is all real numbers? If a statement is true, explain how you know. If a statement is false, give a counterexample.

58. A local minimum of f occurs at a critical point of f.

59. If $x = p$ is not a critical point of f, then $x = p$ is not a local maximum of f.

60. A local maximum of f occurs at a point where

$$f'(x) = 0.$$

61. If $x = p$ is not a local maximum of f, then $x = p$ is not a critical point of f.

62. If $f'(p) = 0$, then $f(x)$ has a local minimum or local maximum at $x = p$.

63. If $f'(x)$ is continuous and $f(x)$ has no critical points, then f is everywhere increasing or everywhere decreasing.

64. If $f''(x)$ is continuous and the graph of f has an inflection point at $x = p$, then $f''(p) = 0$.

65. A critical point of f must be a local maximum or minimum of f.

66. Every cubic polynomial has an inflection point.

In Problems 67–72, give an example of a function f that makes the statement true, or say why such an example is impossible. Assume that f'' exists everywhere.

67. f is concave up and $f(x)$ is positive for all x.

68. f is concave down and $f(x)$ is positive for all x.

69. f is concave down and $f(x)$ is negative for all x.

70. f is concave up and $f(x)$ is negative for all x.

71. $f(x)f''(x) < 0$ for all x.

72. $f(x)f'(x)f''(x)f'''(x) < 0$ for all x.[1]

73. Given that $f'(x)$ is continuous everywhere and changes from negative to positive at $x = a$, which of the following statements must be true?

  (a) a is a critical point of $f(x)$
  (b) $f(a)$ is a local maximum
  (c) $f(a)$ is a local minimum
  (d) $f'(a)$ is a local maximum
  (e) $f'(a)$ is a local minimum

4.2 OPTIMIZATION

The largest and smallest values of a quantity often have practical importance. For example, automobile engineers want to construct a car that uses the least amount of fuel, scientists want to calculate which wavelength carries the maximum radiation at a given temperature, and urban planners want to design traffic patterns to minimize delays. Such problems belong to the field of mathematics called *optimization*. The next three sections show how the derivative provides an efficient way of solving many optimization problems.

Global Maxima and Minima

The single greatest (or least) value of a function f over a specified domain is called the *global maximum* (or *minimum*) of f. Recall that the local maxima and minima tell us where a function is locally largest or smallest. Now we are interested in where the function is absolutely largest or smallest in a given domain. We say

> Suppose p is a point in the domain of f:
> - f has a **global minimum** at p if $f(p)$ is less than or equal to all values of f.
> - f has a **global maximum** at p if $f(p)$ is greater than or equal to all values of f.

Global maxima and minima are sometimes called *extrema* or *optimal values*.

Existence of Global Extrema

The following theorem describes when global extrema are guaranteed to exist:

> **Theorem 4.2: The Extreme Value Theorem**
>
> If f is continuous on the closed interval $a \le x \le b$, then f has a global maximum and a global minimum on that interval.

For a proof of Theorem 4.2, see www.wiley.com/college/hughes-hallett.

---

[1]From the 1998 William Lowell Putnam Mathematical Competition, by permission of the Mathematical Association of America.

How Do We Find Global Maxima and Minima?

If f is a continuous function defined on a closed interval $a \leq x \leq b$ (that is, an interval containing its endpoints), then Theorem 4.2 guarantees that global maxima and minima exist. Figure 4.18 illustrates that the global maximum or minimum of f occurs either at a critical point or at an endpoint of the interval, $x = a$ or $x = b$. These points are the candidates for global extrema.

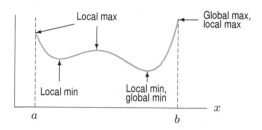

Figure 4.18: Global maximum and minimum on a closed interval $a \leq x \leq b$

Global Maxima and Minima on a Closed Interval: Test the Candidates

For a continuous function f on a closed interval $a \leq x \leq b$:
- Find the critical points of f in the interval.
- Evaluate the function at the critical points and at the endpoints, a and b. The largest value of the function is the global maximum; the smallest value is the global minimum.

If the function is defined on an open interval $a < x < b$ (that is, an interval not including its endpoints) or on all real numbers, there may or may not be a global maximum or minimum. For example, there is no global maximum in Figure 4.19 because the function has no actual largest value. The global minimum in Figure 4.19 coincides with the local minimum. There is a global minimum but no global maximum in Figure 4.20.

Global Maxima and Minima on an Open Interval or on All Real Numbers

For a continuous function, f, find the value of f at all the critical points and sketch a graph. Look at values of f when x approaches the endpoints of the interval, or approaches $\pm\infty$, as appropriate. If there is only one critical point, look at the sign of f' on either side of the critical point.

Figure 4.19: Global minimum on $a < x < b$

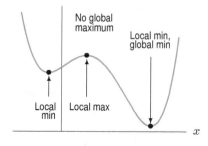

Figure 4.20: Global minimum when the domain is all real numbers

Example 1   Find the global maxima and minima of $f(x) = x^3 - 9x^2 - 48x + 52$ on the following intervals:

(a) $-5 \le x \le 12$ (b) $-5 \le x \le 14$ (c) $-5 \le x < \infty$.

Solution   (a) We have previously obtained the critical points $x = -2$ and $x = 8$ using

$$f'(x) = 3x^2 - 18x - 48 = 3(x + 2)(x - 8).$$

We evaluate f at the critical points and the endpoints of the interval:

$$f(-5) = (-5)^3 - 9(-5)^2 - 48(-5) + 52 = -58$$
$$f(-2) = 104$$
$$f(8) = -396$$
$$f(12) = -92.$$

Comparing these function values, we see that the global maximum on $[-5, 12]$ is 104 and occurs at $x = -2$, and the global minimum on $[-5, 12]$ is -396 and occurs at $x = 8$.

(b) For the interval $[-5, 14]$, we compare

$$f(-5) = -58, \quad f(-2) = 104, \quad f(8) = -396, \quad f(14) = 360.$$

The global maximum is now 360 and occurs at $x = 14$, and the global minimum is still -396 and occurs at $x = 8$. Since the function is increasing for $x > 8$, changing the right-hand end of the interval from $x = 12$ to $x = 14$ alters the global maximum but not the global minimum. See Figure 4.21.

(c) Figure 4.21 shows that for $-5 \le x < \infty$ there is no global maximum, because we can make $f(x)$ as large as we please by choosing x large enough. The global minimum remains -396 at $x = 8$.

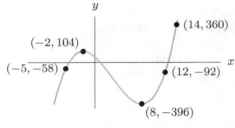

Figure 4.21: Graph of $f(x) = x^3 - 9x^2 - 48x + 52$

Figure 4.22: Graph of $g(x) = x - \sin(2x)$

Example 2   Find the global maximum and minimum of $g(x) = x - \sin(2x)$ on the interval $0 \le x \le \pi/2$.

Solution   Since $g(x) = x - \sin(2x)$ is continuous and the interval $0 \le x \le \pi/2$ is closed, there must be a global maximum and minimum. The possible candidates are critical points in the interval and endpoints. Since there are no points where $g'(x)$ is undefined, we solve $g'(x) = 0$ to find all the critical points:

$$g'(x) = 1 - 2\cos(2x) = 0,$$

so $\cos(2x) = 1/2$. Therefore $2x = \pi/3, 5\pi/3, \ldots$. Thus the only critical point in the interval is $x = \pi/6$. We compare values of g at the critical points and the endpoints:

$$g(0) = 0, \quad g(\pi/6) = \pi/6 - \sqrt{3}/2 = -0.342, \quad g(\pi/2) = \pi/2 = 1.571.$$

Thus the global maximum is 1.571 at $x = \pi/2$ and the global minimum is -0.342 at $x = \pi/6$. See Figure 4.22.

Example 3   Jared is coughing. The speed in m/sec, $v(r)$, with which he expels air depends on the radius, r, of his windpipe, given for $0 \leq r \leq 9$ in mm by

$$v(r) = 0.1(9 - r)r^2.$$

What value of r maximizes the speed? For what value is the speed minimized?

Solution   Notice that $v(0) = v(9) = 0$, and that $v(r)$ is positive for $0 < r < 9$. Therefore the maximum occurs somewhere between $r = 0$ and $r = 9$. Since

$$v(r) = 0.1(9 - r)r^2 = 0.9r^2 - 0.1r^3,$$

the derivative is

$$v'(r) = 1.8r - 0.3r^2 = 0.3r(6 - r).$$

The derivative is zero if $r = 0$ or $r = 6$. These are the critical points of v. We already know $v(0) = v(9) = 0$, and

$$v(6) = 0.1(9 - 6)6^2 = 10.8 \text{ m/sec}.$$

Thus, v has a global maximum at $r = 6$ mm. The global minimum of $v = 0$ m/sec occurs at both endpoints $r = 0$ mm and $r = 9$ mm.

In applications of optimization, the function being optimized often contains a parameter whose value depends on the situation, and the maximum or minimum depends on the parameter.

Example 4   (a) For a positive constant b, the surge function $f(t) = te^{-bt}$ gives the quantity of a drug in the body for time $t \geq 0$. Find the global maximum and minimum of $f(t)$ for $t \geq 0$.
(b) Find the value of b making $t = 10$ the global maximum.

Solution   (a) Differentiating and factoring gives

$$f'(t) = 1 \cdot e^{-bt} - bte^{-bt} = (1 - bt)e^{-bt},$$

so there is a critical point at $t = 1/b$.

The sign of f' is determined by the sign of $(1 - bt)$, so f' is positive to the left of $t = 1/b$ and negative to the right of $t = 1/b$. Since f increases to the left of $t = 1/b$ and decreases to the right of $t = 1/b$, the global maximum occurs at $t = 1/b$. In addition, $f(0) = 0$ and $f(t) \geq 0$ for all $t \geq 0$, so the global minimum occurs at $t = 0$. Thus

The global maximum value is $f\left(\dfrac{1}{b}\right) = \dfrac{1}{b}e^{-b(1/b)} = \dfrac{e^{-1}}{b}$.

The global minimum value is $f(0) = 0$.
(b) Since $t = 10$ gives the global maximum, we have $1/b = 10$, so $b = 0.1$. See Figure 4.23.

Figure 4.23: Graph of $f(t) = te^{-bt}$ for $b = 0.1$

Example 5   When an arrow is shot into the air, its range, R, is defined as the horizontal distance from the archer to the point where the arrow hits the ground. If the ground is horizontal and we neglect air resistance, it can be shown that

$$R = \frac{v_0^2 \sin(2\theta)}{g},$$

where v_0 is the initial velocity of the arrow, g is the (constant) acceleration due to gravity, and θ is the angle above horizontal, so $0 \le \theta \le \pi/2$. (See Figure 4.24.) What angle θ maximizes R?

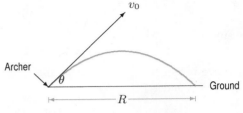

Figure 4.24: Arrow's path

Solution   We can find the maximum of this function without using calculus. The maximum value of R occurs when $\sin(2\theta) = 1$, so $\theta = \arcsin(1)/2 = \pi/4$, giving $R = v_0^2/g$.

Let's see how we can do the same problem with calculus. We want to find the global maximum of R for $0 \le \theta \le \pi/2$. First we look for critical points:

$$\frac{dR}{d\theta} = 2\frac{v_0^2 \cos(2\theta)}{g}.$$

Setting $dR/d\theta$ equal to 0, we get

$$0 = \cos(2\theta), \quad \text{or} \quad 2\theta = \pm\frac{\pi}{2}, \pm\frac{3\pi}{2}, \pm\frac{5\pi}{2}, \ldots$$

so $\pi/4$ is the only critical point in the interval $0 \le \theta \le \pi/2$. The range at $\theta = \pi/4$ is $R = v_0^2/g$.

Now we must check the value of R at the endpoints $\theta = 0$ and $\theta = \pi/2$. Since $R = 0$ at each endpoint (the arrow is shot horizontally or vertically), the critical point $\theta = \pi/4$ gives both a local and a global maximum on $0 \le \theta \le \pi/2$. Therefore, the arrow goes farthest if shot at an angle of $\pi/4$, or $45°$.

Finding Upper and Lower Bounds

A problem which is closely related to finding maxima and minima is finding the *bounds* of a function. In Example 1 on page 198, the value of $f(x)$ on the interval $[-5, 12]$ ranges from -396 to 104. Thus

$$-396 \le f(x) \le 104,$$

and we say that -396 is a *lower bound* for f and 104 is an *upper bound* for f on $[-5, 12]$. (See Appendix A for more on bounds.) Of course, we could also say that

$$-400 \le f(x) \le 150,$$

so that f is also bounded below by -400 and above by 150 on $[-5, 12]$. However, we consider the -396 and 104 to be the *best possible bounds* because they describe more accurately how the function $f(x)$ behaves on $[-5, 12]$.

Example 6   An object on a spring oscillates about its equilibrium position at $y = 0$. See Figure 4.25. Its displacement, y, from equilibrium is given as a function of time, t, by

$$y = e^{-t} \cos t.$$

Find the greatest distance the object goes above and below the equilibrium for $t \geq 0$.

Solution   We are looking for bounds for y as a function of t. What does the graph look like? We can think of it as a cosine curve with a decreasing amplitude of e^{-t}; in other words, it is a cosine curve squashed between the graphs of $y = e^{-t}$ and $y = -e^{-t}$, forming a wave with lower and lower crests and shallower and shallower troughs. (See Figure 4.26.)

Equilibrium

Figure 4.25: Object on spring
($y < 0$ below equilibrium)

Figure 4.26: $f(t) = e^{-t} \cos t$ for $t \geq 0$

From the graph, we see that for $t \geq 0$, the curve lies between the horizontal lines $y = -1$ and $y = 1$. This means that -1 and 1 are bounds:

$$-1 \leq e^{-t} \cos t \leq 1.$$

The line $y = 1$ is the best possible upper bound because the graph does come up that high (at $t = 0$). However, we can find a better lower bound if we find the global minimum value of y for $t \geq 0$; this minimum occurs in the first trough between $t = \pi/2$ and $t = 3\pi/2$ because later troughs are squashed closer to the t-axis. At the minimum, $dy/dt = 0$. The product rule gives

$$\frac{dy}{dt} = (-e^{-t}) \cos t + e^{-t}(-\sin t) = -e^{-t}(\cos t + \sin t) = 0.$$

Since e^{-t} is never 0, we must have

$$\cos t + \sin t = 0, \quad \text{so} \quad \frac{\sin t}{\cos t} = -1.$$

The smallest positive solution of

$$\tan t = -1 \quad \text{is} \quad t = \frac{3\pi}{4}.$$

Thus, the global minimum we see on the graph occurs at $t = 3\pi/4$. The value of y there is

$$y = e^{-3\pi/4} \cos\left(\frac{3\pi}{4}\right) \approx -0.07.$$

The greatest distance the object goes below equilibrium is 0.07. Thus, for all $t \geq 0$,

$$-0.07 \leq e^{-t} \cos t \leq 1.$$

Notice how much smaller in magnitude the lower bound is than the upper. This is a reflection of how quickly the factor e^{-t} causes the oscillation to die out.

Exercises and Problems for Section 4.2

Exercises

For Exercises 1–2, indicate all critical points on the given graphs. Determine which correspond to local minima, local maxima, global minima, global maxima, or none of these. (Note that the graphs are on closed intervals.)

1.

2.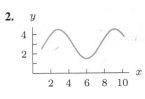

3. For $x > 0$, find the x-value and the corresponding y-value that maximizes $y = 25 + 6x^2 - x^3$, by

(a) Estimating the values from a graph of y.

(b) Finding the values using calculus.

In Exercises 4–10, find the global maximum and minimum for the function on the closed interval.

4. $f(x) = x^3 - 3x^2 + 20, \quad -1 \le x \le 3$

5. $f(x) = x^4 - 8x^2, \quad -3 \le x \le 1$

6. $f(x) = xe^{-x^2/2}, \quad -2 \le x \le 2$

7. $f(x) = 3x^{1/3} - x, \quad -1 \le x \le 8$

8. $f(x) = x - 2\ln(x+1), \quad 0 \le x \le 2$

9. $f(x) = x^2 - 2|x|, \quad -3 \le x \le 4$

10. $f(x) = \dfrac{x+1}{x^2+3}, \quad -1 \le x \le 2$

In Exercises 11–13, find the value(s) of x for which:

(a) $f(x)$ has a local maximum or local minimum. Indicate which ones are maxima and which are minima.

(b) $f(x)$ has a global maximum or global minimum.

11. $f(x) = x^{10} - 10x$, and $0 \le x \le 2$

12. $f(x) = x - \ln x$, and $0.1 \le x \le 2$

13. $f(x) = \sin^2 x - \cos x$, and $0 \le x \le \pi$

In Exercises 14–19, find the exact global maximum and minimum values of the function. The domain is all real numbers unless otherwise specified.

14. $g(x) = 4x - x^2 - 5$

15. $f(x) = x + 1/x$ for $x > 0$

16. $g(t) = te^{-t}$ for $t > 0$

17. $f(x) = x - \ln x$ for $x > 0$

18. $f(t) = \dfrac{t}{1+t^2}$

19. $f(t) = (\sin^2 t + 2)\cos t$

In Exercises 20–25, find the best possible bounds for the function.

20. $x^3 - 4x^2 + 4x$, for $0 \le x \le 4$

21. e^{-x^2}, for $|x| \le 0.3$

22. $x^3 e^{-x}$, for $x \ge 0$

23. $x + \sin x$, for $0 \le x \le 2\pi$

24. $\ln(1+x)$, for $x \ge 0$

25. $\ln(1+x^2)$, for $-1 \le x \le 2$

Problems

26. A grapefruit is tossed straight up with an initial velocity of 50 ft/sec. The grapefruit is 5 feet above the ground when it is released. Its height, in feet, at time t seconds is given by
$$y = -16t^2 + 50t + 5.$$
How high does it go before returning to the ground?

27. Find the value(s) of x that give critical points of $y = ax^2 + bx + c$, where a, b, c are constants. Under what conditions on a, b, c is the critical value a maximum? A minimum?

28. What value of w minimizes S if $S - 5pw = 3qw^2 - 6pq$ and p and q are positive constants?

29. Let $y = at^2 e^{-bt}$ with a and b positive constants. For $t \ge 0$, what value of t maximizes y? Sketch the curve if $a = 1$ and $b = 1$.

30. For some positive constant C, a patient's temperature change, T, due to a dose, D, of a drug is given by
$$T = \left(\frac{C}{2} - \frac{D}{3}\right)D^2.$$

(a) What dosage maximizes the temperature change?

(b) The sensitivity of the body to the drug is defined as dT/dD. What dosage maximizes sensitivity?

31. A warehouse selling cement has to decide how often and in what quantities to reorder. It is cheaper, on average, to place large orders, because this reduces the ordering cost per unit. On the other hand, larger orders mean higher storage costs. The warehouse always reorders cement in the same quantity, q. The total weekly cost, C, of ordering and storage is given by
$$C = \frac{a}{q} + bq, \quad \text{where } a, b \text{ are positive constants.}$$

(a) Which of the terms, a/q and bq, represents the ordering cost and which represents the storage cost?

(b) What value of q gives the minimum total cost?

32. The bending moment M of a beam, supported at one end, at a distance x from the support is given by

$$M = \tfrac{1}{2}wLx - \tfrac{1}{2}wx^2,$$

where L is the length of the beam, and w is the uniform load per unit length. Find the point on the beam where the moment is greatest.

33. A chemical reaction converts substance A to substance Y. At the start of the reaction, the quantity of A present is a grams. At time t seconds later, the quantity of Y present is y grams. The rate of the reaction, in grams/sec, is given by

$$\text{Rate} = ky(a - y), \quad k \text{ is a positive constant.}$$

(a) For what values of y is the rate nonnegative? Graph the rate against y.

(b) For what values of y is the rate a maximum?

34. The potential energy, U, of a particle moving along the x-axis is given by

$$U = b\left(\frac{a^2}{x^2} - \frac{a}{x}\right),$$

where a and b are positive constants and $x > 0$. What value of x minimizes the potential energy?

35. For positive constants A and B, the force between two atoms in a molecule is given by

$$f(r) = -\frac{A}{r^2} + \frac{B}{r^3},$$

where $r > 0$ is the distance between the atoms. What value of r minimizes the force between the atoms?

36. When an electric current passes through two resistors with resistance r_1 and r_2, connected in parallel, the combined resistance, R, can be calculated from the equation

$$\frac{1}{R} = \frac{1}{r_1} + \frac{1}{r_2},$$

where R, r_1, and r_2 are positive. Assume that r_2 is constant.

(a) Show that R is an increasing function of r_1.

(b) Where on the interval $a \le r_1 \le b$ does R take its maximum value?

37. As an epidemic spreads through a population, the number of infected people, I, is expressed as a function of the number of susceptible people, S, by

$$I = k\ln\left(\frac{S}{S_0}\right) - S + S_0 + I_0, \quad \text{for } k, S_0, I_0 > 0.$$

(a) Find the maximum number of infected people.

(b) The constant k is a characteristic of the particular disease; the constants S_0 and I_0 are the values of S and I when the disease starts. Which of the following affects the maximum possible value of I? Explain.

- The particular disease, but not how it starts.
- How the disease starts, but not the particular disease.
- Both the particular disease and how it starts.

38. Two points on the curve $y = \dfrac{x^3}{1 + x^4}$ have opposite x-values, x and $-x$. Find the points making the slope of the line joining them greatest.

39. The function $y = t(x)$ is positive and continuous with a global maximum at the point $(3, 3)$. Graph $t(x)$ if $t'(x)$ and $t''(x)$ have the same sign for $x < 3$, but opposite signs for $x > 3$.

40. Figure 4.27 gives the derivative of $g(x)$ on $-2 \le x \le 2$.

(a) Write a few sentences describing the behavior of $g(x)$ on this interval.

(b) Does the graph of $g(x)$ have any inflection points? If so, give the approximate x-coordinates of their locations. Explain your reasoning.

(c) What are the global maxima and minima of g on $[-2, 2]$?

(d) If $g(-2) = 5$, what do you know about $g(0)$ and $g(2)$? Explain.

Figure 4.27

41. Figure 4.28 shows the second derivative of $h(x)$ for $-2 \le x \le 1$. If $h'(-1) = 0$ and $h(-1) = 2$,

(a) Explain why $h'(x)$ is never negative on this interval.

(b) Explain why $h(x)$ has a global maximum at $x = 1$.

(c) Sketch a possible graph of $h(x)$ for $-2 \le x \le 1$.

Figure 4.28

42. Show that if $f''(x)$ is continuous and $f(x)$ has exactly two critical points, then $f'(x)$ has a local maximum or local minimum between the two critical points.

43. You are given the n numbers $a_1, a_2, a_3, \cdots, a_n$. For a variable x, consider the expression

$$D = (x-a_1)^2 + (x-a_2)^2 + (x-a_3)^2 + \cdots + (x-a_n)^2.$$

Show that D is a minimum when x is the average of $a_1, a_2, a_3, \cdots, a_n$.

44. In this problem we prove a special case of the Mean Value Theorem where $f(a) = f(b) = 0$. This special case is called Rolle's Theorem: If f is continuous on $[a, b]$ and differentiable on (a, b), and if $f(a) = f(b) = 0$, then there is a number c, with $a < c < b$, such that

$$f'(c) = 0.$$

By the Extreme Value Theorem, f has a global maximum and a global minimum on $[a, b]$.

(a) Prove Rolle's Theorem in the case that both the global maximum and the global minimum are at endpoints of $[a, b]$. [Hint: $f(x)$ must be a very simple function in this case.]

(b) Prove Rolle's Theorem in the case that either the global maximum or the global minimum is not at an endpoint. [Hint: Think about local maxima and minima.]

45. Use Rolle's Theorem to prove the Mean Value Theorem. Suppose that $f(x)$ is continuous on $[a, b]$ and differentiable on (a, b). Let $g(x)$ be the difference between $f(x)$ and the y-value on the secant line joining $(a, f(a))$ to $(b, f(b))$, so

$$g(x) = f(x) - f(a) - \frac{f(b) - f(a)}{b - a}(x - a).$$

(a) Show $g(x)$ on a sketch of $f(x)$.
(b) Use Rolle's Theorem (Problem 44) to show that there must be a point c in (a, b) such that $g'(c) = 0$.
(c) Show that if c is the point in part (b), then

$$f'(c) = \frac{f(b) - f(a)}{b - a}.$$

Strengthen Your Understanding

In Problems 46–48, explain what is wrong with the statement.

46. The function $f(x) = (x - 1)^2(x - 2), 0 \le x \le 3$ has a global maximum at $x = 1$.

47. The global minimum of $f(x) = x^4$ on any closed interval $a \le x \le b$ occurs at $x = 0$.

48. The best possible bounds for $f(x) = 1/(1 - x)$ on the interval $0 \le x \le 2$ are $f(0) \le f(x) \le f(2)$.

In Problems 49–52, give an example of:

49. A function which has a global maximum at $x = 0$ and a global minimum at $x = 1$ on the interval $0 \le x \le 1$ but no critical points in between $x = 0$ and $x = 1$.

50. A function for which the global maximum is equal to the global minimum.

51. An interval where the best possible bounds for $f(x) = x^2$ are $2 \le f(x) \le 5$.

52. A differentiable function f with best possible bounds $-1 \le f(x) \le 1$ on the interval $-4 \le x \le 4$.

In Problems 53–57, let $f(x) = x^2$. Decide if the following statements are true or false. Explain your answer.

53. f has an upper bound on the interval $(0, 2)$.

54. f has a global maximum on the interval $(0, 2)$.

55. f does not have a global minimum on the interval $(0, 2)$.

56. f does not have a global minimum on any interval (a, b).

57. f has a global minimum on any interval $[a, b]$.

58. Which of the following statements is implied by the statement "If f is continuous on $[a, b]$ then f has a global maximum on $[a, b]$?"

(a) If f has a global maximum on $[a, b]$ then f must be continuous on $[a, b]$.
(b) If f is not continuous on $[a, b]$ then f does not have a global maximum on $[a, b]$.
(c) If f does not have a global maximum on $[a, b]$ then f is not continuous on $[a, b]$.

Are the statements in Problems 59–63 true of false? Give an explanation for your answer.

59. Since the function $f(x) = 1/x$ is continuous for $x > 0$ and the interval $(0, 1)$ is bounded, f has a maximum on the interval $(0, 1)$.

60. The Extreme Value Theorem says that only continuous functions have global maxima and minima on every closed, bounded interval.

61. The global maximum of $f(x) = x^2$ on every closed interval is at one of the endpoints of the interval.

62. A function can have two different upper bounds.

63. If a differentiable function $f(x)$ has a global maximum on the interval $0 \le x \le 10$ at $x = 0$, then $f'(0) \le 0$.

4.3 OPTIMIZATION AND MODELING

Finding global maxima and minima is often made possible by having a formula for the function to be maximized or minimized. The process of translating a problem into a function with a known formula is called *mathematical modeling*. The examples that follow give the flavor of modeling.

Example 1   What are the dimensions of an aluminum can that holds 40 in^3 of juice and that uses the least material? Assume that the can is cylindrical, and is capped on both ends.

Solution   It is often a good idea to think about a problem in general terms before trying to solve it. Since we're trying to use as little material as possible, why not make the can very small, say, the size of a peanut? We can't, since the can must hold 40 in^3. If we make the can short, to try to use less material in the sides, we'll have to make it fat as well, so that it can hold 40 in^3. See Figure 4.29(a).

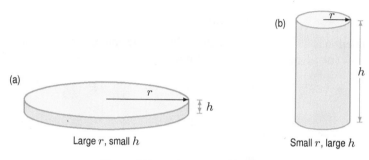

Figure 4.29: Various cylindrical-shaped cans

Table 4.1   *Height, h, and material, M, used in can for various choices of radius, r*

r (in)	h (in)	M (in^2)
0.2	318.31	400.25
1	12.73	86.28
2	3.18	65.13
3	1.41	83.22
4	0.80	120.53
10	0.13	636.32

If we try to save material by making the top and bottom small, the can has to be tall to accommodate the 40 in^3 of juice. So any savings we get by using a small top and bottom may be outweighed by the height of the sides. See Figure 4.29(b).

Table 4.1 gives the height h and amount of material M used in the can for some choices of the radius, r. You can see that r and h change in opposite directions, and that more material is used at the extremes (very large or very small r) than in the middle. It appears that the radius needing the smallest amount of material, M, is somewhere between 1 and 3 inches. Thinking of M as a function of the radius, r, we get the graph in Figure 4.30. The graph shows that the global minimum we want is at a critical point.

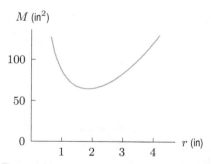

Figure 4.30: Total material used in can, M, as a function of radius, r

Both the table and the graph were obtained from a mathematical model, which in this case is a formula for the material used in making the can. Finding such a formula depends on knowing the geometry of a cylinder, in particular its area and volume. We have

$$M = \text{Material used in the can} = \text{Material in ends} + \text{Material in the side}$$

where

Material in ends $= 2 \cdot$ Area of a circle with radius $r = 2 \cdot \pi r^2$,

Material in the side $=$ Area of curved side of cylinder with height h and radius $r = 2\pi rh$.

We have

$$M = 2\pi r^2 + 2\pi rh.$$

However, h is not independent of r: if r grows, h shrinks, and vice-versa. To find the relationship, we use the fact that the volume of the cylinder, $\pi r^2 h$, is equal to the constant 40 in^3:

$$\text{Volume of can } = \pi r^2 h = 40, \quad \text{giving} \quad h = \frac{40}{\pi r^2}.$$

This means

$$\text{Material in the side} = 2\pi rh = 2\pi r\frac{40}{\pi r^2} = \frac{80}{r}.$$

Thus we obtain the formula for the total material, M, used in a can of radius r if the volume is 40 in^3:

$$M = 2\pi r^2 + \frac{80}{r}.$$

The domain of this function is all $r > 0$ because the radius of the can cannot be negative or zero.

To find the minimum of M, we look for critical points:

$$\frac{dM}{dr} = 4\pi r - \frac{80}{r^2} = 0 \quad \text{at a critical point,} \quad \text{so} \quad 4\pi r = \frac{80}{r^2}.$$

Therefore,

$$\pi r^3 = 20, \quad \text{so} \quad r = \left(\frac{20}{\pi}\right)^{1/3} = 1.85 \text{ inches,}$$

which agrees with the graph in Figure 4.30. We also have

$$h = \frac{40}{\pi r^2} = \frac{40}{\pi(1.85)^2} = 3.7 \text{ inches.}$$

The material used is $M = 2\pi(1.85)^2 + 80/1.85 = 64.7$ in^2.

To confirm that we have found the global minimum, we look at the formula for dM/dr. For small r, the $-80/r^2$ term dominates and for large r, the $4\pi r$ term dominates, so dM/dr is negative for $r < 1.85$ and positive for $r > 1.85$. Thus, M is decreasing for $r < 1.85$ and increasing for $r > 1.85$, so the global minimum occurs at $r = 1.85$.

Practical Tips for Modeling Optimization Problems

1. Make sure that you know what quantity or function is to be optimized.

2. If possible, make several sketches showing how the elements that vary are related. Label your sketches clearly by assigning variables to quantities which change.

3. Try to obtain a formula for the function to be optimized in terms of the variables that you identified in the previous step. If necessary, eliminate from this formula all but one variable. Identify the domain over which this variable varies.

4. Find the critical points and evaluate the function at these points and the endpoints (if relevant) to find the global maxima and/or minima.

The next example, another problem in geometry, illustrates this approach.

Example 2   Alaina wants to get to the bus stop as quickly as possible. The bus stop is across a grassy park, 2000 feet west and 600 feet north of her starting position. Alaina can walk west along the edge of the park on the sidewalk at a speed of 6 ft/sec. She can also travel through the grass in the park, but only at a rate of 4 ft/sec. What path gets her to the bus stop the fastest?

Solution

Figure 4.31: Three possible paths to the bus stop

We might first think that she should take a path that is the shortest distance. Unfortunately, the path that follows the shortest distance to the bus stop is entirely in the park, where her speed is slow. (See Figure 4.31(a).) That distance is $\sqrt{2000^2 + 600^2} = 2088$ feet, which takes her about 522 seconds to traverse. She could instead walk quickly the entire 2000 feet along the sidewalk, which leaves her just the 600-foot northward journey through the park. (See Figure 4.31(b).) This method would take $2000/6 + 600/4 \approx 483$ seconds total walking time.

But can she do even better? Perhaps another combination of sidewalk and park gives a shorter travel time. For example, what is the travel time if she walks 1000 feet west along the sidewalk and the rest of the way through the park? (See Figure 4.31(c).) The answer is about 458 seconds.

We make a model for this problem. We label the distance that Alaina walks west along the sidewalk x and the distance she walks through the park y, as in Figure 4.32. Then the total time, t, is

$$t = t_{\text{sidewalk}} + t_{\text{park}}.$$

Since

$$\text{Time} = \text{Distance/Speed},$$

and she can walk 6 ft/sec on the sidewalk and 4 ft/sec in the park, we have

$$t = \frac{x}{6} + \frac{y}{4}.$$

Now, by the Pythagorean Theorem, $y = \sqrt{(2000 - x)^2 + 600^2}$. Therefore

$$t = \frac{x}{6} + \frac{\sqrt{(2000 - x)^2 + 600^2}}{4} \qquad \text{for } 0 \leq x \leq 2000.$$

We can find the critical points of this function analytically. (See Problem 15 on page 211.) Alternatively, we can graph the function on a calculator and estimate the critical point, which is $x \approx 1463$ feet. This gives a minimum total time of about 445 seconds.

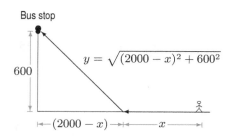

Figure 4.32: Modeling time to bus stop

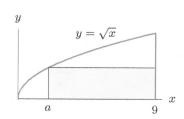

Figure 4.33: Find the rectangle of maximum area with one corner on $y = \sqrt{x}$

Example 3   Figure 4.33 shows the curves $y = \sqrt{x}$, $x = 9$, $y = 0$, and a rectangle with vertical sides at $x = a$ and $x = 9$. Find the dimensions of the rectangle having the maximum possible area.

Solution   We want to choose a to maximize the area of the rectangle with corners at $(a, \sqrt{a})$ and $(9, \sqrt{a})$. The area of this rectangle is given by

$$R = \text{Height} \cdot \text{Length} = \sqrt{a}(9 - a) = 9a^{1/2} - a^{3/2}.$$

We are restricted to $0 \le a \le 9$. To maximize this area, we first set $dR/da = 0$ to find critical points:

$$\frac{dR}{da} = \frac{9}{2}a^{-1/2} - \frac{3}{2}a^{1/2} = 0$$

$$\frac{9}{2\sqrt{a}} = \frac{3\sqrt{a}}{2}$$

$$18 = 6a$$

$$a = 3.$$

Notice that $R = 0$ at the endpoints $a = 0$ and $a = 9$, and R is positive between these values. Since $a = 3$ is the only critical point, the rectangle with the maximum area has length $9 - 3 = 6$ and height $\sqrt{3}$.

Example 4   A closed box has a fixed surface area A and a square base with side x.

(a) Find a formula for the volume, V, of the box as a function of x. What is the domain of V?
(b) Graph V as a function of x.
(c) Find the maximum value of V.

Solution   (a) The height of the box is h, as shown in Figure 4.34. The box has six sides, four with area xh and two, the top and bottom, with area x^2. Thus,

$$4xh + 2x^2 = A.$$

So

$$h = \frac{A - 2x^2}{4x}.$$

Then, the volume, V, is given by

$$V = x^2h = x^2\left(\frac{A - 2x^2}{4x}\right) = \frac{x}{4}(A - 2x^2) = \frac{A}{4}x - \frac{1}{2}x^3.$$

Since the area of the top and bottom combined must be less than A, we have $2x^2 \le A$. Thus, the domain of V is $0 \le x \le \sqrt{A/2}$.
(b) Figure 4.35 shows the graph for $x \ge 0$. (Note that A is a positive constant.)
(c) To find the maximum, we differentiate, regarding A as a constant:

$$\frac{dV}{dx} = \frac{A}{4} - \frac{3}{2}x^2 = 0$$

so

$$x = \pm\sqrt{\frac{A}{6}}.$$

Since $x \ge 0$ in the domain of V, we use $x = \sqrt{A/6}$. Figure 4.35 indicates that at this value of x, the volume is a maximum.

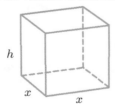

Figure 4.34: Box with base of side x, height h, surface area A, and volume V

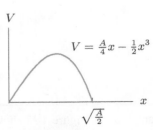

$$V = \tfrac{A}{4}x - \tfrac{1}{2}x^3$$

$$\sqrt{\tfrac{A}{2}}$$

Figure 4.35: Volume, V, against length of side of base, x

From the formula, we see that $dV/dx > 0$ for $x < \sqrt{A/6}$, so V is increasing, and that $dV/dx < 0$ for $x > \sqrt{A/6}$, so V is decreasing. Thus, $x = \sqrt{A/6}$ gives the global maximum. Evaluating V at $x = \sqrt{A/6}$ and simplifying, we get

$$V = \frac{A}{4}\sqrt{\frac{A}{6}} - \frac{1}{2}\left(\sqrt{\frac{A}{6}}\right)^3 = \left(\frac{A}{6}\right)^{3/2}.$$

Example 5   A light is suspended at a height h above the floor. (See Figure 4.36.) The illumination at the point P is inversely proportional to the square of the distance from the point P to the light and directly proportional to the cosine of the angle θ. How far from the floor should the light be to maximize the illumination at the point P?

Figure 4.36: How high should the light be?

Solution   If the illumination is represented by I and r is the distance from the light to the point P, then we know that for some $k \geq 0$,

$$I = \frac{k\cos\theta}{r^2}.$$

Since $r^2 = h^2 + 10^2$ and $\cos\theta = h/r = h/\sqrt{h^2 + 10^2}$, we have, for $h \geq 0$,

$$I = \frac{kh}{(h^2 + 10^2)^{3/2}}.$$

To find the height at which I is maximized, we differentiate using the quotient rule:

$$\frac{dI}{dh} = \frac{k(h^2 + 10^2)^{3/2} - kh(\frac{3}{2}(h^2 + 10^2)^{1/2}(2h))}{[(h^2 + 10^2)^{3/2}]^2}$$

$$= \frac{(h^2 + 10^2)^{1/2}[k(h^2 + 10^2) - 3kh^2]}{(h^2 + 10^2)^3}$$

$$= \frac{k(h^2 + 10^2) - 3kh^2}{(h^2 + 10^2)^{5/2}}$$

$$= \frac{k(10^2 - 2h^2)}{(h^2 + 10^2)^{5/2}}.$$

Setting $dI/dh = 0$ for $h \geq 0$ gives

$$10^2 - 2h^2 = 0$$

$$h = \sqrt{50} \text{ meters.}$$

Since $dI/dh > 0$ for $h < \sqrt{50}$ and $dI/dh < 0$ for $h > \sqrt{50}$, there is a local maximum at $h = \sqrt{50}$ meters. There is only one critical point, so the global maximum of I occurs at that point. Thus, the illumination is greatest if the light is suspended at a height of $\sqrt{50} \approx 7$ meters above the floor.

A Graphical Example: Minimizing Gas Consumption

Next we look at an example in which a function is given graphically and the optimum values are read from a graph. We already know how to estimate the optimum values of $f(x)$ from a graph of $f(x)$—read off the highest and lowest values. In this example, we see how to estimate the optimum value of the quantity $f(x)/x$ from a graph of $f(x)$ against x. The question we investigate is how to set driving speeds to maximize fuel efficiency.[2]

Example 6   Gas consumption, g (in gallons/hour), as a function of velocity, v (in mph), is given in Figure 4.37. What velocity minimizes the gas consumption per mile, represented by g/v?

Figure 4.37: Gas consumption versus velocity

Solution   Figure 4.38 shows that g/v is the slope of the line from the origin to the point P. Where on the curve should P be to make the slope a minimum? From the possible positions of the line shown in Figure 4.38, we see that the slope of the line is both a local and global minimum when the line is tangent to the curve. From Figure 4.39, we can see that the velocity at this point is about 50 mph. Thus to minimize gas consumption per mile, we should drive about 50 mph.

Figure 4.38: Graphical representation of gas consumption per mile, g/v

Figure 4.39: Velocity for maximum fuel efficiency

Exercises and Problems for Section 4.3

Exercises

1. The sum of two nonnegative numbers is 100. What is the maximum value of the product of these two numbers?

2. The product of two positive numbers is 784. What is the minimum value of their sum?

3. The sum of three nonnegative numbers is 36, and one of the numbers is twice one of the other numbers. What is the maximum value of the product of these three numbers?

4. The perimeter of a rectangle is 64 cm. Find the lengths of the sides of the rectangle giving the maximum area.

5. If you have 100 feet of fencing and want to enclose a

rectangular area up against a long, straight wall, what is the largest area you can enclose?

For the solids in Exercises 6–9, find the dimensions giving the minimum surface area, given that the volume is 8 cm³.

6. A closed rectangular box, with a square base x by x cm and height h cm.

7. An open-topped rectangular box, with a square base x by x cm and height h cm.

8. A closed cylinder with radius r cm and height h cm.

9. A cylinder open at one end with radius r cm and height h cm.

[2] Adapted from Peter D. Taylor, *Calculus: The Analysis of Functions* (Toronto: Wall & Emerson, 1992).

In Exercises 10–11, find the x-value maximizing the shaded area. One vertex is on the graph of $f(x) = x^2/3 - 50x + 1000$, where $0 \le x \le 20$.

10.

11.

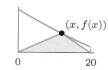

12. A rectangle has one side on the x-axis and two vertices on the curve

$$y = \frac{1}{1 + x^2}.$$

Find the vertices of the rectangle with maximum area.

13. A right triangle has one vertex at the origin and one vertex on the curve $y = e^{-x/3}$ for $1 \le x \le 5$. One of the two perpendicular sides is along the x-axis; the other is parallel to the y-axis. Find the maximum and minimum areas for such a triangle.

14. A rectangle has one side on the x-axis, one side on the y-axis, one vertex at the origin and one on the curve $y = e^{-2x}$ for $x \ge 0$. Find the

(a) Maximum area   **(b)** Minimum perimeter

Problems

15. Find analytically the exact critical point of the function which represents the time, t, to walk to the bus stop in Example 2. Recall that t is given by

$$t = \frac{x}{6} + \frac{\sqrt{(2000 - x)^2 + 600^2}}{4}.$$

16. Of all rectangles with given area, A, which has the shortest diagonals?

17. A rectangular beam is cut from a cylindrical log of radius 30 cm. The strength of a beam of width w and height h is proportional to wh^2. (See Figure 4.40.) Find the width and height of the beam of maximum strength.

Figure 4.40

In Problems 18–19 a vertical line divides a region into two pieces. Find the value of the coordinate x that maximizes the product of the two areas.

18.

19.

In Problems 20–22 the figures are made of rectangles and semicircles.

(a) Find a formula for the area.

(b) Find a formula for the perimeter.

(c) Find the dimensions x and y that maximize the area given that the perimeter is 100.

20.

21.

22.

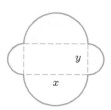

23. A piece of wire of length L cm is cut into two pieces. One piece, of length x cm, is made into a circle; the rest is made into a square.

(a) Find the value of x that makes the sum of the areas of the circle and square a minimum. Find the value of x giving a maximum.

(b) For the values of x found in part (a), show that the ratio of the length of wire in the square to the length of wire in the circle is equal to the ratio of the area of the square to the area of the circle.[3]

(c) Are the values of x found in part (a) the only values of x for which the ratios in part (b) are equal?

[3]From Sally Thomas.

In Problems 24–27, find the minimum and maximum values of the expression where x and y are lengths in Figure 4.41 and $0 \le x \le 10$.

Figure 4.41

24. x **25.** y **26.** $x + 2y$ **27.** $2x + y$

28. Which point on the curve $y = \sqrt{1-x}$ is closest to the origin?

29. Find the point(s) on the ellipse

$$\frac{x^2}{9} + y^2 = 1$$

  (a) Closest to the point $(2, 0)$.
  (b) Closest to the focus $(\sqrt{8}, 0)$.

[Hint: Minimize the square of the distance—this avoids square roots.]

30. What are the dimensions of the closed cylindrical can that has surface area 280 square centimeters and contains the maximum volume?

31. A hemisphere of radius 1 sits on a horizontal plane. A cylinder stands with its axis vertical, the center of its base at the center of the sphere, and its top circular rim touching the hemisphere. Find the radius and height of the cylinder of maximum volume.

32. In a chemical reaction, substance A combines with substance B to form substance Y. At the start of the reaction, the quantity of A present is a grams, and the quantity of B present is b grams. At time t seconds after the start of the reaction, the quantity of Y present is y grams. Assume $a < b$ and $y \le a$. For certain types of reactions, the rate of the reaction, in grams/sec, is given by

Rate $= k(a - y)(b - y)$, k is a positive constant.

  (a) For what values of y is the rate nonnegative? Graph the rate against y.
  (b) Use your graph to find the value of y at which the rate of the reaction is fastest.

33. A smokestack deposits soot on the ground with a concentration inversely proportional to the square of the distance from the stack. With two smokestacks 20 miles apart, the concentration of the combined deposits on the line joining them, at a distance x from one stack, is given by

$$S = \frac{k_1}{x^2} + \frac{k_2}{(20 - x)^2}$$

where k_1 and k_2 are positive constants which depend on the quantity of smoke each stack is emitting. If $k_1 = 7k_2$, find the point on the line joining the stacks where the concentration of the deposit is a minimum.

34. A wave of wavelength λ traveling in deep water has speed, v, given for positive constants c and k, by

$$v = k\sqrt{\frac{\lambda}{c} + \frac{c}{\lambda}}$$

As λ varies, does such a wave have a maximum or minimum velocity? If so, what is it? Explain.

35. A circular ring of wire of radius r_0 lies in a plane perpendicular to the x-axis and is centered at the origin. The ring has a positive electric charge spread uniformly over it. The electric field in the x-direction, E, at the point x on the axis is given by

$$E = \frac{kx}{(x^2 + r_0^2)^{3/2}} \quad \text{for} \quad k > 0.$$

At what point on the x-axis is the field greatest? Least?

36. A woman pulls a sled which, together with its load, has a mass of m kg. If her arm makes an angle of θ with her body (assumed vertical) and the coefficient of friction (a positive constant) is μ, the least force, F, she must exert to move the sled is given by

$$F = \frac{mg\mu}{\sin\theta + \mu\cos\theta}.$$

If $\mu = 0.15$, find the maximum and minimum values of F for $0 \le \theta \le \pi/2$. Give answers as multiples of mg.

37. Four equally massive particles can be made to rotate, equally spaced, around a circle of radius r. This is physically possible provided the radius and period T of the rotation are chosen so that the following *action* function is at its global minimum:

$$A(r) = \frac{r^2}{T} + \frac{T}{r}, \quad r > 0.$$

  (a) Find the radius r at which $A(r)$ has a global minimum.
  (b) If the period of the rotation is doubled, determine whether the radius of the rotation increases or decreases, and by approximately what percentage.

38. You run a small furniture business. You sign a deal with a customer to deliver up to 400 chairs, the exact number to be determined by the customer later. The price will be $90 per chair up to 300 chairs, and above 300, the price will be reduced by $0.25 per chair (on the whole order) for every additional chair over 300 ordered. What are the largest and smallest revenues your company can make under this deal?

39. The cost of fuel to propel a boat through the water (in dollars per hour) is proportional to the cube of the speed. A certain ferry boat uses $100 worth of fuel per hour when cruising at 10 miles per hour. Apart from fuel, the cost of running this ferry (labor, maintenance, and so on) is $675 per hour. At what speed should it travel so as to minimize the cost *per mile* traveled?

40. A business sells an item at a constant rate of r units per month. It reorders in batches of q units, at a cost of $a + bq$ dollars per order. Storage costs are k dollars per item per month, and, on average, $q/2$ items are in storage, waiting to be sold. [Assume r, a, b, k are positive constants.]

   (a) How often does the business reorder?
   (b) What is the average monthly cost of reordering?
   (c) What is the total monthly cost, C of ordering and storage?
   (d) Obtain Wilson's lot size formula, the optimal batch size which minimizes cost.

41. A bird such as a starling feeds worms to its young. To collect worms, the bird flies to a site where worms are to be found, picks up several in its beak, and flies back to its nest. The *loading curve* in Figure 4.42 shows how the number of worms (the load) a starling collects depends on the time it has been searching for them.[4] The curve is concave down because the bird can pick up worms more efficiently when its beak is empty; when its beak is partly full, the bird becomes much less efficient. The traveling time (from nest to site and back) is represented by the distance PO in Figure 4.42. The bird wants to maximize the rate at which it brings worms to the nest, where

$$\text{Rate worms arrive} = \frac{\text{Load}}{\text{Traveling time} + \text{Searching time}}$$

   (a) Draw a line in Figure 4.42 whose slope is this rate.
   (b) Using the graph, estimate the load which maximizes this rate.
   (c) If the traveling time is increased, does the optimal load increase or decrease? Why?

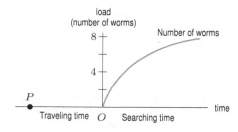

Figure 4.42

42. On the same side of a straight river are two towns, and the townspeople want to build a pumping station, S. See Figure 4.43. The pumping station is to be at the river's edge with pipes extending straight to the two towns. Where should the pumping station be located to minimize the total length of pipe?

Figure 4.43

43. A pigeon is released from a boat (point B in Figure 4.44) floating on a lake. Because of falling air over the cool water, the energy required to fly one meter over the lake is twice the corresponding energy e required for flying over the bank ($e = 3$ joule/meter). To minimize the energy required to fly from B to the loft, L, the pigeon heads to a point P on the bank and then flies along the bank to L. The distance $\overline{AL}$ is 2000 m, and $\overline{AB}$ is 500 m.

   (a) Express the energy required to fly from B to L via P as a function of the angle θ (the angle BPA).
   (b) What is the optimal angle θ?
   (c) Does your answer change if $\overline{AL}$, $\overline{AB}$, and e have different numerical values?

Figure 4.44

44. To get the best view of the Statue of Liberty in Figure 4.45, you should be at the position where θ is a maximum. If the statue stands 92 meters high, including the pedestal, which is 46 meters high, how far from the base should you be? [Hint: Find a formula for θ in terms of your distance from the base. Use this function to maximize θ, noting that $0 \leq \theta \leq \pi/2$.]

© Wesley Hitt/Getty Images

Figure 4.45

---

[4] Alex Kacelnick (1984). Reported by J. R. Krebs and N. B. Davis, *An Introduction to Behavioural Ecology* (Oxford: Blackwell, 1987).

45. A light ray starts at the origin and is reflected off a mirror along the line $y = 1$ to the point $(2, 0)$. See Figure 4.46. Fermat's Principle says that light's path minimizes the time of travel.[5] The speed of light is a constant.

(a) Using Fermat's Principle, find the optimal position of P.

(b) Using your answer to part (a), derive the Law of Reflection, that $\theta_1 = \theta_2$.

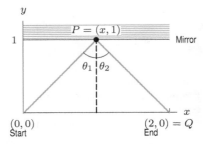

Figure 4.46

46. (a) For which positive number x is $x^{1/x}$ largest? Justify your answer.

[Hint: You may want to write $x^{1/x} = e^{\ln(x^{1/x})}$.]

(b) For which positive integer n is $n^{1/n}$ largest? Justify your answer.

(c) Use your answer to parts (a) and (b) to decide which is larger: $3^{1/3}$ or $\pi^{1/\pi}$.

47. The *arithmetic mean* of two numbers a and b is defined as $(a+b)/2$; the *geometric mean* of two positive numbers a and b is defined as $\sqrt{ab}$.

(a) For two positive numbers, which of the two means is larger? Justify your answer.

[Hint: Define $f(x) = (a+x)/2 - \sqrt{ax}$ for fixed a.]

(b) For three positive numbers a, b, c, the arithmetic and geometric mean are $(a+b+c)/3$ and $\sqrt[3]{abc}$, respectively. Which of the two means of three numbers is larger? [Hint: Redefine $f(x)$ for fixed a *and* b.]

48. A line goes through the origin and a point on the curve $y = x^2 e^{-3x}$, for $x \geq 0$. Find the maximum slope of such a line. At what x-value does it occur?

49. The distance, s, traveled by a cyclist, who starts at 1 pm, is given in Figure 4.47. Time, t, is in hours since noon.

(a) Explain why the quantity s/t is represented by the slope of a line from the origin to the point (t, s) on the graph.

(b) Estimate the time at which the quantity s/t is a maximum.

(c) What is the relationship between the quantity s/t and the instantaneous speed of the cyclist at the time you found in part (b)?

Figure 4.47

50. When birds lay eggs, they do so in clutches of several at a time. When the eggs hatch, each clutch gives rise to a brood of baby birds. We want to determine the clutch size which maximizes the number of birds surviving to adulthood per brood. If the clutch is small, there are few baby birds in the brood; if the clutch is large, there are so many baby birds to feed that most die of starvation. The number of surviving birds per brood as a function of clutch size is shown by the benefit curve in Figure 4.48.[6]

(a) Estimate the clutch size which maximizes the number of survivors per brood.

(b) Suppose also that there is a biological cost to having a larger clutch: the female survival rate is reduced by large clutches. This cost is represented by the dotted line in Figure 4.48. If we take cost into account by assuming that the optimal clutch size in fact maximizes the vertical distance between the curves, what is the new optimal clutch size?

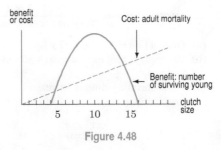

Figure 4.48

51. Let $f(v)$ be the amount of energy consumed by a flying bird, measured in joules per second (a joule is a unit of energy), as a function of its speed v (in meters/sec). Let $a(v)$ be the amount of energy consumed by the same bird, measured in joules per meter.

(a) Suggest a reason in terms of the way birds fly for the shape of the graph of $f(v)$ in Figure 4.49.

(b) What is the relationship between $f(v)$ and $a(v)$?

(c) Where on the graph is $a(v)$ a minimum?

---

[5]See, for example, D. Halliday, R. Resnik, K. Kane, *Physics*, Vol 2, 4th ed, (New York: Wiley, 1992), p. 909.

[6]Data from C. M. Perrins and D. Lack, reported by J. R. Krebs and N. B. Davies in *An Introduction to Behavioural Ecology* (Oxford: Blackwell, 1987).

(d) Should the bird try to minimize $f(v)$ or $a(v)$ when it is flying? Why?

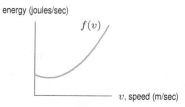

energy (joules/sec)

Figure 4.49

52. The forward motion of an aircraft in level flight is reduced by two kinds of forces, known as *induced drag* and *parasite drag*. Induced drag is a consequence of the downward deflection of air as the wings produce lift. Parasite drag results from friction between the air and the entire surface of the aircraft. Induced drag is inversely proportional to the square of speed and parasite drag is directly proportional to the square of speed. The sum of induced drag and parasite drag is called total drag. The graph in Figure 4.50 shows a certain aircraft's induced drag and parasite drag functions.

(a) Sketch the total drag as a function of air speed.
(b) Estimate two different air speeds which each result in a total drag of 1000 pounds. Does the total drag function have an inverse? What about the induced and parasite drag functions?
(c) Fuel consumption (in gallons per hour) is roughly proportional to total drag. Suppose you are low on fuel and the control tower has instructed you to enter a circular holding pattern of indefinite duration to await the passage of a storm at your landing field. At what air speed should you fly the holding pattern? Why?

Figure 4.50

53. Let $f(v)$ be the fuel consumption, in gallons per hour, of a certain aircraft as a function of its airspeed, v, in miles per hour. A graph of $f(v)$ is given in Figure 4.51.

(a) Let $g(v)$ be the fuel consumption of the same aircraft, but measured in gallons per mile instead of gallons per hour. What is the relationship between $f(v)$ and $g(v)$?
(b) For what value of v is $f(v)$ minimized?
(c) For what value of v is $g(v)$ minimized?
(d) Should a pilot try to minimize $f(v)$ or $g(v)$?

Figure 4.51

Strengthen Your Understanding

In Problems 54–56, explain what is wrong with the statement.

54. If A is the area of a rectangle of sides x and $2x$, for $0 \leq x \leq 10$, the maximum value of A occurs where $dA/dx = 0$.

55. An open box is made from a 20-inch square piece of cardboard by cutting squares of side h from the corners and folding up the edges, giving the box in Figure 4.52. To find the maximum volume of such a box, we work on the domain $h \geq 0$.

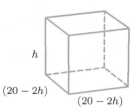

Figure 4.52: Box of volume $V = h(20 - 2h)^2$

56. The solution of an optimization problem modeled by a quadratic function occurs at the vertex of the quadratic.

In Problems 57–59, give an example of:

57. The sides of a rectangle with perimeter 20 cm and area smaller than 10 cm^2.

58. A context for a modeling problem where you are given that $xy = 120$ and you are minimizing the quantity $2x + 6y$.

59. A modeling problem where you are minimizing the cost of the material in a cylindrical can of volume 250 cubic centimeters.

4.4 FAMILIES OF FUNCTIONS AND MODELING

We saw in Chapter 1 that knowledge of one function can provide knowledge of the graphs of many others. The shape of the graph of $y = x^2$ also tells us, indirectly, about the graphs of $y = x^2 + 2$, $y = (x + 2)^2$, $y = 2x^2$, and countless other functions. We say that all functions of the form $y = a(x + b)^2 + c$ form a *family of functions*; their graphs are like that of $y = x^2$, except for shifts and stretches determined by the values of $a, b,$ and c. The constants a, b, c are called *parameters*. Different values of the parameters give different members of the family.

The Bell-Shaped Curve: $y = e^{-(x-a)^2/b}$

The family of bell-shaped curves includes the family of *normal density* functions, used in probability and statistics.[7] We assume that $b > 0$. See Section 8.8 for applications of the normal distribution.
First we let $b = 1$ and examine the role of a.

Example 1   Graph $y = e^{-(x-a)^2}$ for $a = -2, 0, 2$ and explain the role of a in the shape of the graph.

Solution   See Figure 4.53. The role of the parameter a is to shift the graph of $y = e^{-x^2}$ to the right or left. Notice that the value of y is always positive. Since $y \to 0$ as $x \to \pm\infty$, the x-axis is a horizontal asymptote. Thus $y = e^{-(x-a)^2}$ is the family of horizontal shifts of the bell-shaped curve $y = e^{-x^2}$.

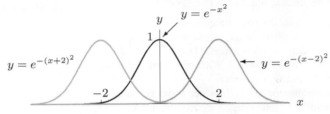

Figure 4.53: The family $y = e^{-(x-a)^2}$

We now consider the role of the parameter b by studying the family with $a = 0$.

Example 2   Find the critical points and points of inflection of $y = e^{-x^2/b}$.

Solution   To investigate the critical points and points of inflection, we calculate

$$\frac{dy}{dx} = -\frac{2x}{b}e^{-x^2/b}$$

and, using the product rule, we get

$$\frac{d^2y}{dx^2} = -\frac{2}{b}e^{-x^2/b} - \frac{2x}{b}\left(-\frac{2x}{b}e^{-x^2/b}\right) = \frac{2}{b}\left(\frac{2x^2}{b} - 1\right)e^{-x^2/b}.$$

Critical points occur where $dy/dx = 0$, that is, where

$$\frac{dy}{dx} = -\frac{2x}{b}\,e^{-x^2/b} = 0.$$

Since $e^{-x^2/b}$ is never zero, the only critical point is $x = 0$. At that point, $y = 1$ and $d^2y/dx^2 < 0$. Hence, by the second derivative test, there is a local maximum at $x = 0$, and this is also a global maximum.

Inflection points occur where the second derivative changes sign; thus, we start by finding values of x for which $d^2y/dx^2 = 0$. Since $e^{-x^2/b}$ is never zero, $d^2y/dx^2 = 0$ when

$$\frac{2x^2}{b} - 1 = 0.$$

[7]Probabilists divide our function by a constant, $\sqrt{\pi b}$, to get the normal density.

Solving for x gives

$$x = \pm\sqrt{\frac{b}{2}}.$$

Looking at the expression for d^2y/dx^2, we see that d^2y/dx^2 is negative for $x = 0$, and positive as $x \to \pm\infty$. Therefore the concavity changes at $x = -\sqrt{b/2}$ and at $x = \sqrt{b/2}$, so we have inflection points at $x = \pm\sqrt{b/2}$.

Returning to the two-parameter family $y = e^{-(x-a)^2/b}$, we conclude that there is a maximum at $x = a$, obtained by horizontally shifting the maximum at $x = 0$ of $y = e^{-x^2/b}$ by a units. There are inflection points at $x = a \pm \sqrt{b/2}$ obtained by shifting the inflection points $x = \pm\sqrt{b/2}$ of $y = e^{-x^2/b}$ by a units. (See Figure 4.54.) At the inflection points $y = e^{-1/2} \approx 0.6$.

With this information we can see the effect of the parameters. The parameter a determines the location of the center of the bell and the parameter b determines how narrow or wide the bell is. (See Figure 4.55.) If b is small, then the inflection points are close to a and the bell is sharply peaked near a; if b is large, the inflection points are farther away from a and the bell is spread out.

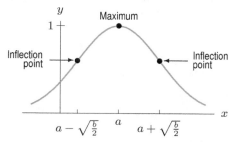

Figure 4.54: Graph of $y = e^{-(x-a)^2/b}$: bell-shaped curve with peak at $x = a$

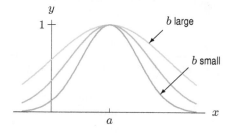

Figure 4.55: Graph of $y = e^{-(x-a)^2/b}$ for fixed a and various b

Modeling with Families of Functions

One reason for studying families of functions is their use in mathematical modeling. Confronted with the problem of modeling some phenomenon, a crucial first step involves recognizing families of functions which might fit the available data.

Motion Under Gravity: $y = -4.9t^2 + v_0t + y_0$

The position of an object moving vertically under the influence of gravity can be described by a function in the two-parameter family

$$y = -4.9t^2 + v_0t + y_0$$

where t is time in seconds and y is the distance in meters above the ground. Why do we need the parameters v_0 and y_0? Notice that at time $t = 0$ we have $y = y_0$. Thus the parameter y_0 gives the height above ground of the object at time $t = 0$. Since $dy/dt = -9.8t + v_0$, the parameter v_0 gives the velocity of the object at time $t = 0$. From this equation we see that $dy/dt = 0$ when $t = v_0/9.8$. This is the time when the object reaches its maximum height.

Example 3   Give a function describing the position of a projectile launched upward from ground level with an initial velocity of 50 m/sec. How high does the projectile rise?

Solution   We have $y_0 = 0$ and $v_0 = 50$, so the height of the projectile after t seconds is $y = -4.9t^2 + 50t$. It reaches its maximum height when $t = 50/9.8 = 5.1$ seconds, and its height at that time is $-4.9(5.1)^2 + 50(5.1) = 127.5$, or about 128 meters.

Exponential Model with a Limit: $y = a(1 - e^{-bx})$

We consider $a, b > 0$. The graph of one member, with $a = 2$ and $b = 1$, is in Figure 4.56. Such a graph represents a quantity which is increasing but leveling off. For example, a body dropped in a thick fluid speeds up initially, but its velocity levels off as it approaches a terminal velocity. Similarly, if a pollutant pouring into a lake builds up toward a saturation level, its concentration may be described in this way. The graph also represents the temperature of an object in an oven.

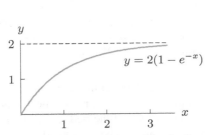

Figure 4.56: One member of the family $y = a(1 - e^{-bx})$, with $a = 2, b = 1$

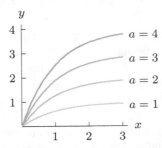

Figure 4.57: Fixing $b = 1$ gives $y = a(1 - e^{-x})$, graphed for various a

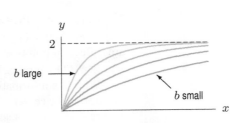

Figure 4.58: Fixing $a = 2$ gives $y = 2(1 - e^{-bx})$, graphed for various b

Example 4 Describe the effect of varying the parameters a and b on the graph of $y = a(1 - e^{-bx})$.

Solution First examine the effect on the graph of varying a. Fix b at some positive number, say $b = 1$. Substitute different values for a and look at the graphs in Figure 4.57. We see that as x gets larger, y approaches a from below, so a is an upper bound for this function. Analytically, this follows from the fact that $e^{-bx} \to 0$ as $x \to \infty$. Physically, the value of a represents the terminal velocity of a falling body or the saturation level of the pollutant in the lake.

Now examine the effect of varying b on the graph. Fix a at some positive number, say $a = 2$. Substitute different values for b and look at the graphs in Figure 4.58. The parameter b determines how sharply the curve rises and how quickly it gets close to the line $y = a$.

Let's confirm the last observation in Example 4 analytically. For $y = a(1 - e^{-bx})$, we have $dy/dx = abe^{-bx}$, so the slope of the tangent to the curve at $x = 0$ is ab. For larger b, the curve rises more rapidly at $x = 0$. How long does it take the curve to climb halfway up from $y = 0$ to $y = a$? When $y = a/2$, we have

$$a(1 - e^{-bx}) = \frac{a}{2}, \qquad \text{which leads to} \qquad x = \frac{\ln 2}{b}.$$

If b is large then $(\ln 2)/b$ is small, so in a short distance the curve is already half way up to a. If b is small, then $(\ln 2)/b$ is large and we have to go a long way out to get up to $a/2$. See Figure 4.59.

Figure 4.59: Tangent at $x = 0$ to $y = a(1 - e^{-bx})$, with fixed a, and large and small b

The following example illustrates an application of this family.

Example 5   The number, N, of people who have heard a rumor spread by mass media by time t is modeled by

$$N(t) = a(1 - e^{-bt}).$$

There are 200,000 people in the population who hear the rumor eventually. If 10% of them heard it the first day, find a and b, assuming t is measured in days.

Solution   Since $\lim_{t \to \infty} N(t) = a$, we have $a = 200{,}000$. When $t = 1$, we have $N = 0.1(200{,}000) = 20{,}000$ people, so substituting into the formula gives

$$N(1) = 20{,}000 = 200{,}000 \left(1 - e^{-b(1)}\right).$$

Solving for b gives

$$0.1 = 1 - e^{-b}$$
$$e^{-b} = 0.9$$
$$b = -\ln 0.9 = 0.105.$$

The Logistic Model: $y = L/(1 + Ae^{-kt})$

The *logistic* family is often used to model population growth when it is limited by the environment. (See Section 11.7.) We assume that $L, A, k > 0$ and we look at the roles of each of the three parameters in turn.

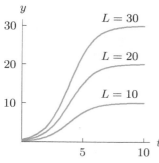

Figure 4.60: Graph of $y = L/(1 + Ae^{-kt})$ varying L with $A = 50, k = 1$

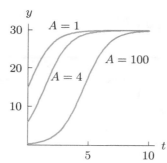

Figure 4.61: Graph of $y = L/(1 + Ae^{-kt})$ varying A with $L = 30, k = 1$

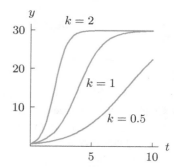

Figure 4.62: Graph of $y = L/(1 + Ae^{-kt})$ varying k, with $L = 30, A = 50$

Logistic curves with varying values of L are shown in Figure 4.60. The values of y level off as $t \to \infty$ because $Ae^{-kt} \to 0$ as $t \to \infty$. Thus, as t increases, the values of y approach L. The line $y = L$ is a horizontal asymptote, called the *limiting value* or *carrying capacity*, and representing the maximum sustainable population. The parameter L stretches or shrinks the graph vertically.

In Figure 4.61 we investigate the effect of the parameter A, with k and L fixed. The parameter A alters the point at which the curve cuts the y-axis—larger values of A move the y-intercept closer to the origin. At $t = 0$ we have $y = L/(1 + A)$, confirming that increasing A decreases the value of y at $t = 0$.

Figure 4.62 shows the effect of the parameter k. With L and A fixed, we see that varying k affects the rate at which the function approaches the limiting value L. If k is small, the graph rises slowly; if k is large, the graph rises steeply. At $t = 0$, we have $dy/dt = LAk/(1 + A)^2$, so the initial slope of a logistic curve is proportional to k.

The graphs suggest that none of the curves has a critical point for $t > 0$. Some curves appear to have a point of inflection; others have none. To investigate, we take derivatives:

$$\frac{dy}{dt} = \frac{LAke^{-kt}}{(1 + Ae^{-kt})^2}.$$

Since every factor of dy/dt is positive, the first derivative is always positive. Thus, there are no critical points and the function is always increasing.

Using a computer algebra system or the quotient rule, we find

$$\frac{d^2y}{dt^2} = \frac{LAk^2e^{-kt}(-1+Ae^{-kt})}{(1+Ae^{-kt})^3}.$$

Since L, A, k, e^{-kt}, and the denominator are always positive, the sign of d^2y/dt^2 is determined by the sign of $(-1+Ae^{-kt})$. Points of inflection may occur where $d^2y/dt^2 = 0$. This is where $-1+Ae^{-kt} = 0$, or

$$Ae^{-kt} = 1.$$

At this value of t,

$$y = \frac{L}{1+Ae^{-kt}} = \frac{L}{1+1} = \frac{L}{2}.$$

In Problem 22 on page 221, we see that d^2y/dt^2 changes sign at $y = L/2$. Since the concavity changes at $y = L/2$, there is a point of inflection when the population is half the carrying capacity. If the initial population is $L/2$ or above, there is no inflection point. (See the top graph in Figure 4.61.)
To find the value of t at the inflection point, we solve for t in the equation

$$Ae^{-kt} = 1$$
$$t = \frac{\ln(1/A)}{-k} = \frac{\ln A}{k}.$$

Thus, increasing the value of A moves the inflection point to the right. (See the bottom two graphs in Figure 4.61.)

Exercises and Problems for Section 4.4

Exercises

In Exercises 1–6, investigate the one-parameter family of functions. Assume that a is positive.

(a) Graph $f(x)$ using three different values for a.

(b) Using your graph in part (a), describe the critical points of f and how they appear to move as a increases.

(c) Find a formula for the x-coordinates of the critical point(s) of f in terms of a.

1. $f(x) = (x-a)^2$ **2.** $f(x) = x^3 - ax$

3. $f(x) = ax^3 - x$ **4.** $f(x) = x - a\sqrt{x}$

5. $f(x) = x^2e^{-ax}$

6. $f(x) = \frac{a}{x^2} + x$ for $x > 0$

7. Consider the family

$$y = \frac{A}{x+B}.$$

(a) If $B = 0$, what is the effect of varying A on the graph?

(b) If $A = 1$, what is the effect of varying B?

(c) On one set of axes, graph the function for several values of A and B.

8. If A and B are positive constants, find all critical points of

$$f(w) = \frac{A}{w^2} - \frac{B}{w}.$$

9. The graphs of $f(x) = 1 + e^{-ax}$ for $a = 1, 2$, and 5, are in Figure 4.63. Without a calculator, identify the graphs by looking at $f'(0)$.

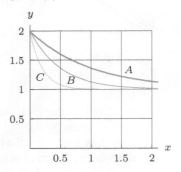

Figure 4.63

10. The graphs of $f(x) = xe^{-ax}$ for $a = 1, 2$, and 3, are in Figure 4.64. Without a calculator, identify the graphs by locating the critical points of $f(x)$.

Figure 4.64

In Exercises 11–16, investigate the given two parameter family of functions. Assume that a and b are positive.

(a) Graph $f(x)$ using $b = 1$ and three different values for a.

(b) Graph $f(x)$ using $a = 1$ and three different values for b.

(c) In the graphs in parts (a) and (b), how do the critical points of f appear to move as a increases? As b increases?

(d) Find a formula for the x-coordinates of the critical point(s) of f in terms of a and b.

11. $f(x) = (x - a)^2 + b$

12. $f(x) = x^3 - ax^2 + b$

13. $f(x) = ax(x - b)^2$

14. $f(x) = \dfrac{ax}{x^2 + b}$

15. $f(x) = \sqrt{b - (x - a)^2}$

16. $f(x) = \dfrac{a}{x} + bx$ for $x > 0$

Problems

17. The graphs of the function $f(x) = x + a^2/x$ for $a = 1$ and 2, and a third integer value of a, are shown in Figure 4.65. Without a calculator, identify the graphs, and estimate the third value of a.

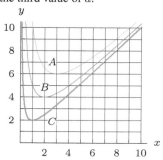

Figure 4.65

18. The graphs of the function $f(x) = x + a\sin x$ for various values of $a > 0$ are shown in Figure 4.66. Explain why, no matter what the positive value of a, the curves intersect in the same points.

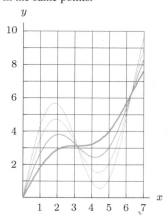

Figure 4.66

19. (a) Sketch graphs of $y = xe^{-bx}$ for $b = 1, 2, 3, 4$. Describe the graphical significance of b.

(b) Find the coordinates of the critical point of $y = xe^{-bx}$ and use it to confirm your answer to part (a).

20. Consider the surge function $y = axe^{-bx}$ for $a, b > 0$.

(a) Find the local maxima, local minima, and points of inflection.

(b) How does varying a and b affect the shape of the graph?

(c) On one set of axes, graph this function for several values of a and b.

21. Find a formula for the family of cubic polynomials with an inflection point at the origin. How many parameters are there?

22. (a) Derive formulas for the first and second derivatives of the logistic function:

$$y = \frac{L}{1 + Ae^{-kt}} \quad \text{for } L, A, \text{ and } k \text{ positive constants.}$$

(b) Derive a formula for the t value of any inflection point(s).

(c) Use the second derivative to determine the concavity on either side of any inflection points.

23. (a) Graph $f(x) = x + a\sin x$ for $a = 0.5$ and $a = 3$.

(b) For what values of a is $f(x)$ increasing for all x?

24. (a) Graph $f(x) = x^2 + a\sin x$ for $a = 1$ and $a = 20$.

(b) For what values of a is $f(x)$ concave up for all x?

25. Consider the family of functions $y = a\cosh(x/a)$ for $a > 0$. Sketch graphs for $a = 1, 2, 3$. Describe in words the effect of increasing a.

26. Sketch several members of the family $y = e^{-ax}\sin bx$ for $b = 1$, and describe the graphical significance of the parameter a.

27. Sketch several members of the family $e^{-ax}\sin bx$ for $a = 1$, and describe the graphical significance of the parameter b.

28. If $a > 0, b > 0$, show that $f(x) = a(1 - e^{-bx})$ is everywhere increasing and everywhere concave down.

29. Let $f(x) = bxe^{1+bx}$, where b is constant and $b > 0$.

(a) What is the x-coordinate of the critical point of f?

(b) Is the critical point a local maximum or a local minimum?

(c) Show that the y-coordinate of the critical point does not depend on the value of b.

30. Let $h(x) = e^{-x} + kx$, where k is any constant. For what value(s) of k does h have

   (a) No critical points?
   (b) One critical point?
   (c) A horizontal asymptote?

31. Let $g(x) = x - ke^x$, where k is any constant. For what value(s) of k does the function g have a critical point?

Find formulas for the functions described in Problems 32–43.

32. A function of the form $y = a(1 - e^{-bx})$ with $a, b > 0$ and a horizontal asymptote of $y = 5$.

33. A function of the form $y = be^{-(x-a)^2/2}$ with its maximum at the point $(0, 3)$.

34. A curve of the form $y = e^{-(x-a)^2/b}$ for $b > 0$ with a local maximum at $x = 2$ and points of inflection at $x = 1$ and $x = 3$.

35. A logistic curve with carrying capacity of 12, y-intercept of 4, and point of inflection at $(0.5, 6)$.

36. A function of the form $y = \dfrac{a}{1 + be^{-t}}$ with y-intercept 2 and an inflection point at $t = 1$.

37. A cubic polynomial with a critical point at $x = 2$, an inflection point at $(1, 4)$, and a leading coefficient of 1.

38. A fourth-degree polynomial whose graph is symmetric about the y-axis, has a y-intercept of 0, and global maxima at $(1, 2)$ and $(-1, 2)$.

39. A function of the form $y = a \sin(bt^2)$ whose first critical point for positive t occurs at $t = 1$ and whose derivative is 3 when $t = 2$.

40. A function of the form $y = a \cos(bt^2)$ whose first critical point for positive t occurs at $t = 1$ and whose derivative is -2 when $t = 1/\sqrt{2}$.

41. A function of the form $y = ae^{-x} + bx$ with the global minimum at $(1, 2)$.

42. A function of the form $y = bxe^{-ax}$ with a local maximum at $(3, 6)$.

43. A function of the form $y = at + b/t$, with a local minimum $(3, 12)$ and a local maximum at $(-3, -12)$.

44. Consider the family of functions $y = f(x) = x - k\sqrt{x}$, with k a positive constant and $x \geq 0$. Show that the graph of $f(x)$ has a local minimum at a point whose x-coordinate is $1/4$ of the way between its x-intercepts.

45. For any constant a, let $f(x) = ax - x \ln x$ for $x > 0$.

   (a) What is the x-intercept of the graph of $f(x)$?
   (b) Graph $f(x)$ for $a = -1$ and $a = 1$.
   (c) For what values of a does $f(x)$ have a critical point for $x > 0$? Find the coordinates of the critical point and decide if it is a local maximum, a local minimum, or neither.

46. Let $f(x) = x^2 + \cos(kx)$, for $k > 0$.

   (a) Graph f for $k = 0.5, 1, 3, 5$. Find the smallest number k at which you see points of inflection in the graph of f.
   (b) Explain why the graph of f has no points of inflection if $k \leq \sqrt{2}$, and infinitely many points of inflection if $k > \sqrt{2}$.
   (c) Explain why f has only a finite number of critical points, no matter what the value of k.

47. Let $f(x) = e^x - kx$, for $k > 0$.

   (a) Graph f for $k = 1/4, 1/2, 1, 2, 4$. Describe what happens as k changes.
   (b) Show that f has a local minimum at $x = \ln k$.
   (c) Find the value of k for which the local minimum is the largest.

48. A family of functions is given by

$$r(x) = \frac{1}{a + (x - b)^2}.$$

   (a) For what values of a and b does the graph of r have a vertical asymptote? Where are the vertical asymptotes in this case?
   (b) Find values of a and b so that the function r has a local maximum at the point $(3, 5)$.

49. **(a)** Find all critical points of $f(x) = x^4 + ax^2 + b$.
   (b) Under what conditions on a and b does this function have exactly one critical point? What is the one critical point, and is it a local maximum, a local minimum, or neither?
   (c) Under what conditions on a and b does this function have exactly three critical points? What are they? Which are local maxima and which are local minima?
   (d) Is it ever possible for this function to have two critical points? No critical points? More than three critical points? Give an explanation in each case.

50. Let $y = Ae^x + Be^{-x}$ for any constants A, B.

   (a) Sketch the graph of the function for

     (i) $A = 1, B = 1$ (ii) $A = 1, B = -1$
     (iii) $A = 2, B = 1$ (iv) $A = 2, B = -1$
     (v) $A = -2, B = -1$ (vi) $A = -2, B = 1$

   (b) Describe in words the general shape of the graph if A and B have the same sign. What effect does the sign of A have on the graph?
   (c) Describe in words the general shape of the graph if A and B have different signs. What effect does the sign of A have on the graph?
   (d) For what values of A and B does the function have a local maximum? A local minimum? Justify your answer using derivatives.

51. The temperature, T, in $^\circ$ C, of a yam put into a 200°C oven is given as a function of time, t, in minutes, by

$$T = a(1 - e^{-kt}) + b.$$

(a) If the yam starts at 20°C, find a and b.

(b) If the temperature of the yam is initially increasing at 2°C per minute, find k.

52. For positive a, b, the potential energy, U, of a particle is

$$U = b\left(\frac{a^2}{x^2} - \frac{a}{x}\right) \quad \text{for } x > 0.$$

(a) Find the intercepts and asymptotes.

(b) Compute the local maxima and minima.

(c) Sketch the graph.

53. The force, F, on a particle with potential energy U is given by

$$F = -\frac{dU}{dx}.$$

Using the expression for U in Problem 52, graph F and U on the same axes, labeling intercepts and local maxima and minima.

54. The Lennard-Jones model predicts the potential energy $V(r)$ of a two-atom molecule as a function of the distance r between the atoms to be

$$V(r) = \frac{A}{r^{12}} - \frac{B}{r^6}, \quad r > 0,$$

where A and B are positive constants.

(a) Evaluate $\lim_{r \to 0^+} V(r)$, and interpret your answer.

(b) Find the critical point of $V(r)$. Is it a local maximum or local minimum?

(c) The inter-atomic force is given by $F(r) = -V'(r)$. At what distance r is the inter-atomic force zero? (This is called the equilibrium size of the molecule.)

(d) Describe how the parameters A and B affect the equilibrium size of the molecule.

55. For positive A, B, the force between two atoms is a function of the distance, r, between them:

$$f(r) = -\frac{A}{r^2} + \frac{B}{r^3} \quad r > 0.$$

(a) What are the zeros and asymptotes of f?

(b) Find the coordinates of the critical points and inflection points of f.

(c) Graph f.

(d) Illustrating your answers with a sketch, describe the effect on the graph of f of:

   (i) Increasing B, holding A fixed

   (ii) Increasing A, holding B fixed

56. An organism has size W at time t. For positive constants A, b, and c, the Gompertz growth function gives

$$W = Ae^{-e^{b-ct}}, \quad t \geq 0.$$

(a) Find the intercepts and asymptotes.

(b) Find the critical points and inflection points.

(c) Graph W for various values of A, b, and c.

(d) A certain organism grows fastest when it is about 1/3 of its final size. Would the Gompertz growth function be useful in modeling its growth? Explain.

Strengthen Your Understanding

In Problems 57–58, explain what is wrong with the statement.

57. Every function of the form $f(x) = x^2 + bx + c$, where b and c are constants, has two zeros.

58. Every function of the form $f(x) = a/x + bx$, where a and b are non-zero constants, has two critical points.

In Problems 59–62, give an example of:

59. A family of quadratic functions which has zeros at $x = 0$ and $x = b$.

60. A member of the family $f(x) = ax^3 - bx$ that has no critical points.

61. A family of functions, $f(x)$, depending on a parameter a, such that each member of the family has exactly one critical point.

62. A family of functions, $g(x)$, depending on two parameters, a and b, such that each member of the family has

exactly two critical points and one inflection point. You may want to restrict a and b.

63. Let $f(x) = ax + b/x$. Suppose a and b are positive. What happens to $f(x)$ as b increases?

(a) The critical points move further apart.

(b) The critical points move closer together.

(c) The critical values move further apart.

(d) The critical values move closer together.

64. Let $f(x) = ax + b/x$. Suppose a and b are positive. What happens to $f(x)$ as a increases?

(a) The critical points move further apart.

(b) The critical points move closer together.

(c) The critical values move further apart.

(d) The critical values move closer together.

4.5 APPLICATIONS TO MARGINALITY

Management decisions within a particular business usually aim at maximizing profit for the company. In this section we see how the derivative can be used to maximize profit. Profit depends on both production cost and revenue (or income) from sales. We begin by looking at the cost and revenue functions.

> The **cost function**, $C(q)$, gives the total cost of producing a quantity q of some good.

What sort of function do we expect C to be? The more goods that are made, the higher the total cost, so C is an increasing function. In fact, cost functions usually have the general shape shown in Figure 4.67. The intercept on the C-axis represents the *fixed costs*, which are incurred even if nothing is produced. (This includes, for instance, the machinery needed to begin production.) The cost function increases quickly at first and then more slowly because producing larger quantities of a good is usually more efficient than producing smaller quantities—this is called *economy of scale*. At still higher production levels, the cost function starts to increase faster again as resources become scarce, and sharp increases may occur when new factories have to be built. Thus, the graph of $C(q)$ may start out concave down and become concave up later on.

Figure 4.67: Cost as a function of quantity

> The **revenue function**, $R(q)$, gives the total revenue received by a firm from selling a quantity q of some good.

Revenue is income obtained from sales. If the price per item is p, and the quantity sold is q, then

$$\text{Revenue} = \text{Price} \times \text{Quantity}, \quad \text{so} \quad R = pq.$$

If the price per item does not depend on the quantity sold, then the graph of $R(q)$ is a straight line through the origin with slope equal to the price p. See Figure 4.68. In practice, for large values of q, the market may become glutted, causing the price to drop, giving $R(q)$ the shape in Figure 4.69.

Figure 4.68: Revenue: Constant price

Figure 4.69: Revenue: Decreasing price

The profit is usually written as π. (Economists use π to distinguish it from the price, p; this π has nothing to do with the area of a circle, and merely stands for the Greek equivalent of the letter "p.") The profit resulting from producing and selling q items is defined by

$$\text{Profit} = \text{Revenue} - \text{Cost}, \quad \text{so} \quad \pi(q) = R(q) - C(q).$$

Example 1   If cost, C, and revenue, R, are given by the graph in Figure 4.70, for what production quantities, q, does the firm make a profit? Approximately what production level maximizes profit?

Figure 4.70: Costs and revenues for Example 1

Solution   The firm makes a profit whenever revenues are greater than costs, that is, when $R > C$. The graph of R is above the graph of C approximately when $130 < q < 215$. Production between $q = 130$ units and $q = 215$ units generates a profit. The vertical distance between the cost and revenue curves is largest at q_0, so q_0 units gives maximum profit.

Marginal Analysis

Many economic decisions are based on an analysis of the costs and revenues "at the margin." Let's look at this idea through an example.

Suppose we are running an airline and we are trying to decide whether to offer an additional flight. How should we decide? We'll assume that the decision is to be made purely on financial grounds: if the flight will make money for the company, it should be added. Obviously we need to consider the costs and revenues involved. Since the choice is between adding this flight and leaving things the way they are, the crucial question is whether the *additional costs* incurred are greater or smaller than the *additional revenues* generated by the flight. These additional costs and revenues are called the *marginal costs* and *marginal revenues*.

Suppose $C(q)$ is the function giving the total cost of running q flights. If the airline had originally planned to run 100 flights, its costs would be $C(100)$. With the additional flight, its costs would be $C(101)$. Therefore,

$$\text{Additional cost "at the margin"} = C(101) - C(100).$$

Now

$$C(101) - C(100) = \frac{C(101) - C(100)}{101 - 100},$$

and this quantity is the average rate of change of cost between 100 and 101 flights. In Figure 4.71 the average rate of change is the slope of the line joining the $C(100)$ and $C(101)$ points on the graph. If the graph of the cost function is not curving fast near the point, the slope of this line is close to the slope of the tangent line there. Therefore, the average rate of change is close to the instantaneous rate of change. Since these rates of change are not very different, many economists choose to define marginal cost, MC, as the instantaneous rate of change of cost with respect to quantity:

Figure 4.71: Marginal cost: Slope of one of these lines

> Marginal cost $= MC = C'(q)$ so   Marginal cost $\approx C(q+1) - C(q)$.

Similarly, if the revenue generated by q flights is $R(q)$ and the number of flights increases from 100 to 101, then

$$\text{Additional revenue "at the margin"} = R(101) - R(100).$$

Now $R(101) - R(100)$ is the average rate of change of revenue between 100 and 101 flights. As before, the average rate of change is usually almost equal to the instantaneous rate of change, so economists often define:

> Marginal revenue $= MR = R'(q)$ so   Marginal revenue $\approx R(q+1) - R(q)$.

We often refer to total cost, C, and total revenue, R, to distinguish them from marginal cost, MC, and marginal revenue, MR. If the words cost and revenue are used alone, they are understood to mean total cost and total revenue.

Example 2   If $C(q)$ and $R(q)$ for the airline are given in Figure 4.72, should the company add the 101st flight?

Solution   The marginal revenue is the slope of the revenue curve, and the marginal cost is the slope of the cost curve at the point 100. From Figure 4.72, you can see that the slope at the point A is smaller than the slope at B, so $MC < MR$. This means that the airline will make more in extra revenue than it will spend in extra costs if it runs another flight, so it should go ahead and run the 101st flight.

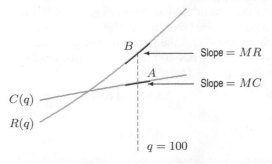

Figure 4.72: Should the company add the 101st flight?

Since MC and MR are derivative functions, they can be estimated from the graphs of total cost and total revenue.

Example 3   If R and C are given by the graphs in Figure 4.73, sketch graphs of $MR = R'(q)$ and $MC = C'(q)$.

Figure 4.73: Total revenue and total cost for Example 3

Solution   The revenue graph is a line through the origin, with equation

$$R = pq$$

where p is the price, which is a constant. The slope is p and

$$MR = R'(q) = p.$$

The total cost is increasing, so the marginal cost is always positive (above the q-axis). For small q values, the total cost curve is concave down, so the marginal cost is decreasing. For larger q, say $q > 100$, the total cost curve is concave up and the marginal cost is increasing. Thus the marginal cost has a minimum at about $q = 100$. (See Figure 4.74.)

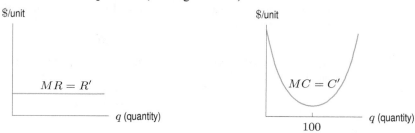

Figure 4.74: Marginal revenue and costs for Example 3

Maximizing Profit

Now let's look at how to maximize profit, given functions for total revenue and total cost.

Example 4   Find the maximum profit if the total revenue and total cost are given, for $0 \le q \le 200$, by the curves R and C in Figure 4.75.

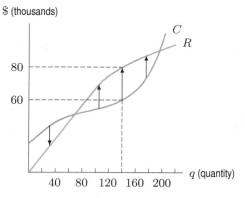

Figure 4.75: Maximum profit at $q = 140$

Solution   The profit is represented by the vertical difference between the curves and is marked by the vertical arrows on the graph. When revenue is below cost, the company is taking a loss; when revenue is above cost, the company is making a profit. We can see that the profit is largest at about $q = 140$, so this is the production level we're looking for. To be sure that the local maximum is a global maximum, we need to check the endpoints. At $q = 0$ and $q = 200$, the profit is negative, so the global maximum is indeed at $q = 140$.

To find the actual maximum profit, we estimate the vertical distance between the curves at $q = 140$. This gives a maximum profit of $80,000 - $60,000 = $20,000$.

Suppose we wanted to find the minimum profit. In this example, we must look at the endpoints, when $q = 0$ or $q = 200$. We see the minimum profit is negative (a loss), and it occurs at $q = 0$.

Maximum Profit Occurs Where $MR = MC$

In Example 4, observe that at $q = 140$ the slopes of the two curves in Figure 4.75 are equal. To the left of $q = 140$, the revenue curve has a larger slope than the cost curve, and the profit increases as q increases. The company will make more money by producing more units, so production should increase toward $q = 140$. To the right of $q = 140$, the slope of the revenue curve is less than the slope of the cost curve, and the profit is decreasing. The company will make more money by producing fewer units so production should decrease toward $q = 140$. At the point where the slopes are equal, the profit has a local maximum; otherwise the profit could be increased by moving toward that point. Since the slopes are equal at $q = 140$, we have $MR = MC$ there.

Now let's look at the general situation. To maximize or minimize profit over an interval, we optimize the profit, π, where

$$\pi(q) = R(q) - C(q).$$

We know that global maxima and minima can only occur at critical points or at endpoints of an interval. To find critical points of π, look for zeros of the derivative:

$$\pi'(q) = R'(q) - C'(q) = 0.$$

So

$$R'(q) = C'(q),$$

that is, the slopes of the revenue and cost curves are equal. This is the same observation that we made in the previous example. In economic language,

---

The maximum (or minimum) profit can occur where

Marginal cost = Marginal revenue.

Of course, maximal or minimal profit does not *have* to occur where $MR = MC$; there are also the endpoints to consider.

Example 5   Find the quantity q which maximizes profit if the total revenue, $R(q)$, and total cost, $C(q)$, are given in dollars by

$$R(q) = 5q - 0.003q^2$$
$$C(q) = 300 + 1.1q,$$

where $0 \leq q \leq 800$ units. What production level gives the minimum profit?

Solution   We look for production levels that give marginal revenue = marginal cost:

$$MR = R'(q) = 5 - 0.006q$$
$$MC = C'(q) = 1.1.$$

So $5 - 0.006q = 1.1$, giving

$$q = 3.9/0.006 = 650 \text{ units.}$$

Does this value of q represent a local maximum or minimum of π? We can tell by looking at production levels of 649 units and 651 units. When $q = 649$ we have $MR = \$1.106$, which is greater than the (constant) marginal cost of $1.10. This means that producing one more unit will bring in more revenue than its cost, so profit will increase. When $q = 651$, $MR = \$1.094$, which is *less* than MC, so it is not profitable to produce the 651st unit. We conclude that $q = 650$ is a local maximum for the profit function π. The profit earned by producing and selling this quantity is $\pi(650) = R(650) - C(650) = \$967.50$.

To check for global maxima we need to look at the endpoints. If $q = 0$, the only cost is $300 (the fixed costs) and there is no revenue, so $\pi(0) = -\$300$. At the upper limit of $q = 800$, we have $\pi(800) = \$900$. Therefore, the maximum profit is at the production level of 650 units, where $MR = MC$. The minimum profit (a loss) occurs when $q = 0$ and there is no production at all.

Exercises and Problems for Section 4.5

Exercises

1. Figure 4.76 shows cost and revenue. For what production levels is the profit function positive? Negative? Estimate the production at which profit is maximized.

Figure 4.76

2. Figure 4.77 gives cost and revenue. What are fixed costs? What quantity maximizes profit, and what is the maximum profit earned?

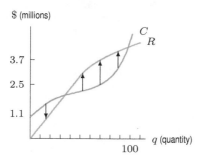

Figure 4.77

3. Total cost and revenue are approximated by the functions $C = 5000 + 2.4q$ and $R = 4q$, both in dollars. Identify the fixed cost, marginal cost per item, and the price at which this commodity is sold.

In Exercises 4–7, give the cost, revenue, and profit functions.

4. An online seller of T-shirts pays $500 to start up the website and $6 per T-shirt, then sells the T-shirts for $12 each.

5. A car wash operator pays $35,000 for a franchise, then spends $10 per car wash, which costs the consumer $15.

6. A couple running a house-cleaning business invests $5000 in equipment, and they spend $15 in supplies to clean a house, for which they charge $60.

7. A lemonade stand operator sets up the stand for free in front of the neighbor's house, makes 5 quarts of lemonade for $4, then sells each 8 oz cup for 25 cents.

8. The revenue from selling q items is $R(q) = 500q - q^2$, and the total cost is $C(q) = 150 + 10q$. Write a function that gives the total profit earned, and find the quantity which maximizes the profit.

9. Revenue is given by $R(q) = 450q$ and cost is given by $C(q) = 10,000 + 3q^2$. At what quantity is profit maximized? What is the total profit at this production level?

10. A company estimates that the total revenue, R, in dollars, received from the sale of q items is $R = \ln(1 + 1000q^2)$. Calculate and interpret the marginal revenue if $q = 10$.

11. Table 4.2 shows cost, $C(q)$, and revenue, $R(q)$.

  (a) At approximately what production level, q, is profit maximized? Explain your reasoning.
  (b) What is the price of the product?
  (c) What are the fixed costs?

Table 4.2

q	0	500	1000	1500	2000	2500	3000
$R(q)$	0	1500	3000	4500	6000	7500	9000
$C(q)$	3000	3800	4200	4500	4800	5500	7400

12. Table 4.3 shows marginal cost, MC, and marginal revenue, MR.

  (a) Use the marginal cost and marginal revenue at a production of $q = 5000$ to determine whether production should be increased or decreased from 5000.
  (b) Estimate the production level that maximizes profit.

Table 4.3

q	5000	6000	7000	8000	9000	10000
MR	60	58	56	55	54	53
MC	48	52	54	55	58	63

Problems

13. Let $C(q)$ be the total cost of producing a quantity q of a certain product. See Figure 4.78.

  (a) What is the meaning of $C(0)$?
  (b) Describe in words how the marginal cost changes as the quantity produced increases.
  (c) Explain the concavity of the graph (in terms of economics).
  (d) Explain the economic significance (in terms of marginal cost) of the point at which the concavity changes.
  (e) Do you expect the graph of $C(q)$ to look like this for all types of products?

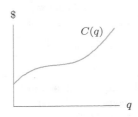

Figure 4.78

14. When production is 2000, marginal revenue is $4 per unit and marginal cost is $3.25 per unit. Do you expect maximum profit to occur at a production level above or below 2000? Explain.

15. If $C'(500) = 75$ and $R'(500) = 100$, should the quantity produced be increased or decreased from $q = 500$ in order to increase profits?

16. An online seller of knitted sweaters finds that it costs $35 to make her first sweater. Her cost for each additional sweater goes down until it reaches $25 for her 100th sweater, and after that it starts to rise again. If she can sell each sweater for $35, is the quantity sold that maximizes her profit less than 100? Greater than 100?

17. The marginal revenue and marginal cost for a certain item are graphed in Figure 4.79. Do the following quantities maximize profit for the company? Explain your answer.

  (a) $q = a$ **(b)** $q = b$

Figure 4.79

18. The total cost $C(q)$ of producing q goods is given by:

$$C(q) = 0.01q^3 - 0.6q^2 + 13q.$$

  (a) What is the fixed cost?
  (b) What is the maximum profit if each item is sold for $7? (Assume you sell everything you produce.)
  (c) Suppose exactly 34 goods are produced. They all sell when the price is $7 each, but for each $1 increase in price, 2 fewer goods are sold. Should the price be raised, and if so by how much?

19. A company manufactures only one product. The quantity, q, of this product produced per month depends on the amount of capital, K, invested (i.e., the number of machines the company owns, the size of its building, and so on) and the amount of labor, L, available each month. We assume that q can be expressed as a *Cobb-Douglas production function*:

$$q = cK^{\alpha}L^{\beta},$$

where c, α, β are positive constants, with $0 < \alpha < 1$ and $0 < \beta < 1$. In this problem we will see how the Russian government could use a Cobb-Douglas function to estimate how many people a newly privatized industry might employ. A company in such an industry has only a small amount of capital available to it and needs to use all of it, so K is fixed. Suppose L is measured in man-hours per month, and that each man-hour costs the company w rubles (a ruble is the unit of Russian currency). Suppose the company has no other costs besides labor, and that each unit of the good can be sold for a fixed price of p rubles. How many man-hours of labor per month should the company use in order to maximize its profit?

20. An agricultural worker in Uganda is planting clover to increase the number of bees making their home in the region. There are 100 bees in the region naturally, and for every acre put under clover, 20 more bees are found in the region.

   (a) Draw a graph of the total number, $N(x)$, of bees as a function of x, the number of acres devoted to clover.
   (b) Explain, both geometrically and algebraically, the shape of the graph of:
      (i) The marginal rate of increase of the number of bees with acres of clover, $N'(x)$.
      (ii) The average number of bees per acre of clover, $N(x)/x$.

21. If you invest x dollars in a certain project, your return is $R(x)$. You want to choose x to maximize your return per dollar invested,[8] which is

$$r(x) = \frac{R(x)}{x}.$$

   (a) The graph of $R(x)$ is in Figure 4.80, with $R(0) = 0$. Illustrate on the graph that the maximum value of $r(x)$ is reached at a point at which the line from the origin to the point is tangent to the graph of $R(x)$.
   (b) Also, the maximum of $r(x)$ occurs at a point at which the slope of the graph of $r(x)$ is zero. On the same axes as part (a), sketch $r(x)$. Illustrate that the maximum of $r(x)$ occurs where its slope is 0.
   (c) Show, by taking the derivative of the formula for $r(x)$, that the conditions in part (a) and (b) are equivalent: the x-value at which the line from the origin is tangent to the graph of R is the same as the x-value at which the graph of r has zero slope.

Figure 4.80

Problems 22–23 involve the *average cost* of manufacturing a quantity q of a good, which is defined to be

$$a(q) = \frac{C(q)}{q}.$$

22. Figure 4.81 shows the cost of production, $C(q)$, as a function of quantity produced, q.

   (a) For some q_0, sketch a line whose slope is the marginal cost, MC, at that point.
   (b) For the same q_0, explain why the average cost $a(q_0)$ can be represented by the slope of the line from that point on the curve to the origin.
   (c) Use the method of Example 6 on page 210 to explain why at the value of q which minimizes $a(q)$, the average and marginal costs are equal.

Figure 4.81

23. The average cost per item to produce q items is given by

$$a(q) = 0.01q^2 - 0.6q + 13, \quad \text{for} \quad q > 0.$$

   (a) What is the total cost, $C(q)$, of producing q goods?
   (b) What is the minimum marginal cost? What is the practical interpretation of this result?
   (c) At what production level is the average cost a minimum? What is the lowest average cost?
   (d) Compute the marginal cost at $q = 30$. How does this relate to your answer to part (c)? Explain this relationship both analytically and in words.

24. The production function $f(x)$ gives the number of units of an item that a manufacturing company can produce from x units of raw material. The company buys the raw material at price w dollars per unit and sells all it produces at a price of p dollars per unit. The quantity of raw material that maximizes profit is denoted by x^*.

   (a) Do you expect the derivative $f'(x)$ to be positive or negative? Justify your answer.
   (b) Explain why the formula $\pi(x) = pf(x) - wx$ gives the profit $\pi(x)$ that the company earns as a function of the quantity x of raw materials that it uses.

[8]From Peter D. Taylor, *Calculus: The Analysis of Functions* (Toronto: Wall & Emerson, 1992).

(c) Evaluate $f'(x^*)$.

(d) Assuming it is nonzero, is $f''(x^*)$ positive or negative?

(e) If the supplier of the raw materials is likely to change the price w, then it is appropriate to treat x^* as a function of w. Find a formula for the derivative dx^*/dw and decide whether it is positive or negative.

(f) If the price w goes up, should the manufacturing company buy more or less of the raw material?

In many applications, we want to maximize or minimize some quantity subject to a condition. Such constrained optimization problems are solved using Lagrange multipliers in multivariable calculus; Problems 25–27 show an alternate method.[9]

25. Minimize $x^2 + y^2$ while satisfying $x + y = 4$ using the following steps.

(a) Graph $x + y = 4$. On the same axes, graph $x^2 + y^2 = 1$, $x^2 + y^2 = 4$, $x^2 + y^2 = 9$.

(b) Explain why the minimum value of $x^2 + y^2$ on $x + y = 4$ occurs at the point at which a graph of $x^2 + y^2 = $ Constant is tangent to the line $x + y = 4$.

(c) Using your answer to part (b) and implicit differentiation to find the slope of the circle, find the minimum value of $x^2 + y^2$ such that $x + y = 4$.

26. The quantity Q of an item which can be produced from

quantities x and y of two raw materials is given by $Q = 10xy$ at a cost of $C = x + 2y$ thousand dollars. If the budget for raw materials is 10 thousand dollars, find the maximum production using the following steps.

(a) Graph $x + 2y = 10$ in the first quadrant. On the same axes, graph $Q = 10xy = 100$, $Q = 10xy = 200$, and $Q = 10xy = 300$.

(b) Explain why the maximum production occurs at a point at which a production curve is tangent to the cost line $C = 10$.

(c) Using your answer to part (b) and implicit differentiation to find the slope of the curve, find the maximum production under this budget.

27. With quantities x and y of two raw materials available, $Q = x^{1/2}y^{1/2}$ thousand items can be produced at a cost of $C = 2x + y$ thousand dollars. Using the following steps, find the minimum cost to produce 1 thousand items.

(a) Graph $x^{1/2}y^{1/2} = 1$. On the same axes, graph $2x + y = 2$, $2x + y = 3$, and $2x + y = 4$.

(b) Explain why the minimum cost occurs at a point at which a cost line is tangent to the production curve $Q = 1$.

(c) Using your answer to part (b) and implicit differentiation to find the slope of the curve, find the minimum cost to meet this production level.

Strengthen Your Understanding

In Problems 28–29, explain what is wrong with the statement.

28. If $C(100) = 90$ and $R(100) = 150$, increasing the quantity produced from 100 increases profit.

29. For the cost, C, and revenue, R, in Figure 4.82, profit is maximized when the quantity produced is about 3,500 units.

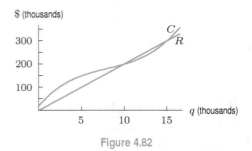

Figure 4.82

In Problems 30–31, give an example of:

30. A quantity, q, in Figure 4.82 where $MC > MR$.

31. Cost and revenue curves such that the item can never be sold for a profit.

32. Which is correct? A company generally wants to

(a) Maximize revenue
(b) Maximize marginal revenue
(c) Minimize cost
(d) Minimize marginal cost
(e) None of the above

33. Which is correct? A company can increase its profit by increasing production if, at its current level of production,

(a) Marginal revenue − Marginal cost > 0
(b) Marginal revenue − Marginal cost = 0
(c) Marginal revenue − Marginal cost < 0
(d) Marginal revenue − Marginal cost is increasing

---

[9]Kelly Black, "Putting Constraints in Optimization for First-Year Calculus Students," pp. 310–312, *SIAM Review*, Vol. 39, No. 2, June 1997.

4.6 RATES AND RELATED RATES

Derivatives represent rates of change. In this section, we see how to calculate rates in a variety of situations.

Example 1

A spherical snowball is melting. Its radius decreases at a constant rate of 2 cm per minute from an initial value of 70 cm. How fast is the volume decreasing half an hour later?

Solution

The radius, r, starts at 70 cm and decreases at 2 cm/min. At time t minutes since the start,

$$r = 70 - 2t \text{ cm}.$$

The volume of the snowball is given by

$$V = \frac{4}{3}\pi r^3 = \frac{4}{3}\pi(70 - 2t)^3 \text{ cm}^3.$$

The rate at which the volume is changing at time t is

$$\frac{dV}{dt} = \frac{4}{3}\pi \cdot 3(70 - 2t)^2(-2) = -8\pi(70 - 2t)^2 \text{ cm}^3/\text{min}.$$

The volume is measured in cm^3, and time is in minutes, so after half an hour $t = 30$, and

$$\left.\frac{dV}{dt}\right|_{t=30} = -8\pi(70 - 2 \cdot 30)^2 = -800\pi \text{ cm}^3/\text{min}.$$

Thus, the rate at which the volume is increasing is $-800\pi \approx -2500$ cm^3/min; the rate at which the volume is decreasing is about 2500 cm^3/min.

Example 2

A skydiver of mass m jumps from a plane at time $t = 0$. Under certain assumptions, the distance, $s(t)$, he has fallen in time t is given by

$$s(t) = \frac{m^2 g}{k^2}\left(\frac{kt}{m} + e^{-kt/m} - 1\right) \quad \text{for some positive constant } k.$$

(a) Find $s'(0)$ and $s''(0)$ and interpret in terms of the skydiver.
(b) Relate the units of $s'(t)$ and $s''(t)$ to the units of t and $s(t)$.

Solution

(a) Differentiating using the chain rule gives

$$s'(t) = \frac{m^2 g}{k^2}\left(\frac{k}{m} + e^{-kt/m}\left(-\frac{k}{m}\right)\right) = \frac{mg}{k}\left(1 - e^{-kt/m}\right)$$

$$s''(t) = \frac{mg}{k}(-e^{kt/m})\left(-\frac{k}{m}\right) = ge^{-kt/m}.$$

Since $e^{-k \cdot 0/m} = 1$, evaluating at $t = 0$ gives

$$s'(0) = \frac{mg}{k}(1 - 1) = 0 \quad \text{and} \quad s''(0) = g.$$

The first derivative of distance is velocity, so the fact that $s'(0) = 0$ tells us that the skydiver starts with zero velocity. The second derivative of distance is acceleration, so the fact that $s''(0) = g$ tells us that the skydiver's initial acceleration is g, the acceleration due to gravity.

(b) The units of velocity, $s'(t)$, and acceleration, $s''(t)$, are given by

$$\text{Units of } s'(t) \text{ are } \frac{\text{Units of } s(t)}{\text{Units of } t} = \frac{\text{Units of distance}}{\text{Units of time}}; \quad \text{for example, meters/sec.}$$

$$\text{Units of } s''(t) \text{ are } \frac{\text{Units of } s'(t)}{\text{Units of } t} = \frac{\text{Units of distance}}{(\text{Units of time})^2}; \quad \text{for example, meters/sec}^2.$$

Related Rates

In Example 1, the radius of the snowball decreased at a constant rate. A more realistic scenario is that the radius decreases at a varying rate. In this case, we may not be able to write a formula for V as a function of t. However, we may still be able to calculate dV/dt, as in the following example.

Example 3   A spherical snowball melts in such a way that the instant at which its radius is 20 cm, its radius is decreasing at 3 cm/min. At what rate is the volume of the ball of snow changing at that instant?

Solution   Since the snowball is spherical, we again have that

$$V = \frac{4}{3}\pi r^3.$$

We can no longer write a formula for r in terms of t, but we know that

$$\frac{dr}{dt} = -3 \quad \text{when} \quad r = 20.$$

We want to know dV/dt when $r = 20$. Think of r as an (unknown) function of t and differentiate the expression for V with respect to t using the chain rule:

$$\frac{dV}{dt} = \frac{4}{3}\pi \cdot 3r^2 \frac{dr}{dt} = 4\pi r^2 \frac{dr}{dt}.$$

At the instant at which $r = 20$ and $dr/dt = -3$, we have

$$\frac{dV}{dt} = 4\pi \cdot 20^2 \cdot (-3) = -4800\pi \approx -15{,}080 \text{ cm}^3/\text{min}.$$

So the volume of the ball is decreasing at a rate of 15,080 cm^3 per minute at the moment when $r = 20$ cm. Notice that we have sidestepped the problem of not knowing r as a function of t by calculating the derivatives only at the moment we are interested in.

Example 4   Figure 4.83 shows the fuel consumption, g, in miles per gallon (mpg), of a car traveling at v mph. At one moment, the car was going 70 mph and its deceleration was 8000 miles/hour^2. How fast was the fuel consumption changing at that moment? Include units.

Figure 4.83: Fuel consumption versus velocity

Solution   Acceleration is rate of change of velocity, dv/dt, and we are told that the deceleration is 8000 miles/hour^2, so we know $dv/dt = -8000$ when $v = 70$. We want dg/dt. The chain rule gives

$$\frac{dg}{dt} = \frac{dg}{dv} \cdot \frac{dv}{dt}.$$

The value of dg/dv is the slope of the curve in Figure 4.83 at $v = 70$. Since the points $(30, 40)$ and $(100, 20)$ lie approximately on the tangent to the curve at $v = 70$, we can estimate the derivative

$$\frac{dg}{dv} \approx \frac{20 - 40}{100 - 30} = -\frac{2}{7} \text{ mpg/mph.}$$

Thus,

$$\frac{dg}{dt} = \frac{dg}{dv} \cdot \frac{dv}{dt} \approx -\frac{2}{7}(-8000) \approx 2300 \text{ mpg/hr.}$$

In other words, fuel consumption is increasing at about $2300/60 \approx 38$ mpg per minute. Since we approximated dg/dv, we can only get a rough estimate for dg/dt.

A famous problem involves the rate at which the top of a ladder slips down a wall as the foot of the ladder moves.

Example 5   (a) A 3-meter ladder stands against a high wall. The foot of the ladder moves outward at a constant speed of 0.1 meter/sec. When the foot is 1 meter from the wall, how fast is the top of the ladder falling? What about when the foot is 2 meters from the wall?

   (b) If the foot of the ladder moves out at a constant speed, how does the speed at which the top falls change as the foot gets farther out?

Solution   (a) Let the foot be x meters from the base of the wall and let the top be y meters from the base. See Figure 4.84. Then, since the ladder is 3 meters long, by Pythagoras' Theorem,

$$x^2 + y^2 = 3^2 = 9.$$

Thinking of x and y as functions of t, we differentiate with respect to t using the chain rule:

$$2x\frac{dx}{dt} + 2y\frac{dy}{dt} = 0.$$

We are interested in the moment at which $dx/dt = 0.1$ and $x = 1$. We want to know dy/dt, so we solve, giving

$$\frac{dy}{dt} = -\frac{x}{y}\frac{dx}{dt}.$$

When the foot of the ladder is 1 meter from the wall, $x = 1$ and $y = \sqrt{9 - 1^2} = \sqrt{8}$, so

$$\frac{dy}{dt} = -\frac{1}{\sqrt{8}}0.1 = -0.035 \text{ meter/sec.}$$

Thus, the top falls at 0.035 meter/sec.
   When the foot is 2 meters from the wall, $x = 2$ and $y = \sqrt{9 - 2^2} = \sqrt{5}$, so

$$\frac{dy}{dt} = -\frac{2}{\sqrt{5}}0.1 = -0.089 \text{ meter/sec.}$$

Thus, the top falls at 0.089 meter/sec. Notice that the top falls faster when the base of the ladder is farther from the wall.

   (b) As the foot of the ladder moves out, x increases and y decreases. Looking at the expression

$$\frac{dy}{dt} = -\frac{x}{y}\frac{dx}{dt},$$

we see that if dx/dt is constant, the magnitude of dy/dt increases as the foot gets farther out. Thus, the top falls faster and faster.

Wall

Ladder
3 meters

y

Ground

x

Figure 4.84: Side view of ladder standing against wall (x, y in meters)

Example 6   An airplane, flying at 450 km/hr at a constant altitude of 5 km, is approaching a camera mounted on the ground. Let θ be the angle of elevation above the ground at which the camera is pointed. See Figure 4.85. When $\theta = \pi/3$, how fast does the camera have to rotate in order to keep the plane in view?

Solution   Suppose the camera is at point C and the plane is vertically above point B. Let x km be the distance between B and C. The fact that the plane is moving horizontally toward C at 450 km/hr means that x is decreasing and $dx/dt = -450$ km/hr. From Figure 4.85, we see that $\tan\theta = 5/x$.

Differentiating $\tan\theta = 5/x$ with respect to t and using the chain rule gives

$$\frac{1}{\cos^2\theta}\frac{d\theta}{dt} = -5x^{-2}\frac{dx}{dt}.$$

Plane

5 km

Camera
C x B

Ground

Figure 4.85: Plane approaching a camera at C (side view; x in km)

We want to calculate $d\theta/dt$ when $\theta = \pi/3$. At that moment, $\cos\theta = 1/2$ and $\tan\theta = \sqrt{3}$, so $x = 5/\sqrt{3}$. Substituting gives

$$\frac{1}{(1/2)^2}\frac{d\theta}{dt} = -5\left(\frac{5}{\sqrt{3}}\right)^{-2}\cdot(-450)$$

$$\frac{d\theta}{dt} = 67.5 \text{ radians/hour.}$$

Since there are 60 minutes in an hour, the camera must turn at roughly 1 radian per minute if it is to remain pointed at the plane. With 1 radian $\approx 60°$, this is a rotation of about one degree per second.

Exercises and Problems for Section 4.6

Exercises

1. With time, t, in minutes, the temperature, H, in degrees Celsius, of a bottle of water put in the refrigerator at $t = 0$ is given by

$$H = 4 + 16e^{-0.02t}.$$

How fast is the water cooling initially? After 10 minutes? Give units.

2. According to the US Census, the world population P, in billions, was approximately

$$P = 6.7e^{0.011t},$$

where t is in years since January 1, 2007. At what rate was the world's population increasing on that date? Give your answer in millions of people per year. [The world population growth rate has actually decreased since 2007.]

3. The power, P, dissipated when a 9-volt battery is put across a resistance of R ohms is given by

$$P = \frac{81}{R}.$$

What is the rate of change of power with respect to resistance?

4. With length, l, in meters, the period T, in seconds, of a pendulum is given by

$$T = 2\pi\sqrt{\frac{l}{9.8}}.$$

(a) How fast does the period increase as l increases?
(b) Does this rate of change increase or decrease as l increases?

5. A plane is climbing at 500 feet per minute, and the air temperature outside the plane is falling at $2°C$ per 1000 feet. What is the rate of change (as a function of time) of the air temperature just outside the plane?

6. Atmospheric pressure decays exponentially as altitude increases. With pressure, P, in inches of mercury and altitude, h, in feet above sea level, we have

$$P = 30e^{-3.23 \times 10^{-5} h}.$$

(a) At what altitude is the atmospheric pressure 25 inches of mercury?
(b) A glider measures the pressure to be 25 inches of mercury and experiences a pressure increase of 0.1 inches of mercury per minute. At what rate is it changing altitude?

7. The gravitational force, F, on a rocket at a distance, r, from the center of the earth is given by

$$F = \frac{k}{r^2},$$

where $k = 10^{13}$ newton $\cdot$ km^2. When the rocket is 10^4 km from the center of the earth, it is moving away at 0.2 km/sec. How fast is the gravitational force changing at that moment? Give units. (A newton is a unit of force.)

8. A voltage V across a resistance R generates a current

$$I = \frac{V}{R}.$$

A constant voltage of 9 volts is put across a resistance that is increasing at a rate of 0.2 ohms per second when the resistance is 5 ohms. At what rate is the current changing?

9. If θ is the angle between a line through the origin and the positive x-axis, the area, in cm^2, of part of a rose petal is

$$A = \frac{9}{16}(4\theta - \sin(4\theta)).$$

If the angle θ is increasing at a rate of 0.2 radians per minute, at what rate is the area changing when $\theta = \pi/4$?

10. The potential, ϕ, of a charge distribution at a point on the positive x-axis is given, for x in centimeters, by

$$\phi = 2\pi\left(\sqrt{x^2 + 4} - x\right).$$

A particle at $x = 3$ is moving to the left at a rate of 0.2 cm/sec. At what rate is its potential changing?

11. The average cost per item, C, in dollars, of manufacturing a quantity q of cell phones is given by

$$C = \frac{a}{q} + b \qquad \text{where } a, b \text{ are positive constants.}$$

(a) Find the rate of change of C as q increases. What are its units?
(b) If production increases at a rate of 100 cell phones per week, how fast is the average cost changing? Is the average cost increasing or decreasing?

12. If $x^2 + y^2 = 25$ and $dx/dt = 6$, find dy/dt when y is positive and

(a) $x = 0$ (b) $x = 3$ (c) $x = 4$

13. A pyramid has height h and a square base with side x. The volume of a pyramid is $V = \frac{1}{3}x^2 h$. If the height remains fixed and the side of the base is decreasing by 0.002 meter/yr, what rate is the volume decreasing when the height is 120 meters and the width is 150 meters?

14. A thin uniform rod of length l cm and a small particle lie on a line separated by a distance of a cm. If K is a positive constant and F is measured in newtons, the gravitational force between them is

$$F = \frac{K}{a(a+l)}.$$

(a) If a is increasing at the rate 2 cm/min when $a = 15$ and $l = 5$, how fast is F decreasing?

(b) If l is decreasing at the rate 2 cm/min when $a = 15$ and $l = 5$, how fast is F increasing?

15. The Dubois formula relates a person's surface area, s, in meters^2, to weight, w, in kg, and height, h, in cm, by

$$s = 0.01 w^{0.25} h^{0.75}.$$

(a) What is the surface area of a person who weighs 60 kg and is 150 cm tall?

(b) The person in part (a) stays constant height but increases in weight by 0.5 kg/year. At what rate is his surface area increasing when his weight is 62 kg?

Problems

16. A rectangle has one side of 10 cm. How fast is the area of the rectangle changing at the instant when the other side is 12 cm and increasing at 3 cm per minute?

17. A rectangle has one side of 8 cm. How fast is the diagonal of the rectangle changing at the instant when the other side is 6 cm and increasing at 3 cm per minute?

18. A right triangle has one leg of 7 cm. How fast is its area changing at the instant that the other leg has length 10 cm and is decreasing at 2 cm per second?

19. The area, A, of a square is increasing at 3 cm^2 per minute. How fast is the side length of the square changing when $A = 576$ cm^2?

20. If two electrical resistances, R_1 and R_2, are connected in parallel, their combined resistance, R, is given by

$$\frac{1}{R} = \frac{1}{R_1} + \frac{1}{R_2}.$$

Suppose R_1 is held constant at 10 ohms, and that R_2 is increasing at 2 ohms per minute when R_2 is 20 ohms. How fast is R changing at that moment?

21. A dose, D, of a drug causes a temperature change, T, in a patient. For C a positive constant, T is given by

$$T = \left(\frac{C}{2} - \frac{D}{3}\right) D^2.$$

(a) What is the rate of change of temperature change with respect to dose?

(b) For what doses does the temperature change increase as the dose increases?

22. An item costs $500 at time $t = 0$ and costs P in year t. When inflation is $r\%$ per year, the price is given by

$$P = 500 e^{rt/100}.$$

(a) If r is a constant, at what rate is the price rising (in dollars per year)

(i) Initially?   (ii) After 2 years?

(b) Now suppose that r is increasing by 0.3 per year when $r = 4$ and $t = 2$. At what rate (dollars per year) is the price increasing at that time?

23. For positive constants A and B, the force, F, between two atoms in a molecule at a distance r apart is given by

$$F = -\frac{A}{r^2} + \frac{B}{r^3}.$$

(a) How fast does force change as r increases? What type of units does it have?

(b) If at some time t the distance is changing at a rate k, at what rate is the force changing with time? What type of units does this rate of change have?

24. For positive constants k and g, the velocity, v, of a particle of mass m at time t is given by

$$v = \frac{mg}{k}\left(1 - e^{-kt/m}\right).$$

At what rate is the velocity changing at time 0? At $t = 1$? What do your answers tell you about the motion?

25. A 10 m ladder leans against a vertical wall and the bottom of the ladder slides away from the wall at a rate of 0.5 m/sec. How fast is the top of the ladder sliding down the wall when the bottom of the ladder is

(a)   4 m from the wall?   (b)   8 m from the wall?

26. Gasoline is pouring into a vertical cylindrical tank of radius 3 feet. When the depth of the gasoline is 4 feet, the depth is increasing at 0.2 ft/sec. How fast is the volume of gasoline changing at that instant?

27. Water is being pumped into a vertical cylinder of radius 5 meters and height 20 meters at a rate of 3 meters^3/min. How fast is the water level rising when the cylinder is half full?

28. A spherical snowball is melting. Its radius is decreasing at 0.2 cm per hour when the radius is 15 cm. How fast is its volume decreasing at that time?

29. The radius of a spherical balloon is increasing by 2 cm/sec. At what rate is air being blown into the balloon at the moment when the radius is 10 cm? Give units in your answer.

30. The circulation time of a mammal (that is, the average time it takes for all the blood in the body to circulate once and return to the heart) is proportional to the fourth root of the body mass of the mammal. The constant of proportionality is 17.40 if circulation time is in seconds and body mass is in kilograms. The body mass of a growing child is 45 kg and is increasing at a rate of 0.1 kg/month. What is the rate of change of the circulation time of the child?

31. A certain quantity of gas occupies a volume of $20\,\text{cm}^3$ at a pressure of 1 atmosphere. The gas expands without the addition of heat, so, for some constant k, its pressure, P, and volume, V, satisfy the relation

$$PV^{1.4} = k.$$

(a) Find the rate of change of pressure with volume. Give units.

(b) The volume is increasing at $2\,\text{cm}^3/\text{min}$ when the volume is $30\,\text{cm}^3$. At that moment, is the pressure increasing or decreasing? How fast? Give units.

32. The metal frame of a rectangular box has a square base. The horizontal rods in the base are made out of one metal and the vertical rods out of a different metal. If the horizontal rods expand at a rate of 0.001 cm/hr and the vertical rods expand at a rate of 0.002 cm/hr, at what rate is the volume of the box expanding when the base has an area of $9\,\text{cm}^2$ and the volume is $180\,\text{cm}^3$?

33. A ruptured oil tanker causes a circular oil slick on the surface of the ocean. When its radius is 150 meters, the radius of the slick is expanding by 0.1 meter/minute and its thickness is 0.02 meter. At that moment:

(a) How fast is the area of the slick expanding?

(b) The circular slick has the same thickness everywhere, and the volume of oil spilled remains fixed. How fast is the thickness of the slick decreasing?

34. A potter forms a piece of clay into a cylinder. As he rolls it, the length, L, of the cylinder increases and the radius, r, decreases. If the length of the cylinder is increasing at 0.1 cm per second, find the rate at which the radius is changing when the radius is 1 cm and the length is 5 cm.

35. A cone-shaped coffee filter of radius 6 cm and depth 10 cm contains water, which drips out through a hole at the bottom at a constant rate of $1.5\,\text{cm}^3$ per second.

(a) If the filter starts out full, how long does it take to empty?

(b) Find the volume of water in the filter when the depth of the water is h cm.

(c) How fast is the water level falling when the depth is 8 cm?

36. Water is being poured into the cone-shaped container in Figure 4.86. When the depth of the water is 2.5 in, it is

increasing at 3 in/min. At that time, how fast is the surface area, A, that is covered by water increasing? [Hint: $A = \pi rs$, where r, s are as shown.]

Figure 4.86: Cone and cross section

37. Grit, which is spread on roads in winter, is stored in mounds which are the shape of a cone. As grit is added to the top of a mound at 2 cubic meters per minute, the angle between the slant side of the cone and the vertical remains 45°. How fast is the height of the mound increasing when it is half a meter high? [Hint: Volume $V = \pi r^2 h/3$, where r is radius and h is height.]

38. A gas station stands at the intersection of a north-south road and an east-west road. A police car is traveling toward the gas station from the east, chasing a stolen truck which is traveling north away from the gas station. The speed of the police car is 100 mph at the moment it is 3 miles from the gas station. At the same time, the truck is 4 miles from the gas station going 80 mph. At this moment:

(a) Is the distance between the car and truck increasing or decreasing? How fast? (Distance is measured along a straight line joining the car and the truck.)

(b) How does your answer change if the truck is going 70 mph instead of 80 mph?

39. The London Eye is a large Ferris wheel that has diameter 135 meters and revolves continuously. Passengers enter the cabins at the bottom of the wheel and complete one revolution in about 27 minutes. One minute into the ride a passenger is rising at 0.06 meters per second. How fast is the horizontal motion of the passenger at that moment?

40. Point P moves around the unit circle.[10] (See Figure 4.87.) The angle θ, in radians, changes with time as shown in Figure 4.88.

(a) Estimate the coordinates of P when $t = 2$.

(b) When $t = 2$, approximately how fast is the point P moving in the x-direction? In the y-direction?

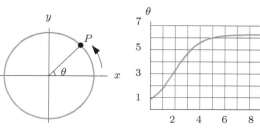

Figure 4.87

Figure 4.88

[10]Based on an idea from Caspar Curjel.

41. Figure 4.89 shows the number of gallons, G, of gasoline used on a trip of M miles.

   (a) The function f is linear on each of the intervals $0 < M < 70$ and $70 < M < 100$. What is the slope of these lines? What are the units of these slopes?

   (b) What is gas consumption (in miles per gallon) during the first 70 miles of this trip? During the next 30 miles?

   (c) Figure 4.90 shows distance traveled, M (in miles), as a function of time t, in hours since the start of the trip. Describe this trip in words. Give a possible explanation for what happens one hour into the trip. What do your answers to part (b) tell you about the trip?

   (d) If we let $G = k(t) = f(h(t))$, estimate $k(0.5)$ and interpret your answer in terms of the trip.

   (e) Find $k'(0.5)$ and $k'(1.5)$. Give units and interpret your answers.

Figure 4.89

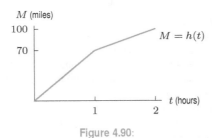

Figure 4.90:

42. On February 16, 2007, paraglider Eva Wisnierska[11] was caught in a freak thunderstorm over Australia and carried upward at a speed of about 3000 ft/min. Table 4.4 gives the temperature at various heights. Approximately how fast (in °F/ per minute) was her temperature decreasing when she was at 4000 feet?

Table 4.4

y (thousand ft)	2	4	6	8	10	12	14	16
H (°F)	60	52	38	31	23	16	9	2

---

43. Coroners estimate time of death using the rule of thumb that a body cools about 2°F during the first hour after death and about 1°F for each additional hour. Assuming an air temperature of 68°F and a living body temperature of 98.6°F, the temperature $T(t)$ in °F of a body at a time t hours since death is given by

$$T(t) = 68 + 30.6e^{-kt}.$$

   (a) For what value of k will the body cool by 2°F in the first hour?

   (b) Using the value of k found in part (a), after how many hours will the temperature of the body be decreasing at a rate of 1°F per hour?

   (c) Using the value of k found in part (a), show that, 24 hours after death, the coroner's rule of thumb gives approximately the same temperature as the formula.

44. A train is traveling at 0.8 km/min along a long straight track, moving in the direction shown in Figure 4.91. A movie camera, 0.5 km away from the track, is focused on the train.

   (a) Express z, the distance between the camera and the train, as a function of x.

   (b) How fast is the distance from the camera to the train changing when the train is 1 km from the camera? Give units.

   (c) How fast is the camera rotating (in radians/min) at the moment when the train is 1 km from the camera?

Figure 4.91

45. A lighthouse is 2 km from the long, straight coastline shown in Figure 4.92. Find the rate of change of the distance of the spot of light from the point O with respect to the angle θ.

Figure 4.92

---

[11]www.sciencedaily.com, accessed May 15, 2007.

46. When the growth of a spherical cell depends on the flow of nutrients through the surface, it is reasonable to assume that the growth rate, dV/dt, is proportional to the surface area, S. Assume that for a particular cell $dV/dt = \frac{1}{3}S$. At what rate is its radius r increasing?

47. The length of each side of a cube is increased at a constant rate. Which is greater, the relative rate of change of the volume of the cube, $\frac{1}{V}\frac{dV}{dt}$, or the relative change of the surface area of the cube, $\frac{1}{A}\frac{dA}{dt}$?

48. A circular region is irrigated by a 20 meter long pipe, fixed at one end and rotating horizontally, spraying water. One rotation takes 5 minutes. A road passes 30 meters from the edge of the circular area. See Figure 4.93.

  (a) How fast is the end of the pipe, P, moving?

  (b) How fast is the distance PQ changing when θ is $\pi/2$? When θ is 0?

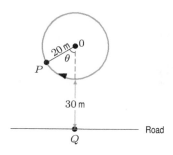

Figure 4.93

49. A water tank is in the shape of an inverted cone with depth 10 meters and top radius 8 meters. Water is flowing into the tank at 0.1 cubic meters/min but leaking out at a rate of $0.004h^2$ cubic meters/min, where h is the depth of the water in meters. Can the tank ever overflow?

50. For the amusement of the guests, some hotels have elevators on the outside of the building. One such hotel is 300 feet high. You are standing by a window 100 feet above the ground and 150 feet away from the hotel, and the elevator descends at a constant speed of 30 ft/sec, starting at time $t = 0$, where t is time in seconds. Let θ be the angle between the line of your horizon and your line of sight to the elevator. (See Figure 4.94.)

  (a) Find a formula for $h(t)$, the elevator's height above the ground as it descends from the top of the hotel.

  (b) Using your answer to part (a), express θ as a function of time t and find the rate of change of θ with respect to t.

  (c) The rate of change of θ is a measure of how fast the elevator appears to you to be moving. At what height is the elevator when it appears to be moving fastest?

Figure 4.94

51. In a romantic relationship between Angela and Brian, who are unsuited for each other, $a(t)$ represents the affection Angela has for Brian at time t days after they meet, while $b(t)$ represents the affection Brian has for Angela at time t. If $a(t) > 0$ then Angela likes Brian; if $a(t) < 0$ then Angela dislikes Brian; if $a(t) = 0$ then Angela neither likes nor dislikes Brian. Their affection for each other is given by the relation $(a(t))^2 + (b(t))^2 = c$, where c is a constant.

  (a) Show that $a(t) \cdot a'(t) = -b(t) \cdot b'(t)$.

  (b) At any time during their relationship, the rate per day at which Brian's affection for Angela changes is $b'(t) = -a(t)$. Explain what this means if Angela

    (i) Likes Brian,   (ii) Dislikes Brian.

  (c) Use parts (a) and (b) to show that $a'(t) = b(t)$. Explain what this means if Brian

    (i) Likes Angela,   (ii) Dislikes Angela.

  (d) If $a(0) = 1$ and $b(0) = 1$ who first dislikes the other?

52. In a 19th century sea-battle, the number of ships on each side remaining t hours after the start are given by $x(t)$ and $y(t)$. If the ships are equally equipped, the relation between them is $(x(t))^2 - (y(t))^2 = c$, where c is a positive constant. The battle ends when one side has no ships remaining.

  (a) If, at the start of the battle, 50 ships on one side oppose 40 ships on the other, what is the value of c?

  (b) If $y(3) = 16$, what is $x(3)$? What does this represent in terms of the battle?

  (c) There is a time T when $y(T) = 0$. What does this T represent in terms of the battle?

  (d) At the end of the battle, how many ships remain on the victorious side?

  (e) At any time during the battle, the rate per hour at which y loses ships is directly proportional to the number of x ships, with constant of proportionality k. Write an equation that represents this. Is k positive or negative?

  (f) Show that the rate per hour at which x loses ships is directly proportional to the number of y ships, with constant of proportionality k.

  (g) Three hours after the start of the battle, x is losing ships at the rate of 32 ships per hour. What is k? At what rate is y losing ships at this time?

In Problems 53–54, explain what is wrong with the statement.

53. If the radius, R, of a circle increases at a constant rate, its diameter, D, increases at the same constant rate.

54. If two variables x and y are functions of t and are related by the equation $y = 1 - x^2$ then $dy/dt = -2x$.

In Problems 55–56, give an example of:

55. Two functions f and g where $y = f(x)$ and $x = g(t)$ such that dy/dt and dx/dt are both constant.

56. Two functions g and f where $x = g(t)$ and $y = f(x)$ such that dx/dt is constant and dy/dt is not constant.

Are the statements in Problems 57–58 true of false? Give an explanation for your answer.

57. If the radius of a circle is increasing at a constant rate, then so is the circumference.

58. If the radius of a circle is increasing at a constant rate, then so is the area.

59. The light in the lighthouse in Figure 4.95 rotates at 2 revolutions per minute. To calculate the speed at which the spot of light moves along the shore, it is best to differentiate:

(a) $r^2 = 5^2 + x^2$
(b) $x = r \sin \theta$
(c) $x = 5 \tan \theta$
(d) $r^2 = 2^2 + x^2$

Figure 4.95

4.7 L'HOPITAL'S RULE, GROWTH, AND DOMINANCE

Suppose we want to calculate the exact value of the limit

$$\lim_{x \to 0} \frac{e^{2x} - 1}{x}.$$

Substituting $x = 0$ gives us $0/0$, which is undefined:

$$\frac{e^{2(0)} - 1}{0} = \frac{1 - 1}{0} = \frac{0}{0}.$$

Substituting values of x near 0 gives us an approximate value for the limit.

However, the limit can be calculated exactly using local linearity. Suppose we let $f(x)$ be the numerator, so $f(x) = e^{2x} - 1$, and $g(x)$ be the denominator, so $g(x) = x$. Then $f(0) = 0$ and $f'(x) = 2e^{2x}$, so $f'(0) = 2$. When we zoom in on the graph of $f(x) = e^{2x} - 1$ near the origin, we see its tangent line $y = 2x$ shown in Figure 4.96. We are interested in the ratio $f(x)/g(x)$, which is approximately the ratio of the y-values in Figure 4.96. So, for x near 0,

$$\frac{f(x)}{g(x)} = \frac{e^{2x} - 1}{x} \approx \frac{2x}{x} = \frac{2}{1} = \frac{f'(0)}{g'(0)}.$$

As $x \to 0$, this approximation gets better, and we have

$$\lim_{x \to 0} \frac{e^{2x} - 1}{x} = 2.$$

Figure 4.96: Ratio $(e^{2x} - 1)/x$ is approximated by ratio of slopes as we zoom in near the origin

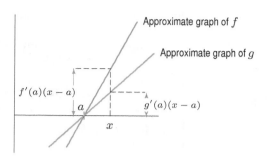

Figure 4.97: Ratio $f(x)/g(x)$ is approximated by ratio of slopes, $f'(a)/g'(a)$, as we zoom in at a

L'Hopital's Rule

If $f(a) = g(a) = 0$, we can use the same method to investigate limits of the form

$$\lim_{x \to a} \frac{f(x)}{g(x)}.$$

As in the previous case, we zoom in on the graphs of $f(x)$ and $g(x)$. Figure 4.97 shows that both graphs cross the x-axis at $x = a$. This suggests that the limit of $f(x)/g(x)$ as $x \to a$ is the ratio of slopes, giving the following result:

L'Hopital's rule:[12] If f and g are differentiable, $f(a) = g(a) = 0$, and $g'(a) \neq 0$, then

$$\lim_{x \to a} \frac{f(x)}{g(x)} = \frac{f'(a)}{g'(a)}.$$

Example 1   Use l'Hopital's rule to confirm that $\lim\limits_{x \to 0} \dfrac{\sin x}{x} = 1$.

Solution   Let $f(x) = \sin x$ and $g(x) = x$. Then $f(0) = g(0) = 0$ and $f'(x) = \cos x$ and $g'(x) = 1$. Thus,

$$\lim_{x \to 0} \frac{\sin x}{x} = \frac{\cos 0}{1} = 1.$$

If we also have $f'(a) = g'(a) = 0$, then we can use the following result:

More general form of l'Hopital's rule: If f and g are differentiable and $f(a) = g(a) = 0$, then

$$\lim_{x \to a} \frac{f(x)}{g(x)} = \lim_{x \to a} \frac{f'(x)}{g'(x)},$$

provided the limit on the right exists.

Example 2   Calculate $\lim\limits_{t \to 0} \dfrac{e^t - 1 - t}{t^2}$.

Solution   Let $f(t) = e^t - 1 - t$ and $g(t) = t^2$. Then $f(0) = e^0 - 1 - 0 = 0$ and $g(0) = 0$, and $f'(t) = e^t - 1$ and $g'(t) = 2t$. So

$$\lim_{t \to 0} \frac{e^t - 1 - t}{t^2} = \lim_{t \to 0} \frac{e^t - 1}{2t}.$$

---

[12]Marquis de l'Hopital (1661–1704) was a French nobleman who wrote the first calculus text.

Since $f'(0) = g'(0) = 0$, the ratio $f'(0)/g'(0)$ is not defined. So we use l'Hopital's rule again:

$$\lim_{t \to 0} \frac{e^t - 1 - t}{t^2} = \lim_{t \to 0} \frac{e^t - 1}{2t} = \lim_{t \to 0} \frac{e^t}{2} = \frac{1}{2}.$$

We can also use l'Hopital's rule in cases involving infinity.

L'Hopital's rule applies to limits involving infinity, provided f and g are differentiable. For a any real number or $\pm\infty$:

- When $\lim_{x \to a} f(x) = \pm\infty$ and $\lim_{x \to a} g(x) = \pm\infty$,

or

- When $\lim_{x \to \infty} f(x) = \lim_{x \to \infty} g(x) = 0$.

it can be shown that:

$$\lim_{x \to a} \frac{f(x)}{g(x)} = \lim_{x \to a} \frac{f'(x)}{g'(x)},$$

provided the limit on the right-hand side exists.

The next example shows how this version of l'Hopital's rule is used.

Example 3   Calculate $\lim_{x \to \infty} \dfrac{5x + e^{-x}}{7x}$.

Solution   Let $f(x) = 5x + e^{-x}$ and $g(x) = 7x$. Then $\lim_{x \to \infty} f(x) = \lim_{x \to \infty} g(x) = \infty$, and $f'(x) = 5 - e^{-x}$ and $g'(x) = 7$, so

$$\lim_{x \to \infty} \frac{5x + e^{-x}}{7x} = \lim_{x \to \infty} \frac{(5 - e^{-x})}{7} = \frac{5}{7}.$$

Dominance: Powers, Polynomials, Exponentials, and Logarithms

In Chapter 1, we see that some functions are much larger than others as $x \to \infty$. For positive functions f and g, we say that g *dominates* f as $x \to \infty$ if $\lim_{x \to \infty} \dfrac{f(x)}{g(x)} = 0$. L'Hopital's rule gives us an easy way of checking this.

Example 4   Check that $x^{1/2}$ dominates $\ln x$ as $x \to \infty$.

Solution   We apply l'Hopital's rule to $(\ln x)/x^{1/2}$:

$$\lim_{x \to \infty} \frac{\ln x}{x^{1/2}} = \lim_{x \to \infty} \frac{1/x}{\frac{1}{2} x^{-1/2}}.$$

To evaluate this limit, we simplify and get

$$\lim_{x \to \infty} \frac{1/x}{\frac{1}{2} x^{-1/2}} = \lim_{x \to \infty} \frac{2x^{1/2}}{x} = \lim_{x \to \infty} \frac{2}{x^{1/2}} = 0.$$

Therefore we have

$$\lim_{x \to \infty} \frac{\ln x}{x^{1/2}} = 0,$$

which tells us that $x^{1/2}$ dominates $\ln x$ as $x \to \infty$.

Example 5   Check that any exponential function of the form e^{kx} (with $k > 0$) dominates any power function of the form Ax^p (with A and p positive) as $x \to \infty$.

Solution   We apply l'Hopital's rule repeatedly to Ax^p/e^{kx}:

$$\lim_{x \to \infty} \frac{Ax^p}{e^{kx}} = \lim_{x \to \infty} \frac{Apx^{p-1}}{ke^{kx}} = \lim_{x \to \infty} \frac{Ap(p-1)x^{p-2}}{k^2 e^{kx}} = \cdots$$

Keep applying l'Hopital's rule until the power of x is no longer positive. Then the limit of the numerator must be a finite number, while the limit of the denominator must be ∞. Therefore we have

$$\lim_{x \to \infty} \frac{Ax^p}{e^{kx}} = 0,$$

so e^{kx} dominates Ax^p.

Recognizing the Form of a Limit

Although expressions like $0/0$ and ∞/∞ have no numerical value, they are useful in describing the form of a limit. We can also use l'Hopital's rule to calculate some limits of the form $0 \cdot \infty$, $\infty - \infty$, 1^∞, 0^0, and ∞^0.

Example 6   Calculate $\lim\limits_{x \to \infty} xe^{-x}$.

Solution   Since $\lim\limits_{x \to \infty} x = \infty$ and $\lim\limits_{x \to \infty} e^{-x} = 0$, we see that

$$xe^{-x} \to \infty \cdot 0 \qquad \text{as } x \to \infty.$$

Rewriting

$$\infty \cdot 0 \quad \text{as} \quad \frac{\infty}{\frac{1}{0}} = \frac{\infty}{\infty}$$

gives a form whose value can be determined using l'Hopital's rule, so we rewrite the function xe^{-x} as

$$xe^{-x} = \frac{x}{e^x} \to \frac{\infty}{\infty} \qquad \text{as } x \to \infty.$$

Taking $f(x) = x$ and $g(x) = e^x$ gives $f'(x) = 1$ and $g'(x) = e^x$, so

$$\lim_{x \to \infty} xe^{-x} = \lim_{x \to \infty} \frac{x}{e^x} = \lim_{x \to \infty} \frac{1}{e^x} = 0.$$

A Famous Limit

In the following example, l'Hopital's rule is applied to calculate a limit that can be used to define e.

Example 7   Evaluate $\lim\limits_{x \to \infty} \left(1 + \dfrac{1}{x}\right)^x$.

Solution   As $x \to \infty$, we see that $\left(1 + \dfrac{1}{x}\right)^x \to 1^\infty$, a form whose value in this context is to be determined. Since $\ln 1^\infty = \infty \cdot \ln 1 = \infty \cdot 0$, we write

$$y = \left(1 + \frac{1}{x}\right)^x$$

and find the limit of $\ln y$:

$$\lim_{x \to \infty} \ln y = \lim_{x \to \infty} \ln \left(1 + \frac{1}{x}\right)^x = \lim_{x \to \infty} x \ln \left(1 + \frac{1}{x}\right) = \infty \cdot 0.$$

As in the previous example, we rewrite

$$\infty \cdot 0 \quad \text{as} \quad \frac{0}{\frac{1}{\infty}} = \frac{0}{0},$$

which suggests rewriting

$$\lim_{x\to\infty} x\ln\left(1+\frac{1}{x}\right) \quad \text{as} \quad \lim_{x\to\infty} \frac{\ln(1+1/x)}{1/x}.$$

Since $\lim_{x\to\infty}\ln(1+1/x) = 0$ and $\lim_{x\to\infty}(1/x) = 0$, we can use l'Hopital's rule with $f(x) = \ln(1+1/x)$ and $g(x) = 1/x$. We have

$$f'(x) = \frac{1}{1+1/x}\left(-\frac{1}{x^2}\right) \quad \text{and} \quad g'(x) = -\frac{1}{x^2},$$

so

$$\lim_{x\to\infty}\ln y = \lim_{x\to\infty}\frac{\ln(1+1/x)}{1/x} = \lim_{x\to\infty}\frac{1}{1+1/x}\left(-\frac{1}{x^2}\right)\bigg/\left(-\frac{1}{x^2}\right)$$

$$= \lim_{x\to\infty}\frac{1}{1+1/x} = 1.$$

Since $\lim_{x\to\infty}\ln y = 1$, we have

$$\lim_{x\to\infty} y = e^1 = e.$$

Example 8   Put the following limits in a form that can be evaluated using l'Hopital's rule:

(a) $\displaystyle\lim_{x\to 0^+} x\ln x$ (b) $\displaystyle\lim_{x\to\infty} x^{1/x}$ (c) $\displaystyle\lim_{x\to 0^+} x^x$ (d) $\displaystyle\lim_{x\to 0}\frac{1}{x} - \frac{1}{\sin x}$

Solution   (a) We have

$$\lim_{x\to 0^+} x\ln x = 0\cdot\infty.$$

We can rewrite

$$0\cdot\infty \quad \text{as} \quad \frac{\infty}{1/0} = \frac{\infty}{\infty}.$$

This corresponds to rewriting

$$\lim_{x\to 0^+} x\ln x \quad \text{as} \quad \lim_{x\to 0^+}\frac{\ln x}{1/x}.$$

This is an ∞/∞ form that can be evaluated using l'Hopital's rule. (Note that we could also have written

$$0\cdot\infty \quad \text{as} \quad \frac{0}{1/\infty} = \frac{0}{0},$$

but this leads to rewriting

$$\lim_{x\to 0^+} x\ln x \quad \text{as} \quad \lim_{x\to 0^+}\frac{x}{1/\ln x}.$$

It turns out that l'Hopital's rule fails to simplify this limit.)

(b) In this case we have a ∞^0 form, so we take the logarithm and get a $0\cdot\infty$ form:

$$\lim_{x\to\infty}\ln(x^{1/x}) = \lim_{x\to\infty}\frac{1}{x}\ln x = \lim_{x\to\infty}\frac{\ln x}{x}.$$

This is an ∞/∞ form that can be evaluated using l'Hopital's rule. Once we get the answer, we exponentiate it to get the original limit.

(c) Since $\lim_{x\to 0^+} x = 0$, this is a 0^0 form. If we take the logarithm, we get

$$\ln 0^0 = 0\cdot\ln 0 = 0\cdot\infty.$$

This corresponds to the limit

$$\lim_{x\to 0^+}\ln x^x = \lim_{x\to 0^+} x\ln x,$$

which is considered in part (a).

(d) We have

$$\lim_{x \to 0} \frac{1}{x} - \frac{1}{\sin x} = \frac{1}{0} - \frac{1}{0} = \infty - \infty.$$

Limits like this can often be calculated by adding the fractions:

$$\lim_{x \to 0} \frac{1}{x} - \frac{1}{\sin x} = \lim_{x \to 0} \frac{\sin x - x}{x \sin x},$$

giving a $0/0$ form that can be evaluated using l'Hopital's rule twice.

Exercises and Problems for Section 4.7

Exercises

In Exercises 1–11, find the limit. Use l'Hopital's rule if it applies.

1. $\lim_{x \to 2} \dfrac{x - 2}{x^2 - 4}$

2. $\lim_{x \to 1} \dfrac{x^2 + 3x - 4}{x - 1}$

3. $\lim_{x \to 1} \dfrac{x^6 - 1}{x^4 - 1}$

4. $\lim_{x \to 0} \dfrac{e^x - 1}{\sin x}$

5. $\lim_{x \to 0} \dfrac{\sin x}{e^x}$

6. $\lim_{x \to 1} \dfrac{\ln x}{x - 1}$

7. $\lim_{x \to \infty} \dfrac{\ln x}{x}$

8. $\lim_{x \to \infty} \dfrac{(\ln x)^3}{x^2}$

9. $\lim_{x \to 0} \dfrac{e^{4x} - 1}{\cos x}$

10. $\lim_{x \to 1} \dfrac{x^a - 1}{x^b - 1}, b \neq 0$

11. $\lim_{x \to a} \dfrac{\sqrt[3]{x} - \sqrt[3]{a}}{x - a}, a \neq 0$

In Exercises 12–15, which function dominates as $x \to \infty$?

12. x^5 and $0.1x^7$

13. $0.01x^3$ and $50x^2$

14. $\ln(x + 3)$ and $x^{0.2}$

15. x^{10} and $e^{0.1x}$

Problems

16. The functions f and g and their tangent lines at $(4, 0)$ are shown in Figure 4.98. Find $\lim_{x \to 4} \dfrac{f(x)}{g(x)}$.

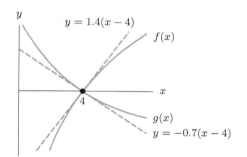

Figure 4.98

For Problems 17–20, find the sign of $\lim_{x \to a} \dfrac{f(x)}{g(x)}$ from the figure.

17.

18.

19. **20.**

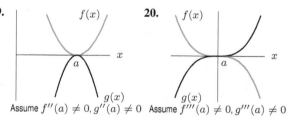

Assume $f''(a) \neq 0, g''(a) \neq 0$ Assume $f'''(a) \neq 0, g'''(a) \neq 0$

Based on your knowledge of the behavior of the numerator and denominator, predict the value of the limits in Problems 21–24. Then find each limit using l'Hopital's rule.

21. $\lim_{x \to 0} \dfrac{x^2}{\sin x}$

22. $\lim_{x \to 0} \dfrac{\sin^2 x}{x}$

23. $\lim_{x \to 0} \dfrac{\sin x}{x^{1/3}}$

24. $\lim_{x \to 0} \dfrac{x}{(\sin x)^{1/3}}$

In Problems 25–30, describe the form of the limit ($0/0$, ∞/∞, $\infty \cdot 0$, $\infty - \infty$, 1^∞, 0^0, ∞^0, or none of these). Does l'Hopital's rule apply? If so, explain how.

25. $\lim_{x \to \infty} \dfrac{x}{e^x}$

26. $\lim_{x \to 1} \dfrac{x}{x - 1}$

27. $\lim_{t \to \infty} \left(\dfrac{1}{t} - \dfrac{2}{t^2} \right)$

28. $\lim_{t \to 0^+} \dfrac{1}{t} - \dfrac{1}{e^t - 1}$

29. $\lim_{x \to 0} (1 + x)^x$

30. $\lim_{x \to \infty} (1 + x)^{1/x}$

In Problems 31–44 determine whether the limit exists, and where possible evaluate it.

31. $\lim\limits_{x \to 1} \dfrac{\ln x}{x^2 - 1}$

32. $\lim\limits_{t \to \pi} \dfrac{\sin^2 t}{t - \pi}$

33. $\lim\limits_{n \to \infty} \sqrt[n]{n}$

34. $\lim\limits_{x \to 0^+} x \ln x$

35. $\lim\limits_{x \to 0} \dfrac{\sinh(2x)}{x}$

36. $\lim\limits_{x \to 0} \dfrac{1 - \cosh(3x)}{x}$

37. $\lim\limits_{x \to 1^-} \dfrac{\cos^{-1} x}{x - 1}$

38. $\lim\limits_{x \to 0} \left(\dfrac{1}{x} - \dfrac{1}{\sin x} \right)$

39. $\lim\limits_{t \to 0^+} \left(\dfrac{2}{t} - \dfrac{1}{e^t - 1} \right)$

40. $\lim\limits_{t \to 0} \left(\dfrac{1}{t} - \dfrac{1}{e^t - 1} \right)$

41. $\lim\limits_{x \to \infty} \left(1 + \sin\left(\dfrac{3}{x} \right) \right)^x$

42. $\lim\limits_{t \to 0} \dfrac{\sin^2 At}{\cos At - 1}, A \neq 0$

43. $\lim\limits_{t \to \infty} e^t - t^n$, where n is a positive integer

44. $\lim\limits_{x \to 0^+} x^a \ln x$, where a is a positive constant.

In Problems 45–47, explain why l'Hopital's rule cannot be used to calculate the limit. Then evaluate the limit if it exists.

45. $\lim\limits_{x \to 1} \dfrac{\sin(2x)}{x}$

46. $\lim\limits_{x \to 0} \dfrac{\cos x}{x}$

47. $\lim\limits_{x \to \infty} \dfrac{e^{-x}}{\sin x}$

In Problems 48–50, evaluate the limit using the fact that

$$\lim\limits_{n \to \infty} \left(1 + \dfrac{1}{n} \right)^n = e.$$

48. $\lim\limits_{x \to 0^+} (1 + x)^{1/x}$

49. $\lim\limits_{n \to \infty} \left(1 + \dfrac{2}{n} \right)^n$

50. $\lim\limits_{x \to 0^+} (1 + kx)^{t/x}; k > 0$

51. Show that $\lim\limits_{n \to \infty} \left(1 - \dfrac{1}{n} \right)^n = e^{-1}$.

52. Use the result of Problem 51 to evaluate

$$\lim\limits_{n \to \infty} \left(1 - \dfrac{\lambda}{n} \right)^n.$$

Evaluate the limits in Problems 53–55 where

$$f(t) = \left(\dfrac{3^t + 5^t}{2} \right)^{1/t} \quad \text{for } t \neq 0.$$

53. $\lim\limits_{t \to -\infty} f(t)$ **54.** $\lim\limits_{t \to +\infty} f(t)$ **55.** $\lim\limits_{t \to 0} f(t)$

In Problems 56–59, evaluate the limits as x approaches 0.

56. $\dfrac{\sinh(2x)}{x}$

57. $\dfrac{1 - \cosh(3x)}{x}$

58. $\dfrac{1 - \cosh(5x)}{x^2}$

59. $\dfrac{x - \sinh(x)}{x^3}$

Problems 60–62 are examples Euler used to illustrate l'Hopital's rule. Find the limit.

60. $\lim\limits_{x \to 0} \dfrac{e^x - 1 - \ln(1 + x)}{x^2}$

61. $\lim\limits_{x \to \pi/2} \dfrac{1 - \sin x + \cos x}{\sin x + \cos x - 1}$

62. $\lim\limits_{x \to 1} \dfrac{x^x - x}{1 - x + \ln x}$

Strengthen Your Understanding

In Problems 63–64, explain what is wrong with the statement.

63. There is a positive integer n such that function x^n dominates e^x as $x \to \infty$.

64. L'Hopital's rule shows that

$$\lim\limits_{x \to \infty} \dfrac{5x + \cos x}{x} = 5.$$

In Problems 65–66, give an example of:

65. A limit of a rational function for which l'Hopital's rule cannot be applied.

66. A function f such that L'Hopital's rule can be applied to find

$$\lim\limits_{x \to \infty} \dfrac{f(x)}{\ln x}.$$

67. Is the following statement true of false? If $g'(a) \neq 0$, then $\lim\limits_{x \to a} \dfrac{f(x)}{g(x)} = \dfrac{f'(a)}{g'(a)}$. Give an explanation for your answer.

68. Which of the limits cannot be computed with l'Hopital's rule?

(a) $\lim\limits_{x \to 0} \dfrac{\sin x}{x}$

(b) $\lim\limits_{x \to 0} \dfrac{\cos x}{x}$

(c) $\lim\limits_{x \to 0} \dfrac{x}{\sin x}$

(d) $\lim\limits_{x \to \infty} \dfrac{x}{e^x}$

4.8 PARAMETRIC EQUATIONS

Representing Motion in the Plane

To represent the motion of a particle in the xy-plane we use two equations, one for the x-coordinate of the particle, $x = f(t)$, and another for the y-coordinate, $y = g(t)$. Thus at time t the particle is at the point $(f(t), g(t))$. The equation for x describes the right-left motion; the equation for y describes the up-down motion. The two equations for x and y are called *parametric equations* with *parameter t*.

Example 1   Describe the motion of the particle whose coordinates at time t are $x = \cos t$ and $y = \sin t$.

Solution   Since $(\cos t)^2 + (\sin t)^2 = 1$, we have $x^2 + y^2 = 1$. That is, at any time t the particle is at a point (x, y) on the unit circle $x^2 + y^2 = 1$. We plot points at different times to see how the particle moves on the circle. (See Figure 4.99 and Table 4.5.) The particle completes one full trip counterclockwise around the circle every 2π units of time. Notice how the x-coordinate goes repeatedly back and forth from -1 to 1 while the y-coordinate goes repeatedly up and down from -1 to 1. The two motions combine to trace out a circle.

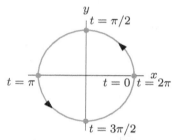

Figure 4.99: The circle parameterized by $x = \cos t$, $y = \sin t$

Table 4.5   *Points on the circle with $x = \cos t$, $y = \sin t$*

t	x	y
0	1	0
$\pi/2$	0	1
π	-1	0
$3\pi/2$	0	-1
2π	1	0

Example 2   Figure 4.100 shows the graphs of two functions, $f(t)$ and $g(t)$. Describe the motion of the particle whose coordinates at time t are $x = f(t)$ and $y = g(t)$.

 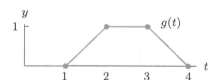

Figure 4.100: Graphs of $x = f(t)$ and $y = g(t)$ used to trace out the path $(f(t), g(t))$ in Figure 4.101

Solution   Between times $t = 0$ and $t = 1$, the x-coordinate goes from 0 to 1, while the y-coordinate stays fixed at 0. So the particle moves along the x-axis from $(0, 0)$ to $(1, 0)$. Then, between times $t = 1$ and $t = 2$, the x-coordinate stays fixed at $x = 1$, while the y-coordinate goes from 0 to 1. Thus, the particle moves along the vertical line from $(1, 0)$ to $(1, 1)$. Similarly, between times $t = 2$ and $t = 3$, it moves horizontally back to $(0, 1)$, and between times $t = 3$ and $t = 4$ it moves down the y-axis to $(0, 0)$. Thus, it traces out the square in Figure 4.101.

Figure 4.101: The square parameterized by $(f(t), g(t))$

Different Motions Along the Same Path

Example 3   Describe the motion of the particle whose x and y coordinates at time t are given by the equations

$$x = \cos(3t), \quad y = \sin(3t).$$

Solution   Since $(\cos(3t))^2 + (\sin(3t))^2 = 1$, we have $x^2 + y^2 = 1$, giving motion around the unit circle. But from Table 4.6, we see that the particle in this example is moving three times as fast as the particle in Example 1. (See Figure 4.102.)

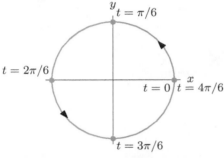

Figure 4.102: The circle parameterized by $x = \cos(3t), y = \sin(3t)$

Table 4.6   *Points on circle with* $x = \cos(3t), y = \sin(3t)$

t	x	y
0	1	0
$\pi/6$	0	1
$2\pi/6$	-1	0
$3\pi/6$	0	-1
$4\pi/6$	1	0

Example 3 is obtained from Example 1 by replacing t by $3t$; this is called a *change in parameter*. If we make a change in parameter, the particle traces out the same curve (or a part of it) but at a different speed or in a different direction.

Example 4   Describe the motion of the particle whose x and y coordinates at time t are given by

$$x = \cos(e^{-t^2}), \quad y = \sin(e^{-t^2}).$$

Solution   As in Examples 1 and 3, we have $x^2 + y^2 = 1$ so the motion lies on the unit circle. As time t goes from $-\infty$ (way back in the past) to 0 (the present) to ∞ (way off in the future), e^{-t^2} goes from near 0 to 1 back to near 0. So $(x, y) = (\cos(e^{-t^2}), \sin(e^{-t^2}))$ goes from near $(1, 0)$ to $(\cos 1, \sin 1)$ and back to near $(1, 0)$. The particle does not actually reach the point $(1, 0)$. (See Figure 4.103 and Table 4.7.)

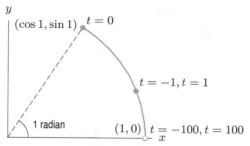

Figure 4.103: The circle parameterized by
$x = \cos\left(e^{-t^2}\right), y = \sin\left(e^{-t^2}\right)$

Table 4.7 Points on circle with $x = \cos(e^{-t^2})$, $y = \sin(e^{-t^2})$		
t	x	y
-100	~ 1	~ 0
-1	0.93	0.36
0	0.54	0.84
1	0.93	0.36
100	~ 1	~ 0

Motion in a Straight Line

An object moves with constant speed along a straight line through the point (x_0, y_0). Both the x- and y-coordinates have a constant rate of change. Let $a = dx/dt$ and $b = dy/dt$. Then at time t the object has coordinates $x = x_0 + at$, $y = y_0 + bt$. (See Figure 4.104.) Notice that a represents the change in x in one unit of time, and b represents the change in y. Thus the line has slope $m = b/a$.

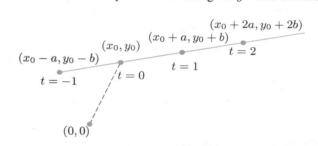

Figure 4.104: The line $x = x_0 + at, y = y_0 + bt$

This yields the following:

Parametric Equations for a Straight Line

An object moving along a line through the point (x_0, y_0), with $dx/dt = a$ and $dy/dt = b$, has parametric equations

$$x = x_0 + at, \quad y = y_0 + bt.$$

The slope of the line is $m = b/a$.

Example 5 Find parametric equations for:

(a) The line passing through the points $(2, -1)$ and $(-1, 5)$.
(b) The line segment from $(2, -1)$ to $(-1, 5)$.

Solution (a) Imagine an object moving with constant speed along a straight line from $(2, -1)$ to $(-1, 5)$, making the journey from the first point to the second in one unit of time. Then $dx/dt = ((-1) - 2)/1 = -3$ and $dy/dt = (5 - (-1))/1 = 6$. Thus the parametric equations are

$$x = 2 - 3t, \quad y = -1 + 6t.$$

(b) In the parameterization in part (a), $t = 0$ corresponds to the point $(2, -1)$ and $t = 1$ corresponds to the point $(-1, 5)$. So the parameterization of the segment is

$$x = 2 - 3t, \quad y = -1 + 6t, \qquad 0 \le t \le 1.$$

There are many other possible parametric equations for this line.

Speed and Velocity

An object moves along a straight line at a constant speed, with $dx/dt = a$ and $dy/dt = b$. In one unit of time, the object moves a units horizontally and b units vertically. Thus, by the Pythagorean Theorem, it travels a distance $\sqrt{a^2 + b^2}$. So its speed is

$$\text{Speed} = \frac{\text{Distance traveled}}{\text{Time taken}} = \frac{\sqrt{a^2 + b^2}}{1} = \sqrt{a^2 + b^2}.$$

For general motion along a curve with varying speed, we make the following definition:

> The **instantaneous speed** of a moving object is defined to be
>
> $$v = \sqrt{\left(\frac{dx}{dt}\right)^2 + \left(\frac{dy}{dt}\right)^2}.$$
>
> The quantity $v_x = dx/dt$ is the **instantaneous velocity** in the x-direction; $v_y = dy/dt$ is the **instantaneous velocity** in the y-direction. The **velocity vector** $\vec{v}$ is written $\vec{v} = v_x \vec{i} + v_y \vec{j}$.

The quantities v_x and v_y are called the *components* of the velocity in the x- and y-directions. The velocity vector $\vec{v}$ is a useful way to keep track of the velocities in both directions using one mathematical object. The symbols $\vec{i}$ and $\vec{j}$ represent vectors of length one in the positive x and y-directions, respectively. For more about vectors, see Appendix D.

Example 6 A particle moves along a curve in the xy-plane with $x(t) = 2t + e^t$ and $y(t) = 3t - 4$, where t is time. Find the velocity vector and speed of the particle when $t = 1$.

Solution Differentiating gives

$$\frac{dx}{dt} = 2 + e^t, \quad \frac{dy}{dt} = 3.$$

When $t = 1$ we have $v_x = 2 + e, v_y = 3$. So the velocity vector is $\vec{v} = (2 + e)\vec{i} + 3\vec{j}$ and the speed is $\sqrt{(2 + e)^2 + 3^2} = \sqrt{13 + 4e + e^2} = 5.591$.

Example 7 A particle moves in the xy-plane with $x = 2t^3 - 9t^2 + 12t$ and $y = 3t^4 - 16t^3 + 18t^2$, where t is time.

(a) At what times is the particle
   (i) Stopped   (ii) Moving parallel to the x- or y- axis?
(b) Find the speed of the particle at time t.

Solution (a) Differentiating gives

$$\frac{dx}{dt} = 6t^2 - 18t + 12, \quad \frac{dy}{dt} = 12t^3 - 48t^2 + 36t.$$

We are interested in the points at which $dx/dt = 0$ or $dy/dt = 0$. Solving gives

$$\frac{dx}{dt} = 6(t^2 - 3t + 2) = 6(t - 1)(t - 2) \quad \text{so} \quad \frac{dx}{dt} = 0 \quad \text{if } t = 1 \text{ or } t = 2.$$

$$\frac{dy}{dt} = 12t(t^2 - 4t + 3) = 12t(t - 1)(t - 3) \quad \text{so} \quad \frac{dy}{dt} = 0 \quad \text{if } t = 0, t = 1, \text{ or } t = 3.$$

(i) The particle is stopped if both dx/dt and dy/dt are 0, which occurs at $t = 1$.

(ii) The particle is moving parallel to the x-axis if $dy/dt = 0$ but $dx/dt \neq 0$. This occurs at $t = 0$ and $t = 3$. The particle is moving parallel to the y-axis if $dx/dt = 0$ but $dy/dt \neq 0$. This occurs at $t = 2$.

(b) We have

$$\text{Speed} = \sqrt{\left(\frac{dx}{dt}\right)^2 + \left(\frac{dy}{dt}\right)^2} = \sqrt{(6t^2 - 18t + 12)^2 + (12t^3 - 48t^2 + 36t)^2}.$$

Example 8   A child is sitting on a Ferris wheel of diameter 10 meters, making one revolution every 2 minutes. Find the speed of the child

(a) Using geometry.   (b) Using a parameterization of the motion.

Solution   (a) The child moves at a constant speed around a circle of radius 5 meters, completing one revolution every 2 minutes. One revolution around a circle of radius 5 is a distance of 10π, so the child's speed is $10\pi/2 = 5\pi \approx 15.7$ m/min. See Figure 4.105.

Speed
15.7 m/min

5 m

5 m

Speed
15.7 m/min

Figure 4.105: Motion of a child on a Ferris wheel at two different times is represented by the arrows. The direction of each arrow is the direction of motion at that time.

(b) The Ferris wheel has radius 5 meters and completes 1 revolution counterclockwise every 2 minutes. If the origin is at the center of the circle and we measure x and y in meters, the motion is parameterized by equations of the form

$$x = 5\cos(\omega t), \quad y = 5\sin(\omega t),$$

where ω is chosen to make the period 2 minutes. Since the period of $\cos(\omega t)$ and $\sin(\omega t)$ is $2\pi/\omega$, we must have

$$\frac{2\pi}{\omega} = 2, \quad \text{so} \quad \omega = \pi.$$

Thus, for t in minutes, the motion is described by the equations

$$x = 5\cos(\pi t), \quad y = 5\sin(\pi t).$$

So the speed is given by

$$v = \sqrt{\left(\frac{dx}{dt}\right)^2 + \left(\frac{dy}{dt}\right)^2}$$

$$= \sqrt{(-5\pi)^2 \sin^2(\pi t) + (5\pi)^2 \cos^2(\pi t)} = 5\pi\sqrt{\sin^2(\pi t) + \cos^2(\pi t)} = 5\pi \approx 15.7 \text{ m/min},$$

which agrees with the speed we calculated in part (a).

Tangent Lines

To find the tangent line at a point (x_0, y_0) to a curve given parametrically, we find the straight line motion through (x_0, y_0) with the same velocity in the x and y directions as a particle moving along the curve.

Example 9   Find the tangent line at the point $(1, 2)$ to the curve defined by the parametric equations

$$x = t^3, \quad y = 2t.$$

Solution   At time $t = 1$ the particle is at the point $(1, 2)$. The velocity in the x-direction at time t is $v_x = dx/dt = 3t^2$, and the velocity in the y-direction is $v_y = dy/dt = 2$. So at $t = 1$ the velocity in the x-direction is 3 and the velocity in the y-direction is 2. Thus the tangent line has parametric equations

$$x = 1 + 3t, \quad y = 2 + 2t.$$

Parametric Representations of Curves in the Plane

Sometimes we are more interested in the curve traced out by the particle than we are in the motion itself. In that case we call the parametric equations a *parameterization* of the curve. As we can see by comparing Examples 1 and 3, two different parameterizations can describe the same curve in the xy-plane. Though the parameter, which we usually denote by t, may not have physical meaning, it is often helpful to think of it as time.

Example 10   Give a parameterization of the semicircle of radius 1 shown in Figure 4.106.

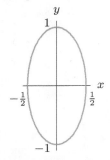

Figure 4.106: Parameterization of   Figure 4.107: Parameterization of the
semicircle for Example 10   ellipse $4x^2 + y^2 = 1$ for Example 11

Solution   We can use the equations $x = \cos t$ and $y = \sin t$ for counterclockwise motion in a circle, from Example 1 on page 249. The particle passes $(0, 1)$ at $t = \pi/2$, moves counterclockwise around the circle, and reaches $(0, -1)$ at $t = 3\pi/2$. So a parameterization is

$$x = \cos t, \; y = \sin t, \quad \frac{\pi}{2} \le t \le \frac{3\pi}{2}.$$

To find the xy-equation of a curve given parametrically, we eliminate the parameter t in the parametric equations. In the previous example, we use the Pythagorean identity, so

$$\cos^2 t + \sin^2 t = 1 \quad \text{gives} \quad x^2 + y^2 = 1.$$

Example 11   Give a parameterization of the ellipse $4x^2 + y^2 = 1$ shown in Figure 4.107.

Solution   Since $(2x)^2 + y^2 = 1$, we adapt the parameterization of the circle in Example 1. Replacing x by $2x$ gives the equations $2x = \cos t, y = \sin t$. A parameterization of the ellipse is thus

$$x = \tfrac{1}{2}\cos t, \qquad y = \sin t, \qquad 0 \le t \le 2\pi.$$

We usually require that the parameterization of a curve go from one end of the curve to the other without retracing any portion of the curve. This is different from parameterizing the motion of a particle, where, for example, a particle may move around the same circle many times.

Parameterizing the Graph of a Function

The graph of any function $y = f(x)$ can be parameterized by letting the parameter t be x:

$$x = t, \quad y = f(t).$$

Example 12 Give parametric equations for the curve $y = x^3 - x$. In which direction does this parameterization trace out the curve?

Solution Let $x = t$, $y = t^3 - t$. Thus, $y = t^3 - t = x^3 - x$. Since $x = t$, as time increases the x-coordinate moves from left to right, so the particle traces out the curve $y = x^3 - x$ from left to right.

Curves Given Parametrically

Some complicated curves can be graphed more easily using parametric equations; the next example shows such a curve.

Example 13 Assume t is time in seconds. Sketch the curve traced out by the particle whose motion is given by

$$x = \cos(3t), \quad y = \sin(5t).$$

Solution The x-coordinate oscillates back and forth between 1 and -1, completing 3 oscillations every 2π seconds. The y-coordinate oscillates up and down between 1 and -1, completing 5 oscillations every 2π seconds. Since both the x- and y-coordinates return to their original values every 2π seconds, the curve is retraced every 2π seconds. The result is a pattern called a Lissajous figure. (See Figure 4.108.) Problems 57–60 concern Lissajous figures $x = \cos(at)$, $y = \sin(bt)$ for other values of a and b.

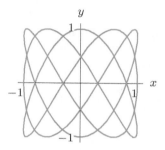

Figure 4.108: A Lissajous figure: $x = \cos(3t), y = \sin(5t)$

Slope and Concavity of Parametric Curves

Suppose we have a curve traced out by the parametric equations $x = f(t)$, $y = g(t)$. To find the slope at a point on the curve, we could, in theory, eliminate the parameter t and then differentiate the function we obtain. However, the chain rule gives us an easier way.

Suppose the curve traced out by the parametric equations is represented by $y = h(x)$. (It may be represented by an implicit function.) Thinking of x and y as functions of t, the chain rule gives

$$\frac{dy}{dt} = \frac{dy}{dx} \cdot \frac{dx}{dt},$$

so we obtain the slope of the curve as a function of t:

$$\boxed{\text{Slope of curve} = \frac{dy}{dx} = \frac{dy/dt}{dx/dt}.}$$

We can find the second derivative, d^2y/dx^2, by a similar method and use it to investigate the concavity of the curve. The chain rule tells us that if w is any differentiable function of x, then

$$\frac{dw}{dx} = \frac{dw/dt}{dx/dt}.$$

For $w = dy/dx$, we have

$$\frac{dw}{dx} = \frac{d}{dx}\left(\frac{dy}{dx}\right) = \frac{d^2y}{dx^2},$$

so the chain rule gives the second derivative at any point on a parametric curve:

$$\frac{d^2y}{dx^2} = \frac{d}{dt}\left(\frac{dy}{dx}\right)\bigg/\frac{dx}{dt}.$$

Example 14   If $x = \cos t$, $y = \sin t$, find the point corresponding to $t = \pi/4$, the slope of the curve at the point, and d^2y/dx^2 at the point.

Solution   The point corresponding to $t = \pi/4$ is $(\cos(\pi/4), \sin(\pi/4)) = (1/\sqrt{2}, 1/\sqrt{2})$.
    To find the slope, we use

$$\frac{dy}{dx} = \frac{dy/dt}{dx/dt} = \frac{\cos t}{-\sin t},$$

so when $t = \pi/4$,

$$\text{Slope} = \frac{\cos(\pi/4)}{-\sin(\pi/4)} = -1.$$

Thus, the curve has slope -1 at the point $(1/\sqrt{2}, 1/\sqrt{2})$. This is as we would expect, since the curve traced out is the circle of Example 1.
    To find d^2y/dx^2, we use $w = dy/dx = -(\cos t)/(\sin t)$, so

$$\frac{d^2y}{dx^2} = \frac{d}{dt}\left(-\frac{\cos t}{\sin t}\right)\bigg/(-\sin t) = -\frac{(-\sin t)(\sin t) - (\cos t)(\cos t)}{\sin^2 t} \cdot \left(-\frac{1}{\sin t}\right) = -\frac{1}{\sin^3 t}.$$

Thus, at $t = \pi/4$

$$\frac{d^2y}{dx^2}\bigg|_{t=\pi/4} = -\frac{1}{(\sin(\pi/4))^3} = -2\sqrt{2}.$$

Since the second derivative is negative, the concavity is negative. This is as expected, since the point is on the top half of the circle where the graph is bending downward.

Exercises and Problems for Section 4.8

Exercises

For Exercises 1–4, use the graphs of f and g to describe the motion of a particle whose position at time t is given by $x = f(t)$, $y = g(t)$.

1.

2.

3.

4.

In Exercises 5–11, write a parameterization for the curves in the xy-plane.

5. A circle of radius 3 centered at the origin and traced out clockwise.

6. A vertical line through the point $(-2, -3)$.

7. A circle of radius 5 centered at the point $(2, 1)$ and traced out counterclockwise.

8. A circle of radius 2 centered at the origin traced clockwise starting from $(-2, 0)$ when $t = 0$.

9. The line through the points $(2, -1)$ and $(1, 3)$.

10. An ellipse centered at the origin and crossing the x-axis at ± 5 and the y-axis at ± 7.

11. An ellipse centered at the origin, crossing the x-axis at ± 3 and the y-axis at ± 7. Start at the point $(-3, 0)$ and trace out the ellipse counterclockwise.

Exercises 12–17 give parameterizations of the unit circle or a part of it. Describe in words how the circle is traced out, including when and where the particle is moving clockwise and when and where the particle is moving counterclockwise.

12. $x = \sin t, \quad y = \cos t$

13. $x = \cos t, \quad y = -\sin t$

14. $x = \cos(t^2), \quad y = \sin(t^2)$

15. $x = \cos(t^3 - t), \quad y = \sin(t^3 - t)$

16. $x = \cos(\ln t), \quad y = \sin(\ln t)$

17. $x = \cos(\cos t), \quad y = \sin(\cos t)$

In Exercises 18–20, what curves do the parametric equations trace out? Find the equation for each curve.

18. $x = 2 + \cos t, \ y = 2 - \sin t$

19. $x = 2 + \cos t, \ y = 2 - \cos t$

20. $x = 2 + \cos t, \ y = \cos^2 t$

In Exercises 21–26, the parametric equations describe the motion of a particle. Find an equation of the curve along which the particle moves.

21. $x = 3t + 1$
$y = t - 4$

22. $x = t^2 + 3$
$y = t^2 - 2$

23. $x = t + 4$
$y = t^2 - 3$

24. $x = \cos 3t$
$y = \sin 3t$

25. $x = 3\cos t$
$y = 3\sin t$

26. $x = 2 + 5\cos t$
$y = 7 + 5\sin t$

In Exercises 27–29, find an equation of the tangent line to the curve for the given value of t.

27. $x = t^3 - t, \quad y = t^2 \quad$ when $t = 2$

28. $x = t^2 - 2t, \quad y = t^2 + 2t \quad$ when $t = 1$

29. $x = \sin(3t), \quad y = \sin(4t) \quad$ when $t = \pi$

For Exercises 30–33, find the speed for the given motion of a particle. Find any times when the particle comes to a stop.

30. $x = t^2, \quad y = t^3$

31. $x = \cos(t^2), \quad y = \sin(t^2)$

32. $x = \cos 2t, \quad y = \sin t$

33. $x = t^2 - 4t, \ y = t^3 - 12t$

34. Find parametric equations for the tangent line at $t = 2$ for Problem 30.

Problems

Problems 35–36 show motion twice around a square, beginning at the origin at time $t = 0$ and parameterized by $x = f(t), y = g(t)$. Sketch possible graphs of f and g consisting of line segments.

35.

36.

37. A line is parameterized by $x = 10 + t$ and $y = 2t$.

(a) What part of the line do we get by restricting t to $t < 0$?

(b) What part of the line do we get by restricting t to $0 \le t \le 1$?

38. A line is parameterized by $x = 2 + 3t$ and $y = 4 + 7t$.

(a) What part of the line is obtained by restricting t to nonnegative numbers?

(b) What part of the line is obtained if t is restricted to $-1 \le t \le 0$?

(c) How should t be restricted to give the part of the line to the left of the y-axis?

39. (a) Explain how you know that the following two pairs of equations parameterize the same line:

$$x = 2 + t, y = 4 + 3t \text{ and } x = 1 - 2t, y = 1 - 6t.$$

(b) What are the slope and y intercept of this line?

40. Describe the similarities and differences among the motions in the plane given by the following three pairs of parametric equations:
(a) $x = t, \quad y = t^2$ (b) $x = t^2, \quad y = t^4$
(c) $x = t^3, \quad y = t^6$.

41. What can you say about the values of a, b and k if the equations

$$x = a + k \cos t, \quad y = b + k \sin t, \qquad 0 \le t \le 2\pi,$$

trace out the following circles in Figure 4.109?
(a) C_1 (b) C_2 (c) C_3

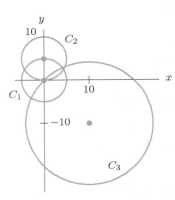

Figure 4.109

42. Suppose $a, b, c, d, m, n, p, q > 0$. Match each pair of parametric equations with one of the lines l_1, l_2, l_3, l_4 in Figure 4.110.

I. $\begin{cases} x = a + ct, \\ y = -b + dt. \end{cases}$ II. $\begin{cases} x = m + pt, \\ y = n - qt. \end{cases}$

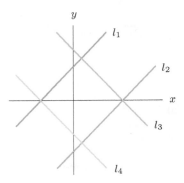

Figure 4.110

43. Describe in words the curve represented by the parametric equations

$$x = 3 + t^3, \quad y = 5 - t^3.$$

44. (a) Sketch the parameterized curve $x = t \cos t$, $y = t \sin t$ for $0 \le t \le 4\pi$.
(b) By calculating the position at $t = 2$ and $t = 2.01$, estimate the speed at $t = 2$.
(c) Use derivatives to calculate the speed at $t = 2$ and compare your answer to part (b).

45. The position of a particle at time t is given by $x = e^t$ and $y = 2e^{2t}$.
(a) Find dy/dx in terms of t.
(b) Eliminate the parameter and write y in terms of x.
(c) Using your answer to part (b), find dy/dx in terms of x.

46. For x and y in meters, the motion of the particle given by

$$x = t^3 - 3t, \quad y = t^2 - 2t,$$

where the y-axis is vertical and the x-axis is horizontal.
(a) Does the particle ever come to a stop? If so, when and where?
(b) Is the particle ever moving straight up or down? If so, when and where?
(c) Is the particle ever moving straight horizontally right or left? If so, when and where?

47. At time t, the position of a particle moving on a curve is given by $x = e^{2t} - e^{-2t}$ and $y = 3e^{2t} + e^{-2t}$.
(a) Find all values of t at which the curve has
    (i) A horizontal tangent.
    (ii) A vertical tangent.
(b) Find dy/dx in terms of t.
(c) Find $\lim\limits_{t \to \infty} dy/dx$.

48. Figure 4.111 shows the graph of a parameterized curve $x = f(t), y = f'(t)$ for a function $f(t)$.
(a) Is $f(t)$ an increasing or decreasing function?
(b) As t increases, is the curve traced from P to Q or from Q to P?
(c) Is $f(t)$ concave up or concave down?

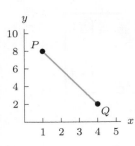

Figure 4.111

49. At time t, the position of a particle is $x(t) = 5\sin(2t)$ and $y(t) = 4\cos(2t)$, with $0 \le t < 2\pi$.

    (a) Graph the path of the particle for $0 \le t < 2\pi$, indicating the direction of motion.

    (b) Find the position and velocity of the particle when $t = \pi/4$.

    (c) How many times does the particle pass through the point found in part (b)?

    (d) What does your answer to part (b) tell you about the direction of the motion relative to the coordinate axes when $t = \pi/4$?

    (e) What is the speed of the particle at time $t = \pi$?

50. At time t, a projectile launched with angle of elevation α and initial velocity v_0 has position $x(t) = (v_0\cos\alpha)t$ and $y(t) = (v_0\sin\alpha)t - \frac{1}{2}gt^2$, where g is the acceleration due to gravity.

    (a) A football player kicks a ball at an angle of $36°$ above the ground with an initial velocity of 60 feet per second. Write the parametric equations for the position of the football at time t seconds. Use $g = 32$ ft/sec^2.

    (b) Graph the path that the football follows.

    (c) How long does it take for the football to hit the ground? How far is it from the spot where the football player kicked it?

    (d) What is the maximum height the football reaches during its flight?

    (e) At what speed is the football traveling 1 second after it was kicked?

51. Two particles move in the xy-plane. At time t, the position of particle A is given by $x(t) = 4t - 4$ and $y(t) = 2t - k$, and the position of particle B is given by $x(t) = 3t$ and $y(t) = t^2 - 2t - 1$.

    (a) If $k = 5$, do the particles ever collide? Explain.

    (b) Find k so that the two particles do collide.

    (c) At the time that the particles collide in part (b), which particle is moving faster?

52. **(a)** Find d^2y/dx^2 for $x = t^3 + t, y = t^2$.

    (b) Is the curve concave up or down at $t = 1$?

53. **(a)** An object moves along the path $x = 3t$ and $y = \cos(2t)$, where t is time. Write the equation for the line tangent to this path at $t = \pi/3$.

    (b) Find the smallest positive value of t for which the y-coordinate is a local maximum.

    (c) Find d^2y/dx^2 when $t = 2$. What does this tell you about the concavity of the graph at $t = 2$?

54. The position of a particle at time t is given by $x = e^t + 3$ and $y = e^{2t} + 6e^t + 9$.

    (a) Find dy/dx in terms of t.

    (b) Find d^2y/dx^2. What does this tell you about the concavity of the graph?

    (c) Eliminate the parameter and write y in terms of x.

    (d) Using your answer from part (c), find dy/dx and d^2y/dx^2 in terms of x. Show that these answers are the same as the answers to parts (a) and (b).

55. A particle moves in the xy-plane so that its position at time t is given by $x = \sin t$ and $y = \cos(2t)$ for $0 \le t < 2\pi$.

    (a) At what time does the particle first touch the x-axis? What is the speed of the particle at that time?

    (b) Is the particle ever at rest?

    (c) Discuss the concavity of the graph.

56. Derive the general formula for the second derivative d^2y/dx^2 of a parametrically defined curve:

$$\frac{d^2y}{dx^2} = \frac{(dx/dt)(d^2y/dt^2) - (dy/dt)(d^2x/dt^2)}{(dx/dt)^3}.$$

Graph the Lissajous figures in Problems 57–60 using a calculator or computer.

57. $x = \cos 2t, \quad y = \sin 5t$

58. $x = \cos 3t, \quad y = \sin 7t$

59. $x = \cos 2t, \quad y = \sin 4t$

60. $x = \cos 2t, \quad y = \sin\sqrt{3}t$

61. A hypothetical moon orbits a planet which in turn orbits a star. Suppose that the orbits are circular and that the moon orbits the planet 12 times in the time it takes for the planet to orbit the star once. In this problem we will investigate whether the moon could come to a stop at some instant. (See Figure 4.112.)

    (a) Suppose the radius of the moon's orbit around the planet is 1 unit and the radius of the planet's orbit around the star is R units. Explain why the motion of the moon relative to the star can be described by the parametric equations

$$x = R\cos t + \cos(12t), \quad y = R\sin t + \sin(12t).$$

    (b) Find values for R and t such that the moon stops relative to the star at time t.

    (c) On a graphing calculator, plot the path of the moon for the value of R you obtained in part (b). Experiment with other values for R.

Figure 4.112

Strengthen Your Understanding

In Problems 62–63, explain what is wrong with the statement.

62. The line segment from $(2, 2)$ to $(0, 0)$ is parameterized by $x = 2t$, $y = 2t$, $0 \leq t \leq 1$.

63. A circle of radius 2 centered at $(0, 1)$ is parameterized by $x = 2 \cos \pi t$, $y = 2 \sin \pi t$, $0 \leq t \leq 2$.

In Problems 64–65, give an example of:

64. A parameterization of a quarter circle centered at the origin of radius 2 in the first quadrant.

65. A parameterization of the line segment between $(0, 0)$ and $(1, 2)$.

Are the statements in Problems 66–67 true of false? Give an explanation for your answer.

66. The curve given parametrically by $x = f(t)$ and $y = g(t)$ has no sharp corners if f and g are differentiable.

67. If a curve is given parametrically by $x = \cos(t^2)$, $y = \sin(t^2)$, then its slope is $\tan(t^2)$.

CHAPTER SUMMARY (see also Ready Reference at the end of the book)

- **Local extrema**
  Maximum, minimum, critical point, tests for local maxima/minima.

- **Using the second derivative**
  Concavity, inflection point.

- **Families of curves**
  Role of parameters

- **Optimization**
  Global extremum, modeling problems, graphical optimization, upper and lower bounds, extreme value theorem.

- **Marginality**
  Cost/revenue functions, marginal cost/marginal revenue functions.

- **Rates and Related Rates**

- **L'Hopital's Rule**
  Limits, growth, dominance

- **Parametric equations**
  Motion of a particle in the plane, parametric equations for lines and other curves, velocity, tangent lines, slope, concavity.

REVIEW EXERCISES AND PROBLEMS FOR CHAPTER FOUR

Exercises

For Exercises 1–2, indicate all critical points on the given graphs. Which correspond to local minima, local maxima, global maxima, global minima, or none of these? (Note that the graphs are on closed intervals.)

1.

2.

In Exercises 3–6, do the following:
(a) Find f' and f''.
(b) Find the critical points of f.
(c) Find any inflection points.
(d) Evaluate f at the critical points and the endpoints. Identify the global maxima and minima of f.
(e) Sketch f. Indicate clearly where f is increasing or decreasing, and its concavity.

3. $f(x) = x^3 - 3x^2$ $(-1 \leq x \leq 3)$

4. $f(x) = x + \sin x$ $(0 \leq x \leq 2\pi)$

5. $f(x) = e^{-x} \sin x$ $(0 \leq x \leq 2\pi)$

6. $f(x) = x^{-2/3} + x^{1/3}$ $(1.2 \leq x \leq 3.5)$

In Exercises 7–9, find the limits as x tends to $+\infty$ and $-\infty$, and then proceed as in Exercises 3–6. (That is, find f', etc.).

7. $f(x) = 2x^3 - 9x^2 + 12x + 1$

8. $f(x) = \dfrac{4x^2}{x^2 + 1}$

9. $f(x) = xe^{-x}$

In Exercises 10–13, find the global maximum and minimum for the function on the closed interval.

10. $f(x) = e^{-x} \sin x$, $0 \leq x \leq 2\pi$

11. $f(x) = e^x + \cos x$, $0 \leq x \leq \pi$

12. $f(x) = x^2 + 2x + 1$, $0 \leq x \leq 3$

13. $f(x) = e^{-x^2}$, $0 \leq x \leq 10$

In Exercises 14–16, find the exact global maximum and minimum values of the function.

14. $h(z) = \dfrac{1}{z} + 4z^2$ for $z > 0$

15. $g(t) = \dfrac{1}{t^3 + 1}$ for $t \geq 0$

16. $f(x) = \dfrac{1}{(x-1)^2 + 2}$

In Exercises 17–23, use derivatives to identify local maxima and minima and points of inflection. Graph the function.

17. $f(x) = x^3 + 3x^2 - 9x - 15$

18. $f(x) = x^5 - 15x^3 + 10$

19. $f(x) = x - 2\ln x$ for $x > 0$

20. $f(x) = e^{-x^2}$

21. $f(x) = x^2 e^{5x}$

22. $f(x) = \dfrac{x^2}{x^2 + 1}$

23. When you cough, your windpipe contracts. The speed, $v(r)$, with which you expel air depends on the radius, r, of your windpipe. If a is the normal (rest) radius of your windpipe, then for $0 \le r \le a$, the speed is given by:
$$v(r) = k(a-r)r^2 \quad \text{where k is a positive constant.}$$
What value of r maximizes the speed? For what value is the speed minimized?

24. Find the point where the following curve is steepest:
$$y = \frac{50}{1 + 6e^{-2t}} \qquad \text{for } t \ge 0.$$

25. The graphs of the function $f(x) = x/(x^2 + a^2)$ for $a = 1, 2$, and 3, are shown in Figure 4.113. Without a calculator, identify the graphs by locating the critical points of $f(x)$.

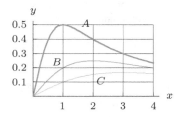

Figure 4.113

26. The graphs of the function $f(x) = 1 - e^{-ax}$ for $a = 1, 2$, and 3, are shown in Figure 4.114. Without a calculator, identify the graphs.

Figure 4.114

27. (a) Find all critical points and all inflection points of the function $f(x) = x^4 - 2ax^2 + b$. Assume a and b are positive constants.
   (b) Find values of the parameters a and b if f has a critical point at the point $(2, 5)$.
   (c) If there is a critical point at $(2, 5)$, where are the inflection points?

28. (a) For a a positive constant, find all critical points of $f(x) = x - a\sqrt{x}$.
   (b) What value of a gives a critical point at $x = 5$? Does $f(x)$ have a local maximum or a local minimum at this critical point?

29. If a and b are nonzero constants, find the domain and all critical points of
$$f(x) = \frac{ax^2}{x - b}.$$

30. The average of two nonnegative numbers is 180. What is the largest possible product of these two numbers?

31. The product of three positive numbers is 192, and one of the numbers is twice one of the other numbers. What is the minimum value of their sum?

32. The difference between two numbers is 24. If both numbers are 100 or greater, what is the minimum value of their product?

33. (a) Fixed costs are \$3 million; variable costs are \$0.4 million per item. Write a formula for total cost as a function of quantity, q.
   (b) The item in part (a) is sold for \$0.5 million each. Write a formula for revenue as a function of q.
   (c) Write a formula for the profit function for this item.

34. A number x is increasing. When $x = 10$, the square of x is increasing at 5 units per second. How fast is x increasing at that time?

35. The mass of a cube in grams is $M = x^3 + 0.1x^4$, where x is the length of one side in centimeters. If the length is increasing at a rate of 0.02 cm/hr, at what rate is the mass of the cube increasing when its length is 5 cm?

36. If θ is the angle between a line through the origin and the positive x-axis, the area, in cm^2, of part of a cardioid is
$$A = 3\theta + 4\sin\theta + \frac{1}{2}\sin(2\theta).$$
If the angle θ is increasing at a rate of 0.3 radians per minute, at what rate is the area changing when $\theta = \pi/2$?

In Exercises 37–38, describe the motion of a particle moving according to the parametric equations. Find an equation of the curve along which the particle moves.

37. $x = 4 - 2t$
$y = 4t + 1$

38. $x = 2\sin t$
$y = 2\cos t$

Problems

39. Figure 4.115 is the graph of f', the derivative of a function f. At which of the points $0, x_1, x_2, x_3, x_4, x_5$, is the function f:

(a) At a local maximum value?
(b) At a local minimum value?
(c) Climbing fastest?
(d) Falling most steeply?

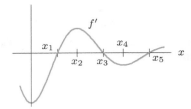

Figure 4.115: Graph of f' not f

40. Figure 4.116 is a graph of f'. For what values of x does f have a local maximum? A local minimum?

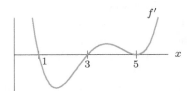

Figure 4.116: Graph of f' (not f)

41. On the graph of f' in Figure 4.117, indicate the x-values that are critical points of the function f itself. Are they local maxima, local minima, or neither?

Figure 4.117: Graph of f' (not f)

42. Graph f given that:

- $f'(x) = 0$ at $x = 2$, $f'(x) < 0$ for $x < 2$, $f'(x) > 0$ for $x > 2$,
- $f''(x) = 0$ at $x = 4$, $f''(x) > 0$ for $x < 4$, $f''(x) < 0$ for $x > 4$.

In Problems 43–47, find formulas for the functions.

43. A cubic polynomial with a local maximum at $x = 1$, a local minimum at $x = 3$, a y-intercept of 5, and an x^3 term whose coefficient is 1.

44. A quartic polynomial whose graph is symmetric about the y-axis and has local maxima at $(-1, 4)$ and $(1, 4)$ and a y-intercept of 3.

45. A function of the form $y = ax^b \ln x$, where a and b are nonzero constants, which has a local maximum at the point $(e^2, 6e^{-1})$.

46. A function of the form $y = A \sin(Bx) + C$ with a maximum at $(5, 2)$, a minimum at $(15, 1.5)$, and no critical points between these two points.

47. A function of the form $y = axe^{-bx^2}$ with a global maximum at $(1, 2)$ and a global minimum at $(-1, -2)$.

In Problems 48–51, find the dimensions of the solid giving the maximum volume, given that the surface area is 8 cm^2.

48. A closed rectangular box, with a square base x by x cm and height h cm.

49. A open-topped rectangular box, with a square base x by x cm and height h cm.

50. A closed cylinder with radius r cm and height h cm.

51. A cylinder open at one end with radius r cm and height h cm.

In Problems 52–54, find the best possible bounds for the functions.

52. $e^{-x} \sin x$,   for $x \geq 0$

53. $x \sin x$,   for $0 \leq x \leq 2\pi$

54. $x^3 - 6x^2 + 9x + 5$ for $0 \leq x \leq 5$

55. Find the value(s) of m, if any, that give the global maximum and minimum of P as a function of m where

$$6jm^2 + P = 4jk - 5km, \quad \text{for positive constants } j \text{ and } k.$$

56. Find values of a and b so that the function $y = axe^{-bx}$ has a local maximum at the point $(2, 10)$.

57. (a) Find all critical points of $f(t) = at^2 e^{-bt}$, assuming a and b are nonzero constants.
(b) Find values of the parameters a and b so that f has a critical point at the point $(5, 12)$.
(c) Identify each critical point as a local maximum or local minimum of the function f in part (b).

58. What effect does increasing the value of a have on the graph of $f(x) = x^2 + 2ax$? Consider roots, maxima and minima, and both positive and negative values of a.

59. Sketch several members of the family $y = x^3 - ax^2$ on the same axes. Show that the critical points lie on the curve $y = -\frac{1}{2}x^3$.

60. A drug is injected into a patient at a rate given by $r(t) = ate^{-bt}$ ml/sec, where t is in seconds since the injection started, $0 \leq t \leq 5$, and a and b are constants. The maximum rate of 0.3 ml/sec occurs half a second after the injection starts. Find a formula for a and b.

61. An object at a distance p from a thin glass lens produces an image at a distance q from the lens, where

$$\frac{1}{p} + \frac{1}{q} = \frac{1}{f}.$$

The constant f is called the focal length of the lens. Suppose an object is moving at 3 mm per second toward a lens of focal length 15 mm. How fast and in what direction is the image moving at the moment at which the object is 35 mm from the lens?

62. Any body radiates energy at various wavelengths. Figure 4.118 shows the intensity of the radiation of a black body at a temperature $T = 3000$ kelvins as a function of the wavelength. The intensity of the radiation is highest in the infrared range, that is, at wavelengths longer than that of visible light (0.4–0.7μm). Max Planck's radiation law, announced to the Berlin Physical Society on October 19, 1900, states that

$$r(\lambda) = \frac{a}{\lambda^5(e^{b/\lambda} - 1)}.$$

Find constants a and b so that the formula fits the graph. (Later in 1900 Planck showed from theory that $a = 2\pi c^2 h$ and $b = \frac{hc}{Tk}$ where c = speed of light, h = Planck's constant, and k = Boltzmann's constant.)

intensity of radiation
$r(\lambda)$ (MW/m^2/μm)

(0.96, 3.13)

wavelength
λ (μm)

4

Figure 4.118

63. An electric current, I, in amps, is given by

$$I = \cos(wt) + \sqrt{3}\sin(wt),$$

where $w \neq 0$ is a constant. What are the maximum and minimum values of I?

64. The efficiency of a screw, E, is given by

$$E = \frac{(\theta - \mu\theta^2)}{\mu + \theta}, \quad \theta > 0,$$

where θ is the angle of pitch of the thread and μ is the coefficient of friction of the material, a (positive) constant. What value of θ maximizes E?

65. A rectangle has one side on the x-axis and two corners on the top half of the circle of radius 1 centered at the origin. Find the maximum area of such a rectangle. What are the coordinates of its vertices?

66. The hypotenuse of a right triangle has one end at the origin and one end on the curve $y = x^2e^{-3x}$, with $x \geq 0$. One of the other two sides is on the x-axis, the other side is parallel to the y-axis. Find the maximum area of such a triangle. At what x-value does it occur?

67. Which point on the parabola $y = x^2$ is nearest to $(1, 0)$? Find the coordinates to two decimals. [Hint: Minimize the square of the distance—this avoids square roots.]

68. Find the coordinates of the point on the parabola $y = x^2$ which is closest to the point (3,0).

69. The cross-section of a tunnel is a rectangle of height h surmounted by a semicircular roof section of radius r (See Figure 4.119). If the cross-sectional area is A, determine the dimensions of the cross section which minimize the perimeter.

Figure 4.119

70. A landscape architect plans to enclose a 3000 square-foot rectangular region in a botanical garden. She will use shrubs costing $45 per foot along three sides and fencing costing $20 per foot along the fourth side. Find the minimum total cost.

71. A rectangular swimming pool is to be built with an area of 1800 square feet. The owner wants 5-foot wide decks along either side and 10-foot wide decks at the two ends. Find the dimensions of the smallest piece of property on which the pool can be built satisfying these conditions.

72. **(a)** A cruise line offers a trip for $2000 per passenger. If at least 100 passengers sign up, the price is reduced for *all* the passengers by $10 for every additional passenger (beyond 100) who goes on the trip. The boat can accommodate 250 passengers. What number of passengers maximizes the cruise line's total revenue? What price does each passenger pay then?
(b) The cost to the cruise line for n passengers is $80,000 + 400n$. What is the maximum profit that the cruise line can make on one trip? How many passengers must sign up for the maximum to be reached and what price will each pay?

73. A manufacturer's cost of producing a product is given in Figure 4.120. The manufacturer can sell the product for a price p each (regardless of the quantity sold), so that the total revenue from selling a quantity q is $R(q) = pq$.

   (a) The difference $\pi(q) = R(q) - C(q)$ is the total profit. For which quantity q_0 is the profit a maximum? Mark your answer on a sketch of the graph.
   (b) What is the relationship between p and $C'(q_0)$? Explain your result both graphically and analytically. What does this mean in terms of economics? (Note that p is the slope of the line $R(q) = pq$. Note also that $\pi(q)$ has a maximum at $q = q_0$, so $\pi'(q_0) = 0$.)
   (c) Graph $C'(q)$ and p (as a horizontal line) on the same axes. Mark q_0 on the q-axis.

74. Using the cost and revenue graphs in Figure 4.120, sketch the following functions. Label the points q_1 and q_2.

   (a) Total profit   **(b)** Marginal cost
   (c) Marginal revenue

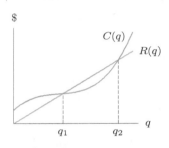

Figure 4.120

75. A ship is steaming due north at 12 knots (1 knot = 1.85 kilometers/hour) and sights a large tanker 3 kilometers away northwest steaming at 15 knots due east. For reasons of safety, the ships want to maintain a distance of at least 100 meters between them. Use a calculator or computer to determine the shortest distance between them if they remain on their current headings, and hence decide if they need to change course.

76. A polystyrene cup is in the shape of a frustum (the part of a cone between two parallel planes cutting the cone), has top radius $2r$, base radius r and height h. The surface area S of such a cup is given by $S = 3\pi r\sqrt{r^2 + h^2}$ and its volume V by $V = 7\pi r^2 h/3$. If the cup is to hold 200 ml, use a calculator or a computer to estimate the value of r that minimizes its surface area.

77. Suppose $g(t) = (\ln t)/t$ for $t > 0$.

   (a) Does g have either a global maximum or a global minimum on $0 < t < \infty$? If so, where, and what are their values?
   (b) What does your answer to part (a) tell you about the number of solutions to the equation
   $$\frac{\ln x}{x} = \frac{\ln 5}{5}?$$

(Note: There are many ways to investigate the number of solutions to this equation. We are asking you to draw a conclusion from your answer to part (a).)
   (c) Estimate the solution(s).

78. For $a > 0$, the following line forms a triangle in the first quadrant with the x- and y-axes:
$$a(a^2 + 1)y = a - x.$$

   (a) In terms of a, find the x- and y-intercepts of the line.
   (b) Find the area of the triangle, as a function of a.
   (c) Find the value of a making the area a maximum.
   (d) What is this greatest area?
   (e) If you want the triangle to have area $1/5$, what choices do you have for a?

79. **(a)** Water is flowing at a constant rate (i.e., constant volume per unit time) into a cylindrical container standing vertically. Sketch a graph showing the depth of water against time.
   (b) Water is flowing at a constant rate into a cone-shaped container standing on its point. Sketch a graph showing the depth of the water against time.

80. The vase in Figure 4.121 is filled with water at a constant rate (i.e., constant volume per unit time).

   (a) Graph $y = f(t)$, the depth of the water, against time, t. Show on your graph the points at which the concavity changes.
   (b) At what depth is $y = f(t)$ growing most quickly? Most slowly? Estimate the ratio between the growth rates at these two depths.

Figure 4.121

81. A chemical storage tank is in the shape of an inverted cone with depth 12 meters and top radius 5 meters. When the depth of the chemical in the tank is 1 meter, the level is falling at 0.1 meters per minute. How fast is the volume of chemical changing?

In Problems 82–83, describe the form of the limit ($0/0$, ∞/∞, $\infty \cdot 0$, $\infty - \infty$, 1^∞, 0^0, ∞^0, or none of these). Does l'Hopital's rule apply? If so, explain how.

82. $\displaystyle\lim_{x \to 0} \frac{x}{e^x}$

83. $\displaystyle\lim_{x \to 1} \frac{\sin \pi x}{x - 1}$

In Problems 84–87, determine whether the limit exists, and where possible evaluate it.

84. $\displaystyle\lim_{t \to 0} \frac{e^t - 1 - t}{t^2}$

85. $\displaystyle\lim_{t \to 0^+} \frac{3 \sin t - \sin 3t}{3 \tan t - \tan 3t}$

86. $\displaystyle\lim_{x \to 0} \frac{1 - \cosh(5x)}{x^2}$

87. $\displaystyle\lim_{x \to 0} \frac{x - \sinh(x)}{x^3}$

88. The rate of change of a population depends on the current population, P, and is given by

$$\frac{dP}{dt} = kP(L - P) \qquad \text{for positive constants } k, L.$$

(a) For what nonnegative values of P is the population increasing? Decreasing? For what values of P does the population remain constant?

(b) Find $d^2 P/dt^2$ as a function of P.

89. A spherical cell is growing at a constant rate of $400 \ \mu\text{m}^3/\text{day}$ ($1 \ \mu\text{m} = 10^{-6}$ m). At what rate is its radius increasing when the radius is $10 \ \mu\text{m}$?

90. A raindrop is a perfect sphere with radius r cm and surface area S cm^2. Condensation accumulates on the raindrop at a rate equal to kS, where $k = 2$ cm/sec. Show that the radius of the raindrop increases at a constant rate and find that rate.

91. A horizontal disk of radius a centered at the origin in the xy-plane is rotating about a vertical axis through the center. The angle between the positive x-axis and a radial line painted on the disk is θ radians.

(a) What does $d\theta/dt$ represent?

(b) What is the relationship between $d\theta/dt$ and the speed v of a point on the rim?

92. The depth of soot deposited from a smokestack is given by $D = K(r + 1)e^{-r}$, where r is the distance from the smokestack. What is the relationship between the rate of change of r with respect to time and the rate of change of D with respect to time?

93. The mass of a circular oil slick of radius r is $M = K(r - \ln(1 + r))$, where K is a positive constant. What is the relationship between the rate of change of the radius with respect to t and the rate of change of the mass with respect to time?

94. Ice is being formed in the shape of a circular cylinder with inner radius 1 cm and height 3 cm. The outer radius of the ice is increasing at 0.03 cm per hour when the outer radius is 1.5 cm. How fast is the volume of the ice increasing at this time?

95. Sand falls from a hopper at a rate of 0.1 cubic meters per hour and forms a conical pile beneath. If the side of the cone makes an angle of $\pi/6$ radians with the vertical, find the rate at which the height of the cone increases. At what rate does the radius of the base increase? Give both answers in terms of h, the height of the pile in meters.

96. (a) A hemispherical bowl of radius 10 cm contains water to a depth of h cm. Find the radius of the surface of the water as a function of h.

(b) The water level drops at a rate of 0.1 cm per hour. At what rate is the radius of the water decreasing when the depth is 5 cm?

97. A particle lies on a line perpendicular to a thin circular ring and through its center. The radius of the ring is a, and the distance from the point to the center of the ring is y. For a positive constant K, the gravitational force exerted by the ring on the particle is given by

$$F = \frac{Ky}{(a^2 + y^2)^{3/2}},$$

If y is increasing, how is F changing with respect to time, t, when

(a) $y = 0$ (b) $y = a/\sqrt{2}$ (c) $y = 2a$

98. A voltage, V volts, applied to a resistor of R ohms produces an electric current of I amps where $V = IR$. As the current flows the resistor heats up and its resistance falls. If 100 volts is applied to a resistor of 1000 ohms the current is initially 0.1 amps but rises by 0.001 amps/minute. At what rate is the resistance falling if the voltage remains constant?

99. A train is heading due west from St. Louis. At noon, a plane flying horizontally due north at a fixed altitude of 4 miles passes directly over the train. When the train has traveled another mile, it is going 80 mph, and the plane has traveled another 5 miles and is going 500 mph. At that moment, how fast is the distance between the train and the plane increasing?

Problems 100–101 involve Boyle's Law, which states that for a fixed quantity of gas at a constant temperature, the pressure, P, and the volume, V, are inversely related. Thus, for some constant k

$$PV = k.$$

100. A fixed quantity of gas is allowed to expand at constant temperature. Find the rate of change of pressure with respect to volume.

101. A certain quantity of gas occupies 10 cm^3 at a pressure of 2 atmospheres. The pressure is increased, while keeping the temperature constant.

(a) Does the volume increase or decrease?

(b) If the pressure is increasing at a rate of 0.05 atmospheres/minute when the pressure is 2 atmospheres, find the rate at which the volume is changing at that moment. What are the units of your answer?

CAS Challenge Problems

102. A population, P, in a restricted environment may grow with time, t, according to the *logistic function*

$$P = \frac{L}{1 + Ce^{-kt}}$$

where L is called the carrying capacity and L, C and k are positive constants.

(a) Find $\lim_{t \to \infty} P$. Explain why L is called the carrying capacity.

(b) Using a computer algebra system, show that the graph of P has an inflection point at $P = L/2$.

103. For positive a, consider the family of functions

$$y = \arctan\left(\frac{\sqrt{x} + \sqrt{a}}{1 - \sqrt{ax}}\right), \qquad x > 0.$$

(a) Graph several curves in the family and describe how the graph changes as a varies.

(b) Use a computer algebra system to find dy/dx, and graph the derivative for several values of a. What do you notice?

(c) Do your observations in part (b) agree with the answer to part (a)? Explain. [Hint: Use the fact that $\sqrt{ax} = \sqrt{a}\sqrt{x}$ for $a > 0$, $x > 0$.]

104. The function $\operatorname{arcsinh} x$ is the inverse function of $\sinh x$.

(a) Use a computer algebra system to find a formula for the derivative of $\operatorname{arcsinh} x$.

(b) Derive the formula by hand by differentiating both sides of the equation

$$\sinh(\operatorname{arcsinh} x) = x.$$

[Hint: Use the identity $\cosh^2 x - \sinh^2 x = 1$.]

105. The function $\operatorname{arccosh} x$, for $x \geq 0$, is the inverse function of $\cosh x$, for $x \geq 0$.

(a) Use a computer algebra system to find the derivative of $\operatorname{arccosh} x$.

(b) Derive the formula by hand by differentiating both sides of the equation

$$\cosh(\operatorname{arccosh} x) = x, \quad x \geq 1.$$

[Hint: Use the identity $\cosh^2 x - \sinh^2 x = 1$.]

106. Consider the family of functions

$$f(x) = \frac{\sqrt{a + x}}{\sqrt{a} + \sqrt{x}}, \quad x \geq 0, \quad \text{for positive } a.$$

(a) Using a computer algebra system, find the local maxima and minima of f.

(b) On one set of axes, graph this function for several values of a. How does varying a affect the shape of the graph? Explain your answer in terms of the answer to part (a).

(c) Use your computer algebra system to find the inflection points of f when $a = 2$.

107. (a) Use a computer algebra system to find the derivative of

$$y = \arctan\left(\sqrt{\frac{1 - \cos x}{1 + \cos x}}\right).$$

(b) Graph the derivative. Does the graph agree with the answer you got in part (a)? Explain using the identity $\cos(x) = \cos^2(x/2) - \sin^2(x/2)$.

108. In 1696, the first calculus textbook was published by the Marquis de l'Hopital. The following problem is a simplified version of a problem from this text.

In Figure 4.122, two ropes are attached to the ceiling at points $\sqrt{3}$ meters apart. The rope on the left is 1 meter long and has a pulley attached at its end. The rope on the right is 3 meters long; it passes through the pulley and has a weight tied to its end. When the weight is released, the ropes and pulley arrange themselves so that the distance from the weight to the ceiling is maximized.

(a) Show that the maximum distance occurs when the weight is exactly halfway between the the points where the ropes are attached to the ceiling. [Hint: Write the vertical distance from the weight to the ceiling in terms of its horizontal distance to the point at which the left rope is tied to the ceiling. A computer algebra system will be useful.]

(b) Does the weight always end up halfway between the ceiling anchor points no matter how long the left-hand rope is? Explain.

Figure 4.122

PROJECTS FOR CHAPTER FOUR

1. **Medical Case Study: Impact of Asthma on Breathing**[13]

   Asthma is a common breathing disease in which inflammation in the airways of the lungs causes episodes of shortness of breath, coughing, and chest tightness. Patients with asthma often have wheezing, an abnormal sound heard on exhalation due to turbulent airflow. Turbulent airflow is caused by swelling, mucus secretion, and constriction of muscle in the walls of the airways, shrinking the radius of the air passages leading to increased resistance to airflow and making it harder for patients to exhale.

   An important breathing test for asthma is called *spirometry*. In this test, a patient takes in as deep a breath as he or she can, and then exhales as rapidly, forcefully, and for as long as possible through a tube connected to an analyzer. The analyzer measures a number of parameters and generates two graphs.

   (a) Figure 4.123 is a volume-time curve for an asthma-free patient, showing the volume of air exhaled, V, as a function of time, t, since the test began.[14]

      (i) What is the physical interpretation of the slope of the volume-time curve?

      (ii) The volume VC shown on the volume-time graph is called the (forced) vital capacity (FVC or simply VC). Describe the physical meaning of VC.

   (b) Figure 4.124 is the flow-volume curve for the same patient.[15] The flow-volume curve shows the flow rate, dV/dt, of air as a function of V, the volume of air exhaled.

      (i) What is the physical interpretation of the slope of the flow-volume curve?

      (ii) Describe how the slope of the flow-volume curve changes as V increases from 0 to 5.5 liters. Explain what this means for the patient's breath.

      (iii) Sketch the slope of the flow-volume curve.

      (iv) What is the volume of air that has been exhaled when the flow rate is a maximum, and what is that maximal rate, the *peak expiratory flow*? Explain how this maximal rate is identified on the flow-volume curve and how the volume at which the maximal rate occurs is identified on the slope curve in part (b)(iii).

   (c) How do you imagine the volume-time curve and the flow-volume curve would be different for a patient with acute asthma? Draw curves to illustrate your thinking.

Figure 4.123: Volume-time curve

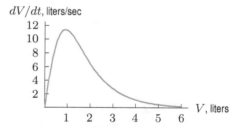

Figure 4.124: Flow-volume curve

2. **Building a Greenhouse**

   Your parents are going to knock out the bottom of the entire length of the south wall of their house and turn it into a greenhouse by replacing the bottom portion of the wall with a huge sloped piece of glass (which is expensive). They have already decided they are going to spend a certain fixed amount. The triangular ends of the greenhouse will be made of various materials they already have lying around.[16]

---

[13]From David E. Sloane, M.D.

[14]Image based on www.aafp.org/afp/2004/0301/p1107.html, accessed July 9, 2011.

[15]Image from http://www.aafp.org/afp/2004/0301/p1107.html, accessed July 9, 2011.

[16]Adapted from M. Cohen, E. Gaughan, A. Knoebel, D. Kurtz, D. Pengelley, *Student Research Projects in Calculus* (Washington DC: Mathematical Association of America, 1992).

The floor space in the greenhouse is only considered usable if they can both stand up in it, so part of it will be unusable. They want to choose the dimensions of the greenhouse to get the most usable floor space. What should the dimensions of the greenhouse be and how much usable space will your parents get?

3. Fitting a Line to Data

(a) The line which best fits the data points $(x_1, y_1), (x_2, y_2) \ldots (x_n, y_n)$ is the one which minimizes the sum of the squares of the vertical distances from the points to the line. These are the distances marked in Figure 4.125. Find the best fitting line of the form $y = mx$ for the points $(2, 3.5), (3, 6.8), (5, 9.1)$.

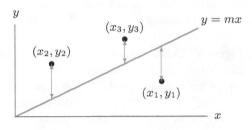

Figure 4.125

(b) A cone with height and radius both equal to r has volume, V, proportional to r^3; that is, $V = kr^3$ for some constant k. A lab experiment is done to measure the volume of several cones; the results are in the following table. Using the method of part (a), determine the best value of k. [Note: Since the volumes were determined experimentally, the values may not be accurate. Assume that the radii were measured accurately.]

Radius (cm)	2	5	7	8
Volume (cm^3)	8.7	140.3	355.8	539.2

(c) Using the method of part (a), show that the best fitting line of the form $y = mx$ for the points $(x_1, y_1), (x_2, y_2) \ldots (x_n, y_n)$ has

$$m = \frac{x_1 y_1 + x_2 y_2 + \cdots + x_n y_n}{x_1^2 + x_2^2 + \cdots + x_n^2}.$$

4. Firebreaks

The summer of 2000 was devastating for forests in the western US: over 3.5 million acres of trees were lost to fires, making this the worst fire season in 30 years. This project studies a fire management technique called *firebreaks*, which reduce the damage done by forest fires. A firebreak is a strip where trees have been removed in a forest so that a fire started on one side of the strip will not spread to the other side. Having many firebreaks helps confine a fire to a small area. On the other hand, having too many firebreaks involves removing large swaths of trees.[17]

(a) A forest in the shape of a 50 km by 50 km square has firebreaks in rectangular strips 50 km by 0.01 km. The trees between two firebreaks are called a stand of trees. All firebreaks in this forest are parallel to each other and to one edge of the forest, with the first firebreak at the edge of the forest. The firebreaks are evenly spaced throughout the forest. (For example, Figure 4.126 shows four firebreaks.) The total area lost in the case of a fire is the area of the stand of trees in which the fire started plus the area of all the firebreaks.

---

[17]Adapted from D. Quinney and R. Harding, *Calculus Connections* (New York: John Wiley & Sons, 1996).

Figure 4.126

(i) Find the number of firebreaks that minimizes the total area lost to the forest in the case of a fire.

(ii) If a firebreak is 50 km by b km, find the optimal number of firebreaks as a function of b. If the width, b, of a firebreak is quadrupled, how does the optimal number of firebreaks change?

(b) Now suppose firebreaks are arranged in two equally spaced sets of parallel lines, as shown in Figure 4.127. The forest is a 50 km by 50 km square, and each firebreak is a rectangular strip 50 km by 0.01 km. Find the number of firebreaks in each direction that minimizes the total area lost to the forest in the case of a fire.

Figure 4.127

Chapter Five

KEY CONCEPT: THE DEFINITE INTEGRAL

Contents

5.1 How Do We Measure Distance Traveled? 272

A Thought Experiment: How Far Did the Car
    Go? 272

Velocity Data Every Two Seconds . . . 272

Velocity Data Every One Second 272

Visualizing Distance on the Velocity
    Graph: Two-Second Data . . 273

Visualizing Distance on the Velocity
    Graph: One-Second Data . . 274

Visualizing Distance on the Velocity Graph:
    Area Under Curve 274

Negative Velocity and Change in
    Position 275

Left and Right Sums 276

Accuracy of Estimates 277

5.2 The Definite Integral 281

Sigma Notation 281

Taking the Limit to Obtain the Definite Integral . 281

Computing a Definite Integral 282

The Definite Integral as an Area 283

When $f(x)$ Is Not Positive 284

More General Riemann Sums 285

5.3 The Fundamental Theorem and Interpretations 289

The Notation and Units for the Definite Integral 289

The Fundamental Theorem of Calculus 290

The Definite Integral of a Rate of Change:
    Applications of the Fundamental
    Theorem 291

Calculating Definite Integrals: Computational
    Use of the Fundamental Theorem 294

5.4 Theorems About Definite Integrals 298

Properties of the Definite Integral 298

Why Do These Properties Hold? 300

Area Between Curves 301

Using Symmetry to Evaluate Integrals 302

Comparing Integrals 303

The Definite Integral as an Average 304

How to Visualize the Average on a
    Graph. 304

REVIEW PROBLEMS 309

PROJECTS 316

5.1 HOW DO WE MEASURE DISTANCE TRAVELED?

For positive constant velocities, we can find the distance a moving object travels using the formula

$$\text{Distance} = \text{Velocity} \times \text{Time}.$$

In this section we see how to estimate the distance when the velocity is not a constant.

A Thought Experiment: How Far Did the Car Go?

Velocity Data Every Two Seconds

A car is moving with increasing velocity. Table 5.1 shows the velocity every two seconds:

Table 5.1   *Velocity of car every two seconds*

Time (sec)	0	2	4	6	8	10
Velocity (ft/sec)	20	30	38	44	48	50

How far has the car traveled? Since we don't know how fast the car is moving at every moment, we can't calculate the distance exactly, but we can make an estimate. The velocity is increasing, so the car is going at least 20 ft/sec for the first two seconds. Since Distance = Velocity × Time, the car goes at least $20 \cdot 2 = 40$ feet during the first two seconds. Likewise, it goes at least $30 \cdot 2 = 60$ feet during the next two seconds, and so on. During the ten-second period it goes at least

$$20 \cdot 2 + 30 \cdot 2 + 38 \cdot 2 + 44 \cdot 2 + 48 \cdot 2 = 360 \text{ feet}.$$

Thus, 360 feet is an underestimate of the total distance traveled during the ten seconds.

To get an overestimate, we can reason this way: During the first two seconds, the car's velocity is at most 30 ft/sec, so it moved at most $30 \cdot 2 = 60$ feet. In the next two seconds it moved at most $38 \cdot 2 = 76$ feet, and so on. Therefore, over the ten-second period it moved at most

$$30 \cdot 2 + 38 \cdot 2 + 44 \cdot 2 + 48 \cdot 2 + 50 \cdot 2 = 420 \text{ feet}.$$

Therefore,

$$360 \text{ feet} \leq \text{Total distance traveled} \leq 420 \text{ feet}.$$

There is a difference of 60 feet between the upper and lower estimates.

Velocity Data Every One Second

What if we want a more accurate estimate? Then we make more frequent velocity measurements, say every second, as in Table 5.2.

As before, we get a lower estimate for each second by using the velocity at the beginning of that second. During the first second the velocity is at least 20 ft/sec, so the car travels at least $20 \cdot 1 = 20$ feet. During the next second the car moves at least 26 feet, and so on. We have

$$\text{New lower estimate} = 20 \cdot 1 + 26 \cdot 1 + 30 \cdot 1 + 34 \cdot 1 + 38 \cdot 1$$
$$+ 41 \cdot 1 + 44 \cdot 1 + 46 \cdot 1 + 48 \cdot 1 + 49 \cdot 1$$
$$= 376 \text{ feet}.$$

Table 5.2   *Velocity of car every second*

Time (sec)	0	1	2	3	4	5	6	7	8	9	10
Velocity (ft/sec)	20	26	30	34	38	41	44	46	48	49	50

Notice that this lower estimate is greater than the old lower estimate of 360 feet.

We get a new upper estimate by considering the velocity at the end of each second. During the first second the velocity is at most 26 ft/sec, so the car moves at most $26 \cdot 1 = 26$ feet; in the next second it moves at most 30 feet, and so on.

$$\text{New upper estimate} = 26 \cdot 1 + 30 \cdot 1 + 34 \cdot 1 + 38 \cdot 1 + 41 \cdot 1$$
$$+ 44 \cdot 1 + 46 \cdot 1 + 48 \cdot 1 + 49 \cdot 1 + 50 \cdot 1$$
$$= 406 \text{ feet.}$$

This is less than the old upper estimate of 420 feet. Now we know that

$$376 \text{ feet} \leq \text{Total distance traveled} \leq 406 \text{ feet.}$$

The difference between upper and lower estimates is now 30 feet, half of what it was before. By halving the interval of measurement, we have halved the difference between the upper and lower estimates.

Visualizing Distance on the Velocity Graph: Two-Second Data

We can represent both upper and lower estimates on a graph of the velocity. The graph also shows how changing the time interval between velocity measurements changes the accuracy of our estimates.

The velocity can be graphed by plotting the two-second data in Table 5.1 and drawing a curve through the data points. (See Figure 5.1.) The area of the first dark rectangle is $20 \cdot 2 = 40$, the lower estimate of the distance moved during the first two seconds. The area of the second dark rectangle is $30 \cdot 2 = 60$, the lower estimate for the distance moved in the next two seconds. The total area of the dark rectangles represents the lower estimate for the total distance moved during the ten seconds.

If the dark and light rectangles are considered together, the first area is $30 \cdot 2 = 60$, the upper estimate for the distance moved in the first two seconds. The second area is $38 \cdot 2 = 76$, the upper estimate for the next two seconds. The upper estimate for the total distance is represented by the sum of the areas of the dark and light rectangles. Therefore, the area of the light rectangles alone represents the difference between the two estimates.

To visualize the difference between the two estimates, look at Figure 5.1 and imagine the light rectangles all pushed to the right and stacked on top of each other. This gives a rectangle of width 2 and height 30. The height, 30, is the difference between the initial and final values of the velocity: $30 = 50 - 20$. The width, 2, is the time interval between velocity measurements.

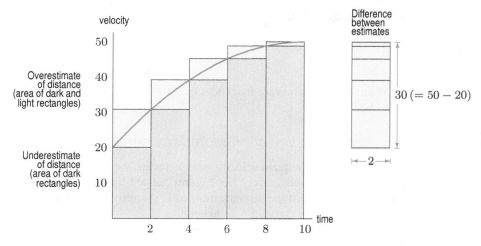

Figure 5.1: Velocity measured every 2 seconds

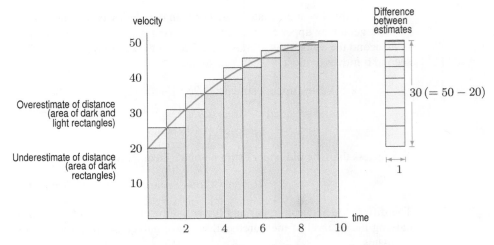

Figure 5.2: Velocity measured every second

Visualizing Distance on the Velocity Graph: One-Second Data

Figure 5.2 shows the velocities measured every second. The area of the dark rectangles again represents the lower estimate, and the area of the dark and light rectangles together represent the upper estimate. As before, the difference between the two estimates is represented by the area of the light rectangles. This difference can be calculated by stacking the light rectangles vertically, giving a rectangle of the same height as before but of half the width. Its area is therefore half what it was before. Again, the height of this stack is $50 - 20 = 30$, but its width is now 1.

Example 1   What would be the difference between the upper and lower estimates if the velocity were given every tenth of a second? Every hundredth of a second? Every thousandth of a second?

Solution   Every tenth of a second: Difference between estimates $= (50 - 20)(1/10) = 3$ feet.
Every hundredth of a second: Difference between estimates $= (50 - 20)(1/100) = 0.3$ feet.
Every thousandth of a second: Difference between estimates $= (50 - 20)(1/1000) = 0.03$ feet.

Example 2   How frequently must the velocity be recorded in order to estimate the total distance traveled to within 0.1 feet?

Solution   The difference between the velocity at the beginning and end of the observation period is $50 - 20 = 30$. If the time between successive measurements is Δt, then the difference between the upper and lower estimates is $(30)\Delta t$. We want

$$(30)\Delta t < 0.1,$$

or

$$\Delta t < \frac{0.1}{30} = 0.0033.$$

So if the measurements are made less than 0.0033 seconds apart, the distance estimate is accurate to within 0.1 feet.

Visualizing Distance on the Velocity Graph: Area Under Curve

As we make more frequent velocity measurements, the rectangles used to estimate the distance traveled fit the curve more closely. See Figures 5.3 and 5.4. In the limit, as the number of subdivisions increases, we see that the distance traveled is given by the area between the velocity curve and the horizontal axis. See Figure 5.5. In general:

If the velocity is positive, the total distance traveled is the area under the velocity curve.

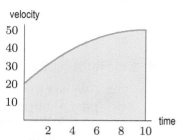

Figure 5.3: Velocity measured every 1/2 second

Figure 5.4: Velocity measured every 1/4 second

Figure 5.5: Distance traveled is area under curve

Example 3   With time t in seconds, the velocity of a bicycle, in feet per second, is given by $v(t) = 5t$. How far does the bicycle travel in 3 seconds?

Solution   The velocity is linear. See Figure 5.6. The distance traveled is the area between the line $v(t) = 5t$ and the t-axis. Since this region is a triangle of height 15 and base 3,

$$\text{Distance traveled} = \text{Area of triangle} = \frac{1}{2} \cdot 15 \cdot 3 = 22.5 \text{ feet.}$$

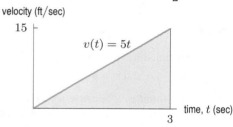

Figure 5.6: Shaded area represents distance traveled

Negative Velocity and Change in Position

In the thought experiment, the velocity is positive and our sums represent distance traveled. What if the velocity is sometimes negative?

Example 4   A particle moves along the y-axis with velocity 30 cm/sec for 5 seconds and velocity -10 cm/sec for the next 5 seconds. Positive velocity indicates upward motion; negative velocity represents downward motion. What is represented by the sum

$$30 \cdot 5 + (-10) \cdot 5?$$

Solution   The first term in the sum represents an upward motion of $30 \cdot 5 = 150$ centimeters. The second term represents a motion of $(-10) \cdot 5 = -50$ centimeters, that is, 50 centimeters downward. Thus, the sum represents a change in position of $150 - 50 = 100$ centimeters upward.

Figure 5.7 shows velocity versus time. The area of the rectangle above the t-axis represents upward distance, while the area of the rectangle below the t-axis represents downward distance.

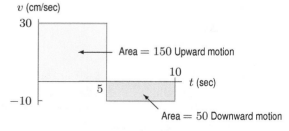

Figure 5.7: Difference in areas gives change in position

In general, if the velocity can be negative as well as positive, the limit of the sums represents change in position, rather than distance traveled.

Left and Right Sums

We now write the estimates for the distance traveled by the car in new notation. Let $v = f(t)$ denote any nonnegative velocity function. We want to find the distance traveled between times $t = a$ and $t = b$. We take measurements of $f(t)$ at equally spaced times $t_0, t_1, t_2, \ldots, t_n$, with time $t_0 = a$ and time $t_n = b$. The time interval between any two consecutive measurements is

$$\Delta t = \frac{b-a}{n},$$

where Δt means the change, or increment, in t.

During the first time interval, from t_0 and t_1, the velocity can be approximated by $f(t_0)$, so the distance traveled is approximately

$$f(t_0)\Delta t.$$

During the second time interval, the velocity is about $f(t_1)$, so the distance traveled is about

$$f(t_1)\Delta t.$$

Continuing in this way and adding all the estimates, we get an estimate for the total distance traveled. In the last interval, the velocity is approximately $f(t_{n-1})$, so the last term is $f(t_{n-1})\Delta t$:

$$\begin{array}{l} \text{Total distance traveled} \\ \text{between } t = a \text{ and } t = b \end{array} \approx f(t_0)\Delta t + f(t_1)\Delta t + f(t_2)\Delta t + \cdots + f(t_{n-1})\Delta t.$$

This is called a *left-hand sum* because we used the value of velocity from the left end of each time interval. It is represented by the sum of the areas of the rectangles in Figure 5.8.

We can also calculate a *right-hand sum* by using the value of the velocity at the right end of each time interval. In that case the estimate for the first interval is $f(t_1)\Delta t$, for the second interval it is $f(t_2)\Delta t$, and so on. The estimate for the last interval is now $f(t_n)\Delta t$, so

$$\begin{array}{l} \text{Total distance traveled} \\ \text{between } t = a \text{ and } t = b \end{array} \approx f(t_1)\Delta t + f(t_2)\Delta t + f(t_3)\Delta t + \cdots + f(t_n)\Delta t.$$

The right-hand sum is represented by the area of the rectangles in Figure 5.9.

If f is an increasing function, as in Figures 5.8 and 5.9, the left-hand sum is an underestimate and the right-hand sum is an overestimate of the total distance traveled. If f is decreasing, as in Figure 5.10, then the roles of the two sums are reversed.

Figure 5.8: Left-hand sums

Figure 5.9: Right-hand sums

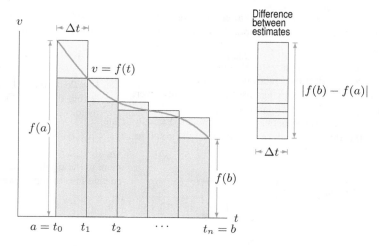

Figure 5.10: Left and right sums if f is decreasing

Accuracy of Estimates

For either increasing or decreasing velocity functions, the exact value of the distance traveled lies somewhere between the two estimates. Thus, the accuracy of our estimate depends on how close these two sums are. For a function which is increasing throughout or decreasing throughout the interval $[a, b]$:

$$\left| \begin{array}{c} \text{Difference between} \\ \text{upper and lower estimates} \end{array} \right| = \left| \begin{array}{c} \text{Difference between} \\ f(a) \text{ and } f(b) \end{array} \right| \cdot \Delta t = |f(b) - f(a)| \cdot \Delta t.$$

(Absolute values make the differences nonnegative.) In Figure 5.10, the area of the light rectangles is the difference between estimates. By making the time interval, Δt, between measurements small enough, we can make this difference between lower and upper estimates as small as we like.

Exercises and Problems for Section 5.1

Exercises

1. Figure 5.11 shows the velocity of a car for $0 \le t \le 12$ and the rectangles used to estimate of the distance traveled.

   (a) Do the rectangles represent a left or a right sum?
   (b) Do the rectangles lead to an upper or a lower estimate?
   (c) What is the value of n?
   (d) What is the value of Δt?
   (e) Give an approximate value for the estimate.

Figure 5.11

2. The velocity $v(t)$ in Table 5.3 is increasing, $0 \le t \le 12$.

   (a) Find an upper estimate for the total distance traveled using

     (i) $n = 4$ (ii) $n = 2$

   (b) Which of the two answers in part (a) is more accurate? Why?
   (c) Find a lower estimate of the total distance traveled using $n = 4$.

Table 5.3

t	0	3	6	9	12
$v(t)$	34	37	38	40	45

3. The velocity $v(t)$ in Table 5.4 is decreasing, $2 \le t \le 12$. Using $n = 5$ subdivisions to approximate the total distance traveled, find

   (a) An upper estimate   **(b)** A lower estimate

Table 5.4

t	2	4	6	8	10	12
$v(t)$	44	42	41	40	37	35

4. A car comes to a stop five seconds after the driver applies the brakes. While the brakes are on, the velocities in the table are recorded.

(a) Give lower and upper estimates of the distance the car traveled after the brakes were applied.

(b) On a sketch of velocity against time, show the lower and upper estimates of part (a).

(c) Find the difference between the estimates. Explain how this difference can be visualized on the graph in part (b).

Time since brakes applied (sec)	0	1	2	3	4	5
Velocity (ft/sec)	88	60	40	25	10	0

5. Figure 5.12 shows the velocity, v, of an object (in meters/sec). Estimate the total distance the object traveled between $t = 0$ and $t = 6$.

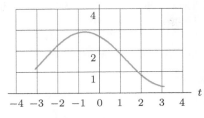

Figure 5.12

6. At time, t, in seconds, your velocity, v, in meters/second, is given by

$$v(t) = 1 + t^2 \quad \text{for} \quad 0 \le t \le 6.$$

Use $\Delta t = 2$ to estimate the distance traveled during this time. Find the upper and lower estimates, and then average the two.

7. Figure 5.13 shows the velocity of a particle, in cm/sec, along a number line for time $-3 \le t \le 3$.

(a) Describe the motion in words: Is the particle changing direction or always moving in the same direction? Is the particle speeding up or slowing down?

(b) Make over and underestimates of the distance traveled for $-3 \le t \le 3$.

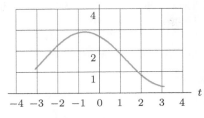

Figure 5.13

8. For time, t, in hours, $0 \le t \le 1$, a bug is crawling at a velocity, v, in meters/hour given by

$$v = \frac{1}{1+t}.$$

Use $\Delta t = 0.2$ to estimate the distance that the bug crawls during this hour. Find an overestimate and an underestimate. Then average the two to get a new estimate.

Exercises 9–12 show the velocity, in cm/sec, of a particle moving along a number line. (Positive velocities represent movement to the right; negative velocities to the left.) Compute the change in position between times $t = 0$ and $t = 5$ seconds.

9.

10.

11.

12.
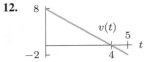

13. Use the expressions for left and right sums on page 276 and Table 5.5.

(a) If $n = 4$, what is Δt? What are t_0, t_1, t_2, t_3, t_4? What are $f(t_0), f(t_1), f(t_2), f(t_3), f(t_4)$?

(b) Find the left and right sums using $n = 4$.

(c) If $n = 2$, what is Δt? What are t_0, t_1, t_2? What are $f(t_0), f(t_1), f(t_2)$?

(d) Find the left and right sums using $n = 2$.

Table 5.5

t	15	17	19	21	23
$f(t)$	10	13	18	20	30

14. Use the expressions for left and right sums on page 276 and Table 5.6.

(a) If $n = 4$, what is Δt? What are t_0, t_1, t_2, t_3, t_4? What are $f(t_0), f(t_1), f(t_2), f(t_3), f(t_4)$?

(b) Find the left and right sums using $n = 4$.

(c) If $n = 2$, what is Δt? What are t_0, t_1, t_2? What are $f(t_0), f(t_1), f(t_2)$?

(d) Find the left and right sums using $n = 2$.

Table 5.6

t	0	4	8	12	16
$f(t)$	25	23	22	20	17

Problems

15. Roger runs a marathon. His friend Jeff rides behind him on a bicycle and clocks his speed every 15 minutes. Roger starts out strong, but after an hour and a half he is so exhausted that he has to stop. Jeff's data follow:

Time since start (min)	0	15	30	45	60	75	90
Speed (mph)	12	11	10	10	8	7	0

(a) Assuming that Roger's speed is never increasing, give upper and lower estimates for the distance Roger ran during the first half hour.

(b) Give upper and lower estimates for the distance Roger ran in total during the entire hour and a half.

(c) How often would Jeff have needed to measure Roger's speed in order to find lower and upper estimates within 0.1 mile of the actual distance he ran?

16. The velocity of a particle moving along the x-axis is given by $f(t) = 6 - 2t$ cm/sec. Use a graph of $f(t)$ to find the exact change in position of the particle from time $t = 0$ to $t = 4$ seconds.

In Problems 17–20, find the difference between the upper and lower estimates of the distance traveled at velocity $f(t)$ on the interval $a \le t \le b$ for n subdivisions.

17. $f(t) = 5t + 8, a = 1, b = 3, n = 100$

18. $f(t) = 25 - t^2, a = 1, b = 4, n = 500$

19. $f(t) = \sin t, a = 0, b = \pi/2, n = 100$

20. $f(t) = e^{-t^2/2}, a = 0, b = 2, n = 20$

21. A baseball thrown directly upward at 96 ft/sec has velocity $v(t) = 96 - 32t$ ft/sec at time t seconds.

(a) Graph the velocity from $t = 0$ to $t = 6$.

(b) When does the baseball reach the peak of its flight? How high does it go?

(c) How high is the baseball at time $t = 5$?

22. Figure 5.14 gives your velocity during a trip starting from home. Positive velocities take you away from home and negative velocities take you toward home. Where are you at the end of the 5 hours? When are you farthest from home? How far away are you at that time?

Figure 5.14

23. When an aircraft attempts to climb as rapidly as possible, its climb rate decreases with altitude. (This occurs because the air is less dense at higher altitudes.) The table shows performance data for a single-engine aircraft.

Altitude (1000 ft)	0	1	2	3	4	5
Climb rate (ft/min)	925	875	830	780	730	685
Altitude (1000 ft)	6	7	8	9	10	
Climb rate (ft/min)	635	585	535	490	440	

(a) Calculate upper and lower estimates for the time required for this aircraft to climb from sea level to 10,000 ft.

(b) If climb rate data were available in increments of 500 ft, what would be the difference between a lower and upper estimate of climb time based on 20 subdivisions?

24. A bicyclist is pedaling along a straight road for one hour with a velocity v shown in Figure 5.15. She starts out five kilometers from the lake and positive velocities take her toward the lake. [Note: The vertical lines on the graph are at 10 minute (1/6 hour) intervals.]

(a) Does the cyclist ever turn around? If so, at what time(s)?

(b) When is she going the fastest? How fast is she going then? Toward the lake or away?

(c) When is she closest to the lake? Approximately how close to the lake does she get?

(d) When is she farthest from the lake? Approximately how far from the lake is she then?

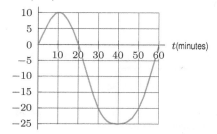

Figure 5.15

25. Two cars travel in the same direction along a straight road. Figure 5.16 shows the velocity, v, of each car at time t. Car B starts 2 hours after car A and car B reaches a maximum velocity of 50 km/hr.

(a) For approximately how long does each car travel?

(b) Estimate car A's maximum velocity.

(c) Approximately how far does each car travel?

Figure 5.16

26. Two cars start at the same time and travel in the same direction along a straight road. Figure 5.17 gives the velocity, v, of each car as a function of time, t. Which car:

(a) Attains the larger maximum velocity?

(b) Stops first?

(c) Travels farther?

Figure 5.17

27. A car initially going 50 ft/sec brakes at a constant rate (constant negative acceleration), coming to a stop in 5 seconds.

(a) Graph the velocity from $t = 0$ to $t = 5$.

(b) How far does the car travel?

(c) How far does the car travel if its initial velocity is doubled, but it brakes at the same constant rate?

28. A woman drives 10 miles, accelerating uniformly from rest to 60 mph. Graph her velocity versus time. How long does it take for her to reach 60 mph?

29. An object has zero initial velocity and a constant acceleration of 32 ft/sec^2. Find a formula for its velocity as a function of time. Use left and right sums with $\Delta t = 1$ to find upper and lower bounds on the distance that the object travels in four seconds. Find the precise distance using the area under the curve.

Problems 30–31 concern hybrid cars such as the Toyota Prius that are powered by a gas-engine, electric-motor combination, but can also function in Electric-Vehicle (EV) only mode. Figure 5.18 shows the velocity, v, of a 2010 Prius Plug-in Hybrid Prototype operating in normal hybrid mode and EV-only mode, respectively, while accelerating from a stoplight.[1]

Figure 5.18

30. Could the car travel half a mile in EV-only mode during the first 25 seconds of movement?

31. Assume two identical cars, one running in normal hybrid mode and one running in EV-only mode, accelerate together in a straight path from a stoplight. Approximately how far apart are the cars after 15 seconds?

Strengthen Your Understanding

In Problems 32–33, explain what is wrong with the statement.

32. If a car accelerates from 0 to 50 ft/sec in 10 seconds, then it travels 250 ft.

33. For any acceleration, you can estimate the total distance traveled by a car in 1 second to within 0.1 feet by recording its velocity every 0.1 second.

In Problems 34–35, give an example of:

34. A velocity function f and an interval $[a, b]$ such that the distance denoted by the right-hand sum for f on $[a, b]$ is less than the distance denoted by the left-hand sum, no matter what the number of subdivisions.

35. A velocity $f(t)$ and an interval $[a, b]$ such that at least 100 subdivisions are needed in order for the difference between the upper and lower estimates to be less than or equal to 0.1.

Are the statements in Problems 36–38 true or false? Give an explanation for your answer.

36. For an increasing velocity function on a fixed time interval, the left-hand sum with a given number of subdivisions is always less than the corresponding right-hand sum.

37. For a decreasing velocity function on a fixed time interval, the difference between the left-hand sum and right-hand sum is halved when the number of subdivisions is doubled.

38. For a given velocity function on a given interval, the difference between the left-hand sum and right-hand sum gets smaller as the number of subdivisions gets larger.

39. A bicyclist starts from home and rides back and forth along a straight east/west highway. Her velocity is given

---

[1]www.motortrend.com/, accessed May 2011.

in Figure 5.19 (positive velocities indicate travel toward the east, negative toward the west).

(a) On what time intervals is she stopped?
(b) How far from home is she the first time she stops, and in what direction?
(c) At what time does she bike past her house?
(d) If she maintains her velocity at $t = 11$, how long will it take her to get back home?

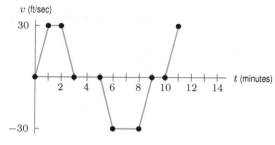

Figure 5.19

5.2 THE DEFINITE INTEGRAL

In Section 5.1, we saw how distance traveled can be approximated by a sum of areas of rectangles. We also saw how the approximation improves as the width of the rectangles gets smaller. In this section, we construct these sums for any function f, whether or not it represents a velocity.

Sigma Notation

Suppose $f(t)$ is a continuous function for $a \leq t \leq b$. We divide the interval from a to b into n equal subdivisions, and we call the width of an individual subdivision Δt, so

$$\Delta t = \frac{b - a}{n}.$$

Let $t_0, t_1, t_2, \ldots, t_n$ be endpoints of the subdivisions. Both the left-hand and right-hand sums can be written more compactly using *sigma*, or summation, notation. The symbol $\sum$ is a capital sigma, or Greek letter "S." We write

$$\text{Right-hand sum} = f(t_1)\Delta t + f(t_2)\Delta t + \cdots + f(t_n)\Delta t = \sum_{i=1}^{n} f(t_i)\Delta t.$$

The $\sum$ tells us to add terms of the form $f(t_i)\Delta t$. The "$i = 1$" at the base of the sigma sign tells us to start at $i = 1$, and the "n" at the top tells us to stop at $i = n$.

In the left-hand sum we start at $i = 0$ and stop at $i = n - 1$, so we write

$$\text{Left-hand sum} = f(t_0)\Delta t + f(t_1)\Delta t + \cdots + f(t_{n-1})\Delta t = \sum_{i=0}^{n-1} f(t_i)\Delta t.$$

Taking the Limit to Obtain the Definite Integral

Now we take the limit of these sums as n goes to infinity. If f is continuous for $a \leq t \leq b$, the limits of the left- and right-hand sums exist and are equal. The *definite integral* is the limit of these sums. A formal definition of the definite integral is given in the online supplement to the text at www.wiley.com/college/hughes-hallett.

Suppose f is continuous for $a \leq t \leq b$. The **definite integral** of f from a to b, written

$$\int_a^b f(t)\, dt,$$

is the limit of the left-hand or right-hand sums with n subdivisions of $a \leq t \leq b$ as n gets arbitrarily large. In other words,

$$\int_a^b f(t)\, dt = \lim_{n \to \infty} (\text{Left-hand sum}) = \lim_{n \to \infty} \left(\sum_{i=0}^{n-1} f(t_i) \Delta t \right)$$

and

$$\int_a^b f(t)\, dt = \lim_{n \to \infty} (\text{Right-hand sum}) = \lim_{n \to \infty} \left(\sum_{i=1}^{n} f(t_i) \Delta t \right).$$

Each of these sums is called a *Riemann sum*, f is called the *integrand*, and a and b are called the *limits of integration*.

The "$\int$" notation comes from an old-fashioned "S," which stands for "sum" in the same way that $\sum$ does. The "dt" in the integral comes from the factor Δt. Notice that the limits on the $\sum$ symbol are 0 and $n-1$ for the left-hand sum, and 1 and n for the right-hand sum, whereas the limits on the $\int$ sign are a and b.

Computing a Definite Integral

In practice, we often approximate definite integrals numerically using a calculator or computer. They use programs which compute sums for larger and larger values of n, and eventually give a value for the integral. Some (but not all) definite integrals can be computed exactly. However, any definite integral can be approximated numerically.

In the next example, we see how numerical approximation works. For each value of n, we show an over- and an under-estimate for the integral $\int_1^2 (1/t)\, dt$. As we increase the value of n, the over- and under-estimates get closer together, trapping the value of the integral between them. By increasing the value of n sufficiently, we can calculate the integral to any desired accuracy.

Example 1   Calculate the left-hand and right-hand sums with $n = 2$ for $\int_1^2 \dfrac{1}{t}\, dt$. What is the relation between the left- and right-hand sums for $n = 10$ and $n = 250$ and the integral?

Solution   Here $a = 1$ and $b = 2$, so for $n = 2$, $\Delta t = (2-1)/2 = 0.5$. Therefore, $t_0 = 1$, $t_1 = 1.5$ and $t_2 = 2$. (See Figure 5.20.) We have

$$\text{Left-hand sum} = f(1)\Delta t + f(1.5)\Delta t = 1(0.5) + \frac{1}{1.5}(0.5) = 0.8333,$$

$$\text{Right-hand sum} = f(1.5)\Delta t + f(2)\Delta t = \frac{1}{1.5}(0.5) + \frac{1}{2}(0.5) = 0.5833.$$

In Figure 5.20 we see that the left-hand sum is bigger than the area under the curve and the right-hand sum is smaller. So the area under the curve $f(t) = 1/t$ from $t = 1$ to $t = 2$ is between them:

$$0.5833 < \int_1^2 \frac{1}{t}\, dt < 0.8333.$$

Since $1/t$ is decreasing, when $n = 10$ in Figure 5.21 we again see that the left-hand sum is larger than the area under the curve, and the right-hand sum smaller. A calculator or computer gives

$$0.6688 < \int_1^2 \frac{1}{t}\, dt < 0.7188.$$

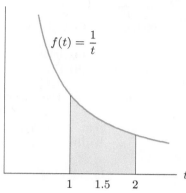

Figure 5.20: Approximating $\int_1^2 \frac{1}{t} \, dt$ with $n = 2$

Figure 5.21: Approximating $\int_1^2 \frac{1}{t} \, dt$ with $n = 10$

Figure 5.22: Shaded area is exact value of $\int_1^2 \frac{1}{t} \, dt$

The left- and right-hand sums trap the exact value of the integral between them. As the subdivisions become finer, the left- and right-hand sums get closer together.

When $n = 250$, a calculator or computer gives

$$0.6921 < \int_1^2 \frac{1}{t} \, dt < 0.6941.$$

So, to two decimal places, we can say that

$$\int_1^2 \frac{1}{t} \, dt \approx 0.69.$$

The exact value is known to be $\int_1^2 \frac{1}{t} \, dt = \ln 2 = 0.693147\ldots$. See Figure 5.22.

The Definite Integral as an Area

If $f(x)$ is positive we can interpret each term $f(x_0)\Delta x, f(x_1)\Delta x, \ldots$ in a left- or right-hand Riemann sum as the area of a rectangle. See Figure 5.23. As the width Δx of the rectangles approaches zero, the rectangles fit the curve of the graph more exactly, and the sum of their areas gets closer and closer to the area under the curve shaded in Figure 5.24. This suggests that:

> When $f(x) \geq 0$ and $a < b$:
>
> $$\text{Area under graph of } f \text{ and above } x\text{-axis between } a \text{ and } b = \int_a^b f(x) \, dx.$$

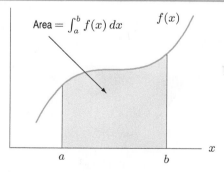

Figure 5.23: Area of rectangles approximating the area under the curve

Figure 5.24: The definite integral $\int_a^b f(x) \, dx$

Example 2   Consider the integral $\int_{-1}^{1} \sqrt{1 - x^2}\, dx$.

(a) Interpret the integral as an area, and find its exact value.

(b) Estimate the integral using a calculator or computer. Compare your answer to the exact value.

Solution   (a) The integral is the area under the graph of $y = \sqrt{1 - x^2}$ between -1 and 1. See Figure 5.25. Rewriting this equation as $x^2 + y^2 = 1$, we see that the graph is a semicircle of radius 1 and area $\pi/2$.

(b) A calculator gives the value of the integral as $1.5707963\ldots$.

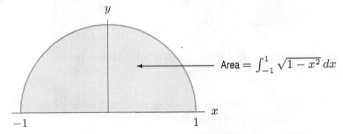

Figure 5.25: Area interpretation of $\int_{-1}^{1} \sqrt{1 - x^2}\, dx$

When $f(x)$ Is Not Positive

We have assumed in drawing Figure 5.24 that the graph of $f(x)$ lies above the x-axis. If the graph lies below the x-axis, then each value of $f(x)$ is negative, so each $f(x)\Delta x$ is negative, and the area gets counted negatively. In that case, the definite integral is the negative of the area.

> When $f(x)$ is positive for some x values and negative for others, and $a < b$:
>
> $\int_{a}^{b} f(x)\, dx$ is the sum of areas above the x-axis, counted positively, and areas below the x-axis, counted negatively.

Example 3   How does the definite integral $\int_{-1}^{1} (x^2 - 1)\, dx$ relate to the area between the parabola $y = x^2 - 1$ and the x-axis?

Solution   A calculator gives $\int_{-1}^{1} (x^2 - 1)\, dx = -1.33$. Since the parabola lies below the axis between $x = -1$ and $x = 1$ (see Figure 5.26), the area between the parabola and the x-axis is approximately 1.33.

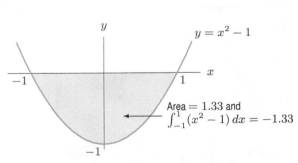

Figure 5.26: Integral $\int_{-1}^{1} (x^2 - 1)\, dx$ is negative of shaded area

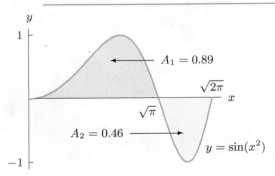

Figure 5.27: Integral $\int_{0}^{\sqrt{2\pi}} \sin(x^2)\, dx = A_1 - A_2$

Example 4   Interpret the definite integral $\int_0^{\sqrt{2\pi}} \sin(x^2)\,dx$ in terms of areas.

Solution   The integral is the area above the x-axis, A_1, minus the area below the x-axis, A_2. See Figure 5.27. Estimating the integral with a calculator gives

$$\int_0^{\sqrt{2\pi}} \sin(x^2)\,dx = 0.43.$$

The graph of $y = \sin(x^2)$ crosses the x-axis where $x^2 = \pi$, that is, at $x = \sqrt{\pi}$. The next crossing is at $x = \sqrt{2\pi}$. Breaking the integral into two parts and calculating each one separately gives

$$\int_0^{\sqrt{\pi}} \sin(x^2)\,dx = 0.89 \quad \text{and} \quad \int_{\sqrt{\pi}}^{\sqrt{2\pi}} \sin(x^2)\,dx = -0.46.$$

So $A_1 = 0.89$ and $A_2 = 0.46$. Then, as we would expect,

$$\int_0^{\sqrt{2\pi}} \sin(x^2)\,dx = A_1 - A_2 = 0.89 - 0.46 = 0.43.$$

More General Riemann Sums

Left- and right-hand sums are special cases of Riemann sums. For a general Riemann sum we allow subdivisions to have different lengths. Also, instead of evaluating f only at the left or right endpoint of each subdivision, we allow it to be evaluated anywhere in the subdivision. Thus, a general Riemann sum has the form

$$\sum_{i=1}^{n} \text{Value of } f(t) \text{ at some point in } i^{\text{th}} \text{ subdivision} \times \text{Length of } i^{\text{th}} \text{ subdivision}.$$

(See Figure 5.28.) As before, we let $t_0, t_1, \ldots, t_n$ be the endpoints of the subdivisions, so the length of the ith subdivision is $\Delta t_i = t_i - t_{i-1}$. For each i we choose a point c_i in the ith subinterval at which to evaluate f, leading to the following definition:

A general Riemann sum for f on the interval $[a, b]$ is a sum of the form

$$\sum_{i=1}^{n} f(c_i)\Delta t_i,$$

where $a = t_0 < t_1 < \cdots < t_n = b$, and, for $i = 1, \ldots, n$, $\Delta t_i = t_i - t_{i-1}$, and $t_{i-1} \leq c_i \leq t_i$.

If f is continuous, we can make a general Riemann sum as close as we like to the value of the definite integral by making the interval lengths small enough. Thus, in approximating definite integrals or in proving theorems about them, we can use general Riemann sums rather than left- or right-hand sums. Generalized Riemann sums are especially useful in establishing properties of the definite integral; see www.wiley.com/college/hughes-hallett.

Figure 5.28: A general Riemann sum approximating $\int_a^b f(t)\,dt$

Exercises and Problems for Section 5.2

Exercises

In Exercises 1–2, rectangles have been drawn to approximate $\int_0^6 g(x)\,dx$.

(a) Do the rectangles represent a left or a right sum?
(b) Do the rectangles lead to an upper or a lower estimate?
(c) What is the value of n?
(d) What is the value of Δx?

1.

2.

3. Figure 5.29 shows a Riemann sum approximation with n subdivisions to $\int_a^b f(x)\,dx$.

(a) Is it a left- or right-hand approximation? Would the other one be larger or smaller?
(b) What are a, b, n and Δx?

Figure 5.29

4. Using Figure 5.30, draw rectangles representing each of the following Riemann sums for the function f on the interval $0 \le t \le 8$. Calculate the value of each sum.

(a) Left-hand sum with $\Delta t = 4$
(b) Right-hand sum with $\Delta t = 4$
(c) Left-hand sum with $\Delta t = 2$
(d) Right-hand sum with $\Delta t = 2$

Figure 5.30

In Exercises 5–10, use a calculator or a computer to find the value of the definite integral.

5. $\displaystyle\int_1^4 (x^2 + x)\,dx$ **6.** $\displaystyle\int_0^3 2^x\,dx$

7. $\displaystyle\int_{-1}^1 e^{-x^2}\,dx$ **8.** $\displaystyle\int_0^3 \ln(y^2 + 1)\,dy$

9. $\displaystyle\int_0^1 \sin(t^2)\,dt$ **10.** $\displaystyle\int_3^4 \sqrt{e^z + z}\,dz$

11. Use the table to estimate $\int_0^{40} f(x)\,dx$. What values of n and Δx did you use?

x	0	10	20	30	40
$f(x)$	350	410	435	450	460

12. Use the table to estimate $\int_0^{12} f(x)\,dx$.

x	0	3	6	9	12
$f(x)$	32	22	15	11	9

13. Use the table to estimate $\int_0^{15} f(x)\,dx$.

x	0	3	6	9	12	15
$f(x)$	50	48	44	36	24	8

14. Write out the terms of the right-hand sum with $n = 5$ that could be used to approximate $\displaystyle\int_3^7 \frac{1}{1+x}\,dx$. Do not evaluate the terms or the sum.

15. Use Figure 5.31 to estimate $\int_0^{20} f(x)\,dx$.

Figure 5.31

16. Use Figure 5.32 to estimate $\int_{-10}^{15} f(x)dx$.

Figure 5.32

17. Using Figure 5.33, estimate $\int_{-3}^{5} f(x)dx$.

Figure 5.33

Problems

18. The graph of $f(t)$ is in Figure 5.34. Which of the following four numbers could be an estimate of $\int_{0}^{1} f(t)dt$ accurate to two decimal places? Explain your choice.

    I. -98.35 II. 71.84 III. 100.12 IV. 93.47

Figure 5.34

19. (a) What is the area between the graph of $f(x)$ in Figure 5.35 and the x-axis, between $x = 0$ and $x = 5$?
  (b) What is $\int_{0}^{5} f(x)\,dx$?

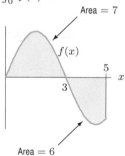

Figure 5.35

20. Find the total area between $y = 4 - x^2$ and the x-axis for $0 \le x \le 3$.

21. (a) Find the total area between $f(x) = x^3 - x$ and the x-axis for $0 \le x \le 3$.
  (b) Find $\int_{0}^{3} f(x)dx$.
  (c) Are the answers to parts (a) and (b) the same? Explain.

In Problems 22–28, find the area of the regions between the curve and the horizontal axis

22. Under $y = 6x^3 - 2$ for $5 \le x \le 10$.

23. Under the curve $y = \cos t$ for $0 \le t \le \pi/2$.

24. Under $y = \ln x$ for $1 \le x \le 4$.

25. Under $y = 2\cos(t/10)$ for $1 \le t \le 2$.

26. Under the curve $y = \cos\sqrt{x}$ for $0 \le x \le 2$.

27. Under the curve $y = 7 - x^2$ and above the x-axis.

28. Above the curve $y = x^4 - 8$ and below the x-axis.

29. Use Figure 5.36 to find the values of

  (a) $\int_{a}^{b} f(x)\,dx$ **(b)** $\int_{b}^{c} f(x)\,dx$
  (c) $\int_{a}^{c} f(x)\,dx$ **(d)** $\int_{a}^{c} |f(x)|\,dx$

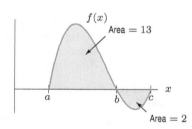

Figure 5.36

30. Given $\int_{-2}^{0} f(x)dx = 4$ and Figure 5.37, estimate:

  (a) $\int_{0}^{2} f(x)dx$ **(b)** $\int_{-2}^{2} f(x)dx$
  (c) The total shaded area.

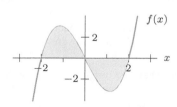

Figure 5.37

31. **(a)** Using Figure 5.38, find $\int_{-3}^{0} f(x)\,dx$.
   (b) If the area of the shaded region is A, estimate $\int_{-3}^{4} f(x)\,dx$.

Figure 5.38

32. Use Figure 5.39 to find the values of
   (a) $\int_{0}^{2} f(x)\,dx$ **(b)** $\int_{3}^{7} f(x)\,dx$
   (c) $\int_{2}^{7} f(x)\,dx$ **(d)** $\int_{5}^{8} f(x)\,dx$

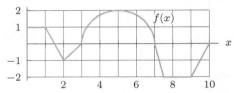

Figure 5.39: Graph consists of a semicircle and line segments

33. **(a)** Graph $f(x) = x(x+2)(x-1)$.
   (b) Find the total area between the graph and the x-axis between $x = -2$ and $x = 1$.
   (c) Find $\int_{-2}^{1} f(x)\,dx$ and interpret it in terms of areas.

34. Compute the definite integral $\int_{0}^{4} \cos \sqrt{x}\,dx$ and interpret the result in terms of areas.

35. Without computation, decide if $\int_{0}^{2\pi} e^{-x} \sin x\,dx$ is positive or negative. [Hint: Sketch $e^{-x} \sin x$.]

36. Estimate $\int_{0}^{1} e^{-x^2}\,dx$ using $n = 5$ rectangles to form a
   (a) Left-hand sum   **(b)** Right-hand sum

37. **(a)** On a sketch of $y = \ln x$, represent the left Riemann sum with $n = 2$ approximating $\int_{1}^{2} \ln x\,dx$. Write out the terms in the sum, but do not evaluate it.
   (b) On another sketch, represent the right Riemann sum with $n = 2$ approximating $\int_{1}^{2} \ln x\,dx$. Write out the terms in the sum, but do not evaluate it.
   (c) Which sum is an overestimate? Which sum is an underestimate?

38. **(a)** Draw the rectangles that give the left-hand sum approximation to $\int_{0}^{\pi} \sin x\,dx$ with $n = 2$.
   (b) Repeat part (a) for $\int_{-\pi}^{0} \sin x\,dx$.
   (c) From your answers to parts (a) and (b), what is the value of the left-hand sum approximation to $\int_{-\pi}^{\pi} \sin x\,dx$ with $n = 4$?

39. **(a)** Use a calculator or computer to find $\int_{0}^{6} (x^2 + 1)\,dx$. Represent this value as the area under a curve.
   (b) Estimate $\int_{0}^{6} (x^2 + 1)\,dx$ using a left-hand sum with $n = 3$. Represent this sum graphically on a sketch of $f(x) = x^2 + 1$. Is this sum an overestimate or underestimate of the true value found in part (a)?
   (c) Estimate $\int_{0}^{6} (x^2 + 1)\,dx$ using a right-hand sum with $n = 3$. Represent this sum on your sketch. Is this sum an overestimate or underestimate?

40. **(a)** Graph $f(x) = \begin{cases} 1 - x & 0 \le x \le 1 \\ x - 1 & 1 < x \le 2. \end{cases}$
   (b) Find $\int_{0}^{2} f(x)\,dx$.
   (c) Calculate the 4-term left Riemann sum approximation to the definite integral. How does the approximation compare to the exact value?

41. Estimate $\int_{1}^{2} x^2\,dx$ using left- and right-hand sums with four subdivisions. How far from the true value of the integral could your estimate be?

42. Without computing the sums, find the difference between the right- and left-hand Riemann sums if we use $n = 500$ subintervals to approximate $\int_{-1}^{1} (2x^3 + 4)\,dx$.

43. Sketch the graph of a function f (you do not need to give a formula for f) on an interval $[a, b]$ with the property that with $n = 2$ subdivisions,
$$\int_{a}^{b} f(x)\,dx < \text{Left-hand sum} < \text{Right-hand sum}.$$

44. Write a few sentences in support of or in opposition to the following statement:
   "If a left-hand sum underestimates a definite integral by a certain amount, then the corresponding right-hand sum will overestimate the integral by the same amount."

45. Consider the integral $\int_{1}^{2} (1/t)\,dt$ in Example 1. By dividing the interval $1 \le t \le 2$ into 10 equal parts, we can show that
$$0.1\left(\frac{1}{1.1} + \frac{1}{1.2} + \ldots + \frac{1}{2}\right) \le \int_{1}^{2} \frac{1}{t}\,dt$$
and
$$\int_{1}^{2} \frac{1}{t}\,dt \le 0.1\left(\frac{1}{1} + \frac{1}{1.1} + \ldots + \frac{1}{1.9}\right).$$
   (a) Now divide the interval $1 \le t \le 2$ into n equal parts to show that
$$\sum_{r=1}^{n} \frac{1}{n+r} < \int_{1}^{2} \frac{1}{t}\,dt < \sum_{r=0}^{n-1} \frac{1}{n+r}.$$
   (b) Show that the difference between the upper and lower sums in part (a) is $1/(2n)$.
   (c) The exact value of $\int_{1}^{2} (1/t)\,dt$ is $\ln 2$. How large should n be to approximate $\ln 2$ with an error of at most $5 \cdot 10^{-6}$, using one of the sums in part (a)?

Strengthen Your Understanding

In Problems 46–47, explain what is wrong with the statement.

46. For any function, $\int_1^3 f(x)\, dx$ is the area between the the graph of f and the x-axis on $1 \leq x \leq 3$.

47. The left-hand sum with 10 subdivisions for the integral $\int_1^2 \sin(x)\, dx$ is

$$0.1\left(\sin(1) + \sin(1.1) + \cdots + \sin(2)\right).$$

In Problems 48–49, give an example of:

48. A function f and an interval $[a, b]$ such that $\int_a^b f(x)\, dx$ is negative.

49. A function f such that $\int_1^3 f(x)\, dx < \int_1^2 f(x)\, dx$.

In Problems 50–52 decide whether the statement is true or false. Justify your answer.

50. On the interval $a \leq t \leq b$, the integral of the velocity is the total distance traveled from $t = a$ to $t = b$.

51. A 4-term left-hand Riemann sum approximation cannot give the exact value of a definite integral.

52. If $f(x)$ is decreasing and $g(x)$ is increasing, then $\int_a^b f(x)\, dx \neq \int_a^b g(x)\, dx$.

In Problems 53–55, is the statement true for all continuous functions $f(x)$ and $g(x)$? Explain your answer.

53. $\int_0^2 f(x)\, dx \leq \int_0^3 f(x)\, dx$.

54. $\int_0^2 f(x)\, dx = \int_0^2 f(t)\, dt$.

55. If $\int_2^6 f(x)\, dx \leq \int_2^6 g(x)\, dx$, then $f(x) \leq g(x)$ for $2 \leq x \leq 6$.

In Problems 56–57, graph a continuous function $f(x) \geq 0$ on $[0, 10]$ with the given properties.

56. The maximum value taken on by $f(x)$ for $0 \leq x \leq 10$ is 1. In addition $\int_0^{10} f(x)\, dx = 5$.

57. The maximum value taken on by $f(x)$ for $0 \leq x \leq 10$ is 5. In addition $\int_0^{10} f(x)\, dx = 1$.

5.3 THE FUNDAMENTAL THEOREM AND INTERPRETATIONS

The Notation and Units for the Definite Integral

Just as the Leibniz notation dy/dx for the derivative reminds us that the derivative is the limit of a ratio of differences, the notation for the definite integral helps us recall the meaning of the integral. The symbol

$$\int_a^b f(x)\, dx$$

reminds us that an integral is a limit of sums of terms of the form "$f(x)$ times a small difference of x." Officially, dx is not a separate entity, but a part of the whole integral symbol. Just as one thinks of d/dx as a single symbol meaning "the derivative with respect to x of...," one can think of $\int_a^b \ldots dx$ as a single symbol meaning "the integral of ... with respect to x."

However, many scientists and mathematicians informally think of dx as an "infinitesimally" small bit of x multiplied by $f(x)$. This viewpoint is often the key to interpreting the meaning of a definite integral. For example, if $f(t)$ is the velocity of a moving particle at time t, then $f(t)\, dt$ may by thought of informally as velocity $\times$ time, giving the distance traveled by the particle during a small bit of time dt. The integral $\int_a^b f(t)\, dt$ may then be thought of as the sum of all these small distances, giving us the net change in position of the particle between $t = a$ and $t = b$. The notation for the integral suggests units for the value of the integral. Since the terms being added up are products of the form "$f(x)$ times a difference in x," the unit of measurement for $\int_a^b f(x)\, dx$ is the product of the units for $f(x)$ and the units for x. For example, if $f(t)$ is velocity measured in meters/second and t is time measured in seconds, then

$$\int_a^b f(t)\, dt$$

has units of (meters/sec)$\times$(sec) $=$ meters. This is what we expect, since the value of this integral represents change in position.

As another example, graph $y = f(x)$ with the same units of measurement of length along the x- and y-axes, say cm. Then $f(x)$ and x are measured in the same units, so

$$\int_a^b f(x)\, dx$$

is measured in square units of cm $\times$ cm $=$ cm^2. Again, this is what we would expect since in this context the integral represents an area.

The Fundamental Theorem of Calculus

We have seen that change in position can be calculated as the limit of Riemann sums of the velocity function $v = f(t)$. Thus, change in position is given by the definite integral $\int_a^b f(t)\, dt$. If we let $F(t)$ denote the position function, then the change in position can also be written as $F(b) - F(a)$. Thus we have:

$$\int_a^b f(t)\, dt = \begin{matrix} \text{Change in position from} \\ t = a \text{ to } t = b \end{matrix} = F(b) - F(a)$$

We also know that the position F and velocity f are related using derivatives: $F'(t) = f(t)$. Thus, we have uncovered a connection between the integral and derivative, which is so important it is called the Fundamental Theorem of Calculus. It applies to any function F with a continuous derivative $f = F'$.

Theorem 5.1: The Fundamental Theorem of Calculus[2]

If f is continuous on the interval $[a, b]$ and $f(t) = F'(t)$, then

$$\int_a^b f(t)\, dt = F(b) - F(a).$$

To understand the Fundamental Theorem of Calculus, think of $f(t) = F'(t)$ as the rate of change of the quantity $F(t)$. To calculate the total change in $F(t)$ between times $t = a$ and $t = b$, we divide the interval $a \le t \le b$ into n subintervals, each of length Δt. For each small interval, we estimate the change in $F(t)$, written ΔF, and add these. In each subinterval we assume the rate of change of $F(t)$ is approximately constant, so that we can say

$$\Delta F \approx \text{Rate of change of } F \times \text{Time elapsed.}$$

For the first subinterval, from t_0 to t_1, the rate of change of $F(t)$ is approximately $F'(t_0)$, so

$$\Delta F \approx F'(t_0)\, \Delta t.$$

Similarly, for the second interval

$$\Delta F \approx F'(t_1)\, \Delta t.$$

Summing over all the subintervals, we get

$$\begin{matrix} \text{Total change in } F(t) \\ \text{between } t = a \text{ and } t = b \end{matrix} = \sum_{i=0}^{n-1} \Delta F \approx \sum_{i=0}^{n-1} F'(t_i)\, \Delta t.$$

We have approximated the change in $F(t)$ as a left-hand sum.

However, the total change in $F(t)$ between the times $t = a$ and $t = b$ is simply $F(b) - F(a)$. Taking the limit as n goes to infinity converts the Riemann sum to a definite integral and suggests the following interpretation of the Fundamental Theorem of Calculus:[3]

---

[2]This result is sometimes called the First Fundamental Theorem of Calculus, to distinguish it from the Second Fundamental Theorem of Calculus discussed in Section 6.4.

[3]We could equally well have used a right-hand sum, since the definite integral is their common limit.

$$F(b) - F(a) = \begin{array}{c} \text{Total change in } F(t) \\ \text{between } t = a \text{ and } t = b \end{array} = \int_a^b F'(t)\, dt.$$

In words, the definite integral of a rate of change gives the total change.

This argument does not, however, constitute a proof of the Fundamental Theorem. The errors in the various approximations must be investigated using the definition of limit. A proof is given in Section 6.4 where we learn how to construct antiderivatives using the Second Fundamental Theorem of Calculus.

Example 1   If $F'(t) = f(t)$ and $f(t)$ is velocity in miles/hour, with t in hours, what are the units of $\int_a^b f(t)\, dt$ and $F(b) - F(a)$?

Solution   Since the units of $f(t)$ are miles/hour and the units of t are hours, the units of $\int_a^b f(t)\, dt$ are (miles/hour) $\times$ hours $=$ miles. Since F measures change in position, the units of $F(b) - F(a)$ are miles. As expected, the units of $\int_a^b f(t)\, dt$ and $F(b) - F(a)$ are the same.

The Definite Integral of a Rate of Change: Applications of the Fundamental Theorem

Many applications are based on the Fundamental Theorem, which tells us that the definite integral of a rate of change gives the total change.

Example 2   Let $F(t)$ represent a bacteria population which is 5 million at time $t = 0$. After t hours, the population is growing at an instantaneous rate of 2^t million bacteria per hour. Estimate the total increase in the bacteria population during the first hour, and the population at $t = 1$.

Solution   Since the rate at which the population is growing is $F'(t) = 2^t$, we have

$$\text{Change in population} = F(1) - F(0) = \int_0^1 2^t\, dt.$$

Using a calculator to evaluate the integral,

$$\text{Change in population} = \int_0^1 2^t\, dt = 1.44 \text{ million bacteria.}$$

Since $F(0) = 5$, the population at $t = 1$ is given by

$$\text{Population} = F(1) = F(0) + \int_0^1 2^t\, dt = 5 + 1.44 = 6.44 \text{ million.}$$

The following example shows how representing a quantity as a definite integral, and thereby as an area, can be helpful even if we don't evaluate the integral.

Example 3   Two cars start from rest at a traffic light and accelerate for several minutes. Figure 5.40 shows their velocities as a function of time.

(a)   Which car is ahead after one minute?   (b)   Which car is ahead after two minutes?

Figure 5.40: Velocities of two cars in Example 3.
Which is ahead when?

Solution

(a) For the first minute car 1 goes faster than car 2, and therefore car 1 must be ahead at the end of one minute.

(b) At the end of two minutes the situation is less clear, since car 1 was going faster for the first minute and car 2 for the second. However, if $v = f(t)$ is the velocity of a car after t minutes, then we know that

$$\text{Distance traveled in two minutes} = \int_0^2 f(t)\, dt,$$

since the integral of velocity is distance traveled. This definite integral may also be interpreted as the area under the graph of f between 0 and 2. Since the area representing the distance traveled by car 2 is clearly larger than the area for car 1 (see Figure 5.40), we know that car 2 has traveled farther than car 1.

Example 4   Biological activity in water is reflected in the rate at which carbon dioxide, CO_2, is added or removed. Plants take CO_2 out of the water during the day for photosynthesis and put CO_2 into the water at night. Animals put CO_2 into the water all the time as they breathe. Figure 5.41 shows the rate of change of the CO_2 level in a pond.[4] At dawn, there were 2.600 mmol of CO_2 per liter of water.

(a) At what time was the CO_2 level lowest? Highest?

(b) Estimate how much CO_2 enters the pond during the night ($t = 12$ to $t = 24$).

(c) Estimate the CO_2 level at dusk (twelve hours after dawn).

(d) Does the CO_2 level appear to be approximately in equilibrium?

Figure 5.41: Rate at which CO_2 enters a pond over a 24-hour period

[4]Data from R. J. Beyers, *The Pattern of Photosynthesis and Respiration in Laboratory Microsystems* (Mem. 1st. Ital. Idrobiol., 1965).

Solution   Let $f(t)$ be the rate at which CO_2 is entering the water at time t and let $F(t)$ be the concentration of CO_2 in the water at time t, so $F'(t) = f(t)$.

(a) From Figure 5.41, we see $f(t)$ is negative for $0 \leq t \leq 12$, so the CO_2 level is decreasing during this interval (daytime). Since $f(t)$ is positive for $12 < t < 24$, the CO_2 level is increasing during this interval (night). The CO_2 is lowest at $t = 12$ (dusk) and highest at $t = 0$ and $t = 24$ (dawn).

(b) We want to calculate the total change in the CO_2 level in the pond, $F(24) - F(12)$. By the Fundamental Theorem of Calculus,

$$F(24) - F(12) = \int_{12}^{24} f(t) \, dt.$$

We use values of $f(t)$ from the graph (displayed in Table 5.7) to construct a left Riemann sum approximation to this integral with $n = 6$, $\Delta t = 2$:

$$\int_{12}^{24} f(t) \, dt \approx f(12) \cdot 2 + f(14) \cdot 2 + f(16) \cdot 2 + \cdots + f(22) \cdot 2$$

$$\approx (0.000)2 + (0.045)2 + (0.035)2 + \cdots + (0.012)2 = 0.278.$$

Thus, between $t = 12$ and $t = 24$,

$$\text{Change in } CO_2 \text{ level } = F(24) - F(12) = \int_{12}^{24} f(t) \, dt \approx 0.278 \text{ mmol/liter}.$$

(c) To find the CO_2 level at $t = 12$, we use the Fundamental Theorem to estimate the change in CO_2 level during the day:

$$F(12) - F(0) = \int_{0}^{12} f(t) \, dt$$

Using a left Riemann sum as in part (b), we have

$$F(12) - F(0) = \int_{0}^{12} f(t) \, dt \approx -0.328.$$

Since initially there were $F(0) = 2.600$ mmol/liter, we have

$$F(12) = F(0) - 0.328 = 2.272 \text{ mmol/liter}.$$

(d) The amount of CO_2 removed during the day is represented by the area of the region below the t-axis; the amount of CO_2 added during the night is represented by the area above the t-axis. These areas look approximately equal, so the CO_2 level is approximately in equilibrium.

Using Riemann sums to estimate these areas, we find that about 0.278 mmol/l of CO_2 was released into the pond during the night and about 0.328 mmol/l of CO_2 was absorbed from the pond during the day. These quantities are sufficiently close that the difference could be due to measurement error, or to errors from the Riemann sum approximation.

Table 5.7   Rate, $f(t)$, at which CO_2 is entering or leaving water (read from Figure 5.41)

t	$f(t)$	t	$f(t)$	t	$f(t)$	t	$f(t)$	t	$f(t)$	t	$f(t)$
0	0.000	4	−0.039	8	−0.026	12	0.000	16	0.035	20	0.020
2	−0.044	6	−0.035	10	−0.020	14	0.045	18	0.027	22	0.012

Calculating Definite Integrals: Computational Use of the Fundamental Theorem

The Fundamental Theorem of Calculus owes its name to its central role in linking rates of change (derivatives) to total change. However, the Fundamental Theorem also provides an exact way of computing certain definite integrals.

Example 5 Compute $\int_1^3 2x\,dx$ by two different methods.

Solution Using left- and right-hand sums, we can approximate this integral as accurately as we want. With $n = 100$, for example, the left-sum is 7.96 and the right sum is 8.04. Using $n = 500$ we learn

$$7.992 < \int_1^3 2x\,dx < 8.008.$$

The Fundamental Theorem, on the other hand, allows us to compute the integral exactly. We take $f(x) = 2x$. We know that if $F(x) = x^2$, then $F'(x) = 2x$. So we use $f(x) = 2x$ and $F(x) = x^2$ and obtain

$$\int_1^3 2x\,dx = F(3) - F(1) = 3^2 - 1^2 = 8.$$

Notice that to use the Fundamental Theorem to calculate a definite integral, we need to know the antiderivative, F. Chapter 6 discusses how antiderivatives are computed.

Exercises and Problems for Section 5.3

Exercises

1. If $f(t)$ is measured in dollars per year and t is measured in years, what are the units of $\int_a^b f(t)\,dt$?

2. If $f(t)$ is measured in meters/second^2 and t is measured in seconds, what are the units of $\int_a^b f(t)\,dt$?

3. If $f(x)$ is measured in pounds and x is measured in feet, what are the units of $\int_a^b f(x)\,dx$?

In Exercises 4–7, explain in words what the integral represents and give units.

4. $\int_1^3 v(t)\,dt$, where $v(t)$ is velocity in meters/sec and t is time in seconds.

5. $\int_0^6 a(t)\,dt$, where $a(t)$ is acceleration in km/hr^2 and t is time in hours.

6. $\int_{2005}^{2011} f(t)\,dt$, where $f(t)$ is the rate at which the world's population is growing in year t, in billion people per year.

7. $\int_0^5 s(x)\,dx$, where $s(x)$ is rate of change of salinity (salt concentration) in gm/liter per cm in sea water, and where x is depth below the surface of the water in cm.

8. For the two cars in Example 3, page 291, estimate:
   (a) The distances moved by car 1 and car 2 during the first minute.
   (b) The time at which the two cars have gone the same distance.

In Exercises 9–14, let $f(t) = F'(t)$. Write the integral $\int_a^b f(t)\,dt$ and evaluate it using the Fundamental Theorem of Calculus.

9. $F(t) = t^2$; $a = 1, b = 3$

10. $F(t) = 3t^2 + 4t$; $a = 2, b = 5$

11. $F(t) = \ln t$; $a = 1, b = 5$

12. $F(t) = \sin t$; $a = 0, b = \pi/2$

13. $F(t) = 7 \cdot 4^t$; $a = 2, b = 3$

14. $F(t) = \tan t$; $a = 0, b = \pi$

Problems

15. (a) Differentiate $x^3 + x$.
    (b) Use the Fundamental Theorem of Calculus to find
    $$\int_0^2 (3x^2 + 1)\,dx.$$

16. (a) What is the derivative of $\sin t$?
    (b) The velocity of a particle at time t is $v(t) = \cos t$. Use the Fundamental Theorem of Calculus to find the total distance traveled by the particle between $t = 0$ and $t = \pi/2$.

17. **(a)** If $F(t) = \frac{1}{2}\sin^2 t$, find $F'(t)$.

    (b) Find $\displaystyle\int_{0.2}^{0.4} \sin t \cos t \, dt$ two ways:

      (i) Numerically.

      (ii) Using the Fundamental Theorem of Calculus.

18. **(a)** If $F(x) = e^{x^2}$, find $F'(x)$.

    (b) Find $\displaystyle\int_{0}^{1} 2xe^{x^2} \, dx$ two ways:

      (i) Numerically.

      (ii) Using the Fundamental Theorem of Calculus.

19. Pollution is removed from a lake on day t at a rate of $f(t)$ kg/day.

    (a) Explain the meaning of the statement $f(12) = 500$.

    (b) If $\int_{5}^{15} f(t)\,dt = 4000$, give the units of the 5, the 15, and the 4000.

    (c) Give the meaning of $\int_{5}^{15} f(t)\,dt = 4000$.

20. Oil leaks out of a tanker at a rate of $r = f(t)$ gallons per minute, where t is in minutes. Write a definite integral expressing the total quantity of oil which leaks out of the tanker in the first hour.

21. Water is leaking out of a tank at a rate of $R(t)$ gallons/hour, where t is measured in hours.

    (a) Write a definite integral that expresses the total amount of water that leaks out in the first two hours.

    (b) In Figure 5.42, shade the region whose area represents the total amount of water that leaks out in the first two hours.

    (c) Give an upper and lower estimate of the total amount of water that leaks out in the first two hours.

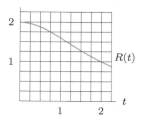

Figure 5.42

22. As coal deposits are depleted, it becomes necessary to strip-mine larger areas for each ton of coal. Figure 5.43 shows the number of acres of land per million tons of coal that will be defaced during strip-mining as a function of the number of million tons removed, starting from the present day.

    (a) Estimate the total number of acres defaced in extracting the next 4 million tons of coal (measured from the present day). Draw four rectangles under the curve, and compute their area.

    (b) Re-estimate the number of acres defaced using rectangles above the curve.

    (c) Use your answers to parts (a) and (b) to get a better estimate of the actual number of acres defaced.

Figure 5.43

23. The rate at which the world's oil is consumed (in billions of barrels per year) is given by $r = f(t)$, where t is in years and $t = 0$ is the start of 2004.

    (a) Write a definite integral representing the total quantity of oil consumed between the start of 2004 and the start of 2009.

    (b) Between 2004 and 2009, the rate was modeled by $r = 32e^{0.05t}$. Using a left-hand sum with five subdivisions, find an approximate value for the total quantity of oil consumed between the start of 2004 and the start of 2009.

    (c) Interpret each of the five terms in the sum from part (b) in terms of oil consumption.

24. A bungee jumper leaps off the starting platform at time $t = 0$ and rebounds once during the first 5 seconds. With velocity measured downward, for t in seconds and $0 \le t \le 5$, the jumper's velocity is approximated[5] by $v(t) = -4t^2 + 16t$ meters/sec.

    (a) How many meters does the jumper travel during the first five seconds?

    (b) Where is the jumper relative to the starting position at the end of the five seconds?

    (c) What does $\int_{0}^{5} v(t)\,dt$ represent in terms of the jump?

25. An old rowboat has sprung a leak. Water is flowing into the boat at a rate, $r(t)$, given in the table.

    (a) Compute upper and lower estimates for the volume of water that has flowed into the boat during the 15 minutes.

    (b) Draw a graph to illustrate the lower estimate.

t minutes	0	5	10	15
$r(t)$ liters/min	12	20	24	16

---

[5]Based on www.itforus.oeiizk.waw.pl/tresc/activ//modules/bj.pdf. Accessed Feb 12, 2012.

26. Annual coal production in the US (in billion tons per year) is given in the table.[6] Estimate the total amount of coal produced in the US between 1997 and 2009. If $r = f(t)$ is the rate of coal production t years since 1997, write an integral to represent the 1997–2009 coal production.

Year	1997	1999	2001	2003	2005	2007	2009
Rate	1.090	1.094	1.121	1.072	1.132	1.147	1.073

27. The amount of waste a company produces, W, in tons per week, is approximated by $W = 3.75e^{-0.008t}$, where t is in weeks since January 1, 2005. Waste removal for the company costs \$15/ton. How much does the company pay for waste removal during the year 2005?

28. A two-day environmental cleanup started at 9 am on the first day. The number of workers fluctuated as shown in Figure 5.44. If the workers were paid \$10 per hour, how much was the total personnel cost of the cleanup?

Figure 5.44

29. Suppose in Problem 28 that the workers were paid \$10 per hour for work during the time period 9 am to 5 pm and were paid \$15 per hour for work during the rest of the day. What would the total personnel costs of the cleanup have been under these conditions?

30. A warehouse charges its customers \$5 per day for every 10 cubic feet of space used for storage. Figure 5.45 records the storage used by one company over a month. How much will the company have to pay?

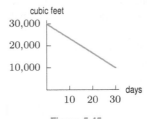

Figure 5.45

31. A cup of coffee at $90°C$ is put into a $20°C$ room when $t = 0$. The coffee's temperature is changing at a rate of $r(t) = -7e^{-0.1t}$ °C per minute, with t in minutes. Estimate the coffee's temperature when $t = 10$.

32. Water is pumped out of a holding tank at a rate of $5 - 5e^{-0.12t}$ liters/minute, where t is in minutes since the pump is started. If the holding tank contains 1000 liters of water when the pump is started, how much water does it hold one hour later?

Problems 33–34 concern the graph of f' in Figure 5.46.

Figure 5.46: Graph of f', not f

33. Which is greater, $f(0)$ or $f(1)$?

34. List the following in increasing order:
$$\frac{f(4) - f(2)}{2}, \quad f(3) - f(2), \quad f(4) - f(3).$$

35. A force F parallel to the x-axis is given by the graph in Figure 5.47. Estimate the work, W, done by the force, where $W = \int_0^{16} F(x)\, dx$.

Figure 5.47

36. Let $f(1) = 7, f'(t) = e^{-t^2}$. Use left- and right-hand sums of 5 rectangles each to estimate $f(2)$.

37. The graph of a continuous function f is given in Figure 5.48. Rank the following integrals in ascending numerical order. Explain your reasons.

(i) $\int_0^2 f(x)\, dx$ (ii) $\int_0^1 f(x)\, dx$

(iii) $\int_0^2 (f(x))^{1/2}\, dx$ (iv) $\int_0^2 (f(x))^2\, dx$.

Figure 5.48

---

[6]http://www.eia.doe.gov/cneaf/coal/page/special/tbl1.html. Accessed May 2011.

38. The graphs in Figure 5.49 represent the velocity, v, of a particle moving along the x-axis for time $0 \leq t \leq 5$. The vertical scales of all graphs are the same. Identify the graph showing which particle:

(a) Has a constant acceleration.
(b) Ends up farthest to the left of where it started.
(c) Ends up the farthest from its starting point.
(d) Experiences the greatest initial acceleration.
(e) Has the greatest average velocity.
(f) Has the greatest average acceleration.

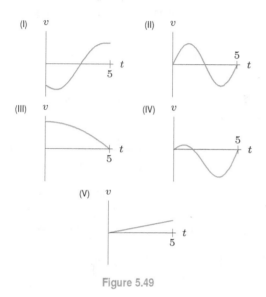

Figure 5.49

39. A car speeds up at a constant rate from 10 to 70 mph over a period of half an hour. Its fuel efficiency (in miles per gallon) increases with speed; values are in the table. Make lower and upper estimates of the quantity of fuel used during the half hour.

Speed (mph)	10	20	30	40	50	60	70
Fuel efficiency (mpg)	15	18	21	23	24	25	26

In Problems 40–41, oil is pumped from a well at a rate of $r(t)$ barrels per day. Assume that t is in days, $r'(t) < 0$ and $t_0 > 0$.

40. What does the value of $\int_0^{t_0} r(t)\, dt$ tells us about the oil well?

41. Rank in order from least to greatest:

$$\int_0^{2t_0} r(t)\, dt, \int_{t_0}^{2t_0} r(t)\, dt, \int_{2t_0}^{3t_0} r(t)\, dt.$$

42. Height velocity graphs are used by endocrinologists to follow the progress of children with growth deficiencies. Figure 5.50 shows the height velocity curves of an average boy and an average girl between ages 3 and 18.

(a) Which curve is for girls and which is for boys? Explain how you can tell.
(b) About how much does the average boy grow between ages 3 and 10?
(c) The growth spurt associated with adolescence and the onset of puberty occurs between ages 12 and 15 for the average boy and between ages 10 and 12.5 for the average girl. Estimate the height gained by each average child during this growth spurt.
(d) When fully grown, about how much taller is the average man than the average woman? (The average boy and girl are about the same height at age 3.)

Figure 5.50

In Problems 43–45, evaluate the expressions using Table 5.8. Give exact values if possible; otherwise, make the best possible estimates using left-hand Riemann sums.

Table 5.8

t	0.0	0.1	0.2	0.3	0.4	0.5
$f(t)$	0.3	0.2	0.2	0.3	0.4	0.5
$g(t)$	2.0	2.9	5.1	5.1	3.9	0.8

43. $\displaystyle\int_0^{0.5} f(t)\, dt$

44. $\displaystyle\int_{0.2}^{0.5} g'(t)\, dt$

45. $\displaystyle\int_0^{0.3} g\left(f(t)\right) dt$

In Problems 46–48, let $C(n)$ be a city's cost, in millions of dollars, for plowing the roads, when n inches of snow have fallen. Let $c(n) = C'(n)$. Evaluate the expressions and interpret your answers in terms of the cost of plowing snow, given

$$c'(n) < 0, \qquad \int_0^{15} c(n)\, dn = 7.5, \qquad c(15) = 0.7,$$

$$c(24) = 0.4, \qquad C(15) = 8, \qquad C(24) = 13.$$

46. $\displaystyle\int_{15}^{24} c(n)\, dn$

47. $C(0)$

48. $c(15) + \displaystyle\int_{15}^{24} c'(n)\, dn$

Problems 49–51 refer to a May 2, 2010, article:[7]

"The crisis began around 10 am yesterday when a 10-foot wide pipe in Weston sprang a leak, which worsened throughout the afternoon and eventually cut off Greater Boston from the Quabbin Reservoir, where most of its water supply is stored… Before water was shut off to the ruptured pipe [at 6:40 pm], brown water had been roaring from a massive crater [at a rate of] 8 million gallons an hour rushing into the nearby Charles River."

Let $r(t)$ be the rate in gallons/hr that water flowed from the pipe t hours after it sprang its leak.

49. Which is larger: $\displaystyle\int_0^2 r(t)\, dt$ or $\displaystyle\int_2^4 r(t)\, dt$?

50. Which is larger: $\displaystyle\int_0^4 r(t)\, dt$ or $4r(4)$?

51. Give a reasonable overestimate of $\displaystyle\int_0^8 r(t)\, dt$.

Strengthen Your Understanding

In Problems 52–53, explain what is wrong with the statement.

52. If $f(t)$ represents the rate, in lbs per year, at which a dog gains weight t years after it is born, then $\int_0^4 f(t)\, dt$ represents the weight of the dog when the dog is four years old.

53. If $f(x) = \sqrt{x}$ the Fundamental Theorem of Calculus states that $\int_4^9 \sqrt{x}\, dx = \sqrt{9} - \sqrt{4}$.

In Problems 54–55, give an example of:

54. A function $f(x)$ and limits of integration a and b such that $\int_a^b f(x)\, dx = e^4 - e^2$.

55. The graph of a velocity function of a car that travels 200 miles in 4 hours.

56. True or False? The units for an integral of a function $f(x)$ are the same as the units for $f(x)$.

5.4   THEOREMS ABOUT DEFINITE INTEGRALS

Properties of the Definite Integral

For the definite integral $\int_a^b f(x)\, dx$, we have so far only considered the case $a < b$. We now allow $a \geq b$. We still set $x_0 = a$, $x_n = b$, and $\Delta x = (b - a)/n$. As before, we have $\int_a^b f(x)\, dx = \lim_{n\to\infty} \sum_{i=1}^{n} f(x_i)\Delta x$.

Theorem 5.2: Properties of Limits of Integration

If a, b, and c are any numbers and f is a continuous function, then

1. $\displaystyle\int_b^a f(x)\, dx = -\int_a^b f(x)\, dx.$

2. $\displaystyle\int_a^c f(x)\, dx + \int_c^b f(x)\, dx = \int_a^b f(x)\, dx.$

In words:

1. The integral from b to a is the negative of the integral from a to b.

2. The integral from a to c plus the integral from c to b is the integral from a to b.

---

[7]"A catastrophic rupture hits region's water system," *The Boston Globe*, May 2, 2010.

By interpreting the integrals as areas, we can justify these results for $f \geq 0$. In fact, they are true for all functions for which the integrals make sense.

Why is $\int_b^a f(x)\,dx = -\int_a^b f(x)\,dx$**?**

By definition, both integrals are approximated by sums of the form $\sum f(x_i)\Delta x$. The only difference in the sums for $\int_b^a f(x)\,dx$ and $\int_a^b f(x)\,dx$ is that in the first $\Delta x = (a-b)/n = -(b-a)/n$ and in the second $\Delta x = (b-a)/n$. Since everything else about the sums is the same, we must have $\int_b^a f(x)\,dx = -\int_a^b f(x)\,dx$.

Why is $\int_a^c f(x)\,dx + \int_c^b f(x)\,dx = \int_a^b f(x)\,dx$**?**

Suppose $a < c < b$. Figure 5.51 suggests that $\int_a^c f(x)\,dx + \int_c^b f(x)\,dx = \int_a^b f(x)\,dx$ since the area under f from a to c plus the area under f from c to b together make up the whole area under f from a to b.

This property holds for all numbers a, b, and c, not just those satisfying $a < c < b$. (See Figure 5.52.) For example, the area under f from 3 to 6 is equal to the area from 3 to 8 *minus* the area from 6 to 8, so

$$\int_3^6 f(x)\,dx = \int_3^8 f(x)\,dx - \int_6^8 f(x)\,dx = \int_3^8 f(x)\,dx + \int_8^6 f(x)\,dx.$$

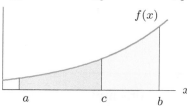

Figure 5.51: Additivity of the definite integral ($a < c < b$)

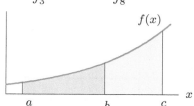

Figure 5.52: Additivity of the definite integral ($a < b < c$)

Example 1   Given that $\int_0^{1.25} \cos(x^2)\,dx = 0.98$ and $\int_0^1 \cos(x^2)\,dx = 0.90$, what are the values of the following integrals? (See Figure 5.53.)

(a) $\displaystyle\int_1^{1.25} \cos(x^2)\,dx$ (b) $\displaystyle\int_{-1}^1 \cos(x^2)\,dx$ (c) $\displaystyle\int_{1.25}^{-1} \cos(x^2)\,dx$

Figure 5.53: Graph of $f(x) = \cos(x^2)$

Solution   (a) Since, by the additivity property,

$$\int_0^{1.25} \cos(x^2)\,dx = \int_0^1 \cos(x^2)\,dx + \int_1^{1.25} \cos(x^2)\,dx,$$

we get

$$0.98 = 0.90 + \int_1^{1.25} \cos(x^2)\,dx,$$

so

$$\int_1^{1.25} \cos(x^2)\,dx = 0.08.$$

(b) By the additivity property, we have

$$\int_{-1}^{1} \cos(x^2)\, dx = \int_{-1}^{0} \cos(x^2)\, dx + \int_{0}^{1} \cos(x^2)\, dx.$$

By the symmetry of $\cos(x^2)$ about the y-axis,

$$\int_{-1}^{0} \cos(x^2)\, dx = \int_{0}^{1} \cos(x^2)\, dx = 0.90.$$

So

$$\int_{-1}^{1} \cos(x^2)\, dx = 0.90 + 0.90 = 1.80.$$

(c) Using both properties in Theorem 5.2, we have

$$\int_{1.25}^{-1} \cos(x^2)\, dx = -\int_{-1}^{1.25} \cos(x^2)\, dx = -\left(\int_{-1}^{0} \cos(x^2)\, dx + \int_{0}^{1.25} \cos(x^2)\, dx \right)$$
$$= -(0.90 + 0.98) = -1.88.$$

Theorem 5.3: Properties of Sums and Constant Multiples of the Integrand

Let f and g be continuous functions and let c be a constant.

1. $\displaystyle \int_{a}^{b} (f(x) \pm g(x))\, dx = \int_{a}^{b} f(x)\, dx \pm \int_{a}^{b} g(x)\, dx.$

2. $\displaystyle \int_{a}^{b} cf(x)\, dx = c \int_{a}^{b} f(x)\, dx.$

In words:

1. The integral of the sum (or difference) of two functions is the sum (or difference) of their integrals.

2. The integral of a constant times a function is that constant times the integral of the function.

Why Do These Properties Hold?

Both can be visualized by thinking of the definite integral as the limit of a sum of areas of rectangles.

For property 1, suppose that f and g are positive on the interval $[a, b]$ so that the area under $f(x) + g(x)$ is approximated by the sum of the areas of rectangles like the one shaded in Figure 5.54. The area of this rectangle is

$$(f(x_i) + g(x_i))\Delta x = f(x_i)\Delta x + g(x_i)\Delta x.$$

Since $f(x_i)\Delta x$ is the area of a rectangle under the graph of f, and $g(x_i)\Delta x$ is the area of a rectangle under the graph of g, the area under $f(x) + g(x)$ is the sum of the areas under $f(x)$ and $g(x)$. For property 2, notice that multiplying a function by c stretches or shrinks the graph in the vertical direction by a factor of c. Thus, it stretches or shrinks the height of each approximating rectangle by c, and hence multiplies the area by c.

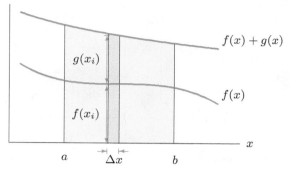

Figure 5.54: Area $= \int_a^b [f(x) + g(x)]\, dx = \int_a^b f(x)\, dx + \int_a^b g(x)\, dx$

Example 2   Evaluate the definite integral $\displaystyle\int_0^2 (1 + 3x)\, dx$ exactly.

Solution   We can break this integral up as follows:

$$\int_0^2 (1 + 3x)\, dx = \int_0^2 1\, dx + \int_0^2 3x\, dx = \int_0^2 1\, dx + 3\int_0^2 x\, dx.$$

From Figures 5.55 and 5.56 and the area interpretation of the integral, we see that

$$\int_0^2 1\, dx = \begin{array}{c}\text{Area of}\\ \text{rectangle}\end{array} = 2 \quad \text{and} \quad \int_0^2 x\, dx = \begin{array}{c}\text{Area of}\\ \text{triangle}\end{array} = \frac{1}{2} \cdot 2 \cdot 2 = 2.$$

Therefore,

$$\int_0^2 (1 + 3x)\, dx = \int_0^2 1\, dx + 3\int_0^2 x\, dx = 2 + 3 \cdot 2 = 8.$$

Figure 5.55: Area representing $\int_0^2 1\, dx$

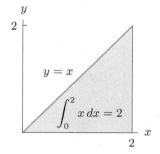

Figure 5.56: Area representing $\int_0^2 x\, dx$

Area Between Curves

Theorem 5.3 enables us to find the area of a region between curves. We have the following result:

If the graph of $f(x)$ lies above the graph of $g(x)$ for $a \leq x \leq b$, then

$$\begin{array}{c}\text{Area between } f \text{ and } g\\ \text{for } a \leq x \leq b\end{array} = \int_a^b (f(x) - g(x))\, dx.$$

Example 3   Find the area of the shaded region in Figure 5.57.

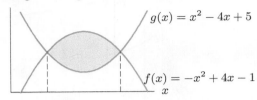

Figure 5.57: Area between two parabolas

Solution   The curves cross where

$$x^2 - 4x + 5 = -x^2 + 4x - 1$$
$$2x^2 - 8x + 6 = 0$$
$$2(x - 1)(x - 3) = 0$$
$$x = 1, 3.$$

Since $f(x) = -x^2 + 4x - 1$ is above $g(x) = x^2 - 4x + 5$ for x between 1 and 3, we find the shaded area by subtraction:

$$\text{Area} = \int_1^3 f(x)\, dx - \int_1^3 g(x)\, dx = \int_1^3 (f(x) - g(x))\, dx$$
$$= \int_1^3 ((-x^2 + 4x - 1) - (x^2 - 4x + 5))\, dx$$
$$= \int_1^3 (-2x^2 + 8x - 6)\, dx = 2.667.$$

Using Symmetry to Evaluate Integrals

Symmetry can be useful in evaluating definite integrals. An even function is symmetric about the y-axis. An odd function is symmetric about the origin. Figures 5.58 and 5.59 suggest the following results:

> If f is even, then $\int_{-a}^a f(x)\, dx = 2\int_0^a f(x)\, dx.$ If g is odd, then $\int_{-a}^a g(x)\, dx = 0.$

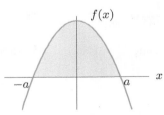

Figure 5.58: For an even function, $\int_{-a}^a f(x)\, dx = 2\int_0^a f(x)\, dx$

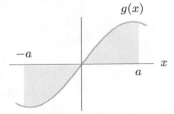

Figure 5.59: For an odd function, $\int_{-a}^a g(x)\, dx = 0$

Example 4   Given that $\int_0^\pi \sin t\, dt = 2$, find (a) $\int_{-\pi}^\pi \sin t\, dt$ (b) $\int_{-\pi}^\pi |\sin t|\, dt$

Solution   Graphs of $\sin t$ and $|\sin t|$ are in Figures 5.60 and 5.61.

(a) Since $\sin t$ is an odd function

$$\int_{-\pi}^\pi \sin t\, dt = 0.$$

(b) Since $|\sin t|$ is an even function

$$\int_{-\pi}^{\pi} |\sin t|\, dt = 2 \int_{0}^{\pi} |\sin t|\, dt = 4.$$

Figure 5.60

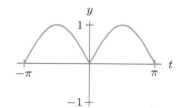

Figure 5.61

Comparing Integrals

Suppose we have constants m and M such that $m \leq f(x) \leq M$ for $a \leq x \leq b$. We say f is *bounded above* by M and *bounded below* by m. Then the graph of f lies between the horizontal lines $y = m$ and $y = M$. So the definite integral lies between $m(b - a)$ and $M(b - a)$. See Figure 5.62.

Suppose $f(x) \leq g(x)$ for $a \leq x \leq b$, as in Figure 5.63. Then the definite integral of f is less than or equal to the definite integral of g. This leads us to the following results:

Figure 5.62: The area under the graph of f lies between the areas of the rectangles

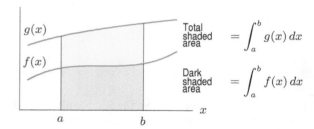

Figure 5.63: If $f(x) \leq g(x)$ then $\int_{a}^{b} f(x)\, dx \leq \int_{a}^{b} g(x)\, dx$

Theorem 5.4: Comparison of Definite Integrals

Let f and g be continuous functions.

1. If $m \leq f(x) \leq M$ for $a \leq x \leq b$, then $\quad m(b - a) \leq \displaystyle\int_{a}^{b} f(x)\, dx \leq M(b - a).$

2. If $f(x) \leq g(x)$ for $a \leq x \leq b$, then $\quad \displaystyle\int_{a}^{b} f(x)\, dx \leq \int_{a}^{b} g(x)\, dx.$

Example 5   Explain why $\displaystyle\int_{0}^{\sqrt{\pi}} \sin(x^2)\, dx \leq \sqrt{\pi}.$

Solution   Since $\sin(x^2) \leq 1$ for all x (see Figure 5.64), part 2 of Theorem 5.4 gives

$$\int_{0}^{\sqrt{\pi}} \sin(x^2)\, dx \leq \int_{0}^{\sqrt{\pi}} 1\, dx = \sqrt{\pi}.$$

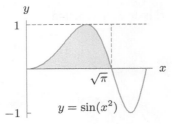

Figure 5.64: Graph showing that $\int_0^{\sqrt{\pi}} \sin(x^2)\, dx < \sqrt{\pi}$

The Definite Integral as an Average

We know how to find the average of n numbers: Add them and divide by n. But how do we find the average value of a continuously varying function? Let us consider an example. Suppose $f(t)$ is the temperature at time t, measured in hours since midnight, and that we want to calculate the average temperature over a 24-hour period. One way to start is to average the temperatures at n equally spaced times, $t_1, t_2, \ldots, t_n$, during the day.

$$\text{Average temperature} \approx \frac{f(t_1) + f(t_2) + \cdots + f(t_n)}{n}.$$

The larger we make n, the better the approximation. We can rewrite this expression as a Riemann sum over the interval $0 \le t \le 24$ if we use the fact that $\Delta t = 24/n$, so $n = 24/\Delta t$:

$$\begin{aligned}
\text{Average temperature} &\approx \frac{f(t_1) + f(t_2) + \cdots + f(t_n)}{24/\Delta t} \\
&= \frac{f(t_1)\Delta t + f(t_2)\Delta t + \cdots + f(t_n)\Delta t}{24} \\
&= \frac{1}{24} \sum_{i=1}^{n} f(t_i)\Delta t.
\end{aligned}$$

As $n \to \infty$, the Riemann sum tends toward an integral, and $1/24$ of the sum also approximates the average temperature better. It makes sense, then, to write

$$\text{Average temperature} = \lim_{n \to \infty} \frac{1}{24} \sum_{i=1}^{n} f(t_i)\Delta t = \frac{1}{24} \int_0^{24} f(t)\, dt.$$

We have found a way of expressing the average temperature over an interval in terms of an integral. Generalizing for any function f, if $a < b$, we define

$$\boxed{\begin{array}{l}
\text{Average value of } f \\
\text{from } a \text{ to } b
\end{array} = \frac{1}{b-a} \int_a^b f(x)\, dx.}$$

How to Visualize the Average on a Graph

The definition of average value tells us that

$$(\text{Average value of } f) \cdot (b - a) = \int_a^b f(x)\, dx.$$

Let's interpret the integral as the area under the graph of f. Then the average value of f is the height of a rectangle whose base is $(b - a)$ and whose area is the same as the area under the graph of f. (See Figure 5.65.)

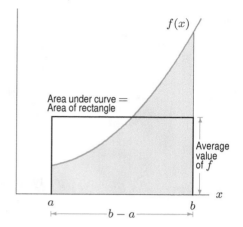

Figure 5.65: Area and average value

Example 6   Suppose that $C(t)$ represents the daily cost of heating your house, measured in dollars per day, where t is time measured in days and $t = 0$ corresponds to January 1, 2008. Interpret $\int_0^{90} C(t)\, dt$ and $\dfrac{1}{90 - 0} \int_0^{90} C(t)\, dt$.

Solution   The units for the integral $\int_0^{90} C(t)\, dt$ are (dollars/day) × (days) = dollars. The integral represents the total cost in dollars to heat your house for the first 90 days of 2008, namely the months of January, February, and March. The second expression is measured in (1/days)(dollars) or dollars per day, the same units as $C(t)$. It represents the average cost per day to heat your house during the first 90 days of 2008.

Example 7   In the year 2000, the population of Nevada was modeled by the function
$$P = f(t) = 2.020(1.036)^t,$$
where P is in millions of people and t is in years since 2000. Use this function to predict the average population of Nevada between the years 2000 and 2020.

Solution   We want the average value of $f(t)$ between $t = 0$ and $t = 20$. This is given by
$$\text{Average population} = \frac{1}{20 - 0} \int_0^{20} f(t)\, dt = \frac{1}{20}(58.748) = 2.937.$$
We used a calculator to evaluate the integral. The average population of Nevada between 2000 and 2020 is predicted to be about 2.9 million people.

Exercises and Problems for Section 5.4

Exercises

In Exercises 1–6, find the integral, given that $\int_a^b f(x)\, dx = 8$, $\int_a^b (f(x))^2\, dx = 12$, $\int_a^b g(t)\, dt = 2$, and $\int_a^b (g(t))^2\, dt = 3$.

1. $\int_a^b (f(x) + g(x))\, dx$ **2.** $\int_a^b cf(z)\, dz$

3. $\int_a^b \left((f(x))^2 - (g(x))^2\right) dx$

4. $\int_a^b (f(x))^2\, dx - \left(\int_a^b f(x)\, dx\right)^2$

5. $\int_a^b \left(c_1 g(x) + (c_2 f(x))^2\right)\, dx$

6. $\int_{a+5}^{b+5} f(x - 5)\, dx$

In Exercises 7–10, find the average value of the function over the given interval.

7. $g(t) = 1 + t$ over $[0, 2]$ **8.** $g(t) = e^t$ over $[0, 10]$

9. $f(x) = 2$ over $[a, b]$ **10.** $f(x) = 4x + 7$ over $[1, 3]$

11. (a) Using Figure 5.66, find $\int_1^6 f(x)\,dx$.

(b) What is the average value of f on $[1, 6]$?

Figure 5.66

12. How do the units for the average value of f relate to the units for $f(x)$ and the units for x?

Find the area of the regions in Exercises 13–20.

13. Under $y = e^x$ and above $y = 1$ for $0 \le x \le 2$.

14. Under $y = 5\ln(2x)$ and above $y = 3$ for $3 \le x \le 5$.

15. Between $y = x^2$ and $y = x^3$ for $0 \le x \le 1$.

16. Between $y = x^{1/2}$ and $y = x^{1/3}$ for $0 \le x \le 1$.

17. Between $y = \sin x + 2$ and $y = 0.5$ for $6 \le x \le 10$.

18. Between $y = \cos t$ and $y = \sin t$ for $0 \le t \le \pi$.

19. Between $y = e^{-x}$ and $y = 4(x - x^2)$.

20. Between $y = e^{-x}$ and $y = \ln x$ for $1 \le x \le 2$.

Problems

21. (a) Let $\int_0^3 f(x)\,dx = 6$. What is the average value of $f(x)$ on the interval $x = 0$ to $x = 3$?

(b) If $f(x)$ is even, what is $\int_{-3}^3 f(x)\,dx$? What is the average value of $f(x)$ on the interval $x = -3$ to $x = 3$?

(c) If $f(x)$ is odd, what is $\int_{-3}^3 f(x)\,dx$? What is the average value of $f(x)$ on the interval $x = -3$ to $x = 3$?

22. Using Figure 5.67, write $\int_0^3 f(x)\,dx$ in terms of $\int_{-1}^1 f(x)\,dx$ and $\int_1^3 f(x)\,dx$.

Figure 5.67

23. (a) Assume $a \le b$. Use geometry to construct a formula in terms of a and b for

$$\int_a^b 1\,dx.$$

(b) Use the result of part (a) to find:

(i) $\int_2^5 1\,dx$ (ii) $\int_{-3}^8 1\,dx$ (iii) $\int_1^3 23\,dx$

24. If $\int_2^5 (2f(x) + 3)\,dx = 17$, find $\int_2^5 f(x)\,dx$.

25. The value, V, of a Tiffany lamp, worth \$225 in 1975, increases at 15% per year. Its value in dollars t years after 1975 is given by

$$V = 225(1.15)^t.$$

Find the average value of the lamp over the period 1975–2010.

26. (a) Assume that $0 \le a \le b$. Use geometry to construct a formula in terms of a and b for

$$\int_a^b x\,dx.$$

(b) Use the result of part (a) to find:

(i) $\int_2^5 x\,dx$ (ii) $\int_{-3}^8 x\,dx$ (iii) $\int_1^3 5x\,dx$

27. If $f(x)$ is odd and $\int_{-2}^3 f(x)\,dx = 30$, find $\int_2^3 f(x)\,dx$.

28. If $f(x)$ is even and $\int_{-2}^2 (f(x) - 3)\,dx = 8$, find $\int_0^2 f(x)\,dx$.

29. Without any computation, find $\int_{-\pi/4}^{\pi/4} x^3 \cos x^2\,dx$.

30. If the average value of f on the interval $2 \le x \le 5$ is 4, find $\int_2^5 (3f(x) + 2)\,dx$.

31. Suppose $\int_1^3 3x^2\,dx = 26$ and $\int_1^3 2x\,dx = 8$. What is $\int_1^3 (x^2 - x)\,dx$?

32. Figure 5.68 shows the rate, $f(x)$, in thousands of algae per hour, at which a population of algae is growing, where x is in hours.

(a) Estimate the average value of the rate over the interval $x = -1$ to $x = 3$.

(b) Estimate the total change in the population over the interval $x = -3$ to $x = 3$.

Figure 5.68

33. (a) Using Figure 5.69, estimate $\int_{-3}^{3} f(x)\,dx$.

    (b) Which of the following average values of $f(x)$ is larger?

       (i) Between $x = -3$ and $x = 3$

       (ii) Between $x = 0$ and $x = 3$

Figure 5.69

34. A bar of metal is cooling from $1000°$C to room temperature, $20°$C. The temperature, H, of the bar t minutes after it starts cooling is given, in $°$C, by

$$H = 20 + 980e^{-0.1t}.$$

(a) Find the temperature of the bar at the end of one hour.

(b) Find the average value of the temperature over the first hour.

(c) Is your answer to part (b) greater or smaller than the average of the temperatures at the beginning and the end of the hour? Explain this in terms of the concavity of the graph of H.

35. In 2010, the population of Mexico[8] was growing at 1.1% a year. Assuming that this growth rate continues into the future and that t is in years since 2010, the Mexican population, P, in millions, is given by

$$P = 112(1.011)^t.$$

(a) Predict the average population of Mexico between 2010 and 2050.

(b) Find the average of the population in 2010 and the predicted population in 2050.

(c) Explain, in terms of the concavity of the graph of P, why your answer to part (b) is larger or smaller than your answer to part (a).

36. (a) Using a graph, decide if the area under $y = e^{-x^2/2}$ between 0 and 1 is more or less than 1.

(b) Find the area.

37. Without computation, show that $2 \le \int_{0}^{2} \sqrt{1 + x^3}\,dx \le 6$.

38. Without calculating the integral, explain why the following statements are false.

(a) $\int_{-2}^{-1} e^{x^2}\,dx = -3$ (b) $\int_{-1}^{1} \left| \dfrac{\cos(x + 2)}{1 + \tan^2 x} \right|\,dx = 0$

For Problems 39–42, mark the quantity on a copy of the graph of f in Figure 5.70.

Figure 5.70

39. A length representing $f(b) - f(a)$.

40. A slope representing $\dfrac{f(b) - f(a)}{b - a}$.

41. An area representing $F(b) - F(a)$, where $F' = f$.

42. A length roughly approximating

$$\dfrac{F(b) - F(a)}{b - a}, \text{ where } F' = f.$$

43. Using the graph of f in Figure 5.71, arrange the following quantities in increasing order, from least to greatest.

(i) $\int_{0}^{1} f(x)\,dx$ (ii) $\int_{1}^{2} f(x)\,dx$

(iii) $\int_{0}^{2} f(x)\,dx$ (iv) $\int_{2}^{3} f(x)\,dx$

(v) $-\int_{1}^{2} f(x)\,dx$ (vi) The number 0

(vii) The number 20   (viii) The number -10

Figure 5.71

44. (a) Using Figures 5.72 and 5.73, find the average value on $0 \le x \le 2$ of

      (i) $f(x)$ (ii) $g(x)$ (iii) $f(x){\cdot}g(x)$

(b) Is the following statement true? Explain your answer.

$$\text{Average}(f) \cdot \text{Average}(g) = \text{Average}(f \cdot g)$$

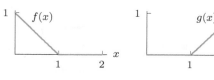

Figure 5.72   Figure 5.73

[8]http://www.indexmundi.com/mexico/population_growth_rate.html. Accessed April 29, 2011.

45. (a) Without computing any integrals, explain why the average value of $f(x) = \sin x$ on $[0, \pi]$ must be between 0.5 and 1.
  (b) Compute this average.

46. Figure 5.74 shows the *standard normal distribution* from statistics, which is given by

$$\frac{1}{\sqrt{2\pi}} e^{-x^2/2}.$$

Statistics books often contain tables such as the following, which show the area under the curve from 0 to b for various values of b.

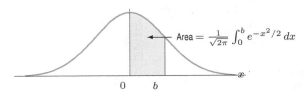

Figure 5.74

b	$\frac{1}{\sqrt{2\pi}} \int_0^b e^{-x^2/2}\, dx$
1	0.3413
2	0.4772
3	0.4987
4	0.5000

Use the information given in the table and the symmetry of the curve about the y-axis to find:

(a) $\dfrac{1}{\sqrt{2\pi}} \displaystyle\int_1^3 e^{-x^2/2}\, dx$ **(b)** $\dfrac{1}{\sqrt{2\pi}} \displaystyle\int_{-2}^3 e^{-x^2/2}\, dx$

In Problems 47–48, evaluate the expression, if possible, or say what additional information is needed, given that $\int_{-4}^4 g(x)\, dx = 12$.

47. $\displaystyle\int_0^4 g(x)\, dx$ **48.** $\displaystyle\int_{-4}^4 g(-x)\, dx$

In Problems 49–52, evaluate the expression if possible, or say what extra information is needed, given $\int_0^7 f(x)\, dx = 25$.

49. $\sqrt{\displaystyle\int_0^7 f(x)\, dx}$ **50.** $\displaystyle\int_0^{3.5} f(x)\, dx$

51. $\displaystyle\int_{-2}^5 f(x+2)\, dx$ **52.** $\displaystyle\int_0^7 (f(x) + 2)\, dx$

53. (a) Sketch a graph of $f(x) = \sin(x^2)$ and mark on it the points $x = \sqrt{\pi}, \sqrt{2\pi}, \sqrt{3\pi}, \sqrt{4\pi}$.
  (b) Use your graph to decide which of the four numbers

$$\int_0^{\sqrt{n\pi}} \sin(x^2)\, dx \quad n = 1, 2, 3, 4$$

is largest. Which is smallest? How many of the numbers are positive?

For Problems 54–56, assuming $F' = f$, mark the quantity on a copy of Figure 5.75.

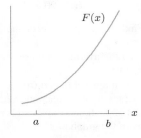

Figure 5.75

54. A slope representing $f(a)$.

55. A length representing $\displaystyle\int_a^b f(x)\, dx$.

56. A slope representing $\dfrac{1}{b-a} \displaystyle\int_a^b f(x)\, dx$.

57. In Chapter 2, the average velocity over the time interval $a \le t \le b$ was defined to be $(s(b) - s(a))/(b - a)$, where $s(t)$ is the position function. Use the Fundamental Theorem of Calculus to show that the average value of the velocity function $v(t)$, on the interval $a \le t \le b$, is also $(s(b) - s(a))/(b - a)$.

Strengthen Your Understanding

In Problems 58–60, explain what is wrong with the statement.

58. If $f(x)$ is a continuous function on $[a, b]$ such that $\int_a^b f(x)\, dx \ge 0$, then $f(x) \ge 0$ for all x in $[a, b]$.

59. If $f(x)$ is a continuous function on the interval $[a, b]$, then $\int_a^b (5 + 3f(x))\, dx = 5 + 3 \int_a^b f(x)\, dx$.

60. If $f(t)$ is the population of fish in a lake on day t, then the average population over a 6-month period is given by

$$\frac{1}{6} \int_0^6 f(t)\, dt.$$

In Problems 61–63, give an example of:

61. A continuous function $f(x)$ on the interval $[0, 1]$ such that $\int_0^1 2f(x)\,dx < \int_0^1 f(x)\,dx$.

62. A continuous function $f(x)$ on the interval $[0, 4]$ such that $\int_0^4 f(x)\,dx = 0$, but $f(x)$ is not equal to 0 everywhere on $[0, 4]$.

63. An expression involving a definite integral that can be interpreted as the average speed for a car over a 5-hour journey.

In Problems 64–78, are the statements true for all continuous functions $f(x)$ and $g(x)$? Give an explanation for your answer.

64. If $\int_0^2 (f(x) + g(x))\,dx = 10$ and $\int_0^2 f(x)\,dx = 3$, then $\int_0^2 g(x)\,dx = 7$.

65. If $\int_0^2 (f(x) + g(x))\,dx = 10$, then $\int_0^2 f(x)\,dx = 3$ and $\int_0^2 g(x)\,dx = 7$.

66. If $\int_0^2 f(x)\,dx = 6$, then $\int_0^4 f(x)\,dx = 12$.

67. If $\int_0^2 f(x)\,dx = 6$ and $g(x) = 2f(x)$, then $\int_0^2 g(x)\,dx = 12$.

68. If $\int_0^2 f(x)\,dx = 6$ and $h(x) = f(5x)$, then $\int_0^2 h(x)\,dx = 30$.

69. If $a = b$, then $\int_a^b f(x)\,dx = 0$.

70. If $a \neq b$, then $\int_a^b f(x)\,dx \neq 0$.

71. $\int_1^2 f(x)\,dx + \int_2^3 g(x)\,dx = \int_1^3 (f(x) + g(x))\,dx$.

72. $\int_{-1}^1 f(x)\,dx = 2\int_0^1 f(x)\,dx$.

73. If $f(x) \leq g(x)$ on the interval $[a, b]$, then the average value of f is less than or equal to the average value of g on the interval $[a, b]$.

74. The average value of f on the interval $[0, 10]$ is the average of the average value of f on $[0, 5]$ and the average value of f on $[5, 10]$.

75. If $a < c < d < b$, then the average value of f on the interval $[c, d]$ is less than the average value of f on the interval $[a, b]$.

76. Suppose that A is the average value of f on the interval $[1, 4]$ and B is the average value of f on the interval $[4, 9]$. Then the average value of f on $[1, 9]$ is the weighted average $(3/8)A + (5/8)B$.

77. On the interval $[a, b]$, the average value of $f(x) + g(x)$ is the average value of $f(x)$ plus the average value of $g(x)$.

78. The average value of the product, $f(x)g(x)$, of two functions on an interval equals the product of the average values of $f(x)$ and $g(x)$ on the interval.

79. Which of the following statements follow directly from the rule

$$\int_a^b (f(x) + g(x))\,dx = \int_a^b f(x)\,dx + \int_a^b g(x)\,dx?$$

(a) If $\int_a^b (f(x) + g(x))\,dx = 5 + 7$, then $\int_a^b f(x)\,dx = 5$ and $\int_a^b g(x)\,dx = 7$.

(b) If $\int_a^b f(x)\,dx = \int_a^b g(x)\,dx = 7$, then $\int_a^b (f(x) + g(x))\,dx = 14$.

(c) If $h(x) = f(x) + g(x)$, then $\int_a^b (h(x) - g(x))\,dx = \int_a^b h(x)\,dx - \int_a^b g(x)\,dx$.

CHAPTER SUMMARY (see also Ready Reference at the end of the book)

- **Definite integral as limit of right or left sums**
- **Fundamental Theorem of Calculus**
- **Interpretations of the definite integral**
  Area, total change from rate of change, change in position given velocity, $(b - a)\cdot$ average value.
- **Properties of the definite integral**

Properties involving integrand, properties involving limits, comparison between integrals.

- **Working with the definite integral**
  Estimate definite integral from graph, table of values, or formula. Units of the definite integral.
- **Theorems about definite integrals**

REVIEW EXERCISES AND PROBLEMS FOR CHAPTER FIVE

Exercises

1. A car comes to a stop six seconds after the driver applies the brakes. While the brakes are on, the velocities recorded are in Table 5.9.

Table 5.9

Time since brakes applied (sec)	0	2	4	6
Velocity (ft/sec)	88	45	16	0

(a) Give lower and upper estimates for the distance the car traveled after the brakes were applied.
(b) On a sketch of velocity against time, show the lower and upper estimates of part (a).

2. A student is speeding down Route 11 in his fancy red Porsche when his radar system warns him of an obstacle 400 feet ahead. He immediately applies the brakes, starts to slow down, and spots a skunk in the road directly ahead of him. The "black box" in the Porsche records the car's speed every two seconds, producing the following table. The speed decreases throughout the 10 seconds it takes to stop, although not necessarily at a constant rate.

Time since brakes applied (sec)	0	2	4	6	8	10
Speed (ft/sec)	100	80	50	25	10	0

(a) What is your best estimate of the total distance the student's car traveled before coming to rest?

(b) Which one of the following statements can you justify from the information given?

   (i) The car stopped before getting to the skunk.

   (ii) The "black box" data is inconclusive. The skunk may or may not have been hit.

   (iii) The skunk was hit by the car.

3. Use Figure 5.76 to estimate $\int_0^3 f(x)\,dx$.

Figure 5.76   Figure 5.77

4. Use Figure 5.77 to estimate $\int_{-15}^{20} f(x)\,dx$.

5. Using the table, estimate $\int_0^{100} f(t)\,dt$.

t	0	20	40	60	80	100
$f(t)$	1.2	2.8	4.0	4.7	5.1	5.2

6. A village wishes to measure the quantity of water that is piped to a factory during a typical morning. A gauge on the water line gives the flow rate (in cubic meters per hour) at any instant. The flow rate is about 100 m³/hr at 6 am and increases steadily to about 280 m³/hr at 9 am.

(a) Using only this information, give your best estimate of the total volume of water used by the factory between 6 am and 9 am.

(b) How often should the flow rate gauge be read to obtain an estimate of this volume to within 6 m³?

7. You jump out of an airplane. Before your parachute opens you fall faster and faster, but your acceleration decreases as you fall because of air resistance. The table gives your acceleration, a (in m/sec²), after t seconds.

t	0	1	2	3	4	5
a	9.81	8.03	6.53	5.38	4.41	3.61

(a) Give upper and lower estimates of your speed at $t = 5$.

(b) Get a new estimate by taking the average of your upper and lower estimates. What does the concavity of the graph of acceleration tell you about your new estimate?

In Exercises 8–9, let $f(t) = F'(t)$. Write the integral $\int_a^b f(t)\,dt$ and evaluate it using the Fundamental Theorem of Calculus.

8. $F(t) = t^4$, $a = -1$, $b = 1$

9. $F(t) = 3t^4 - 5t^3 + 5t$; $a = -2$, $b = 1$

Find the area of the regions in Exercises 10–16.

10. Between the parabola $y = 4 - x^2$ and the x-axis.

11. Between $y = x^2 - 9$ and the x-axis.

12. Under one arch of $y = \sin x$ and above the x-axis.

13. Between the line $y = 1$ and one arch of $y = \sin \theta$.

14. Between $y = -x^2 + 5x - 4$ and the x-axis, $0 \le x \le 3$.

15. Between $y = \cos x + 7$ and $y = \ln(x - 3)$, $5 \le x \le 7$.

16. Above the curve $y = -e^x + e^{2(x-1)}$ and below the x-axis, for $x \ge 0$.

Problems

17. Find $\int_{-1}^1 |x|\,dx$ geometrically.

18. A car accelerates smoothly from 0 to 60 mph in 10 seconds with the velocity given in Figure 5.78. Estimate how far the car travels during the 10-second period.

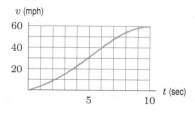

Figure 5.78

19. A car going 80 ft/sec (about 55 mph) brakes to a stop in 8 seconds. Its velocity is recorded every 2 seconds and is given in the following table.

(a) Give your best estimate of the distance traveled by the car during the 8 seconds.

(b) To estimate the distance traveled accurate to within 20 feet, how often should you record the velocity?

t (seconds)	0	2	4	6	8
$v(t)$ (ft/sec)	80	52	28	10	0

20. Using the graph of $2 + \cos x$, for $0 \leq x \leq 4\pi$, list the following quantities in increasing order: the value of the integral $\int_0^{4\pi} (2 + \cos x)\, dx$, the left sum with $n = 2$ subdivisions, and the right sum with $n = 2$ subdivisions.

21. Your velocity is $v(t) = \sin(t^2)$ mph for t in hours, $0 \leq t \leq 1.1$. Find the distance traveled during this time.

22. Your velocity is $v(t) = \ln(t^2 + 1)$ ft/sec for t in seconds, $0 \leq t \leq 3$. Find the distance traveled during this time.

23. The following table gives the emissions, E, of nitrogen oxides in millions of metric tons per year in the US.[9] Let t be the number of years since 1970 and $E = f(t)$.

   (a) What are the units and meaning of $\int_0^{30} f(t)dt$?

   (b) Estimate $\int_0^{30} f(t)dt$.

Year	1970	1975	1980	1985	1990	1995	2000
E	26.9	26.4	27.1	25.8	25.5	25.0	22.6

24. After a spill of radioactive iodine, measurements showed the ambient radiation levels at the site of the spill to be four times the maximum acceptable limit. The level of radiation from an iodine source decreases according to the formula

$$R(t) = R_0 e^{-0.004t}$$

where R is the radiation level (in millirems/hour) at time t in hours and R_0 is the initial radiation level (at $t = 0$).

   (a) How long will it take for the site to reach an acceptable level of radiation?

   (b) How much total radiation (in millirems) will have been emitted by that time, assuming the maximum acceptable limit is 0.6 millirems/hour?

25. Coal gas is produced at a gasworks. Pollutants in the gas are removed by scrubbers, which become less and less efficient as time goes on. The following measurements, made at the start of each month, show the rate at which pollutants are escaping (in tons/month) in the gas:

Time (months)	0	1	2	3	4	5	6
Rate pollutants escape	5	7	8	10	13	16	20

   (a) Make an overestimate and an underestimate of the total quantity of pollutants that escape during the first month.

   (b) Make an overestimate and an underestimate of the total quantity of pollutants that escape during the six months.

   (c) How often would measurements have to be made to find overestimates and underestimates which differ by less than 1 ton from the exact quantity of pollutants that escaped during the first six months?

26. Figure 5.79 shows the rate of change of the quantity of water in a water tower, in liters per day, during the month of April. If the tower had 12,000 liters of water in it on April 1, estimate the quantity of water in the tower on April 30.

rate (liters/day)

Figure 5.79

27. For the function f in Figure 5.80, write an expression involving one or more definite integrals of f that denote:

   (a) The average value of f for $0 \leq x \leq 5$.

   (b) The average value of $|f|$ for $0 \leq x \leq 5$.

Figure 5.80

28. For the even function f in Figure 5.80, consider the average value of f over the following intervals:

   I. $0 \leq x \leq 1$ II. $0 \leq x \leq 2$

   III. $0 \leq x \leq 5$ IV. $-2 \leq x \leq 2$

   (a) For which interval is the average value of f least?

   (b) For which interval is the average value of f greatest?

   (c) For which pair of intervals are the average values equal?

29. **(a)** Suppose $f'(x) = \sin(x^2)$ and $f(0) = 2$. Use a graph of $f'(x)$ to decide which is larger:

   (i) $f(0)$ or $f(1)$ (ii) $f(2)$ or $f(2.5)$

   (b) Estimate $f(b)$ for $b = 0, 1, 2, 3$.

30. **(a)** If $F(t) = t(\ln t) - t$, find $F'(t)$.

   (b) Find $\int_{10}^{12} \ln t\, dt$ two ways:

   (i) Numerically.

   (ii) Using the Fundamental Theorem of Calculus.

[9]*The World Almanac and Book of Facts 2005*, p. 177 (New York: World Almanac Books).

31. Statisticians sometimes use values of the function

$$F(b) = \int_0^b e^{-x^2} \, dx.$$

(a) What is $F(0)$?

(b) Does the value of F increase or decrease as b increases? (Assume $b \geq 0$.)

(c) Find $F(1)$, $F(2)$, and $F(3)$.

In Problems 32–35, find $\int_2^5 f(x) \, dx$.

32. $f(x)$ is odd and $\int_{-2}^5 f(x) \, dx = 8$

33. $f(x)$ is even, $\int_{-2}^2 f(x) \, dx = 6$, and $\int_{-5}^5 f(x) \, dx = 14$

34. $\int_2^5 (3f(x) + 4) \, dx = 18$

35. $\int_2^4 2f(x) \, dx = 8$ and $\int_5^4 f(x) \, dx = 1$

36. Without any computation, find the values of

(a) $\int_{-2}^2 \sin x \, dx$,   (b) $\int_{-\pi}^{\pi} x^{113} \, dx$.

37. Suppose f is periodic, its graph repeating every p units. Given that $\int_0^p f(x) \, dx > 0$, evaluate and simplify

$$\frac{\displaystyle\int_0^{2p} f(x) \, dx + \int_p^{5p} f(x) \, dx}{\displaystyle\int_{5p}^{7p} f(x) \, dx}.$$

38. The function f is even (that is, its graph is symmetric about the y-axis). Use this fact to evaluate and simplify

$$\frac{\int_{-r}^{r} f(x) \, dx + \int_0^r f(x) \, dx}{\displaystyle\int_{-r}^0 f(x) \, dx}, \quad \text{for } r > 0.$$

[Hint: Use the area interpretation of the integral.]

39. (a) Use Figure 5.81 to explain why $\int_{-3}^3 x e^{-x^2} \, dx = 0$.

(b) Find the left-hand sum approximation with $n = 3$ to $\int_0^3 x e^{-x^2} \, dx$. Give your answer to four decimal places.

(c) Repeat part (b) for $\int_{-3}^0 x e^{-x^2} \, dx$.

(d) Do your answers to parts (b) and (c) add to 0? Explain.

Figure 5.81

40. Two trains travel along parallel tracks. The velocity, v, of the trains as functions of time t are shown in Figure 5.82.

(a) Describe in words the trips taken by each train.

(b) Estimate the ratio of the following quantities for Train A to Train B:

(i) Maximum velocity   (ii) Time traveled

(iii) Distance traveled

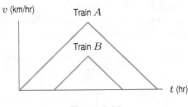

Figure 5.82

41. Worldwide, wind energy generating capacity, W megawatts, t years after 2000, can be modeled[10] by $W = 21{,}000e^{0.22t}$.

(a) What was wind energy generating capacity in 2000? in 2010?

(b) What annual continuous percent increase is indicated by the model?

(c) Estimate average wind energy generating capacity between 2000 and 2010.

In Problems 42–45, let $r(t)$ be the rate, in kg/sec, at which a spaceship burns fuel at time t sec. Assume that $r(t) > 0$ and $r'(t) < 0$ for $0 \leq t \leq T$, where T is the time at which all the fuel has burned. Let T_h be the time at which half the fuel has burned and Q be the initial amount of fuel in kg. State which of the following two expressions is larger, or that they are equal, or that there is not enough information to decide.

42. $\displaystyle\int_0^T r(t) \, dt$ and Q

43. $\displaystyle\int_0^{0.5T} r(t) \, dt$ and $\displaystyle\int_{0.5T}^T r(t) \, dt$

44. $\displaystyle\int_0^{T/3} r(t) \, dt$ and $Q/3$

45. $\displaystyle\int_0^{T_h} r(t) \, dt$ and $\displaystyle\int_0^{0.5T} r(t) \, dt$

46. Use the property $\int_b^a f(x) \, dx = -\int_a^b f(x) \, dx$ to show that $\int_a^a f(x) \, dx = 0$.

47. The average value of $y = v(x)$ equals 4 for $1 \leq x \leq 6$, and equals 5 for $6 \leq x \leq 8$. What is the average value of $v(x)$ for $1 \leq x \leq 8$?

---

[10]Global Wind Energy Council - Global Trends, www.gwec.net, accessed October 2010.

48. (a) For any continuous function f, is
$$\int_1^2 f(x)\,dx + \int_2^3 f(x)\,dx = \int_1^3 f(x)\,dx?$$

(b) For any function f, add the left-hand sum approximation with 10 subdivisions to $\int_1^2 f(x)\,dx$ to the left-hand sum approximation with 10 subdivisions to $\int_2^3 f(x)\,dx$. Do you get the left-sum approximations with 10 subdivisions to $\int_1^3 f(x)\,dx$? If not, interpret the result as a different Riemann Sum.

49. Using Figure 5.83, list the following integrals in increasing order (from smallest to largest). Which integrals are negative, which are positive? Give reasons.

I. $\int_a^b f(x)\,dx$ II. $\int_a^c f(x)\,dx$ III. $\int_a^e f(x)\,dx$
IV. $\int_b^e f(x)\,dx$ V. $\int_b^c f(x)\,dx$

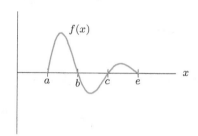

Figure 5.83

In Problems 50–52, the function $F(t)$ gives the thickness, in inches, of ice on a roof t hours after midnight, where $f(t) = F'(t)$, $f(2) = 0.5$, $F(7) = 4$, $F(9) = 5$, and
$$\int_2^{3.5} f'(t)\,dt = 0.75 \quad \text{and} \quad \int_4^7 f(t)\,dt = 1.5.$$

Evaluate the expressions and explain what your answers tell you about the ice on the roof.

50. $\displaystyle\int_7^9 f(t)\,dt$ **51.** $F(4)$ **52.** $F'(3.5)$

53. For the even function f graphed in Figure 5.84:

(a) Suppose you know $\int_0^2 f(x)\,dx$. What is $\int_{-2}^2 f(x)\,dx$?

(b) Suppose you know $\int_0^5 f(x)\,dx$ and $\int_2^5 f(x)\,dx$. What is $\int_0^2 f(x)\,dx$?

(c) Suppose you know $\int_{-2}^5 f(x)\,dx$ and $\int_{-2}^2 f(x)\,dx$. What is $\int_0^5 f(x)\,dx$?

Figure 5.84

54. For the even function f graphed in Figure 5.84:

(a) Suppose you know $\int_{-2}^2 f(x)\,dx$ and $\int_0^5 f(x)\,dx$. What is $\int_2^5 f(x)\,dx$?

(b) Suppose you know $\int_{-2}^5 f(x)\,dx$ and $\int_{-2}^0 f(x)\,dx$. What is $\int_2^5 f(x)\,dx$?

(c) Suppose you know $\int_2^5 f(x)\,dx$ and $\int_{-2}^5 f(x)\,dx$. What is $\int_0^2 f(x)\,dx$?

55. A mouse moves back and forth in a straight tunnel, attracted to bits of cheddar cheese alternately introduced to and removed from the ends (right and left) of the tunnel. The graph of the mouse's velocity, v, is given in Figure 5.85, with positive velocity corresponding to motion toward the right end. Assuming that the mouse starts ($t = 0$) at the center of the tunnel, use the graph to estimate the time(s) at which:

(a) The mouse changes direction.

(b) The mouse is moving most rapidly to the right; to the left.

(c) The mouse is farthest to the right of center; farthest to the left.

(d) The mouse's speed (i.e., the magnitude of its velocity) is decreasing.

(e) The mouse is at the center of the tunnel.

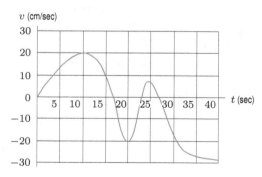

Figure 5.85

Problems 56–57 concern hybrid cars such as the Toyota Prius that are powered by a gas-engine, electric-motor combination, but can also function in Electric-Vehicle (EV) only mode, without power from the engine. Figure 5.86[11] shows the velocity, v, of a 2010 Prius Plug-in Hybrid Prototype operating in normal hybrid mode and EV-only mode, respectively, while accelerating from a stoplight.

Figure 5.86

56. About how far, in feet, does the 2010 Prius Prototype travel in EV-only mode during the first 15 seconds of movement?

57. Assume two identical cars, one running in normal hybrid mode and one running in EV-only mode, accelerate together in a straight path from a stoplight. Approximately how far apart are the cars after 5 seconds?

58. The Montgolfier brothers (Joseph and Etienne) were eighteenth-century pioneers in the field of hot-air ballooning. Had they had the appropriate instruments, they might have left us a record, like that shown in Figure 5.87, of one of their early experiments. The graph shows their vertical velocity, v, with upward as positive.

(a) Over what intervals was the acceleration positive? Negative?

(b) What was the greatest altitude achieved, and at what time?

(c) At what time was the upward acceleration greatest?

(d) At what time was the deceleration greatest?

(e) What might have happened during this flight to explain the answer to part (d)?

(f) This particular flight ended on top of a hill. How do you know that it did, and what was the height of the hill above the starting point?

Figure 5.87

59. The Glen Canyon Dam at the top of the Grand Canyon prevents natural flooding. In 1996, scientists decided an artificial flood was necessary to restore the environmental balance. Water was released through the dam at a controlled rate[12] shown in Figure 5.88. The figure also shows the rate of flow of the last natural flood in 1957.

(a) At what rate was water passing through the dam in 1996 before the artificial flood?

(b) At what rate was water passing down the river in the pre-flood season in 1957?

(c) Estimate the maximum rates of discharge for the 1996 and 1957 floods.

(d) Approximately how long did the 1996 flood last? How long did the 1957 flood last?

(e) Estimate how much additional water passed down the river in 1996 as a result of the artificial flood.

(f) Estimate how much additional water passed down the river in 1957 as a result of the flood.

Figure 5.88

60. Using Figure 5.89, list from least to greatest,

(a) $f'(1)$.

(b) The average value of $f(x)$ on $0 \le x \le a$.

(c) The average value of the rate of change of $f(x)$, for $0 \le x \le a$.

(d) $\int_0^a f(x)\, dx$.

Figure 5.89

---

[11] www.motortrend.com/. Retrieved May 2011.

[12] Adapted from M. Collier, R. Webb, E. Andrews, "Experimental Flooding in Grand Canyon," *Scientific American* (January 1997).

In Problems 61–64, let $f(x) = F'(x)$ where, for all x,

$$f'(x) > 0 \quad \text{and} \quad f''(x) < 0.$$

Explain whether the expression gives the exact value of $f(3.1)$, an underestimate of $f(3.1)$, or an overestimate of $f(3.1)$, or if there is not enough information to decide.

Table 5.10

t	1	2	3	4	5	6	7	8	9	10	11	12
H	20	22	27	28	27	31	29	30	28	25	24	26

61. $f(3) + 0.1f'(3)$

62. $f(3) + \displaystyle\int_3^{3.1} f'(t)\,dt$

63. $\dfrac{F(3.11) - F(3.1)}{0.01}$

64. $f(3) + \displaystyle\sum_{i=1}^{n} f'(x_i)\,\Delta x$, where $n > 0, \Delta x = 0.1/n, x_0 = 3, x_n = 3.1$, with $x_0, x_1, \ldots, x_n$ evenly spaced.

65. The number of days a cold-blooded organism, such as an insect, takes to mature depends on the surrounding temperature, H. Each organism has a minimum temperature $H_{\min}$ below which no development takes place.[13] For an interval of time, Δt, on which the temperature is constant, the increase in maturity of the organism can be measured by the number of degree-days, ΔS, where t is in days and

$$\Delta S = (H - H_{\min})\Delta t.$$

(a) If H varies with time, so $H = f(t)$, write an integral that represents the total number of degree-days, S, required if development to maturity takes T days.

(b) An organism which has $H_{\min} = 15°C$ requires 125 degree-days to develop to maturity. Estimate the development time if the temperature, $H°C$, at time t days is in Table 5.10.

66. Let $\theta(x)$ be the angle of the tangent line at x of the graph of f with the horizontal, as in Figure 5.90. Show that

(a) $\tan \theta = f'(x)$

(b) $1 + (f'(x))^2 = \dfrac{1}{\cos^2 \theta}$

(c) $\dfrac{d\theta}{dx} = \cos^2 \theta \dfrac{d}{dx}(\tan \theta) = \dfrac{f''(x)}{1 + (f'(x))^2}$

(d) $\theta(b) - \theta(a) = \displaystyle\int_a^b \dfrac{f''(x)}{1 + (f'(x))^2}\,dx$

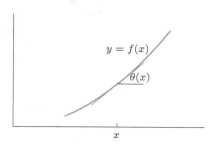

$y = f(x)$

$\theta(x)$

x

Figure 5.90

CAS Challenge Problems

67. Consider the definite integral $\int_0^1 x^4\,dx$.

(a) Write an expression for a right-hand Riemann sum approximation for this integral using n subdivisions. Express each x_i, $i = 1, 2, \ldots, n$, in terms of i.

(b) Use a computer algebra system to obtain a formula for the sum you wrote in part (a) in terms of n.

(c) Take the limit of this expression for the sum as $n \to \infty$, thereby finding the exact value of this integral.

68. Repeat Problem 67, using the definite integral $\int_0^1 x^5\,dx$.

For Problems 69–71, you will write a Riemann sum approximating a definite integral and use a computer algebra system to find a formula for the Riemann sum. By evaluating the limit of this sum as the number of subdivisions approaches infinity, you will obtain the definite integral.

69. (a) Using summation notation, write the left-hand Rie-

mann sum with n subdivisions for $\int_1^2 t\,dt$.

(b) Use a computer algebra system to find a formula for the Riemann sum.

(c) Evaluate the limit of the sum as n approaches infinity.

(d) Calculate directly the area under the graph of $y = t$ between $t = 1$ and $t = 2$, and compare it with your answer to part (c).

70. (a) Using summation notation, write the left-hand Riemann sum with n subdivisions for $\int_1^2 t^2\,dt$.

(b) Use a computer algebra system to find a formula for the Riemann sum.

(c) Evaluate the limit of the sum as n approaches infinity.

(d) What is the area under the graph of $y = t^2$ between $t = 1$ and $t = 2$?

71. (a) Using summation notation, write the right-hand Riemann sum with n subdivisions for $\int_0^\pi \sin x\,dx$.

---

[13]Information from http://www.ento.vt.edu/~sharov/PopEcol/popecol.html (Accessed Nov. 18, 2003).

(b) Use a computer algebra system to find a formula for the Riemann sum. [Note: Not all computer algebra systems can evaluate this sum.]

(c) Use a computer algebra system to evaluate the limit of the sum as n approaches infinity.

(d) Confirm your answer to part (c) by calculating the definite integral with the computer algebra system.

In Problems 72–73:

(a) Use a computer algebra system to compute the given definite integral.

(b) From your answer to part (a) and the Fundamental Theorem of Calculus, guess a function whose derivative is the integrand. Check your guess using the computer algebra system.

[Hint: Make sure that the constants a, b, and c do not have previously assigned values in your computer algebra system.]

72. $\displaystyle\int_a^b \sin(cx)\,dx$

73. $\displaystyle\int_a^c \frac{x}{1+bx^2}\,dx, \quad b > 0$

PROJECTS FOR CHAPTER FIVE

1. Medical Case Study: Cardiac Cycle[14]

Physiologists who study the heart measure and plot quantities that reflect many aspects of cardiac function. One of the most famous plots is the pressure-volume loop, which shows the blood pressure versus the volume of blood in the left ventricle (LV). Both pressure and volume change during the cardiac cycle, the periodic relaxation and contraction of the heart, reflected in the lub-dub sounds of a heartbeat.

The LV is a hollow chamber with walls made of muscle. The LV pumps blood from the heart to all the organs of the body. When the LV contracts, a phase of the cardiac cycle called systole, the walls move in and blood is expelled from the heart and flows out to the organs. When the LV relaxes, a phase called diastole, its walls move out and it fills up with new blood, ready to be pumped out with the next LV contraction.

The cardiac cycle for the LV can be simplified into four phases. Points on the pressure-volume loop in Figure 5.91 represent the pressure and volume at different times during the cycle, and the arrows show the direction of change. When the LV has just finished contracting (so systole ends, and diastole begins), the volume of blood is at a minimum ($D1$). In Phase 1, isometric relaxation, the LV relaxes, causing a drop in the LV pressure, while the volume stays the same, as no new blood can flow into the LV yet. At $D2$, isometric relaxation ends and Phase 2 begins: the LV starts to fill up with new blood, causing an increase in LV volume and a small increase in pressure. At $S1$, diastole ends and the muscular walls of the LV start to contract, initiating systole. In Phase 3, isometric contraction pressure rises rapidly, but no blood is ejected yet, so LV volume remains constant. Phase 4 starts at $S2$, and blood is rapidly expelled from the LV, so the volume decreases, and there is a mild decrease in pressure. This brings the cycle back to $D1$ as systole ends and diastole is ready to begin again.

(a) For each of the four phases of the cardiac cycle, decide whether the work done by the LV wall on the blood is positive, negative, or zero.

(b) Using the units of pressure and volume, find the units of area of regions in the pressure-volume plane.

(c) Suppose Phases 2 and 4 are the graphs of two functions, $g(V)$ and $f(V)$, respectively. Explain why the integral represents the work done by the LV wall on the blood in each phase.

(i) Phase 4, $\int_a^b f(V)\,dV$

(ii) Phase 2, $-\int_a^b g(V)\,dV$

(d) Express the area enclosed by the pressure-volume loop as an integral. Using part (c), give the physical meaning of this area.

---

[14]From David E. Sloane, M.D.

Left ventrical pressure (nt/cm²)

Phase 4

$D1$ $f(V)$ $S2$

Phase 3

Phase 1

$g(V)$ $S1$

$D2$ Phase 2

Left ventrical volume, V (cm³)

a b

Figure 5.91: Pressure-volume loop

2. The Car and the Truck

A car starts at noon and travels along a straight road with the velocity shown in Figure 5.92. A truck starts at 1 pm from the same place and travels along the same road at a constant velocity of 50 mph.

(a) How far away is the car when the truck starts?

(b) How fast is the distance between the car and the truck increasing or decreasing at 3 pm? What is the practical significance (in terms of the distance between the car and the truck) of the fact that the car's velocity is maximized at about 2 pm?

(c) During the period when the car is ahead of the truck, when is the distance between them greatest, and what is that greatest distance?

(d) When does the truck overtake the car, and how far have both traveled then?

(e) Suppose the truck starts at noon. (Everything else remains the same.) Sketch a new graph showing the velocities of both car and truck against time.

(f) How many times do the two graphs in part (e) intersect? What does each intersection mean in terms of the distance between the two?

velocity (mph)

time since noon (hours)

Figure 5.92: Velocity of car starting at noon

3. An Orbiting Satellite

A NASA satellite orbits the earth every 90 minutes. During an orbit, the satellite's electric power comes either from solar array wings, when these are illuminated by the sun, or from batteries. The batteries discharge whenever the satellite uses more electricity than the solar array can provide or whenever the satellite is in the shadow of the earth (where the solar array cannot be used). If the batteries are overused, however, they can be damaged.[15]

---

[15] Adapted from Amy C. R. Gerson, "Electrical Engineering: Space Systems," in *She Does Math! Real Life Problems from Women on the Job*, ed. Marla Parker, p. 61 (Washington, DC: Mathematical Association of America, 1995).

You are to determine whether the batteries could be damaged in either of the following operations. You are told that the battery capacity is 50 ampere-hours. If the total battery discharge does not exceed 40% of battery capacity, the batteries will not be damaged.

(a) Operation 1 is performed by the satellite while orbiting the earth. At the beginning of a given 90-minute orbit, the satellite performs a 15-minute maneuver which requires more current than the solar array can deliver, causing the batteries to discharge. The maneuver causes a sinusoidally varying battery discharge of period 30 minutes with a maximum discharge of ten amperes at 7.5 minutes. For the next 45 minutes the solar array meets the total satellite current demand, and the batteries do not discharge. During the last 30 minutes, the satellite is in the shadow of the earth and the batteries supply the total current demand of 30 amperes.

   (i) The battery current in amperes is a function of time. Plot the function, showing the current in amperes as a function of time for the 90-minute orbit. Write a formula (or formulas) for the battery current function.

   (ii) Calculate the total battery discharge (in units of ampere-hours) for the 90-minute orbit for Operation 1.

   (iii) What is your recommendation regarding the advisability of Operation 1?

(b) Operation 2 is simulated at NASA's laboratory in Houston. The following graph was produced by the laboratory simulation of the current demands on the battery during the 90-minute orbit required for Operation 2.

Figure 5.93: Battery discharge simulation graph for Operation 2

   (i) Calculate the total battery discharge (in units of ampere-hours) for the 90-minute orbit for Operation 2.

   (ii) What is your recommendation regarding the advisability of Operation 2?

Chapter Six

CONSTRUCTING ANTIDERIVATIVES

Contents

6.1 Antiderivatives Graphically and Numerically 320

The Family of Antiderivatives 320

Visualizing Antiderivatives Using Slopes 320

Computing Values of an Antiderivative Using
Definite Integrals 321

6.2 Constructing Antiderivatives Analytically . . . 326

An Antiderivative of $f(x) = 0$ 326

What Is the Most General Antiderivative of f ?. 326

The Indefinite Integral 326

An Antiderivative of $f(x) = k$ 327

Finding Antiderivatives 327

Using Antiderivatives to Compute Definite
Integrals 329

6.3 Differential Equations and Motion 332

How Can We Pick One Solution
to the Differential Equation
$\frac{dy}{dx} = f(x)$? 333

Equations of Motion 334

History of the Equations of Motion 336

6.4 Second Fundamental Theorem of Calculus . . 340

Construction of Antiderivatives Using the
Definite Integral. 340

Relationship Between the Construct-
ion Theorem and the
Fundamental Theorem of
Calculus. 341

Using the Construction Theorem for
Antiderivatives. 342

REVIEW PROBLEMS. 345

PROJECTS 350

6.1 ANTIDERIVATIVES GRAPHICALLY AND NUMERICALLY

The Family of Antiderivatives

If the derivative of F is f, we call F an *antiderivative* of f. For example, since the derivative of x^2 is $2x$, we say that

$$x^2 \text{ is an antiderivative of } 2x.$$

Notice that $2x$ has many antiderivatives, since $x^2 + 1$, $x^2 + 2$, and $x^2 + 3$, all have derivative $2x$. In fact, if C is any constant, we have

$$\frac{d}{dx}(x^2 + C) = 2x + 0 = 2x,$$

so any function of the form $x^2 + C$ is an antiderivative of $2x$. The function $f(x) = 2x$ has a *family of antiderivatives*.

Let us look at another example. If v is the velocity of a car and s is its position, then $v = ds/dt$ and s is an antiderivative of v. As before, $s + C$ is an antiderivative of v for any constant C. In terms of the car, adding C to s is equivalent to adding C to the odometer reading. Adding a constant to the odometer reading simply means measuring distance from a different point, which does not alter the car's velocity.

Visualizing Antiderivatives Using Slopes

Suppose we have the graph of f', and we want to sketch an approximate graph of f. We are looking for the graph of f whose slope at any point is equal to the value of f' there. Where f' is above the x-axis, f is increasing; where f' is below the x-axis, f is decreasing. If f' is increasing, f is concave up; if f' is decreasing, f is concave down.

Example 1   The graph of f' is given in Figure 6.1. Sketch a graph of f in the cases when $f(0) = 0$ and $f(0) = 1$.

Figure 6.1: Graph of f'

Figure 6.2: Two different f's which have the same derivative f'

Solution   For $0 \leq x \leq 2$, the function f has a constant slope of 1, so the graph of f is a straight line. For $2 \leq x \leq 4$, the function f is increasing but more and more slowly; it has a maximum at $x = 4$ and decreases thereafter. (See Figure 6.2.) The solutions with $f(0) = 0$ and $f(0) = 1$ start at different points on the vertical axis but have the same shape.

Example 2   Sketch a graph of the antiderivative F of $f(x) = e^{-x^2}$ satisfying $F(0) = 0$.

Solution   The graph of $f(x) = e^{-x^2}$ is shown in Figure 6.3. The slope of the antiderivative $F(x)$ is given by $f(x)$. Since $f(x)$ is always positive, the antiderivative $F(x)$ is always increasing. Since $f(x)$ is increasing for negative x, we know that $F(x)$ is concave up for negative x. Since $f(x)$ is decreasing for positive x, we know that $F(x)$ is concave down for positive x. Since $f(x) \to 0$ as $x \to \pm\infty$, the graph of $F(x)$ levels off at both ends. See Figure 6.4.

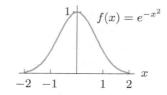

Figure 6.3: Graph of $f(x) = e^{-x^2}$

Figure 6.4: An antiderivative $F(x)$ of
$f(x) = e^{-x^2}$

Example 3   For the function f' given in Figure 6.5, sketch a graph of three antiderivative functions f, one with $f(0) = 0$, one with $f(0) = 1$, and one with $f(0) = 2$.

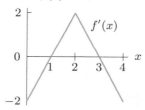

Figure 6.5: Slope function, f'

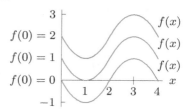

Figure 6.6: Antiderivatives f

Solution   To graph f, start at the point on the vertical axis specified by the initial condition and move with slope given by the value of f' in Figure 6.5. Different initial conditions lead to different graphs for f, but for a given x-value they all have the same slope (because the value of f' is the same for each). Thus, the different f curves are obtained from one another by a vertical shift. See Figure 6.6.

- Where f' is positive ($1 < x < 3$), we see f is increasing; where f' is negative ($0 < x < 1$ or $3 < x < 4$), we see f is decreasing.
- Where f' is increasing ($0 < x < 2$), we see f is concave up; where f' is decreasing ($2 < x < 4$), we see f is concave down.
- Where $f' = 0$, we see f has a local maximum at $x = 3$ and a local minimum at $x = 1$.
- Where f' has a maximum ($x = 2$), we see f has a point of inflection.

Computing Values of an Antiderivative Using Definite Integrals

A graph of f' shows where f is increasing and where f is decreasing. We can calculate the actual value of the function f using the Fundamental Theorem of Calculus (Theorem 5.1 on page 290): If f' is continuous, then

$$\int_a^b f'(x)\, dx = f(b) - f(a).$$

If we know $f(a)$, we can estimate $f(b)$ by computing the definite integral using area or Riemann sums.

Example 4   Figure 6.7 is the graph of the derivative $f'(x)$ of a function $f(x)$. It is given that $f(0) = 100$. Sketch the graph of $f(x)$, showing all critical points and inflection points of f and giving their coordinates.

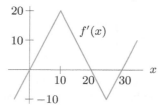

Figure 6.7: Graph of derivative

Solution   The critical points of f occur at $x = 0$, $x = 20$, and $x = 30$, where $f'(x) = 0$. The inflection points of f occur at $x = 10$ and $x = 25$, where $f'(x)$ has a maximum or minimum. To find the coordinates of the critical points and inflection points of f, we evaluate $f(x)$ for $x = 0, 10, 20, 25, 30$. Using the Fundamental Theorem, we can express the values of $f(x)$ in terms of definite integrals. We evaluate the definite integrals using the areas of triangular regions under the graph of $f'(x)$, remembering that areas below the x-axis are subtracted. (See Figure 6.8.)

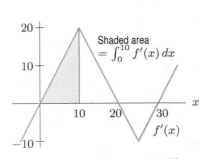

Figure 6.8: Finding $f(10) = f(0) + \int_0^{10} f'(x)\, dx$

Figure 6.9: Graph of $f(x)$

Since $f(0) = 100$, the Fundamental Theorem gives us the following values of f, which are marked in Figure 6.9.

$$f(10) = f(0) + \int_0^{10} f'(x)\, dx = 100 + \text{(Shaded area in Figure 6.8)} = 100 + \frac{1}{2}(10)(20) = 200,$$

$$f(20) = f(10) + \int_{10}^{20} f'(x)\, dx = 200 + \frac{1}{2}(10)(20) = 300,$$

$$f(25) = f(20) + \int_{20}^{25} f'(x)\, dx = 300 - \frac{1}{2}(5)(10) = 275,$$

$$f(30) = f(25) + \int_{25}^{30} f'(x)\, dx = 275 - \frac{1}{2}(5)(10) = 250.$$

Example 5   Suppose $F'(t) = t \cos t$ and $F(0) = 2$. Find $F(b)$ at the points $b = 0, 0.1, 0.2, \ldots, 1.0$.

Solution   We apply the Fundamental Theorem with $f(t) = t \cos t$ and $a = 0$ to get values for $F(b)$:

$$F(b) - F(0) = \int_0^b F'(t)\, dt = \int_0^b t \cos t\, dt.$$

Since $F(0) = 2$, we have

$$F(b) = 2 + \int_0^b t \cos t\, dt.$$

Calculating the definite integral $\int_0^b t \cos t\, dt$ numerically for $b = 0, 0.1, 0.2, \ldots, 1.0$ gives the values for F in Table 6.1:

Table 6.1   *Approximate values for F*

b	0	0.1	0.2	0.3	0.4	0.5	0.6	0.7	0.8	0.9	1.0
$F(b)$	2.000	2.005	2.020	2.044	2.077	2.117	2.164	2.216	2.271	2.327	2.382

Notice that $F(b)$ appears to be increasing between $b = 0$ and $b = 1$. This could have been predicted from the fact that $t \cos t$, the derivative of $F(t)$, is positive for t between 0 and 1.

Exercises and Problems for Section 6.1

Exercises

1. Fill in the blanks in the following statements, assuming that $F(x)$ is an antiderivative of $f(x)$:

    (a) If $f(x)$ is positive over an interval, then $F(x)$ is _____ over the interval.

    (b) If $f(x)$ is increasing over an interval, then $F(x)$ is _____ over the interval.

2. Use Figure 6.10 and the fact that $P = 0$ when $t = 0$ to find values of P when $t = 1, 2, 3, 4$ and 5.

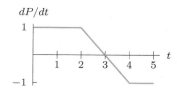

Figure 6.10

3. Use Figure 6.11 and the fact that $P = 2$ when $t = 0$ to find values of P when $t = 1, 2, 3, 4$ and 5.

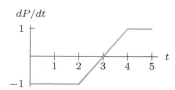

Figure 6.11

In Exercises 4–11, sketch two functions F such that $F' = f$. In one case let $F(0) = 0$ and in the other, let $F(0) = 1$.

4.

5.

6.

7.

8.

9.

10.

11.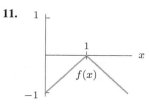

Problems

12. Let $F(x)$ be an antiderivative of $f(x)$.

    (a) If $\int_2^5 f(x)\,dx = 4$ and $F(5) = 10$, find $F(2)$.

    (b) If $\int_0^{100} f(x)\,dx = 0$, what is the relationship between $F(100)$ and $F(0)$?

13. Estimate $f(x)$ for $x = 2, 4, 6$, using the given values of $f'(x)$ and the fact that $f(0) = 100$.

x	0	2	4	6
$f'(x)$	10	18	23	25

14. Estimate $f(x)$ for $x = 2, 4, 6$, using the given values of $f'(x)$ and the fact that $f(0) = 50$.

x	0	2	4	6
$f'(x)$	17	15	10	2

15. A particle moves back and forth along the x-axis. Figure 6.12 approximates the velocity of the particle as a function of time. Positive velocities represent movement to the right and negative velocities represent movement to the left. The particle starts at the point $x = 5$. Graph the distance of the particle from the origin, with distance measured in kilometers and time in hours.

Figure 6.12

16. Assume f' is given by the graph in Figure 6.13. Suppose f is continuous and that $f(0) = 0$.

(a) Find $f(3)$ and $f(7)$.
(b) Find all x with $f(x) = 0$.
(c) Sketch a graph of f over the interval $0 \le x \le 7$.

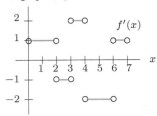

Figure 6.13

17. The graph of dy/dt against t is in Figure 6.14. The three shaded regions each have area 2. If $y = 0$ when $t = 0$, draw the graph of y as a function of t, labeling the known y-values, maxima and minima, and inflection points. Mark $t_1, t_2, \ldots, t_5$ on the t axis.[1]

Figure 6.14

18. Repeat Problem 17 for the graph of dy/dt given in Figure 6.15. (Each of the three shaded regions has area 2.)

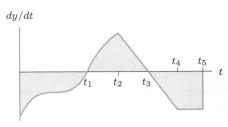

Figure 6.15

19. Using Figure 6.16, sketch a graph of an antiderivative $G(t)$ of $g(t)$ satisfying $G(0) = 5$. Label each critical point of $G(t)$ with its coordinates.

Figure 6.16

20. Using the graph of g' in Figure 6.17 and the fact that $g(0) = 50$, sketch the graph of $g(x)$. Give the coordinates of all critical points and inflection points of g.

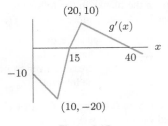

Figure 6.17

21. Figure 6.18 shows the rate of change of the concentration of adrenaline, in micrograms per milliliter per minute, in a person's body. Sketch a graph of the concentration of adrenaline, in micrograms per milliliter, in the body as a function of time, in minutes.

Figure 6.18

22. Urologists are physicians who specialize in the health of the bladder. In a common diagnostic test, urologists monitor the emptying of the bladder using a device that produces two graphs. In one of the graphs the flow rate (in milliliters per second) is measured as a function of time (in seconds). In the other graph, the volume emptied from the bladder is measured (in milliliters) as a function of time (in seconds). See Figure 6.19.

(a) Which graph is the flow rate and which is the volume?
(b) Which one of these graphs is an antiderivative of the other?

Figure 6.19

[1]From *Calculus: The Analysis of Functions*, by Peter D. Taylor (Toronto: Wall & Emerson, Inc., 1992).

In Problems 23–26, sketch two functions F with $F'(x) = f(x)$. In one, let $F(0) = 0$; in the other, let $F(0) = 1$. Mark x_1, x_2, and x_3 on the x-axis of your graph. Identify local maxima, minima, and inflection points of $F(x)$.

23.

24.

25.

26.

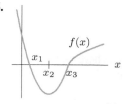

27. Use a graph of $f(x) = 2\sin(x^2)$ to determine where an antiderivative, F, of this function reaches its maximum on $0 \le x \le 3$. If $F(1) = 5$, find the maximum value attained by F.

28. Two functions, $f(x)$ and $g(x)$, are shown in Figure 6.20. Let F and G be antiderivatives of f and g, respectively. On the same axes, sketch graphs of the antiderivatives $F(x)$ and $G(x)$ satisfying $F(0) = 0$ and $G(0) = 0$. Compare F and G, including a discussion of zeros and x- and y-coordinates of critical points.

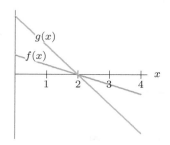

Figure 6.20

29. The graph in Figure 6.21 records the spillage rate at a toxic waste treatment plant over the 50 minutes it took to plug the leak.

    (a) Complete the table for the total quantity spilled in liters in time t minutes since the spill started.

Time t (min)	0	10	20	30	40	50
Quantity (liters)	0					

    (b) Graph the total quantity leaked against time for the entire fifty minutes. Label axes and include units.

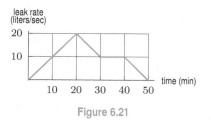

Figure 6.21

30. The Quabbin Reservoir in the western part of Massachusetts provides most of Boston's water. The graph in Figure 6.22 represents the flow of water in and out of the Quabbin Reservoir throughout 2007.

    (a) Sketch a graph of the quantity of water in the reservoir, as a function of time.

    (b) When, in the course of 2007, was the quantity of water in the reservoir largest? Smallest? Mark and label these points on the graph you drew in part (a).

    (c) When was the quantity of water increasing most rapidly? Decreasing most rapidly? Mark and label these times on both graphs.

    (d) By July 2008 the quantity of water in the reservoir was about the same as in January 2007. Draw plausible graphs for the flow into and the flow out of the reservoir for the first half of 2008.

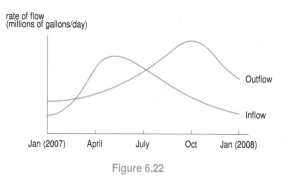

Figure 6.22

In Problems 31–32, explain what is wrong with the statement.

31. Let $F(x)$ be an antiderivative of $f(x)$. If $f(x)$ is everywhere increasing, then $F(x) \geq 0$.

32. If $F(x)$ and $G(x)$ are both antiderivatives of $f(x)$, then $H(x) = F(x) + G(x)$ must also be an antiderivative of $f(x)$.

In Problems 33–34, give an example of:

33. A graph of a function $f(x)$ such that $\int_0^2 f(x)\,dx = 0$.

34. A graph of a function $f(x)$ whose antiderivative is increasing everywhere.

Are the statements in Problems 35–36 true or false? Give an explanation for your answer.

35. A function $f(x)$ has at most one derivative.

36. If $f(t)$ is a linear function with positive slope, then an antiderivative, F, is a linear function.

6.2   CONSTRUCTING ANTIDERIVATIVES ANALYTICALLY

What Is an Antiderivative of $f(x) = 0$?

A function whose derivative is zero everywhere on an interval must have a horizontal tangent line at every point of its graph, and the only way this can happen is if the function is constant. Alternatively, if we think of the derivative as a velocity, and if the velocity is always zero, then the object is standing still; the position function is constant. A rigorous proof of this result using the definition of the derivative is surprisingly subtle. (See the Constant Function Theorem on page 177.)

If $F'(x) = 0$ on an interval, then $F(x) = C$ on this interval, for some constant C.

What Is the Most General Antiderivative of f ?

We know that if a function f has an antiderivative F, then it has a family of antiderivatives of the form $F(x) + C$, where C is any constant. You might wonder if there are any others. To decide, suppose that we have two functions F and G with $F' = f$ and $G' = f$: that is, F and G are both antiderivatives of the same function f. Since $F' = G'$ we have $(G - F)' = 0$. But this means that we must have $G - F = C$, so $G(x) = F(x) + C$, where C is a constant. Thus, any two antiderivatives of the same function differ only by a constant.

If F and G are both antiderivatives of f on an interval, then $G(x) = F(x) + C$.

The Indefinite Integral

All antiderivatives of $f(x)$ are of the form $F(x) + C$. We introduce a notation for the general antiderivative that looks like the definite integral without the limits and is called the *indefinite integral*:

$$\int f(x)\,dx = F(x) + C.$$

It is important to understand the difference between

$$\int_a^b f(x)\,dx \qquad \text{and} \qquad \int f(x)\,dx.$$

The first is a number and the second is a family of *functions*. The word "integration" is frequently used for the process of finding the antiderivative as well as of finding the definite integral. The context usually makes clear which is intended.

What Is an Antiderivative of $f(x) = k$?

If k is a constant, the derivative of kx is k, so we have

An antiderivative of k is kx.

Using the indefinite integral notation, we have

> If k is constant,
> $$\int k \, dx = kx + C.$$

Finding Antiderivatives

Finding antiderivatives of functions is like taking square roots of numbers: if we pick a number at random, such as 7 or 493, we may have trouble finding its square root without a calculator. But if we happen to pick a number such as 25 or 64, which we know is a perfect square, then we can find its square root exactly. Similarly, if we pick a function which we recognize as a derivative, then we can find its antiderivative easily.

For example, to find an antiderivative of $f(x) = x$, notice that $2x$ is the derivative of x^2; this tells us that x^2 is an antiderivative of $2x$. If we divide by 2, then we guess that

An antiderivative of x is $\dfrac{x^2}{2}$.

To check this statement, take the derivative of $x^2/2$:

$$\frac{d}{dx}\left(\frac{x^2}{2}\right) = \frac{1}{2} \cdot \frac{d}{dx} x^2 = \frac{1}{2} \cdot 2x = x.$$

What about an antiderivative of x^2? The derivative of x^3 is $3x^2$, so the derivative of $x^3/3$ is $3x^2/3 = x^2$. Thus,

An antiderivative of x^2 is $\dfrac{x^3}{3}$.

The pattern looks like

An antiderivative of x^n is $\dfrac{x^{n+1}}{n+1}$.

(We assume $n \neq -1$, or we would have $x^0/0$, which does not make sense.) It is easy to check this formula by differentiation:

$$\frac{d}{dx}\left(\frac{x^{n+1}}{n+1}\right) = \frac{(n+1)x^n}{n+1} = x^n.$$

In indefinite integral notation, we have shown that

> $$\int x^n \, dx = \frac{x^{n+1}}{n+1} + C, \quad n \neq -1.$$

What about when $n = -1$? In other words, what is an antiderivative of $1/x$? Fortunately, we know a function whose derivative is $1/x$, namely, the natural logarithm. Thus, since

$$\frac{d}{dx}(\ln x) = \frac{1}{x},$$

we know that

$$\int \frac{1}{x}\, dx = \ln x + C, \quad \text{for } x > 0.$$

If $x < 0$, then $\ln x$ is not defined, so it can't be an antiderivative of $1/x$. In this case, we can try $\ln(-x)$:

$$\frac{d}{dx}\ln(-x) = (-1)\frac{1}{-x} = \frac{1}{x}$$

so

$$\int \frac{1}{x}\, dx = \ln(-x) + C, \quad \text{for } x < 0.$$

This means $\ln x$ is an antiderivative of $1/x$ if $x > 0$, and $\ln(-x)$ is an antiderivative of $1/x$ if $x < 0$. Since $|x| = x$ when $x > 0$ and $|x| = -x$ when $x < 0$, we can collapse these two formulas into:

An antiderivative of $\dfrac{1}{x}$ is $\ln|x|$.

Therefore

$$\int \frac{1}{x}\, dx = \ln|x| + C.$$

Since the exponential function is its own derivative, it is also its own antiderivative; thus

$$\int e^x\, dx = e^x + C.$$

Also, antiderivatives of the sine and cosine are easy to guess. Since

$$\frac{d}{dx}\sin x = \cos x \quad \text{and} \quad \frac{d}{dx}\cos x = -\sin x,$$

we get

$$\int \cos x\, dx = \sin x + C \quad \text{and} \quad \int \sin x\, dx = -\cos x + C.$$

Example 1   Find $\displaystyle\int (3x + x^2)\, dx$.

Solution   We know that $x^2/2$ is an antiderivative of x and that $x^3/3$ is an antiderivative of x^2, so we expect

$$\int (3x + x^2)\, dx = 3\left(\frac{x^2}{2}\right) + \frac{x^3}{3} + C.$$

You should always check your antiderivatives by differentiation—it's easy to do. Here

$$\frac{d}{dx}\left(\frac{3}{2}x^2 + \frac{x^3}{3} + C\right) = \frac{3}{2}\cdot 2x + \frac{3x^2}{3} = 3x + x^2.$$

The preceding example illustrates that the sum and constant multiplication rules of differentiation work in reverse:

Theorem 6.1: Properties of Antiderivatives: Sums and Constant Multiples

In indefinite integral notation,

1. $\int (f(x) \pm g(x))\, dx = \int f(x)\, dx \pm \int g(x)\, dx$

2. $\int c f(x)\, dx = c \int f(x)\, dx.$

In words,

1. An antiderivative of the sum (or difference) of two functions is the sum (or difference) of their antiderivatives.

2. An antiderivative of a constant times a function is the constant times an antiderivative of the function.

These properties are analogous to the properties for definite integrals given on page 300 in Section 5.4, even though definite integrals are numbers and antiderivatives are functions.

Example 2   Find $\int (\sin x + 3 \cos x)\, dx.$

Solution   We break the antiderivative into two terms:

$$\int (\sin x + 3 \cos x)\, dx = \int \sin x\, dx + 3 \int \cos x\, dx = -\cos x + 3 \sin x + C.$$

Check by differentiating:

$$\frac{d}{dx}(-\cos x + 3 \sin x + C) = \sin x + 3 \cos x.$$

Using Antiderivatives to Compute Definite Integrals

As we saw in Section 5.3, the Fundamental Theorem of Calculus gives us a way of calculating definite integrals. Denoting $F(b) - F(a)$ by $F(x)\big|_a^b$, the theorem says that if $F' = f$ and f is continuous, then

$$\int_a^b f(x)\, dx = F(x)\bigg|_a^b = F(b) - F(a).$$

To find $\int_a^b f(x)\, dx$, we first find F, and then calculate $F(b) - F(a)$. This method of computing definite integrals gives an exact answer. However, the method only works in situations where we can find the antiderivative $F(x)$. This is not always easy; for example, none of the functions we have encountered so far is an antiderivative of $\sin(x^2)$.

Example 3   Compute $\int_1^2 3x^2\, dx$ using the Fundamental Theorem.

Solution   Since $F(x) = x^3$ is an antiderivative of $f(x) = 3x^2$,

$$\int_1^2 3x^2\, dx = F(x)\bigg|_1^2 = F(2) - F(1),$$

gives

$$\int_1^2 3x^2\, dx = x^3\bigg|_1^2 = 2^3 - 1^3 = 7.$$

Notice in this example we used the antiderivative x^3, but $x^3 + C$ works just as well because the constant C cancels out:

$$\int_1^2 3x^2\, dx = (x^3 + C)\Big|_1^2 = (2^3 + C) - (1^3 + C) = 7.$$

Example 4   Compute $\int_0^{\pi/4} \dfrac{1}{\cos^2 \theta}\, d\theta$ exactly.

Solution   We use the Fundamental Theorem. Since $F(\theta) = \tan \theta$ is an antiderivative of $f(\theta) = 1/\cos^2 \theta$, we get

$$\int_0^{\pi/4} \frac{1}{\cos^2 \theta}\, d\theta = \tan \theta \Big|_0^{\pi/4} = \tan\left(\frac{\pi}{4}\right) - \tan(0) = 1.$$

Exercises and Problems for Section 6.2

Exercises

In Exercises 1–16, find an antiderivative.

1. $f(x) = 5$

2. $f(t) = 5t$

3. $f(x) = x^2$

4. $g(t) = t^2 + t$

5. $g(z) = \sqrt{z}$

6. $h(z) = \dfrac{1}{z}$

7. $r(t) = \dfrac{1}{t^2}$

8. $h(t) = \cos t$

9. $g(z) = \dfrac{1}{z^3}$

10. $q(y) = y^4 + \dfrac{1}{y}$

11. $f(z) = e^z$

12. $g(t) = \sin t$

13. $f(t) = 2t^2 + 3t^3 + 4t^4$

14. $p(t) = t^3 - \dfrac{t^2}{2} - t$

15. $f(t) = \dfrac{t^2 + 1}{t}$

16. $f(x) = 5x - \sqrt{x}$

In Exercises 17–28, find the general antiderivative.

17. $f(t) = 6t$

18. $h(x) = x^3 - x$

19. $f(x) = x^2 - 4x + 7$

20. $g(t) = \sqrt{t}$

21. $r(t) = t^3 + 5t - 1$

22. $f(z) = z + e^z$

23. $g(x) = \sin x + \cos x$

24. $h(x) = 4x^3 - 7$

25. $p(t) = \dfrac{1}{\sqrt{t}}$

26. $p(t) = 2 + \sin t$

27. $g(x) = \dfrac{5}{x^3}$

28. $h(t) = \dfrac{7}{\cos^2 t}$

In Exercises 29–36, find an antiderivative $F(x)$ with $F'(x) = f(x)$ and $F(0) = 0$. Is there only one possible solution?

29. $f(x) = 3$

30. $f(x) = 2x$

31. $f(x) = -7x$

32. $f(x) = 2 + 4x + 5x^2$

33. $f(x) = \dfrac{1}{4}x$

34. $f(x) = x^2$

35. $f(x) = \sqrt{x}$

36. $f(x) = \sin x$

In Exercises 37–50, find the indefinite integrals.

37. $\displaystyle\int (5x + 7)\, dx$

38. $\displaystyle\int \left(4t + \frac{1}{t}\right) dt$

39. $\displaystyle\int (2 + \cos t)\, dt$

40. $\displaystyle\int 7e^x\, dx$

41. $\displaystyle\int (3e^x + 2\sin x)\, dx$

42. $\displaystyle\int (4e^x - 3\sin x)\, dx$

43. $\displaystyle\int \left(5x^2 + 2\sqrt{x}\right) dx$

44. $\displaystyle\int (x + 3)^2\, dx$

45. $\displaystyle\int \frac{8}{\sqrt{x}}\, dx$

46. $\displaystyle\int \left(\frac{3}{t} - \frac{2}{t^2}\right) dt$

47. $\displaystyle\int (e^x + 5)\, dx$

48. $\displaystyle\int t^3(t^2 + 1)\, dt$

49. $\displaystyle\int \left(\sqrt{x^3} - \frac{2}{x}\right) dx$

50. $\displaystyle\int \left(\frac{x + 1}{x}\right) dx$

In Exercises 51–60, evaluate the definite integrals exactly [as in $\ln(3\pi)$], using the Fundamental Theorem, and numerically [$\ln(3\pi) \approx 2.243$]:

51. $\int_0^3 (x^2 + 4x + 3)\,dx$

52. $\int_1^3 \frac{1}{t}\,dt$

53. $\int_0^{\pi/4} \sin x\,dx$

54. $\int_0^1 2e^x\,dx$

55. $\int_0^2 3e^x\,dx$

56. $\int_2^5 (x^3 - \pi x^2)\,dx$

57. $\int_0^1 \sin\theta\,d\theta$

58. $\int_1^2 \frac{1 + y^2}{y}\,dy$

59. $\int_0^2 \left(\frac{x^3}{3} + 2x\right)dx$

60. $\int_0^{\pi/4} (\sin t + \cos t)\,dt$

Problems

61. Water is pumped into a cylindrical tank, standing vertically, at a decreasing rate given at time t minutes by

$$r(t) = 120 - 6t \text{ ft}^3/\text{min} \quad \text{for } 0 \le t \le 10.$$

The tank has radius 5 ft and is empty when $t = 0$. Find the depth of water in the tank at $t = 4$.

62. A car moves along a straight line with velocity, in feet/second, given by

$$v(t) = 6 - 2t \quad \text{for } t \ge 0.$$

(a) Describe the car's motion in words. (When is it moving forward, backward, and so on?)

(b) The car's position is measured from its starting point. When is it farthest forward? Backward?

(c) Find s, the car's position measured from its starting point, as a function of time.

63. A helicopter rotor slows down at a constant rate from 350 revs/min to 260 revs/min in 1.5 minutes.

(a) Find the angular acceleration during this time interval. What are the units of this acceleration?

(b) Assuming the angular acceleration remains constant, how long does it take for the rotor to stop? (Measure time from the moment when speed was 350 revs/min.)

(c) How many revolutions does the rotor make between the time the angular speed was 350 revs/min and stopping?

64. In drilling an oil well, the total cost, C, consists of fixed costs (independent of the depth of the well) and marginal costs, which depend on depth; drilling becomes more expensive, per meter, deeper into the earth. Suppose the fixed costs are 1,000,000 riyals (the riyal is the unit of currency of Saudi Arabia), and the marginal costs are

$$C'(x) = 4000 + 10x \text{ riyals/meter},$$

where x is the depth in meters. Find the total cost of drilling a well x meters deep.

65. Use the Fundamental Theorem to find the area under $f(x) = x^2$ between $x = 0$ and $x = 3$.

66. Find the exact area of the region bounded by the x-axis and the graph of $y = x^3 - x$.

67. Calculate the exact area above the graph of $y = \frac{1}{2}\left(\frac{3}{\pi}x\right)^2$ and below the graph of $y = \cos x$. The curves intersect at $x = \pm\pi/3$.

68. Find the exact area of the shaded region in Figure 6.23 between $y = 3x^2 - 3$ and the x-axis.

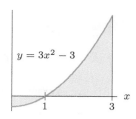

$y = 3x^2 - 3$

Figure 6.23

69. (a) Find the exact area between $f(x) = x^3 - 7x^2 + 10x$, the x-axis, $x = 0$, and $x = 5$.

(b) Find $\int_0^5 (x^3 - 7x^2 + 10x)\,dx$ exactly and interpret this integral in terms of areas.

70. Find the exact area between the curve $y = e^x - 2$ and the x-axis for $0 \le x \le 2$.

71. Find the exact area between the curves $y = x^2$ and $y = 2 - x^2$.

72. Find the exact area between the x-axis and the graph of $f(x) = (x - 1)(x - 2)(x - 3)$.

73. Consider the area between the curve $y = e^x - 2$ and the x-axis, between $x = 0$ and $x = c$ for $c > 0$. Find the value of c making the area above the axis equal to the area below the axis.

74. The area under $1/\sqrt{x}$ on the interval $1 \le x \le b$ is equal to 6. Find the value of b using the Fundamental Theorem.

75. Find the exact positive value of c which makes the area under the graph of $y = c(1 - x^2)$ and above the x-axis equal to 1.

76. Sketch the parabola $y = x(x - \pi)$ and the curve $y = \sin x$, showing their points of intersection. Find the exact area between the two graphs.

77. Find the exact average value of $f(x) = \sqrt{x}$ on the interval $0 \leq x \leq 9$. Illustrate your answer on a graph of $f(x) = \sqrt{x}$.

In Problems 78–79, evaluate the integral using $f(x) = 4x^{-3}$.

78. $\int_1^3 f\left(x^{-1}\right) \, dx$

79. $\int_1^3 f'(x) \, dx$

80. If A_n is the area between the curves $y = x$ and $y = x^n$, show that $A_n \to \frac{1}{2}$ as $n \to \infty$ and explain this result graphically.

81. (a) Explain why you can rewrite x^x as $x^x = e^{x \ln x}$ for $x > 0$.

    (b) Use your answer to part (a) to find $\dfrac{d}{dx}(x^x)$.

    (c) Find $\displaystyle\int x^x(1 + \ln x)dx$.

    (d) Find $\displaystyle\int_1^2 x^x(1 + \ln x)dx$ exactly using part (c). Check your answer numerically.

82. (a) What is the average value of $f(t) = \sin t$ over $0 \leq t \leq 2\pi$? Why is this a reasonable answer?

    (b) Find the average of $f(t) = \sin t$ over $0 \leq t \leq \pi$.

83. The origin and the point (a, a) are at opposite corners of a square. Calculate the ratio of the areas of the two parts into which the curve $\sqrt{x} + \sqrt{y} = \sqrt{a}$ divides the square.

Strengthen Your Understanding

In Problems 84–85, explain what is wrong with the statement.

84. $\displaystyle\int \frac{3x^2 + 1}{2x} \, dx = \frac{x^3 + x}{x^2} + C$

85. For all n, $\displaystyle\int x^n \, dx = \frac{x^{n+1}}{n+1} + C$.

In Problems 86–87, give an example of:

86. Two different functions $F(x)$ and $G(x)$ that have the same derivative.

87. A function $f(x)$ whose antiderivative $F(x)$ has a graph which is a line with negative slope.

Are the statements in Problems 88–96 true or false? Give an explanation for your answer.

88. An antiderivative of $3\sqrt{x + 1}$ is $2(x + 1)^{3/2}$.

89. An antiderivative of $3x^2$ is $x^3 + \pi$.

90. An antiderivative of $1/x$ is $\ln |x| + \ln 2$.

91. An antiderivative of e^{-x^2} is $-e^{-x^2}/2x$.

92. $\int f(x) \, dx = (1/x) \int x f(x) \, dx$.

93. If $F(x)$ is an antiderivative of $f(x)$ and $G(x) = F(x) + 2$, then $G(x)$ is an antiderivative of $f(x)$.

94. If $F(x)$ and $G(x)$ are two antiderivatives of $f(x)$ for $-\infty < x < \infty$ and $F(5) > G(5)$, then $F(10) > G(10)$.

95. If $F(x)$ is an antiderivative of $f(x)$ and $G(x)$ is an antiderivative of $g(x)$, then $F(x) \cdot G(x)$ is an antiderivative of $f(x) \cdot g(x)$.

96. If $F(x)$ and $G(x)$ are both antiderivatives of $f(x)$ on an interval, then $F(x) - G(x)$ is a constant function.

6.3 DIFFERENTIAL EQUATIONS AND MOTION

An equation of the form

$$\frac{dy}{dx} = f(x)$$

is an example of a *differential equation*. Finding the *general solution* to the differential equation means finding the general antiderivative $y = F(x) + C$ with $F'(x) = f(x)$. Chapter 11 gives more details.

Example 1   Find and graph the general solution of the differential equation

$$\frac{dy}{dx} = 2x.$$

Solution   We are asking for a function whose derivative is $2x$. One antiderivative of $2x$ is

$$y = x^2.$$

The general solution is therefore

$$y = x^2 + C,$$

where C is any constant. Figure 6.24 shows several curves in this family.

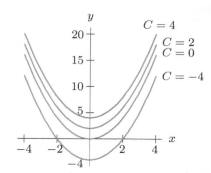

Figure 6.24: Solution curves of
$dy/dx = 2x$

How Can We Pick One Solution to the Differential Equation $\dfrac{dy}{dx} = f(x)$?

Picking one antiderivative is equivalent to selecting a value of C. To do this, we need an extra piece of information, usually that the solution curve passes through a particular point (x_0, y_0). The differential equation plus the extra condition

$$\frac{dy}{dx} = f(x), \qquad y(x_0) = y_0$$

is called an *initial value problem*. (The *initial condition* $y(x_0) = y_0$ is shorthand for $y = y_0$ when $x = x_0$.) An initial value problem usually has a unique solution, called the *particular solution*.

Example 2   Find the solution of the initial value problem

$$\frac{dy}{dx} = 2x, \quad y(3) = 5.$$

Solution   We have already seen that the general solution to the differential equation is $y = x^2 + C$. The initial condition allows us to determine the constant C. Substituting $y(3) = 5$ gives

$$5 = y(3) = 3^2 + C,$$

so C is given by

$$C = -4.$$

Thus, the (unique) solution is

$$y = x^2 - 4$$

Figure 6.24 shows this particular solution, marked $C = -4$.

Equations of Motion

We now use differential equations to analyze the motion of an object falling freely under the influence of gravity. It has been known since Galileo's time that an object moving under the influence of gravity (ignoring air resistance) has constant acceleration, g. In the most frequently used units, its value is approximately

$$g = 9.8 \text{ m/sec}^2, \quad \text{or} \quad g = 32 \text{ ft/sec}^2.$$

Thus, if v is the upward velocity and t is the time, we have the differential equation

$$\frac{dv}{dt} = -g.$$

The negative sign represents the fact that positive velocity is measured upward, whereas gravity acts downward.

Example 3   A stone is dropped from a 100-foot-high building. Find, as functions of time, its position and velocity. When does it hit the ground, and how fast is it going at that time?

Solution   Suppose t is measured in seconds from the time when the stone was dropped. If we measure distance, s, in feet above the ground, then the velocity, v, is in ft/sec upward, and the acceleration due to gravity is 32 ft/sec^2 downward, so we have the differential equation

$$\frac{dv}{dt} = -32.$$

From what we know about antiderivatives, the general solution is

$$v = -32t + C,$$

where C is some constant. Since $v = C$ when $t = 0$, the constant C represents the initial velocity, v_0. The fact that the stone is dropped rather than thrown tells us that the initial velocity is zero, so the initial condition is $v_0 = 0$. Substituting gives

$$0 = -32(0) + C \quad \text{so} \quad C = 0.$$

Thus,

$$v = -32t.$$

But now we can write a second differential equation:

$$v = \frac{ds}{dt} = -32t.$$

The general solution is

$$s = -16t^2 + K,$$

where K is another constant.

Since the stone starts at the top of the building, we have the initial condition $s = 100$ when $t = 0$. Substituting gives

$$100 = -16(0^2) + K, \quad \text{so} \quad K = 100,$$

and therefore

$$s = -16t^2 + 100.$$

Thus, we have found both v and s as functions of time.

The stone hits the ground when $s = 0$, so we must solve

$$0 = -16t^2 + 100$$

giving $t^2 = 100/16$ or $t = \pm 10/4 = \pm 2.5$ sec. Since t must be positive, $t = 2.5$ sec. At that time, $v = -32(2.5) = -80$ ft/sec. (The velocity is negative because we are considering moving up as positive and down as negative.) After the stone hits the ground, the differential equation no longer applies.

Example 4   An object is thrown vertically upward with a speed of 10 m/sec from a height of 2 meters above the ground. Find the highest point it reaches and the time when it hits the ground.

Solution   We must find the position as a function of time. In this example, the velocity is in m/sec, so we use $g = 9.8$ m/sec^2. Measuring distance in meters upward from the ground, we have the differential equation

$$\frac{dv}{dt} = -9.8.$$

As before, v is a function whose derivative is constant, so

$$v = -9.8t + C.$$

Since the initial velocity is 10 m/sec upward, we know that $v = 10$ when $t = 0$. Substituting gives

$$10 = -9.8(0) + C \quad \text{so} \quad C = 10.$$

Thus,

$$v = -9.8t + 10.$$

To find s, we use

$$v = \frac{ds}{dt} = -9.8t + 10$$

and look for a function that has $-9.8t + 10$ as its derivative. The general solution is

$$s = -4.9t^2 + 10t + K,$$

where K is any constant. To find K, we use the fact that the object starts at a height of 2 meters above the ground, so $s = 2$ when $t = 0$. Substituting gives

$$2 = -4.9(0)^2 + 10(0) + K, \quad \text{so} \quad K = 2,$$

and therefore

$$s = -4.9t^2 + 10t + 2.$$

The object reaches its highest point when the velocity is 0, so at that time

$$v = -9.8t + 10 = 0.$$

This occurs when

$$t = \frac{10}{9.8} \approx 1.02 \text{ sec.}$$

When $t = 1.02$ seconds,

$$s = -4.9(1.02)^2 + 10(1.02) + 2 \approx 7.10 \text{ meters.}$$

So the maximum height reached is 7.10 meters. The object reaches the ground when $s = 0$:

$$0 = -4.9t^2 + 10t + 2.$$

Solving this using the quadratic formula gives

$$t \approx -0.18 \quad \text{and} \quad t \approx 2.22 \text{ sec.}$$

Since the time at which the object hits the ground must be positive, $t \approx 2.22$ seconds.

History of the Equations of Motion

The problem of a body moving freely under the influence of gravity near the surface of the earth intrigued mathematicians and philosophers from Greek times onward and was finally solved by Galileo and Newton. The question to be answered was: How do the velocity and the position of the body vary with time? We define s to be the position, or height, of the body above a fixed point (often ground level), v is the velocity of the body measured upward, and a is the acceleration. The velocity and position at time $t = 0$ are represented by v_0 and s_0 respectively. We assume that the acceleration of the body is a constant, $-g$ (the negative sign means that the acceleration is downward), so

$$\frac{dv}{dt} = a = -g.$$

Problem 35 asks you to show that the motion satisfies

$$v = -gt + v_0,$$
$$s = -\frac{g}{2}t^2 + v_0 t + s_0.$$

Our derivation of the formulas for the velocity and the position of the body hides an almost 2000-year struggle to understand the mechanics of falling bodies, from Aristotle's *Physics* to Galileo's *Dialogues Concerning Two New Sciences*.

Though it is an oversimplification of his ideas, we can say that Aristotle's conception of motion was primarily in terms of *change of position*. This seems entirely reasonable; it is what we commonly observe, and this view dominated discussions of motion for centuries. But it misses a subtlety that was brought to light by Descartes, Galileo, and, with a different emphasis, by Newton. That subtlety is now usually referred to as the *principle of inertia*.

This principle holds that a body traveling undisturbed at constant velocity in a straight line will continue in this motion indefinitely. Stated another way, it says that one cannot distinguish in any absolute sense (that is, by performing an experiment), between being at rest and moving with constant velocity in a straight line. If you are reading this book in a closed room and have no external reference points, there is no experiment that will tell you, one way or the other, whether you are at rest or whether you, the room, and everything in it are moving with constant velocity in a straight line. Therefore, as Newton saw, an understanding of motion should be based on *change of velocity* rather than change of position. Since acceleration is the rate of change of velocity, it is acceleration that must play a central role in the description of motion.

Newton placed a new emphasis on the importance of *forces*. Newton's laws of motion do not say what a force *is*, they say how it *acts*. His first law is the principle of inertia, which says what happens in the *absence* of a force—there is no change in velocity. His second law says that a force acts to produce a change in velocity, that is, an acceleration. It states that $F = ma$, where m is the mass of the object, F is the net force, and a is the acceleration produced by this force.

Galileo demonstrated that a body falling under the influence of gravity does so with constant acceleration. Assuming we can neglect air resistance, this constant acceleration is independent of the mass of the body. This last fact was the outcome of Galileo's famous observation around 1600 that a heavy ball and a light ball dropped off the Leaning Tower of Pisa hit the ground at the same time. Whether or not he actually performed this experiment, Galileo presented a very clear thought experiment in the *Dialogues* to prove the same point. (This point was counter to Aristotle's more common-sense notion that the heavier ball would reach the ground first.) Galileo showed that the mass of the object did not appear as a variable in the equation of motion. Thus, the same constant-acceleration equation applies to all bodies falling under the influence of gravity.

Nearly a hundred years after Galileo's experiment, Newton formulated his laws of motion and gravity, which gave a theoretical explanation of Galileo's experimental observation that the acceleration due to gravity is independent of the mass of the body. According to Newton, acceleration is caused by force, and in the case of falling bodies, that force is the force of gravity.

Exercises and Problems for Section 6.3

Exercises

1. Show that $y = xe^{-x} + 2$ is a solution of the initial value problem

$$\frac{dy}{dx} = (1 - x)e^{-x}, \quad y(0) = 2.$$

2. Show that $y = \sin(2t)$, for $0 \le t < \pi/4$, is a solution to the initial value problem

$$\frac{dy}{dt} = 2\sqrt{1 - y^2}, \quad y(0) = 0.$$

In Exercises 3–8, find the general solution to the differential equation.

3. $\dfrac{dy}{dx} = 2x$

4. $\dfrac{dy}{dt} = t^2$

5. $\dfrac{dy}{dx} = x^3 + 5x^4$

6. $\dfrac{dy}{dt} = e^t$

7. $\dfrac{dy}{dx} = \cos x$

8. $\dfrac{dy}{dx} = \dfrac{1}{x}$, where $x > 0$

In Exercises 9–12, find the solution of the initial value problem.

9. $\dfrac{dy}{dx} = 3x^2, \quad y(0) = 5$

10. $\dfrac{dy}{dx} = x^5 + x^6, \quad y(1) = 2$

11. $\dfrac{dy}{dx} = e^x, \quad y(0) = 7$

12. $\dfrac{dy}{dx} = \sin x, \quad y(0) = 3$

Problems

13. A rock is thrown downward with velocity 10 ft/sec from a bridge 100 ft above the water. How fast is the rock going when it hits the water?

14. A water balloon launched from the roof of a building at time $t = 0$ has vertical velocity $v(t) = -32t + 40$ feet/sec at time t seconds, with $v > 0$ corresponding to upward motion.

   (a) If the roof of the building is 30 feet above the ground, find an expression for the height of the water balloon above the ground at time t.

   (b) What is the average velocity of the balloon between $t = 1.5$ and $t = 3$ seconds?

   (c) A 6-foot person is standing on the ground. How fast is the water balloon falling when it strikes the person on the top of the head?

15. A car starts from rest at time $t = 0$ and accelerates at $-0.6t + 4$ meters/sec^2 for $0 \le t \le 12$. How long does it take for the car to go 100 meters?

16. Ice is forming on a pond at a rate given by

$$\frac{dy}{dt} = k\sqrt{t},$$

where y is the thickness of the ice in inches at time t measured in hours since the ice started forming, and k is a positive constant. Find y as a function of t.

17. A revenue $R(p)$ is obtained by a farmer from selling grain at price p dollars/unit. The marginal revenue is given by $R'(p) = 25 - 2p$.

   (a) Find $R(p)$. Assume the revenue is zero when the price is zero.

   (b) For what prices does the revenue increase as the price increases? For what prices does the revenue decrease as price increases?

18. A firm's marginal cost function is $MC = 3q^2 + 6q + 9$.

   (a) Write a differential equation for the total cost, $C(q)$.

   (b) Find the total cost function if the fixed costs are 400.

19. A tomato is thrown upward from a bridge 25 m above the ground at 40 m/sec.

   (a) Give formulas for the acceleration, velocity, and height of the tomato at time t.

   (b) How high does the tomato go, and when does it reach its highest point?

   (c) How long is it in the air?

20. A car going 80 ft/sec (about 55 mph) brakes to a stop in five seconds. Assume the deceleration is constant.

   (a) Graph the velocity against time, t, for $0 \le t \le 5$ seconds.

   (b) Represent, as an area on the graph, the total distance traveled from the time the brakes are applied until the car comes to a stop.

   (c) Find this area and hence the distance traveled.

   (d) Now find the total distance traveled using antidifferentiation.

21. An object is shot vertically upward from the ground with an initial velocity of 160 ft/sec.

   (a) At what rate is the velocity decreasing? Give units.
   (b) Explain why the graph of velocity of the object against time (with upward positive) is a line.
   (c) Using the starting velocity and your answer to part (b), find the time at which the object reaches the highest point.
   (d) Use your answer to part (c) to decide when the object hits the ground.
   (e) Graph the velocity against time. Mark on the graph when the object reaches its highest point and when it lands.
   (f) Find the maximum height reached by the object by considering an area on the graph.
   (g) Now express velocity as a function of time, and find the greatest height by antidifferentiation.

22. A stone thrown upward from the top of a 320-foot cliff at 128 ft/sec eventually falls to the beach below.

   (a) How long does the stone take to reach its highest point?
   (b) What is its maximum height?
   (c) How long before the stone hits the beach?
   (d) What is the velocity of the stone on impact?

23. A 727 jet needs to attain a speed of 200 mph to take off. If it can accelerate from 0 to 200 mph in 30 seconds, how long must the runway be? (Assume constant acceleration.)

24. A cat, walking along the window ledge of a New York apartment, knocks off a flower pot, which falls to the street 200 feet below. How fast is the flower pot traveling when it hits the street? (Give your answer in ft/sec and in mph, given that 1 ft/sec $= 15/22$ mph.)

25. An Acura NSX going at 70 mph stops in 157 feet. Find the acceleration, assuming it is constant.

26. (a) Find the general solution of the differential equation $dy/dx = 2x + 1$.
   (b) Sketch a graph of at least three solutions.
   (c) Find the solution satisfying $y(1) = 5$. Graph this solution with the others from part (b).

27. (a) Find and graph the general solution of the differential equation

$$\frac{dy}{dx} = \sin x + 2.$$

   (b) Find the solution of the initial value problem

$$\frac{dy}{dx} = \sin x + 2, \quad y(3) = 5.$$

28. On the moon, the acceleration due to gravity is about 1.6 m/sec^2 (compared to $g \approx 9.8$ m/sec^2 on earth). If you drop a rock on the moon (with initial velocity 0), find formulas for:

   (a) Its velocity, $v(t)$, at time t.
   (b) The distance, $s(t)$, it falls in time t.

29. (a) Imagine throwing a rock straight up in the air. What is its initial velocity if the rock reaches a maximum height of 100 feet above its starting point?
   (b) Now imagine being transplanted to the moon and throwing a moon rock vertically upward with the same velocity as in part (a). How high will it go? (On the moon, $g = 5$ ft/sec^2.)

30. An object is dropped from a 400-foot tower. When does it hit the ground and how fast is it going at the time of the impact?

31. The object in Problem 30 falls off the same 400-foot tower. What would the acceleration due to gravity have to be to make it reach the ground in half the time?

32. A ball that is dropped from a window hits the ground in five seconds. How high is the window? (Give your answer in feet.)

33. On the moon the acceleration due to gravity is 5 ft/sec^2. An astronaut jumps into the air with an initial upward velocity of 10 ft/sec. How high does he go? How long is the astronaut off the ground?

34. A particle of mass, m, acted on by a force, F, moves in a straight line. Its acceleration, a, is given by Newton's Law:

$$F = ma.$$

The work, W, done by a constant force when the particle moves through a displacement, d, is

$$W = Fd.$$

The velocity, v, of the particle as a function of time, t, is given in Figure 6.25. What is the sign of the work done during each of the time intervals: $[0, t_1], [t_1, t_2], [t_2, t_3], [t_3, t_4], [t_2, t_4]$?

Figure 6.25

35. Assume the acceleration of a moving body is $-g$ and its initial velocity and position are v_0 and s_0 respectively. Find velocity, v, and position, s, as a function of t.

36. Galileo was the first person to show that the distance traveled by a body falling from rest is proportional to the square of the time it has traveled, and independent of the mass of the body. Derive this result from the fact that the acceleration due to gravity is a constant.

37. While attempting to understand the motion of bodies under gravity, Galileo stated that:

> The time in which any space is traversed by a body starting at rest and uniformly accelerated is equal to the time in which that same space would be traversed by the same body moving at a uniform speed whose value is the mean of the highest velocity and the velocity just before acceleration began.

(a) Write Galileo's statement in symbols, defining all the symbols you use.

(b) Check Galileo's statement for a body dropped off a 100-foot building accelerating from rest under gravity until it hits the ground.

(c) Show why Galileo's statement is true in general.

38. Newton's law of gravity says that the gravitational force between two bodies is attractive and given by

$$F = \frac{GMm}{r^2},$$

where G is the gravitational constant, m and M are the masses of the two bodies, and r is the distance between them. This is the famous *inverse square law*. For a falling body, we take M to be the mass of the earth and r to be the distance from the body to the center of the earth. So, actually, r changes as the body falls, but for anything we can easily observe (say, a ball dropped from the Tower of Pisa), it won't change significantly over the course of the motion. Hence, as an approximation, it is reasonable to assume that the force is constant. According to Newton's second law, acceleration is caused by a force and

$$\text{Force} = \text{Mass} \times \text{Acceleration}.$$

(a) Find the differential equation for the position, s of a moving body as a function of time.

(b) Explain how the differential equation shows the acceleration of the body is independent of its mass.

39. In his *Dialogues Concerning Two New Sciences*, Galileo wrote:

> The distances traversed during equal intervals of time by a body falling from rest stand to one another in the same ratio as the odd numbers beginning with unity.

Assume, as is now believed, that $s = -(gt^2)/2$, where s is the total distance traveled in time t, and g is the acceleration due to gravity.

(a) How far does a falling body travel in the first second (between $t = 0$ and $t = 1$)? During the second second (between $t = 1$ and $t = 2$)? The third second? The fourth second?

(b) What do your answers tell you about the truth of Galileo's statement?

Strengthen Your Understanding

In Problems 40–43, explain what is wrong with the statement.

40. A rock dropped from a 400-foot cliff takes twice as long to hit the ground as it would if it were dropped from a 200-foot cliff.

41. The function $y = \cos(t^2)$ is a solution to the initial value problem

$$\frac{dy}{dt} = -\sin(t^2), \quad y(0) = 1.$$

42. Two solutions to a differential equation $dy/dx = f(x)$ have graphs which cross at the initial value.

43. A differential equation cannot have a constant solution.

In Problems 44–45, give an example of:

44. Two different solutions to the differential equation

$$\frac{dy}{dt} = t + 3.$$

45. A differential equation that has solution $y = \cos(5x)$.

Are the statements in Problems 46–54 true or false? Give an explanation for your answer.

46. If $F(x)$ is an antiderivative of $f(x)$, then $y = F(x)$ is a solution to the differential equation $dy/dx = f(x)$.

47. If $y = F(x)$ is a solution to the differential equation $dy/dx = f(x)$, then $F(x)$ is an antiderivative of $f(x)$.

48. If an object has constant nonzero acceleration, then the position of the object as a function of time is a quadratic polynomial.

49. In an initial value problem for the differential equation $dy/dx = f(x)$, the value of y at $x = 0$ is always specified.

50. If $f(x)$ is positive for all x, then there is a solution of the differential equation $dy/dx = f(x)$ where $y(x)$ is positive for all x.

51. If $f(x) > 0$ for all x then every solution of the differential equation $dy/dx = f(x)$ is an increasing function.

52. If two solutions of a differential equation $dy/dx = f(x)$ have different values at $x = 3$ then they have different values at every x.

53. If the function $y = f(x)$ is a solution of the differential equation $dy/dx = \sin x/x$, then the function $y = f(x) + 5$ is also a solution.

54. There is only one solution $y(t)$ to the initial value problem $dy/dt = 3t^2$, $y(1) = \pi$.

6.4   SECOND FUNDAMENTAL THEOREM OF CALCULUS

Suppose f is an elementary function, that is, a combination of constants, powers of x, $\sin x$, $\cos x$, e^x, and $\ln x$. Then we have to be lucky to find an antiderivative F which is also an elementary function. But if we can't find F as an elementary function, how can we be sure that F exists at all? In this section we use the definite integral to construct antiderivatives.

Construction of Antiderivatives Using the Definite Integral

Consider the function $f(x) = e^{-x^2}$. We would like to find a way of calculating values of its antiderivative, F, which is not an elementary function. However, assuming F exists, we know from the Fundamental Theorem of Calculus that

$$F(b) - F(a) = \int_a^b e^{-t^2}\, dt.$$

Setting $a = 0$ and replacing b by x, we have

$$F(x) - F(0) = \int_0^x e^{-t^2}\, dt.$$

Suppose we want the antiderivative that satisfies $F(0) = 0$. Then we get

$$F(x) = \int_0^x e^{-t^2}\, dt.$$

This is a formula for F. For any value of x, there is a unique value for $F(x)$, so F is a function. For any fixed x, we can calculate $F(x)$ numerically. For example,

$$F(2) = \int_0^2 e^{-t^2}\, dt = 0.88208\ldots.$$

Notice that our expression for F is not an elementary function; we have *created* a new function using the definite integral. The next theorem says that this method of constructing antiderivatives works in general. This means that if we define F by

$$F(x) = \int_a^x f(t)\, dt,$$

then F must be an antiderivative of f.

Theorem 6.2: Construction Theorem for Antiderivatives

(Second Fundamental Theorem of Calculus) If f is a continuous function on an interval, and if a is any number in that interval, then the function F defined on the interval as follows is an antiderivative of f:

$$F(x) = \int_a^x f(t)\, dt.$$

Proof Our task is to show that F, defined by this integral, is an antiderivative of f. We want to show that $F'(x) = f(x)$. By the definition of the derivative,

$$F'(x) = \lim_{h \to 0} \frac{F(x+h) - F(x)}{h}.$$

To gain some geometric insight, let's suppose f is positive and h is positive. Then we can visualize

$$F(x) = \int_a^x f(t)\, dt \quad \text{and} \quad F(x+h) = \int_a^{x+h} f(t)\, dt$$

as areas, which leads to representing

$$F(x + h) - F(x) = \int_x^{x+h} f(t)\, dt$$

as a difference of two areas. From Figure 6.26, we see that $F(x + h) - F(x)$ is roughly the area of a rectangle of height $f(x)$ and width h (shaded darker in Figure 6.26), so we have

$$F(x + h) - F(x) \approx f(x)h,$$

hence

$$\frac{F(x + h) - F(x)}{h} \approx f(x).$$

More precisely, we can use Theorem 5.4 on comparing integrals on page 303 to conclude that

$$mh \leq \int_x^{x+h} f(t)\, dt \leq Mh,$$

where m is the greatest lower bound for f on the interval from x to $x + h$ and M is the least upper bound on that interval. (See Figure 6.27.) Hence

$$mh \leq F(x + h) - F(x) \leq Mh,$$

so

$$m \leq \frac{F(x + h) - F(x)}{h} \leq M.$$

Since f is continuous, both m and M approach $f(x)$ as h approaches zero. Thus

$$f(x) \leq \lim_{h \to 0} \frac{F(x + h) - F(x)}{h} \leq f(x).$$

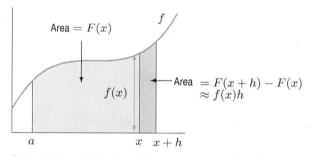

Figure 6.26: $F(x + h) - F(x)$ is area of roughly rectangular region

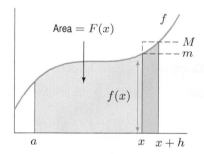

Figure 6.27: Upper and lower bounds for $F(x + h) - F(x)$

Thus both inequalities must actually be equalities, so we have the result we want:

$$f(x) = \lim_{h \to 0} \frac{F(x + h) - F(x)}{h} = F'(x).$$

Relationship Between the Construction Theorem and the Fundamental Theorem of Calculus

If F is constructed as in Theorem 6.2, then we have just shown that $F' = f$. Suppose G is any other antiderivative of f, so $G' = f$, and therefore $F' = G'$. Since the derivative of $F - G$ is zero, the Constant Function Theorem on page 177 tells us that $F - G$ is a constant, so $F(x) = G(x) + C$.

Since we know $F(a) = 0$ (by the definition of F), we can write

$$\int_a^b f(t)\, dt = F(b) = F(b) - F(a) = (G(b) + C) - (G(a) + C) = G(b) - G(a).$$

This result, that the definite integral $\int_a^b f(t)\,dt$ can be evaluated using any antiderivative of f, is the (First) Fundamental Theorem of Calculus. Thus, we have shown that the First Fundamental Theorem of Calculus can be obtained from the Construction Theorem (the Second Fundamental Theorem of Calculus).

Using the Construction Theorem for Antiderivatives

The construction theorem enables us to write down antiderivatives of functions that do not have elementary antiderivatives. For example, an antiderivative of $(\sin x)/x$ is

$$F(x) = \int_0^x \frac{\sin t}{t}\,dt.$$

Notice that F is a function; we can calculate its values to any degree of accuracy.[2] This function already has a name: it is called the *sine-integral*, and it is denoted $\text{Si}(x)$.

Example 1   Construct a table of values of $\text{Si}(x)$ for $x = 0, 1, 2, 3$.

Solution   Using numerical methods, we calculate the values of $\text{Si}(x) = \int_0^x (\sin t)/t\,dt$ given in Table 6.2. Since the integrand is undefined at $t = 0$, we took the lower limit as 0.00001 instead of 0.

Table 6.2   *A table of values of Si(x)*

x	0	1	2	3
$\text{Si}(x)$	0	0.95	1.61	1.85

The reason the sine-integral has a name is that some scientists and engineers use it all the time (for example, in optics). For them, it is just another common function like sine or cosine. Its derivative is given by

$$\frac{d}{dx}\,\text{Si}(x) = \frac{\sin x}{x}.$$

Example 2   Find the derivative of $x\,\text{Si}(x)$.

Solution   Using the product rule,

$$\frac{d}{dx}\,(x\,\text{Si}(x)) = \left(\frac{d}{dx}\,x\right)\text{Si}(x) + x\left(\frac{d}{dx}\,\text{Si}(x)\right)$$
$$= 1 \cdot \text{Si}(x) + x\frac{\sin x}{x}$$
$$= \text{Si}(x) + \sin x.$$

Exercises and Problems for Section 6.4

Exercises

1. For $x = 0, 0.5, 1.0, 1.5$, and 2.0, make a table of values for $I(x) = \int_0^x \sqrt{t^4 + 1}\,dt$.

2. Assume that $F'(t) = \sin t \cos t$ and $F(0) = 1$. Find $F(b)$ for $b = 0,\ 0.5,\ 1,\ 1.5,\ 2,\ 2.5$, and 3.

3. (a) Continue the table of values for $\text{Si}(x) = \int_0^x (\sin t/t)\,dt$ on page 342 for $x = 4$ and $x = 5$.
   (b) Why is $\text{Si}(x)$ decreasing between $x = 4$ and $x = 5$?

In Exercises 4–6, write an expression for the function, $f(x)$, with the given properties.

4. $f'(x) = \sin(x^2)$ and $f(0) = 7$

5. $f'(x) = (\sin x)/x$ and $f(1) = 5$

6. $f'(x) = \text{Si}(x)$ and $f(0) = 2$

[2]You may notice that the integrand, $(\sin t)/t$, is undefined at $t = 0$; such improper integrals are treated in more detail in Chapter 7.

In Exercises 7–10, let $F(x) = \int_0^x f(t)\, dt$. Graph $F(x)$ as a function of x.

7.

8.

9.

10.

Find the derivatives in Exercises 11–16.

11. $\dfrac{d}{dx} \displaystyle\int_0^x \cos(t^2)\, dt$

12. $\dfrac{d}{dt} \displaystyle\int_4^t \sin(\sqrt{x})\, dx$

13. $\dfrac{d}{dx} \displaystyle\int_1^x (1+t)^{200}\, dt$

14. $\dfrac{d}{dx} \displaystyle\int_2^x \ln(t^2+1)\, dt$

15. $\dfrac{d}{dx} \displaystyle\int_{0.5}^x \arctan(t^2)\, dt$

16. $\dfrac{d}{dx}\left[\mathrm{Si}(x^2)\right]$

Problems

17. Find intervals where the graph of $F(x) = \int_0^x e^{-t^2}\, dt$ is concave up and concave down.

18. Use properties of the function $f(x) = xe^{-x}$ to determine the number of values x that make $F(x) = 0$, given $F(x) = \int_1^x f(t)\, dt$.

For Problems 19–21, let $F(x) = \int_0^x \sin(t^2)\, dt$.

19. Approximate $F(x)$ for $x = 0,\ 0.5,\ 1,\ 1.5,\ 2,\ 2.5$.

20. Using a graph of $F'(x)$, decide where $F(x)$ is increasing and where $F(x)$ is decreasing for $0 \le x \le 2.5$.

21. Does $F(x)$ have a maximum value for $0 \le x \le 2.5$? If so, at what value of x does it occur, and approximately what is that maximum value?

22. Use Figure 6.28 to sketch a graph of $F(x) = \int_0^x f(t)\, dt$. Label the points x_1, x_2, x_3.

Figure 6.28

23. The graph of the derivative F' of some function F is given in Figure 6.29. If $F(20) = 150$, estimate the maximum value attained by F.

Figure 6.29

24. Let $g(x) = \int_0^x f(t)\, dt$. Using Figure 6.30, find

   (a) $g(0)$ (b) $g'(1)$

   (c) The interval where g is concave up.

   (d) The value of x where g takes its maximum on the interval $0 \le x \le 8$.

Figure 6.30

25. Let $F(x) = \int_0^x \sin(2t)\, dt$.

   (a) Evaluate $F(\pi)$.

   (b) Draw a sketch to explain geometrically why the answer to part (a) is correct.

   (c) For what values of x is $F(x)$ positive? negative?

26. Let $F(x) = \int_2^x (1/\ln t)\, dt$ for $x \ge 2$.

   (a) Find $F'(x)$.

   (b) Is F increasing or decreasing? What can you say about the concavity of its graph?

   (c) Sketch a graph of $F(x)$.

27. Let $R(x) = \displaystyle\int_0^x \sqrt{1+t^2}\, dt$

   (a) Evaluate $R(0)$ and determine if R is an even or an odd function.

   (b) Is R increasing or decreasing?

   (c) What can you say about concavity?

   (d) Sketch a graph of $R(x)$.

   (e) Show that $\lim_{x \to \infty} (R(x)/x^2)$ exists and find its value.

28. Suppose that $f(x)$ is a continuous function and $\int_a^b f(t)\,dt = 0$ for all a and b.

    (a) Show that $F(x) = \int_a^x f(t)\,dt = 0$ for all x.

    (b) Show that $f(x) = 0$ for all x.

In Problems 29–30, find the value of the function with the given properties.

29. $F(1)$, where $F'(x) = e^{-x^2}$ and $F(0) = 2$

30. $G(-1)$, where $G'(x) = \cos(x^2)$ and $G(0) = -3$

In Problems 31–34, estimate the value of each expression, given $w(t) = \int_0^t q(x)\,dx$ and $v(t) = \int_0^t q'(x)\,dx$. Table 6.3 gives values for $q(x)$, a function with negative first and second derivatives. Are your answers under- or overestimates?

Table 6.3

x	0.0	0.1	0.2	0.3	0.4	0.5
$q(x)$	5.3	5.2	4.9	4.5	3.9	3.1

31. $w(0.4)$

32. $v(0.4)$

33. $w'(0.4)$

34. $v'(0.4)$

In Problems 35–38, use the chain rule to calculate the derivative.

35. $\dfrac{d}{dx}\int_0^{x^2} \ln(1+t^2)\,dt$

36. $\dfrac{d}{dt}\int_1^{\sin t} \cos(x^2)\,dx$

37. $\dfrac{d}{dt}\int_{2t}^{4} \sin(\sqrt{x})\,dx$

38. $\dfrac{d}{dx}\int_{-x^2}^{x^2} e^{t^2}\,dt$

In Problems 39–42, find the given quantities. The *error function*, erf(x), is defined by

$$\mathrm{erf}(x) = \frac{2}{\sqrt{\pi}}\int_0^x e^{-t^2}\,dt.$$

39. $\dfrac{d}{dx}(x\,\mathrm{erf}(x))$

40. $\dfrac{d}{dx}(\mathrm{erf}(\sqrt{x}))$

41. $\dfrac{d}{dx}\left(\int_0^{x^3} e^{-t^2}\,dt\right)$

42. $\dfrac{d}{dx}\left(\int_x^{x^3} e^{-t^2}\,dt\right)$

Strengthen Your Understanding

In Problems 43–45, explain what is wrong with the statement.

43. $\dfrac{d}{dx}\int_0^5 t^2\,dt = x^2.$

44. $F(x) = \displaystyle\int_{-2}^x t^2\,dt$ has a local minimum at $x = 0$.

45. For the function $f(x)$ shown in Figure 6.31, $F(x) = \int_0^x f(t)\,dt$ has a local minimum at $x = 2$.

Figure 6.31:

In Problems 46–47, give an example of:

46. A function, $F(x)$, constructed using the Second Fundamental Theorem of Calculus such that F is a nondecreasing function and $F(0) = 0$.

47. A function $G(x)$, constructed using the Second Fundamental Theorem of Calculus such that G is concave up and $G(7) = 0$.

Are the statements in Problems 48–53 true or false? Give an explanation for your answer.

48. Every continuous function has an antiderivative.

49. $\int_0^x \sin(t^2)\,dt$ is an antiderivative of $\sin(x^2)$.

50. If $F(x) = \int_0^x f(t)\,dt$, then $F(5) - F(3) = \int_3^5 f(t)\,dt$.

51. If $F(x) = \int_0^x f(t)\,dt$, then $F(x)$ must be increasing.

52. If $F(x) = \int_0^x f(t)\,dt$ and $G(x) = \int_2^x f(t)\,dt$, then $F(x) = G(x) + C$.

53. If $F(x) = \int_0^x f(t)\,dt$ and $G(x) = \int_0^x g(t)\,dt$, then $F(x) + G(x) = \int_0^x (f(t) + g(t))\,dt$.

CHAPTER SUMMARY (see also Ready Reference at the end of the book)

- **Constructing antiderivatives**
  Graphically, numerically, analytically.
- **The family of antiderivatives**
  The indefinite integral.
- **Differential equations**

Initial value problems, uniform motion.
- **Construction theorem (Second Fundamental Theorem of Calculus)**
  Constructing antiderivatives using definite integrals.
- **Equations of motion**

REVIEW EXERCISES AND PROBLEMS FOR CHAPTER SIX

Exercises

1. The graph of a derivative $f'(x)$ is shown in Figure 6.32. Fill in the table of values for $f(x)$ given that $f(0) = 2$.

x	0	1	2	3	4	5	6
$f(x)$	2						

Figure 6.32: Graph of f', not f

2. Figure 6.33 shows f. If $F' = f$ and $F(0) = 0$, find $F(b)$ for $b = 1, 2, 3, 4, 5, 6$.

Figure 6.33

In Exercises 3–4, graph $F(x)$ such that $F'(x) = f(x)$ and $F(0) = 0$.

3.

4.

5. (a) Using Figure 6.34, estimate $\int_0^7 f(x)\,dx$.
  (b) If F is an antiderivative of the same function f and $F(0) = 25$, estimate $F(7)$.

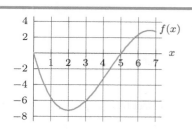

Figure 6.34

In Exercises 6–27, find the indefinite integrals.

6. $\displaystyle\int 5x\,dx$

7. $\displaystyle\int x^3\,dx$

8. $\displaystyle\int \sin\theta\,d\theta$

9. $\displaystyle\int (x^3 - 2)\,dx$

10. $\displaystyle\int \left(t^2 + \frac{1}{t^2}\right)\,dt$

11. $\displaystyle\int \frac{4}{t^2}\,dt$

12. $\displaystyle\int (x^2 + 5x + 8)\,dx$

13. $\displaystyle\int 4\sqrt{w}\,dw$

14. $\displaystyle\int (4t + 7)\,dt$

15. $\displaystyle\int \cos\theta\,d\theta$

16. $\displaystyle\int \left(t\sqrt{t} + \frac{1}{t\sqrt{t}}\right)\,dt$

17. $\displaystyle\int \left(x + \frac{1}{\sqrt{x}}\right)\,dx$

18. $\displaystyle\int (\pi + x^{11})\,dx$

19. $\displaystyle\int \left(3\cos t + 3\sqrt{t}\right)\,dt$

20. $\displaystyle\int \left(\frac{y^2 - 1}{y}\right)^2\,dy$

21. $\displaystyle\int \frac{1}{\cos^2 x}\,dx$

22. $\displaystyle\int \left(\frac{2}{x} + \pi\sin x\right)\,dx$

23. $\displaystyle\int \left(\frac{x^2 + x + 1}{x}\right)\,dx$

24. $\displaystyle\int 5e^z\,dz$

25. $\displaystyle\int 2^x\,dx$

26. $\displaystyle\int (3\cos x - 7\sin x)\,dx$

27. $\displaystyle\int (2e^x - 8\cos x)\,dx$

In Exercises 28–29, evaluate the definite integral exactly [as in $\ln(3\pi)$], using the Fundamental Theorem, and numerically [$\ln(3\pi) \approx 2.243$]:

28. $\displaystyle\int_{-3}^{-1} \frac{2}{r^3}\, dr$

29. $\displaystyle\int_{-\pi/2}^{\pi/2} 2\cos\phi\, d\phi$

For Exercises 30–35, find an antiderivative $F(x)$ with $F'(x) = f(x)$ and $F(0) = 4$.

30. $f(x) = x^2$

31. $f(x) = x^3 + 6x^2 - 4$

32. $f(x) = \sqrt{x}$

33. $f(x) = e^x$

34. $f(x) = \sin x$

35. $f(x) = \cos x$

36. Use the fact that $(x^x)' = x^x(1 + \ln x)$ to evaluate exactly: $\displaystyle\int_{1}^{3} x^x(1 + \ln x)\, dx$.

37. Show that $y = x + \sin x - \pi$ satisfies the initial value problem

$$\frac{dy}{dx} = 1 + \cos x, \quad y(\pi) = 0.$$

38. Show that $y = x^n + A$ is a solution of the differential equation $y' = nx^{n-1}$ for any value of A.

In Exercises 39–42, find the general solution of the differential equation.

39. $\dfrac{dy}{dx} = x^3 + 5$

40. $\dfrac{dy}{dx} = 8x + \dfrac{1}{x}$

41. $\dfrac{dW}{dt} = 4\sqrt{t}$

42. $\dfrac{dr}{dp} = 3\sin p$

In Exercises 43–46, find the solution of the initial value problem.

43. $\dfrac{dy}{dx} = 6x^2 + 4x, \quad y(2) = 10$

44. $\dfrac{dP}{dt} = 10e^t, \quad P(0) = 25$

45. $\dfrac{ds}{dt} = -32t + 100, \quad s = 50$ when $t = 0$

46. $\dfrac{dq}{dz} = 2 + \sin z, \quad q = 5$ when $z = 0$

Find the derivatives in Exercises 47–48.

47. $\dfrac{d}{dt} \displaystyle\int_{t}^{\pi} \cos(z^3)\, dz$

48. $\dfrac{d}{dx} \displaystyle\int_{x}^{1} \ln t\, dt$

Problems

49. Use Figure 6.35 and the fact that $F(2) = 3$ to sketch the graph of $F(x)$. Label the values of at least four points.

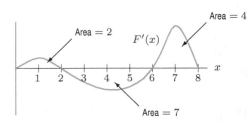

Figure 6.35

50. The vertical velocity of a cork bobbing up and down on the waves in the sea is given by Figure 6.36. Upward is considered positive. Describe the motion of the cork at each of the labeled points. At which point(s), if any, is the acceleration zero? Sketch a graph of the height of the cork above the sea floor as a function of time.

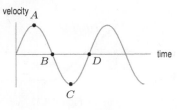

Figure 6.36

In Problems 51–52, a graph of f is given. Let $F'(x) = f(x)$.

(a) What are the x-coordinates of the critical points of $F(x)$?

(b) Which critical points are local maxima, which are local minima, and which are neither?

(c) Sketch a possible graph of $F(x)$.

51.

52.

53. The graph of f'' is given in Figure 6.37. Draw graphs of f and f', assuming both go through the origin, and use them to decide at which of the labeled x-values:

   (a) $f(x)$ is greatest.
   (b) $f(x)$ is least.
   (c) $f'(x)$ is greatest.
   (d) $f'(x)$ is least.
   (e) $f''(x)$ is greatest.
   (f) $f''(x)$ is least.

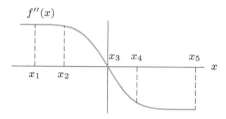

Figure 6.37: Graph of f''

54. Assume f' is given by the graph in Figure 6.38. Suppose f is continuous and that $f(3) = 0$.

   (a) Sketch a graph of f.
   (b) Find $f(0)$ and $f(7)$.
   (c) Find $\int_0^7 f'(x)\,dx$ in two different ways.

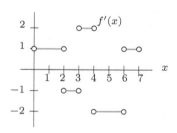

Figure 6.38

55. Use the Fundamental Theorem to find the area under $f(x) = x^2$ between $x = 1$ and $x = 4$.

56. Calculate the exact area between the x-axis and the graph of $y = 7 - 8x + x^2$.

57. Find the exact area below the curve $y = x^3(1 - x)$ and above the x-axis.

58. Find the exact area enclosed by the curve $y = x^2(1-x)^2$ and the x-axis.

59. Find the exact area between the curves $y = x^2$ and $x = y^2$.

60. Calculate the exact area above the graph of $y = \sin\theta$ and below the graph of $y = \cos\theta$ for $0 \le \theta \le \pi/4$.

61. Find the exact area between $f(\theta) = \sin\theta$ and $g(\theta) = \cos\theta$ for $0 \le \theta \le 2\pi$.

62. Find the exact value of the area between the graphs of $y = \cos x$ and $y = e^x$ for $0 \le x \le 1$.

63. Find the exact value of the area between the graphs of $y = \sinh x$, $y = \cosh x$, for $-1 \le x \le 1$.

64. Use the Fundamental Theorem to determine the value of b if the area under the graph of $f(x) = 8x$ between $x = 1$ and $x = b$ is equal to 192. Assume $b > 1$.

65. Find the exact positive value of c if the area between the graph of $y = x^2 - c^2$ and the x-axis is 36.

66. Use the Fundamental Theorem to find the average value of $f(x) = x^2 + 1$ on the interval $x = 0$ to $x = 10$. Illustrate your answer on a graph of $f(x)$.

67. The average value of the function $v(x) = 6/x^2$ on the interval $[1, c]$ is equal to 1. Find the value of c.

In Problems 68–70, evaluate the expression using $f(x) = 5\sqrt{x}$.

68. $\displaystyle\int_1^4 f^{-1}(x)\,dx$ **69.** $\displaystyle\int_1^4 (f(x))^{-1}\,dx$

70. $\displaystyle\left(\int_1^4 f(x)\,dx\right)^{-1}$

In Problems 71–72, evaluate and simplify the expressions given that $f(t) = \displaystyle\int_0^t tx^2\,dx$.

71. $f(2)$ **72.** $f(n)$

Calculate the derivatives in Problems 73–76.

73. $\displaystyle\frac{d}{dx}\int_2^{x^3} \sin(t^2)\,dt$ **74.** $\displaystyle\frac{d}{dx}\int_{\cos x}^3 e^{t^2}\,dt$

75. $\displaystyle\frac{d}{dx}\int_{-x}^x e^{-t^4}\,dt$ **76.** $\displaystyle\frac{d}{dt}\int_{e^t}^{t^3} \sqrt{1+x^2}\,dx$

77. A store has an inventory of Q units of a product at time $t = 0$. The store sells the product at the steady rate of Q/A units per week, and it exhausts the inventory in A weeks.

   (a) Find a formula $f(t)$ for the amount of product in inventory at time t. Graph $f(t)$.
   (b) Find the average inventory level during the period $0 \le t \le A$. Explain why your answer is reasonable.

78. For $0 \leq t \leq 10$ seconds, a car moves along a straight line with velocity

$$v(t) = 2 + 10t \text{ ft/sec.}$$

  (a) Graph $v(t)$ and find the total distance the car has traveled between $t = 0$ and $t = 10$ seconds using the formula for the area of a trapezoid.
  (b) Find the function $s(t)$ that gives the position of the car as a function of time. Explain the meaning of any new constants.
  (c) Use your function $s(t)$ to find the total distance traveled by the car between $t = 0$ and $t = 10$ seconds. Compare with your answer in part (a).
  (d) Explain how your answers to parts (a) and (c) relate to the Fundamental Theorem of Calculus.

79. For a function f, you are given the graph of the derivative f' in Figure 6.39 and that $f(0) = 50$.

  (a) On the interval $0 \leq t \leq 5$, at what value of t does f appear to reach its maximum value? Its minimum value?
  (b) Estimate these maximum and minimum values.
  (c) Estimate $f(5) - f(0)$.

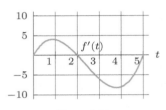

Figure 6.39

80. The acceleration, a, of a particle as a function of time is shown in Figure 6.40. Sketch graphs of velocity and position against time. The particle starts at rest at the origin.

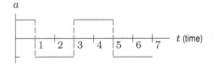

Figure 6.40

81. The angular speed of a car engine increases from 1100 revs/min to 2500 revs/min in 6 sec.

  (a) Assuming that it is constant, find the angular acceleration in revs/min².
  (b) How many revolutions does the engine make in this time?

82. Figure 6.41 is a graph of

$$f(x) = \begin{cases} -x + 1, & \text{for } 0 \leq x \leq 1; \\ x - 1, & \text{for } 1 < x \leq 2. \end{cases}$$

  (a) Find a function F such that $F' = f$ and $F(1) = 1$.
  (b) Use geometry to show the area under the graph of f above the x-axis between $x = 0$ and $x = 2$ is equal to $F(2) - F(0)$.
  (c) Use parts (a) and (b) to check the Fundamental Theorem of Calculus.

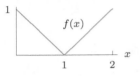

Figure 6.41

83. If a car goes from 0 to 80 mph in six seconds with constant acceleration, what is that acceleration?

84. A car going at 30 ft/sec decelerates at a constant 5 ft/sec².

  (a) Draw up a table showing the velocity of the car every half second. When does the car come to rest?
  (b) Using your table, find left and right sums which estimate the total distance traveled before the car comes to rest. Which is an overestimate, and which is an underestimate?
  (c) Sketch a graph of velocity against time. On the graph, show an area representing the distance traveled before the car comes to rest. Use the graph to calculate this distance.
  (d) Now find a formula for the velocity of the car as a function of time, and then find the total distance traveled by antidifferentiation. What is the relationship between your answer to parts (c) and (d) and your estimates in part (b)?

85. An object is thrown vertically upward with a velocity of 80 ft/sec.

  (a) Make a table showing its velocity every second.
  (b) When does it reach its highest point? When does it hit the ground?
  (c) Using your table, write left and right sums which under- and overestimate the height the object attains.
  (d) Use antidifferentiation to find the greatest height it reaches.

86. If $A(r)$ represents the area of a circle of radius r and $C(r)$ represents its circumference, it can be shown that $A'(r) = C(r)$. Use the fact that $C(r) = 2\pi r$ to obtain the formula for $A(r)$.

87. If $V(r)$ represents the volume of a sphere of radius r and $S(r)$ represents its surface area, it can be shown that $V'(r) = S(r)$. Use the fact that $S(r) = 4\pi r^2$ to obtain the formula for $V(r)$.

88. A car, initially moving at 60 mph, has a constant deceleration and stops in a distance of 200 feet. What is its deceleration? (Give your answer in ft/sec². Note that 1 mph = 22/15 ft/sec.)

89. The birth rate, B, in births per hour, of a bacteria population is given in Figure 6.42. The curve marked D gives the death rate, in deaths per hour, of the same population.

    (a) Explain what the shape of each of these graphs tells you about the population.

    (b) Use the graphs to find the time at which the net rate of increase of the population is at a maximum.

    (c) At time $t = 0$ the population has size N. Sketch the graph of the total number born by time t. Also sketch the graph of the number alive at time t. Estimate the time at which the population is a maximum.

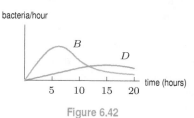

bacteria/hour

time (hours)

Figure 6.42

90. Water flows at a constant rate into the left side of the W-shaped container in Figure 6.43. Sketch a graph of the height, H, of the water in the left side of the container as a function of time, t. The container starts empty.

Figure 6.43

In Problems 91–92, the quantity, $N(t)$ in kg, of pollutant that has leeched from a toxic waste site after t days, is given by

$$N(t) = \int_0^t r(x)\, dx, \quad \text{where } r(x) > 0, \ r'(x) < 0.$$

91. If there is enough information to decide, determine whether $N(t)$ is an increasing or a decreasing function and whether its graph concave up or concave down.

92. Rank in order from least to greatest:

$$N(20), N(10), N(20) - N(10), N(15) - N(5).$$

93. Let $f(x)$ have one zero, at $x = 3$, and suppose $f'(x) < 0$ for all x and that

$$\int_0^3 f(t)\, dt = -\int_3^5 f(t)\, dt.$$

Define $F(x) = \int_0^x f(t)\, dt$ and $G(x) = \int_1^x F(t)\, dt$.

    (a) Find the zeros and critical points of F.

    (b) Find the zeros and critical points of G.

94. Let $P(x) = \int_0^x \arctan(t^2)\, dt$.

    (a) Evaluate $P(0)$ and determine if P is an even or an odd function.

    (b) Is P increasing or decreasing?

    (c) What can you say about concavity?

    (d) Sketch a graph of $P(x)$.

CAS Challenge Problems

95. **(a)** Set up a right-hand Riemann sum for $\int_a^b x^3 dx$ using n subdivisions. What is Δx? Express each x_i, for $i = 1,2,\ldots,n$, in terms of i.

    (b) Use a computer algebra system to find an expression for the Riemann sum in part (a); then find the limit of this expression as $n \to \infty$.

    (c) Simplify the final expression and compare the result to that obtained using the Fundamental Theorem of Calculus.

96. **(a)** Use a computer algebra system to find $\int e^{2x}\, dx$, $\int e^{3x}\, dx$, and $\int e^{3x+5}\, dx$.

    (b) Using your answers to part (a), conjecture a formula for $\int e^{ax+b}\, dx$, where a and b are constants.

    (c) Check your formula by differentiation. Explain which differentiation rules you are using.

97. **(a)** Use a computer algebra system to find $\int \sin(3x)\, dx$,

$\int \sin(4x)\, dx$, and $\int \sin(3x - 2)\, dx$.

    (b) Using your answers to part (a), conjecture a formula for $\int \sin(ax + b)\, dx$, where a and b are constants.

    (c) Check your formula by differentiation. Explain which differentiation rules you are using.

98. **(a)** Use a computer algebra system to find

$$\int \frac{x-2}{x-1}\, dx, \quad \int \frac{x-3}{x-1}\, dx, \quad \text{and} \quad \int \frac{x-1}{x-2}\, dx.$$

    (b) If a and b are constants, use your answers to part (a) to conjecture a formula for

$$\int \frac{x-a}{x-b}\, dx.$$

    (c) Check your formula by differentiation. Explain which rules of differentiation you are using.

99. (a) Use a computer algebra system to find

$$\int \frac{1}{(x-1)(x-3)}\, dx, \quad \int \frac{1}{(x-1)(x-4)}\, dx$$

and

$$\int \frac{1}{(x-1)(x+3)}\, dx.$$

(b) If a and b are constants, use your answers to part (a) to conjecture a formula for

$$\int \frac{1}{(x-a)(x-b)}\, dx.$$

(c) Check your formula by differentiation. Explain which rules of differentiation you are using.

PROJECTS FOR CHAPTER SIX

1. Distribution of Resources

Whether a resource is distributed evenly among members of a population is often an important political or economic question. How can we measure this? How can we decide if the distribution of wealth in this country is becoming more or less equitable over time? How can we measure which country has the most equitable income distribution? This problem describes a way of making such measurements. Suppose the resource is distributed evenly. Then any 20% of the population will have 20% of the resource. Similarly, any 30% will have 30% of the resource and so on. If, however, the resource is not distributed evenly, the poorest $p\%$ of the population (in terms of this resource) will not have $p\%$ of the goods. Suppose $F(x)$ represents the fraction of the resource owned by the poorest fraction x of the population. Thus $F(0.4) = 0.1$ means that the poorest 40% of the population owns 10% of the resource.

(a) What would F be if the resource were distributed evenly?

(b) What must be true of any such F? What must $F(0)$ and $F(1)$ equal? Is F increasing or decreasing? Is the graph of F concave up or concave down?

(c) Gini's index of inequality, G, is one way to measure how evenly the resource is distributed. It is defined by

$$G = 2 \int_0^1 (x - F(x))\, dx.$$

Show graphically what G represents.

2. Yield from an Apple Orchard

Figure 6.44 is a graph of the annual yield, $y(t)$, in bushels per year, from an orchard t years after planting. The trees take about 10 years to get established, but for the next 20 years they give a substantial yield. After about 30 years, however, age and disease start to take their toll, and the annual yield falls off.[3]

(a) Represent on a sketch of Figure 6.44 the total yield, $F(M)$, up to M years, with $0 \le M \le 60$. Write an expression for $F(M)$ in terms of $y(t)$.

(b) Sketch a graph of $F(M)$ against M for $0 \le M \le 60$.

(c) Write an expression for the average annual yield, $a(M)$, up to M years.

(d) When should the orchard be cut down and replanted? Assume that we want to maximize average revenue per year, and that fruit prices remain constant, so that this is achieved by maximizing average annual yield. Use the graph of $y(t)$ to estimate the time at which the average annual yield is a maximum. Explain your answer geometrically and symbolically.

---

[3]From Peter D. Taylor, *Calculus: The Analysis of Functions* (Toronto: Wall & Emerson, Inc., 1992).

Figure 6.44

3. Slope Fields

Suppose we want to sketch the antiderivative, F, of the function f. To get an accurate graph of F, we must be careful about making F have the right slope at every point. The slope of F at any point (x, y) on its graph should be $f(x)$, since $F'(x) = f(x)$. We arrange this as follows: at the point (x, y) in the plane, draw a small line segment with slope $f(x)$. Do this at many points. We call such a diagram a *slope field*. If $f(x) = x$, we get the slope field in Figure 6.45.

Figure 6.45: Slope field of
$f(x) = x$

Figure 6.46: Slope field of
$f(x) = e^{-x^2}$

Notice how the lines in Figure 6.45 seem to be arranged in a parabolic pattern. This is because the general antiderivative of x is $x^2/2 + C$, so the lines are all the tangent lines to the family of parabolas $y = x^2/2 + C$. This suggests a way of finding antiderivatives graphically even if we can't write down a formula for them: plot the slopes, and see if they suggest the graph of an antiderivative. For example, if you do this with $f(x) = e^{-x^2}$, which is one of the functions that does not have an elementary antiderivative, you get Figure 6.46.

You can see the ghost of the graph of a function lurking behind the slopes in Figure 6.46; in fact there is a whole stack of them. If you move across the plane in the direction suggested by the slope field at every point, you will trace out a curve. The slope field is tangent to the curve everywhere, so this is the graph of an antiderivative of e^{-x^2}.

(a) (i) Sketch a graph of $f(t) = \dfrac{\sin t}{t}$.

(ii) What does your graph tell you about the behavior of

$$\text{Si}(x) = \int_0^x \frac{\sin(t)}{t}\, dt$$

for $x > 0$? Is $\text{Si}(x)$ always increasing or always decreasing? Does $\text{Si}(x)$ cross the x-axis for $x > 0$?

(iii) By drawing the slope field for $f(t) = \dfrac{\sin t}{t}$, decide whether $\lim\limits_{x \to \infty} \text{Si}(x)$ exists.

(b) (i) Use your calculator or computer to sketch a graph of $y = x^{\sin x}$ for $0 < x \le 20$.

(ii) Using your answer to part (i), sketch by hand a graph of the function F, where

$$F(x) = \int_0^x t^{\sin t}\, dt.$$

(iii) Use a slope field program to check your answer to part (ii).

(c) Let $F(x)$ be the antiderivative of $\sin(x^2)$ satisfying $F(0) = 0$.

(i) Describe any general features of the graph of F that you can deduce by looking at the graph of $\sin(x^2)$ in Figure 6.47.

(ii) By drawing a slope field (using a calculator or computer), sketch a graph of F. Does F ever cross the x-axis in the region $x > 0$? Does $\displaystyle\lim_{x \to \infty} F(x)$ exist?

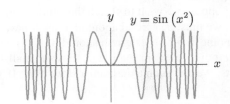

Figure 6.47

Chapter Seven

INTEGRATION

Contents

7.1 Integration by Substitution **354**

The Guess-and-Check Method 354

The Method of Substitution 355

Definite Integrals by Substitution 358

More Complex Substitutions 359

7.2 Integration by Parts **364**

The General Formula for Integration by Parts . . 364

7.3 Tables of Integrals **371**

Using the Table of Integrals 371

Transforming the Integrand 373

Using Factoring 373

Long Division 373

Completing the Square 373

Substitution 374

**7.4 Algebraic Identities and Trigonometric
    Substitutions** **376**

Method of Partial Fractions 376

Trigonometric Substitutions 380

Sine Substitutions 380

Tangent Substitutions 382

Completing the Square 383

7.5 Numerical Methods for Definite Integrals . . . **387**

The Midpoint Rule 387

The Trapezoid Rule 388

Over- or Underestimate? 389

The Midpoint Rule 389

Error in Left and Right Rules 390

Error in Trapezoid and Midpoint Rules 390

Simpson's Rule 391

Alternate Approach to Numerical Integration:
    Approximating by Lines and Parabolas 392

7.6 Improper Integrals **395**

When the Limit of Integration Is Infinite 395

When the Integrand Becomes Infinite 398

7.7 Comparison of Improper Integrals **403**

Making Comparisons 403

How Do We Know What to Compare
    With? 404

REVIEW PROBLEMS **408**

PROJECTS **412**

7.1 INTEGRATION BY SUBSTITUTION

In Chapter 3, we learned rules to differentiate any function obtained by combining constants, powers of x, $\sin x$, $\cos x$, e^x, and $\ln x$, using addition, multiplication, division, or composition of functions. Such functions are called *elementary*.

In this chapter, we introduce several methods of antidifferentiation. However, there is a great difference between looking for derivatives and looking for antiderivatives. Every elementary function has elementary derivatives, but most elementary functions—such as $\sqrt{x^3 + 1}$, $(\sin x)/x$, and e^{-x^2}—do not have elementary antiderivatives.

All commonly occurring antiderivatives can be found with a computer algebra system (CAS). However, just as it is useful to be able to calculate $3 + 4$ without a calculator, we usually calculate some antiderivatives by hand.

The Guess-and-Check Method

A good strategy for finding simple antiderivatives is to *guess* an answer (using knowledge of differentiation rules) and then *check* the answer by differentiating it. If we get the expected result, then we're done; otherwise, we revise the guess and check again.

The method of guess-and-check is useful in reversing the chain rule. According to the chain rule,

$$\frac{d}{dx}(f(g(x))) = f'\overbrace{(g(x))}^{\text{Inside}} \cdot \underbrace{g'(x)}.$$

Derivative of outside $\nearrow$ $\qquad$ $\searrow$ Derivative of inside

Thus, any function which is the result of applying the chain rule is the product of two factors: the "derivative of the outside" and the "derivative of the inside." If a function has this form, its antiderivative is $f(g(x))$.

Example 1 Find $\displaystyle\int 3x^2 \cos(x^3)\, dx$.

Solution The function $3x^2 \cos(x^3)$ looks like the result of applying the chain rule: there is an "inside" function x^3 and its derivative $3x^2$ appears as a factor. Since the outside function is a cosine which has a sine as an antiderivative, we guess $\sin(x^3)$ for the antiderivative. Differentiating to check gives

$$\frac{d}{dx}(\sin(x^3)) = \cos(x^3) \cdot (3x^2).$$

Since this is what we began with, we know that

$$\int 3x^2 \cos(x^3)\, dx = \sin(x^3) + C.$$

The basic idea of this method is to try to find an inside function whose derivative appears as a factor. This works even when the derivative is missing a constant factor, as in the next example.

Example 2 Find $\displaystyle\int x^3 \sqrt{x^4 + 5}\, dx$.

Solution Here the inside function is $x^4 + 5$, and its derivative appears as a factor, with the exception of a missing 4. Thus, the integrand we have is more or less of the form

$$g'(x)\sqrt{g(x)},$$

with $g(x) = x^4 + 5$. Since $x^{3/2}/(3/2)$ is an antiderivative of the outside function $\sqrt{x}$, we might guess that an antiderivative is

$$\frac{(g(x))^{3/2}}{3/2} = \frac{(x^4 + 5)^{3/2}}{3/2}.$$

Let's check and see:

$$\frac{d}{dx}\left(\frac{(x^4+5)^{3/2}}{3/2}\right) = \frac{3}{2}\frac{(x^4+5)^{1/2}}{3/2}\cdot 4x^3 = 4x^3(x^4+5)^{1/2},$$

so $\dfrac{(x^4+5)^{3/2}}{3/2}$ is too big by a factor of 4. The correct antiderivative is

$$\frac{1}{4}\frac{(x^4+5)^{3/2}}{3/2} = \frac{1}{6}(x^4+5)^{3/2}.$$

Thus

$$\int x^3\sqrt{x^4+5}\,dx = \frac{1}{6}(x^4+5)^{3/2}+C.$$

As a final check:

$$\frac{d}{dx}\left(\frac{1}{6}(x^4+5)^{3/2}\right) = \frac{1}{6}\cdot\frac{3}{2}(x^4+5)^{1/2}\cdot 4x^3 = x^3(x^4+5)^{1/2}.$$

As we see in the preceding example, antidifferentiating a function often involves "correcting for" constant factors: if differentiation produces an extra factor of 2, antidifferentiation will require a factor of $\frac{1}{2}$.

The Method of Substitution

When the integrand is complicated, it helps to formalize this guess-and-check method as follows:

> ### To Make a Substitution
>
> Let w be the "inside function" and $dw = w'(x)\,dx = \dfrac{dw}{dx}dx.$

Let's redo the first example using a substitution.

Example 3   Find $\displaystyle\int 3x^2\cos(x^3)\,dx.$

Solution   As before, we look for an inside function whose derivative appears—in this case x^3. We let $w = x^3$. Then $dw = w'(x)\,dx = 3x^2\,dx$. The original integrand can now be completely rewritten in terms of the new variable w:

$$\int 3x^2\cos(x^3)\,dx = \int \cos\underbrace{(x^3)}_{w}\cdot\underbrace{3x^2\,dx}_{dw} = \int\cos w\,dw = \sin w + C = \sin(x^3)+C.$$

By changing the variable to w, we can simplify the integrand. We now have $\cos w$, which can be antidifferentiated more easily. The final step, after antidifferentiating, is to convert back to the original variable, x.

Why Does Substitution Work?

The substitution method makes it look as if we can treat dw and dx as separate entities, even canceling them in the equation $dw = (dw/dx)dx$. Let's see why this works. Suppose we have an integral of the form $\int f(g(x))g'(x)\,dx$, where $g(x)$ is the inside function and $f(x)$ is the outside function. If F is an antiderivative of f, then $F' = f$, and by the chain rule $\frac{d}{dx}(F(g(x))) = f(g(x))g'(x)$. Therefore,

$$\int f(g(x))g'(x)\,dx = F(g(x))+C.$$

Now write $w = g(x)$ and $dw/dx = g'(x)$ on both sides of this equation:

$$\int f(w)\frac{dw}{dx}\,dx = F(w) + C.$$

On the other hand, knowing that $F' = f$ tells us that

$$\int f(w)\,dw = F(w) + C.$$

Thus, the following two integrals are equal:

$$\int f(w)\frac{dw}{dx}\,dx = \int f(w)\,dw.$$

Substituting w for the inside function and writing $dw = w'(x)dx$ leaves the indefinite integral unchanged.

Let's revisit the second example that we did by guess-and-check.

Example 4   Find $\int x^3\sqrt{x^4 + 5}\,dx$.

Solution   The inside function is $x^4 + 5$, with derivative $4x^3$. The integrand has a factor of x^3, and since the only thing missing is a constant factor, we try

$$w = x^4 + 5.$$

Then

$$dw = w'(x)\,dx = 4x^3\,dx,$$

giving

$$\frac{1}{4}dw = x^3\,dx.$$

Thus,

$$\int x^3\sqrt{x^4 + 5}\,dx = \int \sqrt{w}\,\frac{1}{4}dw = \frac{1}{4}\int w^{1/2}\,dw = \frac{1}{4}\cdot\frac{w^{3/2}}{3/2} + C = \frac{1}{6}(x^4 + 5)^{3/2} + C.$$

Once again, we get the same result as with guess-and-check.

Warning

We saw in the preceding example that we can apply the substitution method when a *constant* factor is missing from the derivative of the inside function. However, we may not be able to use substitution if anything other than a constant factor is missing. For example, setting $w = x^4 + 5$ to find

$$\int x^2\sqrt{x^4 + 5}\,dx$$

does us no good because $x^2\,dx$ is not a constant multiple of $dw = 4x^3\,dx$. Substitution works if the integrand contains the derivative of the inside function, *to within a constant factor*.

Some people prefer the substitution method over guess-and-check since it is more systematic, but both methods achieve the same result. For simple problems, guess-and-check can be faster.

Example 5   Find $\int e^{\cos\theta}\sin\theta\,d\theta$.

Solution   We let $w = \cos\theta$ since its derivative is $-\sin\theta$ and there is a factor of $\sin\theta$ in the integrand. This gives

$$dw = w'(\theta)\,d\theta = -\sin\theta\,d\theta,$$

so

$$-dw = \sin\theta\,d\theta.$$

Thus

$$\int e^{\cos\theta}\sin\theta\,d\theta = \int e^w\,(-dw) = (-1)\int e^w\,dw = -e^w + C = -e^{\cos\theta} + C.$$

Example 6   Find $\displaystyle\int \frac{e^t}{1+e^t}\,dt.$

Solution   Observing that the derivative of $1 + e^t$ is e^t, we see $w = 1 + e^t$ is a good choice. Then $dw = e^t\,dt$, so that

$$\int \frac{e^t}{1+e^t}\,dt = \int \frac{1}{1+e^t}\,e^t\,dt = \int \frac{1}{w}\,dw = \ln|w| + C$$
$$= \ln|1 + e^t| + C$$
$$= \ln(1 + e^t) + C. \qquad \text{(Since } (1 + e^t) \text{ is always positive.)}$$

Since the numerator is $e^t\,dt$, we might also have tried $w = e^t$. This substitution leads to the integral $\int (1/(1 + w))dw$, which is better than the original integral but requires another substitution, $u = 1 + w$, to finish. There are often several different ways of doing an integral by substitution.

Notice the pattern in the previous example: having a function in the denominator and its derivative in the numerator leads to a natural logarithm. The next example follows the same pattern.

Example 7   Find $\displaystyle\int \tan\theta\,d\theta.$

Solution   Recall that $\tan\theta = (\sin\theta)/(\cos\theta)$. If $w = \cos\theta$, then $dw = -\sin\theta\,d\theta$, so

$$\int \tan\theta\,d\theta = \int \frac{\sin\theta}{\cos\theta}\,d\theta = \int \frac{-dw}{w} = -\ln|w| + C = -\ln|\cos\theta| + C.$$

One way to think of integration is in terms of standard forms, whose antiderivatives are known. Substitution is useful for putting a complicated integral in a standard form.

Example 8   Give a substitution w and constants k, n so that the following integral has the form $\int kw^n\,dw$:

$$\int e^x \cos^3(e^x) \sin(e^x)\,dx.$$

Solution   We notice that one of the factors in the integrand is $(\cos(e^x))^3$, so if we let $w = \cos(e^x)$, this factor is w^3. Then $dw = (-\sin(e^x))e^x\,dx$, so

$$\int e^x \cos^3(e^x) \sin(e^x)\,dx = \int \cos^3(e^x)(\sin(e^x))e^x\,dx = \int w^3\,(-dw).$$

Therefore, we choose $w = \cos(e^x)$ and then $k = -1, n = 3$.

Definite Integrals by Substitution

Example 9   Compute $\int_0^2 xe^{x^2}\, dx$.

Solution   To evaluate this definite integral using the Fundamental Theorem of Calculus, we first need to find an antiderivative of $f(x) = xe^{x^2}$. The inside function is x^2, so we let $w = x^2$. Then $dw = 2x\, dx$, so $\frac{1}{2}\, dw = x\, dx$. Thus,

$$\int xe^{x^2}\, dx = \int e^w \frac{1}{2}\, dw = \frac{1}{2}e^w + C = \frac{1}{2}e^{x^2} + C.$$

Now we find the definite integral

$$\int_0^2 xe^{x^2}\, dx = \frac{1}{2}e^{x^2}\Big|_0^2 = \frac{1}{2}(e^4 - e^0) = \frac{1}{2}(e^4 - 1).$$

There is another way to look at the same problem. After we established that

$$\int xe^{x^2}\, dx = \frac{1}{2}e^w + C,$$

our next two steps were to replace w by x^2, and then x by 2 and 0. We could have directly replaced the original limits of integration, $x = 0$ and $x = 2$, by the corresponding w limits. Since $w = x^2$, the w limits are $w = 0^2 = 0$ (when $x = 0$) and $w = 2^2 = 4$ (when $x = 2$), so we get

$$\int_{x=0}^{x=2} xe^{x^2}\, dx = \frac{1}{2}\int_{w=0}^{w=4} e^w\, dw = \frac{1}{2}e^w\Big|_0^4 = \frac{1}{2}\left(e^4 - e^0\right) = \frac{1}{2}(e^4 - 1).$$

As we would expect, both methods give the same answer.

To Use Substitution to Find Definite Integrals

Either
- Compute the indefinite integral, expressing an antiderivative in terms of the original variable, and then evaluate the result at the original limits,

or
- Convert the original limits to new limits in terms of the new variable and do not convert the antiderivative back to the original variable.

Example 10   Evaluate $\int_0^{\pi/4} \dfrac{\tan^3 \theta}{\cos^2 \theta}\, d\theta$.

Solution   To use substitution, we must decide what w should be. There are two possible inside functions, $\tan \theta$ and $\cos \theta$. Now

$$\frac{d}{d\theta}(\tan \theta) = \frac{1}{\cos^2 \theta} \quad \text{and} \quad \frac{d}{d\theta}(\cos \theta) = -\sin \theta,$$

and since the integral contains a factor of $1/\cos^2 \theta$ but not of $\sin \theta$, we try $w = \tan \theta$. Then $dw = (1/\cos^2 \theta)d\theta$. When $\theta = 0$, $w = \tan 0 = 0$, and when $\theta = \pi/4$, $w = \tan(\pi/4) = 1$, so

$$\int_0^{\pi/4} \frac{\tan^3 \theta}{\cos^2 \theta}\, d\theta = \int_0^{\pi/4} (\tan \theta)^3 \cdot \frac{1}{\cos^2 \theta}\, d\theta = \int_0^1 w^3\, dw = \frac{1}{4}w^4\Big|_0^1 = \frac{1}{4}.$$

Example 11   Evaluate $\int_1^3 \dfrac{dx}{5 - x}$.

Solution   Let $w = 5 - x$, so $dw = -dx$. When $x = 1$, $w = 4$, and when $x = 3$, $w = 2$, so

$$\int_1^3 \frac{dx}{5 - x} = \int_4^2 \frac{-dw}{w} = -\ln|w|\Big|_4^2 = -(\ln 2 - \ln 4) = \ln\left(\frac{4}{2}\right) = \ln 2 = 0.693.$$

Notice that we write the limit $w = 4$ at the bottom, even though it is larger than $w = 2$, because $w = 4$ corresponds to the lower limit $x = 1$.

More Complex Substitutions

In the examples of substitution presented so far, we guessed an expression for w and hoped to find dw (or some constant multiple of it) in the integrand. What if we are not so lucky? It turns out that it often works to let w be some messy expression contained inside, say, a cosine or under a root, even if we cannot see immediately how such a substitution helps.

Example 12   Find $\displaystyle\int \sqrt{1 + \sqrt{x}}\, dx$.

Solution   This time, the derivative of the inside function is nowhere to be seen. Nevertheless, we try $w = 1 + \sqrt{x}$. Then $w - 1 = \sqrt{x}$, so $(w - 1)^2 = x$. Therefore $2(w - 1)\, dw = dx$. We have

$$\int \sqrt{1 + \sqrt{x}}\, dx = \int \sqrt{w}\, 2(w - 1)\, dw = 2\int w^{1/2}(w - 1)\, dw$$

$$= 2\int (w^{3/2} - w^{1/2})\, dw = 2\left(\frac{2}{5}w^{5/2} - \frac{2}{3}w^{3/2}\right) + C$$

$$= 2\left(\frac{2}{5}(1 + \sqrt{x})^{5/2} - \frac{2}{3}(1 + \sqrt{x})^{3/2}\right) + C.$$

Notice that the substitution in the preceding example again converts the inside of the messiest function into something simple. In addition, since the derivative of the inside function is not waiting for us, we have to solve for x so that we can get dx entirely in terms of w and dw.

Example 13   Find $\displaystyle\int (x + 7)\sqrt[3]{3 - 2x}\, dx$.

Solution   Here, instead of the derivative of the inside function (which is -2), we have the factor $(x + 7)$. However, substituting $w = 3 - 2x$ turns out to help anyway. Then $dw = -2\, dx$, so $(-1/2)\, dw = dx$. Now we must convert everything to w, including $x + 7$. If $w = 3 - 2x$, then $2x = 3 - w$, so $x = 3/2 - w/2$, and therefore we can write $x + 7$ in terms of w. Thus

$$\int (x + 7)\sqrt[3]{3 - 2x}\, dx = \int \left(\frac{3}{2} - \frac{w}{2} + 7\right)\sqrt[3]{w}\left(-\frac{1}{2}\right) dw$$

$$= -\frac{1}{2}\int \left(\frac{17}{2} - \frac{w}{2}\right) w^{1/3}\, dw$$

$$= -\frac{1}{4}\int (17 - w)w^{1/3}\, dw$$

$$= -\frac{1}{4}\int (17w^{1/3} - w^{4/3})\, dw$$

$$= -\frac{1}{4}\left(17\frac{w^{4/3}}{4/3} - \frac{w^{7/3}}{7/3}\right) + C$$

$$= -\frac{1}{4}\left(\frac{51}{4}(3 - 2x)^{4/3} - \frac{3}{7}(3 - 2x)^{7/3}\right) + C.$$

Looking back over the solution, the reason this substitution works is that it converts $\sqrt[3]{3 - 2x}$, the messiest part of the integrand, to $\sqrt[3]{w}$, which can be combined with the other factor and then integrated.

Exercises and Problems for Section 7.1

1. Use substitution to express each of the following integrals as a multiple of $\int_a^b (1/w)\, dw$ for some a and b. Then evaluate the integrals.

   (a) $\displaystyle\int_0^1 \frac{x}{1+x^2}\, dx$ (b) $\displaystyle\int_0^{\pi/4} \frac{\sin x}{\cos x}\, dx$

2. (a) Find the derivatives of $\sin(x^2+1)$ and $\sin(x^3+1)$.
   (b) Use your answer to part (a) to find antiderivatives of:

   (i) $x\cos(x^2+1)$ (ii) $x^2\cos(x^3+1)$

   (c) Find the general antiderivatives of:

   (i) $x\sin(x^2+1)$ (ii) $x^2\sin(x^3+1)$

Find the integrals in Exercises 3–48. Check your answers by differentiation.

3. $\displaystyle\int e^{3x}\, dx$

4. $\displaystyle\int te^{t^2}\, dt$

5. $\displaystyle\int e^{-x}\, dx$

6. $\displaystyle\int 25e^{-0.2t}\, dt$

7. $\displaystyle\int \sin(2x)\, dx$

8. $\displaystyle\int t\cos(t^2)\, dt$

9. $\displaystyle\int \sin(3-t)\, dt$

10. $\displaystyle\int xe^{-x^2}\, dx$

11. $\displaystyle\int (r+1)^3\, dr$

12. $\displaystyle\int y(y^2+5)^8\, dy$

13. $\displaystyle\int x^2(1+2x^3)^2\, dx$

14. $\displaystyle\int t^2(t^3-3)^{10}\, dt$

15. $\displaystyle\int x(x^2+3)^2\, dx$

16. $\displaystyle\int x(x^2-4)^{7/2}\, dx$

17. $\displaystyle\int y^2(1+y)^2\, dy$

18. $\displaystyle\int (2t-7)^{73}\, dt$

19. $\displaystyle\int x^2 e^{x^3+1}\, dx$

20. $\displaystyle\int \frac{dy}{y+5}$

21. $\displaystyle\int \frac{1}{\sqrt{4-x}}\, dx$

22. $\displaystyle\int (x^2+3)^2\, dx$

23. $\displaystyle\int \sin\theta(\cos\theta+5)^7\, d\theta$ 24. $\displaystyle\int \sqrt{\cos 3t}\,\sin 3t\, dt$

25. $\displaystyle\int \sin^6\theta \cos\theta\, d\theta$

26. $\displaystyle\int \sin^3\alpha \cos\alpha\, d\alpha$

27. $\displaystyle\int \sin^6(5\theta)\cos(5\theta)\, d\theta$ 28. $\displaystyle\int \tan(2x)\, dx$

29. $\displaystyle\int \frac{(\ln z)^2}{z}\, dz$

30. $\displaystyle\int \frac{e^t+1}{e^t+t}\, dt$

31. $\displaystyle\int \frac{(t+1)^2}{t^2}\, dt$

32. $\displaystyle\int \frac{y}{y^2+4}\, dy$

33. $\displaystyle\int \frac{dx}{1+2x^2}$

34. $\displaystyle\int \frac{dx}{\sqrt{1-4x^2}}$

35. $\displaystyle\int \frac{\cos\sqrt{x}}{\sqrt{x}}\, dx$

36. $\displaystyle\int \frac{e^{\sqrt{y}}}{\sqrt{y}}\, dy$

37. $\displaystyle\int \frac{1+e^x}{\sqrt{x+e^x}}\, dx$

38. $\displaystyle\int \frac{e^x}{2+e^x}\, dx$

39. $\displaystyle\int \frac{x+1}{x^2+2x+19}\, dx$ 40. $\displaystyle\int \frac{t}{1+3t^2}\, dt$

41. $\displaystyle\int \frac{e^x-e^{-x}}{e^x+e^{-x}}\, dx$ 42. $\displaystyle\int \frac{x\cos(x^2)}{\sqrt{\sin(x^2)}}\, dx$

43. $\displaystyle\int \sinh 3t\, dt$

44. $\displaystyle\int \cosh x\, dx$

45. $\displaystyle\int \cosh(2w+1)\, dw$ 46. $\displaystyle\int (\sinh z)e^{\cosh z}\, dz$

47. $\displaystyle\int \cosh^2 x\sinh x\, dx$ 48. $\displaystyle\int x\cosh x^2\, dx$

For the functions in Exercises 49–56, find the general antiderivative. Check your answers by differentiation.

49. $p(t)=\pi t^3+4t$

50. $f(x)=\sin 3x$

51. $f(x)=2x\cos(x^2)$

52. $r(t)=12t^2\cos(t^3)$

53. $f(x)=\sin(2-5x)$

54. $f(x)=e^{\sin x}\cos x$

55. $f(x)=\dfrac{x}{x^2+1}$

56. $f(x)=\dfrac{1}{3\cos^2(2x)}$

For Exercises 57–64, use the Fundamental Theorem to calculate the definite integrals.

57. $\displaystyle\int_0^\pi \cos(x+\pi)\, dx$

58. $\displaystyle\int_0^{1/2} \cos(\pi x)\, dx$

59. $\displaystyle\int_0^{\pi/2} e^{-\cos\theta}\sin\theta\, d\theta$ 60. $\displaystyle\int_1^2 2xe^{x^2}\, dx$

61. $\displaystyle\int_1^4 \frac{e^{\sqrt{x}}}{\sqrt{x}}\, dx$

62. $\displaystyle\int_{-1}^{e-2} \frac{1}{t+2}\, dt$

63. $\displaystyle\int_1^4 \frac{\cos\sqrt{x}}{\sqrt{x}}\, dx$

64. $\displaystyle\int_0^2 \frac{x}{(1+x^2)^2}\, dx$

For Exercises 65–70, evaluate the definite integrals. Whenever possible, use the Fundamental Theorem of Calculus, perhaps after a substitution. Otherwise, use numerical methods.

65. $\int_{-1}^{3} (x^3 + 5x)\, dx$

66. $\int_{-1}^{1} \frac{1}{1+y^2}\, dy$

67. $\int_{1}^{3} \frac{1}{x}\, dx$

68. $\int_{1}^{3} \frac{dt}{(t+7)^2}$

69. $\int_{-1}^{2} \sqrt{x+2}\, dx$

70. $\int_{1}^{2} \frac{\sin t}{t}\, dt$

Find the integrals in Exercises 71–78.

71. $\int y\sqrt{y+1}\, dy$

72. $\int z(z+1)^{1/3}\, dz$

73. $\int \frac{t^2+t}{\sqrt{t+1}}\, dt$

74. $\int \frac{dx}{2+2\sqrt{x}}$

75. $\int x^2\sqrt{x-2}\, dx$

76. $\int (z+2)\sqrt{1-z}\, dz$

77. $\int \frac{t}{\sqrt{t+1}}\, dt$

78. $\int \frac{3x-2}{\sqrt{2x+1}}\, dx$

Problems

In Problems 79–82, show the two integrals are equal using a substitution.

79. $\int_{0}^{\pi/3} 3\sin^2(3x)\, dx = \int_{0}^{\pi} \sin^2(y)\, dy$

80. $\int_{1}^{2} 2\ln(s^2+1)\, ds = \int_{1}^{4} \frac{\ln(t+1)}{\sqrt{t}}\, dt$

81. $\int_{1}^{e} (\ln w)^3\, dw = \int_{0}^{1} z^3 e^z\, dz$

82. $\int_{0}^{\pi} x\cos(\pi - x)\, dx = \int_{0}^{\pi} (\pi - t)\cos t\, dt$

83. Using the substitution $w = x^2$, find a function $g(w)$ such that $\int_{\sqrt{a}}^{\sqrt{b}} dx = \int_{a}^{b} g(w)\, dw$ for all $0 < a < b$.

84. Using the substitution $w = e^x$, find a function $g(w)$ such that $\int_{a}^{b} e^{-x}\, dx = \int_{e^a}^{e^b} g(w)\, dw$ for all $a < b$.

In Problems 85–89, explain why the two antiderivatives are really, despite their apparent dissimilarity, different expressions of the same problem. You do not need to evaluate the integrals.

85. $\int \frac{e^x\, dx}{1+e^{2x}}$ and $\int \frac{\cos x\, dx}{1+\sin^2 x}$

86. $\int \frac{\ln x}{x}\, dx$ and $\int x\, dx$

87. $\int e^{\sin x}\cos x\, dx$ and $\int \frac{e^{\arcsin x}}{\sqrt{1-x^2}}\, dx$

88. $\int (\sin x)^3\cos x\, dx$ and $\int (x^3+1)^3 x^2\, dx$

89. $\int \sqrt{x+1}\, dx$ and $\int \frac{\sqrt{1+\sqrt{x}}}{\sqrt{x}}\, dx$

In Problems 90–96, evaluate the integral. Your answer should not contain f, which is a differentiable function with the following values:

x	0	1	$\pi/2$	e	3
$f(x)$	5	7	8	10	11
$f'(x)$	2	4	6	9	12

90. $\int_{0}^{1} f'(x)\sin f(x)\, dx$

91. $\int_{1}^{3} f'(x)e^{f(x)}\, dx$

92. $\int_{1}^{3} \frac{f'(x)}{f(x)}\, dx$

93. $\int_{0}^{1} e^x f'(e^x)\, dx$

94. $\int_{1}^{e} \frac{f'(\ln x)}{x}\, dx$

95. $\int_{0}^{1} f'(x)(f(x))^2\, dx$

96. $\int_{0}^{\pi/2} \sin x \cdot f'(\cos x)\, dx$

In Problems 97–100, find an expression for the integral which contains g but no integral sign.

97. $\int g'(x)(g(x))^4\, dx$

98. $\int g'(x)e^{g(x)}\, dx$

99. $\int g'(x)\sin g(x)\, dx$

100. $\int g'(x)\sqrt{1+g(x)}\, dx$

In Problems 101–103, find a substitution w and constants k, n so that the integral has the form $\int kw^n\, dw$.

101. $\int x^2\sqrt{1-4x^3}\, dx$

102. $\int \frac{\cos t}{\sin t}\, dt$

103. $\int \frac{2x\, dx}{(x^2-3)^2}$

In Problems 104–106, find constants k, n, w_0, w_1 so the the integral has the form $\int_{w_0}^{w_1} kw^n\, dw$.

104. $\int_{1}^{5} \frac{3x\, dx}{\sqrt{5x^2+7}}$, $w = 5x^2 + 7$

105. $\int_{0}^{5} \frac{2^x\, dx}{2^x+3}$, $w = 2^x + 3$

106. $\int_{\pi/12}^{\pi/4} \sin^7(2x)\cos(2x)\, dx$, $w = \sin 2x$

In Problems 107–111, find a substitution w and a constant k so that the integral has the form $\int k e^w \, dw$.

107. $\int x e^{-x^2} \, dx$

108. $\int e^{\sin \phi} \cos \phi \, d\phi$

109. $\int \sqrt{e^r} \, dr$

110. $\int \dfrac{z^2 \, dz}{e^{-z^3}}$

111. $\int e^{2t} e^{3t-4} \, dt$

In Problems 112–113, find a substitution w and constants a, b, A so that the integral has the form $\int_a^b A e^w \, dw$.

112. $\int_3^7 e^{2t-3} \, dt$

113. $\int_0^1 e^{\cos(\pi t)} \sin(\pi t) \, dt$

114. Integrate:

(a) $\int \dfrac{1}{\sqrt{x}} \, dx$

(b) $\int \dfrac{1}{\sqrt{x}+1} \, dx$

(c) $\int \dfrac{1}{\sqrt{x+1}} \, dx$

115. If appropriate, evaluate the following integrals by substitution. If substitution is not appropriate, say so, and do not evaluate.

(a) $\int x \sin(x^2) \, dx$

(b) $\int x^2 \sin x \, dx$

(c) $\int \dfrac{x^2}{1+x^2} \, dx$

(d) $\int \dfrac{x}{(1+x^2)^2} \, dx$

(e) $\int x^3 e^{x^2} \, dx$

(f) $\int \dfrac{\sin x}{2 + \cos x} \, dx$

In Problems 116–122, find the exact area.

116. Under $f(x) = x e^{x^2}$ between $x = 0$ and $x = 2$.

117. Under $f(x) = 1/(x+1)$ between $x = 0$ and $x = 2$.

118. Under $f(x) = \sinh(x/2)$ between $x = 0$ and $x = 2$.

119. Under $f(\theta) = (e^{\theta+1})^3$ for $0 \le \theta \le 2$.

120. Between e^t and e^{t+1} for $0 \le t \le 2$.

121. Between $y = e^x$, $y = 3$, and the y-axis.

122. Under one arch of the curve $V(t) = V_0 \sin(\omega t)$, where $V_0 > 0$ and $\omega > 0$.

123. Find the exact average value of $f(x) = 1/(x+1)$ on the interval $x = 0$ to $x = 2$. Sketch a graph showing the function and the average value.

124. Let $g(x) = f(2x)$. Show that the average value of f on the interval $[0, 2b]$ is the same as the average value of g on the interval $[0, b]$.

125. Suppose $\int_0^2 g(t) \, dt = 5$. Calculate the following:

(a) $\int_0^4 g(t/2) \, dt$

(b) $\int_0^2 g(2-t) \, dt$

126. Suppose $\int_0^1 f(t) \, dt = 3$. Calculate the following:

(a) $\int_0^{0.5} f(2t) \, dt$

(b) $\int_0^1 f(1-t) \, dt$

(c) $\int_1^{1.5} f(3-2t) \, dt$

127. (a) Calculate exactly: $\int_{-\pi}^{\pi} \cos^2 \theta \sin \theta \, d\theta$.

(b) Calculate the exact area under the curve $y = \cos^2 \theta \sin \theta$ between $\theta = 0$ and $\theta = \pi$.

128. Find $\int 4x(x^2+1) \, dx$ using two methods:

(a) Do the multiplication first, and then antidifferentiate.

(b) Use the substitution $w = x^2 + 1$.

(c) Explain how the expressions from parts (a) and (b) are different. Are they both correct?

129. (a) Find $\int \sin \theta \cos \theta \, d\theta$.

(b) You probably solved part (a) by making the substitution $w = \sin \theta$ or $w = \cos \theta$. (If not, go back and do it that way.) Now find $\int \sin \theta \cos \theta \, d\theta$ by making the *other* substitution.

(c) There is yet another way of finding this integral which involves the trigonometric identities

$$\sin(2\theta) = 2 \sin \theta \cos \theta$$
$$\cos(2\theta) = \cos^2 \theta - \sin^2 \theta.$$

Find $\int \sin \theta \cos \theta \, d\theta$ using one of these identities and then the substitution $w = 2\theta$.

(d) You should now have three different expressions for the indefinite integral $\int \sin \theta \cos \theta \, d\theta$. Are they really different? Are they all correct? Explain.

For Problems 130–131, find a substitution w and constants a, b, k so that the integral has the form $\int_a^b k f(w) \, dw$.

130. $\int_1^9 f\left(6x\sqrt{x}\right) \sqrt{x} \, dx$

131. $\int_2^5 \dfrac{f\left(\ln\left(x^2+1\right)\right) x \, dx}{x^2+1}$

132. Find the solution of the initial value problem

$$y' = \tan x + 1, \quad y(0) = 1.$$

133. Let $I_{m,n} = \int_0^1 x^m (1-x)^n \, dx$ for constant m, n. Show that $I_{m,n} = I_{n,m}$.

134. Let $f(t)$ be the velocity in meters/second of a car at time t in seconds. Give an integral for the change of position of the car

(a) For the time interval $0 \le t \le 60$.

(b) In terms of T in minutes, for the same time interval.

135. Over the past fifty years the carbon dioxide level in the atmosphere has increased. Carbon dioxide is believed to drive temperature, so predictions of future carbon dioxide levels are important. If $C(t)$ is carbon dioxide level in parts per million (ppm) and t is time in years since 1950, three possible models are:[1]

I $C'(t) = 1.3$
II $C'(t) = 0.5 + 0.03t$
III $C'(t) = 0.5e^{0.02t}$

(a) Given that the carbon dioxide level was 311 ppm in 1950, find $C(t)$ for each model.
(b) Find the carbon dioxide level in 2020 predicted by each model.

136. Let $f(t)$ be the rate of flow, in cubic meters per hour, of a flooding river at time t in hours. Give an integral for the total flow of the river

(a) Over the 3-day period $0 \le t \le 72$.
(b) In terms of time T in days over the same 3-day period.

137. With t in years since 2000, the population, P, of the world in billions can be modeled by $P = 6.1e^{0.012t}$.

(a) What does this model predict for the world population in 2010? In 2020?
(b) Use the Fundamental Theorem to predict the average population of the world between 2000 and 2010.

138. Oil is leaking out of a ruptured tanker at the rate of $r(t) = 50e^{-0.02t}$ thousand liters per minute.

(a) At what rate, in liters per minute, is oil leaking out at $t = 0$? At $t = 60$?
(b) How many liters leak out during the first hour?

139. Throughout much of the 20th century, the yearly consumption of electricity in the US increased exponentially at a continuous rate of 7% per year. Assume this trend continues and that the electrical energy consumed in 1900 was 1.4 million megawatt-hours.

(a) Write an expression for yearly electricity consumption as a function of time, t, in years since 1900.
(b) Find the average yearly electrical consumption throughout the 20th century.
(c) During what year was electrical consumption closest to the average for the century?
(d) Without doing the calculation for part (c), how could you have predicted which half of the century the answer would be in?

140. An electric current, $I(t)$, flowing out of a capacitor, decays according to $I(t) = I_0 e^{-t}$, where t is time. Find the charge, $Q(t)$, remaining in the capacitor at time t. The initial charge is Q_0 and $Q(t)$ is related to $I(t)$ by

$$Q'(t) = -I(t).$$

141. If we assume that wind resistance is proportional to velocity, then the downward velocity, v, of a body of mass m falling vertically is given by

$$v = \frac{mg}{k}\left(1 - e^{-kt/m}\right),$$

where g is the acceleration due to gravity and k is a constant. Find the height, h, above the surface of the earth as a function of time. Assume the body starts at height h_0.

142. If we assume that wind resistance is proportional to the square of velocity, then the downward velocity, v, of a falling body is given by

$$v = \sqrt{\frac{g}{k}}\left(\frac{e^{t\sqrt{gk}} - e^{-t\sqrt{gk}}}{e^{t\sqrt{gk}} + e^{-t\sqrt{gk}}}\right).$$

Use the substitution $w = e^{t\sqrt{gk}} + e^{-t\sqrt{gk}}$ to find the height, h, of the body above the surface of the earth as a function of time. Assume the body starts at a height h_0.

143. (a) Between 2000 and 2010, ACME Widgets sold widgets at a continuous rate of $R = R_0 e^{0.125t}$ widgets per year, where t is time in years since January 1, 2000. Suppose they were selling widgets at a rate of 1000 per year on January 1, 2000. How many widgets did they sell between 2000 and 2010? How many did they sell if the rate on January 1, 2000 was 1,000,000 widgets per year?
(b) In the first case (1000 widgets per year on January 1, 2000), how long did it take for half the widgets in the ten-year period to be sold? In the second case (1,000,000 widgets per year on January 1, 2000), when had half the widgets in the ten-year period been sold?
(c) In 2010, ACME advertised that half the widgets it had sold in the previous ten years were still in use. Based on your answer to part (b), how long must a widget last in order to justify this claim?

144. The rate at which water is flowing into a tank is $r(t)$ gallons/minute, with t in minutes.

(a) Write an expression approximating the amount of water entering the tank during the interval from time t to time $t + \Delta t$, where Δt is small.
(b) Write a Riemann sum approximating the total amount of water entering the tank between $t = 0$ and $t = 5$. Write an exact expression for this amount.
(c) By how much has the amount of water in the tank changed between $t = 0$ and $t = 5$ if $r(t) = 20e^{0.02t}$?
(d) If $r(t)$ is as in part (c), and if the tank contains 3000 gallons initially, find a formula for $Q(t)$, the amount of water in the tank at time t.

---

[1] Based on data from www.esrl.noaa.gov/gmd/ccgg.

In Problems 145–147, explain what is wrong with the statement.

145. $\int (f(x))^2 \, dx = (f(x))^3/3 + C$.

146. $\int \cos(x^2) \, dx = \sin(x^2)/(2x) + C$.

147. $\int_0^{\pi/2} \cos(3x) \, dx = (1/3) \int_0^{\pi/2} \cos w \, dw$.

In Problems 148–149, give an example of:

148. A possible $f(\theta)$ so that the following integral can be integrated by substitution:

$$\int f(\theta) e^{\cos \theta} \, d\theta.$$

149. An indefinite integral involving $\sin(x^3 - 3x)$ that can be evaluated by substitution.

In Problems 150–152, decide whether the statements are true or false. Give an explanation for your answer.

150. $\int f'(x) \cos(f(x)) \, dx = \sin(f(x)) + C$.

151. $\int (1/f(x)) \, dx = \ln |f(x)| + C$.

152. $\int t \sin(5 - t^2) \, dt$ can be evaluated using substitution.

7.2 INTEGRATION BY PARTS

The method of substitution reverses the chain rule. Now we introduce *integration by parts*, which is based on the product rule.

Example 1   Find $\int x e^x \, dx$.

Solution   We are looking for a function whose derivative is xe^x. The product rule might lead us to guess xe^x, because we know that the derivative has two terms, one of which is xe^x:

$$\frac{d}{dx}(xe^x) = \frac{d}{dx}(x)e^x + x\frac{d}{dx}(e^x) = e^x + xe^x.$$

Of course, our guess is wrong because of the extra e^x. But we can adjust our guess by subtracting e^x; this leads us to try $xe^x - e^x$. Let's check it:

$$\frac{d}{dx}(xe^x - e^x) = \frac{d}{dx}(xe^x) - \frac{d}{dx}(e^x) = e^x + xe^x - e^x = xe^x.$$

It works, so $\int xe^x \, dx = xe^x - e^x + C$.

Example 2   Find $\int \theta \cos \theta \, d\theta$.

Solution   We guess the antiderivative is $\theta \sin \theta$ and use the product rule to check:

$$\frac{d}{d\theta}(\theta \sin \theta) = \frac{d(\theta)}{d\theta} \sin \theta + \theta \frac{d}{d\theta}(\sin \theta) = \sin \theta + \theta \cos \theta.$$

To correct for the extra $\sin \theta$ term, we must subtract from our original guess something whose derivative is $\sin \theta$. Since $\frac{d}{d\theta}(\cos \theta) = -\sin \theta$, we try:

$$\frac{d}{d\theta}(\theta \sin \theta + \cos \theta) = \frac{d}{d\theta}(\theta \sin \theta) + \frac{d}{d\theta}(\cos \theta) = \sin \theta + \theta \cos \theta - \sin \theta = \theta \cos \theta.$$

Thus, $\int \theta \cos \theta \, d\theta = \theta \sin \theta + \cos \theta + C$.

The General Formula for Integration by Parts

We can formalize the process illustrated in the last two examples in the following way. We begin with the product rule:

$$\frac{d}{dx}(uv) = u'v + uv'$$

where u and v are functions of x with derivatives u' and v', respectively. We rewrite this as:

$$uv' = \frac{d}{dx}(uv) - u'v$$

and then integrate both sides:

$$\int uv' \, dx = \int \frac{d}{dx}(uv) \, dx - \int u'v \, dx.$$

Since an antiderivative of $\frac{d}{dx}(uv)$ is just uv, we get the following formula:

Integration by Parts

$$\int uv' \, dx = uv - \int u'v \, dx.$$

This formula is useful when the integrand can be viewed as a product and when the integral on the right-hand side is simpler than that on the left. In effect, we were using integration by parts in the previous two examples. In Example 1, we let $xe^x = (x) \cdot (e^x) = uv'$, and choose $u = x$ and $v' = e^x$. Thus, $u' = 1$ and $v = e^x$, so

$$\int \underbrace{(x)}_{u} \underbrace{(e^x)}_{v'} \, dx = \underbrace{(x)}_{u} \underbrace{(e^x)}_{v} - \int \underbrace{(1)}_{u'} \underbrace{(e^x)}_{v} \, dx = xe^x - e^x + C.$$

So uv represents our first guess, and $\int u'v \, dx$ represents the correction to our guess.

Notice what would have happened if, instead of $v = e^x$, we took $v = e^x + C_1$. Then

$$\int xe^x \, dx = x(e^x + C_1) - \int (e^x + C_1) \, dx$$
$$= xe^x + C_1 x - e^x - C_1 x + C$$
$$= xe^x - e^x + C,$$

as before. Thus, it is not necessary to include an arbitrary constant in the antiderivative for v; any antiderivative will do.

What would have happened if we had picked u and v' the other way around? If $u = e^x$ and $v' = x$, then $u' = e^x$ and $v = x^2/2$. The formula for integration by parts then gives

$$\int xe^x \, dx = \frac{x^2}{2}e^x - \int \frac{x^2}{2} \cdot e^x \, dx,$$

which is true but not helpful since the integral on the right is worse than the one on the left. To use this method, we must choose u and v' to make the integral on the right easier to find than the integral on the left.

How to Choose u and v'

- Whatever you let v' be, you need to be able to find v.
- It helps if u' is simpler than u (or at least no more complicated than u).
- It helps if v is simpler than v' (or at least no more complicated than v').

If we pick $v' = x$ in Example 1, then $v = x^2/2$, which is certainly "worse" than v'.

There are some examples which don't look like good candidates for integration by parts because they don't appear to involve products, but for which the method works well. Such examples often involve $\ln x$ or the inverse trigonometric functions. Here is one:

Example 3   Find $\displaystyle\int_2^3 \ln x \, dx$.

Solution   This does not look like a product unless we write $\ln x = (1)(\ln x)$. Then we might say $u = 1$ so $u' = 0$, which certainly makes things simpler. But if $v' = \ln x$, what is v? If we knew, we would not need integration by parts. Let's try the other way: if $u = \ln x$, $u' = 1/x$ and if $v' = 1$, $v = x$, so

$$\int_2^3 \underbrace{(\ln x)}_{u} \underbrace{(1)}_{v'} \, dx = \underbrace{(\ln x)}_{u} \underbrace{(x)}_{v} \Big|_2^3 - \int_2^3 \underbrace{\left(\frac{1}{x}\right)}_{u'} \cdot \underbrace{(x)}_{v} \, dx$$

$$= x \ln x \Big|_2^3 - \int_2^3 1 \, dx = (x \ln x - x) \Big|_2^3$$

$$= 3 \ln 3 - 3 - 2 \ln 2 + 2 = 3 \ln 3 - 2 \ln 2 - 1.$$

Notice that when doing a definite integral by parts, we must remember to put the limits of integration (here 2 and 3) on the uv term (in this case $x \ln x$) as well as on the integral $\int u'v \, dx$.

Example 4   Find $\displaystyle\int x^6 \ln x \, dx$.

Solution   View $x^6 \ln x$ as uv' where $u = \ln x$ and $v' = x^6$. Then $v = \frac{1}{7}x^7$ and $u' = 1/x$, so integration by parts gives us:

$$\int x^6 \ln x \, dx = \int (\ln x) x^6 \, dx = (\ln x)\left(\frac{1}{7}x^7\right) - \int \frac{1}{7}x^7 \cdot \frac{1}{x} \, dx$$

$$= \frac{1}{7}x^7 \ln x - \frac{1}{7}\int x^6 \, dx$$

$$= \frac{1}{7}x^7 \ln x - \frac{1}{49}x^7 + C.$$

In Example 4 we did not choose $v' = \ln x$, because it is not immediately clear what v would be. In fact, we used integration by parts in Example 3 to find the antiderivative of $\ln x$. Also, using $u = \ln x$, as we have done, gives $u' = 1/x$, which can be considered simpler than $u = \ln x$. This shows that u does not have to be the first factor in the integrand (here x^6).

Example 5   Find $\displaystyle\int x^2 \sin 4x \, dx$.

Solution   If we let $v' = \sin 4x$, then $v = -\frac{1}{4}\cos 4x$, which is no worse than v'. Also letting $u = x^2$, we get $u' = 2x$, which is simpler than $u = x^2$. Using integration by parts:

$$\int x^2 \sin 4x \, dx = x^2 \left(-\frac{1}{4}\cos 4x\right) - \int 2x \left(-\frac{1}{4}\cos 4x\right) \, dx$$

$$= -\frac{1}{4}x^2 \cos 4x + \frac{1}{2}\int x \cos 4x \, dx.$$

The trouble is we still have to grapple with $\int x \cos 4x \, dx$. This can be done by using integration by parts again with a new u and v, namely $u = x$ and $v' = \cos 4x$:

$$\int x \cos 4x \, dx = x \left(\frac{1}{4} \sin 4x \right) - \int 1 \cdot \frac{1}{4} \sin 4x \, dx$$

$$= \frac{1}{4} x \sin 4x - \frac{1}{4} \cdot \left(-\frac{1}{4} \cos 4x \right) + C$$

$$= \frac{1}{4} x \sin 4x + \frac{1}{16} \cos 4x + C.$$

Thus,

$$\int x^2 \sin 4x \, dx = -\frac{1}{4} x^2 \cos 4x + \frac{1}{2} \int x \cos 4x \, dx$$

$$= -\frac{1}{4} x^2 \cos 4x + \frac{1}{2} \left(\frac{1}{4} x \sin 4x + \frac{1}{16} \cos 4x + C \right)$$

$$= -\frac{1}{4} x^2 \cos 4x + \frac{1}{8} x \sin 4x + \frac{1}{32} \cos 4x + C.$$

Notice that, in this example, each time we used integration by parts, the exponent of x went down by 1. In addition, when the arbitrary constant C is multiplied by $\frac{1}{2}$, it is still represented by C.

Example 6   Find $\int \cos^2 \theta \, d\theta$.

Solution   Using integration by parts with $u = \cos \theta$, $v' = \cos \theta$ gives $u' = -\sin \theta$, $v = \sin \theta$, so we get

$$\int \cos^2 \theta \, d\theta = \cos \theta \sin \theta + \int \sin^2 \theta \, d\theta.$$

Substituting $\sin^2 \theta = 1 - \cos^2 \theta$ leads to

$$\int \cos^2 \theta \, d\theta = \cos \theta \sin \theta + \int (1 - \cos^2 \theta) \, d\theta$$

$$= \cos \theta \sin \theta + \int 1 \, d\theta - \int \cos^2 \theta \, d\theta.$$

Looking at the right side, we see that the original integral has reappeared. If we move it to the left, we get

$$2 \int \cos^2 \theta \, d\theta = \cos \theta \sin \theta + \int 1 \, d\theta = \cos \theta \sin \theta + \theta + C.$$

Dividing by 2 gives

$$\int \cos^2 \theta \, d\theta = \frac{1}{2} \cos \theta \sin \theta + \frac{1}{2} \theta + C.$$

Problem 53 asks you to do this integral by another method.

The previous example illustrates a useful technique: Use integration by parts to transform the integral into an expression containing another copy of the same integral, possibly multiplied by a coefficient, then solve for the original integral.

Example 7   Use integration by parts twice to find $\int e^{2x} \sin(3x) \, dx$.

Solution   Using integration by parts with $u = e^{2x}$ and $v' = \sin(3x)$ gives $u' = 2e^{2x}$, $v = -\frac{1}{3} \cos(3x)$, so we get

$$\int e^{2x} \sin(3x) \, dx = -\frac{1}{3} e^{2x} \cos(3x) + \frac{2}{3} \int e^{2x} \cos(3x) \, dx.$$

On the right side we have an integral similar to the original one, with the sine replaced by a cosine. Using integration by parts on that integral in the same way gives

$$\int e^{2x}\cos(3x)\,dx = \frac{1}{3}e^{2x}\sin(3x) - \frac{2}{3}\int e^{2x}\sin(3x)\,dx.$$

Substituting this into the expression we obtained for the original integral gives

$$\int e^{2x}\sin(3x)\,dx = -\frac{1}{3}e^{2x}\cos(3x) + \frac{2}{3}\left(\frac{1}{3}e^{2x}\sin(3x) - \frac{2}{3}\int e^{2x}\sin(3x)\,dx\right)$$

$$= -\frac{1}{3}e^{2x}\cos(3x) + \frac{2}{9}e^{2x}\sin(3x) - \frac{4}{9}\int e^{2x}\sin(3x)\,dx.$$

The right side now has a copy of the original integral, multiplied by $-4/9$. Moving it to the left, we get

$$\left(1+\frac{4}{9}\right)\int e^{2x}\sin(3x)\,dx = -\frac{1}{3}e^{2x}\cos(3x) + \frac{2}{9}e^{2x}\sin(3x).$$

Dividing through by the coefficient on the left, $(1+4/9) = 13/9$ and adding a constant of integration C, we get

$$\int e^{2x}\sin(3x)\,dx = \frac{9}{13}\left(-\frac{1}{3}e^{2x}\cos(3x) + \frac{2}{9}e^{2x}\sin(3x)\right) + C$$

$$= \frac{1}{13}e^{2x}\left(2\sin(3x) - 3\cos(3x)\right) + C.$$

Example 8   Use a computer algebra system to investigate $\int \sin(x^2)\,dx$.

Solution   It can be shown that $\sin(x^2)$ has no elementary antiderivative. A computer algebra system gives an antiderivative involving a non-elementary function, the Fresnel Integral, which you may not recognize.

Exercises and Problems for Section 7.2

Exercises

1. Use integration by parts to express $\int x^2 e^x\,dx$ in terms of

   (a) $\int x^3 e^x\,dx$ (b) $\int x e^x\,dx$

2. Write $\arctan x = 1 \cdot \arctan x$ to find $\int \arctan x\,dx$.

Find the integrals in Exercises 3–32.

3. $\int t\sin t\,dt$

4. $\int t^2 \sin t\,dt$

5. $\int t e^{5t}\,dt$

6. $\int t^2 e^{5t}\,dt$

7. $\int p e^{-0.1p}\,dp$

8. $\int (z+1)e^{2z}\,dz$

9. $\int x\ln x\,dx$

10. $\int x^3 \ln x\,dx$

11. $\int q^5 \ln 5q\,dq$

12. $\int \theta^2 \cos 3\theta\,d\theta$

13. $\int \sin^2 \theta\,d\theta$

14. $\int \cos^2(3\alpha+1)\,d\alpha$

15. $\int (\ln t)^2\,dt$

16. $\int \ln(x^2)\,dx$

17. $\int y\sqrt{y+3}\,dy$

18. $\int (t+2)\sqrt{2+3t}\,dt$

19. $\int (\theta+1)\sin(\theta+1)\,d\theta$

20. $\int \frac{z}{e^z}\,dz$

21. $\int \frac{\ln x}{x^2}\,dx$

22. $\int \frac{y}{\sqrt{5-y}}\,dy$

23. $\int \frac{t+7}{\sqrt{5-t}}\,dt$

24. $\int x(\ln x)^4\,dx$

25. $\int r(\ln r)^2 \, dr$ **26.** $\int \arcsin w \, dw$

27. $\int \arctan 7z \, dz$ **28.** $\int x \arctan x^2 \, dx$

29. $\int x^3 e^{x^2} \, dx$ **30.** $\int x^5 \cos x^3 \, dx$

31. $\int x \sinh x \, dx$ **32.** $\int (x-1) \cosh x \, dx$

Evaluate the integrals in Exercises 33–40 both exactly [e.g. $\ln(3\pi)$] and numerically [e.g. $\ln(3\pi) \approx 2.243$].

33. $\int_1^5 \ln t \, dt$ **34.** $\int_3^5 x \cos x \, dx$

35. $\int_0^{10} z e^{-z} \, dz$ **36.** $\int_1^3 t \ln t \, dt$

37. $\int_0^1 \arctan y \, dy$ **38.** $\int_0^5 \ln(1+t) \, dt$

39. $\int_0^1 \arcsin z \, dz$ **40.** $\int_0^1 u \arcsin u^2 \, du$

41. For each of the following integrals, indicate whether integration by substitution or integration by parts is more appropriate. Do not evaluate the integrals.

    (a) $\int x \sin x \, dx$ **(b)** $\int \dfrac{x^2}{1+x^3} \, dx$

    (c) $\int x e^{x^2} \, dx$ **(d)** $\int x^2 \cos(x^3) \, dx$

    (e) $\int \dfrac{1}{\sqrt{3x+1}} \, dx$ **(f)** $\int x^2 \sin x \, dx$

    (g) $\int \ln x \, dx$

42. Find $\int_1^2 \ln x \, dx$ numerically. Find $\int_1^2 \ln x \, dx$ using antiderivatives. Check that your answers agree.

Problems

In Problems 43–45, using properties of ln, find a substitution w and constant k so that the integral has the form $\int k \ln w \, dw$.

43. $\int \ln \left((5-3x)^2 \right) \, dx$ **44.** $\int \ln \left(\dfrac{1}{\sqrt{4-5x}} \right) \, dx$

45. $\int \dfrac{\ln \left((\ln x)^3 \right)}{x} \, dx$

In Problems 46–51, find the exact area.

46. Under $y = te^{-t}$ for $0 \le t \le 2$.

47. Under $f(z) = \arctan z$ for $0 \le z \le 2$.

48. Under $f(y) = \arcsin y$ for $0 \le y \le 1$.

49. Between $y = \ln x$ and $y = \ln(x^2)$ for $1 \le x \le 2$.

50. Between $f(t) = \ln(t^2 - 1)$ and $g(t) = \ln(t-1)$ for $2 \le t \le 3$.

51. Under the first arch of $f(x) = x \sin x$.

52. In Exercise 13, you evaluated $\int \sin^2 \theta \, d\theta$ using integration by parts. (If you did not do it by parts, do so now!) Redo this integral using the identity $\sin^2 \theta = (1 - \cos 2\theta)/2$. Explain any differences in the form of the answer obtained by the two methods.

53. Compute $\int \cos^2 \theta \, d\theta$ in two different ways and explain any differences in the form of your answers. (The identity $\cos^2 \theta = (1 + \cos 2\theta)/2$ may be useful.)

54. Use integration by parts twice to find $\int e^x \sin x \, dx$.

55. Use integration by parts twice to find $\int e^\theta \cos \theta \, d\theta$.

56. Use the results from Problems 54 and 55 and integration by parts to find $\int x e^x \sin x \, dx$.

57. Use the results from Problems 54 and 55 and integration by parts to find $\int \theta e^\theta \cos \theta \, d\theta$.

58. If f is a twice differentiable function, find

$$\int f''(x) \ln x \, dx + \int \frac{f(x)}{x^2} \, dx$$

(Your answer should contain f, but no integrals.)

59. If f is a twice differentiable function, find $\int x f''(x) \, dx$. (Your answer should contain f, but no integrals.)

60. Use the table with $f(x) = F'(x)$ to find $\displaystyle\int_0^5 x f'(x) \, dx$.

x	0	1	2	3	4	5
$f(x)$	2	-5	-6	-1	10	27
$F(x)$	10	8	2	-2	2	20

In Problems 61–64, derive the given formulas.

61. $\int x^n e^x \, dx = x^n e^x - n \int x^{n-1} e^x \, dx$

62. $\int x^n \cos ax \, dx = \dfrac{1}{a} x^n \sin ax - \dfrac{n}{a} \int x^{n-1} \sin ax \, dx$

63. $\int x^n \sin ax \, dx = -\dfrac{1}{a} x^n \cos ax + \dfrac{n}{a} \int x^{n-1} \cos ax \, dx$

64. $\int \cos^n x \, dx = \dfrac{1}{n} \cos^{n-1} x \sin x + \dfrac{n-1}{n} \int \cos^{n-2} x \, dx$

65. Integrating $e^{ax} \sin bx$ by parts twice gives

$$\int e^{ax} \sin bx \, dx = e^{ax} (A \sin bx + B \cos bx) + C.$$

    (a) Find the constants A and B in terms of a and b. [Hint: Don't actually perform the integration.]

    (b) Evaluate $\int e^{ax} \cos bx \, dx$ by modifying the method in part (a). [Again, do not perform the integration.]

66. Estimate $\int_0^{10} f(x)g'(x)\, dx$ if $f(x) = x^2$ and g has the values in the following table.

x	0	2	4	6	8	10
$g(x)$	2.3	3.1	4.1	5.5	5.9	6.1

67. Let f be a function with $f(0) = 6$, $f(1) = 5$, and $f'(1) = 2$. Evaluate the integral $\int_0^1 x f''(x)\, dx$.

68. Given $h(x) = f(x)\sqrt{x}$ and $g'(x) = f(x)/\sqrt{x}$, rewrite in terms of $h(x)$ and $g(x)$:

$$\int f'(x)\sqrt{x}\, dx.$$

Your answer should not include integrals, $f(x)$, $h'(x)$, or $g'(x)$.

69. Given that $f(7) = 0$ and $\int_0^7 f(x)\, dx = 5$, evaluate

$$\int_0^7 x f'(x)\, dx.$$

70. Let $F(a)$ be the area under the graph of $y = x^2 e^{-x}$ between $x = 0$ and $x = a$, for $a > 0$.

(a) Find a formula for $F(a)$.
(b) Is F an increasing or decreasing function?
(c) Is F concave up or concave down for $0 < a < 2$?

71. The concentration, C, in ng/ml, of a drug in the blood as a function of the time, t, in hours since the drug was administered is given by $C = 15te^{-0.2t}$. The area under the concentration curve is a measure of the overall effect of the drug on the body, called the bioavailability. Find the bioavailability of the drug between $t = 0$ and $t = 3$.

72. The voltage, V, in an electric circuit is given as a function of time, t, by

$$V = V_0 \cos(\omega t + \phi).$$

Each of the positive constants, V_0, ω, ϕ is increased (while the other two are held constant). What is the effect of each increase on the following quantities:

(a) The maximum value of V?

(b) The maximum value of dV/dt?
(c) The average value of V^2 over one period of V?

73. During a surge in the demand for electricity, the rate, r, at which energy is used can be approximated by

$$r = te^{-at},$$

where t is the time in hours and a is a positive constant.

(a) Find the total energy, E, used in the first T hours. Give your answer as a function of a.
(b) What happens to E as $T \to \infty$?

74. Given $h(x) = f(x)\ln|x|$ and $g'(x) = \dfrac{f(x)}{x}$, rewrite

$$\int f'(x)\ln|x|\, dx. \text{ in terms of } h(x) \text{ and } g(x).$$

75. The *error function*, $\mathrm{erf}(x)$, is defined by

$$\mathrm{erf}(x) = \frac{2}{\sqrt{\pi}}\int_0^x e^{-t^2}\, dt.$$

(a) Let $u = \mathrm{erf}(x)$. Use integration by parts to write $\int \mathrm{erf}(x)\, dx = uv - \int v\, u'\, dx$. Give u' and v'.

(b) Evaluate the integral $\int v\, u'\, dx$ from part (a) by making a substitution w. Give the values of w and dw.

(c) Use your answers to parts (a) and (b) to find $\int \mathrm{erf}(x)\, dx$. Your answer may involve $\mathrm{erf}(x)$.

76. The *Eulerian logarithmic integral* $\mathrm{Li}(x)$ is defined[2] as $\mathrm{Li}(x) = \int_2^x \dfrac{1}{\ln t}\, dt$. Letting $u = \mathrm{Li}(x)$ and $v = \ln x$, use integration by parts to evaluate $\int \mathrm{Li}(x)x^{-1}\, dx$. Your answer will involve $\mathrm{Li}(x)$.

Strengthen Your Understanding

In Problems 77–79, explain what is wrong with the statement.

77. To integrate $\int t \ln t\, dt$ by parts, use $u = t$, $v' = \ln t$.

78. The integral $\int \arctan x\, dx$ cannot be evaluated using integration by parts since the integrand is not a product of two functions.

79. Using integration by parts, we can show that

$$\int f(x)\, dx = x f'(x) - \int x f'(x)\, dx.$$

In Problems 80–82, give an example of:

80. An integral using only powers of θ and $\sin\theta$ which can be evaluated using integration by parts twice.

81. An integral that requires three applications of integration by parts.

82. An integral of the form $\int f(x)g(x)\, dx$ that can be evaluated using integration by parts either with $u = f(x)$ or with $u = g(x)$.

---

[2]http://en.wikipedia.org/wiki/Logarithmic_integral_function#Offset_logarithmic_integral, accessed February 17, 2011.

In Problems 83–85, decide whether the statements are true or false. Give an explanation for your answer.

83. $\int t\sin(5-t)\,dt$ can be evaluated by parts.

84. The integral $\int t^2 e^{3-t}\,dt$ can be done by parts.

85. When integrating by parts, it does not matter which factor we choose for u.

7.3 TABLES OF INTEGRALS

Today, many integrals are done using a CAS. Traditionally, the antiderivatives of commonly used functions were compiled in a table, such as the one in the back of this book. Other tables include *CRC Standard Mathematical Tables* (Boca Raton, Fl: CRC Press). The key to using these tables is being able to recognize the general class of function that you are trying to integrate, so you can know in what section of the table to look.

Warning: This section involves long division of polynomials and completing the square. You may want to review these topics!

Using the Table of Integrals

Part I of the table inside the back cover gives the antiderivatives of the basic functions x^n, a^x, $\ln x$, $\sin x$, $\cos x$, and $\tan x$. (The antiderivative for $\ln x$ is found using integration by parts and is a special case of the more general formula III-13.) Most of these are already familiar.

Part II of the table contains antiderivatives of functions involving products of e^x, $\sin x$, and $\cos x$. All of these antiderivatives were obtained using integration by parts.

Example 1 Find $\int \sin 7z \sin 3z\,dz$.

Solution Since the integrand is the product of two sines, we should use II-10 in the table,

$$\int \sin 7z \sin 3z\,dz = -\frac{1}{40}(7\cos 7z \sin 3z - 3\cos 3z \sin 7z) + C.$$

Part III of the table contains antiderivatives for products of a polynomial and e^x, $\sin x$, or $\cos x$. It also has an antiderivative for $x^n \ln x$, which can easily be used to find the antiderivatives of the product of a general polynomial and $\ln x$. Each *reduction formula* is used repeatedly to reduce the degree of the polynomial until a zero-degree polynomial is obtained.

Example 2 Find $\int (x^5 + 2x^3 - 8)e^{3x}\,dx$.

Solution Since $p(x) = x^5 + 2x^3 - 8$ is a polynomial multiplied by e^{3x}, this is of the form in III-14. Now $p'(x) = 5x^4 + 6x^2$ and $p''(x) = 20x^3 + 12x$, and so on, giving

$$\int (x^5 + 2x^3 - 8)e^{3x}\,dx = e^{3x}\left(\frac{1}{3}(x^5 + 2x^3 - 8) - \frac{1}{9}(5x^4 + 6x^2) + \frac{1}{27}(20x^3 + 12x)\right.$$
$$\left. - \frac{1}{81}(60x^2 + 12) + \frac{1}{243}(120x) - \frac{1}{729}\cdot 120\right) + C.$$

Here we have the successive derivatives of the original polynomial $x^5 + 2x^3 - 8$, occurring with alternating signs and multiplied by successive powers of $1/3$.

Part IV of the table contains reduction formulas for the antiderivatives of $\cos^n x$ and $\sin^n x$, which can be obtained by integration by parts. When n is a positive integer, formulas IV-17 and IV-18 can be used repeatedly to reduce the power n until it is 0 or 1.

Example 3   Find $\int \sin^6 \theta \, d\theta$.

Solution   Use IV-17 repeatedly:

$$\int \sin^6 \theta \, d\theta = -\frac{1}{6} \sin^5 \theta \cos \theta + \frac{5}{6} \int \sin^4 \theta \, d\theta$$

$$\int \sin^4 \theta \, d\theta = -\frac{1}{4} \sin^3 \theta \cos \theta + \frac{3}{4} \int \sin^2 \theta \, d\theta$$

$$\int \sin^2 \theta \, d\theta = -\frac{1}{2} \sin \theta \cos \theta + \frac{1}{2} \int 1 \, d\theta.$$

Calculate $\int \sin^2 \theta \, d\theta$ first, and use this to find $\int \sin^4 \theta \, d\theta$; then calculate $\int \sin^6 \theta \, d\theta$. Putting this all together, we get

$$\int \sin^6 \theta \, d\theta = -\frac{1}{6} \sin^5 \theta \cos \theta - \frac{5}{24} \sin^3 \theta \cos \theta - \frac{15}{48} \sin \theta \cos \theta + \frac{15}{48} \theta + C.$$

The last item in **Part IV** of the table is not a formula: it is advice on how to antidifferentiate products of integer powers of $\sin x$ and $\cos x$. There are various techniques to choose from, depending on the nature (odd or even, positive or negative) of the exponents.

Example 4   Find $\int \cos^3 t \sin^4 t \, dt$.

Solution   Here the exponent of $\cos t$ is odd, so IV-23 recommends making the substitution $w = \sin t$. Then $dw = \cos t \, dt$. To make this work, we'll have to separate off one of the cosines to be part of dw. Also, the remaining even power of $\cos t$ can be rewritten in terms of $\sin t$ by using $\cos^2 t = 1 - \sin^2 t = 1 - w^2$, so that

$$\int \cos^3 t \sin^4 t \, dt = \int \cos^2 t \sin^4 t \cos t \, dt$$

$$= \int (1 - w^2) w^4 \, dw = \int (w^4 - w^6) \, dw$$

$$= \frac{1}{5} w^5 - \frac{1}{7} w^7 + C = \frac{1}{5} \sin^5 t - \frac{1}{7} \sin^7 t + C.$$

Example 5   Find $\int \cos^2 x \sin^4 x \, dx$.

Solution   In this example, both exponents are even. The advice given in IV-23 is to convert to all sines or all cosines. We'll convert to all sines by substituting $\cos^2 x = 1 - \sin^2 x$, and then we'll multiply out the integrand:

$$\int \cos^2 x \sin^4 x \, dx = \int (1 - \sin^2 x) \sin^4 x \, dx = \int \sin^4 x \, dx - \int \sin^6 x \, dx.$$

In Example 3 we found $\int \sin^4 x \, dx$ and $\int \sin^6 x \, dx$. Put them together to get

$$\int \cos^2 x \sin^4 x \, dx = -\frac{1}{4} \sin^3 x \cos x - \frac{3}{8} \sin x \cos x + \frac{3}{8} x$$

$$- \left(-\frac{1}{6} \sin^5 x \cos x - \frac{5}{24} \sin^3 x \cos x - \frac{15}{48} \sin x \cos x + \frac{15}{48} x \right) + C$$

$$= \frac{1}{6} \sin^5 x \cos x - \frac{1}{24} \sin^3 x \cos x - \frac{3}{48} \sin x \cos x + \frac{3}{48} x + C.$$

The last two parts of the table are concerned with quadratic functions: **Part V** has expressions with quadratic denominators; **Part VI** contains square roots of quadratics. The quadratics that appear in these formulas are of the form $x^2 \pm a^2$ or $a^2 - x^2$, or in factored form $(x - a)(x - b)$, where a and b are different constants. Quadratics can be converted to these forms by factoring or completing the square.

Preparing to Use the Table: Transforming the Integrand

To use the integral table, we often need to manipulate or reshape integrands to fit entries in the table. The manipulations that tend to be useful are factoring, long division, completing the square, and substitution.

Using Factoring

Example 6 Find $\displaystyle\int \frac{3x + 7}{x^2 + 6x + 8}\, dx$.

Solution In this case we factor the denominator to get it into a form in the table:

$$x^2 + 6x + 8 = (x + 2)(x + 4).$$

Now in V-27 we let $a = -2$, $b = -4$, $c = 3$, and $d = 7$, to obtain

$$\int \frac{3x + 7}{x^2 + 6x + 8}\, dx = \frac{1}{2}(\ln |x + 2| - (-5) \ln |x + 4|) + C.$$

Long Division

Example 7 Find $\displaystyle\int \frac{x^2}{x^2 + 4}\, dx$.

Solution A good rule of thumb when integrating a rational function whose numerator has a degree greater than or equal to that of the denominator is to start by doing *long division*. This results in a polynomial plus a simpler rational function as a remainder. Performing long division here, we obtain:

$$\frac{x^2}{x^2 + 4} = 1 - \frac{4}{x^2 + 4}.$$

Then, by V-24 with $a = 2$, we obtain:

$$\int \frac{x^2}{x^2 + 4}\, dx = \int 1\, dx - 4 \int \frac{1}{x^2 + 4}\, dx = x - 4 \cdot \frac{1}{2} \arctan \frac{x}{2} + C.$$

Completing the Square to Rewrite the Quadratic in the Form $w^2 + a^2$

Example 8 Find $\displaystyle\int \frac{1}{x^2 + 6x + 14}\, dx$.

Solution By completing the square, we can get this integrand into a form in the table:

$$x^2 + 6x + 14 = (x^2 + 6x + 9) - 9 + 14$$
$$= (x + 3)^2 + 5.$$

Let $w = x + 3$. Then $dw = dx$ and so the substitution gives

$$\int \frac{1}{x^2 + 6x + 14}\, dx = \int \frac{1}{w^2 + 5}\, dw = \frac{1}{\sqrt{5}} \arctan \frac{w}{\sqrt{5}} + C = \frac{1}{\sqrt{5}} \arctan \frac{x + 3}{\sqrt{5}} + C,$$

where the antidifferentiation uses V-24 with $a^2 = 5$.

Substitution

Getting an integrand into the right form to use a table of integrals involves substitution and a variety of algebraic techniques.

Example 9   Find $\int e^t \sin(5t + 7)\, dt$.

Solution   This looks similar to II-8. To make the correspondence more complete, let's try the substitution $w = 5t + 7$. Then $dw = 5\, dt$, so $dt = \frac{1}{5}\, dw$. Also, $t = (w - 7)/5$. Then the integral becomes

$$\int e^t \sin(5t + 7)\, dt = \int e^{(w-7)/5} \sin w\, \frac{dw}{5}$$

$$= \frac{e^{-7/5}}{5} \int e^{w/5} \sin w\, dw. \qquad \text{(Since } e^{(w-7)/5} = e^{w/5} e^{-7/5} \text{ and } e^{-7/5} \text{ is a constant)}$$

Now we can use II-8 with $a = \frac{1}{5}$ and $b = 1$ to write

$$\int e^{w/5} \sin w\, dw = \frac{1}{(\frac{1}{5})^2 + 1^2} e^{w/5} \left(\frac{\sin w}{5} - \cos w \right) + C,$$

so

$$\int e^t \sin(5t + 7)\, dt = \frac{e^{-7/5}}{5} \left(\frac{25}{26} e^{(5t+7)/5} \left(\frac{\sin(5t + 7)}{5} - \cos(5t + 7) \right) \right) + C$$

$$= \frac{5e^t}{26} \left(\frac{\sin(5t + 7)}{5} - \cos(5t + 7) \right) + C.$$

Example 10   Find a substitution w and constants k, n so that the following integral has the form $\int kw^n \ln w\, dw$, found in III-15:

$$\int \frac{\ln(x + 1) + \ln(x - 1)}{\sqrt{x^2 - 1}} x\, dx$$

Solution   First we use properties of ln to simplify the integral:

$$\int \frac{\ln(x + 1) + \ln(x - 1)}{\sqrt{x^2 - 1}} x\, dx = \int \frac{\ln((x + 1)(x - 1))}{\sqrt{x^2 - 1}} x\, dx = \int \frac{\ln(x^2 - 1)}{\sqrt{x^2 - 1}} x\, dx.$$

Let $w = x^2 - 1$, $dw = 2x\, dx$, so that $x\, dx = (1/2)\, dw$. Then

$$\int \frac{\ln(x^2 - 1)}{\sqrt{x^2 - 1}} x\, dx = \int w^{-1/2} \ln w\, \frac{1}{2} dw = \int \frac{1}{2} w^{-1/2} \ln w\, dw,$$

so $k = 1/2$, $n = -1/2$.

Exercises and Problems for Section 7.3

Exercises

For Exercises 1–40, antidifferentiate using the table of integrals. You may need to transform the integrand first.

1. $\int x^5 \ln x\, dx$

2. $\int e^{-3\theta} \cos \theta\, d\theta$

3. $\int x^3 \sin 5x\, dx$.

4. $\int (x^2 + 3) \ln x\, dx$.

5. $\int (x^3 + 5)^2\, dx$.

6. $\int \sin w \cos^4 w\, dw$

7. $\int \sin^4 x\, dx$

8. $\int x^3 e^{2x}\, dx$

9. $\int x^2 e^{3x}\, dx$

10. $\int x^2 e^{x^3}\, dx$

11. $\int x^4 e^{3x}\, dx$

12. $\int u^5 \ln(5u)\, du$

13. $\int \frac{1}{3 + y^2}\, dy$

14. $\int \frac{dx}{9x^2 + 16}$

15. $\displaystyle\int \frac{dx}{\sqrt{25-16x^2}}$

16. $\displaystyle\int \frac{dx}{\sqrt{9x^2+25}}$

17. $\displaystyle\int \sin 3\theta \cos 5\theta \, d\theta$

18. $\displaystyle\int \sin 3\theta \sin 5\theta \, d\theta$

19. $\displaystyle\int \frac{1}{\cos^3 x}\, dx$

20. $\displaystyle\int \frac{t^2+1}{t^2-1}\, dt$

21. $\displaystyle\int e^{5x}\sin 3x\, dx$

22. $\displaystyle\int \cos 2y \cos 7y\, dy$

23. $\displaystyle\int y^2 \sin 2y\, dy$

24. $\displaystyle\int x^3 \sin x^2\, dx$

25. $\displaystyle\int \frac{1}{\cos^4 7x}\, dx$

26. $\displaystyle\int \frac{1}{\sin^3 3\theta}\, d\theta$

27. $\displaystyle\int \frac{1}{\sin^2 2\theta}\, d\theta$

28. $\displaystyle\int \frac{1}{\cos^5 x}\, dx.$

29. $\displaystyle\int \frac{1}{x^2+4x+3}\, dx$

30. $\displaystyle\int \frac{1}{x^2+4x+4}\, dx$

31. $\displaystyle\int \frac{dz}{z(z-3)}$

32. $\displaystyle\int \frac{dy}{4-y^2}$

33. $\displaystyle\int \frac{1}{1+(z+2)^2}\, dz$

34. $\displaystyle\int \frac{1}{y^2+4y+5}\, dy$

35. $\displaystyle\int \sin^3 x\, dx$

36. $\displaystyle\int \tan^4 x\, dx$

37. $\displaystyle\int \sinh^3 x \cosh^2 x\, dx$

38. $\displaystyle\int \sinh^2 x \cosh^3 x\, dx$

39. $\displaystyle\int \sin^3 3\theta \cos^2 3\theta\, d\theta$

40. $\displaystyle\int ze^{2z^2}\cos(2z^2)\, dz$

For Exercises 41–50, evaluate the definite integrals. Whenever possible, use the Fundamental Theorem of Calculus, perhaps after a substitution. Otherwise, use numerical methods.

41. $\displaystyle\int_0^{\pi/12} \sin(3\alpha)\, d\alpha$

42. $\displaystyle\int_{-\pi}^{\pi} \sin 5x \cos 6x\, dx$

43. $\displaystyle\int_1^2 (x-2x^3)\ln x\, dx$

44. $\displaystyle\int_0^1 \sqrt{3-x^2}\, dx$

45. $\displaystyle\int_0^1 \frac{1}{x^2+2x+1}\, dx$

46. $\displaystyle\int_0^1 \frac{dx}{x^2+2x+5}$

47. $\displaystyle\int_0^{1/\sqrt{2}} \frac{x}{\sqrt{1-x^4}}\, dx$

48. $\displaystyle\int_0^1 \frac{(x+2)}{(x+2)^2+1}\, dx$

49. $\displaystyle\int_{\pi/4}^{\pi/3} \frac{dx}{\sin^3 x}$

50. $\displaystyle\int_{-3}^{-1} \frac{dx}{\sqrt{x^2+6x+10}}$

Problems

In Problems 51–52, using properties of ln, find a substitution w and constants k, n so that the integral has the form

$$\int kw^n \ln w\, dw.$$

51. $\displaystyle\int (2x+1)^3 \ln(2x+1)\, dx$

52. $\displaystyle\int (2x+1)^3 \ln\frac{1}{\sqrt{2x+1}}\, dx$

In Problems 53–55, find constants a, b, c, m, n so that the integral is in one of the following forms from a table of integrals.[3] Give the form (i)–(iii) you use.

(i) $\displaystyle\int \frac{dx}{ax^2+bx+c}$

(ii) $\displaystyle\int \frac{mx+n}{ax^2+bx+c}\, dx$

(iii) $\displaystyle\int \frac{dx}{(ax^2+bx+c)^n},\ n>0$

53. $\displaystyle\int \frac{dx}{5-\dfrac{x}{4}-\dfrac{x^2}{6}}$

54. $\displaystyle\int \frac{dx}{2x+\dfrac{5}{7+3x}}$

55. $\displaystyle\int \frac{dx}{(x^2-5x+6)^3(x^2-4x+4)^2(x^2-6x+9)^2}$

In Problems 56–57, find constants a, b, λ so that the integral has the form found in some tables of integrals:[4]

$$\int \frac{e^{2\lambda x}}{ae^{\lambda x}+b}\, dx.$$

56. $\displaystyle\int \frac{e^{6x}}{4+e^{3x+1}}\, dx$

57. $\displaystyle\int \frac{e^{8x}}{4e^{4x}+5e^{6x}}\, dx$

58. According to a table of integrals,[5]

$$\int x^2 e^{bx}\, dx = e^{bx}\left(\frac{x^2}{b}-\frac{2x}{b^2}+\frac{2}{b^3}\right)+C.$$

(a) Find a substitution w and constant k so that the integral $\int x^5 e^{bx^2}\, dx$ can be rewritten in the form

$$\int kw^2 e^{bw}\, dw.$$

(b) Evaluate the integral in terms of x. Your answer may involve the constant b.

59. Show that for all integers m and n, with $m \neq \pm n$, $\int_{-\pi}^{\pi} \sin m\theta \sin n\theta\, d\theta = 0$.

60. Show that for all integers m and n, with $m \neq \pm n$, $\int_{-\pi}^{\pi} \cos m\theta \cos n\theta\, d\theta = 0$.

---

[3]http://en.wikipedia.org/wiki/List_of_integrals_of_rational_functions, page accessed February 24, 2010.
[4]http://en.wikipedia.org/wiki/List_of_integrals_of_exponential_functions, page accessed May 5, 2010.
[5]http://en.wikipedia.org/wiki/List_of_integrals_of_exponential_functions, page accessed February 17, 2011.

61. The voltage, V, in an electrical outlet is given as a function of time, t, by the function $V = V_0 \cos(120\pi t)$, where V is in volts and t is in seconds, and V_0 is a positive constant representing the maximum voltage.

   (a) What is the average value of the voltage over 1 second?

   (b) Engineers do not use the average voltage. They use the root mean square voltage defined by $\overline{V} = \sqrt{\text{average of } (V^2)}$. Find $\overline{V}$ in terms of V_0. (Take the average over 1 second.)

   (c) The standard voltage in an American house is 110 volts, meaning that $\overline{V} = 110$. What is V_0?

62. For some constants A and B, the rate of production, $R(t)$, of oil in a new oil well is modeled by:

$$R(t) = A + Be^{-t}\sin(2\pi t)$$

where t is the time in years, A is the equilibrium rate, and B is the "variability" coefficient.

   (a) Find the total amount of oil produced in the first N years of operation. (Take N to be an integer.)

   (b) Find the average amount of oil produced per year over the first N years (where N is an integer).

   (c) From your answer to part (b), find the average amount of oil produced per year as $N \to \infty$.

   (d) Looking at the function $R(t)$, explain how you might have predicted your answer to part (c) without doing any calculations.

   (e) Do you think it is reasonable to expect this model to hold over a very long period? Why or why not?

Strengthen Your Understanding

In Problems 63–67, explain what is wrong with the statement.

63. The table of integrals cannot be used to find $\int \dfrac{dt}{7 - t^2}$.

64. If $a > 0$, then $\int 1/(x^2 + 4x + a)\,dx$ always involves arctan.

65. By Formula II-8 of the table with $a = 1, b = 1$,

$$\int e^x \sin x\,dx = \frac{1}{2}e^x(\sin x - \cos x) + C.$$

Therefore

$$\int e^{2x+1}\sin(2x + 1)\,dx =$$

$$\frac{1}{2}e^{2x+1}(\sin(2x + 1) - \cos(2x + 1)) + C.$$

66. The integral $\int \sin x \cos x\,dx$ with $a = 1, b = 1$ is undefined according to Table Formula II-12 since, for $a \neq b$,

$$\int \sin(ax)\cos(bx)\,dx =$$

$$\frac{1}{b^2 - a^2}(b\sin(ax)\sin(bx) + a\cos(ax)\cos(bx)) + C.$$

67. The table can be used to evaluate $\int \sin x/x\,dx$.

In Problems 68–69, give an example of:

68. An indefinite integral involving a square root that can be evaluated by first completing a square.

69. An indefinite integral involving $\sin x$ that can be evaluated with a reduction formula

In Problems 70–73, decide whether the statements are true or false. Give an explanation for your answer.

70. $\int \sin^7\theta \cos^6\theta\,d\theta$ can be written as a polynomial with $\cos\theta$ as the variable.

71. $\int 1/(x^2 + 4x + 5)\,dx$ involves a natural logarithm.

72. $\int 1/(x^2 + 4x - 5)\,dx$ involves an arctangent.

73. $\int x^{-1}((\ln x)^2 + (\ln x)^3)\,dx$ is a polynomial with $\ln x$ as the variable.

7.4 ALGEBRAIC IDENTITIES AND TRIGONOMETRIC SUBSTITUTIONS

Although not all functions have elementary antiderivatives, many do. In this section we introduce two powerful methods of integration which show that large classes of functions have elementary antiderivatives. The first is the method of partial fractions, which depends on an algebraic identity, and allows us to integrate rational functions. The second is the method of trigonometric substitutions, which allows us to handle expressions involving the square root of a quadratic polynomial. Some of the formulas in the table of integrals can be derived using the techniques of this section.

Method of Partial Fractions

The integral of some rational functions can be obtained by splitting the integrand into *partial fractions*. For example, to find

$$\int \frac{1}{(x - 2)(x - 5)}\,dx,$$

the integrand is split into partial fractions with denominators $(x-2)$ and $(x-5)$. We write

$$\frac{1}{(x-2)(x-5)} = \frac{A}{x-2} + \frac{B}{x-5},$$

where A and B are constants that need to be found. Multiplying by $(x-2)(x-5)$ gives the identity

$$1 = A(x-5) + B(x-2)$$

so

$$1 = (A+B)x - 5A - 2B.$$

Since this equation holds for all x, the constant terms on both sides must be equal.[6] Similarly, the coefficients of x on both sides must be equal. So

$$-5A - 2B = 1$$
$$A + B = 0.$$

Solving these equations gives $A = -1/3$, $B = 1/3$. Thus,

$$\frac{1}{(x-2)(x-5)} = \frac{-1/3}{x-2} + \frac{1/3}{x-5}.$$

(Check the answer by writing the right-hand side over the common denominator $(x-2)(x-5)$.)

Example 1   Use partial fractions to integrate $\displaystyle\int \frac{1}{(x-2)(x-5)}\, dx$.

Solution   We split the integrand into partial fractions, each of which can be integrated:

$$\int \frac{1}{(x-2)(x-5)}\, dx = \int \left(\frac{-1/3}{x-2} + \frac{1/3}{x-5} \right) dx = -\frac{1}{3}\ln|x-2| + \frac{1}{3}\ln|x-5| + C.$$

You can check that using formula V-26 in the integral table gives the same result.

This method can be used to derive formulas V-26 and V-27 in the integral table. A similar method works whenever the denominator of the integrand factors into distinct linear factors and the numerator has degree less than the denominator.

Example 2   Find $\displaystyle\int \frac{x+2}{x^2+x}\, dx$.

Solution   We factor the denominator and split the integrand into partial fractions:

$$\frac{x+2}{x^2+x} = \frac{x+2}{x(x+1)} = \frac{A}{x} + \frac{B}{x+1}.$$

Multiplying by $x(x+1)$ gives the identity

$$x + 2 = A(x+1) + Bx$$
$$= (A+B)x + A.$$

Equating constant terms and coefficients of x gives $A = 2$ and $A + B = 1$, so $B = -1$. Then we split the integrand into two parts and integrate:

$$\int \frac{x+2}{x^2+x}\, dx = \int \left(\frac{2}{x} - \frac{1}{x+1} \right) dx = 2\ln|x| - \ln|x+1| + C.$$

The next example illustrates what to do if there is a repeated factor in the denominator.

Example 3   Calculate $\displaystyle\int \frac{10x - 2x^2}{(x-1)^2(x+3)}\, dx$ using partial fractions of the form $\dfrac{A}{x-1}, \dfrac{B}{(x-1)^2}, \dfrac{C}{x+3}$.

---

[6]We have not shown that the equation holds for $x = 2$ and $x = 5$, but these values do not affect the argument.

Solution   We are given that the squared factor, $(x-1)^2$, leads to partial fractions of the form:

$$\frac{10x - 2x^2}{(x-1)^2(x+3)} = \frac{A}{x-1} + \frac{B}{(x-1)^2} + \frac{C}{x+3}.$$

Multiplying through by $(x-1)^2(x+3)$ gives

$$10x - 2x^2 = A(x-1)(x+3) + B(x+3) + C(x-1)^2$$
$$= (A+C)x^2 + (2A + B - 2C)x - 3A + 3B + C.$$

Equating the coefficients of x^2 and x and the constant terms, we get the simultaneous equations:

$$A + C = -2$$
$$2A + B - 2C = 10$$
$$-3A + 3B + C = 0.$$

Solving gives $A = 1, B = 2, C = -3$. Thus, we obtain three integrals which can be evaluated:

$$\int \frac{10x - 2x^2}{(x-1)^2(x+3)}\, dx = \int \left(\frac{1}{x-1} + \frac{2}{(x-1)^2} - \frac{3}{x+3} \right) dx$$
$$= \ln|x-1| - \frac{2}{(x-1)} - 3\ln|x+3| + K.$$

For the second integral, we use the fact that $\int 2/(x-1)^2 dx = 2\int (x-1)^{-2} dx = -2(x-1)^{-1} + K$.

If there is a quadratic in the denominator which cannot be factored, we need an expression of the form $Ax + B$ in the numerator, as the next example shows.

Example 4   Find $\displaystyle \int \frac{2x^2 - x - 1}{(x^2+1)(x-2)}\, dx$ using partial fractions of the form $\dfrac{Ax + B}{x^2 + 1}$ and $\dfrac{C}{x-2}$.

Solution   We are given that the quadratic denominator, $(x^2 + 1)$, which cannot be factored further, has a numerator of the form $Ax + B$, so we have

$$\frac{2x^2 - x - 1}{(x^2+1)(x-2)} = \frac{Ax + B}{x^2 + 1} + \frac{C}{x-2}.$$

Multiplying by $(x^2 + 1)(x-2)$ gives

$$2x^2 - x - 1 = (Ax + B)(x-2) + C(x^2 + 1)$$
$$= (A+C)x^2 + (B - 2A)x + C - 2B.$$

Equating the coefficients of x^2 and x and the constant terms gives the simultaneous equations

$$A + C = 2$$
$$B - 2A = -1$$
$$C - 2B = -1.$$

Solving gives $A = B = C = 1$, so we rewrite the integral as follows:

$$\int \frac{2x^2 - x - 1}{(x^2+1)(x-2)}\, dx = \int \left(\frac{x+1}{x^2+1} + \frac{1}{x-2} \right) dx.$$

This identity is useful provided we can perform the integration on the right-hand side. The first integral can be done if it is split into two; the second integral is similar to those in the previous examples. We have

$$\int \frac{2x^2 - x - 1}{(x^2 + 1)(x - 2)}\, dx = \int \frac{x}{x^2 + 1}\, dx + \int \frac{1}{x^2 + 1}\, dx + \int \frac{1}{x - 2}\, dx.$$

To calculate $\int (x/(x^2 + 1))\, dx$, substitute $w = x^2 + 1$, or guess and check. The final result is

$$\int \frac{2x^2 - x - 1}{(x^2 + 1)(x - 2)}\, dx = \frac{1}{2}\ln|x^2 + 1| + \arctan x + \ln|x - 2| + K.$$

The next example shows what to do if the numerator has degree larger than the denominator.

Example 5   Calculate $\displaystyle\int \frac{x^3 - 7x^2 + 10x + 1}{x^2 - 7x + 10}\, dx$ using long division before integrating.

Solution

The degree of the numerator is greater than the degree of the denominator, so we divide first:

$$\frac{x^3 - 7x^2 + 10x + 1}{x^2 - 7x + 10} = \frac{x(x^2 - 7x + 10) + 1}{x^2 - 7x + 10} = x + \frac{1}{x^2 - 7x + 10}.$$

The remainder, in this case $1/(x^2 - 7x + 10)$, is a rational function on which we try to use partial fractions. We have

$$\frac{1}{x^2 - 7x + 10} = \frac{1}{(x - 2)(x - 5)}$$

so in this case we use the result of Example 1 to obtain

$$\int \frac{x^3 - 7x^2 + 10x + 1}{x^2 - 7x + 10}\, dx = \int \left(x + \frac{1}{(x - 2)(x - 5)} \right) dx = \frac{x^2}{2} - \frac{1}{3}\ln|x - 2| + \frac{1}{3}\ln|x - 5| + C.$$

Many, though not all, rational functions can be integrated by the strategy suggested by the previous examples.

Strategy for Integrating a Rational Function, $\frac{P(x)}{Q(x)}$

- If degree of $P(x) \geq$ degree of $Q(x)$, try long division and the method of partial fractions on the remainder.
- If $Q(x)$ is the product of distinct linear factors, use partial fractions of the form

$$\frac{A}{(x - c)}.$$

- If $Q(x)$ contains a repeated linear factor, $(x - c)^n$, use partial fractions of the form

$$\frac{A_1}{(x - c)} + \frac{A_2}{(x - c)^2} + \cdots + \frac{A_n}{(x - c)^n}.$$

- If $Q(x)$ contains an unfactorable quadratic $q(x)$, try a partial fraction of the form

$$\frac{Ax + B}{q(x)}.$$

To use this method, we must be able to integrate each partial fraction. We can integrate terms of the form $A/(x-c)^n$ using the power rule (if $n > 1$) and logarithms (if $n = 1$). Next we see how to integrate terms of the form $(Ax + B)/q(x)$, where $q(x)$ is an unfactorable quadratic.

Trigonometric Substitutions

Section 7.1 showed how substitutions could be used to transform complex integrands. Now we see how substitution of $\sin \theta$ or $\tan \theta$ can be used for integrands involving square roots of quadratics or unfactorable quadratics.

Sine Substitutions

Substitutions involving $\sin \theta$ make use of the Pythagorean identity, $\cos^2 \theta + \sin^2 \theta = 1$, to simplify an integrand involving $\sqrt{a^2 - x^2}$.

Example 6   Find $\displaystyle \int \frac{1}{\sqrt{1 - x^2}} \, dx$ using the substitution $x = \sin \theta$.

Solution   If $x = \sin \theta$, then $dx = \cos \theta \, d\theta$, and substitution converts $1 - x^2$ to a perfect square:

$$\int \frac{1}{\sqrt{1 - x^2}} \, dx = \int \frac{1}{\sqrt{1 - \sin^2 \theta}} \cos \theta \, d\theta = \int \frac{\cos \theta}{\sqrt{\cos^2 \theta}} \, d\theta.$$

Now either $\sqrt{\cos^2 \theta} = \cos \theta$ or $\sqrt{\cos^2 \theta} = -\cos \theta$ depending on the values taken by θ. If we choose $-\pi/2 \leq \theta \leq \pi/2$, then $\cos \theta \geq 0$, so $\sqrt{\cos^2 \theta} = \cos \theta$. Then

$$\int \frac{\cos \theta}{\sqrt{\cos^2 \theta}} \, d\theta = \int \frac{\cos \theta}{\cos \theta} \, d\theta = \int 1 \, d\theta = \theta + C = \arcsin x + C.$$

The last step uses the fact that $\theta = \arcsin x$ if $x = \sin \theta$ and $-\pi/2 \leq \theta \leq \pi/2$.

From now on, when we substitute $\sin \theta$, we assume that the interval $-\pi/2 \leq \theta \leq \pi/2$ has been chosen. Notice that the previous example is the case $a = 1$ of VI-28 in the table of integrals. The next example illustrates how to choose the substitution when $a \neq 1$.

Example 7   Use a trigonometric substitution to find $\displaystyle \int \frac{1}{\sqrt{4 - x^2}} \, dx$.

Solution   This time we choose $x = 2 \sin \theta$, with $-\pi/2 \leq \theta \leq \pi/2$, so that $4 - x^2$ becomes a perfect square:

$$\sqrt{4 - x^2} = \sqrt{4 - 4\sin^2 \theta} = 2\sqrt{1 - \sin^2 \theta} = 2\sqrt{\cos^2 \theta} = 2\cos \theta.$$

Then $dx = 2 \cos \theta \, d\theta$, so substitution gives

$$\int \frac{1}{\sqrt{4 - x^2}} \, dx = \int \frac{1}{2 \cos \theta} 2 \cos \theta \, d\theta = \int 1 \, d\theta = \theta + C = \arcsin \left(\frac{x}{2} \right) + C.$$

The general rule for choosing a sine substitution is:

> To simplify $\sqrt{a^2 - x^2}$, for constant a, try $x = a \sin \theta$, with $-\pi/2 \leq \theta \leq \pi/2$.

Notice $\sqrt{a^2 - x^2}$ is only defined on the interval $[-a, a]$. Assuming that the domain of the integrand is $[-a, a]$, the substitution $x = a \sin \theta$, with $-\pi/2 \leq \theta \leq \pi/2$, is valid for all x in the domain, because its range is $[-a, a]$ and it has an inverse $\theta = \arcsin(x/a)$ on $[-a, a]$.

Example 8   Find the area of the ellipse $4x^2 + y^2 = 9$.

Solution   Solving for y shows that $y = \sqrt{9 - 4x^2}$ gives the upper half of the ellipse. From Figure 7.1, we see that

$$\text{Area} = 4 \int_0^{3/2} \sqrt{9 - 4x^2} \, dx.$$

To decide which trigonometric substitution to use, we write the integrand as

$$\sqrt{9 - 4x^2} = 2\sqrt{\frac{9}{4} - x^2} = 2\sqrt{\left(\frac{3}{2}\right)^2 - x^2}.$$

This suggests that we should choose $x = (3/2) \sin\theta$, so that $dx = (3/2) \cos\theta \, d\theta$ and

$$\sqrt{9 - 4x^2} = 2\sqrt{\left(\frac{3}{2}\right)^2 - \left(\frac{3}{2}\right)^2 \sin^2\theta} = 2\left(\frac{3}{2}\right)\sqrt{1 - \sin^2\theta} = 3\cos\theta.$$

When $x = 0$, $\theta = 0$, and when $x = 3/2$, $\theta = \pi/2$, so

$$4 \int_0^{3/2} \sqrt{9 - 4x^2} \, dx = 4 \int_0^{\pi/2} 3\cos\theta \left(\frac{3}{2}\right) \cos\theta \, d\theta = 18 \int_0^{\pi/2} \cos^2\theta \, d\theta.$$

Using Example 6 on page 367 or table of integrals IV-18, we find

$$\int \cos^2\theta \, d\theta = \frac{1}{2} \cos\theta \sin\theta + \frac{1}{2}\theta + C.$$

So we have

$$\text{Area} = 4 \int_0^{3/2} \sqrt{9 - 4x^2} \, dx = \frac{18}{2} \left.(\cos\theta \sin\theta + \theta)\right|_0^{\pi/2} = 9\left(0 + \frac{\pi}{2}\right) = \frac{9\pi}{2}.$$

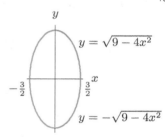

Figure 7.1: The ellipse $4x^2 + y^2 = 9$

In Example 8, we did not return to the original variable x after making the substitution because we had also converted the limits of the definite integral. However, if we are calculating an indefinite integral, we have to return to the original variable. In the next example, we see how a triangle representing the substitution can be useful.

Example 9   Find the indefinite integral $\int \sqrt{9 - 4x^2} \, dx$ corresponding to Example 8.

Solution   From Example 8, we know if $x = (3/2) \sin\theta$, then

$$\int \sqrt{9 - 4x^2} \, dx = \frac{1}{2} \cos\theta \sin\theta + \frac{1}{2}\theta + C.$$

To rewrite the antiderivative in terms of the original variable x, we use the fact that $\sin\theta = 2x/3$ to write $\theta = \arcsin(2x/3)$. To express $\cos\theta$ in terms of x, we draw the right triangle in Figure 7.2

with opposite side $2x$ and hypotenuse 3, so $\sin\theta = 2x/3$. Then we use the Pythagorean Theorem to see that $\cos\theta = \sqrt{9 - 4x^2}/3$, so

$$\int \sqrt{9 - 4x^2}\, dx = \frac{1}{2}\cos\theta\sin\theta + \frac{1}{2}\theta + C$$

$$= \frac{1}{2}\cdot\frac{2x}{3}\cdot\frac{\sqrt{9 - 4x^2}}{3} + \frac{1}{2}\arcsin\frac{2x}{3} + C = \frac{x\sqrt{9 - 4x^2}}{9} + \frac{1}{2}\arcsin\frac{2x}{3} + C.$$

Figure 7.2: Triangle with $\sin\theta = 2x/3$

Tangent Substitutions

Integrals involving $a^2 + x^2$ may be simplified by a substitution involving $\tan\theta$ and the trigonometric identities $\tan\theta = \sin\theta/\cos\theta$ and $\cos^2\theta + \sin^2\theta = 1$.

Example 10   Find $\displaystyle\int \frac{1}{x^2 + 9}\, dx$ using the substitution $x = 3\tan\theta$.

Solution   If $x = 3\tan\theta$, then $dx = (3/\cos^2\theta)\, d\theta$, so

$$\int \frac{1}{x^2 + 9}\, dx = \int \left(\frac{1}{9\tan^2\theta + 9}\right)\left(\frac{3}{\cos^2\theta}\right) d\theta = \frac{1}{3}\int \frac{1}{\left(\frac{\sin^2\theta}{\cos^2\theta} + 1\right)\cos^2\theta}\, d\theta$$

$$= \frac{1}{3}\int \frac{1}{\sin^2\theta + \cos^2\theta}\, d\theta = \frac{1}{3}\int 1\, d\theta = \frac{1}{3}\theta + C = \frac{1}{3}\arctan\left(\frac{x}{3}\right) + C.$$

To simplify $a^2 + x^2$ or $\sqrt{a^2 + x^2}$, for constant a, try $x = a\tan\theta$, with $-\pi/2 < \theta < \pi/2$.

Note that $a^2 + x^2$ and $\sqrt{a^2 + x^2}$ are defined on $(-\infty, \infty)$. Assuming that the domain of the integrand is $(-\infty, \infty)$, the substitution $x = a\tan\theta$, with $-\pi/2 < \theta < \pi/2$, is valid for all x in the domain, because its range is $(-\infty, \infty)$ and it has an inverse $\theta = \arctan(x/a)$ on $(-\infty, \infty)$.

Example 11   Use a tangent substitution to show that the following two integrals are equal:

$$\int_0^1 \sqrt{1 + x^2}\, dx = \int_0^{\pi/4} \frac{1}{\cos^3\theta}\, d\theta.$$

What area do these integrals represent?

Solution   We put $x = \tan\theta$, with $-\pi/2 < \theta < \pi/2$, so that $dx = (1/\cos^2\theta)\, d\theta$, and

$$\sqrt{1 + x^2} = \sqrt{1 + \frac{\sin^2\theta}{\cos^2\theta}} = \sqrt{\frac{\cos^2\theta + \sin^2\theta}{\cos^2\theta}} = \frac{1}{\cos\theta}.$$

When $x = 0$, $\theta = 0$, and when $x = 1$, $\theta = \pi/4$, so

$$\int_0^1 \sqrt{1 + x^2}\, dx = \int_0^{\pi/4} \left(\frac{1}{\cos\theta}\right)\left(\frac{1}{\cos^2\theta}\right) d\theta = \int_0^{\pi/4} \frac{1}{\cos^3\theta}\, d\theta.$$

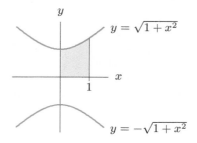

Figure 7.3: The hyperbola $y^2 - x^2 = 1$

The integral $\int_0^1 \sqrt{1+x^2}\,dx$ represents the area under the hyperbola $y^2 - x^2 = 1$ in Figure 7.3.

Completing the Square to Use a Trigonometric Substitution

To make a trigonometric substitution, we may first need to complete the square.

Example 12   Find $\displaystyle\int \frac{3}{\sqrt{2x - x^2}}\,dx$.

Solution   To use a sine or tangent substitution, the expression under the square root sign should be in the form $a^2 + x^2$ or $a^2 - x^2$. Completing the square, we get

$$2x - x^2 = 1 - (x-1)^2.$$

This suggests we substitute $x - 1 = \sin\theta$, or $x = \sin\theta + 1$. Then $dx = \cos\theta\,d\theta$, and

$$\int \frac{3}{\sqrt{2x - x^2}}\,dx = \int \frac{3}{\sqrt{1 - (x-1)^2}}\,dx = \int \frac{3}{\sqrt{1 - \sin^2\theta}}\cos\theta\,d\theta$$

$$= \int \frac{3}{\cos\theta}\cos\theta\,d\theta = \int 3\,d\theta = 3\theta + C.$$

Since $x - 1 = \sin\theta$, we have $\theta = \arcsin(x-1)$, so

$$\int \frac{3}{\sqrt{2x - x^2}}\,dx = 3\arcsin(x - 1) + C.$$

Example 13   Find $\displaystyle\int \frac{1}{x^2 + x + 1}\,dx$.

Solution   Completing the square, we get

$$x^2 + x + 1 = \left(x + \frac{1}{2}\right)^2 + \frac{3}{4} = \left(x + \frac{1}{2}\right)^2 + \left(\frac{\sqrt{3}}{2}\right)^2.$$

This suggests we substitute $x + 1/2 = (\sqrt{3}/2)\tan\theta$, or $x = -1/2 + (\sqrt{3}/2)\tan\theta$. Then $dx = (\sqrt{3}/2)(1/\cos^2\theta)\,d\theta$, so

$$\int \frac{1}{x^2 + x + 1}\,dx = \int \left(\frac{1}{(x + \frac{1}{2})^2 + \frac{3}{4}}\right)\left(\frac{\sqrt{3}}{2}\frac{1}{\cos^2\theta}\right)d\theta$$

$$= \frac{\sqrt{3}}{2}\int\left(\frac{1}{\frac{3}{4}\tan^2\theta + \frac{3}{4}}\right)\left(\frac{1}{\cos^2\theta}\right)d\theta = \frac{2}{\sqrt{3}}\int \frac{1}{(\tan^2\theta + 1)\cos^2\theta}\,d\theta$$

$$= \frac{2}{\sqrt{3}}\int \frac{1}{\sin^2\theta + \cos^2\theta}\,d\theta = \frac{2}{\sqrt{3}}\int 1\,d\theta = \frac{2}{\sqrt{3}}\theta + C.$$

Since $x + 1/2 = (\sqrt{3}/2) \tan\theta$, we have $\theta = \arctan((2/\sqrt{3})x + 1/\sqrt{3})$, so

$$\int \frac{1}{x^2 + x + 1}\, dx = \frac{2}{\sqrt{3}} \arctan\left(\frac{2}{\sqrt{3}}x + \frac{1}{\sqrt{3}}\right) + C.$$

Alternatively, using a computer algebra system gives[7]

$$\frac{2 \tan^{-1}\left(\dfrac{2x+1}{\sqrt{3}}\right)}{\sqrt{3}},$$

essentially the same as we obtained by hand. You can check either answer by differentiation.

Exercises and Problems for Section 7.4

Exercises

Split the functions in Exercises 1–7 into partial fractions.

1. $\dfrac{x+1}{6x+x^2}$

2. $\dfrac{20}{25 - x^2}$

3. $\dfrac{1}{w^4 - w^3}$

4. $\dfrac{2y}{y^3 - y^2 + y - 1}$

5. $\dfrac{8}{y^3 - 4y}$

6. $\dfrac{2(1+s)}{s(s^2 + 3s + 2)}$

7. $\dfrac{2}{s^4 - 1}$

In Exercises 8–14, find the antiderivative of the function in the given exercise.

8. Exercise 1

9. Exercise 2

10. Exercise 3

11. Exercise 4

12. Exercise 5

13. Exercise 6

14. Exercise 7

In Exercises 15–19, evaluate the integral.

15. $\displaystyle\int \frac{3x^2 - 8x + 1}{x^3 - 4x^2 + x + 6}\, dx;$ use $\dfrac{A}{x-2} + \dfrac{B}{x+1} + \dfrac{C}{x-3}$.

16. $\displaystyle\int \frac{dx}{x^3 - x^2};$ use $\dfrac{A}{x} + \dfrac{B}{x^2} + \dfrac{C}{x-1}$.

17. $\displaystyle\int \frac{10x + 2}{x^3 - 5x^2 + x - 5}\, dx;$ use $\dfrac{A}{x-5} + \dfrac{Bx + C}{x^2 + 1}$.

18. $\displaystyle\int \frac{x^4 + 12x^3 + 15x^2 + 25x + 11}{x^3 + 12x^2 + 11x}\, dx;$

use division and $\dfrac{A}{x} + \dfrac{B}{x+1} + \dfrac{C}{x+11}$.

19. $\displaystyle\int \frac{x^4 + 3x^3 + 2x^2 + 1}{x^2 + 3x + 2}\, dx;$ use division.

In Exercises 20–22, use the substitution to find the integral.

20. $\displaystyle\int \frac{1}{\sqrt{9 - 4x^2}}\, dx, \quad x = \frac{3}{2}\sin t$

21. $\displaystyle\int \frac{1}{\sqrt{4x - 3 - x^2}}\, dx, \quad x = \sin t + 2$

22. $\displaystyle\int \frac{1}{x^2 + 4x + 5}\, dx, \quad x = \tan t - 2$

23. Which of the following integrals are best done by a trigonometric substitution, and what substitution?

   (a) $\displaystyle\int \sqrt{9 - x^2}\, dx$ (b) $\displaystyle\int x\sqrt{9 - x^2}\, dx$

24. Give a substitution (not necessarily trigonometric) which could be used to compute the following integrals:

   (a) $\displaystyle\int \frac{x}{\sqrt{x^2 + 10}}\, dx$ (b) $\displaystyle\int \frac{1}{\sqrt{x^2 + 10}}\, dx$

Problems

25. Find a value of k and a substitution w such that

$$\int \frac{12x - 2}{(3x + 2)(x - 1)}\, dx = k \int \frac{dw}{w}.$$

26. Find values of A and B such that

$$\int \frac{12x - 2}{(3x + 2)(x - 1)}\, dx = \int \frac{A\, dx}{3x + 2} + \int \frac{B\, dx}{x - 1}.$$

---

[7]wolframalpha.com, January 11, 2011.

27. Write the integral $\displaystyle\int \frac{2x+9}{(3x+5)(4-5x)}\,dx$ in the form

$\displaystyle\int \frac{cx+d}{(x-a)(x-b)}\,dx$. Give the values of a, b, c, d. You need not evaluate the integral.

28. Write the integral $\displaystyle\int \frac{dx}{\sqrt{12-4x^2}}$ in the form

$\displaystyle\int \frac{k\,dx}{\sqrt{a^2-x^2}}$. Give the values of the positive constants a and k. You need not evaluate the integral.

29. Using the fact that $e^{2x} = (e^x)^2$, write the integral

$$\int_0^{\ln 7} \frac{2e^x+1}{e^{2x}-4e^x+3}\cdot e^x\,dx$$

in the form

$$\int_r^s \left(\frac{A}{w-3}+\frac{B}{w-1}\right)dw.$$

State the values of A, B, w, dw, r, s. (Note that r and s are values of w, not x.) You need not evaluate the integral.

30. (a) Evaluate $\displaystyle\int \frac{3x+6}{x^2+3x}\,dx$ by partial fractions.

   (b) Show that your answer to part (a) agrees with the answer you get by using the integral tables.

Complete the square and give a substitution (not necessarily trigonometric) which could be used to compute the integrals in Problems 31–38.

31. $\displaystyle\int \frac{1}{x^2+2x+2}\,dx$ **32.** $\displaystyle\int \frac{1}{x^2+6x+25}\,dx$

33. $\displaystyle\int \frac{dy}{y^2+3y+3}$ **34.** $\displaystyle\int \frac{x+1}{x^2+2x+2}\,dx$

35. $\displaystyle\int \frac{4}{\sqrt{2z-z^2}}\,dz$ **36.** $\displaystyle\int \frac{z-1}{\sqrt{2z-z^2}}\,dz$

37. $\displaystyle\int (t+2)\sin(t^2+4t+7)\,dt$

38. $\displaystyle\int (2-\theta)\cos(\theta^2-4\theta)\,d\theta$

Calculate the integrals in Problems 39–54.

39. $\displaystyle\int \frac{1}{(x-5)(x-3)}\,dx$ **40.** $\displaystyle\int \frac{1}{(x+2)(x+3)}\,dx$

41. $\displaystyle\int \frac{1}{(x+7)(x-2)}\,dx$ **42.** $\displaystyle\int \frac{x}{x^2-3x+2}\,dx$

43. $\displaystyle\int \frac{dz}{z^2+z}$ **44.** $\displaystyle\int \frac{dx}{x^2+5x+4}$

45. $\displaystyle\int \frac{dP}{3P-3P^2}$ **46.** $\displaystyle\int \frac{3x+1}{x^2-3x+2}\,dx$

47. $\displaystyle\int \frac{y+2}{2y^2+3y+1}\,dy$ **48.** $\displaystyle\int \frac{x+1}{x^3+x}\,dx$

49. $\displaystyle\int \frac{x-2}{x^2+x^4}\,dx$ **50.** $\displaystyle\int \frac{y^2}{25+y^2}\,dy$

51. $\displaystyle\int \frac{dz}{(4-z^2)^{3/2}}$ **52.** $\displaystyle\int \frac{10}{(s+2)(s^2+1)}\,ds$

53. $\displaystyle\int \frac{1}{x^2+4x+13}\,dx$ **54.** $\displaystyle\int \frac{e^x\,dx}{(e^x-1)(e^x+2)}$

In Problems 55–64, evaluate the indefinite integral, using a trigonometric substitution and a triangle to express the answer in terms of x. Assume $-\pi/2 \le \theta \le \pi/2$.

55. $\displaystyle\int \frac{1}{x^2\sqrt{1+x^2}}\,dx$ **56.** $\displaystyle\int \frac{x^2}{\sqrt{9-x^2}}\,dx$

57. $\displaystyle\int \frac{\sqrt{1-4x^2}}{x^2}\,dx$ **58.** $\displaystyle\int \frac{\sqrt{25-9x^2}}{x}\,dx$

59. $\displaystyle\int \frac{1}{x\sqrt{9-4x^2}}\,dx$ **60.** $\displaystyle\int \frac{1}{x\sqrt{1+16x^2}}\,dx$

61. $\displaystyle\int \frac{1}{x^2\sqrt{4-x^2}}\,dx$ **62.** $\displaystyle\int \frac{1}{(25+4x^2)^{3/2}}\,dx$

63. $\displaystyle\int \frac{1}{(16-x^2)^{3/2}}\,dx$ **64.** $\displaystyle\int \frac{x^2}{(1+9x^2)^{3/2}}\,dx$

Find the exact area of the regions in Problems 65–70.

65. Bounded by $y = 3x/((x-1)(x-4))$, $y = 0$, $x = 2$, $x = 3$.

66. Bounded by $y = (3x^2+x)/((x^2+1)(x+1))$, $y = 0$, $x = 0$, $x = 1$.

67. Bounded by $y = x^2/\sqrt{1-x^2}$, $y = 0$, $x = 0$, $x = 1/2$.

68. Bounded by $y = x^3/\sqrt{4-x^2}$, $y = 0$, $x = 0$, $x = \sqrt{2}$.

69. Bounded by $y = 1/\sqrt{x^2+9}$, $y = 0$, $x = 0$, $x = 3$.

70. Bounded by $y = 1/(x\sqrt{x^2+9})$, $y = 0$, $x = \sqrt{3}$, $x = 3$.

Calculate the integrals in Problems 71–73 by partial fractions and then by using the indicated substitution. Show that the results you get are the same.

71. $\displaystyle\int \frac{dx}{1-x^2}$; substitution $x = \sin\theta$.

72. $\displaystyle\int \frac{2x}{x^2-1}\,dx$; substitution $w = x^2 - 1$.

73. $\int \dfrac{3x^2 + 1}{x^3 + x}\, dx$; substitution $w = x^3 + x$.

74. (a) Show $\int \dfrac{1}{\sin^2 \theta}\, d\theta = -\dfrac{1}{\tan \theta} + C.$

(b) Calculate $\int \dfrac{dy}{y^2 \sqrt{5 - y^2}}.$

Solve Problems 75–77 without using integral tables.

75. Calculate the integral $\int \dfrac{1}{(x - a)(x - b)}\, dx$ for

(a) $a \neq b$ (b) $a = b$

76. Calculate the integral $\int \dfrac{x}{(x - a)(x - b)}\, dx$ for

(a) $a \neq b$ (b) $a = b$

77. Calculate the integral $\int \dfrac{1}{x^2 - a}\, dx$ for

(a) $a > 0$ (b) $a = 0$ (c) $a < 0$

78. A rumor is spread in a school. For $0 < a < 1$ and $b > 0$, the time t at which a fraction p of the school population has heard the rumor is given by

$$t(p) = \int_a^p \dfrac{b}{x(1 - x)}\, dx.$$

(a) Evaluate the integral to find an explicit formula for $t(p)$. Write your answer so it has only one ln term.

(b) At time $t = 0$ one percent of the school population ($p = 0.01$) has heard the rumor. What is a?

(c) At time $t = 1$ half the school population ($p = 0.5$) has heard the rumor. What is b?

(d) At what time has 90% of the school population ($p = 0.9$) heard the rumor?

79. The Law of Mass Action tells us that the time, T, taken by a chemical to create a quantity x_0 of the product (in molecules) is given by

$$T = \int_0^{x_0} \dfrac{k\, dx}{(a - x)(b - x)}$$

where a and b are initial quantities of the two ingredients used to make the product, and k is a positive constant. Suppose $0 < a < b$.

(a) Find the time taken to make a quantity $x_0 = a/2$ of the product.

(b) What happens to T as $x_0 \to a$?

80. The moment-generating function, $m(t)$, which gives useful information about the normal distribution of statistics, is defined by

$$m(t) = \int_{-\infty}^{\infty} e^{tx} \dfrac{e^{-x^2/2}}{\sqrt{2\pi}}\, dx.$$

Find a formula for $m(t)$. [Hint: Complete the square and use the fact that $\int_{-\infty}^{\infty} e^{-x^2/2}\, dx = \sqrt{2\pi}$.]

Strengthen Your Understanding

In Problems 81–82, explain what is wrong with the statement.

81. To integrate

$$\int \dfrac{1}{(x - 1)^2 (x - 2)}\, dx$$

using a partial fraction decomposition, let

$$\dfrac{1}{(x - 1)^2 (x - 2)} = \dfrac{A}{(x - 1)^2} + \dfrac{B}{x - 2}.$$

82. Use the substitution $x = 2 \sin \theta$ to integrate the following integral:

$$\int \dfrac{1}{(x^2 + 4)^{3/2}}\, dx.$$

In Problems 83–86, give an example of:

83. A rational function whose antiderivative is not a rational function.

84. An integral whose evaluation requires factoring a cubic.

85. A linear polynomial $P(x)$ and a quadratic polynomial $Q(x)$ such that the rational function $P(x)/Q(x)$ does not have a partial fraction decomposition of the form

$$\dfrac{P(x)}{Q(x)} = \dfrac{A}{x - r} + \dfrac{B}{x - s}$$

for some constants A, B, r, and s.

86. An integral that can be made easier to evaluate by using the trigonometric substitution $x = \frac{3}{2} \sin \theta$.

In Problems 87–88, decide whether the statements are true or false. Give an explanation for your answer.

87. The integral $\int \dfrac{1}{\sqrt{9 - t^2}}\, dt$ can be made easier to evaluate by using the substitution $t = 3 \tan \theta$.

88. To calculate $\int \dfrac{1}{x^3 + x^2}\, dx$, we can split the integrand into

$$\int \left(\dfrac{A}{x} + \dfrac{B}{x^2} + \dfrac{C}{x + 1} \right)\, dx$$

For Problems 89–90, which technique is useful in evaluating the integral?

(a)   Integration by parts   (b)   Partial fractions
(c)   Long division   (d)   Completing the square
(e)   A trig substitution   (f)   Other substitutions

89. $\int \dfrac{x^2}{\sqrt{1 - x^2}}\, dx$ **90.** $\int \dfrac{x^2}{1 - x^2}\, dx$

7.5 NUMERICAL METHODS FOR DEFINITE INTEGRALS

Many functions do not have elementary antiderivatives. To evaluate the definite integrals of such functions, we cannot use the Fundamental Theorem; we must use numerical methods. We know how to approximate a definite integral numerically using left- and right-hand Riemann sums; in this section, we introduce more accurate methods.

The Midpoint Rule

In the left- and right-hand Riemann sums, the heights of the rectangles are found using the left-hand or right-hand endpoints, respectively, of the subintervals. For the *midpoint rule*, we use the midpoint of each of the subintervals.

For example, in approximating $\int_1^2 f(x)\, dx$ by a Riemann sum with two subdivisions, we first divide the interval $1 \le x \le 2$ into two pieces. The midpoint of the first subinterval is 1.25 and the midpoint of the second is 1.75. The heights of the two rectangles are $f(1.25)$ and $f(1.75)$, respectively. (See Figure 7.4.) The Riemann sum is

$$f(1.25)0.5 + f(1.75)0.5.$$

Figure 7.4 shows that evaluating f at the midpoint of each subdivision often gives a better approximation to the area under the curve than evaluating f at either end.

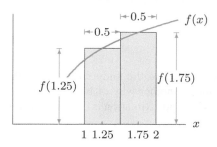

Figure 7.4: Midpoint rule with two subdivisions

Thus, we have three ways of estimating an integral using a Riemann sum:

1. The **left rule** uses the left endpoint of each subinterval.
2. The **right rule** uses the right endpoint of each subinterval.
3. The **midpoint rule** uses the midpoint of each subinterval.

We write $\text{LEFT}(n)$, $\text{RIGHT}(n)$, and $\text{MID}(n)$ to denote the results obtained by using these rules with n subdivisions.

Example 1   For $\int_1^2 \dfrac{1}{x}\, dx$, compute $\text{LEFT}(2)$, $\text{RIGHT}(2)$ and $\text{MID}(2)$, and compare your answers with the exact value of the integral.

Solution   For $n = 2$ subdivisions of the interval $[1, 2]$, we use $\Delta x = 0.5$. Then, to four decimal places,

$$\text{LEFT}(2) = f(1)(0.5) + f(1.5)(0.5) = \frac{1}{1}(0.5) + \frac{1}{1.5}(0.5) = 0.8333$$

$$\text{RIGHT}(2) = f(1.5)(0.5) + f(2)(0.5) = \frac{1}{1.5}(0.5) + \frac{1}{2}(0.5) = 0.5833$$

$$\text{MID}(2) = f(1.25)(0.5) + f(1.75)(0.5) = \frac{1}{1.25}(0.5) + \frac{1}{1.75}(0.5) = 0.6857.$$

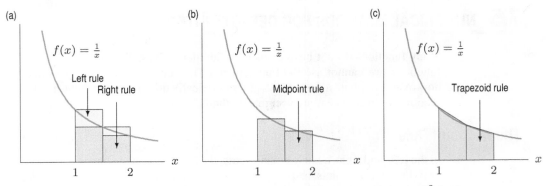

Figure 7.5: Left, right, midpoint, and trapezoid approximations to $\int_1^2 \frac{1}{x}\, dx$

All three Riemann sums in this example are approximating

$$\int_1^2 \frac{1}{x}\, dx = \ln x \Big|_1^2 = \ln 2 - \ln 1 = \ln 2 = 0.6931.$$

With only two subdivisions, the left and right rules give quite poor approximations but the midpoint rule is already fairly close to the exact answer. Figures 7.5(a) and (b) show that the midpoint rule is more accurate than the left and right rules because the error to the left of the midpoint tends to cancel the error to the right of the midpoint.

The Trapezoid Rule

We have just seen how the midpoint rule can have the effect of balancing out the errors of the left and right rules. Another way of balancing these errors is to average the results from the left and right rules. This approximation is called the *trapezoid rule*:

$$\text{TRAP}(n) = \frac{\text{LEFT}(n) + \text{RIGHT}(n)}{2}.$$

The trapezoid rule averages the values of f at the left and right endpoints of each subinterval and multiplies by Δx. This is the same as approximating the area under the graph of f in each subinterval by a trapezoid (see Figure 7.6).

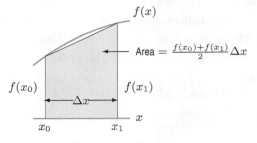

Figure 7.6: Area used in the trapezoid rule

Example 2   For $\int_1^2 \frac{1}{x}\, dx$, compare the trapezoid rule with two subdivisions with the left, right, and midpoint rules.

Solution   In the previous example we got $\text{LEFT}(2) = 0.8333$ and $\text{RIGHT}(2) = 0.5833$. The trapezoid rule is the average of these, so $\text{TRAP}(2) = 0.7083$. (See Figure 7.5(c).) The exact value of the integral is 0.6931, so the trapezoid rule is better than the left or right rules. The midpoint rule is still the best, however, since $\text{MID}(2) = 0.6857$.

Is the Approximation an Over- or Underestimate?

It is useful to know when a rule is producing an overestimate and when it is producing an underestimate. In Chapter 5 we saw that if the integrand is increasing, the left rule underestimates and the right rule overestimates the integral. If the integrand is decreasing, the roles reverse. Now we see how concavity relates to the errors in the trapezoid and midpoint rules.

The Trapezoid Rule

If the graph of the function is concave down on $[a, b]$, then each trapezoid lies below the graph and the trapezoid rule underestimates. If the graph is concave up on $[a, b]$, the trapezoid rule overestimates. (See Figure 7.7.)

f concave down:
Trapezoid underestimates

f concave up:
Trapezoid overestimates

Figure 7.7: Error in the trapezoid rule

The Midpoint Rule

To understand the relationship between the midpoint rule and concavity, take a rectangle whose top intersects the curve at the midpoint of a subinterval. Draw a tangent to the curve at the midpoint; this gives a trapezoid. See Figure 7.8. (This is *not* the same trapezoid as in the trapezoid rule.) The midpoint rectangle and the new trapezoid have the same area, because the shaded triangles in Figure 7.8 are congruent. Hence, if the graph of the function is concave down, the midpoint rule overestimates; if the graph is concave up, the midpoint rule underestimates. (See Figure 7.9.)

If the graph of f is concave down on $[a, b]$, then

$$\text{TRAP}(n) \leq \int_a^b f(x)\,dx \leq \text{MID}(n).$$

If the graph of f is concave up on $[a, b]$, then

$$\text{MID}(n) \leq \int_a^b f(x)\,dx \leq \text{TRAP}(n).$$

Figure 7.8: Midpoint rectangle and
trapezoid with same area

f concave down: f concave up:
Midpoint overestimates   Midpoint underestimates

Figure 7.9: Error in the midpoint rule

When we compute an approximation, we are always concerned about the error, namely the difference between the exact answer and the approximation. We usually do not know the exact error; if we did, we would also know the exact answer. We take

$$\text{Error} = \text{Actual value} - \text{Approximate value}.$$

The errors for some methods are much smaller than those for others. In general, the midpoint and trapezoid rules are more accurate than the left or right rules. Comparing the errors in the midpoint and trapezoid rules suggests an even better method, called Simpson's rule.

Error in Left and Right Rules

We work with the example $\int_1^2 (1/x) \, dx$ because we know the exact value of this integral ($\ln 2$) and we can investigate the behavior of the errors.

Let us see what happens to the error in the left and right rules as we increase n. The results are in Table 7.1. A positive error indicates that the Riemann sum is less than the exact value, $\ln 2$. Notice that the errors for the left and right rules have opposite signs but are approximately equal in magnitude. (See Figure 7.10.) This leads us to want to average the left and right rules; this average is the trapezoid rule.

Table 7.1   *Errors for the left and right rule approximation to $\int_1^2 \frac{1}{x} \, dx = \ln 2 \approx 0.6931471806$*

n	Error in left rule	Error in right rule
2	-0.1402	0.1098
10	-0.0256	0.0244
50	-0.0050	0.0050
250	-0.0010	0.0010

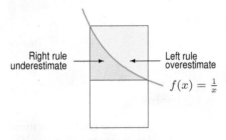

Figure 7.10: Errors in left and right sums

There is another pattern to the errors in Table 7.1. If we compute the *ratio* of the errors in Table 7.2, we see that the error[8] in both the left and right rules decreases by a factor of about 5 as n increases by a factor of 5.

There is nothing special about the number 5; the same holds for any factor. To get one extra digit of accuracy in any calculation, we must make the error $1/10$ as big, so we must increase n by a factor of 10. In fact, *for the left or right rules, each extra digit of accuracy requires about 10 times the work.*

Table 7.2   *Ratio of the errors as n increases for $\int_1^2 \frac{1}{x} \, dx$*

	Ratio of errors in left rule	Ratio of errors in right rule
Error(2)/Error(10)	5.47	4.51
Error(10)/Error(50)	5.10	4.90
Error(50)/Error(250)	5.02	4.98

Error in Trapezoid and Midpoint Rules

Table 7.3 shows that the trapezoid and midpoint rules generally produce better approximations to $\int_1^2 (1/x) \, dx$ than the left and right rules.

Again there is a pattern to the errors. For each n, the midpoint rule is noticeably better than the trapezoid rule; the error for the midpoint rule, in absolute value, seems to be about half the error of the trapezoid rule. To see why, compare the shaded areas in Figure 7.11. Also, notice in Table 7.3 that the errors for the two rules have opposite signs; this is due to concavity.

---

[8]The values in Table 7.1 are rounded to 4 decimal places; those in Table 7.2 were computed using more decimal places and then rounded.

Table 7.3   *The errors for the trapezoid and midpoint rules for $\int_1^2 \frac{1}{x}\, dx$*

n	Error in trapezoid rule	Error in midpoint rule
2	-0.0152	0.0074
10	-0.00062	0.00031
50	-0.0000250	0.0000125
250	-0.0000010	0.0000005

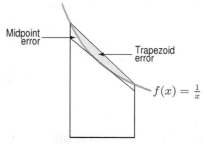

Figure 7.11: Errors in the midpoint and trapezoid rules

We are interested in how the errors behave as n increases. Table 7.4 gives the ratios of the errors for each rule. For each rule, we see that as n increases by a factor of 5, the error decreases by a factor of about $25 = 5^2$. In fact, it can be shown that this squaring relationship holds for any factor, so increasing n by a factor of 10 will decrease the error by a factor of about $100 = 10^2$. Reducing the error by a factor of 100 is equivalent to adding two more decimal places of accuracy to the result. In other words: *In the trapezoid or midpoint rules, each extra 2 digits of accuracy requires about 10 times the work.*

Table 7.4   *Ratios of the errors as n increases for $\int_1^2 \frac{1}{x}\, dx$*

	Ratio of errors in trapezoid rule	Ratio of errors in midpoint rule
$\mathrm{Error}(2)/\mathrm{Error}(10)$	24.33	23.84
$\mathrm{Error}(10)/\mathrm{Error}(50)$	24.97	24.95
$\mathrm{Error}(50)/\mathrm{Error}(250)$	25.00	25.00

Simpson's Rule

Observing that the trapezoid error has the opposite sign and about twice the magnitude of the midpoint error, we may guess that a weighted average of the two rules, with the midpoint rule weighted twice the trapezoid rule, has a smaller error. This approximation is called *Simpson's rule*[9]:

$$\mathrm{SIMP}(n) = \frac{2 \cdot \mathrm{MID}(n) + \mathrm{TRAP}(n)}{3}.$$

Table 7.5 gives the errors for Simpson's rule. Notice how much smaller the errors are than the previous errors. Of course, it is a little unfair to compare Simpson's rule at $n = 50$, say, with the previous rules, because Simpson's rule must compute the value of f at both the midpoint and the endpoints of each subinterval and hence involves evaluating the function at twice as many points.

We see in Table 7.5 that as n increases by a factor of 5, the errors decrease by a factor of about 600, or about 5^4. Again this behavior holds for any factor, so increasing n by a factor of 10 decreases the error by a factor of about 10^4. In other words: *In Simpson's rule, each extra 4 digits of accuracy requires about 10 times the work.*

Table 7.5   *The errors for Simpson's rule and the ratios of the errors*

n	Error	Ratio
2	-0.0001067877	550.15
10	-0.0000001940	632.27
50	-0.0000000003	

---

[9]Some books and computer programs use slightly different terminology for Simpson's rule; what we call $n = 50$, they call $n = 100$.

Alternate Approach to Numerical Integration: Approximating by Lines and Parabolas

These rules for numerical integration can be obtained by approximating $f(x)$ on subintervals by a function:

- The left and right rules use constant functions.
- The trapezoid and midpoint rules use linear functions.
- Simpson's rule uses quadratic functions.

Problems 36 and 37 on page 394 show how a quadratic approximation leads to Simpson's rule.

Exercises and Problems for Section 7.5

Exercises

In Exercises 1–6, sketch the area given by the following approximations to $\int_a^b f(x)\,dx$. Identify each approximation as an overestimate or an underestimate.

(a) LEFT(2)   (b) RIGHT(2)
(c) TRAP(2)   (d) MID(2)

1.

2.

3.

4.

5.

6.

7. Calculate the following approximations to $\int_0^6 x^2\,dx$.

(a) LEFT(2)   (b) RIGHT(2)
(c) TRAP(2)   (d) MID(2)

8. (a) Find LEFT(2) and RIGHT(2) for $\int_0^4 (x^2 + 1)\,dx$.
   (b) Illustrate your answers to part (a) graphically. Is each approximation an underestimate or overestimate?

9. (a) Find MID(2) and TRAP(2) for $\int_0^4 (x^2 + 1)\,dx$.
   (b) Illustrate your answers to part (a) graphically. Is each approximation an underestimate or overestimate?

10. Calculate the following approximations to $\int_0^\pi \sin\theta\,d\theta$.

(a) LEFT(2)   (b) RIGHT(2)
(c) TRAP(2)   (d) MID(2)

Problems

11. Use Table 7.6 to estimate $\int_1^2 g(t)\,dt$ by MID(5).

Table 7.6

t	1.0	1.1	1.2	1.3	1.4	1.5
$g(t)$	−2.1	−2.9	−3.4	−3.7	−3.6	−3.2
t	1.6	1.7	1.8	1.9	2.0	2.1
$g(t)$	−2.5	−1.7	−0.7	0.5	2.1	4.1

12. Compute MID(4) for the integral $\int_0^2 f(x)\,dx$ using the values in Table 7.7.

Table 7.7

x	0	0.25	0.50	0.75	1.00	1.25
$f(x)$	2.3	5.8	7.8	9.3	10.3	10.8
x	1.50	1.75	2.00	2.25	2.50	2.75
$f(x)$	10.8	10.3	9.3	7.8	5.8	3.3

In Problems 13–14, compute approximations to $\int_2^3 (1/x^2)\,dx$.

13. TRAP(2)   **14.** MID(2)

15. (a) Estimate $\int_0^1 1/(1 + x^2)\,dx$ by subdividing the interval into eight parts using:
   (i) the left Riemann sum
   (ii) the right Riemann sum
   (iii) the trapezoidal rule
   (b) Since the exact value of the integral is $\pi/4$, you can estimate the value of π using part (a). Explain why your first estimate is too large and your second estimate too small.

16. Using the table, estimate the total distance traveled from time $t = 0$ to time $t = 6$ using LEFT, RIGHT, and TRAP.

Time, t	0	1	2	3	4	5	6
Velocity, v	3	4	5	4	7	8	11

17. Using Figure 7.12, order the following approximations to the integral $\int_0^3 f(x)dx$ and its exact value from smallest to largest:
LEFT(n), RIGHT(n), MID(n), TRAP(n), Exact value.

Figure 7.12

18. The results from the left, right, trapezoid, and midpoint rules used to approximate $\int_0^1 g(t)\,dt$, with the same number of subdivisions for each rule, are as follows:
0.601, 0.632, 0.633, 0.664.

(a) Using Figure 7.13, match each rule with its approximation.
(b) Between which two consecutive approximations does the true value of the integral lie?

Figure 7.13

In Problems 19–22, decide which approximation—left, right, trapezoid, or midpoint—is guaranteed to give an overestimate for $\int_0^5 f(x)\,dx$, and which is guaranteed to give an underestimate. (There may be more than one.)

19.

20.

21.

22.
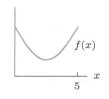

23. Consider the integral $\int_0^4 3\sqrt{x}dx$.

(a) Estimate the value of the integral using MID(2).
(b) Use the Fundamental Theorem of Calculus to find the exact value of the definite integral.
(c) What is the error for MID(2)?
(d) Use your knowledge of how errors change and your answer to part (c) to estimate the error for MID(20).
(e) Use your answer to part (d) to estimate the approximation MID(20).

24. Using a fixed number of subdivisions, we approximate the integrals of f and g on the interval in Figure 7.14.

(a) For which function, f or g, is LEFT more accurate? RIGHT? Explain.
(b) For which function, f or g, is TRAP more accurate? MID? Explain.

Figure 7.14

25. (a) Values for $f(x)$ are in the table. Which of the four approximation methods in this section is most likely to give the best estimate of $\int_0^{12} f(x)\,dx$? Estimate the integral using this method.
(b) Assume $f(x)$ is continuous with no critical points or points of inflection on the interval $0 \leq x \leq 12$. Is the estimate found in part (a) an over- or underestimate? Explain.

x	0	3	6	9	12
$f(x)$	100	97	90	78	55

26. (a) Find the exact value of $\int_0^{2\pi} \sin\theta\,d\theta$.
(b) Explain, using pictures, why the MID(1) and MID(2) approximations to this integral give the exact value.
(c) Does MID(3) give the exact value of this integral? How about MID(n)? Explain.

27. To investigate the relationship between the integrand and the errors in the left and right rules, imagine integrating a linear function. For one subinterval of integration, sketch lines with small f' and large f'. How do the errors compare?

28. To investigate the relationship between the integrand and the errors in the midpoint and trapezoid rules, imagine an integrand whose graph is concave down over one subinterval of integration. Sketch graphs where f'' has small magnitude and where f'' has large magnitude. How do the errors compare?

29. (a) Show geometrically why $\int_0^1 \sqrt{2 - x^2}\, dx = \frac{\pi}{4} + \frac{1}{2}$.
[Hint: Break up the area under $y = \sqrt{2 - x^2}$ from $x = 0$ to $x = 1$ into two pieces: a sector of a circle and a right triangle.]

(b) Approximate $\int_0^1 \sqrt{2 - x^2}\, dx$ for $n = 5$ using the left, right, trapezoid, and midpoint rules. Compute the error in each case using the answer to part (a), and compare the errors.

30. The width, in feet, at various points along the fairway of a hole on a golf course is given in Figure 7.15. If one pound of fertilizer covers 200 square feet, estimate the amount of fertilizer needed to fertilize the fairway.

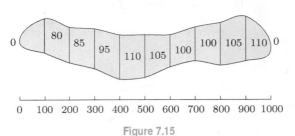

0   100 200 300 400 500 600 700 800 900 1000

Figure 7.15

Problems 31–35 involve approximating $\int_a^b f(x)\, dx$.

31. Show $\text{RIGHT}(n) = \text{LEFT}(n) + f(b)\Delta x - f(a)\Delta x$.

32. Show $\text{TRAP}(n) = \text{LEFT}(n) + \frac{1}{2}\left(f(b) - f(a)\right)\Delta x$.

33. Show $\text{LEFT}(2n) = \frac{1}{2}\left(\text{LEFT}(n) + \text{MID}(n)\right)$.

34. Check that the equations in Problems 31 and 32 hold for $\int_1^2 (1/x)\, dx$ when $n = 10$.

35. Suppose that $a = 2$, $b = 5$, $f(2) = 13$, $f(5) = 21$ and that $\text{LEFT}(10) = 3.156$ and $\text{MID}(10) = 3.242$. Use Problems 31–33 to compute $\text{RIGHT}(10)$, $\text{TRAP}(10)$, $\text{LEFT}(20)$, $\text{RIGHT}(20)$, and $\text{TRAP}(20)$.

Problems 36–37 show how Simpson's rule can be obtained by approximating the integrand, f, by quadratic functions.

36. Suppose that $a < b$ and that m is the midpoint $m = (a + b)/2$. Let $h = b - a$. The purpose of this problem is to show that if f is a quadratic function, then

$$\int_a^b f(x)\, dx = \frac{h}{3}\left(\frac{f(a)}{2} + 2f(m) + \frac{f(b)}{2}\right).$$

(a) Show that this equation holds for the functions $f(x) = 1$, $f(x) = x$, and $f(x) = x^2$.

(b) Use part (a) and the properties of the integral on page 300 to show that the equation holds for any quadratic function, $f(x) = Ax^2 + Bx + C$.

37. Consider the following method for approximating $\int_a^b f(x)\, dx$. Divide the interval $[a, b]$ into n equal subintervals. On each subinterval approximate f by a quadratic function that agrees with f at both endpoints and at the midpoint of the subinterval.

(a) Explain why the integral of f on the subinterval $[x_i, x_{i+1}]$ is approximately equal to the expression

$$\frac{h}{3}\left(\frac{f(x_i)}{2} + 2f(m_i) + \frac{f(x_{i+1})}{2}\right),$$

where m_i is the midpoint of the subinterval, $m_i = (x_i + x_{i+1})/2$. (See Problem 36.)

(b) Show that if we add up these approximations for each subinterval, we get Simpson's rule:

$$\int_a^b f(x)\, dx \approx \frac{2 \cdot \text{MID}(n) + \text{TRAP}(n)}{3}.$$

Strengthen Your Understanding

In Problems 38–41, explain what is wrong with the statement.

38. The midpoint rule never gives the exact value of a definite integral.

39. $\text{TRAP}(n) \to 0$ as $n \to \infty$.

40. For any integral, $\text{TRAP}(n) \geq \text{MID}(n)$.

41. If, for a certain integral, it takes 3 nanoseconds to improve the accuracy of TRAP from one digit to three digits, then it also takes 3 nanoseconds to improve the accuracy from 8 digits to 10 digits.

In Problems 42–43, give an example of:

42. A continuous function $f(x)$ on the interval $[0, 1]$ such that $\text{RIGHT}(10) < \int_0^1 f(x)\, dx < \text{MID}(10)$.

43. A continuous function $f(x)$ on the interval $[0, 10]$ such that $\text{TRAP}(40) > \text{TRAP}(80)$.

In Problems 44–45, decide whether the statements are true or false. Give an explanation for your answer.

44. The midpoint rule approximation to $\int_0^1 (y^2 - 1)\, dy$ is always smaller than the exact value of the integral.

45. The trapezoid rule approximation is never exact.

The left and right Riemann sums of a function f on the interval $[2, 6]$ are denoted by $\text{LEFT}(n)$ and $\text{RIGHT}(n)$, respectively, when the interval is divided into n equal parts. In Problems 46–56, decide whether the statements are true for all continuous functions, f. Give an explanation for your answer.

46. If $n = 10$, then the subdivision size is $\Delta x = 1/10$.

47. If we double the value of n, we make Δx half as large.

48. $\text{LEFT}(10) \leq \text{RIGHT}(10)$

49. As n approaches infinity, LEFT(n) approaches 0.

50. LEFT(n) − RIGHT(n) = $(f(2) - f(6))\Delta x$.

51. Doubling n decreases the difference LEFT(n) − RIGHT(n) by exactly the factor 1/2.

52. If LEFT(n) = RIGHT(n) for all n, then f is a constant function.

53. The trapezoid estimate TRAP(n) = (LEFT(n) + RIGHT(n))/2 is always closer to $\int_2^6 f(x)\,dx$ than

LEFT(n) or RIGHT(n).

54. $\int_2^6 f(x)\,dx$ lies between LEFT(n) and RIGHT(n).

55. If LEFT(2) $<$ $\int_a^b f(x)\,dx$, then LEFT(4) $<$ $\int_a^b f(x)\,dx$.

56. If $0 < f' < g'$ everywhere, then the error in approximating $\int_a^b f(x)\,dx$ by LEFT(n) is less than the error in approximating $\int_a^b g(x)\,dx$ by LEFT(n).

7.6 IMPROPER INTEGRALS

Our original discussion of the definite integral $\int_a^b f(x)\,dx$ assumed that the interval $a \le x \le b$ was of finite length and that f was continuous. Integrals that arise in applications do not necessarily have these nice properties. In this section we investigate a class of integrals, called *improper* integrals, in which one limit of integration is infinite or the integrand is unbounded. As an example, to estimate the mass of the earth's atmosphere, we might calculate an integral which sums the mass of the air up to different heights. In order to represent the fact that the atmosphere does not end at a specific height, we let the upper limit of integration get larger and larger, or tend to infinity.

We consider improper integrals with positive integrands since they are the most common.

One Type of Improper Integral: When the Limit of Integration Is Infinite

Here is an example of an improper integral:

$$\int_1^{\infty} \frac{1}{x^2}\,dx.$$

To evaluate this integral, we first compute the definite integral $\int_1^b (1/x^2)\,dx$:

$$\int_1^b \frac{1}{x^2}\,dx = -x^{-1}\Big|_1^b = -\frac{1}{b} + \frac{1}{1}.$$

Now take the limit as $b \to \infty$. Since

$$\lim_{b \to \infty} \int_1^b \frac{1}{x^2}\,dx = \lim_{b \to \infty}\left(-\frac{1}{b} + 1\right) = 1,$$

we say that the improper integral $\int_1^{\infty}(1/x^2)\,dx$ *converges* to 1.

If we think in terms of areas, the integral $\int_1^{\infty}(1/x^2)\,dx$ represents the area under $f(x) = 1/x^2$ from $x = 1$ extending infinitely far to the right. (See Figure 7.16(a).) It may seem strange that this region has finite area. What our limit computations are saying is that

When $b = 10$: $\int_1^{10} \frac{1}{x^2}\,dx = -\frac{1}{x}\Big|_1^{10} = -\frac{1}{10} + 1 = 0.9$

When $b = 100$: $\int_1^{100} \frac{1}{x^2}\,dx = -\frac{1}{100} + 1 = 0.99$

When $b = 1000$: $\int_1^{1000} \frac{1}{x^2}\,dx = -\frac{1}{1000} + 1 = 0.999$

and so on. In other words, as b gets larger and larger, the area between $x = 1$ and $x = b$ tends to 1. See Figure 7.16(b). Thus, it does make sense to declare that $\int_1^{\infty}(1/x^2)\,dx = 1$.

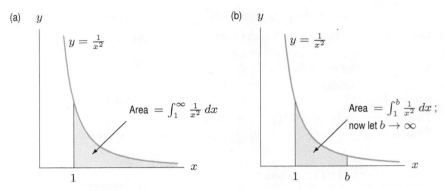

Figure 7.16: Area representation of improper integral

Of course, in another example, we might not get a finite limit as b gets larger and larger. In that case we say the improper integral *diverges*.

Suppose $f(x)$ is positive for $x \geq a$.

If $\displaystyle\lim_{b \to \infty} \int_a^b f(x)\, dx$ is a finite number, we say that $\displaystyle\int_a^\infty f(x)\, dx$ **converges** and define

$$\int_a^\infty f(x)\, dx = \lim_{b \to \infty} \int_a^b f(x)\, dx.$$

Otherwise, we say that $\displaystyle\int_a^\infty f(x)\, dx$ **diverges**. We define $\displaystyle\int_{-\infty}^b f(x)\, dx$ similarly.

Similar definitions apply if $f(x)$ is negative.

Example 1   Does the improper integral $\displaystyle\int_1^\infty \frac{1}{\sqrt{x}}\, dx$ converge or diverge?

Solution   We consider

$$\int_1^b \frac{1}{\sqrt{x}}\, dx = \int_1^b x^{-1/2}\, dx = 2x^{1/2}\Big|_1^b = 2b^{1/2} - 2.$$

We see that $\int_1^b (1/\sqrt{x})\, dx$ grows without bound as $b \to \infty$. We have shown that the area under the curve in Figure 7.17 is not finite. Thus we say the integral $\int_1^\infty (1/\sqrt{x})\, dx$ *diverges*. We could also say $\int_1^\infty (1/\sqrt{x})\, dx = \infty$.

Notice that $f(x) \to 0$ as $x \to \infty$ does not guarantee convergence of $\int_a^\infty f(x)\, dx$.

Figure 7.17: $\int_1^\infty \frac{1}{\sqrt{x}}\, dx$ diverges

What is the difference between the functions $1/x^2$ and $1/\sqrt{x}$ that makes the area under the graph of $1/x^2$ approach 1 as $x \to \infty$, whereas the area under $1/\sqrt{x}$ grows very large? Both functions approach 0 as x grows, so as b grows larger, smaller bits of area are being added to the definite integral. The difference between the functions is subtle: the values of the function $1/\sqrt{x}$ *don't shrink fast enough* for the integral to have a finite value. Of the two functions, $1/x^2$ drops to 0 much faster than $1/\sqrt{x}$, and this feature keeps the area under $1/x^2$ from growing beyond 1.

Example 2   Find $\int_0^\infty e^{-5x}\,dx$.

Solution   First we consider $\int_0^b e^{-5x}\,dx$:

$$\int_0^b e^{-5x}\,dx = -\frac{1}{5}e^{-5x}\bigg|_0^b = -\frac{1}{5}e^{-5b} + \frac{1}{5}.$$

Since $e^{-5b} = \dfrac{1}{e^{5b}}$, this term tends to 0 as b approaches infinity, so $\int_0^\infty e^{-5x}\,dx$ converges. Its value is

$$\int_0^\infty e^{-5x}\,dx = \lim_{b\to\infty}\int_0^b e^{-5x}\,dx = \lim_{b\to\infty}\left(-\frac{1}{5}e^{-5b} + \frac{1}{5}\right) = 0 + \frac{1}{5} = \frac{1}{5}.$$

Since e^{5x} grows very rapidly, we expect that e^{-5x} will approach 0 rapidly. The fact that the area approaches $1/5$ instead of growing without bound is a consequence of the speed with which the integrand e^{-5x} approaches 0.

Example 3   Determine for which values of the exponent, p, the improper integral $\int_1^\infty \dfrac{1}{x^p}\,dx$ diverges.

Solution   For $p \neq 1$,

$$\int_1^b x^{-p}\,dx = \frac{1}{-p+1}x^{-p+1}\bigg|_1^b = \left(\frac{1}{-p+1}b^{-p+1} - \frac{1}{-p+1}\right).$$

The important question is whether the exponent of b is positive or negative. If it is negative, then as b approaches infinity, b^{-p+1} approaches 0. If the exponent is positive, then b^{-p+1} grows without bound as b approaches infinity. What happens if $p = 1$? In this case we get

$$\int_1^\infty \frac{1}{x}\,dx = \lim_{b\to\infty}\ln x\bigg|_1^b = \lim_{b\to\infty}\ln b - \ln 1.$$

Since $\ln b$ becomes arbitrarily large as b approaches infinity, the integral grows without bound. We conclude that $\int_1^\infty (1/x^p)\,dx$ diverges precisely when $p \leq 1$. For $p > 1$ the integral has the value

$$\int_1^\infty \frac{1}{x^p}\,dx = \lim_{b\to\infty}\int_1^b \frac{1}{x^p}\,dx = \lim_{b\to\infty}\left(\frac{1}{-p+1}b^{-p+1} - \frac{1}{-p+1}\right) = -\left(\frac{1}{-p+1}\right) = \frac{1}{p-1}.$$

Application of Improper Integrals to Energy

The energy, E, required to separate two charged particles, originally a distance a apart, to a distance b, is given by the integral

$$E = \int_a^b \frac{kq_1q_2}{r^2}\,dr$$

where q_1 and q_2 are the magnitudes of the charges and k is a constant. If q_1 and q_2 are in coulombs, a and b are in meters, and E is in joules, the value of the constant k is $9 \cdot 10^9$.

Example 4   A hydrogen atom consists of a proton and an electron, with opposite charges of magnitude $1.6 \cdot 10^{-19}$ coulombs. Find the energy required to take a hydrogen atom apart (that is, to move the electron from its orbit to an infinite distance from the proton). Assume that the initial distance between the electron and the proton is the Bohr radius, $R_B = 5.3 \cdot 10^{-11}$ meter.

Solution   Since we are moving from an initial distance of R_B to a final distance of ∞, the energy is represented by the improper integral

$$E = \int_{R_B}^{\infty} k\frac{q_1 q_2}{r^2}\, dr = kq_1 q_2 \lim_{b\to\infty} \int_{R_B}^{b} \frac{1}{r^2}\, dr$$

$$= kq_1 q_2 \lim_{b\to\infty} -\frac{1}{r}\bigg|_{R_B}^{b} = kq_1 q_2 \lim_{b\to\infty}\left(-\frac{1}{b} + \frac{1}{R_B}\right) = \frac{kq_1 q_2}{R_B}.$$

Substituting numerical values, we get

$$E = \frac{(9\cdot 10^9)(1.6\cdot 10^{-19})^2}{5.3\cdot 10^{-11}} \approx 4.35\cdot 10^{-18}\ \text{joules.}$$

This is about the amount of energy needed to lift a speck of dust 0.000000025 inch off the ground. (In other words, not much!)

What happens if the limits of integration are $-\infty$ and ∞? In this case, we break the integral at any point and write the original integral as a sum of two new improper integrals.

For a positive function $f(x)$, we can use any (finite) number c to define

$$\int_{-\infty}^{\infty} f(x)\, dx = \int_{-\infty}^{c} f(x)\, dx + \int_{c}^{\infty} f(x)\, dx.$$

If *either* of the two new improper integrals diverges, we say the original integral diverges. Only if both of the new integrals have a finite value do we add the values to get a finite value for the original integral.

It is not hard to show that the preceding definition does not depend on the choice for c.

Another Type of Improper Integral: When the Integrand Becomes Infinite

There is another way for an integral to be improper. The interval may be finite but the function may be unbounded near some points in the interval. For example, consider $\int_0^1 (1/\sqrt{x})\, dx$. Since the graph of $y = 1/\sqrt{x}$ has a vertical asymptote at $x = 0$, the region between the graph, the x-axis, and the lines $x = 0$ and $x = 1$ is unbounded. Instead of extending to infinity in the horizontal direction as in the previous improper integrals, this region extends to infinity in the vertical direction. See Figure 7.18(a). We handle this improper integral in a similar way as before: we compute $\int_a^1 (1/\sqrt{x})\, dx$ for values of a slightly larger than 0 and look at what happens as a approaches 0 from the positive side. (This is written as $a \to 0^+$.)

First we compute the integral:

$$\int_a^1 \frac{1}{\sqrt{x}}\, dx = 2x^{1/2}\bigg|_a^1 = 2 - 2a^{1/2}.$$

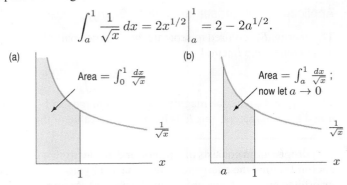

Figure 7.18: Area representation of improper integral

Now we take the limit:

$$\lim_{a \to 0^+} \int_a^1 \frac{1}{\sqrt{x}}\, dx = \lim_{a \to 0^+} (2 - 2a^{1/2}) = 2.$$

Since the limit is finite, we say the improper integral converges, and that

$$\int_0^1 \frac{1}{\sqrt{x}}\, dx = 2.$$

Geometrically, what we have done is to calculate the finite area between $x = a$ and $x = 1$ and take the limit as a tends to 0 from the right. See Figure 7.18(b). Since the limit exists, the integral converges to 2. If the limit did not exist, we would say the improper integral diverges.

Example 5 Investigate the convergence of $\int_0^2 \frac{1}{(x-2)^2}\, dx$.

Solution This is an improper integral since the integrand tends to infinity as x approaches 2 and is undefined at $x = 2$. Since the trouble is at the right endpoint, we replace the upper limit by b, and let b tend to 2 from the left. This is written $b \to 2^-$, with the "$-$" signifying that 2 is approached from below. See Figure 7.19.

$$\int_0^2 \frac{1}{(x-2)^2}\, dx = \lim_{b \to 2^-} \int_0^b \frac{1}{(x-2)^2}\, dx = \lim_{b \to 2^-} (-1)(x-2)^{-1}\Big|_0^b = \lim_{b \to 2^-} \left(-\frac{1}{(b-2)} - \frac{1}{2} \right).$$

Therefore, since $\lim_{b \to 2^-} \left(-\frac{1}{b-2} \right)$ does not exist, the integral diverges.

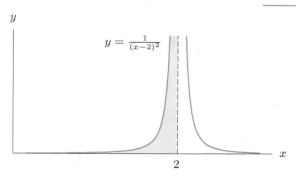

Figure 7.19: Shaded area represents $\int_0^2 \frac{1}{(x-2)^2}\, dx$

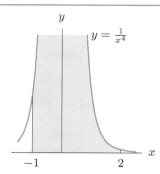

Figure 7.20: Shaded area represents $\int_{-1}^2 \frac{1}{x^4}\, dx$

Suppose $f(x)$ is positive and continuous on $a \le x < b$ and tends to infinity as $x \to b$. If $\lim_{c \to b^-} \int_a^c f(x)\, dx$ is a finite number, we say that $\int_a^b f(x)\, dx$ **converges** and define

$$\int_a^b f(x)\, dx = \lim_{c \to b^-} \int_a^c f(x)\, dx.$$

Otherwise, we say that $\int_a^b f(x)\, dx$ **diverges**.

When $f(x)$ tends to infinity as x approaches a, we define convergence in a similar way. In addition, an integral can be improper because the integrand tends to infinity *inside* the interval of integration rather than at an endpoint. In this case, we break the given integral into two (or more) improper integrals so that the integrand tends to infinity only at endpoints.

Suppose that $f(x)$ is positive and continuous on $[a, b]$ except at the point c. If $f(x)$ tends to infinity as $x \to c$, then we define

$$\int_a^b f(x)\, dx = \int_a^c f(x)\, dx + \int_c^b f(x)\, dx.$$

If *either* of the two new improper integrals diverges, we say the original integral diverges. Only if *both* of the new integrals have a finite value do we add the values to get a finite value for the original integral.

Example 6   Investigate the convergence of $\int_{-1}^2 \frac{1}{x^4}\, dx$.

Solution   See Figure 7.20. The trouble spot is $x = 0$, rather than $x = -1$ or $x = 2$. We break the given improper integral into two improper integrals each of which has $x = 0$ as an endpoint:

$$\int_{-1}^2 \frac{1}{x^4}\, dx = \int_{-1}^0 \frac{1}{x^4}\, dx + \int_0^2 \frac{1}{x^4}\, dx.$$

We can now use the previous technique to evaluate the new integrals, if they converge. Since

$$\int_0^2 \frac{1}{x^4}\, dx = \lim_{a \to 0^+} -\frac{1}{3}x^{-3}\Big|_a^2 = \lim_{a \to 0^+} \left(-\frac{1}{3}\right)\left(\frac{1}{8} - \frac{1}{a^3}\right)$$

the integral $\int_0^2 (1/x^4)\, dx$ diverges. Thus, the original integral diverges. A similar computation shows that $\int_{-1}^0 (1/x^4)\, dx$ also diverges.

It is easy to miss an improper integral when the integrand tends to infinity inside the interval. For example, it is fundamentally incorrect to say that $\int_{-1}^2 (1/x^4)\, dx = -\frac{1}{3}x^{-3}\Big|_{-1}^2 = -\frac{1}{24} - \frac{1}{3} = -\frac{3}{8}$.

Example 7   Find $\int_0^6 \frac{1}{(x-4)^{2/3}}\, dx$.

Solution   Figure 7.21 shows that the trouble spot is at $x = 4$, so we break the integral at $x = 4$ and consider the separate parts.

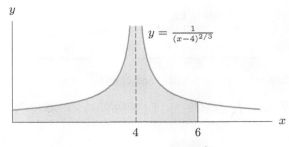

Figure 7.21: Shaded area represents $\int_0^6 \frac{1}{(x-4)^{2/3}}\, dx$

We have

$$\int_0^4 \frac{1}{(x-4)^{2/3}}\, dx = \lim_{b \to 4^-} 3(x-4)^{1/3}\Big|_0^b = \lim_{b \to 4^-} \left(3(b-4)^{1/3} - 3(-4)^{1/3}\right) = 3(4)^{1/3}.$$

Similarly,

$$\int_4^6 \frac{1}{(x-4)^{2/3}}\, dx = \lim_{a \to 4^+} 3(x-4)^{1/3}\Big|_a^6 = \lim_{a \to 4^+} \left(3 \cdot 2^{1/3} - 3(a-4)^{1/3}\right) = 3(2)^{1/3}.$$

Since both of these integrals converge, the original integral converges:

$$\int_0^6 \frac{1}{(x-4)^{2/3}} \, dx = 3(4)^{1/3} + 3(2)^{1/3} = 8.542.$$

Finally, there is a question of what to do when an integral is improper at both endpoints. In this case, we just break the integral at any interior point of the interval. The original integral diverges if either or both of the new integrals diverge.

Example 8   Investigate the convergence of $\int_0^\infty \frac{1}{x^2} \, dx$.

Solution   This integral is improper both because the upper limit is ∞ and because the function is undefined at $x = 0$. We break the integral into two parts at, say, $x = 1$. We know by Example 3 that $\int_1^\infty (1/x^2) \, dx$ has a finite value. However, the other part, $\int_0^1 (1/x^2) \, dx$, diverges since:

$$\int_0^1 \frac{1}{x^2} \, dx = \lim_{a \to 0^+} \left. -x^{-1} \right|_a^1 = \lim_{a \to 0^+} \left(\frac{1}{a} - 1 \right).$$

Therefore $\int_0^\infty \frac{1}{x^2} \, dx$ diverges as well.

Exercises and Problems for Section 7.6

Exercises

1. Shade the area represented by:

   (a) $\int_1^\infty (1/x^2) \, dx$ (b) $\int_0^1 (1/\sqrt{x}) \, dx$

2. Evaluate the improper integral $\int_0^\infty e^{-0.4x} \, dx$ and sketch the area it represents.

3. (a) Use a calculator or computer to estimate $\int_0^b xe^{-x} \, dx$ for $b = 5, 10, 20$.

   (b) Use your answers to part (a) to estimate the value of $\int_0^\infty xe^{-x} \, dx$, assuming it is finite.

4. (a) Sketch the the area represented by the improper integral $\int_{-\infty}^\infty e^{-x^2} \, dx$.

   (b) Use a calculator or computer to estimate $\int_{-a}^a e^{-x^2} \, dx$ for $a = 1,2,3,4,5$.

   (c) Use the answers to part (b) to estimate the value of $\int_{-\infty}^\infty e^{-x^2} \, dx$, assuming it is finite.

Calculate the integrals in Exercises 5–33, if they converge. You may calculate the limits by appealing to the dominance of one function over another, or by l'Hopital's rule.

5. $\int_1^\infty \frac{1}{5x+2} \, dx$

6. $\int_1^\infty \frac{1}{(x+2)^2} \, dx$

7. $\int_0^1 \ln x \, dx$

8. $\int_0^\infty e^{-\sqrt{x}} \, dx$

9. $\int_0^\infty xe^{-x^2} \, dx$

10. $\int_1^\infty e^{-2x} \, dx$

11. $\int_0^\infty \frac{x}{e^x} \, dx$

12. $\int_1^\infty \frac{x}{4+x^2} \, dx$

13. $\int_{-\infty}^0 \frac{e^x}{1+e^x} \, dx$

14. $\int_{-\infty}^\infty \frac{dz}{z^2+25}$

15. $\int_0^4 \frac{1}{\sqrt{x}} \, dx$

16. $\int_{\pi/4}^{\pi/2} \frac{\sin x}{\sqrt{\cos x}} \, dx$

17. $\int_0^1 \frac{1}{v} \, dv$

18. $\int_0^1 \frac{x^4+1}{x} \, dx$

19. $\int_1^\infty \frac{1}{x^2+1} \, dx$

20. $\int_1^\infty \frac{1}{\sqrt{x^2+1}} \, dx$

21. $\int_0^4 \frac{-1}{u^2-16} \, du$

22. $\int_1^\infty \frac{y}{y^4+1} \, dy$

23. $\int_2^\infty \frac{dx}{x \ln x}$

24. $\int_0^1 \frac{\ln x}{x} \, dx$

25. $\int_{16}^{20} \frac{1}{y^2-16} \, dy$

26. $\int_0^\pi \frac{1}{\sqrt{x}} e^{-\sqrt{x}} \, dx$

27. $\int_3^\infty \frac{dx}{x(\ln x)^2}$

28. $\int_0^2 \frac{1}{\sqrt{4-x^2}} \, dx$

29. $\int_4^\infty \frac{dx}{(x-1)^2}$

30. $\int_4^\infty \frac{dx}{x^2-1}$

31. $\int_7^\infty \frac{dy}{\sqrt{y-5}}$

32. $\int_0^3 \frac{y \, dy}{\sqrt{9-y^2}}$

33. $\int_3^6 \frac{d\theta}{(4-\theta)^2}$

Problems

34. Find a formula (not involving integrals) for

$$f(x) = \int_{-\infty}^{x} e^t \, dt.$$

35. In statistics we encounter $P(x)$, a function defined by

$$P(x) = \frac{1}{\sqrt{\pi}} \int_0^x e^{-t^2} \, dt.$$

Use a calculator or computer to evaluate

   (a) $P(1)$ **(b)** $P(\infty)$

36. Find the area under the curve $y = xe^{-x}$ for $x \geq 0$.

37. Find the area under the curve $y = 1/\cos^2 t$ between $t = 0$ and $t = \pi/2$.

In Problems 38–41, evaluate $f(3)$.

38. $f(x) = \int_0^{\infty} x^{-t} \, dt$ **39.** $f(x) = \int_1^{\infty} t^{-x} \, dt$

40. $f(x) = \int_0^{\infty} xe^{-xt} \, dt$ **41.** $f(x) = \int_0^{\infty} 2txe^{-tx^2} \, dt$

42. For $\alpha > 0$, calculate

  (a) $\int_0^{\infty} \frac{e^{-y/\alpha}}{\alpha} \, dy$ **(b)** $\int_0^{\infty} \frac{ye^{-y/\alpha}}{\alpha} \, dy$

  (c) $\int_0^{\infty} \frac{y^2 e^{-y/\alpha}}{\alpha} \, dy$

43. The rate, r, at which people get sick during an epidemic of the flu can be approximated by $r = 1000te^{-0.5t}$, where r is measured in people/day and t is measured in days since the start of the epidemic.

  (a) Sketch a graph of r as a function of t.
  (b) When are people getting sick fastest?
  (c) How many people get sick altogether?

44. Find the energy required to separate opposite electric charges of magnitude 1 coulomb. The charges are initially 1 meter apart and one is moved infinitely far from the other. (The definition of energy is on page 397.)

45. Given that $\int_{-\infty}^{\infty} e^{-x^2} \, dx = \sqrt{\pi}$, calculate the exact value of

$$\int_{-\infty}^{\infty} e^{-(x-a)^2/b} \, dx.$$

46. Assuming $g(x)$ is a differentiable function whose values are bounded for all x, derive Stein's identity, which is used in statistics:

$$\int_{-\infty}^{\infty} g'(x)e^{-x^2/2} \, dx = \int_{-\infty}^{\infty} xg(x)e^{-x^2/2} \, dx.$$

47. Given that

$$\int_0^{\infty} \frac{x^4 e^x}{(e^x - 1)^2} \, dx = \frac{4\pi^4}{15}$$

evaluate

$$\int_0^{\infty} \frac{x^4 e^{2x}}{(e^{2x} - 1)^2} \, dx.$$

48. The gamma function is defined for all $x > 0$ by the rule

$$\Gamma(x) = \int_0^{\infty} t^{x-1} e^{-t} \, dt.$$

  (a) Find $\Gamma(1)$ and $\Gamma(2)$.
  (b) Integrate by parts with respect to t to show that, for positive n,

$$\Gamma(n+1) = n\Gamma(n).$$

  (c) Find a simple expression for $\Gamma(n)$ for positive integers n.

Strengthen Your Understanding

In Problems 49–50, explain what is wrong with the statement.

49. If both $\int_1^{\infty} f(x) \, dx$ and $\int_1^{\infty} g(x) \, dx$ diverge, then so does $\int_1^{\infty} f(x)g(x) \, dx$.

50. If $\int_1^{\infty} f(x) \, dx$ diverges, then $\lim_{x \to \infty} f(x) \neq 0$.

In Problems 51–52, give an example of:

51. A function $f(x)$, continuous for $x \geq 1$, such that $\lim_{x \to \infty} f(x) = 0$, but $\int_1^{\infty} f(x) \, dx$ diverges.

52. A function $f(x)$, continuous at $x = 2$ and $x = 5$, such that the integral $\int_2^5 f(x) \, dx$ is improper and divergent.

In Problems 53–58, decide whether the statements are true or false. Give an explanation for your answer.

53. If f is continuous for all x and $\int_0^{\infty} f(x) \, dx$ converges, then so does $\int_a^{\infty} f(x) \, dx$ for all positive a.

54. If $f(x)$ is a positive periodic function, then $\int_0^{\infty} f(x) \, dx$ diverges.

55. If $f(x)$ is continuous and positive for $x > 0$ and if $\lim_{x \to \infty} f(x) = 0$, then $\int_0^{\infty} f(x) \, dx$ converges.

56. If $f(x)$ is continuous and positive for $x > 0$ and if $\lim_{x \to \infty} f(x) = \infty$, then $\int_0^{\infty} (1/f(x)) \, dx$ converges.

57. If $\int_0^{\infty} f(x) \, dx$ and $\int_0^{\infty} g(x) \, dx$ both converge, then $\int_0^{\infty} (f(x) + g(x)) \, dx$ converges.

58. If $\int_0^\infty f(x)\,dx$ and $\int_0^\infty g(x)\,dx$ both diverge, then $\int_0^\infty (f(x)+g(x))\,dx$ diverges.

Suppose that f is continuous for all real numbers and that $\int_0^\infty f(x)\,dx$ converges. Let a be any positive number. Decide which of the statements in Problems 59–62 are true and which are false. Give an explanation for your answer.

59. $\int_0^\infty af(x)\,dx$ converges.

60. $\int_0^\infty f(ax)\,dx$ converges.

61. $\int_0^\infty f(a+x)\,dx$ converges.

62. $\int_0^\infty (a+f(x))\,dx$ converges.

7.7 COMPARISON OF IMPROPER INTEGRALS

Making Comparisons

Sometimes it is difficult to find the exact value of an improper integral by antidifferentiation, but it may be possible to determine whether an integral converges or diverges. The key is to *compare* the given integral to one whose behavior we already know. Let's look at an example.

Example 1 Determine whether $\displaystyle\int_1^\infty \frac{1}{\sqrt{x^3+5}}\,dx$ converges.

Solution First, let's see what this integrand does as $x \to \infty$. For large x, the 5 becomes insignificant compared with the x^3, so

$$\frac{1}{\sqrt{x^3+5}} \approx \frac{1}{\sqrt{x^3}} = \frac{1}{x^{3/2}}.$$

Since

$$\int_1^\infty \frac{1}{\sqrt{x^3}}\,dx = \int_1^\infty \frac{1}{x^{3/2}}\,dx = \lim_{b\to\infty} \int_1^b \frac{1}{x^{3/2}}\,dx = \lim_{b\to\infty} -2x^{-1/2}\Big|_1^b = \lim_{b\to\infty}\left(2 - 2b^{-1/2}\right) = 2,$$

the integral $\int_1^\infty (1/x^{3/2})\,dx$ converges. So we expect our integral to converge as well.
   In order to confirm this, we observe that for $0 \le x^3 \le x^3 + 5$, we have

$$\frac{1}{\sqrt{x^3+5}} \le \frac{1}{\sqrt{x^3}}.$$

and so for $b \ge 1$,

$$\int_1^b \frac{1}{\sqrt{x^3+5}}\,dx \le \int_1^b \frac{1}{\sqrt{x^3}}\,dx.$$

(See Figure 7.22.) Since $\int_1^b (1/\sqrt{x^3+5})\,dx$ increases as b approaches infinity but is always smaller than $\int_1^b (1/x^{3/2})\,dx < \int_1^\infty (1/x^{3/2})\,dx = 2$, we know $\int_1^\infty (1/\sqrt{x^3+5})\,dx$ must have a finite value less than 2. Thus,

$$\int_1^\infty \frac{dx}{\sqrt{x^3+5}} \text{ converges to a value less than 2.}$$

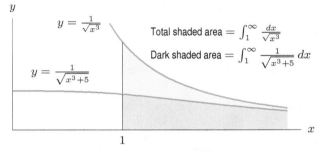

Figure 7.22: Graph showing $\int_1^\infty \frac{1}{\sqrt{x^3+5}}\,dx \le \int_1^\infty \frac{dx}{\sqrt{x^3}}$

Notice that we first looked at the behavior of the integrand as $x \to \infty$. This is useful because the convergence or divergence of the integral is determined by what happens as $x \to \infty$.

The Comparison Test for $\displaystyle\int_a^\infty f(x)\ dx$

Assume $f(x)$ is positive. Making a comparison involves two stages:

1. Guess, by looking at the behavior of the integrand for large x, whether the integral converges or not. (This is the "behaves like" principle.)
2. Confirm the guess by comparison with a positive function $g(x)$:
   - If $f(x) \le g(x)$ and $\int_a^\infty g(x)\,dx$ converges, then $\int_a^\infty f(x)\,dx$ converges.
   - If $g(x) \le f(x)$ and $\int_a^\infty g(x)\,dx$ diverges, then $\int_a^\infty f(x)\,dx$ diverges.

Example 2   Decide whether $\displaystyle\int_4^\infty \frac{dt}{(\ln t) - 1}$ converges or diverges.

Solution   Since $\ln t$ grows without bound as $t \to \infty$, the -1 is eventually going to be insignificant in comparison to $\ln t$. Thus, as far as convergence is concerned,

$$\int_4^\infty \frac{1}{(\ln t) - 1}\, dt \quad \text{behaves like} \quad \int_4^\infty \frac{1}{\ln t}\, dt.$$

Does $\int_4^\infty (1/\ln t)\,dt$ converge or diverge? Since $\ln t$ grows very slowly, $1/\ln t$ goes to zero very slowly, and so the integral probably does not converge. We know that $(\ln t) - 1 < \ln t < t$ for all positive t. So, provided $t > e$, we take reciprocals:

$$\frac{1}{(\ln t) - 1} > \frac{1}{\ln t} > \frac{1}{t}.$$

Since $\int_4^\infty (1/t)\,dt$ diverges, we conclude that

$$\int_4^\infty \frac{1}{(\ln t) - 1}\, dt \text{ diverges.}$$

How Do We Know What to Compare With?

In Examples 1 and 2, we investigated the convergence of an integral by comparing it with an easier integral. How did we pick the easier integral? This is a matter of trial and error, guided by any information we get by looking at the original integrand as $x \to \infty$. We want the comparison integrand to be easy and, in particular, to have a simple antiderivative.

Useful Integrals for Comparison

- $\displaystyle\int_1^\infty \frac{1}{x^p}dx$ converges for $p > 1$ and diverges for $p \le 1$.
- $\displaystyle\int_0^1 \frac{1}{x^p}dx$ converges for $p < 1$ and diverges for $p \ge 1$.
- $\displaystyle\int_0^\infty e^{-ax}dx$ converges for $a > 0$.

Of course, we can use any function for comparison, provided we can determine its behavior.

Example 3   Investigate the convergence of $\displaystyle\int_1^\infty \frac{(\sin x) + 3}{\sqrt{x}}\, dx$.

Solution   Since it looks difficult to find an antiderivative of this function, we try comparison. What happens to this integrand as $x \to \infty$? Since $\sin x$ oscillates between -1 and 1,

$$\frac{2}{\sqrt{x}} = \frac{-1+3}{\sqrt{x}} \leq \frac{(\sin x)+3}{\sqrt{x}} \leq \frac{1+3}{\sqrt{x}} = \frac{4}{\sqrt{x}},$$

the integrand oscillates between $2/\sqrt{x}$ and $4/\sqrt{x}$. (See Figure 7.23.)

What do $\int_1^\infty (2/\sqrt{x})\, dx$ and $\int_1^\infty (4/\sqrt{x})\, dx$ do? As far as convergence is concerned, they certainly do the same thing, and whatever that is, the original integral does it too. It is important to notice that $\sqrt{x}$ grows very slowly. This means that $1/\sqrt{x}$ gets small slowly, which means that convergence is unlikely. Since $\sqrt{x} = x^{1/2}$, the result in the preceding box (with $p = \frac{1}{2}$) tells us that $\int_1^\infty (1/\sqrt{x})\, dx$ diverges. So the comparison test tells us that the original integral diverges.

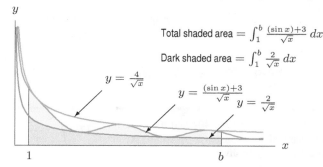

Total shaded area $= \int_1^b \frac{(\sin x)+3}{\sqrt{x}}\, dx$

Dark shaded area $= \int_1^b \frac{2}{\sqrt{x}}\, dx$

$y = \frac{4}{\sqrt{x}}$

$y = \frac{(\sin x)+3}{\sqrt{x}}$ $y = \frac{2}{\sqrt{x}}$

Figure 7.23: Graph showing $\int_1^b \frac{2}{\sqrt{x}}\, dx \leq \int_1^b \frac{(\sin x)+3}{\sqrt{x}}\, dx$, for $b \geq 1$

Notice that there are two possible comparisons we could have made in Example 3:

$$\frac{2}{\sqrt{x}} \leq \frac{(\sin x)+3}{\sqrt{x}} \qquad \text{or} \qquad \frac{(\sin x)+3}{\sqrt{x}} \leq \frac{4}{\sqrt{x}}.$$

Since both $\int_1^\infty (2/\sqrt{x})\, dx$ and $\int_1^\infty (4/\sqrt{x})\, dx$ diverge, only the first comparison is useful. Knowing that an integral is *smaller* than a divergent integral is of no help whatsoever!

The next example shows what to do if the comparison does not hold throughout the interval of integration.

Example 4   Show $\displaystyle\int_1^\infty e^{-x^2/2}\, dx$ converges.

Solution   We know that $e^{-x^2/2}$ goes very rapidly to zero as $x \to \infty$, so we expect this integral to converge. Hence we look for some larger integrand which has a convergent integral. One possibility is $\int_1^\infty e^{-x}\, dx$, because e^{-x} has an elementary antiderivative and $\int_1^\infty e^{-x}\, dx$ converges. What is the relationship between $e^{-x^2/2}$ and e^{-x}? We know that for $x \geq 2$,

$$x \leq \frac{x^2}{2} \qquad \text{so} \qquad -\frac{x^2}{2} \leq -x,$$

and so, for $x \geq 2$

$$e^{-x^2/2} \leq e^{-x}.$$

Since this inequality holds only for $x \geq 2$, we split the interval of integration into two pieces:

$$\int_1^\infty e^{-x^2/2}\, dx = \int_1^2 e^{-x^2/2}\, dx + \int_2^\infty e^{-x^2/2}\, dx.$$

Now $\int_1^2 e^{-x^2/2}\, dx$ is finite (it is not improper) and $\int_2^\infty e^{-x^2/2}\, dx$ is finite by comparison with $\int_2^\infty e^{-x}\, dx$. Therefore, $\int_1^\infty e^{-x^2/2}\, dx$ is the sum of two finite pieces and therefore must be finite.

The previous example illustrates the following general principle:

> If f is positive and continuous on $[a, b]$,
>
> $$\int_a^\infty f(x)\, dx \text{ and } \int_b^\infty f(x)\, dx$$
>
> either both converge or both diverge.

In particular, when the comparison test is applied to $\int_a^\infty f(x)\, dx$, the inequalities for $f(x)$ and $g(x)$ do not need to hold for all $x \geq a$ but only for x greater than some value, say b.

Exercises and Problems for Section 7.7

Exercises

In Exercises 1–9, use the box on page 404 and the behavior of rational and exponential functions as $x \to \infty$ to predict whether the integrals converge or diverge.

1. $\displaystyle\int_1^\infty \frac{x^2}{x^4 + 1}\, dx$

2. $\displaystyle\int_2^\infty \frac{x^3}{x^4 - 1}\, dx$

3. $\displaystyle\int_1^\infty \frac{x^2 + 1}{x^3 + 3x + 2}\, dx$

4. $\displaystyle\int_1^\infty \frac{1}{x^2 + 5x + 1}\, dx$

5. $\displaystyle\int_1^\infty \frac{x}{x^2 + 2x + 4}\, dx$

6. $\displaystyle\int_1^\infty \frac{x^2 - 6x + 1}{x^2 + 4}\, dx$

7. $\displaystyle\int_1^\infty \frac{5x + 2}{x^4 + 8x^2 + 4}\, dx$

8. $\displaystyle\int_1^\infty \frac{1}{e^{5t} + 2}\, dt$

9. $\displaystyle\int_1^\infty \frac{x^2 + 4}{x^4 + 3x^2 + 11}\, dx$

In Exercises 10–25, decide if the improper integral converges or diverges.

10. $\displaystyle\int_{50}^\infty \frac{dz}{z^3}$

11. $\displaystyle\int_1^\infty \frac{dx}{1 + x}$

12. $\displaystyle\int_1^\infty \frac{dx}{x^3 + 1}$

13. $\displaystyle\int_5^8 \frac{6}{\sqrt{t - 5}}\, dt$

14. $\displaystyle\int_0^1 \frac{1}{x^{19/20}}\, dx$

15. $\displaystyle\int_{-1}^5 \frac{dt}{(t + 1)^2}$

16. $\displaystyle\int_{-\infty}^\infty \frac{du}{1 + u^2}$

17. $\displaystyle\int_1^\infty \frac{du}{u + u^2}$

18. $\displaystyle\int_1^\infty \frac{d\theta}{\sqrt{\theta^2 + 1}}$

19. $\displaystyle\int_2^\infty \frac{d\theta}{\sqrt{\theta^3 + 1}}$

20. $\displaystyle\int_0^1 \frac{d\theta}{\sqrt{\theta^3 + \theta}}$

21. $\displaystyle\int_0^\infty \frac{dy}{1 + e^y}$

22. $\displaystyle\int_1^\infty \frac{2 + \cos\phi}{\phi^2}\, d\phi$

23. $\displaystyle\int_0^\infty \frac{dz}{e^z + 2^z}$

24. $\displaystyle\int_0^\pi \frac{2 - \sin\phi}{\phi^2}\, d\phi$

25. $\displaystyle\int_4^\infty \frac{3 + \sin\alpha}{\alpha}\, d\alpha$

Problems

26. The graphs of $y = 1/x$, $y = 1/x^2$ and the functions $f(x)$, $g(x)$, $h(x)$, and $k(x)$ are shown in Figure 7.24.

(a) Is the area between $y = 1/x$ and $y = 1/x^2$ on the interval from $x = 1$ to ∞ finite or infinite? Explain.

(b) Using the graph, decide whether the integral of each of the functions $f(x)$, $g(x)$, $h(x)$ and $k(x)$ on the interval from $x = 1$ to ∞ converges, diverges, or whether it is impossible to tell.

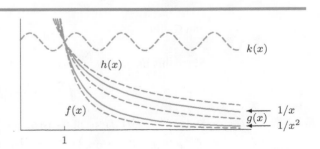

Figure 7.24

27. Suppose $\int_a^\infty f(x)\,dx$ converges. What does Figure 7.25 suggest about the convergence of $\int_a^\infty g(x)\,dx$?

Figure 7.25

For what values of p do the integrals in Problems 28–29 converge or diverge?

28. $\displaystyle\int_2^\infty \frac{dx}{x(\ln x)^p}$

29. $\displaystyle\int_1^2 \frac{dx}{x(\ln x)^p}$

30. (a) Find an upper bound for

$$\int_3^\infty e^{-x^2}\,dx.$$

[Hint: $e^{-x^2} \le e^{-3x}$ for $x \ge 3$.]

(b) For any positive n, generalize the result of part (a) to find an upper bound for

$$\int_n^\infty e^{-x^2}\,dx$$

by noting that $nx \le x^2$ for $x \ge n$.

31. In Planck's Radiation Law, we encounter the integral

$$\int_1^\infty \frac{dx}{x^5(e^{1/x} - 1)}.$$

(a) Explain why a graph of the tangent line to e^t at $t = 0$ tells us that for all t

$$1 + t \le e^t.$$

(b) Substituting $t = 1/x$, show that for all $x \ne 0$

$$e^{1/x} - 1 > \frac{1}{x}.$$

(c) Use the comparison test to show that the original integral converges.

Strengthen Your Understanding

In Problems 32–35, explain what is wrong with the statement.

32. $\int_1^\infty 1/(x^3 + \sin x)\,dx$ converges by comparison with $\int_1^\infty 1/x^3\,dx$.

33. $\int_1^\infty 1/(x^{\sqrt{2}} + 1)\,dx$ is divergent.

34. If $0 \le f(x) \le g(x)$ and $\int_0^\infty g(x)\,dx$ diverges then by the comparison test $\int_0^\infty f(x)\,dx$ diverges.

35. Let $f(x) > 0$. If $\int_1^\infty f(x)\,dx$ is convergent then so is $\int_1^\infty 1/f(x)\,dx$.

In Problems 36–37, give an example of:

36. A continuous function $f(x)$ for $x \ge 1$ such that the improper integral $\int_1^\infty f(x)\,dx$ can be shown to converge by comparison with the integral $\int_1^\infty 3/(2x^2)\,dx$.

37. A positive, continuous function $f(x)$ such that $\int_1^\infty f(x)\,dx$ diverges and

$$f(x) \le \frac{3}{7x - 2\sin x}, \qquad \text{for } x \ge 1.$$

In Problems 38–39, decide whether the statements are true or false. Give an explanation for your answer.

38. The integral $\displaystyle\int_0^\infty \frac{1}{e^x + x}\,dx$ converges.

39. The integral $\displaystyle\int_0^1 \frac{1}{x^2 - 3}\,dx$ diverges.

CHAPTER SUMMARY (see also Ready Reference at the end of the book)

- **Integration techniques**
  Substitution, parts, partial fractions, trigonometric substitution, using tables.
- **Numerical approximations**

Riemann sums (left, right, midpoint), trapezoid rule, Simpson's rule, approximation errors.

- **Improper integrals**
  Convergence/divergence, comparison test for integrals.

REVIEW EXERCISES AND PROBLEMS FOR CHAPTER SEVEN

Exercises

For Exercises 1–4, find an antiderivative.

1. $q(t) = (t + 1)^2$

2. $p(\theta) = 2 \sin(2\theta)$

3. $f(x) = 5^x$

4. $r(t) = e^t + 5e^{5t}$

For Exercises 5–110, evaluate the following integrals. Assume $a, b, c,$ and k are constants. Exercises 7–69 can be done without an integral table, as can some of the later problems.

5. $\int (3w + 7) \, dw$

6. $\int e^{2r} \, dr$

7. $\int \sin t \, dt$

8. $\int \cos 2t \, dt$

9. $\int e^{5z} \, dz$

10. $\int \cos(x + 1) \, dx$

11. $\int \sin 2\theta \, d\theta$

12. $\int (x^3 - 1)^4 x^2 \, dx$

13. $\int \left(x^{3/2} + x^{2/3} \right) \, dx$

14. $\int (e^x + 3^x) \, dx$

15. $\int \frac{1}{e^z} \, dz$

16. $\int \left(\frac{4}{x^2} - \frac{3}{x^3} \right) \, dx$

17. $\int \frac{x^3 + x + 1}{x^2} \, dx$

18. $\int \frac{(1 + \ln x)^2}{x} \, dx$

19. $\int t e^{t^2} \, dt$

20. $\int x \cos x \, dx$

21. $\int x^2 e^{2x} \, dx$

22. $\int x \sqrt{1 - x} \, dx$

23. $\int y \ln y \, dy$

24. $\int y \sin y \, dy$

25. $\int (\ln x)^2 \, dx$

26. $\int e^{0.5 - 0.3t} \, dt$

27. $\int \sin^2 \theta \cos \theta \, d\theta$

28. $\int x \sqrt{4 - x^2} \, dx$

29. $\int \frac{(u + 1)^3}{u^2} \, du$

30. $\int \frac{\cos \sqrt{y}}{\sqrt{y}} \, dy$

31. $\int \frac{1}{\cos^2 z} \, dz$

32. $\int \cos^2 \theta \, d\theta$

33. $\int t^{10}(t - 10) \, dt$

34. $\int \tan(2x - 6) \, dx$

35. $\int \frac{(\ln x)^2}{x} \, dx$

36. $\int \frac{(t + 2)^2}{t^3} \, dt$

37. $\int \left(x^2 + 2x + \frac{1}{x} \right) \, dx$

38. $\int \frac{t + 1}{t^2} \, dt$

39. $\int t e^{t^2 + 1} \, dt$

40. $\int \tan \theta \, d\theta$

41. $\int \sin(5\theta) \cos(5\theta) \, d\theta$

42. $\int \frac{x}{x^2 + 1} \, dx$

43. $\int \frac{dz}{1 + z^2}$

44. $\int \frac{dz}{1 + 4z^2}$

45. $\int \cos^3 2\theta \sin 2\theta \, d\theta$

46. $\int \sin 5\theta \cos^3 5\theta \, d\theta$

47. $\int \sin^3 z \cos^3 z \, dz$

48. $\int t(t - 10)^{10} \, dt$

49. $\int \cos \theta \sqrt{1 + \sin \theta} \, d\theta$

50. $\int x e^x \, dx$

51. $\int t^3 e^t \, dt$

52. $\int_1^3 x(x^2 + 1)^{70} \, dx$

53. $\int (3z + 5)^3 \, dz$

54. $\int \frac{du}{9 + u^2}$

55. $\int \frac{\cos w}{1 + \sin^2 w} \, dw$

56. $\int \frac{1}{x} \tan(\ln x) \, dx$

57. $\int \frac{1}{x} \sin(\ln x) \, dx$

58. $\int \frac{w \, dw}{\sqrt{16 - w^2}}$

59. $\int \frac{e^{2y} + 1}{e^{2y}} \, dy$

60. $\int \frac{\sin w \, dw}{\sqrt{1 - \cos w}}$

61. $\int \frac{dx}{x \ln x}$

62. $\int \frac{du}{3u + 8}$

63. $\int \frac{x \cos \sqrt{x^2 + 1}}{\sqrt{x^2 + 1}} \, dx$

64. $\int \frac{t^3}{\sqrt{1 + t^2}} \, dt$

65. $\int u e^{ku} \, du$

66. $\int (w + 5)^4 w \, dw$

67. $\int e^{\sqrt{2x + 3}} \, dx$

68. $\int (e^x + x)^2 \, dx$

69. $\int u^2 \ln u \, du$

70. $\int \frac{5x + 6}{x^2 + 4} \, dx$

71. $\displaystyle\int \frac{1}{\sin^3(2x)}\,dx$

72. $\displaystyle\int \frac{dr}{r^2 - 100}$

73. $\displaystyle\int y^2 \sin(cy)\,dy$

74. $\displaystyle\int e^{-ct}\sin kt\,dt$

75. $\displaystyle\int e^{5x}\cos(3x)\,dx$

76. $\displaystyle\int \left(x^{\sqrt{k}} + \sqrt{k}^x\right)dx$

77. $\displaystyle\int \sqrt{3 + 12x^2}\,dx.$

78. $\displaystyle\int \frac{1}{\sqrt{x^2 - 3x + 2}}\,dx$

79. $\displaystyle\int \frac{x^3}{x^2 + 3x + 2}\,dx$

80. $\displaystyle\int \frac{x^2 + 1}{x^2 - 3x + 2}\,dx$

81. $\displaystyle\int \frac{dx}{ax^2 + bx}$

82. $\displaystyle\int \frac{ax + b}{ax^2 + 2bx + c}\,dx$

83. $\displaystyle\int \left(\frac{x}{3} + \frac{3}{x}\right)^2 dx$

84. $\displaystyle\int \frac{2^t}{2^t + 1}\,dt$

85. $\displaystyle\int 10^{1-x}\,dx$

86. $\displaystyle\int (x^2 + 5)^3\,dx$

87. $\displaystyle\int v\arcsin v\,dv$

88. $\displaystyle\int \sqrt{4 - x^2}\,dx$

89. $\displaystyle\int \frac{z^3}{z - 5}\,dz$

90. $\displaystyle\int \frac{\sin w\cos w}{1 + \cos^2 w}\,dw$

91. $\displaystyle\int \frac{1}{\tan(3\theta)}\,d\theta$

92. $\displaystyle\int \frac{x}{\cos^2 x}\,dx$

93. $\displaystyle\int \frac{x + 1}{\sqrt{x}}\,dx$

94. $\displaystyle\int \frac{x}{\sqrt{x + 1}}\,dx$

95. $\displaystyle\int \frac{\sqrt{\sqrt{x} + 1}}{\sqrt{x}}\,dx$

96. $\displaystyle\int \frac{e^{2y}}{e^{2y} + 1}\,dy$

97. $\displaystyle\int \frac{z}{(z^2 - 5)^3}\,dz$

98. $\displaystyle\int \frac{z}{(z - 5)^3}\,dz$

99. $\displaystyle\int \frac{(1 + \tan x)^3}{\cos^2 x}\,dx$

100. $\displaystyle\int \frac{(2x - 1)e^{x^2}}{e^x}\,dx$

101. $\displaystyle\int (2x + 1)e^{x^2}e^x\,dx$

102. $\displaystyle\int \sqrt{y^2 - 2y + 1}\,(y - 1)\,dy$

103. $\displaystyle\int \sin x(\sqrt{2 + 3\cos x})\,dx$

104. $\displaystyle\int (x^2 - 3x + 2)e^{-4x}\,dx$

105. $\displaystyle\int \sin^2(2\theta)\cos^3(2\theta)\,d\theta$

106. $\displaystyle\int \cos(2\sin x)\cos x\,dx$

107. $\displaystyle\int (x + \sin x)^3(1 + \cos x)\,dx$

108. $\displaystyle\int \left(2x^3 + 3x + 4\right)\cos(2x)\,dx$

109. $\displaystyle\int \sinh^2 x\cosh x\,dx$

110. $\displaystyle\int (x + 1)\sinh(x^2 + 2x)\,dx$

For Exercises 111–124, evaluate the definite integrals using the Fundamental Theorem of Calculus and check your answers numerically.

111. $\displaystyle\int_0^1 x(1 + x^2)^{20}\,dx$

112. $\displaystyle\int_4^1 x\sqrt{x^2 + 4}\,dx$

113. $\displaystyle\int_0^\pi \sin\theta(\cos\theta + 5)^7\,d\theta$

114. $\displaystyle\int_0^1 \frac{x}{1 + 5x^2}\,dx$

115. $\displaystyle\int_1^2 \frac{x^2 + 1}{x}\,dx$

116. $\displaystyle\int_1^3 \ln(x^3)\,dx$

117. $\displaystyle\int_1^e (\ln x)^2\,dx$

118. $\displaystyle\int_{-\pi}^\pi e^{2x}\sin 2x\,dx$

119. $\displaystyle\int_0^{10} ze^{-z}\,dz$

120. $\displaystyle\int_{-\pi/3}^{\pi/4} \sin^3\theta\cos\theta\,d\theta$

121. $\displaystyle\int_1^8 \frac{e^{\sqrt[3]{x}}}{\sqrt[3]{x^2}}\,dx$

122. $\displaystyle\int_0^1 \frac{dx}{x^2 + 1}$

123. $\displaystyle\int_{-\pi/4}^{\pi/4} \cos^2\theta\sin^5\theta\,d\theta$

124. $\displaystyle\int_{-2}^0 \frac{2x + 4}{x^2 + 4x + 5}\,dx$

125. Use partial fractions on $\dfrac{1}{x^2 - 1}$ to find $\displaystyle\int \frac{1}{x^2 - 1}\,dx$.

126. **(a)** Use partial fractions to find $\displaystyle\int \frac{1}{x^2 - x}\,dx$.

    (b) Show that your answer to part (a) agrees with the answer you get by using the integral tables.

127. Use partial fractions to find $\displaystyle\int \frac{1}{x(L - x)}\,dx$, where L is constant.

Evaluate the integrals in Exercises 128–139 using partial fractions or a trigonometric substitution (a and b are positive constants).

128. $\displaystyle\int \frac{1}{(x - 2)(x + 2)}\,dx$

129. $\displaystyle\int \frac{1}{\sqrt{25 - x^2}}\,dx,$

130. $\displaystyle\int \frac{1}{x(x + 5)}\,dx$

131. $\displaystyle\int \frac{1}{\sqrt{1 - 9x^2}}\,dx$

132. $\int \dfrac{2x+3}{x(x+2)(x-1)} dx$ **133.** $\int \dfrac{3x+1}{x(x^2-1)} dx$

134. $\int \dfrac{1+x^2}{x(1+x)^2} dx$ **135.** $\int \dfrac{1}{x^2+2x+2} dx$

136. $\int \dfrac{1}{x^2+4x+5} dx$ **137.** $\int \dfrac{1}{\sqrt{a^2-(bx)^2}} dx$

138. $\int \dfrac{\cos x}{\sin^3 x + \sin x} dx$ **139.** $\int \dfrac{e^x}{e^{2x}-1} dx$

Calculate the integrals in Exercises 140–143, if they converge. You may calculate the limits by appealing to the dominance of one function over another, or by l'Hopital's rule.

140. $\int_0^4 \dfrac{dx}{\sqrt{16-x^2}}$ **141.** $\int_0^3 \dfrac{5}{x^2} dx$

142. $\int_0^2 \dfrac{1}{x-2} dx$ **143.** $\int_0^8 \dfrac{1}{\sqrt[3]{8-x}} dx$

For Exercises 144–157 decide if the integral converges or diverges. If the integral converges, find its value or give a bound on its value.

144. $\int_4^\infty \dfrac{dt}{t^{3/2}}$ **145.** $\int_{10}^\infty \dfrac{dx}{x \ln x}$

146. $\int_0^\infty we^{-w} dw$ **147.** $\int_{-1}^1 \dfrac{1}{x^4} dx$

148. $\int_{-\pi/4}^{\pi/4} \tan\theta \, d\theta$ **149.** $\int_2^\infty \dfrac{1}{4+z^2} dz$

150. $\int_{10}^\infty \dfrac{1}{z^2-4} dz$ **151.** $\int_{-5}^{10} \dfrac{dt}{\sqrt{t+5}}$

152. $\int_0^{\pi/2} \dfrac{1}{\sin\phi} d\phi$ **153.** $\int_0^{\pi/4} \tan 2\theta \, d\theta$

154. $\int_1^\infty \dfrac{x}{x+1} dx$ **155.** $\int_0^\infty \dfrac{\sin^2\theta}{\theta^2+1} d\theta$

156. $\int_0^\pi \tan^2\theta d\theta$ **157.** $\int_0^1 (\sin x)^{-3/2} dx$

Problems

In Problems 158–160, find the exact area.

158. Under $y = (e^x)^2$ for $0 \le x \le 1$.

159. Between $y = (e^x)^3$ and $y = (e^x)^2$ for $0 \le x \le 3$.

160. Between $y = e^x$ and $y = 5e^{-x}$ and the y-axis.

161. The curves $y = \sin x$ and $y = \cos x$ cross each other infinitely often. What is the area of the region bounded by these two curves between two consecutive crossings?

162. Evaluate $\int_0^2 \sqrt{4-x^2}\, dx$ using its geometric interpretation.

In Problems 163–164, find a substitution w and constants k, p so that the integral has the form $\int kw^p \, dw$.

163. $\int 3x^4 \sqrt{3x^5+2}\, dx$ **164.** $\int \dfrac{5\sin(3\theta)\, d\theta}{\cos^3(3\theta)}$

In Problems 165–168, give the substitution and the values of any constants to rewrite the integral in the desired form.

165. $\int \dfrac{dx}{(2x-3)(3x-2)}$ as $\int \left(\dfrac{A}{2x-3} + \dfrac{B}{3x-2}\right) dx$

166. $\int (x^2+x)\cos(0.5x-1)\, dx$ as $\int p(u)\cos(u)\, du$, where $p(u)$ is a polynomial

167. $\int x^3 e^{-x^2}\, dx$ as $\int kue^u \, du$

168. $\int \dfrac{\cos^4\left(\sqrt{x}\right)\sin\sqrt{x}\, dx}{\sqrt{x}}$ as $\int ku^n \, du$

In Problems 169–172, explain why the following pairs of antiderivatives are really, despite their apparent dissimilarity, different expressions of the same problem. You do not need to evaluate the integrals.

169. $\int \dfrac{1}{\sqrt{1-x^2}} dx$ and $\int \dfrac{x\, dx}{\sqrt{1-x^4}}$

170. $\int \dfrac{dx}{x^2+4x+4}$ and $\int \dfrac{x}{(x^2+1)^2} dx$

171. $\int \dfrac{x}{1-x^2} dx$ and $\int \dfrac{1}{x \ln x} dx$

172. $\int \dfrac{x}{x+1} dx$ and $\int \dfrac{1}{x+1} dx$

In Problems 173–174, show the two integrals are equal using a substitution.

173. $\int_0^2 e^{-w^2}\, dw = \int_0^1 2e^{-4x^2}\, dx$

174. $\int_0^3 \dfrac{\sin t}{t}\, dt = \int_0^1 \dfrac{\sin 3t}{t}\, dt$

175. A function is defined by $f(t) = t^2$ for $0 \le t \le 1$ and $f(t) = 2 - t$ for $1 < t \le 2$. Compute $\int_0^2 f(t)\, dt$.

176. (a) Find $\int (x+5)^2 \, dx$ in two ways:

    (i) By multiplying out

    (ii) By substituting $w = x + 5$

(b) Are the results the same? Explain.

177. Suppose $\int_{-1}^{1} h(z) \, dz = 7$, and that $h(z)$ is even. Calculate the following:

    (a) $\int_{0}^{1} h(z) \, dz$ **(b)** $\int_{-4}^{-2} 5h(z+3) \, dz$

178. Find the average (vertical) height of the shaded area in Figure 7.26.

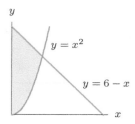

Figure 7.26

179. Find the average (horizontal) width of the shaded area in Figure 7.26.

180. (a) Find the average value of the following functions over one cycle:

    (i) $f(t) = \cos t$

    (ii) $g(t) = |\cos t|$

    (iii) $k(t) = (\cos t)^2$

(b) Write the averages you have just found in ascending order. Using words and graphs, explain why the averages come out in the order they do.

181. What, if anything, is wrong with the following calculation?

$$\int_{-2}^{2} \frac{1}{x^2} \, dx = -\frac{1}{x}\Big|_{-2}^{2} = -\frac{1}{2} - \left(-\frac{1}{-2}\right) = -1.$$

182. Let

$$E(x) = \int \frac{e^x}{e^x + e^{-x}} \, dx \text{ and } F(x) = \int \frac{e^{-x}}{e^x + e^{-x}} \, dx.$$

    (a) Calculate $E(x) + F(x)$.

    (b) Calculate $E(x) - F(x)$.

    (c) Use your results from parts (a) and (b) to calculate $E(x)$ and $F(x)$.

183. Using Figure 7.27, put the following approximations to the integral $\int_{a}^{b} f(x) \, dx$ and its exact value in order from smallest to largest: LEFT(5), LEFT(10), RIGHT(5), RIGHT(10), MID(10), TRAP(10), Exact value

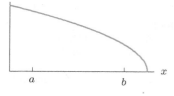

Figure 7.27

184. You estimate $\int_{0}^{0.5} f(x) \, dx$ by the trapezoid and midpoint rules with 100 steps. Which of the two estimates is an overestimate, and which is an underestimate, of the true value of the integral if

    (a) $f(x) = 1 + e^{-x}$ **(b)** $f(x) = e^{-x^2}$

    (c) $f(x)$ is a line

185. (a) Using the left rectangle rule, a computer takes two seconds to compute a particular definite integral accurate to 4 digits to the right of the decimal point. How long (in years) does it take to get 8 digits correct using the left rectangle rule? How about 12 digits? 20 digits?

(b) Repeat part (a) but this time assume that the trapezoidal rule is being used throughout.

186. Given that $\int_{0}^{\infty} e^{-x^2} \, dx = \dfrac{\sqrt{\pi}}{2}$, find $\int_{0}^{\infty} x^2 e^{-x^2} \, dx$.

187. A population, P, is said to be growing logistically if the time, T, taken for it to increase from P_1 to P_2 is given by

$$T = \int_{P_1}^{P_2} \frac{k \, dP}{P(L - P)},$$

where k and L are positive constants and $P_1 < P_2 < L$.

    (a) Calculate the time taken for the population to grow from $P_1 = L/4$ to $P_2 = L/2$.

    (b) What happens to T as $P_2 \to L$?

188. In 2005, the average per-capita income in the US was \$34,586 and increasing at a rate of $r(t) = 1556.37e^{0.045t}$ dollars per year, where t is the number of years since 2005.

    (a) Estimate the average per-capita income in 2015.

    (b) Find a formula for the average per-capita income as a function of time after 2005.

189. A patient is given an injection of Imitrex, a migraine medicine, at a rate of $r(t) = 2te^{-2t}$ ml/sec, where t is the number of seconds since the injection started.

    (a) By letting $t \to \infty$, estimate the total quantity of Imitrex injected.

    (b) What fraction of this dose has the patient received at the end of 5 seconds?

190. In 1990 humans generated $1.4 \cdot 10^{20}$ joules of energy from petroleum. At the time, it was estimated that all of the earth's petroleum would generate approximately 10^{22} joules. Assuming the use of energy generated by petroleum increases by 2% each year, how long will it be before all of our petroleum resources are used up?

191. An organism has a development time of T days at a temperature $H = f(t)°$C. The total the number of degree-days S required for development to maturity is a constant defined by

$$S = \int_0^T (f(t) - H_{min})dt.$$

(a) Evaluate this integral for $T = 18$, $f(t) = 30°$C, and $H_{min} = 10°$C. What are the units of S?

(b) Illustrate this definite integral on a graph. Label the features corresponding to T, $f(t)$, H_{min}, and S.

(c) Now suppose $H = g(t) = 20 + 10\cos(2\pi t/6)°$C. Assuming that S remains constant, write a definite integral which determines the new development time, T_2. Sketch a graph illustrating this new integral. Judging from the graph, how does T_2 compare to T? Find T_2.

192. For a positive integer n, let $\Psi_n(x) = C_n \sin(n\pi x)$ be the wave function used in describing the behavior of an electron. If n and m are different positive integers, find

$$\int_0^1 \Psi_n(x) \cdot \Psi_m(x)\, dx.$$

CAS Challenge Problems

193. (a) Use a computer algebra system to find $\int \dfrac{\ln x}{x}\, dx$, $\int \dfrac{(\ln x)^2}{x}\, dx$, and $\int \dfrac{(\ln x)^3}{x}\, dx$.

(b) Guess a formula for $\int \dfrac{(\ln x)^n}{x}\, dx$ that works for any positive integer n.

(c) Use a substitution to check your formula.

194. (a) Using a computer algebra system, find $\int (\ln x)^n\, dx$ for $n = 1, 2, 3, 4$.

(b) There is a formula relating $\int (\ln x)^n\, dx$ to $\int (\ln x)^{n-1}\, dx$ for any positive integer n. Guess this formula using your answer to part (a). Check your guess using integration by parts.

In Problems 195–197:

(a) Use a computer algebra system to find the indefinite integral of the given function.

(b) Use the computer algebra system again to differentiate the result of part (a). Do not simplify.

(c) Use algebra to show that the result of part (b) is the same as the original function. Show all the steps in your calculation.

195. $\sin^3 x$

196. $\sin x \cos x \cos(2x)$

197. $\dfrac{x^4}{(1+x^2)^2}$

PROJECTS FOR CHAPTER SEVEN

1. Taylor Polynomial Inequalities

(a) Use the fact that $e^x \geq 1 + x$ for all values of x and the formula

$$e^x = 1 + \int_0^x e^t\, dt$$

to show that

$$e^x \geq 1 + x + \frac{x^2}{2}$$

for all positive values of x. Generalize this idea to get inequalities involving higher-degree polynomials.

(b) Use the fact that $\cos x \leq 1$ for all x and repeated integration to show that

$$\cos x \leq 1 - \frac{x^2}{2!} + \frac{x^4}{4!}.$$

Chapter Eleven

DIFFERENTIAL EQUATIONS

Contents

11.1 What is a Differential Equation? **586**

   How Fast Does a Person Learn? 586

   First-and Second-Order Differential Equations 588

11.2 Slope Fields **591**

   Existence and Uniqueness of Solutions 593

11.3 Euler's Method **599**

   The Accuracy of Euler's Method 601

11.4 Separation of Variables **604**

   Justification for Separation of Variables . . . 606

11.5 Growth and Decay **609**

   Continuously Compounded Interest 610

   Newton's Law of Heating and Cooling 613

   Equilibrium Solutions 615

11.6 Applications and Modeling **620**

   How a Layer of Ice Forms 620

   The Net Worth of a Company 621

   Terminal Velocity 622

   Compartmental Analysis: A Reservoir 624

11.7 The Logistic Model **629**

   Peak Oil: US and World 631

   US Population Growth 633

11.8 Systems of Differential Equations **639**

   The S-I-R Model 640

   The Phase Plane 641

   Two Interacting Populations: Predator-Prey 643

11.9 Analyzing the Phase Plane **649**

   Competitive Exclusion: Citrus Tree Parasites 649

   The Phase Plane and Nullclines 650

   Nullclines and the Parasite Populations 651

REVIEW PROBLEMS **655**

PROJECTS **661**

11.1 WHAT IS A DIFFERENTIAL EQUATION?

How Fast Does a Person Learn?

Suppose we are interested in how fast an employee learns a new task. One theory claims that the more the employee already knows of the task, the slower he or she learns. In other words, if $y\%$ is the percentage of the task that has already been mastered and dy/dt the rate at which the employee learns, then dy/dt decreases as y increases.

What can we say about y as a function of time, t? Figure 11.1 shows three graphs whose slope, dy/dt, decreases as y increases. Figure 11.1(a) represents an employee who starts learning at $t = 0$ and who eventually masters 100% of the task. Figure 11.1(b) represents an employee who starts later but eventually masters 100% of the task. Figure 11.1(c) represents an employee who starts learning at $t = 0$ but who does not master the whole task (since y levels off below 100%).

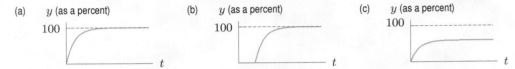

Figure 11.1: Possible graphs showing percentage of task learned, y, as a function of time, t

Setting up a Differential Equation to Model How a Person Learns

To describe more precisely how a person learns, we need more exact information about how dy/dt depends on y. Suppose, if time is measured in weeks, that

$$\text{Rate a person learns} \quad = \quad \text{Percentage of task not yet learned.}$$

Since y is the percentage learned by time t (in weeks), the percentage not yet learned by that time is $100 - y$. So we have

$$\frac{dy}{dt} = 100 - y.$$

Such an equation, which gives information about the rate of change of an unknown function, is called a *differential equation*.

Solving the Differential Equation Numerically

Suppose that the person starts learning at time zero, so $y = 0$ when $t = 0$. Then initially the person is learning at a rate

$$\frac{dy}{dt} = 100 - 0 = 100\% \text{ per week.}$$

In other words, if the person were to continue learning at this rate, the task would be mastered in a week. In fact, however, the rate at which the person learns decreases, so it takes more than a week to get close to mastering the task. Let's assume a five-day work week and that the 100% per week learning rate holds for the whole first day. (It does not, but we assume this for now.) One day is 1/5 of a week, so during the first day the person learns $100(1/5) = 20\%$ of the task. By the end of the first day, the rate at which the person learns has therefore been reduced to

$$\frac{dy}{dt} = 100 - 20 = 80\% \text{ per week.}$$

Thus, during the second day the person learns $80(1/5) = 16\%$, so by the end of the second day, the person knows $20 + 16 = 36\%$ of the task. Continuing in this fashion, we compute the approximate y-values[1] in Table 11.1.

---

[1]The values of y after 6, 7, 8, 9, ..., 19 days were computed by the same method, but omitted from the table.

Table 11.1   *Approximate percentage of task learned as a function of time*

Time (working days)	0	1	2	3	4	5	10	20
Percentage learned	0	20	36	48.8	59.0	67.2	89.3	98.8

A Formula for the Solution to the Differential Equation

A function $y = f(t)$ that satisfies the differential equation is called a *solution*. Figure 11.1(a) shows a possible solution, and Table 11.1 shows approximate numerical values of a solution to the equation

$$\frac{dy}{dt} = 100 - y.$$

Later in this chapter, we see how to obtain a formula for the solution:

$$y = 100 + Ce^{-t},$$

where C is a constant. To check that this formula is correct, we substitute into the differential equation, giving:

$$\text{Left side} = \frac{dy}{dt} = \frac{d}{dt}(100 + Ce^{-t}) = -Ce^{-t}$$
$$\text{Right side} = 100 - y = 100 - (100 + Ce^{-t}) = -Ce^{-t}.$$

Since we get the same result on both sides, $y = 100 + Ce^{-t}$ is a solution of this differential equation.

Finding the Arbitrary Constant: Initial Conditions

To find a value for the arbitrary constant C, we need an additional piece of information—usually the initial value of y. If, for example, we are told that $y = 0$ when $t = 0$, then substituting into

$$y = 100 + Ce^{-t}$$

shows us that

$$0 = 100 + Ce^0, \quad \text{so} \quad C = -100.$$

So the function $y = 100 - 100e^{-t}$ satisfies the differential equation *and* the condition that $y = 0$ when $t = 0$.

The Family of Solutions

Any solution to this differential equation is of the form $y = 100 + Ce^{-t}$ for some constant C. Like a family of antiderivatives, this family contains an arbitrary constant, C. We say that the *general solution* to the differential equation $dy/dt = 100 - y$ is the family of functions $y = 100 + Ce^{-t}$. The solution $y = 100 - 100e^{-t}$ that satisfies the differential equation together with the *initial condition* that $y = 0$ when $t = 0$ is called a *particular solution*. The differential equation and the initial condition together are called an *initial value problem*. Several members of the family of solutions are graphed in Figure 11.2. The horizontal solution curve when $C = 0$ is called an *equilibrium solution*.

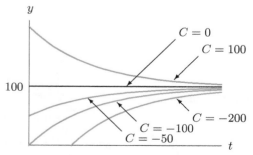

Figure 11.2: Solution curves for $dy/dt = 100 - y$:
Members of the family $y = 100 + Ce^{-t}$

First- and Second-Order Differential Equations

First, some more definitions. We often write y' to represent the derivative of y. The differential equation

$$y' = 100 - y$$

is called *first-order* because it involves the first derivative, but no higher derivatives. By contrast, if s is the height (in meters) of a body moving under the force of gravity and t is time (in seconds), then

$$\frac{d^2 s}{dt^2} = -9.8.$$

This is a *second-order* differential equation because it involves the second derivative of the unknown function, $s = f(t)$, but no higher derivatives.

Example 1   Show that $y = e^{2t}$ is not a solution to the second-order differential equation

$$\frac{d^2 y}{dt^2} + 4y = 0.$$

Solution   To decide whether the function $y = e^{2t}$ is a solution, substitute it into the differential equation:

$$\frac{d^2 y}{dt^2} + 4y = 2(2e^{2t}) + 4e^{2t} = 8e^{2t}.$$

Since $8e^{2t}$ is not identically zero, $y = e^{2t}$ is not a solution.

How Many Arbitrary Constants Should We Expect in the Family of Solutions?

Since a differential equation involves the derivative of an unknown function, solving it usually involves antidifferentiation, which introduces arbitrary constants. The solution to a first-order differential equation usually involves one antidifferentiation and one arbitrary constant (for example, the C in $y = 100 + Ce^{-t}$). Picking out one particular solution involves knowing one additional piece of information, such as an initial condition. Solving a second-order differential equation generally involves two antidifferentiations and so two arbitrary constants. Consequently, finding a particular solution usually involves two initial conditions.

For example, if s is the height (in meters) of a body above the surface of the earth at time t (in seconds), then

$$\frac{d^2 s}{dt^2} = -9.8.$$

Integrating gives

$$\frac{ds}{dt} = -9.8t + C_1,$$

and integrating again gives

$$s = -4.9t^2 + C_1 t + C_2.$$

Thus the general solution for s involves the two arbitrary constants C_1 and C_2. We can find C_1 and C_2 if we are told, for example, that the initial velocity is 30 meters per second upward and that the initial position is 5 meters above the ground. In this case, $C_1 = 30$ and $C_2 = 5$.

Exercises and Problems for Section 11.1

Exercises

1. Is $y = x^3$ a solution to the differential equation

$$xy' - 3y = 0?$$

2. Determine whether each function is a solution to the differential equation and justify your answer:

$$x\frac{dy}{dx} = 4y.$$

(a) $y = x^4$ (b) $y = x^4 + 3$

(c) $y = x^3$ (d) $y = 7x^4$

3. Determine whether each function is a solution to the differential equation and justify your answer:

$$y\frac{dy}{dx} = 6x^2.$$

(a) $y = 4x^3$ (b) $y = 2x^{3/2}$ (c) $y = 6x^{3/2}$

4. Show that $y(x) = Ae^{\lambda x}$ is a solution to the equation $y' = \lambda y$ for any value of A.

5. Show that $y = \sin 2t$ satisfies

$$\frac{d^2y}{dt^2} + 4y = 0.$$

6. Show that, for any constant P_0, the function $P = P_0 e^t$ satisfies the equation

$$\frac{dP}{dt} = P.$$

7. Use implicit differentiation to show that $x^2 + y^2 = r^2$ is a solution to the differential equation $dy/dx = -x/y$.

8. A quantity Q satisfies the differential equation

$$\frac{dQ}{dt} = \frac{t}{Q} - 0.5.$$

(a) If $Q = 8$ when $t = 2$, use dQ/dt to determine whether Q is increasing or decreasing at $t = 2$.

(b) Use your work in part (a) to estimate the value of Q when $t = 3$. Assume the rate of change stays approximately constant over the interval from $t = 2$ to $t = 3$.

9. Fill in the missing values in the table given if you know that $dy/dt = 0.5y$. Assume the rate of growth given by dy/dt is approximately constant over each unit time interval and that the initial value of y is 8.

t	0	1	2	3	4
y	8				

10. Use the method that generated the data in Table 11.1 on page 587 to fill in the missing y-values for $t = 6, 7, \ldots, 19$ days.

In Exercises 11–14, find the particular solution to the differential equation, given the general solution and an initial condition. (C is the constant of integration.)

11. $x(t) = Ce^{3t}$; $x(0) = 5$

12. $P = C/t$; $P = 5$ when $t = 3$

13. $y = \sqrt{2t + C}$; the solution curve passes through $(1, 3)$

14. $Q = 1/(Ct + C)$; $Q = 4$ when $t = 2$

Problems

15. Show that $y = A + Ce^{kt}$ is a solution to the equation

$$\frac{dy}{dt} = k(y - A).$$

16. Find the value(s) of ω for which $y = \cos \omega t$ satisfies

$$\frac{d^2y}{dt^2} + 9y = 0.$$

17. Show that any function of the form

$$x = C_1 \cosh \omega t + C_2 \sinh \omega t$$

satisfies the differential equation

$$x'' - \omega^2 x = 0.$$

18. Suppose $Q = Ce^{kt}$ satisfies the differential equation

$$\frac{dQ}{dt} = -0.03Q.$$

What (if anything) does this tell you about the values of C and k?

19. Find the values of k for which $y = x^2 + k$ is a solution to the differential equation

$$2y - xy' = 10.$$

20. For what values of k (if any) does $y = 5 + 3e^{kx}$ satisfy the differential equation

$$\frac{dy}{dx} = 10 - 2y?$$

21. (a) For what values of C and n (if any) is $y = Cx^n$ a solution to the differential equation

$$x\frac{dy}{dx} - 3y = 0?$$

(b) If the solution satisfies $y = 40$ when $x = 2$, what more (if anything) can you say about C and n?

22. (a) Find the value of A so that the equation $y' - xy - x = 0$ has a solution of the form $y(x) = A + Be^{x^2/2}$ for any constant B.

(b) If $y(0) = 1$, find B.

23. In Figure 11.3, the height, y, of the hanging cable above the horizontal line satisfies

$$\frac{d^2y}{dx^2} = k\sqrt{1 + \left(\frac{dy}{dx}\right)^2}.$$

(a) Show that $y = \dfrac{e^x + e^{-x}}{2}$ satisfies this differential equation if $k = 1$.

(b) For general k, one solution to this differential equation is of the form

$$y = \frac{e^{Ax} + e^{-Ax}}{2A}.$$

Substitute this expression for y into the differential equation to find A in terms of k.

Figure 11.3

24. Match solutions and differential equations. (Note: Each equation may have more than one solution.)

(a) $y'' - y = 0$ (I) $y = e^x$

(b) $x^2y'' + 2xy' - 2y = 0$ (II) $y = x^3$

(c) $x^2y'' - 6y = 0$ (III) $y = e^{-x}$

                              (IV) $y = x^{-2}$

25. Pick out which functions are solutions to which differential equations. (Note: Functions may be solutions to more than one equation or to none; an equation may have more than one solution.)

(a) $\dfrac{dy}{dx} = -2y$ (I) $y = 2\sin x$

(b) $\dfrac{dy}{dx} = 2y$ (II) $y = \sin 2x$

(c) $\dfrac{d^2y}{dx^2} = 4y$ (III) $y = e^{2x}$

(d) $\dfrac{d^2y}{dx^2} = -4y$ (IV) $y = e^{-2x}$

26. Families of curves often arise as solutions of differential equations. Match the families of curves with the differential equations of which they are solutions.

(a) $\dfrac{dy}{dx} = \dfrac{y}{x}$ (I) $y = xe^{kx}$

(b) $\dfrac{dy}{dx} = ky$ (II) $y = x^k$

(c) $\dfrac{dy}{dx} = ky + \dfrac{y}{x}$ (III) $y = e^{kx}$

(d) $\dfrac{dy}{dx} = \dfrac{ky}{x}$ (IV) $y = kx$

27. Is $y(x) = e^{3x}$ the general solution of $y' = 3y$?

28. (a) Let $y = A + Be^{-2t}$. For what values of A and B, if any, is y a solution to the differential equation

$$\frac{dy}{dt} = 100 - 2y?$$

Give the general solution to the differential equation.

(b) If the solution satisfies $y = 85$ when $t = 0$, what more (if anything) can you say about A and B? Give the particular solution to the differential equation with this initial condition.

Strengthen Your Understanding

In Problems 29–30, explain what is wrong with the statement.

29. $Q = 6e^{4t}$ is the general solution to the differential equation $dQ/dt = 4Q$.

30. If $dx/dt = 1/x$ and $x = 3$ when $t = 0$, then x is a decreasing function of t.

In Problems 31–37, give an example of:

31. A differential equation with an initial condition.

32. A second-order differential equation.

33. A differential equation and two different solutions to the differential equation.

34. A differential equation that has a trigonometric function as a solution.

35. A differential equation that has a logarithmic function as a solution.

36. A differential equation all of whose solutions are increasing and concave up.

37. A differential equation all of whose solutions have their critical points on the parabola $y = x^2$.

Are the statements in Problems 38–39 true or false? Give an explanation for your answer.

38. If $y = f(t)$ is a particular solution to a first-order differential equation, then the general solution is $y = f(t)+C$, where C is an arbitrary constant.

39. Polynomials are never solutions to differential equations.

In Problems 40–47, is the statement true or false? Assume that $y = f(x)$ is a solution to the equation $dy/dx = g(x)$. If the statement is true, explain how you know. If the statement is false, give a counterexample.

40. If $g(x)$ is increasing for all x, then the graph of f is concave up for all x .

41. If $g(x)$ is increasing for $x > 0$, then so is $f(x)$.

42. If $g(0) = 1$ and $g(x)$ is increasing for $x \geq 0$, then $f(x)$ is also increasing for $x \geq 0$.

43. If $g(x)$ is periodic, then $f(x)$ is also periodic.

44. If $\lim_{x \to \infty} g(x) = 0$, then $\lim_{x \to \infty} f(x) = 0$.

45. If $\lim_{x \to \infty} g(x) = \infty$, then $\lim_{x \to \infty} f(x) = \infty$.

46. If $g(x)$ is even, then so is $f(x)$.

47. If $g(x)$ is even, then $f(x)$ is odd.

11.2 SLOPE FIELDS

In this section, we see how to visualize a first-order differential equation. We start with the equation

$$\frac{dy}{dx} = y.$$

Any solution to this differential equation has the property that the slope at any point is equal to the y-coordinate at that point. (That's what the equation $dy/dx = y$ is telling us!) If the solution goes through the point $(0, 0.5)$, its slope there is 0.5; if it goes through a point with $y = 1.5$, its slope there is 1.5. See Figure 11.4.

In Figure 11.4 a small line segment is drawn at each of the marked points showing the slope of the curve there. Imagine drawing many of these line segments, but leaving out the curves; this gives the *slope field* for the equation $dy/dx = y$ in Figure 11.5. From this picture, we can see that above the x-axis, the slopes are all positive (because y is positive there), and they increase as we move upward (as y increases). Below the x-axis, the slopes are all negative and get more so as we move downward. On any horizontal line (where y is constant) the slopes are constant.

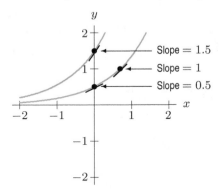

Figure 11.4: Solutions to $dy/dx = y$

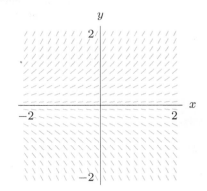

Figure 11.5: Slope field for $dy/dx = y$

In the slope field we can see the ghost of the solution curve lurking. Start anywhere on the plane and move so that the slope lines are tangent to our path; we trace out one of the solution curves. We think of the slope field as a set of signposts pointing in the direction we should go at each point. In this case, the slope field should trace out exponential curves of the form $y = Ce^x$, the solutions to the differential equation $dy/dx = y$.

Example 1   Figure 11.6 shows the slope field of the differential equation $dy/dx = 2x$.

(a) How does the slope field vary as we move around the xy-plane?

(b) Compare the solution curves sketched on the slope field with the formula for the solutions.

Figure 11.6: Slope field for $dy/dx = 2x$

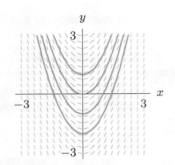

Figure 11.7: Some solutions to $dy/dx = 2x$

Solution   (a) In Figure 11.6 we notice that on a vertical line (where x is constant) the slopes are constant. This is because in this differential equation dy/dx depends on x only. (In the previous example, $dy/dx = y$, the slopes depended on y only.)

(b) The solution curves in Figure 11.7 look like parabolas. By antidifferentiation, we see that the solution to the differential equation $dy/dx = 2x$ is

$$y = \int 2x \, dx = x^2 + C,$$

so the solution curves really are parabolas.

Example 2   Using the slope field, guess the form of the solution curves of the differential equation

$$\frac{dy}{dx} = -\frac{x}{y}.$$

Solution   The slope field is shown in Figure 11.8. On the y-axis, where x is 0, the slope is 0. On the x-axis, where y is 0, the line segments are vertical and the slope is infinite. At the origin the slope is undefined, and there is no line segment.

The slope field suggests that the solution curves are circles centered at the origin. Later we see how to obtain the solution analytically, but even without this, we can check that the circle is a solution. We take the circle of radius r,

$$x^2 + y^2 = r^2,$$

and differentiate implicitly, thinking of y as a function of x. Using the chain rule, we get

$$2x + 2y \cdot \frac{dy}{dx} = 0.$$

Solving for dy/dx gives our differential equation,

$$\frac{dy}{dx} = -\frac{x}{y}.$$

This tells us that $x^2 + y^2 = r^2$ is a solution to the differential equation.

Figure 11.8: Slope field for $dy/dx = -x/y$

The previous example shows that the solution to a differential equation may be an implicit function.

Example 3   The slope fields of $dy/dt = 2 - y$ and $dy/dt = t/y$ are in Figures 11.9 and 11.10.

(a) On each slope field, sketch solution curves with initial conditions

      (i) $y = 1$ when $t = 0$ (ii) $y = 0$ when $t = 1$ (iii) $y = 3$ when $t = 0$

(b) For each solution curve, what can you say about the long-run behavior of y? For example, does $\lim\limits_{t \to \infty} y$ exist? If so, what is its value?

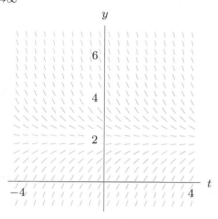

Figure 11.9: Slope field for $dy/dt = 2 - y$ Figure 11.10: Slope field for $dy/dt = t/y$

Solution

(a) See Figures 11.11 and 11.12.

(b) For $dy/dt = 2 - y$, all solution curves have $y = 2$ as a horizontal asymptote, so $\lim\limits_{t \to \infty} y = 2$.

    For $dy/dt = t/y$, as $t \to \infty$, it appears that either $y \to t$ or $y \to -t$.

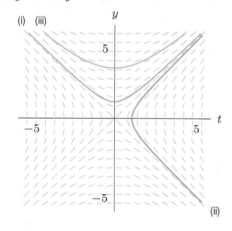

Figure 11.11: Solution curves for $dy/dt = 2 - y$ Figure 11.12: Solution curves for $dy/dt = t/y$

Existence and Uniqueness of Solutions

Since differential equations are used to model many real situations, the question of whether a solution is unique can have great practical importance. If we know how the velocity of a satellite is changing, can we know its velocity at any future time? If we know the initial population of a city and we know how the population is changing, can we predict the population in the future? Common sense says yes: if we know the initial value of some quantity and we know exactly how it is changing, we should be able to figure out its future value.

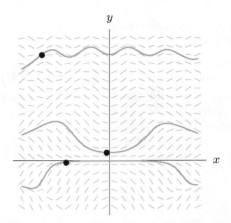

Figure 11.13: There's one and only one solution curve through each
point in the plane for this slope field (dots represent initial conditions).

In the language of differential equations, an initial value problem (that is, a differential equation and an initial condition) almost always has a unique solution. One way to see this is by looking at the slope field. Imagine starting at the point representing the initial condition. Through that point there is usually a line segment pointing in the direction of the solution curve. By following these line segments, we trace out the solution curve. See Figure 11.13. In general, at each point there is one line segment and therefore only one direction for the solution curve to go. The solution curve *exists* and is *unique* provided we are given an initial point. Notice that even though we can draw the solution curves, we may have no simple formula for them.

It can be shown that if the slope field is continuous as we move from point to point in the plane, we can be sure that a solution curve exists everywhere. Ensuring that each point has only one solution curve through it requires a slightly stronger condition.

Exercises and Problems for Section 11.2

Exercises

1. (a) For $dy/dx = x^2 - y^2$, find the slope at the following points:

$$(1,0), \quad (0,1), \quad (1,1), \quad (2,1), \quad (1,2), \quad (2,2)$$

(b) Sketch the slope field at these points.

2. Sketch the slope field for $dy/dx = x/y$ at the points marked in Figure 11.14.

Figure 11.14

3. Sketch the slope field for $dy/dx = y^2$ at the points marked in Figure 11.15.

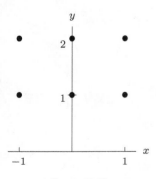

Figure 11.15

4. Match each of the slope field segments in (I)–(VI) with one or more of the differential equations in (a)–(f).

(a) $y' = e^{-x^2}$ **(b)** $y' = \cos y$

(c) $y' = \cos(4 - y)$ **(d)** $y' = y(4 - y)$

(e) $y' = y(3 - y)$ **(f)** $y' = x(3 - x)$

(I)

(II)

(III)

(IV)

(V)

(VI)

5. Sketch three solution curves for each of the slope fields in Figures 11.16 and 11.17.

Figure 11.16   Figure 11.17

6. Sketch three solution curves for each of the slope fields in Figure 11.18.

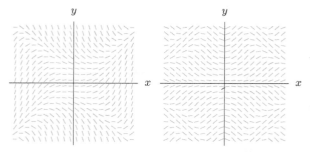

Figure 11.18

7. One of the slope fields in Figure 11.18 is the slope field for $y' = x^2 - y^2$. Which one? On this field, where is the point $(0, 1)$? The point $(1, 0)$? (Assume that the x and y scales are the same.) Sketch the line $x = 1$ and the solution curve passing through $(0, 1)$ until it crosses $x = 1$.

8. The slope field for the equation $y' = x(y - 1)$ is shown in Figure 11.19.

(a) Sketch the solutions that pass through the points

(i) $(0, 1)$ (ii) $(0, -1)$ (iii) $(0, 0)$

(b) From your sketch, write down the equation of the solution with $y(0) = 1$.

(c) Check your solution to part (b) by substituting it into the differential equation.

Figure 11.19

9. The slope field for the equation $y' = x + y$ is shown in Figure 11.20.

(a) Sketch the solutions that pass through the points

(i) $(0, 0)$ (ii) $(-3, 1)$ (iii) $(-1, 0)$

(b) From your sketch, write the equation of the solution passing through $(-1, 0)$.

(c) Check your solution to part (b) by substituting it into the differential equation.

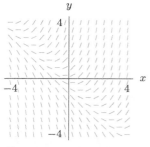

Figure 11.20: Slope field for $y' = x + y$

Problems

10. Sketch a slope field with the following properties. (Draw at least ten line segments, including some with $x < 0$, with $x > 0$, and with $x = 0$.)

$$\frac{dy}{dx} > 0 \text{ for } x < 0,$$

$$\frac{dy}{dx} < 0 \text{ for } x > 0,$$

$$\frac{dy}{dx} = 0 \text{ for } x = 0.$$

11. Sketch a slope field with the following properties. (Draw at least ten line segments, including some with $P < 2$, with $2 < P < 5$, and with $P > 5$.)

$$\frac{dP}{dt} > 0 \text{ for } 2 < P < 5,$$

$$\frac{dP}{dt} < 0 \text{ for } P < 2 \text{ or } P > 5,$$

$$\frac{dP}{dt} = 0 \text{ for } P = 2 \text{ and } P = 5.$$

12. **(a)** Sketch the slope field for the equation $y' = x - y$ in Figure 11.21 at the points indicated.
   (b) Find the equation for the solution that passes through the point $(1, 0)$.

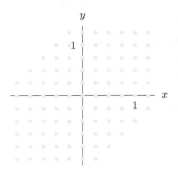

Figure 11.21

13. The slope field for the equation $dP/dt = 0.1P(10-P)$, for $P \geq 0$, is in Figure 11.22.

   (a) Sketch the solutions that pass through the points

   (i) $(0,0)$ (ii) $(1,4)$ (iii) $(4,1)$
   (iv) $(-5,1)$ (v) $(-2,12)$ (vi) $(-2,10)$

   (b) For which positive values of P are the solutions increasing? Decreasing? If $P(0) = 5$, what is the limiting value of P as t gets large?

Figure 11.22

14. The slope field for $y' = 0.5(1 + y)(2 - y)$ is shown in Figure 11.23.

   (a) Plot the following points on the slope field:
   (i)   the origin   (ii) $(0,1)$ (iii) $(1,0)$
   (iv) $(0,-1)$ (v) $(0,-5/2)$ (vi) $(0,5/2)$

   (b) Plot solution curves through the points in part (a).
   (c) For which regions are all solution curves increasing? For which regions are all solution curves decreasing? When can the solution curves have horizontal tangents? Explain why, using both the slope field and the differential equation.

Figure 11.23: Note: x and y scales are equal

15. One of the slope fields in Figure 11.24 is the slope field for $y' = (x + y)/(x - y)$. Which one?

Figure 11.24

16. The slope field for $y' = (\sin x)(\sin y)$ is in Figure 11.25.

    (a) Sketch the solutions that pass through the points

        (i) $(0, -2)$ (ii) $(0, \pi)$

    (b) What is the equation of the solution that passes through $(0, n\pi)$, where n is any integer?

Figure 11.25

17. Match the slope fields in Figure 11.26 with their differential equations. Explain your reasoning.

    (a) $y' = -y$ **(b)** $y' = y$ **(c)** $y' = x$

    (d) $y' = 1/y$ **(e)** $y' = y^2$

(I)

(II)

(III)

(IV)

(V)

Figure 11.26: Each slope field is graphed for $-5 \le x \le 5, -5 \le y \le 5$

18. Match the slope fields in Figure 11.27 to the corresponding differential equations:

    (a) $y' = xe^{-x}$ **(b)** $y' = \sin x$ **(c)** $y' = \cos x$

    (d) $y' = x^2 e^{-x}$ **(e)** $y' = e^{-x^2}$ **(f)** $y' = e^{-x}$

(I)

(II)

(III)

(IV)

(V)

(VI)

Figure 11.27

In Problems 19–22, match an equation with the slope field.

    (a) $y' = 0.05y(10 - y)$ **(b)** $y' = 0.05x(10 - x)$

    (c) $y' = 0.05y(5 - y)$ **(d)** $y' = 0.05x(5 - x)$

    (e) $y' = 0.05y(y - 10)$ **(f)** $y' = 0.05x(x - 10)$

    (g) $y' = 0.05y(y - 5)$ **(h)** $y' = 0.05x(x - 5)$

    (i) $y' = 0.05x(y - 5)$

19.

20.

21.

22.

23. Match the following differential equations with the slope fields shown in Figure 11.28. Explain your reasoning.

(a) $\dfrac{dy}{dx} = e^{x^2}$ **(b)** $\dfrac{dy}{dx} = e^{-2x^2}$

(c) $\dfrac{dy}{dx} = e^{-x^2/2}$ **(d)** $\dfrac{dy}{dx} = e^{-0.5x}\cos x$

(e) $\dfrac{dy}{dx} = \dfrac{1}{(1 + 0.5\cos x)^2}$

(f) $\dfrac{dy}{dx} = -e^{-x^2}$

(I)

(II)

(III)

(IV)

(V)

(VI)

Figure 11.28: Each slope field is graphed for $-3 \le x \le 3$, $-3 \le y \le 3$

24. The Gompertz equation, which models growth of animal tumors, is $y' = -ay\ln(y/b)$, where a and b are positive constants. Use Figures 11.29 and 11.30 to write a paragraph describing the similarities and/or differences between solutions to the Gompertz equation with $a = 1$ and $b = 2$ and solutions to the equation $y' = y(2 - y)$.

Figure 11.29: Slope field for $y' = -y\ln(y/2)$

Figure 11.30: Slope field for $y' = y(2 - y)$

Strengthen Your Understanding

In Problems 25–26, explain what is wrong with the statement.

25. There is a differential equation that has $y = x$ as one of its solutions and a slope field with a slope of 0 at the point $(1, 1)$.

26. Figure 11.31 shows the slope field of $y' = y$.

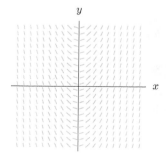

Figure 11.31

In Problems 27–30, give an example of:

27. A differential equation whose slope field has all the slopes positive.

28. A differential equation that has a slope field with all the slopes above the x-axis positive and all the slopes below the x-axis negative.

29. A slope field for a differential equation where the formula for dy/dx depends on x but not y.

30. A slope field for a differential equation where the formula for dy/dx depends on y but not x.

Are the statements in Problems 31–35 true or false? Give an explanation for your answer.

31. All solutions to the differential equation whose slope field is in Figure 11.32 have $\lim_{x \to \infty} y = \infty$.

y

x

Figure 11.32

32. All solutions to the differential equation whose slope field is in Figure 11.33 have $\lim_{x \to \infty} y = 0$.

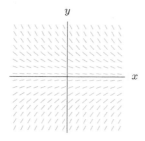

y

x

Figure 11.33

33. All solutions to the differential equation whose slope field is in Figure 11.34 have the same limiting value as $x \to \infty$.

y

x

Figure 11.34

34. The solutions of the differential equation $dy/dx = x^2 + y^2 + 1$ are increasing at every point.

35. The solutions of the differential equation $dy/dx = x^2 + y^2 + 1$ are concave up at every point.

In Problems 36–44, decide whether the statement is true or false. Assume that $y = f(x)$ is a solution to the equation $dy/dx = 2x - y$. Justify your answer.

36. If $f(a) = b$, the slope of the graph of f at (a, b) is $2a - b$.

37. $f'(x) = 2x - f(x)$.

38. There could be more than one value of x such that $f'(x) = 1$ and $f(x) = 5$.

39. If $y = f(x)$, then $d^2y/dx^2 = 2 - (2x - y)$.

40. If $f(1) = 5$, then $(1, 5)$ could be a critical point of f.

41. The graph of f is decreasing whenever it lies above the line $y = 2x$ and is increasing whenever it lies below the line $y = 2x$.

42. All the inflection points of f lie on the line $y = 2x - 2$.

43. If $g(x)$ is another solution to the differential equation $dy/dx = 2x - y$, then $g(x) = f(x) + C$.

44. If $g(x)$ is a different solution to the differential equation $dy/dx = 2x - y$, then $\lim_{x \to \infty} (g(x) - f(x)) = 0$. [Hint: Show that $w = g(x) - f(x)$ satisfies the differential equation $dw/dx = -w$.]

11.3 EULER'S METHOD

In the preceding section we saw how to sketch a solution curve to a differential equation using its slope field. In this section we compute points on a solution curve numerically using *Euler's method*. (Leonhard Euler was an eighteenth-century Swiss mathematician.) In Section 11.4 we find formulas for some solution curves.

Here's the concept behind Euler's method. Think of the slope field as a set of signposts directing you across the plane. Pick a starting point (corresponding to the initial value), and calculate the slope at that point using the differential equation. This slope is a signpost telling you the direction to take. Head off a small distance in that direction. Stop and look at the new signpost. Recalculate the slope from the differential equation, using the coordinates of the new point. Change direction to correspond to the new slope, and move another small distance, and so on.

Example 1 Use Euler's method for $dy/dx = y$. Start at the point $P_0 = (0, 1)$ and take $\Delta x = 0.1$.

Solution The slope at the point $P_0 = (0, 1)$ is $dy/dx = 1$. (See Figure 11.35.) As we move from P_0 to P_1, y increases by Δy, where

$$\Delta y = (\text{slope at } P_0)\Delta x = 1(0.1) = 0.1.$$

So we have

$$y\text{-value at } P_1 = (y \text{ value at } P_0) + \Delta y = 1 + 0.1 = 1.1.$$

Table 11.2 *Euler's method for $dy/dx = y$, starting at $(0, 1)$*

	x	y	$\Delta y = (\text{Slope})\Delta x$
P_0	0	1	$0.1 = (1)(0.1)$
P_1	0.1	1.1	$0.11 = (1.1)(0.1)$
P_2	0.2	1.21	$0.121 = (1.21)(0.1)$
P_3	0.3	1.331	$0.1331 = (1.331)(0.1)$
P_4	0.4	1.4641	$0.14641 = (1.4641)(0.1)$
P_5	0.5	1.61051	$0.161051 = (1.61051)(0.1)$

Figure 11.35: Euler's approximate solution to $dy/dx = y$

Thus the point P_1 is $(0.1, 1.1)$. Now, using the differential equation again, we see that

$$\text{slope at } P_1 = 1.1,$$

so if we move to P_2, then y changes by

$$\Delta y = (\text{slope at } P_1)\Delta x = (1.1)(0.1) = 0.11.$$

This means

$$y\text{-value at } P_2 = (y \text{ value at } P_1) + \Delta y = 1.1 + 0.11 = 1.21.$$

Thus P_2 is $(0.2, 1.21)$. Continuing gives the results in Table 11.2.

Since the solution curves of $dy/dx = y$ are exponentials, they are concave up and bend upward away from the line segments of the slope field. Therefore, in this case, Euler's method produces y-values which are too small.

Notice that Euler's method calculates approximate y-values for points on a solution curve; it does not give a formula for y in terms of x.

Example 2 Show that Euler's method for $dy/dx = y$ starting at $(0, 1)$ and using two steps with $\Delta x = 0.05$ gives $y \approx 1.1025$ when $x = 0.1$.

Solution At $(0, 1)$, the slope is 1 and $\Delta y = (1)(0.05) = 0.05$, so new $y = 1 + 0.05 = 1.05$. At $(0.05, 1.05)$, the slope is 1.05 and $\Delta y = (1.05)(0.05) = 0.0525$, so new $y = 1.05 + 0.0525 = 1.1025$ at $x = 0.1$.

In general, dy/dx may be a function of both x and y. Euler's method still works, as the next example shows.

Example 3   Approximate four points on the solution curve to $dy/dx = -x/y$ starting at $(0, 1)$; use $\Delta x = 0.1$. Are the approximate values overestimates or underestimates?

Solution   The results from Euler's method are in Table 11.3, along with the y-values (to two decimals) calculated from the equation of the circle $x^2 + y^2 = 1$, which is the solution curve through $(0, 1)$. Since the curve is concave down, the approximate y-values are above the exact ones. (See Figure 11.36.)

Table 11.3   *Euler's method for $dy/dx = -x/y$, starting at $(0, 1)$*

x	Approx. y-value	$\Delta y = (\text{Slope})\Delta x$	True y-value
0	1	$0 = (0)(0.1)$	1
0.1	1	$-0.01 = (-0.1/1)(0.1)$	0.99
0.2	0.99	$-0.02 = (-0.2/0.99)(0.1)$	0.98
0.3	0.97		0.95

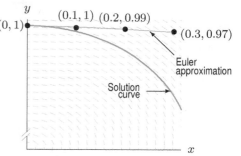

Figure 11.36: Euler's approximate solution to $dy/dx = -x/y$

The Accuracy of Euler's Method

To improve the accuracy of Euler's method, we choose a smaller step size, Δx. Let's go back to the differential equation $dy/dx = y$ and compare the exact and approximate values for different Δx's. The exact solution going through the point $(0, 1)$ is $y = e^x$, so the exact values are calculated using this function. (See Figure 11.37.) Where $x = 0.1$,

$$\text{Exact } y\text{-value } = e^{0.1} \approx 1.1051709.$$

In Example 1 we had $\Delta x = 0.1$, and where $x = 0.1$,

$$\text{Approximate } y\text{-value} = 1.1, \quad \text{so the error} \approx 0.005.$$

In Example 2 we decreased Δx to 0.05. After two steps, $x = 0.1$, and we had

$$\text{Approximate } y\text{-value} = 1.1025, \quad \text{so error} \approx 0.00267.$$

Thus, it appears that halving the step size has approximately halved the error.

Figure 11.37: Euler's approximate solution to $dy/dx = y$

> The *error* in using Euler's method over a fixed interval is Exact value − Approximate value. If the number of steps used is n, the error is approximately proportional to $1/n$.

Just as there are more accurate numerical integration methods than left and right Riemann sums, there are more accurate methods than Euler's for approximating solution curves. However, Euler's method is all we need.

Exercises and Problems for Section 11.3

Exercises

1. Using Euler's method, complete the following table for $y' = (x-2)(y-3)$.

x	y	y'
0.0	4.0	
0.1		
0.2		

2. Using Euler's method, complete the following table for $y' = 4xy$.

x	y	y'
1.00	−3.0	
1.01		
1.02		

3. A population, P, in millions, is 1500 at time $t = 0$ and its growth is governed by

$$\frac{dP}{dt} = 0.00008P(1900 - P).$$

Use Euler's method with $\Delta t = 1$ to estimate P at time $t = 1, 2, 3$.

4. (a) Use Euler's method to approximate the value of y at $x = 1$ on the solution curve to the differential equation $dy/dx = 3$ that passes through $(0, 2)$. Use $\Delta x = 0.2$.

(b) What is the solution to the differential equation $dy/dx = 3$ with initial condition $y = 2$ when $x = 0$?

(c) What is the error for the Euler's method approximation at $x = 1$?

(d) Explain why Euler's method is exact in this case.

5. (a) Use five steps of Euler's method to determine an approximate solution for the differential equation $dy/dx = y - x$ with initial condition $y(0) = 10$, using step size $\Delta x = 0.2$. What is the estimated value of y at $x = 1$?

(b) Does the solution to the differential equation appear to be concave up or concave down?

(c) Are the approximate values overestimates or underestimates?

6. (a) Use ten steps of Euler's method to determine an approximate solution for the differential equation $y' = x^3$, $y(0) = 0$, using a step size $\Delta x = 0.1$.

(b) What is the exact solution? Compare it to the computed approximation.

(c) Use a sketch of the slope field for this equation to explain the results of part (b).

7. Consider the differential equation $y' = x + y$ whose slope field is in Figure 11.20 on page 595. Use Euler's method with $\Delta x = 0.1$ to estimate y when $x = 0.4$ for the solution curves satisfying

(a) $y(0) = 1$ **(b)** $y(-1) = 0$.

8. (a) Using Figure 11.38, sketch the solution curve that passes through $(0, 0)$ for the differential equation

$$\frac{dy}{dx} = x^3 - y^3.$$

(b) Compute the points on the solution curve generated by Euler's method with 5 steps of $\Delta x = 0.2$.

(c) Is your answer to part (b) an overestimate or an underestimate?

Figure 11.38: Slope field for $dy/dx = x^3 - y^3$

9. Consider the solution of the differential equation $y' = y$ passing through $y(0) = 1$.

(a) Sketch the slope field for this differential equation, and sketch the solution passing through the point $(0, 1)$.

(b) Use Euler's method with step size $\Delta x = 0.1$ to estimate the solution at $x = 0.1, 0.2, \ldots, 1$.

(c) Plot the estimated solution on the slope field; compare the solution and the slope field.

(d) Check that $y = e^x$ is the solution of $y' = y$ with $y(0) = 1$.

Problems

10. Consider the differential equation $y' = (\sin x)(\sin y)$.

   (a) Calculate approximate y-values using Euler's method with three steps and $\Delta x = 0.1$, starting at each of the following points:

     (i) $(0, 2)$ (ii) $(0, \pi)$

   (b) Use the slope field in Figure 11.25 on page 597 to explain your solution to part (a)(ii).

11. **(a)** Use Euler's method with five subintervals to approximate the solution curve to the differential equation $dy/dx = x^2 - y^2$ passing through the point $(0, 1)$ and ending at $x = 1$. (Keep the approximate function values to three decimal places.)

   (b) Repeat this computation using ten subintervals, again ending with $x = 1$.

12. Why are the approximate results you obtained in Problem 11 smaller than the true values? (Note: The slope field for this differential equation is one of those in Figure 11.18 on page 595.)

13. How do the errors of the five-step calculation and the ten-step calculation in Problem 11 compare? Estimate the true value of y on the solution through the point $(0, 1)$ when $x = 1$.

14. **(a)** Use ten steps of Euler's method to approximate y-values for $dy/dt = 1/t$, starting at $(1, 0)$ and using $\Delta t = 0.1$.

   (b) Using integration, solve the differential equation to find the exact value of y at the end of these ten steps.

   (c) Is your approximate value of y at the end of ten steps bigger or smaller than the exact value? Use a slope field to explain your answer.

15. Consider the differential equation

$$\frac{dy}{dx} = 2x, \quad \text{with initial condition } y(0) = 1.$$

   (a) Use Euler's method with two steps to estimate y when $x = 1$. Now use four steps.

   (b) What is the formula for the exact value of y?

   (c) Does the error in Euler's approximation behave as predicted in the box on page 601?

16. Consider the differential equation

$$\frac{dy}{dx} = \sin(xy), \quad \text{with initial condition } y(1) = 1.$$

Estimate $y(2)$, using Euler's method with step sizes $\Delta x = 0.2, 0.1, 0.05$. Plot the computed approximations for $y(2)$ against Δx. What do you conclude? Use your observations to estimate the exact value of $y(2)$.

17. Use Euler's method to estimate $B(1)$, given that

$$\frac{dB}{dt} = 0.05B$$

and $B = 1000$ when $t = 0$. Take:

   (a) $\Delta t = 1$ and 1 step   **(b)** $\Delta t = 0.5$ and 2 steps

   (c) $\Delta t = 0.25$ and 4 steps

   (d) Suppose B is the balance in a bank account earning interest. Explain why the result of your calculation in part (a) is equivalent to compounding the interest once a year instead of continuously.

   (e) Interpret the result of your calculations in parts (b) and (c) in terms of compound interest.

18. Consider the differential equation $dy/dx = f(x)$ with initial value $y(0) = 0$. Explain why using Euler's method to approximate the solution curve gives the same results as using left Riemann sums to approximate $\int_0^x f(t)\, dt$.

Strengthen Your Understanding

In Problems 19–20, explain what is wrong with the statement.

19. Euler's method never produces an exact solution to a differential equation at a point. There is always some error.

20. If we use Euler's method on the interval $[0, 1]$ to estimate the value of $x(1)$ where $dx/dt = x$, then we get an underestimate.

In Problems 21–22, give an example of:

21. A differential equation for which the approximate values found using Euler's method lie on a straight line.

22. A differential equation and initial condition such that for

any step size, the approximate y-value found after one step of Euler's method is an underestimate of the solution value.

Are the statements in Problems 23–24 true or false? Give an explanation for your answer.

23. Euler's method gives the arc length of a solution curve.

24. Using Euler's method with five steps and $\Delta x = 0.2$ to approximate $y(1)$ when $dy/dx = f(x)$ and $y(0) = 0$ gives the same answer as the left Riemann sum approximation to $\int_0^1 f(x)\, dx$.

11.4 SEPARATION OF VARIABLES

We have seen how to sketch solution curves of a differential equation using a slope field and how to calculate approximate numerical solutions. Now we see how to solve certain differential equations analytically, finding an equation for the solution curve.

First, we look at a familiar example, the differential equation

$$\frac{dy}{dx} = -\frac{x}{y},$$

whose solution curves are the circles

$$x^2 + y^2 = C.$$

We can check that these circles are solutions by differentiation; the question now is how they were obtained. The method of *separation of variables* works by putting all the x-values on one side of the equation and all the y-values on the other, giving

$$y \, dy = -x \, dx.$$

We then integrate each side separately:

$$\int y \, dy = -\int x \, dx,$$

$$\frac{y^2}{2} = -\frac{x^2}{2} + k.$$

This gives the circles we were expecting:

$$x^2 + y^2 = C \qquad \text{where } C = 2k.$$

You might worry about whether it is legitimate to separate the dx and the dy. The reason it can be done is explained at the end of this section.

Example 1   Using separation of variables, solve the differential equation:

$$\frac{dy}{dx} = ky.$$

Solution   Separating variables,

$$\frac{1}{y} dy = k \, dx,$$

and integrating,

$$\int \frac{1}{y} \, dy = \int k \, dx,$$

gives

$$\ln|y| = kx + C \quad \text{for some constant } C.$$

Solving for $|y|$ leads to

$$|y| = e^{kx+C} = e^{kx}e^C = Ae^{kx}$$

where $A = e^C$, so A is positive. Thus

$$y = (\pm A)e^{kx} = Be^{kx}$$

where $B = \pm A$, so B is any nonzero constant. Even though there's no C leading to $B = 0$, we can have $B = 0$ because $y = 0$ is a solution to the differential equation. We lost this solution when we divided through by y at the first step. Thus, the general solution is $y = Be^{kx}$ for any B.

The differential equation $dy/dx = ky$ always leads to exponential growth (if $k > 0$) or exponential decay (if $k < 0$). Graphs of solution curves for some fixed $k > 0$ are in Figure 11.39. For $k < 0$, the graphs are reflected in the y-axis.

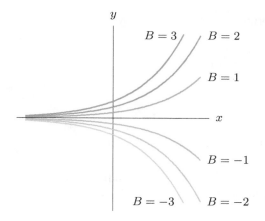

Figure 11.39: Graphs of $y = Be^{kx}$, which are solutions to $dy/dx = ky$, for some fixed $k > 0$

Example 2   For $k > 0$, find and graph solutions of

$$\frac{dH}{dt} = -k(H - 20).$$

Solution   The slope field in Figure 11.40 shows the qualitative behavior of the solutions. To find the equation of the solution curves, we separate variables and integrate:

$$\int \frac{1}{H - 20}\, dH = -\int k\, dt.$$

This gives

$$\ln|H - 20| = -kt + C.$$

Solving for H leads to:

$$|H - 20| = e^{-kt+C} = e^{-kt}e^{C} = Ae^{-kt}$$

or

$$H - 20 = (\pm A)e^{-kt} = Be^{-kt}$$
$$H = 20 + Be^{-kt}.$$

Again, $B = 0$ also gives a solution. Graphs for $k = 1$ and $B = -10, 0, 10$, with $t \geq 0$, are in Figure 11.40.

Figure 11.40: Slope field and some solution curves for $dH/dt = -k(H - 20)$, with $k = 1$

This differential equation can be used to represent the temperature, $H(t)$, in °C at time t of a cup of water standing in a room at 20°C. As Figure 11.40 shows, if the initial temperature is 10°C, the water warms up; if the initial temperature is 30°C, the water cools down. If the initial temperature is 20°C, the water remains 20°C.

Example 3   Find and sketch the solution to

$$\frac{dP}{dt} = 2P - 2Pt \qquad \text{satisfying } P = 5 \text{ when } t = 0.$$

Solution Factoring the right-hand side gives

$$\frac{dP}{dt} = P(2 - 2t).$$

Separating variables, we get

$$\int \frac{dP}{P} = \int (2 - 2t)\,dt,$$

so

$$\ln|P| = 2t - t^2 + C.$$

Solving for P leads to

$$|P| = e^{2t - t^2 + C} = e^C e^{2t - t^2} = Ae^{2t - t^2}$$

with $A = e^C$, so $A > 0$. In addition, $A = 0$ gives a solution. Thus the general solution to the differential equation is

$$P = Be^{2t - t^2} \quad \text{for any } B.$$

To find the value of B, substitute $P = 5$ and $t = 0$ into the general solution, giving

$$5 = Be^{2 \cdot 0 - 0^2} = B,$$

so

$$P = 5e^{2t - t^2}.$$

The graph of this function is in Figure 11.41. Since the solution can be rewritten as

$$P = 5e^{1 - 1 + 2t - t^2} = 5e^1 e^{-1 + 2t - t^2} = (5e)e^{-(t-1)^2},$$

the graph has the same shape as the graph of $y = e^{-t^2}$, the bell-shaped curve of statistics. Here the maximum, normally at $t = 0$, is shifted one unit to the right to $t = 1$.

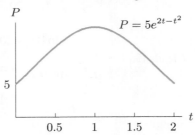

Figure 11.41: Bell-shaped solution curve

Justification for Separation of Variables

Suppose a differential equation can be written in the form

$$\frac{dy}{dx} = g(x)f(y).$$

Provided $f(y) \neq 0$, we write $f(y) = 1/h(y)$, so the right-hand side can be thought of as a fraction,

$$\frac{dy}{dx} = \frac{g(x)}{h(y)}.$$

If we multiply through by $h(y)$, we get

$$h(y)\frac{dy}{dx} = g(x).$$

Thinking of y as a function of x, so $y = y(x)$, and $dy/dx = y'(x)$, we can rewrite the equation as

$$h(y(x)) \cdot y'(x) = g(x).$$

Now integrate both sides with respect to x:

$$\int h(y(x)) \cdot y'(x)\,dx = \int g(x)\,dx.$$

The form of the integral on the left suggests that we use the substitution $y = y(x)$. Since $dy = y'(x)\,dx$, we get

$$\int h(y)\,dy = \int g(x)\,dx.$$

If we can find antiderivatives of h and g, then this gives the equation of the solution curve. Note that transforming the original differential equation,

$$\frac{dy}{dx} = \frac{g(x)}{h(y)},$$

into

$$\int h(y)\,dy = \int g(x)\,dx$$

looks as though we have treated dy/dx as a fraction, cross-multiplied, and then integrated. Although that's not exactly what we have done, you may find this a helpful way of remembering the method. In fact, the dy/dx notation was introduced by Leibniz to allow shortcuts like this (more specifically, to make the chain rule look like cancellation).

Exercises and Problems for Section 11.4

Exercises

1. Determine which of the following differential equations are separable. Do not solve the equations.

   (a) $y' = y$
   (b) $y' = x + y$
   (c) $y' = xy$
   (d) $y' = \sin(x + y)$
   (e) $y' - xy = 0$
   (f) $y' = y/x$
   (g) $y' = \ln(xy)$
   (h) $y' = (\sin x)(\cos y)$
   (i) $y' = (\sin x)(\cos xy)$
   (j) $y' = x/y$
   (k) $y' = 2x$
   (l) $y' = (x+y)/(x+2y)$

In Exercises 2–28, use separation of variables to find the solutions to the differential equations subject to the given initial conditions.

2. $\dfrac{dP}{dt} = -2P, \quad P(0) = 1$

3. $\dfrac{dP}{dt} = 0.02P, \quad P(0) = 20$

4. $\dfrac{dL}{dp} = \dfrac{L}{2}, \quad L(0) = 100$

5. $\dfrac{dQ}{dt} = \dfrac{Q}{5}, \quad Q = 50$ when $t = 0$

6. $P\dfrac{dP}{dt} = 1, \quad P(0) = 1$

7. $\dfrac{dm}{dt} = 3m, \quad m = 5$ when $t = 1$

8. $\dfrac{dI}{dx} = 0.2I, \quad I = 6$ where $x = -1$

9. $\dfrac{1}{z}\dfrac{dz}{dt} = 5, \quad z(1) = 5$

10. $\dfrac{dm}{ds} = m, \quad m(1) = 2$

11. $2\dfrac{du}{dt} = u^2, \quad u(0) = 1$

12. $\dfrac{dz}{dy} = zy, \quad z = 1$ when $y = 0$

13. $\dfrac{dy}{dx} + \dfrac{y}{3} = 0, \quad y(0) = 10$

14. $\dfrac{dy}{dt} = 0.5(y - 200), \quad y = 50$ when $t = 0$

15. $\dfrac{dP}{dt} = P + 4, \quad P = 100$ when $t = 0$

16. $\dfrac{dy}{dx} = 2y - 4, \quad$ through $(2, 5)$

17. $\dfrac{dQ}{dt} = 0.3Q - 120, \quad Q = 50$ when $t = 0$

18. $\dfrac{dm}{dt} = 0.1m + 200, \quad m(0) = 1000$

19. $\dfrac{dR}{dy} + R = 1, \quad R(1) = 0.1$

20. $\dfrac{dB}{dt} + 2B = 50, \quad B(1) = 100$

21. $\dfrac{dy}{dt} = \dfrac{y}{3+t}, \quad y(0) = 1$

22. $\dfrac{dz}{dt} = te^z, \quad$ through the origin

23. $\dfrac{dy}{dx} = \dfrac{5y}{x}, \quad y = 3$ where $x = 1$

24. $\dfrac{dy}{dt} = y^2(1 + t), \quad y = 2$ when $t = 1$

25. $\dfrac{dz}{dt} = z + zt^2, \quad z = 5$ when $t = 0$

26. $\dfrac{dw}{d\theta} = \theta w^2 \sin \theta^2, \quad w(0) = 1$

27. $\dfrac{dw}{d\psi} = -w^2 \tan \psi, \quad w(0) = 2$

28. $x(x + 1)\dfrac{du}{dx} = u^2, \quad u(1) = 1$

Problems

29. (a) Solve the differential equation

$$\frac{dy}{dx} = \frac{4x}{y^2}.$$

Write the solution y as an explicit function of x.

(b) Find the particular solution for each initial condition below and graph the three solutions on the same coordinate plane.

$$y(0) = 1, \qquad y(0) = 2, \qquad y(0) = 3.$$

30. (a) Solve the differential equation

$$\frac{dP}{dt} = 0.2P - 10.$$

Write the solution P as an explicit function of t.

(b) Find the particular solution for each initial condition below and graph the three solutions on the same coordinate plane.

$$P(0) = 40, \qquad P(0) = 50, \qquad P(0) = 60.$$

31. (a) Find the general solution to the differential equation modeling how a person learns:

$$\frac{dy}{dt} = 100 - y.$$

(b) Plot the slope field of this differential equation and sketch solutions with $y(0) = 25$ and $y(0) = 110$.

(c) For each of the initial conditions in part (b), find the particular solution and add to your sketch.

(d) Which of these two particular solutions could represent how a person learns?

32. A circular oil spill grows at a rate given by the differential equation $dr/dt = k/r$, where r represents the radius of the spill in feet, and time is measured in hours. If the radius of the spill is 400 feet 16 hours after the spill begins, what is the value of k? Include units in your answer.

33. Figure 11.42 shows the slope field for $dy/dx = y^2$.

(a) Sketch the solutions that pass through the points

(i) $(0, 1)$ (ii) $(0, -1)$ (iii) $(0, 0)$

(b) In words, describe the end behavior of the solution curves in part (a).

(c) Find a formula for the general solution.

(d) Show that all solution curves except for $y = 0$ have both a horizontal and a vertical asymptote.

Figure 11.42

Solve the differential equations in Problems 34–43. Assume a, b, and k are nonzero constants.

34. $\dfrac{dR}{dt} = kR$

35. $\dfrac{dQ}{dt} - \dfrac{Q}{k} = 0$

36. $\dfrac{dP}{dt} = P - a$

37. $\dfrac{dQ}{dt} = b - Q$

38. $\dfrac{dP}{dt} = k(P - a)$

39. $\dfrac{dR}{dt} = aR + b$

40. $\dfrac{dP}{dt} - aP = b$

41. $\dfrac{dy}{dt} = ky^2(1 + t^2)$

42. $\dfrac{dR}{dx} = a(R^2 + 1)$

43. $\dfrac{dL}{dx} = k(x + a)(L - b)$

Solve the differential equations in Problems 44–47. Assume $x, y, t > 0$.

44. $\dfrac{dy}{dt} = y(2 - y), \quad y(0) = 1$

45. $\dfrac{dx}{dt} = \dfrac{x \ln x}{t}$

46. $t\dfrac{dx}{dt} = (1 + 2 \ln t) \tan x$

47. $\dfrac{dy}{dt} = -y \ln\left(\dfrac{y}{2}\right), \quad y(0) = 1$

48. Figure 11.43 shows the slope field for the equation

$$\frac{dy}{dx} = \begin{cases} y^2 & \text{if } |y| \geq 1 \\ 1 & \text{if } -1 \leq y \leq 1. \end{cases}$$

(a) Sketch the solutions that pass through $(0, 0)$.

(b) What can you say about the end behavior of the solution curve in part (a)?

(c) For each of the following regions, find a formula for the general solution

(i) $-1 \leq y \leq 1$ (ii) $y \leq -1$

(iii) $y \geq 1$

(d) Show that each solution curve has two vertical asymptotes.

(e) How far apart are the two asymptotes of a solution curve?

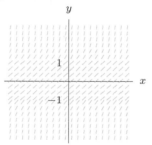

Figure 11.43

49. (a) Sketch the slope field for $y' = x/y$.
  (b) Sketch several solution curves.
  (c) Solve the differential equation analytically.

50. (a) Sketch the slope field for $y' = -y/x$.
  (b) Sketch several solution curves.
  (c) Solve the differential equation analytically.

51. Compare the slope field for $y' = x/y$, Problem 49, with that for $y' = -y/x$, Problem 50. Show that the solution curves of Problem 49 intersect the solution curves of Problem 50 at right angles.

Strengthen Your Understanding

In Problems 52–54, explain what is wrong with the statement.

52. Separating variables in $dy/dx = x + y$ gives $-y\,dy = x\,dx$.

53. The solution to $dP/dt = 0.2t$ is $P = Be^{0.2t}$.

54. Separating variables in $dy/dx = e^{x+y}$ gives $-e^y\,dy = e^x\,dx$.

In Problems 55–58, give an example of:

55. A differential equation that is not separable.

56. An expression for $f(x)$ such that the differential equation $dy/dx = f(x) + xy - \cos x$ is separable.

57. A differential equation all of whose solutions form the family of functions $f(x) = x^2 + C$.

58. A differential equation all of whose solutions form the family of hyperbolas $x^2 - y^2 = C$.

Are the statements in Problems 59–62 true or false? Give an explanation for your answer.

59. For all constants k, the equation $y' + ky = 0$ has exponential functions as solutions.

60. The differential equation $dy/dx = x + y$ can be solved by separation of variables.

61. The differential equation $dy/dx - xy = x$ can be solved by separation of variables.

62. The only solution to the differential equation $dy/dx = 3y^{2/3}$ passing through the point $(0,0)$ is $y = x^3$.

11.5 GROWTH AND DECAY

In this section we look at exponential growth and decay equations. Consider the population of a region. If there is no immigration or emigration, the rate at which the population is changing is often proportional to the population. In other words, the larger the population, the faster it is growing because there are more people to have babies. If the population at time t is P and its continuous growth rate is 2% per unit time, then we know

$$\text{Rate of growth of population} = 2\%(\text{Current population}),$$

and we can write this as

$$\frac{dP}{dt} = 0.02P.$$

The 2% growth rate is called the *relative growth rate* to distinguish it from the *absolute growth rate*, dP/dt. Notice they measure different quantities. Since

$$\text{Relative growth rate} = 2\% = \frac{1}{P}\frac{dP}{dt},$$

the relative growth rate is a percent change per unit time, while

$$\text{Absolute growth rate} = \text{Rate of change of population} = \frac{dP}{dt}$$

is a change in population per unit time.

We showed in Section 11.4 that since the equation $dP/dt = 0.02P$ is of the form $dP/dt = kP$ for $k = 0.02$, it has solution

$$P = P_0 e^{0.02t}.$$

Other processes are described by differential equations similar to that for population growth, but with negative values for k. In summary, we have the following result from the preceding section:

Every solution to the equation

$$\frac{dP}{dt} = kP$$

can be written in the form

$$P = P_0 e^{kt},$$

where P_0 is the value of P at $t = 0$, and $k > 0$ represents growth, whereas $k < 0$ represents decay.

Recall that the *doubling time* of an exponentially growing quantity is the time required for it to double. The *half-life* of an exponentially decaying quantity is the time required for half of it to decay.

Continuously Compounded Interest

At a bank, continuous compounding means that interest is accrued at a rate that is a fixed percentage of the balance at that moment. Thus, the larger the balance, the faster interest is earned and the faster the balance grows.

Example 1   A bank account earns interest continuously at a rate of 5% of the current balance per year. Assume that the initial deposit is $1000 and that no other deposits or withdrawals are made.

(a) Write the differential equation satisfied by the balance in the account.
(b) Solve the differential equation and graph the solution.

Solution   (a) We are looking for B, the balance in the account in dollars, as a function of t, time in years. Interest is being added to the account continuously at a rate of 5% of the balance at that moment. Since no deposits or withdrawals are made, at any instant,

$$\text{Rate balance increasing} = \text{Rate interest earned} = 5\%(\text{Current balance}),$$

which we write as

$$\frac{dB}{dt} = 0.05B.$$

This is the differential equation that describes the process. It does not involve the initial condition $1000 because the initial deposit does not affect the process by which interest is earned.

(b) Solving the differential equation by separation of variables gives

$$B = B_0 e^{0.05t},$$

where B_0 is the value of B at $t = 0$, so $B_0 = 1000$. Thus

$$B = 1000 e^{0.05t}$$

and this function is graphed in Figure 11.44.

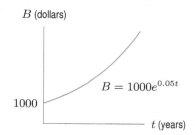

Figure 11.44: Bank balance against time

The Difference Between Continuous and Annual Percentage Growth Rates

If $P = P_0(1 + r)^t$ with t in years, we say that r is the *annual* growth rate, while if $P = P_0 e^{kt}$, we say that k is the *continuous* growth rate.

The constant k in the differential equation $dP/dt = kP$ is not the annual growth rate, but the continuous growth rate. In Example 1, with a continuous interest rate of 5%, we obtain a balance of $B = B_0 e^{0.05t}$, where time, t, is in years. At the end of one year the balance is $B_0 e^{0.05}$. In that one year, our balance has changed from B_0 to $B_0 e^{0.05}$, that is, by a factor of $e^{0.05} = 1.0513$. Thus the annual growth rate is 5.13%. This is what the bank means when it says "5% compounded continuously for an effective annual yield of 5.13%." Since $P_0 e^{0.05t} = P_0(1.0513)^t$, we have two different ways to represent the same function.

Since most growth is measured over discrete time intervals, a continuous growth rate is an idealized concept. A demographer who says a population is growing at the rate of 2% per year usually means that after t years the population is $P = P_0(1.02)^t$. To find the continuous growth rate, k, we express the population as $P = P_0 e^{kt}$. At the end of one year $P = P_0 e^k$, so $e^k = 1.02$. Thus $k = \ln 1.02 \approx 0.0198$. The continuous growth rate, $k = 1.98\%$, is close to the annual growth rate of 2%, but it is not the same. Again, we have two different representations of the same function since $P_0(1.02)^t = P_0 e^{0.0198t}$.

Pollution in the Great Lakes

In the 1960s pollution in the Great Lakes became an issue of public concern. We set up a model for how long it would take for the lakes to flush themselves clean, assuming no further pollutants are being dumped in the lakes.

Suppose Q is the total quantity of pollutant in a lake of volume V at time t. Suppose that clean water is flowing into the lake at a constant rate r and that water flows out at the same rate. Assume that the pollutant is evenly spread throughout the lake and that the clean water coming into the lake immediately mixes with the rest of the water.

We investigate how Q varies with time. Since pollutants are being taken out of the lake but not added, Q decreases, and the water leaving the lake becomes less polluted, so the rate at which the pollutants leave decreases. This tells us that Q is decreasing and concave up. In addition, the pollutants are never completely removed from the lake though the quantity remaining becomes arbitrarily small: in other words, Q is asymptotic to the t-axis. (See Figure 11.45.)

Setting Up a Differential Equation for the Pollution

To model exactly how Q changes with time, we write an equation for the rate at which Q changes. We know that

$$\begin{pmatrix} \text{Rate } Q \\ \text{changes} \end{pmatrix} = - \begin{pmatrix} \text{Rate pollutants} \\ \text{leave in outflow} \end{pmatrix}$$

Q (quantity of pollutant)

t (time)

Figure 11.45: Pollutant in lake versus time

where the negative sign represents the fact that Q is decreasing. At time t, the concentration of pollutants is Q/V, and water containing this concentration is leaving at rate r. Thus

$$\begin{array}{c} \text{Rate pollutants} \\ \text{leave in outflow} \end{array} = \begin{array}{c} \text{Rate of} \\ \text{outflow} \end{array} \times \text{Concentration} = r \cdot \frac{Q}{V}.$$

So the differential equation is

$$\frac{dQ}{dt} = -\frac{r}{V}Q,$$

and its solution is

$$Q = Q_0 e^{-rt/V}.$$

Table 11.4 contains values of r and V for four of the Great Lakes.[2] We use this data to calculate how long it would take for certain fractions of the pollution to be removed.

Table 11.4   *Volume and outflow in Great Lakes*[3]

	V (thousands of km^3)	r (km^3/year)
Superior	12.2	65.2
Michigan	4.9	158
Erie	0.46	175
Ontario	1.6	209

Example 2   According to this model, how long will it take for 90% of the pollution to be removed from Lake Erie? For 99% to be removed?

Solution   Substituting r and V for Lake Erie into the differential equation for Q gives

$$\frac{dQ}{dt} = -\frac{r}{V}Q = \frac{-175}{0.46 \times 10^3}Q = -0.38Q$$

where t is measured in years. Thus Q is given by

$$Q = Q_0 e^{-0.38t}.$$

When 90% of the pollution has been removed, 10% remains, so $Q = 0.1Q_0$. Substituting gives

$$0.1Q_0 = Q_0 e^{-0.38t}.$$

[2]Data from William E. Boyce and Richard C. DiPrima, *Elementary Differential Equations*, 9th Edition (New York: Wiley, 2009), pp. 63–64.

[3]www.epa.gov/greatlakes/

Canceling Q_0 and solving for t, we get

$$t = \frac{-\ln(0.1)}{0.38} \approx 6 \text{ years.}$$

When 99% of the pollution has been removed, $Q = 0.01Q_0$, so t satisfies

$$0.01Q_0 = Q_0 e^{-0.38t}.$$

Solving for t gives

$$t = \frac{-\ln(0.01)}{0.38} \approx 12 \text{ years.}$$

Newton's Law of Heating and Cooling

Newton proposed that the temperature of a hot object decreases at a rate proportional to the difference between its temperature and that of its surroundings. Similarly, a cold object heats up at a rate proportional to the temperature difference between the object and its surroundings.

For example, a hot cup of coffee standing on the kitchen table cools at a rate proportional to the temperature difference between the coffee and the surrounding air. As the coffee cools, the rate at which it cools decreases because the temperature difference between the coffee and the air decreases. In the long run, the rate of cooling tends to zero, and the temperature of the coffee approaches room temperature. See Figure 11.46.

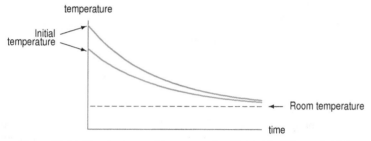

Figure 11.46: Temperature of two cups of coffee with different initial temperatures

---

Example 3   When a murder is committed, the body, originally at 37°C, cools according to Newton's Law of Cooling. Suppose that after two hours the temperature is 35°C and that the temperature of the surrounding air is a constant 20°C.

(a) Find the temperature, H, of the body as a function of t, the time in hours since the murder was committed.
(b) Sketch a graph of temperature against time.
(c) What happens to the temperature in the long run? Show this on the graph and algebraically.
(d) If the body is found at 4 pm at a temperature of 30°C, when was the murder committed?

Solution   (a) We first find a differential equation for the temperature of the body as a function of time. Newton's Law of Cooling says that for some constant α,

$$\text{Rate of change of temperature} = \alpha(\text{Temperature difference}).$$

If H is the temperature of the body, then

$$\text{Temperature difference} = H - 20,$$

so

$$\frac{dH}{dt} = \alpha(H - 20).$$

What about the sign of α? If the temperature difference is positive (i.e., $H > 20$), then H is falling, so the rate of change must be negative. Thus α should be negative, so we write:

$$\frac{dH}{dt} = -k(H - 20), \qquad \text{for some } k > 0.$$

Separating variables and solving, as in Example 2 on page 605, gives:

$$H - 20 = Be^{-kt}.$$

To find B, substitute the initial condition that $H = 37$ when $t = 0$:

$$37 - 20 = Be^{-k(0)} = B,$$

so $B = 17$. Thus,

$$H - 20 = 17e^{-kt}.$$

To find k, we use the fact that after 2 hours, the temperature is $35°C$, so

$$35 - 20 = 17e^{-k(2)}.$$

Dividing by 17 and taking natural logs, we get:

$$\ln\left(\frac{15}{17}\right) = \ln(e^{-2k})$$
$$-0.125 = -2k$$
$$k \approx 0.063.$$

Therefore, the temperature is given by

$$H - 20 = 17e^{-0.063t}$$

or

$$H = 20 + 17e^{-0.063t}.$$

(b) The graph of $H = 20 + 17e^{-0.063t}$ has a vertical intercept of $H = 37$ because the temperature of the body starts at $37°C$. The temperature decays exponentially with $H = 20$ as the horizontal asymptote. (See Figure 11.47.)

Figure 11.47: Temperature of dead body

(c) "In the long run" means as $t \to \infty$. The graph shows that as $t \to \infty$, $H \to 20$. Algebraically, since $e^{-0.063t} \to 0$ as $t \to \infty$, we have

$$H = 20 + \underbrace{17e^{-0.063t}}_{\text{goes to 0 as } t \to \infty} \longrightarrow 20 \quad \text{as } t \to \infty.$$

(d) We want to know when the temperature reaches $30°C$. Substitute $H = 30$ and solve for t:

$$30 = 20 + 17e^{-0.063t}$$
$$\frac{10}{17} = e^{-0.063t}.$$

Taking natural logs:

$$-0.531 = -0.063t,$$

which gives

$$t \approx 8.4 \text{ hours.}$$

Thus the murder must have been committed about 8.4 hours before 4 pm. Since 8.4 hours = 8 hours 24 minutes, the murder was committed at about 7:30 am.

Equilibrium Solutions

Figure 11.48 shows the temperature of several objects in a 20°C room. One is initially hotter than 20°C and cools down toward 20°C; another is initially cooler and warms up toward 20°C. All these curves are solutions to the differential equation

$$\frac{dH}{dt} = -k(H - 20)$$

for some fixed $k > 0$, and all the solutions have the form

$$H = 20 + Ae^{-kt}$$

for some A. Notice that $H \to 20$ as $t \to \infty$ because $e^{-kt} \to 0$ as $t \to \infty$. In other words, in the long run, the temperature of the object always tends toward 20°C, the temperature of the room. This means that what happens in the long run is independent of the initial condition.

In the special case when $A = 0$, we have the *equilibrium solution*

$$H = 20$$

for all t. This means that if the object starts at 20°C, it remains at 20°C for all time. Notice that such a solution can be found directly from the differential equation by solving $dH/dt = 0$:

$$\frac{dH}{dt} = -k(H - 20) = 0$$

giving

$$H = 20.$$

Regardless of the initial temperature, H always gets closer and closer to 20 as $t \to \infty$. As a result, $H = 20$ is called a *stable* equilibrium[4] for H.

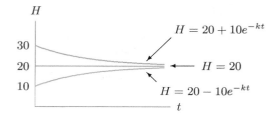

Figure 11.48: $H = 20$ is stable equilibrium ($k > 0$)

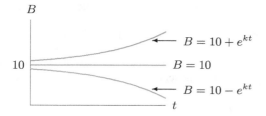

Figure 11.49: $B = 10$ is unstable equilibrium ($k > 0$)

A different situation is displayed in Figure 11.49, which shows solutions to the differential equation

$$\frac{dB}{dt} = k(B - 10)$$

for some fixed $k > 0$. Solving $dB/dt = 0$ gives the equilibrium $B = 10$, which is *unstable* because if B starts near 10, it moves away as $t \to \infty$.

In general, we have the following definitions.

---

[4]In more advanced work, this behavior is described as asymptotic stability.

- An **equilibrium solution** is constant for all values of the independent variable. The graph is a horizontal line.
- An equilibrium is **stable** if a small change in the initial conditions gives a solution that tends toward the equilibrium as the independent variable tends to positive infinity.
- An equilibrium is **unstable** if a small change in the initial conditions gives a solution curve that veers away from the equilibrium as the independent variable tends to positive infinity.

Solutions that do not veer away from an equilibrium solution are also called stable. If the differential equation is of the form $y' = f(y)$, equilibrium solutions can be found by setting y' to zero.

Example 4   Find the equilibrium solution to the differential equation $dP/dt = -50 + 4P$ and determine whether the equilibrium is stable or unstable.

Solution   In order to find the equilibrium solution, we solve $dP/dt = -50 + 4P = 0$. Thus, we have one equilibrium solution at $P = 50/4 = 12.5$. We can determine whether the equilibrium is stable or unstable by analyzing the behavior of solutions with initial conditions near $P = 12.5$. For example, the solution with initial value $P = 13$ has initial slope $dP/dt = -50 + 4(13) = 2 > 0$. Thus, solutions above the equilibrium $P = 12.5$ will increase and move away from the equilibrium.

A solution with an initial value $P = 12$ has initial slope $dP/dt = -50 + 4(12) = -2 < 0$. Thus, solutions that have an initial value less than $P = 12.5$ will decrease and veer away from the equilibrium. Since a small change in the initial condition gives solutions that move away from the equilibrium, $P = 12.5$ is an unstable equilibrium. Notice it is possible to find equilibrium and study their stability without finding a formula for the general solution to the differential equation.

Exercises and Problems for Section 11.5

Exercises

1. Match the graphs in Figure 11.50 with the following descriptions.

   (a) The temperature of a glass of ice water left on the kitchen table.
   (b) The amount of money in an interest-bearing bank account into which $50 is deposited.
   (c) The speed of a constantly decelerating car.
   (d) The temperature of a piece of steel heated in a furnace and left outside to cool.

2. Each curve in Figure 11.51 represents the balance in a bank account into which a single deposit was made at time zero. Assuming continuously compounded interest, find:

   (a) The curve representing the largest initial deposit.
   (b) The curve representing the largest interest rate.
   (c) Two curves representing the same initial deposit.
   (d) Two curves representing the same interest rate.

Figure 11.51

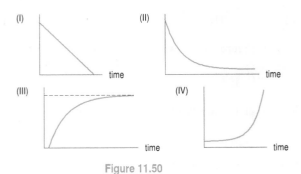

Figure 11.50

3. The slope field for $y' = 0.5(1 + y)(2 - y)$ is given in Figure 11.52.

(a) List equilibrium solutions and state whether each is stable or unstable.

(b) Draw solution curves on the slope field through each of the three marked points.

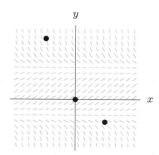

Figure 11.52

4. The slope field for a differential equation is given in Figure 11.53. Estimate all equilibrium solutions for this differential equation, and indicate whether each is stable or unstable.

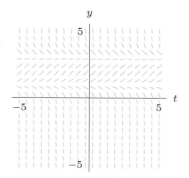

Figure 11.53

For Exercises 5–6, sketch solution curves with a variety of initial values for the differential equations. You do not need to find an equation for the solution.

5. $\dfrac{dy}{dt} = \alpha - y$,

where α is a positive constant.

6. $\dfrac{dw}{dt} = (w - 3)(w - 7)$

7. A yam is put in a 200°C oven and heats up according to the differential equation

$$\frac{dH}{dt} = -k(H - 200), \quad \text{for } k \text{ a positive constant.}$$

(a) If the yam is at 20°C when it is put in the oven, solve the differential equation.

(b) Find k using the fact that after 30 minutes the temperature of the yam is 120°C.

8. (a) Find the equilibrium solution to the differential equation

$$\frac{dy}{dt} = 0.5y - 250.$$

(b) Find the general solution to this differential equation.

(c) Sketch the graphs of several solutions to this differential equation, using different initial values for y.

(d) Is the equilibrium solution stable or unstable?

9. (a) Find all equilibrium solutions for the differential equation

$$\frac{dy}{dx} = 0.5y(y - 4)(2 + y).$$

(b) Draw a slope field and use it to determine whether each equilibrium solution is stable or unstable.

10. (a) A cup of coffee is made with boiling water and stands in a room where the temperature is 20° C. If $H(t)$ is the temperature of the coffee at time t, in minutes, explain what the differential equation

$$\frac{dH}{dt} = -k(H - 20)$$

says in everyday terms. What is the sign of k?

(b) Solve this differential equation. If the coffee cools to 90°C in 2 minutes, how long will it take to cool to 60°C degrees?

11. In Example 2 on page 612, we saw that it would take about 6 years for 90% of the pollution in Lake Erie to be removed and about 12 years for 99% to be removed. Explain why one time is double the other.

12. Using the model in the text and the data in Table 11.4 on page 612, find how long it would take for 90% of the pollution to be removed from Lake Michigan and from Lake Ontario, assuming no new pollutants are added. Explain how you can tell which lake will take longer to be purified just by looking at the data in the table.

13. Use the model in the text and the data in Table 11.4 on page 612 to determine which of the Great Lakes would require the longest time and which would require the shortest time for 80% of the pollution to be removed, assuming no new pollutants are being added. Find the ratio of these two times.

Problems

In Problems 14–17,

(a) Define the variables.

(b) Write a differential equation to describe the relationship.

(c) Solve the differential equation.

14. In 2010, the population of India was 1.15 billion people and increasing at a rate proportional to its population. If the population is measured in billions of people and time is measured in years, the constant of proportionality is 0.0135.

15. Nicotine leaves the body at a rate proportional to the amount present, with constant of proportionality 0.347 if the amount of nicotine is in mg and time is in hours. The amount of nicotine in the body immediately after smoking a cigarette is 0.4 mg.

16. In 2007, world solar photovoltaic (PV) market installations were 2826 megawatts and were growing exponentially at a continuous rate of 48% per year.[5]

17. In 2007, Grinnell Glacier in Glacier National Park covered 142 acres and was estimated to be shrinking exponentially at a continuous rate of 4.3% per year.[6]

18. Since 1980, textbook prices have increased at 6.7% per year while inflation has been 3.3% per year.[7] Assume both rates are continuous growth rates and let time, t, be in years since the start of 1980.

(a) Write a differential equation satisfied by $B(t)$, the price of a textbook at time t.

(b) Write a differential equation satisfied by $P(t)$, the price at time t of an item growing at the inflation rate.

(c) Solve both differential equations.

(d) What is the doubling time of the price of a textbook?

(e) What is the doubling time of the price of an item growing according to the inflation rate?

(f) How is the ratio of the doubling times related to the ratio of the growth rates? Justify your answer.

19. Write a differential equation whose solution is the temperature as a function of time of a bottle of orange juice taken out of a 40°F refrigerator and left in a 65°F room. Solve the equation and graph the solution.

20. A roast is taken from the refrigerator, where the temperature is 40°F, and put in a 350°F oven. One hour later, the meat thermometer shows a temperature of 90°F. If the roast is done when its temperature reaches 140°F, what is the total time the roast should be in the oven?

21. Warfarin is a drug used as an anticoagulant. After administration of the drug is stopped, the quantity remaining in a patient's body decreases at a rate proportional to the

quantity remaining. The half-life of warfarin in the body is 37 hours.

(a) Sketch the quantity, Q, of warfarin in a patient's body as a function of the time, t, since stopping administration of the drug. Mark the 37 hours on your graph.

(b) Write a differential equation satisfied by Q.

(c) How many days does it take for the drug level in the body to be reduced to 25% of the original level?

22. The rate at which a drug leaves the bloodstream and passes into the urine is proportional to the quantity of the drug in the blood at that time. If an initial dose of Q_0 is injected directly into the blood, 20% is left in the blood after 3 hours.

(a) Write and solve a differential equation for the quantity, Q, of the drug in the blood after t hours.

(b) How much of this drug is in a patient's body after 6 hours if the patient is given 100 mg initially?

23. Oil is pumped continuously from a well at a rate proportional to the amount of oil left in the well. Initially there were 1 million barrels of oil in the well; six years later 500,000 barrels remain.

(a) At what rate was the amount of oil in the well decreasing when there were 600,000 barrels remaining?

(b) When will there be 50,000 barrels remaining?

24. The radioactive isotope carbon-14 is present in small quantities in all life forms, and it is constantly replenished until the organism dies, after which it decays to stable carbon-12 at a rate proportional to the amount of carbon-14 present, with a half-life of 5730 years. Suppose $C(t)$ is the amount of carbon-14 present at time t.

(a) Find the value of the constant k in the differential equation $C' = -kC$.

(b) In 1988 three teams of scientists found that the Shroud of Turin, which was reputed to be the burial cloth of Jesus, contained 91% of the amount of carbon-14 contained in freshly made cloth of the same material.[8] How old is the Shroud of Turin, according to these data?

25. The amount of radioactive carbon-14 in a sample is measured using a Geiger counter, which records each disintegration of an atom. Living tissue disintegrates at a rate of about 13.5 atoms per minute per gram of carbon. In 1977 a charcoal fragment found at Stonehenge, England, recorded 8.2 disintegrations per minute per gram of carbon. Assuming that the half-life of carbon-14 is 5730

---

[5]www.solarbuzz.com/marketbuzz2008. Accessed February 2010.

[6]"Warming climate shrinking Glacier Park's glaciers", www.usatoday.com, October 15, 2007.

[7]Data from "Textbooks headed for ash heap of history", http://educationtechnews.com, Vol. 5, 2010.

[8]*The New York Times*, October 18, 1988.

years and that the charcoal was formed during the building of the site, estimate the date at which Stonehenge was built.

26. A detective finds a murder victim at 9 am. The temperature of the body is measured at $90.3°F$. One hour later, the temperature of the body is $89.0°F$. The temperature of the room has been maintained at a constant $68°F$.

    (a) Assuming the temperature, T, of the body obeys Newton's Law of Cooling, write a differential equation for T.

    (b) Solve the differential equation to estimate the time the murder occurred.

27. At 1:00 pm one winter afternoon, there is a power failure at your house in Wisconsin, and your heat does not work without electricity. When the power goes out, it is $68°F$ in your house. At 10:00 pm, it is $57°F$ in the house, and you notice that it is $10°F$ outside.

    (a) Assuming that the temperature, T, in your home obeys Newton's Law of Cooling, write the differential equation satisfied by T.

    (b) Solve the differential equation to estimate the temperature in the house when you get up at 7:00 am the next morning. Should you worry about your water pipes freezing?

    (c) What assumption did you make in part (a) about the temperature outside? Given this (probably incorrect) assumption, would you revise your estimate up or down? Why?

28. Before Galileo discovered that the speed of a falling body with no air resistance is proportional to the time since it was dropped, he mistakenly conjectured that the speed was proportional to the distance it had fallen.

    (a) Assume the mistaken conjecture to be true and write an equation relating the distance fallen, $D(t)$, at time t, and its derivative.

    (b) Using your answer to part (a) and the correct initial conditions, show that D would have to be equal to 0 for all t, and therefore the conjecture must be wrong.

29. **(a)** An object is placed in a $68°F$ room. Write a differential equation for H, the temperature of the object at time t.

    (b) Find the equilibrium solution to the differential equation. Determine from the differential equation whether the equilibrium is stable or unstable.

    (c) Give the general solution for the differential equation.

    (d) The temperature of the object is $40°F$ initially and $48°F$ one hour later. Find the temperature of the object after 3 hours.

30. Hydrocodone bitartrate is used as a cough suppressant. After the drug is fully absorbed, the quantity of drug in the body decreases at a rate proportional to the amount left in the body. The half-life of hydrocodone bitartrate in the body is 3.8 hours, and the usual oral dose is 10 mg.

    (a) Write a differential equation for the quantity, Q, of hydrocodone bitartrate in the body at time t, in hours since the drug was fully absorbed.

    (b) Find the equilibrium solution of the differential equation. Based on the context, do you expect the equilibrium to be stable or unstable?

    (c) Solve the differential equation given in part (a).

    (d) Use the half-life to find the constant of proportionality, k.

    (e) How much of the 10 mg dose is still in the body after 12 hours?

31. **(a)** Let B be the balance at time t of a bank account that earns interest at a rate of $r\%$, compounded continuously. What is the differential equation describing the rate at which the balance changes? What is the constant of proportionality, in terms of r?

    (b) Find the equilibrium solution to the differential equation. Determine whether the equilibrium is stable or unstable and explain what this means about the bank account.

    (c) What is the solution to this differential equation?

    (d) Sketch the graph of B as function of t for an account that starts with $1000 and earns interest at the following rates:

        (i) 4%   (ii) 10%   (iii) 15%

Strengthen Your Understanding

In Problems 32–34, explain what is wrong with the statement.

32. The line $y = 2$ is an equilibrium solution to the differential equation $dy/dx = y^3 - 4xy$.

33. The function $y = x^2$ is an equilibrium solution to the differential equation $dy/dx = y - x^2$.

34. At time $t = 0$, a roast is taken out of a $40°F$ refrigerator and put in a $350°F$ oven. If H represents the temperature of the roast at time t minutes after it is put in the oven, we have $dH/dt = k(H - 40)$.

In Problems 35–37, give an example of:

35. A differential equation for a quantity that is decaying exponentially at a continuous rate per unit time.

36. A differential equation with an equilibrium solution of $Q = 500$.

37. A graph of three possible solutions, with initial P-values of 20, 25, and 30, respectively, to a differential equation that has an unstable equilibrium solution at $P = 25$.

11.6 APPLICATIONS AND MODELING

Much of this book involves functions that represent real processes, such as how the temperature of a yam or the population of the US is changing with time. You may wonder where such functions come from. In some cases, we fit functions to experimental data by trial and error. In other cases, we take a more theoretical approach, leading to a differential equation whose solution is the function we want. In this section we give examples of the more theoretical approach.

How a Layer of Ice Forms

When ice forms on a lake, the water on the surface freezes first. As heat from the water travels up through the ice and is lost to the air, more ice is formed. The question we will consider is: How thick is the layer of ice as a function of time? Since the thickness of the ice increases with time, the thickness function is increasing. In addition, as the ice gets thicker, it insulates better. Therefore, we expect the layer of ice to form more slowly as time goes on. Hence, the thickness function is increasing at a decreasing rate, so its graph is concave down.

A Differential Equation for the Thickness of the Ice

To get more detailed information about the thickness function, we have to make some assumptions. Suppose y represents the thickness of the ice as a function of time, t. Since the thicker the ice, the longer it takes the heat to get through it, we will assume that the rate at which ice is formed is inversely proportional to the thickness. In other words, we assume that for some constant k,

$$\text{Rate thickness is increasing} = \frac{k}{\text{Thickness}},$$

so

$$\frac{dy}{dt} = \frac{k}{y} \quad \text{where} \quad k > 0.$$

This differential equation enables us to find a formula for y. Using separation of variables:

$$\int y \, dy = \int k \, dt$$

$$\frac{y^2}{2} = kt + C.$$

If we measure time so that $y = 0$ when $t = 0$, then $C = 0$. Since y must be non-negative, we have

$$y = \sqrt{2kt}.$$

Graphs of y against t are in Figure 11.54. Notice that the larger y is, the more slowly y increases. In addition, this model suggests that y increases indefinitely as time passes. (Of course, the value of y cannot increase beyond the depth of the lake.)

Figure 11.54: Thickness of ice as a function of time

The Net Worth of a Company

In the preceding section, we saw an example in which money in a bank account was earning interest (Example 1, page 610). Consider a company whose revenues are proportional to its net worth (like interest on a bank account) but that must also make payroll payments. The question is: under what circumstances does the company make money, and under what circumstances does it go bankrupt?

Common sense says that if the payroll exceeds the rate at which revenue is earned, the company will eventually be in trouble, whereas if revenue exceeds payroll, the company should do well. We assume that revenue is earned continuously and that payments are made continuously. (For a large company, this is a good approximation.) We also assume that the only factors affecting net worth are revenue and payroll.

Example 1   A company's revenue is earned at a continuous annual rate of 5% of its net worth. At the same time, the company's payroll obligations amount to $200 million a year, paid out continuously.

(a) Write a differential equation that governs the net worth of the company, W million dollars.
(b) Solve the differential equation, assuming an initial net worth of W_0 million dollars.
(c) Sketch the solution for $W_0 = 3000$, 4000, and 5000.

Solution   First, let's see what we can learn without writing a differential equation. For example, we can ask if there is any initial net worth W_0 that will exactly keep the net worth constant. If there's such an equilibrium, the rate at which revenue is earned must exactly balance the payments made, so

$$\text{Rate revenue is earned} \quad = \quad \text{Rate payments are made.}$$

If net worth is a constant W_0, revenue is earned at a constant rate of $0.05W_0$ per year, so we have

$$0.05W_0 = 200 \quad \text{giving} \quad W_0 = 4000.$$

Therefore, if the net worth starts at $4000 million, the revenue and payments are equal, and the net worth remains constant. Therefore, $4000 million is an equilibrium solution.

Suppose, however, the initial net worth is above $4000 million. Then, the revenue earned is more than the payroll expenses, and the net worth of the company increases, thereby increasing the revenue still further. Thus the net worth increases more and more quickly. On the other hand, if the initial net worth is below $4000 million, the revenue is not enough to meet the payments, and the net worth of the company declines. This decreases the revenue, making the net worth decrease still more quickly. The net worth will eventually go to zero, and the company goes bankrupt. See Figure 11.55.

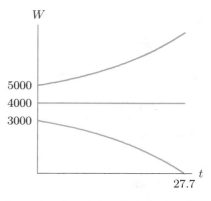

Figure 11.55: Net worth as a function of time: Solutions to $dW/dt = 0.05W - 200$

(a) Now we set up a differential equation for the net worth, using the fact that

$$\begin{pmatrix} \text{Rate net worth} \\ \text{is increasing} \end{pmatrix} = \begin{pmatrix} \text{Rate revenue} \\ \text{is earned} \end{pmatrix} - \begin{pmatrix} \text{Rate payroll payments} \\ \text{are made} \end{pmatrix}.$$

In millions of dollars per year, revenue is earned at a rate of $0.05W$, and payments are made at a rate of 200 per year, so for t in years,

$$\frac{dW}{dt} = 0.05W - 200.$$

The equilibrium solution, $W = 4000$, is obtained by setting $dW/dt = 0$.

(b) We solve this equation by separation of variables. It is helpful to factor out 0.05 before separating, so that the W moves over to the left-hand side without a coefficient:

$$\frac{dW}{dt} = 0.05(W - 4000).$$

Separating and integrating gives

$$\int \frac{dW}{W - 4000} = \int 0.05 \, dt,$$

so

$$\ln|W - 4000| = 0.05t + C,$$

or

$$|W - 4000| = e^{0.05t+C} = e^C e^{0.05t}.$$

This means

$$W - 4000 = Ae^{0.05t} \qquad \text{where } A = \pm e^C.$$

To find A, we use the initial condition that $W = W_0$ when $t = 0$:

$$W_0 - 4000 = Ae^0 = A.$$

Substituting this value for A into $W = 4000 + Ae^{0.05t}$ gives

$$W = 4000 + (W_0 - 4000)e^{0.05t}.$$

(c) If $W_0 = 4000$, then $W = 4000$, the equilibrium solution.
If $W_0 = 5000$, then $W = 4000 + 1000e^{0.05t}$.
If $W_0 = 3000$, then $W = 4000 - 1000e^{0.05t}$. Substituting $t \approx 27.7$ gives $W = 0$, so the company goes bankrupt in its twenty-eighth year. These solutions are shown in Figure 11.55. Notice that if the net worth starts with W_0 near, but not equal to, \$4000 million, then W moves further away. Thus, $W = 4000$ is an unstable equilibrium.

The Velocity of a Falling Body: Terminal Velocity

Think about the velocity of a sky-diver jumping out of a plane. When the sky-diver first jumps, his velocity is zero. The pull of gravity then makes his velocity increase. As the sky-diver speeds up, the air resistance also increases. Since the air resistance partly balances the pull of gravity, the force causing him to accelerate decreases. Thus, the velocity is an increasing function of time, but it is increasing at a decreasing rate. The air resistance increases until it balances gravity, when the sky-diver's velocity levels off. Thus, we expect the the graph of velocity against time to be concave down with a horizontal asymptote.

A Differential Equation: Air Resistance Proportional to Velocity

In order to compute the velocity function, we need to know exactly how air resistance depends on velocity. To decide whether air resistance is, say, proportional to the velocity, or is some other function of velocity, requires either lab experiments or a theoretical idea of how the air resistance is created. We consider a very small object, such as a dust particle settling on a computer component during manufacturing,[9] and assume that air resistance is proportional to velocity. Thus, the net force on the object is $F = mg - kv$, where mg is the gravitational force, which acts downward, and kv is the air resistance, which acts upward, so $k > 0$. (See Figure 11.56.) Then, by Newton's Second Law of Motion,

$$\text{Force} = \text{Mass} \cdot \text{Acceleration},$$

we have

$$mg - kv = m\frac{dv}{dt}.$$

This differential equation can be solved by separation of variables. It is easier if we factor out $-k/m$ before separating, giving

$$\frac{dv}{dt} = -\frac{k}{m}\left(v - \frac{mg}{k}\right).$$

Separating and integrating gives

$$\int \frac{dv}{v - mg/k} = -\frac{k}{m}\int dt$$

$$\ln\left|v - \frac{mg}{k}\right| = -\frac{k}{m}t + C.$$

Solving for v, we have

$$\left|v - \frac{mg}{k}\right| = e^{-kt/m+C} = e^C e^{-kt/m}$$

$$v - \frac{mg}{k} = Ae^{-kt/m},$$

where A is an arbitrary constant. We find A from the initial condition that the object starts from rest, so $v = 0$ when $t = 0$. Substituting

$$0 - \frac{mg}{k} = Ae^0$$

gives

$$A = -\frac{mg}{k}.$$

Figure 11.56: Forces acting on a falling object

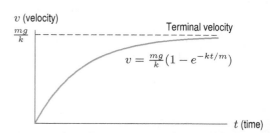

Figure 11.57: Velocity of falling dust particle assuming that air resistance is kv

Thus

$$v = \frac{mg}{k} - \frac{mg}{k}e^{-kt/m} = \frac{mg}{k}(1 - e^{-kt/m}).$$

The graph of this function is in Figure 11.57. The horizontal asymptote represents the *terminal velocity*, mg/k.

Notice that the terminal velocity can also be obtained from the differential equation by setting $dv/dt = 0$ and solving for v:

$$m\frac{dv}{dt} = mg - kv = 0, \quad \text{so} \quad v = \frac{mg}{k}.$$

[9]Example suggested by Howard Stone.

Compartmental Analysis: A Reservoir

Many processes can be modeled as a container with various solutions flowing in and out—for example, drugs given intravenously or the discharge of pollutants into a lake. We consider a city's water reservoir, fed partly by clean water from a spring and partly by run-off from the surrounding land. In New England and many other areas with much snow in the winter, the run-off contains salt that has been put on the roads to make them safe for driving. We consider the concentration of salt in the reservoir. If there is no salt in the reservoir initially, the concentration builds up until the rate at which the salt is entering into the reservoir balances the rate at which salt flows out. If, on the other hand, the reservoir starts with a great deal of salt in it, then initially, the rate at which the salt is entering is less than the rate at which it is flowing out, and the quantity of salt in the reservoir decreases. In either case, the salt concentration levels off at an equilibrium value.

A Differential Equation for Salt Concentration

A water reservoir holds 100 million gallons of water and supplies a city with 1 million gallons a day. The reservoir is partly refilled by a spring that provides 0.9 million gallons a day, and the rest of the water, 0.1 million gallons a day, comes from run-off from the surrounding land. The spring is clean, but the run-off contains salt with a concentration of 0.0001 pound per gallon. There was no salt in the reservoir initially, and the water is well mixed (that is, the outflow contains the concentration of salt in the tank at that instant). We find the concentration of salt in the reservoir as a function of time.

It is important to distinguish between the total quantity, Q, of salt in pounds and the concentration, C, of salt in pounds/gallon where

$$\text{Concentration} = C = \frac{\text{Quantity of salt}}{\text{Volume of water}} = \frac{Q}{100\,\text{million}} \left(\frac{\text{lb}}{\text{gal}} \right).$$

(The volume of the reservoir is 100 million gallons.) We will find Q first, and then C. We know that

$$\begin{array}{l} \text{Rate of change of} \\ \text{quantity of salt} \end{array} = \text{Rate salt entering} - \text{Rate salt leaving}.$$

Salt is entering through the run-off of 0.1 million gallons per day, with each gallon containing 0.0001 pound of salt. Therefore,

$$\begin{aligned} \text{Rate salt entering} &= \text{Concentration} \cdot \text{Volume per day} \\ &= 0.0001 \left(\frac{\text{lb}}{\text{gal}} \right) \cdot 0.1 \left(\frac{\text{million gal}}{\text{day}} \right) \\ &= 0.00001 \left(\frac{\text{million lb}}{\text{day}} \right) = 10\,\text{lb/day}. \end{aligned}$$

Salt is leaving in the million gallons of water used by the city each day . Thus

$$\begin{aligned} \text{Rate salt leaving} &= \text{Concentration} \cdot \text{Volume per day} \\ &= \frac{Q}{100\,\text{million}} \left(\frac{\text{lb}}{\text{gal}} \right) \cdot 1 \left(\frac{\text{million gal}}{\text{day}} \right) = \frac{Q}{100}\,\text{lb/day}. \end{aligned}$$

Therefore, Q satisfies the differential equation

$$\frac{dQ}{dt} = 10 - \frac{Q}{100}.$$

We factor out $-1/100 = -0.01$ and separate variables, giving

$$\frac{dQ}{dt} = -0.01(Q - 1000)$$

$$\int \frac{dQ}{Q - 1000} = -\int 0.01 \, dt$$

$$\ln |Q - 1000| = -0.01t + k$$

$$Q - 1000 = Ae^{-0.01t}.$$

There is no salt initially, so we substitute $Q = 0$ when $t = 0$:

$$0 - 1000 = Ae^0 \quad \text{giving} \quad A = -1000.$$

Thus

$$Q - 1000 = -1000e^{-0.01t},$$

so

$$Q = 1000(1 - e^{-0.01t}) \quad \text{pounds.}$$

Therefore

$$\text{Concentration} = C = \frac{Q}{100 \text{ million}} = \frac{1000}{10^8}(1 - e^{-0.01t}) = 10^{-5}(1 - e^{-0.01t}) \text{ lb/gal.}$$

A sketch of concentration against time is in Figure 11.58.

Figure 11.58: Concentration of salt in reservoir

Exercises and Problems for Section 11.6

Exercises

1. Match the graphs in Figure 11.59 with the following descriptions.

   (a) The population of a new species introduced onto a tropical island.
   (b) The temperature of a metal ingot placed in a furnace and then removed.
   (c) The speed of a car traveling at uniform speed and then braking uniformly.
   (d) The mass of carbon-14 in a historical specimen.
   (e) The concentration of tree pollen in the air over the course of a year.

In Exercises 2–5, write a differential equation for the balance B in an investment fund with time, t, measured in years.

2. The balance is earning interest at a continuous rate of 5% per year, and payments are being made out of the fund at a continuous rate of $12,000 per year.

3. The balance is earning interest at a continuous rate of 3.7% per year, and money is being added to the fund at a continuous rate of $5000 per year.

4. The balance is losing value at a continuous rate of 8% per year, and money is being added to the fund at a continuous rate of $2000 per year.

5. The balance is losing value at a continuous rate of 6.5% per year, and payments are being made out of the fund at a continuous rate of $50,000 per year.

6. A bank account that earns 10% interest compounded continuously has an initial balance of zero. Money is deposited into the account at a constant rate of $1000 per year.

   (a) Write a differential equation that describes the rate of change of the balance $B = f(t)$.
   (b) Solve the differential equation to find the balance as a function of time.

Figure 11.59

7. At time $t = 0$, a bottle of juice at $90°F$ is stood in a mountain stream whose temperature is $50°F$. After 5 minutes, its temperature is $80°F$. Let $H(t)$ denote the temperature of the juice at time t, in minutes.

   (a) Write a differential equation for $H(t)$ using Newton's Law of Cooling.
   (b) Solve the differential equation.
   (c) When will the temperature of the juice have dropped to $60°F$?

8. The velocity, v, of a dust particle of mass m and acceleration a satisfies the equation

$$ma = m\frac{dv}{dt} = mg - kv, \quad \text{where } g, k \text{ are constant.}$$

   By differentiating this equation, find a differential equation satisfied by a. (Your answer may contain m, g, k, but not v.) Solve for a, given that $a(0) = g$.

Problems

9. A deposit is made to a bank account paying 8% interest compounded continuously. Payments totaling $2000 per year are made from this account.

   (a) Write a differential equation for the balance, B, in the account after t years.
   (b) Find the equilibrium solution of the differential equation. Is the equilibrium stable or unstable? Explain what happens to an account that begins with slightly more money or slightly less money than the equilibrium value.
   (c) Write the solution to the differential equation.
   (d) How much is in the account after 5 years if the initial deposit is (i) $20,000?   (ii) $30,000?

10. Dead leaves accumulate on the ground in a forest at a rate of 3 grams per square centimeter per year. At the same time, these leaves decompose at a continuous rate of 75% per year. Write a differential equation for the total quantity of dead leaves (per square centimeter) at time t. Sketch a solution showing that the quantity of dead leaves tends toward an equilibrium level. What is that equilibrium level?

11. A stream flowing into a lake brings with it a pollutant at a rate of 8 metric tons per year. The river leaving the lake removes the pollutant at a rate proportional to the quantity in the lake, with constant of proportionality -0.16 if time is measured in years.

   (a) Is the quantity of pollutant in the lake increasing or decreasing at a moment at which the quantity is 45 metric tons? At which the quantity is 55 metric tons?
   (b) What is the quantity of pollutant in the lake after a long time?

12. Caffeine is metabolized and excreted at a continuous rate of about 17% per hour. A person with no caffeine in the body starts drinking coffee, containing 130 mg of caffeine per cup, at 7 am. The person drinks coffee continuously all day at the rate of one cup an hour. Write a differential equation for A, the amount of caffeine in the body t hours after 7 am and give the particular solution to this differential equation. How much caffeine is in the person's body at 5 pm?

13. The rate (per foot) at which light is absorbed as it passes through water is proportional to the intensity, or brightness, at that point.

   (a) Find the intensity as a function of the distance the light has traveled through the water.
   (b) If 50% of the light is absorbed in 10 feet, how much is absorbed in 20 feet? 25 feet?

14. In 2010, the world population was 6.9 billion. The birth rate had stabilized to 140 million per year and is projected to remain constant. The death rate is projected to increase from 57 million per year in 2010 to 80 million per year in 2040 and to continue increasing at the same rate.

   (a) Assuming the death rate increases linearly, write a differential equation for $P(t)$, the world population in billions t years from 2010.
   (b) Solve the differential equation.
   (c) Find the population predicted for 2050.

15. The rate at which barometric pressure decreases with altitude is proportional to the barometric pressure at that altitude. If the barometric pressure is measured in inches of mercury, and the altitude in feet, then the constant of proportionality is $3.7 \cdot 10^{-5}$. The barometric pressure at sea level is 29.92 inches of mercury.

   (a) Calculate the barometric pressure at the top of Mount Whitney, 14,500 feet (the highest mountain in the US outside Alaska), and at the top of Mount Everest, 29,000 feet (the highest mountain in the world).
   (b) People cannot easily survive at a pressure below 15 inches of mercury. What is the highest altitude to which people can safely go?

16. According to a simple physiological model, an athletic adult male needs 20 calories per day per pound of body weight to maintain his weight. If he consumes more or fewer calories than those required to maintain his weight, his weight changes at a rate proportional to the difference between the number of calories consumed and the number needed to maintain his current weight; the constant of proportionality is $1/3500$ pounds per calorie. Suppose that a particular person has a constant caloric intake of I calories per day. Let $W(t)$ be the person's weight in pounds at time t (measured in days).

   (a) What differential equation has solution $W(t)$?

(b) Find the equilibrium solution of the differential equation. Based on the context, do you expect the equilibrium to be stable or unstable?

(c) Solve this differential equation.

(d) Graph $W(t)$ if the person starts out weighing 160 pounds and consumes 3000 calories a day.

17. Morphine is often used as a pain-relieving drug. The half-life of morphine in the body is 2 hours. Suppose morphine is administered to a patient intravenously at a rate of 2.5 mg per hour, and the rate at which the morphine is eliminated is proportional to the amount present.

(a) Use the half-life to show that, to three decimal places, the constant of proportionality for the rate at which morphine leaves the body (in mg/hour) is $k = -0.347$.

(b) Write a differential equation for the quantity, Q, of morphine in the blood after t hours.

(c) Use the differential equation to find the equilibrium solution. (This is the long-term amount of morphine in the body, once the system has stabilized.)

18. Water leaks out of a barrel at a rate proportional to the square root of the depth of the water at that time. If the water level starts at 36 inches and drops to 35 inches in 1 hour, how long will it take for all of the water to leak out of the barrel?

19. When a gas expands without gain or loss of heat, the rate of change of pressure with respect to volume is proportional to pressure divided by volume. Find a law connecting pressure and volume in this case.

20. A spherical snowball melts at a rate proportional to its surface area.

(a) Write a differential equation for its volume, V.

(b) If the initial volume is V_0, solve the differential equation and graph the solution.

(c) When does the snowball disappear?

21. Water leaks from a vertical cylindrical tank through a small hole in its base at a rate proportional to the square root of the volume of water remaining. If the tank initially contains 200 liters and 20 liters leak out during the first day, when will the tank be half empty? How much water will there be after 4 days?

22. As you know, when a course ends, students start to forget the material they have learned. One model (called the Ebbinghaus model) assumes that the rate at which a student forgets material is proportional to the difference between the material currently remembered and some positive constant, a.

(a) Let $y = f(t)$ be the fraction of the original material remembered t weeks after the course has ended. Set up a differential equation for y. Your equation will contain two constants; the constant a is less than y for all t.

(b) Solve the differential equation.

(c) Describe the practical meaning (in terms of the amount remembered) of the constants in the solution $y = f(t)$.

23. An item is initially sold at a price of \$$p$ per unit. Over time, market forces push the price toward the equilibrium price, \$$p^*$, at which supply balances demand. The Evans Price Adjustment model says that the rate of change in the market price, \$$p$, is proportional to the difference between the market price and the equilibrium price.

(a) Write a differential equation for p as a function of t.

(b) Solve for p.

(c) Sketch solutions for various different initial prices, both above and below the equilibrium price.

(d) What happens to p as $t \to \infty$?

24. Let L, a constant, be the number of people who would like to see a newly released movie, and let $N(t)$ be the number of people who have seen it during the first t days since its release. The rate that people first go see the movie, dN/dt (in people/day), is proportional to the number of people who would like to see it but haven't yet. Write and solve a differential equation describing dN/dt where t is the number of days since the movie's release. Your solution will involve L and a constant of proportionality, k.

25. A drug is administered intravenously at a constant rate of r mg/hour and is excreted at a rate proportional to the quantity present, with constant of proportionality $\alpha > 0$.

(a) Solve a differential equation for the quantity, Q, in milligrams, of the drug in the body at time t hours. Assume there is no drug in the body initially. Your answer will contain r and α. Graph Q against t. What is Q_∞, the limiting long-run value of Q?

(b) What effect does doubling r have on Q_∞? What effect does doubling r have on the time to reach half the limiting value, $\frac{1}{2}Q_\infty$?

(c) What effect does doubling α have on Q_∞? On the time to reach $\frac{1}{2}Q_\infty$?

26. When people smoke, carbon monoxide is released into the air. In a room of volume 60 m^3, air containing 5% carbon monoxide is introduced at a rate of 0.002 m^3/min. (This means that 5% of the volume of the incoming air is carbon monoxide.) The carbon monoxide mixes immediately with the rest of the air, and the mixture leaves the room at the same rate as it enters.

(a) Write a differential equation for $c(t)$, the concentration of carbon monoxide at time t, in minutes.

(b) Solve the differential equation, assuming there is no carbon monoxide in the room initially.

(c) What happens to the value of $c(t)$ in the long run?

27. (Continuation of Problem 26.) Government agencies warn that exposure to air containing 0.02% carbon monoxide can lead to headaches and dizziness.[10] How

---

[10]www.lni.wa.gov/Safety/Topics/AtoZ/CarbonMonoxide/, accessed on June 14, 2007.

long does it take for the concentration of carbon monoxide in the room in Problem 26 to reach this level?

28. An aquarium pool has volume $2 \cdot 10^6$ liters. The pool initially contains pure fresh water. At $t = 0$ minutes, water containing 10 grams/liter of salt is poured into the pool at a rate of 60 liters/minute. The salt water instantly mixes with the fresh water, and the excess mixture is drained out of the pool at the same rate (60 liters/minute).

    (a) Write a differential equation for $S(t)$, the mass of salt in the pool at time t.
    (b) Solve the differential equation to find $S(t)$.
    (c) What happens to $S(t)$ as $t \to \infty$?

29. In 1692, Johann Bernoulli was teaching the Marquis de l'Hopital calculus in Paris. Solve the following problem, which is similar to the one that they did. What is the equation of the curve which has subtangent (distance BC in Figure 11.60) equal to twice its abscissa (distance OC)?

Figure 11.60

30. An object of mass m is thrown vertically upward from the surface of the earth with initial velocity v_0. We will calculate the value of v_0, called the escape velocity, with which the object can escape the pull of the gravity and never return to earth. Since the object is moving far from the surface of the earth, we must take into account the variation of gravity with altitude. If the acceleration due to gravity at sea level is g, and R is the radius of the earth, the gravitational force, F, on the object of mass m at an altitude h above the surface of the earth is given by

$$F = \frac{mgR^2}{(R + h)^2}.$$

(a) The velocity of the object (measured upward) is v at time t. Use Newton's Second Law of Motion to show that

$$\frac{dv}{dt} = -\frac{gR^2}{(R + h)^2}.$$

(b) Rewrite this equation with h instead of t as the independent variable using the chain rule $\frac{dv}{dt} = \frac{dv}{dh} \cdot \frac{dh}{dt}$. Hence, show that

$$v \frac{dv}{dh} = -\frac{gR^2}{(R + h)^2}.$$

(c) Solve the differential equation in part (b).
(d) Find the escape velocity, the smallest value of v_0 such that v is never zero.

31. A bank account earns 5% annual interest, compounded continuously. Money is deposited in a continuous cash flow at a rate of $1200 per year into the account.

    (a) Write a differential equation that describes the rate at which the balance $B = f(t)$ is changing.
    (b) Solve the differential equation given an initial balance $B_0 = 0$.
    (c) Find the balance after 5 years.

32. (Continuation of Problem 31.) Now suppose the money is deposited once a month (instead of continuously) but still at a rate of $1200 per year.

    (a) Write down the sum that gives the balance after 5 years, assuming the first deposit is made one month from today, and today is $t = 0$.
    (b) The sum you wrote in part (a) is a Riemann sum approximation to the integral

$$\int_0^5 1200e^{0.1t} \, dt.$$

    Determine whether it is a left sum or right sum, and determine what Δt and n are. Then use your calculator to evaluate the sum.
    (c) Compare your answer in part (b) to your answer to Problem 31(c).

Strengthen Your Understanding

In Problems 33–34, explain what is wrong with the statement.

33. At a time when a bank balance B, which satisfies $dB/dt = 0.08B - 250$, is $5000, the balance is going down.

34. The differential equation $dQ/dt = -0.15Q + 25$ represents the quantity of a drug in the body if the drug is metabolized at a continuous rate of 15% per day and an IV line is delivering the drug at a constant rate of 25 mg per hour.

In Problems 35–37, give an example of:

35. A differential equation for the quantity of a drug in a patient's body if the patient is receiving the drug at a constant rate through an IV line and is metabolizing the drug at a rate proportional to the quantity present.

36. A differential equation for any quantity which grows in two ways simultaneously: on its own at a rate proportional to the cube root of the amount present and from an external contribution at a constant rate.

37. A differential equation for a quantity that is increasing and grows fastest when the quantity is small and grows more slowly as the quantity gets larger.

11.7 THE LOGISTIC MODEL

Oil prices have a significant impact on the world's economies. In the eighteen months preceding July 2008, the price of oil more than doubled from about $60 a barrel to about $140 a barrel.[11] The impact of the increase was significant, from the auto industry, to family budgets, to how people commute. Even the threat of a price hike can send stock markets tumbling.

Many reasons are suggested for the increase, but one fact is inescapable: there is a finite supply of oil in the world. To fuel its expanding economy, the world consumes more oil each succeeding year. This cannot go on indefinitely. Economists and geologists are interested in estimating the remaining oil reserves and the date at which annual oil production is expected to peak (that is, reach a maximum).

US oil production has already peaked—and the date was predicted in advance. In 1956, geologist M. King Hubbert predicted that annual US oil production would peak some time in the period 1965–1970. Although many did not take his prediction seriously, US oil production did in fact peak in 1970. The economic impact was blunted by the US's increasing reliance on foreign oil.

In this section we introduce the *logistic differential equation* and use it, as Hubbert did, to predict the peak of US oil production.[12] Problems 29–32 investigate the peak of world oil production.

The Logistic Model

The logistic differential equation describes growth subject to a limit. For oil, the limit is the total oil reserves; for a population, the limit is the largest population that the environment can support; for the spread of information or a disease, the limit is the number of people that could be affected. The solution to this differential equation is the family of logistic functions introduced in Section 4.4.

Suppose P is growing logistically toward a limiting value of L, and the relative growth rate, $(1/P)dP/dt$, is k when $P = 0$. In the exponential model, the relative growth rate remains constant at k. But in the logistic model, the relative growth rate decreases linearly to 0 as P approaches L; see Figure 11.61.

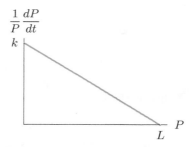

Figure 11.61: Logistic model: Relative growth rate is a linear function of P

So we have

$$\frac{1}{P}\frac{dP}{dt} = k - \frac{k}{L}P = k\left(1 - \frac{P}{L}\right).$$

The logistic differential equation can also be written

$$\frac{dP}{dt} = kP\left(1 - \frac{P}{L}\right).$$

This equation was first proposed as a model for population growth by the Belgian mathematician P. F. Verhulst in the 1830s. In Verhulst's model, L represents the *carrying capacity* of the environment, which is determined by the supply of food and arable land along with the available technology.

---

[11] http://www.nyse.tv/crude-oil-price-history.htm. Accessed February 2012.
[12] Based on an undergraduate project by Brad Ernst, Colgate University.

Qualitative Solution to the Logistic Equation

Figure 11.62 shows the slope field and characteristic *sigmoid*, or *S*-shaped, solution curve for the logistic model. Notice that for each fixed value of P, that is, along each horizontal line, the slopes are constant because dP/dt depends only on P and not on t. The slopes are small near $P = 0$ and near $P = L$; they are steepest around $P = L/2$. For $P > L$, the slopes are negative, so if the population is above the carrying capacity, the population decreases.

Figure 11.62: Slope field for $dP/dt = kP(1 - P/L)$

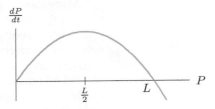

Figure 11.63: $dP/dt = kP(1 - P/L)$

We can locate the inflection point where the slope is greatest using Figure 11.63. This graph is a parabola because dP/dt is a quadratic function of P. The horizontal intercepts are at $P = 0$ and $P = L$, so the maximum, where the slope is greatest, is at $P = L/2$. Figure 11.63 also tells us that for $0 < P < L/2$, the slope dP/dt is positive and increasing, so the graph of P against t is concave up. (See Figure 11.64.) For $L/2 < P < L$, the slope dP/dt is positive and decreasing, so the graph of P is concave down. For $P > L$, the slope dP/dt is negative, so P is decreasing.

Figure 11.64: Logistic growth with inflection point

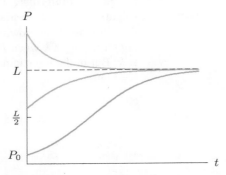

Figure 11.65: Solutions to the logistic equation

If $P = 0$ or $P = L$, there is an equilibrium solution. Figure 11.65 shows that $P = 0$ is an unstable equilibrium because solutions which start near 0 move away. However, $P = L$ is a stable equilibrium.

The Analytic Solution to the Logistic Equation

We have already obtained a lot of information about logistic growth without finding a formula for the solution. However, the equation can be solved analytically by separating variables:

$$\frac{dP}{dt} = kP\left(1 - \frac{P}{L}\right) = kP\left(\frac{L - P}{L}\right)$$

giving

$$\int \frac{dP}{P(L - P)} = \int \frac{k}{L}\, dt.$$

We can integrate the left side using the integral tables (Formula V 26) or by partial fractions:

$$\int \frac{1}{L}\left(\frac{1}{P} + \frac{1}{L - P}\right) dP = \int \frac{k}{L}\, dt.$$

Canceling the constant L, we integrate to get

$$\ln |P| - \ln |L - P| = kt + C.$$

Multiplying through by (-1) and using properties of logarithms, we have

$$\ln \left| \frac{L - P}{P} \right| = -kt - C.$$

Exponentiating both sides gives

$$\left| \frac{L - P}{P} \right| = e^{-kt-C} = e^{-C} e^{-kt}, \qquad \text{so} \qquad \frac{L - P}{P} = \pm e^{-C} e^{-kt}.$$

Then, writing $A = \pm e^{-C}$, we have

$$\frac{L - P}{P} = A e^{-kt}.$$

We find A by substituting $P = P_0$ when $t = 0$, which gives

$$\frac{L - P_0}{P_0} = A e^0 = A.$$

Since $(L - P)/P = (L/P) - 1$, we have

$$\frac{L}{P} = 1 + A e^{-kt},$$

which gives the following result:

The solution to the logistic differential equation:

$$\frac{dP}{dt} = kP \left(1 - \frac{P}{L} \right) \qquad \text{with initial condition } P_0 \text{ when } t = 0$$

is the logistic function

$$P = \frac{L}{1 + A e^{-kt}} \qquad \text{with} \quad A = \frac{L - P_0}{P_0}.$$

The parameter L represents the limiting value. The parameter k represents the relative growth rate when P is small relative to L. The parameter A depends on the initial condition P_0.

Peak Oil: US Production

We apply the logistic model to US oil production as Hubbert did in 1956. To make predictions, we need the values of k and L. We calculate these values from the oil production data Hubbert had available to him in the 1950s; see Table 11.5.

We define P to be the *total* amount of oil, in billions of barrels, produced in the US since 1859, the year the first oil well was built. See Table 11.5. With time, t, in years, dP/dt approximates the *annual* oil production in billions of barrels per year. Peak oil production occurs when dP/dt is a maximum.

Table 11.5   *US oil production[13] for 1931–1950 (billions of barrels)*

Year	dP/dt	P	Year	dP/dt	P	Year	dP/dt	P
1931	0.851	13.8	1938	1.21	21.0	1945	1.71	31.5
1932	0.785	14.6	1939	1.26	22.3	1946	1.73	33.2
1933	0.906	15.5	1940	1.50	23.8	1947	1.86	35.1
1934	0.908	16.4	1941	1.40	25.2	1948	2.02	37.1
1935	0.994	17.4	1942	1.39	26.6	1949	1.84	38.9
1936	1.10	18.5	1943	1.51	28.1	1950	1.97	40.9
1937	1.28	19.8	1944	1.68	29.8			

Figure 11.66 shows a scatterplot of the relative growth rate $(dP/dt)/P$ versus P. If the data follow a logistic differential equation, we see a linear relationship with intercept k and slope $-k/L$:

$$\frac{1}{P}\frac{dP}{dt} = k\left(1 - \frac{P}{L}\right) = k - \frac{k}{L}P.$$

Figure 11.66 shows a line fitted to the data.[14] The vertical intercept gives the value $k = 0.0649$.

The slope of the line is $-k/L = -0.00036$, so we have $L = 0.0649/0.00036 = 180$ billion barrels of oil. Thus, the model predicts that the total oil reserves in the US (the total amount in the ground before drilling started in 1859) were 180 billion barrels of oil.[15]

Figure 11.66: US oil production 1931–1950: Scatterplot and line for $1/P(dP/dt)$ versus P

If we let $t = 0$ be 1950, then $P_0 = 40.9$ billion barrels and $A = (180 - 40.9)/40.9 = 3.401$. The logistic function representing US oil production is

$$P = \frac{180}{1 + 3.401e^{-0.0649t}}.$$

Predicting Peak Oil Production

To predict, as Hubbert did, the year when annual US oil production would peak, we use the fact that the maximum value for dP/dt occurs when $P = L/2$. We derive a formula for the peak year (used again in Problems 29–32 to find peak production in world oil). The crucial observation is that, at the peak, the denominator of the expression for P must equal 2. Since

$$P = \frac{L}{2} = \frac{L}{1 + Ae^{-kt}}, \qquad \text{we have} \quad Ae^{-kt} = 1.$$

Using logarithms to solve the equation $Ae^{-kt} = 1$, we get $t = (1/k)\ln A$. Since $A = (L - P_0)/P_0$, we see that the time to peak oil production is an example of the following result:

---

[13] Data from http://www.eia.gov/dnav/pet/hist/LeafHandler.ashx?n=PET&s=MCRFPUS1&f=A. Accessed Feb, 2012.

[14] The line is a least-squares regression line.

[15] If the same analysis is repeated for other time periods, for example 1900–1950 or 1900–2000, the value for L varies between 120 and 220 billion barrels, while the value of k varies between 0.060 and 0.075.

For a logistic function, the maximum value of dP/dt occurs when $P = L/2$, and

$$\text{Time to the maximum rate of change} = \frac{1}{k}\ln A = \frac{1}{k}\ln\frac{L - P_0}{P_0}.$$

Thus, for the US,

$$\text{Time to peak oil production} = \frac{1}{0.0649}\ln\frac{180 - 40.9}{40.9} \approx 19 \text{ years;}$$

that is, oil production was predicted to peak in the year $1950 + 19 = 1969$. That year, $P = L/2$ and annual production was expected to be

$$\frac{dP}{dt} = kP\left(1 - \frac{P}{L}\right) = 0.0649 \cdot \frac{180}{2}\left(1 - \frac{1}{2}\right) \approx 3 \text{ billion barrels.}$$

The actual peak in US oil production was 3.5 billion barrels in 1970. Repeating the analysis using other time periods gives peak oil years in the range 1965-1970, as Hubbert predicted.

Figure 11.67 shows annual US production data and the parabola predicting its peak around 1970. Figure 11.68 shows P as a logistic function of t, with the limiting value of $P = 180$ and maximum production at $P = 90$. In fact, the first major oil crisis hit the US in the 1970s, with spiraling gas prices and long lines at service stations. The decline in US oil production since 1970 was partly mitigated by the opening of the Alaskan oil fields, which led to a second but lower peak in 1985. However, the US has increasingly depended on foreign oil.

Although Hubbert's predictions of the peak year proved to be accurate, extrapolation into the future is risky. Figure 11.67 and Figure 11.68 show that since 1970, oil production has slowed, though not as much as predicted.

Figure 11.67: US oil production: dP/dt versus P, predicted (parabola) and actual

Figure 11.68: US oil production: P versus t, predicted (logistic) and actual

Interestingly, Hubbert used the logistic model only to estimate k; for L, he relied on geological studies. It is remarkable that using only annual oil production for 1930-1950, we get an estimate for L that is in such close agreement with the geological estimates.

US Population Growth

The logistic equation is often used to model population growth. Table 11.6 gives the annual census figures in millions for the US population from 1790 to 2010.[16] Since we have the population, $P(t)$, of the US at ten-year intervals, we compute the relative growth rate using averages of estimates of the form:

$$\frac{1}{P}\frac{dP}{dt} \text{ in } 1860 = \frac{1}{P(1860)} \cdot \frac{P(1870) - P(1860)}{10}.$$

(See Problem 19 for details.) If we focus on the period 1790–1940, a line fitted to the scatterplot of $(1/P)dP/dt$ versus P has intercept $k = 0.0317$ and slope $-k/L = -0.000165$, so $L \approx 192$. Thus the differential equation modeling the US population during this period is

---

[16]www.census.gov. Accessed February 12, 2012.

$$\frac{dP}{dt} = 0.0317P\left(1 - \frac{P}{192}\right).$$

Using 1790 as $t = 0$, we get

$$A = \frac{L - P_0}{P_0} = \frac{192 - 3.9}{3.9} \approx 48.$$

Thus the solution to the logistic differential equation is

$$P = \frac{192}{1 + 48e^{-0.0317t}}.$$

Table 11.6 shows the actual census data for 1790–1940 with projected values from a logistic model; the largest deviations are 4% in 1840 and 1870 (the Civil War accounts for the second one).[17]

Table 11.6   *US population, in millions, for 1790–2010, actual data and logistic predictions*

Year	Actual	Logistic	Year	Actual	Logistic	Year	Actual	Logistic	Year	Actual	Logistic
1790	3.9	3.9	1850	23.2	23.6	1910	92.2	92.9	1970	203.2	165.7
1800	5.3	5.4	1860	31.4	30.9	1920	106.0	108.0	1980	226.5	172.2
1810	7.2	7.3	1870	38.6	40.1	1930	123.2	122.6	1990	248.7	177.2
1820	9.6	9.8	1880	50.2	51.0	1940	132.2	136.0	2000	281.4	181.0
1830	12.9	13.3	1890	63.0	63.7	1950	151.3	147.7	2010	308.7	183.9
1840	17.1	17.8	1900	76.2	77.9	1960	179.3	157.6			

After 1940, the actual figures leave the logistic model in the dust. The model predicts an increase of 9.9 million from 1950 to 1960 versus the actual change of 28 million. By 1970 the actual population of 203.2 million exceeded the predicted limiting population of $L = 192$ million. The unprecedented surge in US population between 1945 and 1965 is referred to as the baby boom.

Exercises and Problems for Section 11.7

Exercises

1. (a) Show that $P = 1/(1 + e^{-t})$ satisfies the logistic equation
   $$\frac{dP}{dt} = P(1 - P).$$
   (b) What is the limiting value of P as $t \to \infty$?

2. A quantity P satisfies the differential equation
   $$\frac{dP}{dt} = kP\left(1 - \frac{P}{100}\right).$$
   Sketch approximate solutions satisfying each of the following initial conditions:
   (a) $P_0 = 8$ (b) $P_0 = 70$ (c) $P_0 = 125$

3. A quantity Q satisfies the differential equation
   $$\frac{dQ}{dt} = kQ(1 - 0.0004Q).$$
   Sketch approximate solutions satisfying each of the following initial conditions:

   (a) $Q_0 = 300$ (b) $Q_0 = 1500$ (c) $Q_0 = 3500$

4. A quantity P satisfies the differential equation
   $$\frac{dP}{dt} = kP\left(1 - \frac{P}{250}\right), \quad \text{with } k > 0.$$
   Sketch a graph of dP/dt as a function of P.

5. A quantity A satisfies the differential equation
   $$\frac{dA}{dt} = kA(1 - 0.0002A), \quad \text{with } k > 0.$$
   Sketch a graph of dA/dt as a function of A.

[17]Calculations were done with more precise values of the population data and the constants k, L, and A than those shown.

6. Figure 11.69 shows a graph of dP/dt against P for a logistic differential equation. Sketch several solutions of P against t, using different initial conditions. Include a scale on your vertical axis.

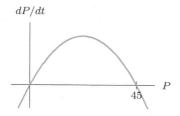

Figure 11.69

7. Figure 11.70 shows a slope field of a differential equation for a quantity Q growing logistically. Sketch a graph of dQ/dt against Q. Include a scale on the horizontal axis.

Figure 11.70

8. (a) On the slope field for $dP/dt = 3P - 3P^2$ in Figure 11.71, sketch three solution curves showing different types of behavior for the population, P.
   (b) Is there a stable value of the population? If so, what is it?
   (c) Describe the meaning of the shape of the solution curves for the population: Where is P increasing? Decreasing? What happens in the long run? Are there any inflection points? Where? What do they mean for the population?
   (d) Sketch a graph of dP/dt against P. Where is dP/dt positive? Negative? Zero? Maximum? How do your observations about dP/dt explain the shapes of your solution curves?

Figure 11.71

Exercises 9–10 give a graph of dP/dt against P.
   (a) What are the equilibrium values of P?
   (b) If $P = 500$, is dP/dt positive or negative? Is P increasing or decreasing?

9.

10.

For the logistic differential equations in Exercises 11–12,
   (a) Give values for k and for L and interpret the meaning of each in terms of the growth of the quantity P.
   (b) Give the value of P when the rate of change is at its peak.

11. $\dfrac{dP}{dt} = 0.035P\left(1 - \dfrac{P}{6000}\right)$

12. $\dfrac{dP}{dt} = 0.1P - 0.00008P^2$

In Exercises 13–16, give the general solution to the logistic differential equation.

13. $\dfrac{dP}{dt} = 0.05P\left(1 - \dfrac{P}{2800}\right)$

14. $\dfrac{dP}{dt} = 0.012P\left(1 - \dfrac{P}{5700}\right)$

15. $\dfrac{dP}{dt} = 0.68P(1 - 0.00025P)$

16. $\dfrac{dP}{dt} = 0.2P - 0.0008P^2$

In Exercises 17–20, give k, L, A, a formula for P as a function of time t, and the time to the peak value of dP/dt.

17. $\dfrac{dP}{dt} = 10P - 5P^2$, $P_0 = L/4$

18. $\dfrac{dP}{dt} = 0.02P - 0.0025P^2$, $P_0 = 1$

19. $\dfrac{1}{P}\dfrac{dP}{dt} = 0.3\left(1 - \dfrac{P}{100}\right)$, $P_0 = 75$

20. $\dfrac{1}{10P}\dfrac{dP}{dt} = 0.012 - 0.002P$, $P_0 = 2$

In Exercises 21–22, give the solution to the logistic differential equation with initial condition.

21. $\dfrac{dP}{dt} = 0.8P\left(1 - \dfrac{P}{8500}\right)$ with $P_0 = 500$

22. $\dfrac{dP}{dt} = 0.04P(1 - 0.0001P)$ with $P_0 = 200$

Problems

23. A rumor spreads among a group of 400 people. The number of people, $N(t)$, who have heard the rumor by time t in hours since the rumor started is approximated by

$$N(t) = \frac{400}{1 + 399e^{-0.4t}}.$$

(a) Find $N(0)$ and interpret it.

(b) How many people will have heard the rumor after 2 hours? After 10 hours?

(c) Graph $N(t)$.

(d) Approximately how long will it take until half the people have heard the rumor? 399 people?

(e) When is the rumor spreading fastest?

24. The Tojolobal Mayan Indian community in southern Mexico has available a fixed amount of land. The proportion, P, of land in use for farming t years after 1935 is modeled with the logistic function in Figure 11.72:[18]

$$P = \frac{1}{1 + 2.968e^{-0.0275t}}.$$

(a) What proportion of the land was in use for farming in 1935?

(b) What is the long-run prediction of this model?

(c) When was half the land in use for farming?

(d) When was the proportion of land used for farming increasing most rapidly?

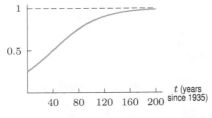

P
(proportion of land in use)

Figure 11.72

25. A model for the population, P, of carp in a landlocked lake at time t is given by the differential equation

$$\frac{dP}{dt} = 0.25P(1 - 0.0004P).$$

(a) What is the long-term equilibrium population of carp in the lake?

(b) A census taken ten years ago found there were 1000 carp in the lake. Estimate the current population.

(c) Under a plan to join the lake to a nearby river, the fish will be able to leave the lake. A net loss of 10% of the carp each year is predicted, but the patterns of birth and death are not expected to change. Revise the differential equation to take this into account. Use the revised differential equation to predict the future development of the carp population.

26. Table 11.7 gives values for a logistic function $P = f(t)$.

(a) Estimate the maximum rate of change of P and estimate the value of t when it occurs.

(b) If P represents the growth of a population, estimate the carrying capacity of the population.

Table 11.7

t	0	10	20	30	40	50	60	70
P	120	125	135	155	195	270	345	385

27. Figure 11.73 shows the spread of the Code-red computer virus during July 2001. Most of the growth took place starting at midnight on July 19; on July 20, the virus attacked the White House, trying (unsuccessfully) to knock its site off-line. The number of computers infected by the virus was a logistic function of time.

(a) Estimate the limiting value of $f(t)$ as t increased. What does this limiting value represent in terms of Code-red?

(b) Estimate the value of t at which $f''(t) = 0$. Estimate the value of n at this time.

(c) What does the answer to part (b) tell us about Code-red?

(d) How are the answers to parts (a) and (b) related?

n (thousands of infected computers)

Figure 11.73

28. According to an article in *The New York Times*,[19] pigweed has acquired resistance to the weedkiller Roundup. Let N be the number of acres, in millions, where Roundup-resistant pigweed is found. Suppose the relative growth rate, $(1/N)dN/dt$, was 15% when $N = 5$ and 14.5% when $N = 10$. Assuming the relative growth rate is a linear function of N, write a differential equation to model N as a function of time, and predict how many acres will eventually be afflicted before the spread of Roundup-resistant pigweed halts.

---

[18] Adapted from J. S. Thomas and M. C. Robbins, "The Limits to Growth in a Tojolobal Maya Ejido," *Geoscience and Man 26* (Baton Rouge: Geoscience Publications, 1988), pp. 9–16.

[19] http://www.nytimes.com/2010/05/04/business/energy-environment/04weed.html, accessed May 3, 2010.

In Problems 29–33, we analyze world oil production.[20] When annual world oil production peaks and starts to decline, major economic restructuring will be needed. We investigate when this slowdown is projected to occur.

29. We define P to be the total oil production worldwide since 1859 in billions of barrels. In 1993, annual world oil production was 22.0 billion barrels and the total production was $P = 724$ billion barrels. In 2008, annual production was 26.9 billion barrels and the total production was $P = 1100$ billion barrels. Let t be time in years since 1993.

    (a) Estimate the rate of production, dP/dt, for 1993 and 2008.

    (b) Estimate the relative growth rate, $(1/P)(dP/dt)$, for 1993 and 2008.

    (c) Find an equation for the relative growth rate, $(1/P)(dP/dt)$, as a function of P, assuming that the function is linear.

    (d) Assuming that P increases logistically and that all oil in the ground will ultimately be extracted, estimate the world oil reserves in 1859 to the nearest billion barrels.

    (e) Write and solve the logistic differential equation modeling P.

30. In Problem 29 we used a logistic function to model P, total world oil production since 1859, as a function of time, t, in years since 1993. Use this function to answer the following questions:

    (a) When does peak annual world oil production occur?

    (b) Geologists have estimated world oil reserves to be as high as 3500 billion barrels.[21] When does peak world oil production occur with this assumption? (Assume k and P_0 are unchanged.)

31. As in Problem 29, let P be total world oil production since 1859. In 1998, annual world production was 24.4 billion barrels and total production was $P = 841$ billion barrels. In 2003, annual production was 25.3 billion barrels and total production was $P = 964$ billion barrels.

    (a) Graph dP/dt versus P from Problem 29 and show the data for 1998 and 2003. How well does the model fit the data?

    (b) Graph the logistic function modeling worldwide oil production (P versus t) from Problem 29 and show the data for 1998 and 2003. How well does the model fit the data?

32. Use the logistic function obtained in Problem 29 to model the growth of P, the total oil produced worldwide in billions of barrels since 1859:

    (a) Find the projected value of P for 2010.

    (b) Estimate the annual world oil production during 2010.

    (c) How much oil is projected to remain in the ground in 2010?

    (d) Compare the projected production in part (b) with the actual figure of 26.9 billion barrels.

33. With P, the total oil produced worldwide since 1859, in billions of barrels, modeled as a function of time t in years since 1993 as in Problem 29:

    (a) Predict the total quantity of oil produced by 2020.

    (b) In what year does the model predict that only 300 billion barrels remain?

34. The total number of people infected with a virus often grows like a logistic curve. Suppose that time, t, is in weeks and that 10 people originally have the virus. In the early stages, the number of people infected is increasing exponentially with $k = 1.78$. In the long run, 5000 people are infected.

    (a) Find a logistic function to model the number of people infected.

    (b) Sketch a graph of your answer to part (a).

    (c) Use your graph to estimate the length of time until the rate at which people are becoming infected starts to decrease. What is the vertical coordinate at this point?

35. Policy makers are interested in modeling the spread of information through a population. For example, agricultural ministries use models to understand the spread of technical innovations or new seed types through their countries. Two models, based on how the information is spread, follow. Assume the population is of a constant size M.

    (a) If the information is spread by mass media (TV, radio, newspapers), the rate at which information is spread is believed to be proportional to the number of people not having the information at that time. Write a differential equation for the number of people having the information by time t. Sketch a solution assuming that no one (except the mass media) has the information initially.

    (b) If the information is spread by word of mouth, the rate of spread of information is believed to be proportional to the product of the number of people who know and the number who don't. Write a differential equation for the number of people having the information by time t. Sketch the solution for the cases in which

      (i) No one   **(ii)** 5% of the population

      (iii) 75% of the population

    knows initially. In each case, when is the information spreading fastest?

---

[20]Data from http://cta.ornl.gov/data/chapter1.shtml. Accessed February 2012.
[21]http://www.hoodriver.k12.or.us/169320618135056660/lib/169320618135056660/peak_oil.pdf. Accessed Feb 2012.

36. In the 1930s, the Soviet ecologist G. F. Gause[22] studied the population growth of yeast. Fit a logistic curve, $dP/dt = kP(1 - P/L)$, to his data below using the method outlined below.

Time (hours)	0	10	18	23	34	42	47
Yeast pop	0.37	8.87	10.66	12.50	13.27	12.87	12.70

(a) Plot the data and use it to estimate (by eye) the carrying capacity, L.

(b) Use the first two pieces of data in the table and your value for L to estimate k.

(c) On the same axes as the data points, use your values for k and L to sketch the solution curve

$$P = \frac{L}{1 + Ae^{-kt}} \quad \text{where} \quad A = \frac{L - P_0}{P_0}.$$

37. The population data from another experiment on yeast by the ecologist G. F. Gause is given.

Time (hours)	0	13	32	56	77	101	125
Yeast pop	1.00	1.70	2.73	4.87	5.67	5.80	5.83

(a) Do you think the population is growing exponentially or logistically? Give reasons for your answer.

(b) Estimate the value of k (for either model) from the first two pieces of data. If you chose a logistic model in part (a), estimate the carrying capacity, L, from the data.

(c) Sketch the data and the approximate growth curve given by the parameters you estimated.

38. The spread of a non-fatal disease through a population of fixed size M can be modeled as follows. The rate that healthy people are infected, in people per day, is proportional to the product of the numbers of healthy and infected people. The constant of proportionality is $0.01/M$. The rate of recovery, in people per day, is 0.009 times the number of people infected. Construct a differential equation that models the spread of the disease. Assuming that initially only a small number of people are infected, plot a graph of the number of infected people against time. What fraction of the population is infected in the long run?

39. Many organ pipes in old European churches are made of tin. In cold climates such pipes can be affected with *tin pest*, when the tin becomes brittle and crumbles into a gray powder. This transformation can appear to take place very suddenly because the presence of the gray powder encourages the reaction to proceed. The rate of the reaction is proportional to the product of the amount of tin left and the quantity of gray powder, p, present at time t. Assume that when metallic tin is converted to gray powder, its mass does not change.

(a) Write a differential equation for p. Let the total quantity of metallic tin present originally be B.

(b) Sketch a graph of the solution $p = f(t)$ if there is a small quantity of powder initially. How much metallic tin has crumbled when it is crumbling fastest?

(c) Suppose there is no gray powder initially. (For example, suppose the tin is completely new.) What does this model predict will happen? How do you reconcile this with the fact that many organ pipes do get tin pest?

40. The logistic model can be applied to a renewable resource that is harvested, like fish. If a fraction c of the population is harvested each year, we have

$$\frac{dP}{dt} = kP\left(1 - \frac{P}{L}\right) - cP.$$

Figure 11.74 assumes $c < k$ and shows two graphs of dP/dt versus P: the parabola $dP/dt = kP(1 - P/L)$ and the line $dP/dt = cP$.

(a) Show that there is an equilibrium at $P = (k-c)L/k$ and that the annual harvest is then $H = c(k-c)L/k$.

(b) If k and L are constant and the population is at the equilibrium in part (a), show that the maximum possible annual harvest is $kL/4$ and occurs when $c = k/2$.

(c) How can the population and the annual harvest at equilibrium be identified on the graph? Explain what happens as c increases beyond $k/2$ toward k. (Assume k and L are constant.)

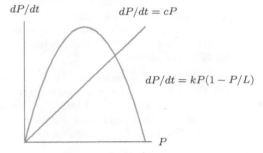

Figure 11.74

41. Federal or state agencies control hunting and fishing by setting a quota on how many animals can be harvested each season. Determining the appropriate quota means achieving a balance between environmental concerns and the interests of hunters and fishers. For example, when a June 8, 2007 decision by the Delaware Superior Court invalidated a two-year moratorium on catching horseshoe crabs, the Delaware Department of Natural Resources and Environmental Control imposed instead an annual quota of 100,000 on male horseshoe crabs. Environmentalists argued this would exacerbate a decrease in the protected Red Knot bird population that depends on the crab for food. For a population P that satisfies the logistic model with harvesting,

$$\frac{dP}{dt} = kP\left(1 - \frac{P}{L}\right) - H,$$

show that the quota, H, must satisfy $H \leq kL/4$, or else the population P may die out. (In fact, H should be kept much less than $kL/4$ to be safe.)

---

[22]Data adapted from G. F. Gause, *The Struggle for Existence* (New York: Hafner Publishing Company, 1969).

Strengthen Your Understanding

In Problems 42–44, explain what is wrong with the statement.

42. The differential equation $dP/dt = 0.08P - 0.0032P^2$ has one equilibrium solution, at $P = 25$.

43. The maximum rate of change occurs at $t = 25$ for a quantity Q growing according to the logistic equation

$$\frac{dQ}{dt} = 0.13Q(1 - 0.02Q).$$

44. Figure 11.75 shows a quantity growing logistically.

Figure 11.75

In Problems 45–48, give an example of:

45. A quantity that increases logistically.

46. A logistic differential equation for a quantity P such that the maximum rate of change of P occurs when $P = 75$.

47. A graph of dQ/dt against Q if Q is growing logistically and has an equilibrium value at $Q = 500$.

48. A graph of dP/dt against P if P is a logistic function which increases when $0 < P < 20$ and which decreases when $P < 0$ or $P > 20$.

Are the statements in Problems 49–50 true or false? Give an explanation for your answer.

49. There is a solution curve for the logistic differential equation $dP/dt = P(2 - P)$ that goes through the points $(0, 1)$ and $(1, 3)$.

50. For any positive values of the constant k and any positive values of the initial value $P(0)$, the solution to the differential equation $dP/dt = kP(L - P)$ has limiting value L as $t \to \infty$.

11.8 SYSTEMS OF DIFFERENTIAL EQUATIONS

In Section 11.7 we modeled the growth of a single population over time. We now consider the growth of two populations that interact, such as a population of sick people infecting the healthy people around them. This involves not just one differential equation, but a system of two.

Diseases and Epidemics

Differential equations can be used to predict when an outbreak of a disease will become so severe that it is called an *epidemic*[23] and to decide what level of vaccination is necessary to prevent an epidemic. Let's consider a specific example.

Flu in a British Boarding School

In January 1978, 763 students returned to a boys' boarding school after their winter vacation. A week later, one boy developed the flu, followed by two others the next day. By the end of the month, nearly half the boys were sick. Most of the school had been affected by the time the epidemic was over in mid-February.[24]

Being able to predict how many people will get sick, and when, is an important step toward controlling an epidemic. This is one of the responsibilities of Britain's Communicable Disease Surveillance Centre and the US's Center for Disease Control and Prevention.

---

[23]Exactly when a disease should be called an epidemic is not always clear. The medical profession generally classifies a disease an epidemic when the frequency is higher than usually expected—leaving open the question of what is usually expected. See, for example, *Epidemiology in Medicine* by C. H. Hennekens and J. Buring (Boston: Little, Brown, 1987).

[24]Data from the Communicable Disease Surveillance Centre (UK); reported in "Influenza in a Boarding School," *British Medical Journal*, March 4, 1978, and by J. D. Murray in *Mathematical Biology* (New York: Springer Verlag, 1990).

The S-I-R Model

We apply one of the most commonly used models for an epidemic, called the S-I-R model, to the boarding school flu example. The population of the school is divided into three groups:

S = the number of *susceptibles*, the people who are not yet sick
   but who could become sick

I = the number of *infecteds*, the people who are currently sick

R = the number of *recovered*, or *removed*, the people who have
   been sick and can no longer infect others or be reinfected.

The number of susceptibles decreases with time as people become infected. We assume that the rate at which people become infected is proportional to the number of contacts between susceptible and infected people. We expect the number of contacts between the two groups to be proportional to both S and I. (If S doubles, we expect the number of contacts to double; similarly, if I doubles, we expect the number of contacts to double.) Thus we assume that the number of contacts is proportional to the product, SI. In other words, we assume that for some constant $a > 0$,

$$\frac{dS}{dt} = -\left(\begin{array}{c} \text{Rate susceptibles} \\ \text{get sick} \end{array} \right) = -aSI.$$

(The negative sign is used because S is decreasing.)

The number of infecteds is changing in two ways: newly sick people are added to the infected group, and others are removed. The newly sick people are exactly those people leaving the susceptible group and so accrue at a rate of aSI (with a positive sign this time). People leave the infected group either because they recover (or die), or because they are physically removed from the rest of the group and can no longer infect others. We assume that people are removed at a rate proportional to the number of sick, or bI, where b is a positive constant. Thus,

$$\frac{dI}{dt} = \begin{array}{c} \text{Rate susceptibles} \\ \text{get sick} \end{array} - \begin{array}{c} \text{Rate infecteds} \\ \text{get removed} \end{array} = aSI - bI.$$

Assuming that those who have recovered from the disease are no longer susceptible, the recovered group increases at the rate of bI, so

$$\frac{dR}{dt} = bI.$$

We are assuming that having the flu confers immunity on a person, that is, that the person cannot get the flu again. (This is true for a given strain of flu, at least in the short run.)

In analyzing the flu, we can use the fact that the total population $S + I + R$ is not changing. (The total population, the total number of boys in the school, did not change during the epidemic.) Thus, once we know S and I, we can calculate R. So we restrict our attention to the two equations

$$\frac{dS}{dt} = -aSI$$
$$\frac{dI}{dt} = aSI - bI.$$

The Constants a and b

The constant a measures how infectious the disease is—that is, how quickly it is transmitted from the infecteds to the susceptibles. In the case of the flu, we know from medical accounts that the epidemic started with one sick boy, with two more becoming sick a day later. Thus, when $I = 1$ and

$S = 762$, we have $dS/dt \approx -2$, enabling us to roughly[25] approximate a:

$$a = -\frac{dS/dt}{SI} = \frac{2}{(762)(1)} = 0.0026.$$

The constant b represents the rate at which infected people are removed from the infected population. In this case of the flu, boys were generally taken to the infirmary within one or two days of becoming sick. About half the infected population was removed each day, so we take $b \approx 0.5$. Thus, our equations are:

$$\frac{dS}{dt} = -0.0026SI$$

$$\frac{dI}{dt} = 0.0026SI - 0.5I.$$

The Phase Plane

We can get a good idea of the progress of the disease from graphs. You might expect that we would look for graphs of S and I against t, and eventually we will. However, we first look at a graph of I against S. If we plot a point (S, I) representing the number of susceptibles and the number of infecteds at any moment in time, then, as the numbers of susceptibles and infecteds change, the point moves. The SI-plane on which the point moves is called the *phase plane*. The path along which the point moves is called the *phase trajectory*, or *orbit*, of the point.

To find the phase trajectory, we need a differential equation relating S and I directly. Thinking of I as a function of S, and S as a function of t, we use the chain rule to get

$$\frac{dI}{dt} = \frac{dI}{dS} \cdot \frac{dS}{dt},$$

giving

$$\frac{dI}{dS} = \frac{dI/dt}{dS/dt}.$$

Substituting for dI/dt and dS/dt, we get

$$\frac{dI}{dS} = \frac{0.0026SI - 0.5I}{-0.0026SI}.$$

Assuming I is not zero, this equation simplifies to approximately

$$\frac{dI}{dS} = -1 + \frac{192}{S}.$$

The slope field of this differential equation is shown in Figure 11.76. The trajectory with initial condition $S_0 = 762$, $I_0 = 1$ is shown in Figure 11.77. Time is represented by the arrow showing the direction that a point moves on the trajectory. The disease starts at the point $S_0 = 762$, $I_0 = 1$. At first, more people become infected and fewer are susceptible. In other words, S decreases and I increases. Later, I decreases as S continues to decrease.

Figure 11.76: Slope field for $dI/dS = -1 + 192/S$

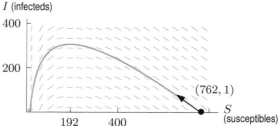

Figure 11.77: Trajectory for $S_0 = 762$, $I_0 = 1$

---

[25]The values of a and b are close to those obtained by J. D. Murray in *Mathematical Biology* (New York: Springer Verlag, 1990).

What Does the SI-Phase Plane Tell Us?

To learn how the disease progresses, look at the shape of the curve in Figure 11.77. The value of I increases to about 300 (the maximum number infected and infectious at any one time); then I decreases to zero. This peak value of I occurs when $S \approx 200$. We can determine exactly when the peak value occurs by solving

$$\frac{dI}{dS} = -1 + \frac{192}{S} = 0,$$

which gives

$$S = 192.$$

Notice that the peak value for I always occurs at the same value of S, namely $S = 192$. The graph shows that if a trajectory starts with $S_0 > 192$, then I first increases and then decreases to zero. On the other hand, if $S_0 < 192$, there is no peak as I decreases right away.

> For this example, the value $S_0 = 192$ is called a *threshold value*. If S_0 is around or below 192, there is no epidemic. If S_0 is significantly greater than 192, an epidemic occurs.[26]

The phase diagram makes clear that the maximum value of I is about 300. Another question answered by the phase plane diagram is the total number of students who are expected to get sick during the epidemic. (This is not the maximum value reached by I, which gives the maximum number infected at any one time.) The point at which the trajectory crosses the S-axis represents the time when the epidemic has passed (since $I = 0$). The S-intercept shows how many boys never get the flu and thus, how many do get it.

How Many People Should Be Vaccinated?

An epidemic can sometimes be avoided by vaccination. How many boys would have had to be vaccinated to prevent the flu epidemic? To answer this, think of vaccination as removing people from the S category (without increasing I), which amounts to moving the initial point on the trajectory to the left, parallel to the S-axis. To avoid an epidemic, the initial value of S_0 should be at or below the threshold value. Therefore, all but 192 boys would need to be vaccinated.

Graphs of S and I Against t

To find out exactly when I reaches its maximum, we need numerical methods. A modification of Euler's method was used to generate the solution curves of S and I against t in Figure 11.78. Notice that the number of susceptibles drops throughout the disease as healthy people get sick. The number of infecteds peaks after about 6 days and then drops. The epidemic has run its course in 20 days.

Analytical Solution for the SI-Phase Trajectory

The differential equation

$$\frac{dI}{dS} = -1 + \frac{192}{S}$$

can be integrated, giving

$$I = -S + 192 \ln S + C.$$

Using $S_0 = 762$ and $I_0 = 1$ gives $1 = -762 + 192 \ln 762 + C$, so we get $C = 763 - 192 \ln 762$. Substituting this value for C, we get:

$$I = -S + 192 \ln S - 192 \ln 762 + 763$$
$$I = -S + 192 \ln \left(\frac{S}{762} \right) + 763.$$

This is the equation of the solution curve in Figure 11.77.

---

[26]Here we are using J. D. Murray's definition of an epidemic as an outbreak in which the number of infecteds increases from the initial value, I_0. See *Mathematical Biology* (New York: Springer Verlag, 1990).

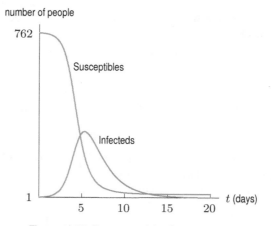

number of people

Figure 11.78: Progress of the flu over time

Two Interacting Populations: Predator-Prey

We now consider two populations which interact. They may compete for food, one may prey on the other, or they may enjoy a symbiotic relationship in which each helps the other. We model a predator-prey system using the *Lotka-Volterra equations*.

Robins and Worms

Let's look at an idealized case[27] in which robins are the predators and worms are the prey. There are r thousand robins and w million worms. If there were no robins, the worms would increase exponentially according to the equation

$$\frac{dw}{dt} = aw \quad \text{where } a \text{ is a constant and } a > 0.$$

If there were no worms, the robins would have no food and their population would decrease according to the equation[28]

$$\frac{dr}{dt} = -br \quad \text{where } b \text{ is a constant and } b > 0.$$

Now we account for the effect of the two populations on one another. Clearly, the presence of the robins is bad for the worms, so

$$\frac{dw}{dt} = aw - \text{Effect of robins on worms.}$$

On the other hand, the robins do better with the worms around, so

$$\frac{dr}{dt} = -br + \text{Effect of worms on robins.}$$

How exactly do the two populations interact? Let's assume the effect of one population on the other is proportional to the number of "encounters." (An encounter is when a robin eats a worm.) The number of encounters is likely to be proportional to the product of the populations because the more there are of either population, the more encounters there will be. So we assume

$$\frac{dw}{dt} = aw - cwr \quad \text{and} \quad \frac{dr}{dt} = -br + kwr,$$

where c and k are positive constants.

To analyze this system of equations, let's look at the specific example with $a = b = c = k = 1$:

$$\frac{dw}{dt} = w - wr \quad \text{and} \quad \frac{dr}{dt} = -r + wr.$$

---

[27] Based on ideas from Thomas A. McMahon.

[28] You might criticize this assumption because it predicts that the number of robins will decay exponentially, rather than die out in finite time.

To visualize the solutions to these equations, we look for trajectories in the phase plane. First we use the chain rule,

$$\frac{dr}{dw} = \frac{dr/dt}{dw/dt},$$

to obtain

$$\frac{dr}{dw} = \frac{-r + wr}{w - wr}.$$

The Slope Field and Equilibrium Points

We can get an idea of what solutions of this equation look like from the slope field in Figure 11.79. At the point $(1, 1)$ there is no slope drawn because at this point the rate of change of the worm population with respect to time is zero:

$$\frac{dw}{dt} = 1 - (1)(1) = 0.$$

The rate of change of the robin population with respect to time is also zero:

$$\frac{dr}{dt} = -1 + (1)(1) = 0.$$

Thus dr/dw is undefined. In terms of worms and robins, this means that if at some moment $w = 1$ and $r = 1$ (that is, there are 1 million worms and 1 thousand robins), then w and r remain constant forever. The point $w = 1$, $r = 1$ is therefore an equilibrium solution. The slope field suggests that there are no other equilibrium points except the origin.

At an **equilibrium point**, both w and r are constant, so

$$\frac{dw}{dt} = 0 \qquad \text{and} \qquad \frac{dr}{dt} = 0.$$

Therefore, we look for equilibrium points by solving

$$\frac{dw}{dt} = w - wr = 0 \quad \text{and} \quad \frac{dr}{dt} = -r + rw = 0,$$

which has $w = 0$, $r = 0$ and $w = 1$, $r = 1$ as the only solutions.

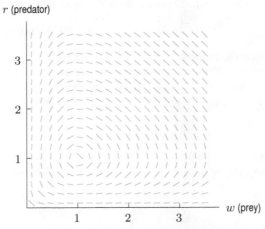

Figure 11.79: Slope field for $\dfrac{dr}{dw} = \dfrac{-r + wr}{w - wr}$

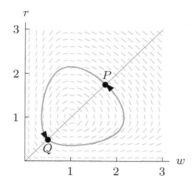

Figure 11.80: Solution curve is closed

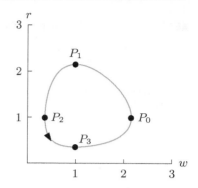

Figure 11.81: Trajectory in the phase plane

Trajectories in the wr-Phase Plane

Let's look at the trajectories in the phase plane. Remember that a point on a curve represents a pair of populations (w, r) existing at the same time t (though t is not shown on the graph). A short time later, the pair of populations is represented by a nearby point. As time passes, the point traces out a trajectory. The direction is marked on the curve by an arrow. (See Figure 11.80.)

How do we figure out which way to move on the trajectory? Approximating the solution numerically shows that the trajectory is traversed counterclockwise. Alternatively, look at the original pair of differential equations. At the point P_0 in Figure 11.81, where $w > 1$ and $r = 1$,

$$\frac{dr}{dt} = -r + wr = -1 + w > 0.$$

Therefore, r is increasing, so the point is moving counterclockwise around the closed curve.

Now let's think about why the solution curves are closed curves (that is, why they come back and meet themselves). Notice that the slope field is symmetric about the line $w = r$. We can confirm this by observing that interchanging w and r does not alter the differential equation for dr/dw. This means that if we start at point P on the line $w = r$ and travel once around the point $(1, 1)$, we arrive back at the same point P. The reason is that the second half of the path, from Q to P, is the reflection of the first half, from P to Q, in the line $w = r$. (See Figure 11.80.) If we did not end up at P again, the second half of our path would have a different shape from the first half.

The Populations as Functions of Time

The shape of the trajectories tells us how the populations vary with time. We start at $t = 0$ at the point P_0 in Figure 11.81. Then we move to P_1 at time t_1, to P_2 at time t_2, to P_3 at time t_3, and so on. At time t_4 we are back at P_0, and the whole cycle repeats. Since the trajectory is a closed curve, both populations oscillate periodically with the same period. The worms (the prey) are at their maximum a quarter of a cycle before the robins. (See Figure 11.82.)

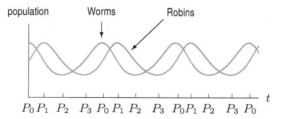

Figure 11.82: Populations of robins (in thousands) and worms (in millions) over time

Exercises and Problems for Section 11.8

Exercises

For Exercises 1–4, suppose x and y are the populations of two different species. Describe in words how each population changes with time.

1.

2.

3.

4.

In Exercises 5–8, find all equilibrium points. Give answers as ordered pairs (x, y).

5. $\dfrac{dx}{dt} = -3x + xy$

$\dfrac{dy}{dt} = 5y - xy$

6. $\dfrac{dx}{dt} = -2x + 4xy$

$\dfrac{dy}{dt} = -8y + 2xy$

7. $\dfrac{dx}{dt} = 15x - 5xy$

$\dfrac{dy}{dt} = 10y + 2xy$

8. $\dfrac{dx}{dt} = x^2 - xy$

$\dfrac{dy}{dt} = 15y - 3y^2$

9. Given the system of differential equations

$$\frac{dx}{dt} = 5x - 3xy$$
$$\frac{dy}{dt} = -8y + xy$$

determine whether x and y are increasing or decreasing at the point

   (a) $x = 3, y = 2$ **(b)** $x = 5, y = 1$

10. Given the system of differential equations

$$\frac{dP}{dt} = 2P - 10$$
$$\frac{dQ}{dt} = Q - 0.2PQ$$

determine whether P and Q are increasing or decreasing at the point

   (a) $P = 2, Q = 3$ **(b)** $P = 6, Q = 5$

Problems

11. Figure 11.83 shows the trajectory through the SI phase plane of a 50-day epidemic.

   (a) Make an approximate table of values for the number of susceptibles and infecteds on the days marked on the trajectory.

   (b) When is the epidemic at its peak? How many people are infected then?

   (c) During the course of the epidemic, how many catch the disease and how many are spared?

Figure 11.83: Days 8 through 44 of an epidemic

12. Figure 11.84 shows the number of susceptibles and infecteds in a population of 4000 through the course of a 60-day epidemic.

   (a) How many are infected on day 20?

   (b) How many have had the disease by day 20?

   (c) How many have had the disease by the time the epidemic is over?

Figure 11.84

13. Humans vs Zombies[29] is a game in which one player starts as a zombie and turns human players into zombies by tagging them. Zombies have to "eat" on a regular basis by tagging human players, or they die of starvation and are out of the game. The game is usually played over a period of about five days. If we let H represent the size of the human population and Z represent the size of the zombie population in the game, then, for constant parameters a, b, and c, we have:

$$\frac{dH}{dt} = aHZ$$

$$\frac{dZ}{dt} = bZ + cHZ$$

(a) Decide whether each of the parameters a, b, c is positive or negative.

(b) What is the relationship, if any, between a and c?

14. Four pairs of species are given, with descriptions of how they interact.

  I. Bees/flowers: each needs the other to survive
  II. Owls/trees: owls need trees but trees are indifferent
  III. Elk/buffalo: in competition and would do fine alone
  IV. Fox/hare: fox eats the hare and needs it to survive

Match each system of differential equations with a species pair, and indicate which species is x and which is y.

(a) $\dfrac{dx}{dt} = -0.2x + 0.03xy$

   $\dfrac{dy}{dt} = 0.4y - 0.08xy$

(b) $\dfrac{dx}{dt} = 0.18x$

   $\dfrac{dy}{dt} = -0.4y + 0.3xy$

(c) $\dfrac{dx}{dt} = -0.6x + 0.18xy$

   $\dfrac{dy}{dt} = -0.1y + 0.09xy$

(d) Write a possible system of differential equations for the species pair that does not have a match.

15. Show that if S, I, and R satisfy the differential equations on page 640, the total population, $S + I + R$, is constant.

For Problems 16–24, let w be the number of worms (in millions) and r the number of robins (in thousands) living on an island. Suppose w and r satisfy the following differential equations, which correspond to the slope field in Figure 11.85.

$$\frac{dw}{dt} = w - wr, \qquad \frac{dr}{dt} = -r + wr.$$

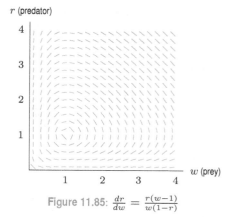

Figure 11.85: $\dfrac{dr}{dw} = \dfrac{r(w-1)}{w(1-r)}$

16. Explain why these differential equations are a reasonable model for interaction between the two populations. Why have the signs been chosen this way?

17. Solve these differential equations in the two special cases when there are no robins and when there are no worms living on the island.

18. Describe and explain the symmetry you observe in the slope field. What consequences does this symmetry have for the solution curves?

19. Assume $w = 2$ and $r = 2$ when $t = 0$. Do the numbers of robins and worms increase or decrease at first? What happens in the long run?

20. For the case discussed in Problem 19, estimate the maximum and the minimum values of the robin population. How many worms are there at the time when the robin population reaches its maximum?

21. On the same axes, graph w and r (the worm and the robin populations) against time. Use initial values of 1.5 for w and 1 for r. You may do this without units for t.

22. People on the island like robins so much that they decide to import 200 robins all the way from England, to increase the initial population from $r = 2$ to $r = 2.2$ when $t = 0$. Does this make sense? Why or why not?

23. Assume that $w = 3$ and $r = 1$ when $t = 0$. Do the numbers of robins and worms increase or decrease initially? What happens in the long run?

24. For the case discussed in Problem 23, estimate the maximum and minimum values of the robin population. Estimate the number of worms when the robin population reaches its minimum.

The systems of differential equations in Problems 25–27 model the interaction of two populations x and y. In each case, answer the following two questions:

(a) What kinds of interaction (symbiosis,[30] competition, predator-prey) do the equations describe?

---

[29]http://humansvszombies.org

[30]Symbiosis takes place when the interaction of two species benefits both. An example is the pollination of plants by insects.

(b) What happens in the long run? (For one of the systems, your answer will depend on the initial populations.) Use a calculator or computer to draw slope fields.

25. $\dfrac{1}{x}\dfrac{dx}{dt} = y - 1$

$\dfrac{1}{y}\dfrac{dy}{dt} = x - 1$

26. $\dfrac{1}{x}\dfrac{dx}{dt} = 1 - \dfrac{x}{2} - \dfrac{y}{2}$

$\dfrac{1}{y}\dfrac{dy}{dt} = 1 - x - y$

27. $\dfrac{1}{x}\dfrac{dx}{dt} = y - 1 - 0.05x$

$\dfrac{1}{y}\dfrac{dy}{dt} = 1 - x - 0.05y$

For Problems 28–31, consider a conflict between two armies of x and y soldiers, respectively. During World War I, F. W. Lanchester assumed that if both armies are fighting a conventional battle within sight of one another, the rate at which soldiers in one army are put out of action (killed or wounded) is proportional to the amount of fire the other army can concentrate on them, which is in turn proportional to the number of soldiers in the opposing army. Thus Lanchester assumed that if there are no reinforcements and t represents time since the start of the battle, then x and y obey the differential equations

$$\frac{dx}{dt} = -ay$$
$$\frac{dy}{dt} = -bx \quad a, b > 0.$$

28. Near the end of World War II a fierce battle took place between US and Japanese troops over the island of Iwo Jima, off the coast of Japan. Applying Lanchester's analysis to this battle, with x representing the number of US troops and y the number of Japanese troops, it has been estimated[31] that $a = 0.05$ and $b = 0.01$.

(a) Using these values for a and b and ignoring reinforcements, write a differential equation involving dy/dx and sketch its slope field.

(b) Assuming that the initial strength of the US forces was 54,000 and that of the Japanese was 21,500, draw the trajectory which describes the battle. What outcome is predicted? (That is, which side do the differential equations predict will win?)

(c) Would knowing that the US in fact had 19,000 reinforcements, while the Japanese had none, alter the outcome predicted?

29. (a) For two armies of strengths x and y fighting a conventional battle governed by Lanchester's differential equations, write a differential equation involving dy/dx and the constants of attrition a and b.

(b) Solve the differential equation and hence show that the equation of the phase trajectory is

$$ay^2 - bx^2 = C$$

for some constant C. This equation is called *Lanchester's square law*. The value of C depends on the initial sizes of the two armies.

30. Consider the battle of Iwo Jima, described in Problem 28. Take $a = 0.05$, $b = 0.01$ and assume the initial strength of the US troops to be 54,000 and that of the Japanese troops to be 21,500. (Again, ignore reinforcements.)

(a) Using Lanchester's square law derived in Problem 29, find the equation of the trajectory describing the battle.

(b) Assuming that the Japanese fought without surrendering until they had all been killed, as was the case, how many US troops does this model predict would be left when the battle ended?

31. In this problem we adapt Lanchester's model for a conventional battle to the case in which one or both of the armies is a guerrilla force. We assume that the rate at which a guerrilla force is put out of action is proportional to the product of the strengths of the two armies.

(a) Give a justification for the assumption that the rate at which a guerrilla force is put out of action is proportional to the product of the strengths of the two armies.

(b) Write the differential equations which describe a conflict between a guerrilla army of strength x and a conventional army of strength y, assuming all the constants of proportionality are 1.

(c) Find a differential equation involving dy/dx and solve it to find equations of phase trajectories.

(d) Describe which side wins in terms of the constant of integration. What happens if the constant is zero?

(e) Use your solution to part (d) to divide the phase plane into regions according to which side wins.

32. To model a conflict between two guerrilla armies, we assume that the rate that each one is put out of action is proportional to the product of the strengths of the two armies.

(a) Write the differential equations which describe a conflict between two guerrilla armies of strengths x and y, respectively.

(b) Find a differential equation involving dy/dx and solve to find equations of phase trajectories.

(c) Describe which side wins in terms of the constant of integration. What happens if the constant is zero?

(d) Use your solution to part (c) to divide the phase plane into regions according to which side wins.

33. The predator-prey model on page 643 for the number of robins, r, in thousands, and the number of worms, w, in millions, was for some positive constants a, b, c, k:

$$\frac{dw}{dt} = aw - cwr \quad \text{and} \quad \frac{dr}{dt} = -br + kwr.$$

(a) Find the equilibrium points of this system of equations.

---

[31] See Martin Braun, *Differential Equations and Their Applications*, 2[nd]ed. (New York: Springer Verlag, 1975).

(b) An insecticide is applied to the ground, causing a decline in the number of worms proportional to their population. What effect does this have on the equi-

librium point? Interpret this in terms of the equilibrium population of worms and robins.

Strengthen Your Understanding

In Problems 34–35, explain what is wrong with the statement.

34. If $dx/dt = 3x - 0.4xy$ and $dy/dt = 4y - 0.5xy$, then an increase in x corresponds to a decrease in y.

35. For a system of differential equations for x and y, at the point $(2, 3)$, we have $dx/dt < 0$ and $dy/dt > 0$ and $dy/dx > 0$.

In Problems 36–38, give an example of:

36. A system of differential equations for two populations X and Y such that Y needs X to survive and X is indifferent to Y and thrives on its own. Let x represent the size of the X population and y represent the size of the Y population.

37. A system of differential equations for the profits of two

companies if each would thrive on its own but the two companies compete for business. Let x and y represent the profits of the two companies.

38. Two diseases D_1 and D_2 such that the parameter a in the S-I-R model on page 640 is larger for disease D_1 than it is for disease D_2. Explain your reasoning.

Are the statements in Problems 39–40 true or false? Give an explanation for your answer.

39. The system of differential equations $dx/dt = -x + xy^2$ and $dy/dt = y - x^2y$ requires initial conditions for both $x(0)$ and $y(0)$ to determine a unique solution.

40. Populations modeled by a system of differential equations never die out.

11.9   ANALYZING THE PHASE PLANE

In the previous section we analyzed a system of differential equations using a slope field. In this section we analyze a system of differential equations using *nullclines*. We consider two species having similar *niches*, or ways of living, and that are in competition for food and space. In such cases, one species often becomes extinct. This phenomenon is called the *Principle of Competitive Exclusion*. We see how differential equations predict this in a particular case.

Competitive Exclusion: Citrus Tree Parasites

The citrus farmers of Southern California are interested in controlling the insects that live on their trees. Some of these insects can be controlled by parasites that live on the trees too. Scientists are, therefore, interested in understanding under what circumstances these parasites flourish or die out. One such parasite was introduced accidentally from the Mediterranean; later, other parasites were introduced from China and India; in each case the previous parasite became extinct over part of its habitat. In 1963 a lab experiment was carried out to determine which one of a pair of species became extinct when they were in competition with each other. The data on one pair of species, called A. *fisheri* and A. *melinus*, with populations P_1 and P_2 respectively, is given in Table 11.8 and shows that A. *melinus* (P_2) became extinct after 8 generations.[32]

Table 11.8   *Population (in thousands) of two species of parasite as a function of time*

Generation number	1	2	3	4	5	6	7	8
Population P_1 (thousands)	0.193	1.093	1.834	5.819	13.705	16.965	18.381	16.234
Population P_2 (thousands)	0.083	0.229	0.282	0.378	0.737	0.507	0.13	0

Data from the same experimenters indicates that, when alone, each population grows logistically. In fact, their data suggests that, when alone, the population of P_1 might grow according to the

[32]Data adapted from Paul DeBach and Ragnhild Sundby, "Competitive Displacement Between Ecological Homologues," *Hilgardia 34*:17 (1963).

equation

$$\frac{dP_1}{dt} = 0.05P_1\left(1 - \frac{P_1}{20}\right),$$

and when alone, the population of P_2 might grow according to the equation

$$\frac{dP_2}{dt} = 0.09P_2\left(1 - \frac{P_2}{15}\right).$$

Now suppose both parasites are present. Each tends to reduce the growth rate of the other, so each differential equation is modified by subtracting a term on the right. The experimental data shows that together P_1 and P_2 can be well described by the equations

$$\frac{dP_1}{dt} = 0.05P_1\left(1 - \frac{P_1}{20}\right) - 0.002P_1P_2$$

$$\frac{dP_2}{dt} = 0.09P_2\left(1 - \frac{P_2}{15}\right) - 0.15P_1P_2.$$

The fact that P_2 dies out with time is reflected in these equations: the coefficient of P_1P_2 is much larger in the equation for P_2 than in the equation for P_1. This indicates that the interaction has a much more devastating effect upon the growth of P_2 than on the growth of P_1.

The Phase Plane and Nullclines

We consider the phase plane with the P_1 axis horizontal and the P_2 axis vertical. To find the trajectories in the P_1P_2 phase plane, we could draw a slope field as in the previous section. Instead, we use a method that gives a good qualitative picture of the behavior of the trajectories even without a calculator or computer. We find the *nullclines* or curves along which $dP_1/dt = 0$ or $dP_2/dt = 0$. At points where $dP_2/dt = 0$, the population P_2 is momentarily constant, so only population P_1 is changing with time. Therefore, at this point the trajectory is horizontal. (See Figure 11.86.) Similarly, at points where $dP_1/dt = 0$, the population P_1 is momentarily constant and population P_2 is the only one changing, so the trajectory is vertical there. A point where both $dP_1/dt = 0$ and $dP_2/dt = 0$ is called an *equilibrium point* because P_1 and P_2 both remain constant if they reach these values.

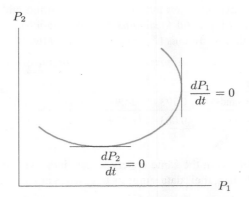

Figure 11.86: Points on a trajectory where
$dP_1/dt = 0$ or $dP_2/dt = 0$

On the $P_1 P_2$ phase plane:

- If $\dfrac{dP_1}{dt} = 0$, the trajectory is vertical.

- If $\dfrac{dP_2}{dt} = 0$, the trajectory is horizontal.

- If $\dfrac{dP_1}{dt} = \dfrac{dP_2}{dt} = 0$, there is an equilibrium point.

Using Nullclines to Analyze the Parasite Populations

In order to see where $dP_1/dt = 0$ or $dP_2/dt = 0$, we factor the right side of our differential equations:

$$\frac{dP_1}{dt} = 0.05P_1\left(1 - \frac{P_1}{20}\right) - 0.002P_1P_2 = 0.001P_1(50 - 2.5P_1 - 2P_2)$$

$$\frac{dP_2}{dt} = 0.09P_2\left(1 - \frac{P_2}{15}\right) - 0.15P_1P_2 = 0.001P_2(90 - 150P_1 - 6P_2).$$

Thus $dP_1/dt = 0$ where $P_1 = 0$ or where $50 - 2.5P_1 - 2P_2 = 0$. Graphing these equations in the phase plane gives two lines, which are nullclines. Since the trajectory is vertical where $dP_1/dt = 0$, in Figure 11.87 we draw small vertical line segments on these nullclines to represent the direction of the trajectories as they cross the nullcline. Similarly $dP_2/dt = 0$ where $P_2 = 0$ or where $90 - 150P_1 - 6P_2 = 0$. These equations are graphed in Figure 11.87 with small horizontal line segments on them.

The equilibrium points are where both $dP_1/dt = 0$ and $dP_2/dt = 0$, namely the points $P_1 = 0, P_2 = 0$ (meaning that both species die out); $P_1 = 0, P_2 = 15$ (where P_1 is extinct); and $P_1 = 20, P_2 = 0$ (where P_2 is extinct).

What Happens in the Regions Between the Nullclines?

Nullclines are useful because they divide the plane into regions in which the signs of dP_1/dt and dP_2/dt are constant. In each region, the direction of every trajectory remains roughly the same.

In Region I, for example, we might try the point $P_1 = 20, P_2 = 25$. Then

$$\frac{dP_1}{dt} = 0.001(20)(50 - 2.5(20) - 2(25)) < 0$$

$$\frac{dP_2}{dt} = 0.001(25)(90 - 150(20) - 6(25)) < 0.$$

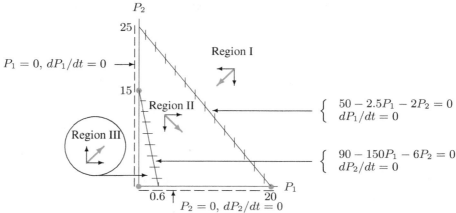

Figure 11.87: Analyzing three regions in the phase plane using nullclines (axes distorted) with equilibrium points represented by dots

Now $dP_1/dt < 0$, so P_1 is decreasing, which can be represented by an arrow in the direction ←. Also, $dP_2/dt < 0$, so P_2 is decreasing, as represented by the arrow ↓. Combining these directions, we know that the trajectories in this region go approximately in the diagonal direction ↙ (See Region I in Figure 11.87.)

In Region II, try, for example, $P_1 = 1, P_2 = 1$. Then we have

$$\frac{dP_1}{dt} = 0.001(1)(50 - 2.5 - 2) > 0$$
$$\frac{dP_2}{dt} = 0.001(1)(90 - 150 - 6) < 0.$$

So here, P_1 is increasing while P_2 is decreasing. (See Region II in Figure 11.87.)

In Region III, try $P_1 = 0.1, P_2 = 0.1$:

$$\frac{dP_1}{dt} = 0.001(0.1)(50 - 2.5(0.1) - 2(0.1)) > 0$$
$$\frac{dP_2}{dt} = 0.001(0.1)(90 - 150(0.1) - 6(0.1)) > 0.$$

So here, both P_1 and P_2 are increasing. (See Region III in Figure 11.87.)

Notice that the behavior of the populations in each region makes biological sense. In region I both populations are so large that overpopulation is a problem, so both populations decrease. In Region III both populations are so small that they are effectively not in competition, so both grow. In Region II competition between the species comes into play. The fact that P_1 increases while P_2 decreases in Region II means that P_1 wins.

Solution Trajectories

Suppose the system starts with some of each population. This means that the initial point of the trajectory is not on one of the axes, and so it is in Region I, II, or III. Then the point moves on a trajectory like one of those computed numerically and shown in Figure 11.88. Notice that *all* these trajectories tend toward the point $P_1 = 20, P_2 = 0$, corresponding to a population of 20,000 for P_1 and extinction for P_2. Consequently, this model predicts that no matter what the initial populations are, provided $P_1 \neq 0$, the population of P_2 is excluded by P_1, and P_1 tends to a constant value. This makes biological sense: in the absence of P_2, we would expect P_1 to settle down to the carrying capacity of the niche, which is 20,000.

Figure 11.88: Trajectories showing exclusion of population P_2 (not to scale)

Exercises and Problems for Section 11.9

Exercises

In Exercises 1–5, use Figure 11.89.

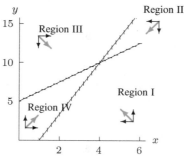

Figure 11.89: Nullclines in the phase plane of a system of differential equations

1. Give the coordinates for each equilibrium point.
2. At each point, give the signs of dx/dt and dy/dt.
   - (a) $(4, 7)$
   - (b) $(4, 10)$
   - (c) $(6, 15)$
3. Draw a possible trajectory that starts at the point $(2, 5)$.
4. Draw a possible trajectory that starts at the point $(2, 10)$.
5. What is the long-run behavior of a trajectory that starts at any point in the first quadrant?

In Exercises 6–10, use Figure 11.90.

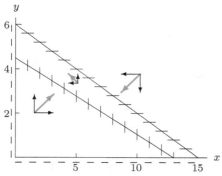

Figure 11.90: Nullclines in the phase plane of a system of differential equations

6. Give the approximate coordinates for each equilibrium point.

7. At each point, give the signs of dx/dt and dy/dt.
   - (a) $(5, 2)$
   - (b) $(10, 2)$
   - (c) $(10, 1)$

8. Draw a possible trajectory that starts at the point $(2, 5)$.

9. Draw a possible trajectory that starts at the point $(10, 4)$.

10. What is the long-run behavior of a trajectory that starts at any point in the first quadrant?

11. Figure 11.91 shows a phase plane for a system of differential equations. Draw the nullclines.

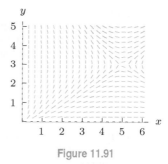

Figure 11.91

12. (a) Find the equilibrium points for the following system of equations

$$\frac{dx}{dt} = 20x - 10xy$$

$$\frac{dy}{dt} = 25y - 5xy.$$

   (b) Explain why $x = 2$, $y = 4$ is not an equilibrium point for this system.

Problems

For Problems 13–18, analyze the phase plane of the differential equations for x, $y \geq 0$. Show the nullclines and equilibrium points, and sketch the direction of the trajectories in each region.

13. $\dfrac{dx}{dt} = x(2 - x - y)$
    $\dfrac{dy}{dt} = y(1 - x - y)$

14. $\dfrac{dx}{dt} = x(2 - x - 3y)$
    $\dfrac{dy}{dt} = y(1 - 2x)$

15. $\dfrac{dx}{dt} = x(2 - x - 2y)$
    $\dfrac{dy}{dt} = y(1 - 2x - y)$

16. $\dfrac{dx}{dt} = x(1 - y - \dfrac{x}{3})$
    $\dfrac{dy}{dt} = y(1 - \dfrac{y}{2} - x)$

17. $\dfrac{dx}{dt} = x\left(1 - x - \dfrac{y}{3}\right)$
    $\dfrac{dy}{dt} = y\left(1 - y - \dfrac{x}{2}\right)$

18. $\dfrac{dx}{dt} = x\left(1 - \dfrac{x}{2} - y\right)$
    $\dfrac{dy}{dt} = y\left(1 - \dfrac{y}{3} - x\right)$

19. The equations describing the flu epidemic in a boarding school are

$$\frac{dS}{dt} = -0.0026SI$$

$$\frac{dI}{dt} = 0.0026SI - 0.5I.$$

(a) Find the nullclines and equilibrium points in the SI phase plane.

(b) Find the direction of the trajectories in each region.

(c) Sketch some typical trajectories and describe their behavior in words.

20. Use the idea of nullclines dividing the plane into sectors to analyze the equations describing the interactions of robins and worms:

$$\frac{dw}{dt} = w - wr$$

$$\frac{dr}{dt} = -r + rw.$$

21. Two companies share the market for a new technology. They have no competition except each other. Let $A(t)$ be the net worth of one company and $B(t)$ the net worth of the other at time t. Suppose that net worth cannot be negative and that A and B satisfy the differential equations

$$A' = 2A - AB$$

$$B' = B - AB.$$

(a) What do these equations predict about the net worth of each company if the other were not present? What effect do the companies have on each other?

(b) Are there any equilibrium points? If so, what are they?

(c) Sketch a slope field for these equations (using a computer or calculator), and hence describe the different possible long-run behaviors.

22. In the 1930s L. F. Richardson proposed that an arms race between two countries could be modeled by a system of differential equations. One arms race that can be reasonably well described by differential equations is the US-Soviet Union arms race between 1945 and 1960. If $x represents the annual Soviet expenditures on armaments (in billions of dollars) and $y represents the corresponding US expenditures, it has been suggested[33] that x and y obey the following differential equations:

$$\frac{dx}{dt} = -0.45x + 10.5$$

$$\frac{dy}{dt} = 8.2x - 0.8y - 142.$$

(a) Find the nullclines and equilibrium points for these differential equations. Which direction do the trajectories go in each region?

(b) Sketch some typical trajectories in the phase plane.

(c) What do these differential equations predict will be the long-term outcome of the US-Soviet arms race?

(d) Discuss these predictions in the light of the actual expenditures in Table 11.9.

Table 11.9   *Arms budgets of the United States and the Soviet Union for the years 1945–1960 (billions of dollars)*

	USSR	USA		USSR	USA
1945	14	97	1953	25.7	71.4
1946	14	80	1954	23.9	61.6
1947	15	29	1955	25.5	58.3
1948	20	20	1956	23.2	59.4
1949	20	22	1957	23.0	61.4
1950	21	23	1958	22.3	61.4
1951	22.7	49.6	1959	22.3	61.7
1952	26.0	69.6	1960	22.1	59.6

23. In the 1930s, the Soviet ecologist G. F. Gause performed a series of experiments on competition among two yeasts with populations P_1 and P_2, respectively. By performing population studies at low density in large volumes, he determined what he called the *coefficients of geometric increase* (and we would call continuous exponential growth rates). These coefficients described the growth of each yeast alone:

$$\frac{1}{P_1}\frac{dP_1}{dt} = 0.2$$

$$\frac{1}{P_2}\frac{dP_2}{dt} = 0.06$$

where P_1 and P_2 are measured in units that Gause established.

He also determined that, in his units, the carrying capacity of P_1 was 13 and the carrying capacity of P_2 was 6. He then observed that one P_2 occupies the niche space of 3 P_1 and that one P_1 occupied the niche space of 0.4 P_2. This led him to the following differential equations to describe the interaction of P_1 and P_2:

$$\frac{dP_1}{dt} = 0.2P_1\left(\frac{13 - (P_1 + 3P_2)}{13}\right)$$

$$\frac{dP_2}{dt} = 0.06P_2\left(\frac{6 - (P_2 + 0.4P_1)}{6}\right).$$

When both yeasts were growing together, Gause recorded the data in Table 11.10.

Table 11.10   *Gause's yeast populations*

Time (hours)	6	16	24	29	48	53
P_1	0.375	3.99	4.69	6.15	7.27	8.30
P_2	0.29	0.98	1.47	1.46	1.71	1.84

(a) Carry out a phase plane analysis of Gause's equations.

(b) Mark the data points on the phase plane and describe what would have happened had Gause continued the experiment.

---

[33]R. Taagepera, G. M. Schiffler, R. T. Perkins and D. L. Wagner, *Soviet-American and Israeli-Arab Arms Races and the Richardson Model* (General Systems, XX, 1975).

Strengthen Your Understanding

In Problems 24–25, explain what is wrong with the statement.

24. A solution trajectory and nullclines for a system of differential equations are shown in Figure 11.92.

Figure 11.92

25. The nullclines for a system of differential equations are shown in Figure 11.93. The system has an equilibrium at the point $(6, 6)$.

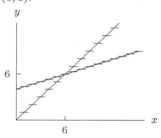

Figure 11.93

In Problems 26–28, give an example of:

26. A graph of the nullclines of a system of differential equations with exactly two equilibrium points in the first quadrant. Label the nullclines to show whether trajectories pass through the nullcline vertically or horizontally.

27. The nullclines of a system of differential equations with the trajectory shown in Figure 11.94.

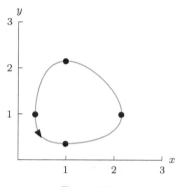

Figure 11.94

28. A trajectory for a system of differential equations with nullclines in Figure 11.95 and initial conditions $x = 1$ and $y = 2$.

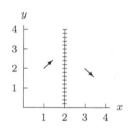

Figure 11.95

CHAPTER SUMMARY (see also Ready Reference at the end of the book)

- **Differential equations terminology**
  Order, initial conditions, families of solutions, stable/unstable equilibrium solutions.

- **Solving first-order differential equations**
  Slope fields (graphical), Euler's method (numerical), separation of variables (analytical).

- **Modeling with differential equations**
  Growth and decay, Newton's Law of Heating and Cooling, compartment models, logistic model.

- **Systems of differential equations**
  $S\text{-}I\text{-}R$ model, predator-prey model, phase plane.

REVIEW EXERCISES AND PROBLEMS FOR CHAPTER ELEVEN

Exercises

1. Which of the differential equations are satisfied by the functions on the right?

(a) $y'' + 2y = 0$

(b) $y'' - 2y = 0$

(c) $y'' + 2y' + y = 0$

(d) $y'' - 2y' + y = 0$

(I) $y = xe^x$

(II) $y = xe^{-x}$

2. Match the slope fields in Figure 11.96 with their differential equations:

(a) $y' = 1 + y^2$ (b) $y' = x$ (c) $y' = \sin x$
(d) $y' = y$ (e) $y' = x - y$ (f) $y' = 4 - y$

Figure 11.96: Each slope field is graphed for
$-5 \le x \le 5, -5 \le y \le 5$

3. The graphs in Figure 11.97 represent the temperature, $H(°C)$, of four eggs as a function of time, t, in minutes. Match three of the graphs with the descriptions (a)–(c). Write a similar description for the fourth graph, including an interpretation of any intercepts and asymptotes.

(a) An egg is taken out of the refrigerator (just above $0°C$) and put into boiling water.
(b) Twenty minutes after the egg in part (a) is taken out of the fridge and put into boiling water, the same thing is done with another egg.
(c) An egg is taken out of the refrigerator at the same time as the egg in part (a) and left to sit on the kitchen table.

(I) $H(°C)$

(II) $H(°C)$

(III) $H(°C)$

(IV) $H(°C)$

Figure 11.97

Find a general solution to the differential equations in Exercises 4–9.

4. $\dfrac{dP}{dt} = t$

5. $\dfrac{dy}{dx} = 0.2y - 8$

6. $\dfrac{dP}{dt} = 10 - 2P$

7. $\dfrac{dH}{dt} = 0.5H + 10$

8. $\dfrac{dR}{dt} = 2R - 6R^2$

9. $\dfrac{dP}{dt} = 0.4P(1 - 0.01P)$

For the differential equations in Exercises 10–25, find a solution which passes through the given point.

10. $\dfrac{dy}{dx} + xy^2 = 0$, $y(1) = 1$

11. $\dfrac{dP}{dt} = 0.03P + 400$, $P(0) = 0$

12. $1 + y^2 - \dfrac{dy}{dx} = 0$, $y(0) = 0$

13. $2\sin x - y^2 \dfrac{dy}{dx} = 0$, $y(0) = 3$

14. $\dfrac{dk}{dt} = (1 + \ln t)k$, $k(1) = 1$

15. $\dfrac{dy}{dx} = \dfrac{y(3 - x)}{x(0.5y - 4)}$, $y(1) = 5$

16. $\dfrac{dy}{dx} = \dfrac{0.2y(18 + 0.1x)}{x(100 + 0.5y)}$, $(10, 10)$

17. $\dfrac{dz}{dt} = z(z - 1)$, $z(0) = 10$

18. $\dfrac{dy}{dt} = y(10 - y)$, $y(0) = 1$

19. $\dfrac{dy}{dx} = \dfrac{y(100 - x)}{x(20 - y)}$, $(1, 20)$

20. $\dfrac{df}{dx} = \sqrt{xf(x)}$, $f(1) = 1$

21. $\dfrac{dy}{dx} = e^{x-y}$, $y(0) = 1$

22. $\dfrac{dy}{dx} = e^{x+y}$, $y = 0$ where $x = 1$

23. $e^{-\cos\theta}\dfrac{dz}{d\theta} = \sqrt{1 - z^2}\sin\theta$, $z(0) = \frac{1}{2}$

24. $(1 + t^2)y\dfrac{dy}{dt} = 1 - y$, $y(1) = 0$

25. $\dfrac{dy}{dt} = 2^y \sin^3 t$, $y(0) = 0$

Problems

26. A population satisfies $dP/dt = 0.025P - 0.00005P^2$.

  (a) What are the equilibrium values for P?

  (b) For each of the following initial conditions, will P increase, decrease, or stay the same? Will the population increase or decrease without bound or to a limiting value? If to a limiting value, what is it?

  (a) $P_0 = 100$ **(b)** $P_0 = 400$

  (c) $P_0 = 500$ **(d)** $P_0 = 800$

27. (a) What are the equilibrium solutions for the differential equation

$$\frac{dy}{dt} = 0.2(y - 3)(y + 2)?$$

  (b) Use a slope field to determine whether each equilibrium solution is stable or unstable.

In Problems 28–29, is the function a solution to

$$y' = xy - y,$$

given that $y = f(x)$ satisfies this equation?

28. $y = 2f(x)$ **29.** $y = 2 + f(x)$

30. Find y when $x = 1/2$ on the solution passing through $(0, 0)$ of the differential equation

$$\frac{dy}{dx} = \frac{1}{(\cos x)(\cos y)}.$$

  (a) Use Euler's method with

    (i) $\Delta x = 1/2$ (1 step)   (ii) $\Delta x = 1/4$ (2 steps)
    (iii) $\Delta x = 1/8$ (4 steps)

  (b) Use separation of variables. Compare with your results in part (a).

31. Consider the initial value problem

$$y' = 5 - y, \quad y(0) = 1.$$

  (a) Use Euler's method with five steps to estimate $y(1)$.

  (b) Sketch the slope field for this differential equation in the first quadrant, and use it to decide if your estimate is an over- or underestimate.

  (c) Find the exact solution to the differential equation and hence find $y(1)$ exactly.

  (d) Without doing the calculation, roughly what would you expect the approximation for $y(1)$ to be with ten steps?

32. In 2007, the population of Switzerland was 7.5 million and was growing at a continuous rate of 0.38% per year.[34] Write an expression for the population as a function of time, t, in years since 2007.

33. The amount of land in use for growing crops increases as the world's population increases. Suppose $A(t)$ represents the total number of hectares of land in use in year t. (A hectare is about $2\frac{1}{2}$ acres.)

  (a) Explain why it is plausible that $A(t)$ satisfies the equation $A'(t) = kA(t)$. What assumptions are you making about the world's population and its relation to the amount of land used?

  (b) In 1966 about 4.55 billion hectares of land were in use; in 1996 the figure was 4.93 billion hectares.[35] If the total amount of land available for growing crops is thought to be 6 billion hectares, when does this model predict it will be exhausted? (Let $t = 0$ in 1966.)

34. The rate of growth of a tumor is proportional to the size of the tumor.

  (a) Write a differential equation satisfied by S, the size of the tumor, in mm, as a function of time, t.

  (b) Find the general solution to the differential equation.

  (c) If the tumor is 5 mm across at time $t = 0$, what does that tell you about the solution?

  (d) If, in addition, the tumor is 8 mm across at time $t = 3$, what does that tell you about the solution?

35. Money in a bank account grows continuously at an annual rate of r (when the interest rate is 5%, $r = 0.05$, and so on). Suppose \$2000 is put into the account in 2010.

  (a) Write a differential equation satisfied by M, the amount of money in the account at time t, measured in years since 2010.

  (b) Solve the differential equation.

  (c) Sketch the solution until the year 2040 for interest rates of 5% and 10%.

36. Radioactive carbon (carbon-14) decays at a rate of approximately 1 part in 10,000 a year. For an initial quantity Q_0, write and solve a differential equation for the quantity of carbon-14 as a function of time. Sketch a graph of the solution.

37. Suppose \$1000 is put into a bank account and earns interest continuously at a rate of i per year, and in addition, continuous payments are made out of the account at a rate of \$100 a year. Find a formula and sketch the amount of money in the account as a function of time if the interest rate is

  (a)   5%   **(b)**   10%   **(c)**   15%

---

[34]http://www.un.org/esa/population/publications/wpp2006/WPP2006_Highlights_rev.pdf, accessed April 24, 2012.
[35]http://www.farmingsolutions.org/facts/factscontent_det.asp, accessed June 6, 2011.

38. A cell contains a chemical (the solute) dissolved in it at a concentration $c(t)$, and the concentration of the same substance outside the cell is a constant k. By Fick's law, if $c(t)$ and k are unequal, solute moves across the cell wall at a rate proportional to the difference between $c(t)$ and k, toward the region of lower concentration.

(a) Write a differential equation satisfied by $c(t)$.

(b) Solve the differential equation with the initial condition $c(0) = c_0$.

(c) Sketch the solution for $c_0 = 0$.

39. A bank account earns 5% annual interest compounded continuously. Continuous payments are made out of the account at a rate of \$12,000 per year for 20 years.

(a) Write a differential equation describing the balance $B = f(t)$, where t is in years.

(b) Solve the differential equation given an initial balance of B_0.

(c) What should the initial balance be such that the account has zero balance after precisely 20 years?

40. In some chemical reactions, the rate at which the amount of a substance changes with time is proportional to the amount present. For example, this is the case as δ-glucono-lactone changes into gluconic acid.

(a) Write a differential equation satisfied by y, the quantity of δ-glucono-lactone present at time t.

(b) If 100 grams of δ-glucono-lactone is reduced to 54.9 grams in one hour, how many grams will remain after 10 hours?

41. When the electromotive force (emf) is removed from a circuit containing inductance and resistance but no capacitors, the rate of decrease of current is proportional to the current. If the initial current is 30 amps but decays to 11 amps after 0.01 seconds, find an expression for the current as a function of time.

42. A mothball is in the shape of a sphere and starts with radius 1 cm. The material in the mothball evaporates at a rate proportional to the surface area. After one month, the radius is 0.5 cm. How many months (from the start) is it before the radius is 0.2 cm?

43. Let P be the number of animals in a colony at time t. The growth of the population satisfies

$$\frac{1000}{P}\frac{dP}{dt} = 100 - P.$$

The initial population is 200 individuals. Sketch a graph of P against t. Will there ever be more than 200 individuals in the colony? Will there ever be fewer than 100 individuals? Explain.

44. Table 11.11 gives the percentage, P, of households with a DVD player as a function of year.

(a) Explain why a logistic model is a reasonable one to fit to this data.

(b) Use the data to estimate the point of inflection of P. What limiting value L does this point of inflection predict?

(c) The best logistic equation for this data, using t as years since 1997, turns out to be

$$P = \frac{86.395}{1 + 72.884.75e^{-0.786t}}.$$

What limiting value does this model predict?

Table 11.11 *Percentage of households with a DVD player*

Year	1998	1999	2000	2001	2002
$P(\%)$	1	5	13	21	35
Year	2003	2004	2005	2006	
$P(\%)$	50	70	75	81	

45. A chemical reaction involves one molecule of a substance A combining with one molecule of substance B to form one molecule of substance C, written $A + B \rightarrow C$. The Law of Mass Action states that the rate at which C is formed is proportional to the product of the quantities of A and B present. Assume a and b are the initial quantities of A and B and x is the quantity of C present at time t.

(a) Write a differential equation for x.

(b) Solve the equation with $x(0) = 0$.

46. If the initial quantities, a and b, in Problem 45 are the same, write and solve a differential equation for x, with $x(0) = 0$.

The differential equations in Problems 47–49 describe the rates of growth of two populations x and y (both measured in thousands) of species A and B, respectively. For each set:

(a) Describe in words what happens to the population of each species in the absence of the other.

(b) Describe in words how the species interact with one another. Give reasons why the populations might behave as described by the equations. Suggest species that might interact as described by the equations.

47. $\dfrac{dx}{dt} = 0.01x - 0.05xy$

$\dfrac{dy}{dt} = -0.2y + 0.08xy$

48. $\dfrac{dx}{dt} = 0.01x - 0.05xy$

$\dfrac{dy}{dt} = 0.2y - 0.08xy$

49. $\dfrac{dx}{dt} = 0.2x$

$\dfrac{dy}{dt} = 0.4xy - 0.1y$

50. A shrimp population P in a bay grows according to the logistic equation

$$\frac{dP}{dt} = 0.8P(1 - 0.01P),$$

with P in tons of shrimp and t in years.

(a) Sketch a graph of dP/dt against P.

(b) What is the predicted long-term population of shrimp in the bay, given any positive initial condition?

(c) If shrimp are harvested out of the bay by fishermen at a rate of 10 tons per year, what is the new differential equation showing both the natural logistic growth and the constant harvesting?

(d) Sketch a graph of dP/dt against P for the differential equation given in part (c).

(e) What are the equilibrium values for the differential equation given in part (c)?

(f) Use the graph in part (d) to determine whether the shrimp population increases or decreases from each of the following populations:

$$P = 12; \qquad P = 25; \qquad P = 75.$$

51. The concentrations of two chemicals A and B as functions of time are denoted by x and y respectively. Each alone decays at a rate proportional to its concentration. Put together, they also interact to form a third substance, at a rate proportional to the product of their concentrations. All this is expressed in the equations:

$$\frac{dx}{dt} = -2x - xy, \qquad \frac{dy}{dt} = -3y - xy.$$

(a) Find a differential equation describing the relationship between x and y, and solve it.

(b) Show that the only equilibrium state is $x = y = 0$. (Note that the concentrations are nonnegative.)

(c) Show that when x and y are positive and very small, y^2/x^3 is roughly constant. [Hint: When x is small, x is negligible compared to $\ln x$.]

If now the initial concentrations are $x(0) = 4$, $y(0) = 8$:

(d) Find the equation of the phase trajectory.

(e) What would be the concentrations of each substance if they become equal?

(f) If $x = e^{-10}$, find an approximate value for y.

52. We apply Lanchester's model to the Battle of Trafalgar (1805), when a fleet of 40 British ships expected to face a combined French and Spanish fleet of 46 ships. Suppose that there were x British ships and y opposing ships at time t. We assume that all the ships are identical so that constants in the differential equations in Lanchester's model are equal:

$$\frac{dx}{dt} = -ay$$

$$\frac{dy}{dt} = -ax.$$

(a) Write a differential equation involving dy/dx, and solve it using the initial sizes of the two fleets.

(b) If the battle were fought until all the British ships were put out of action, how many French/Spanish ships does this model predict would be left at the end of the battle?

Admiral Nelson, who was in command of the British fleet, did not in fact send his 40 ships against the 46 French and Spanish ships. Instead he split the battle into two parts, sending 32 of his ships against 23 of the French/Spanish ships and his other 8 ships against their other 23.

(c) Analyze each of these two sub-battles using Lanchester's model. Find the solution trajectory for each sub-battle. Which side is predicted to win each one? How many ships from each fleet are expected to be left at the end?

(d) Suppose, as in fact happened, that the remaining ships from each sub-battle then fought each other. Which side is predicted to win, and with how many ships remaining?

53. The following equations describe the rates of growth of an insect and bird population in a particular region, where x is the insect population in millions at time t and y is the bird population in thousands:

$$\frac{dx}{dt} = 3x - 0.02xy$$

$$\frac{dy}{dt} = -10y + 0.001xy.$$

(a) Describe in words the growth of each population in the absence of the other, and describe in words their interaction.

(b) Find the two points (x, y) at which the populations are in equilibrium.

(c) When the populations are at the nonzero equilibrium, 10 thousand additional birds are suddenly introduced. Let A be the point in the phase plane representing these populations. Find a differential equation in terms of just x and y (i.e., eliminate t), and find an equation for the particular solution passing through the point A.

(d) Show that the following points lie on the trajectory in the phase plane that passes through point A:

(i) B (9646.91, 150) (ii) C (10,000, 140.43)
(iii) D (10,361.60, 150)

(e) Sketch this trajectory in the phase plane, with x on the horizontal axis, y on the vertical. Show the equilibrium point.

(f) In what order are the points A, B, C, D traversed? [Hint: Find dy/dt, dx/dt at each point.]

(g) On another graph, sketch x and y versus time, t. Use the same initial value as in part (c). You do not need to indicate actual numerical values on the t-axis.

(h) Find dy/dx at points A and C. Find dx/dy at points B and D. [Hint: $dx/dy = 1/(dy/dx)$. Notice that the points A and C are the maximum and minimum values of y, respectively, and B and D are the maximum and minimum values of x, respectively.]

54. When two countries are in an arms race, the rate at which each one spends money on arms is determined by its own current level of spending and by its opponent's level of spending. We expect that the more a country is already spending on armaments, the less willing it will be to increase its military expenditures. On the other hand, the more a country's opponent spends on armaments, the more rapidly the country will arm. If \$$x$ billion is the country's yearly expenditure on arms, and \$$y$ billion is its opponent's, then the *Richardson arms race model* proposes that x and y are determined by differential equations. Suppose that for some particular arms race the equations are

$$\frac{dx}{dt} = -0.2x + 0.15y + 20$$

$$\frac{dy}{dt} = 0.1x - 0.2y + 40.$$

(a) Explain the signs of the three terms on the right side of the equations for dx/dt.

(b) Find the equilibrium points for this system.
(c) Analyze the direction of the trajectories in each region.
(d) Are the equilibrium points stable or unstable?
(e) What does this model predict will happen if both countries disarm?
(f) What does this model predict will happen in the case of unilateral disarmament (one country disarms, and the other country does not)?
(g) What does the model predict will happen in the long run?

In Problems 55–57, a population $P(t)$ of animals satisfies

$$\frac{dP}{dt} = -kP\left(1 - \frac{P}{L}\right)\left(1 - \frac{P}{2L}\right), \quad \text{with } k, L > 0.$$

For the given initial condition, what happens to the animal population over time? [Hint: The equation has equilibrium solutions at $P = 0, L, 2L$.]

55. Initially, there are fewer than L animals.

56. Initially, there are between L and $2L$ animals.

57. Initially, there are more than $2L$ animals.

CAS Challenge Problems

58. Consider the differential equation

$$\frac{dP}{dt} = P(P-1)(2-P).$$

(a) Find all the equilibrium solutions.
(b) Show that the following two functions are solutions:

$$P_1(t) = 1 - \frac{e^t}{\sqrt{3 + e^{2t}}} \quad \text{and} \quad P_2(t) = 1 + \frac{e^t}{\sqrt{3 + e^{2t}}}.$$

[Hint: Use a computer algebra system to simplify the difference between the right and left-hand sides.]
(c) Find $P_1(0)$, $P_2(0)$, $\lim_{t\to\infty} P_1(t)$, and $\lim_{t\to\infty} P_2(t)$. Explain how you could have predicted the limits as $t \to \infty$ from the values at $t = 0$ without knowing the solutions explicitly.

59. In this problem we investigate *Picard's method* for approximating the solutions of differential equations. Consider the differential equation

$$y'(t) = y(t)^2 + t^2, \quad y(a) = b.$$

Integrating both sides with respect to t gives

$$y(s) - y(a) = \int_a^s y'(t)\, dt = \int_a^s (y(t)^2 + t^2)\, dt.$$

Since $y(a) = b$, we have

$$y(s) = b + \int_a^s (y(t)^2 + t^2)\, dt.$$

We have put the differential equation into the form of an *integral equation*. If we have an approximate solution $y_0(s)$, we can use the integral form to make a new approximation

$$y_1(s) = b + \int_a^s (y_0(t)^2 + t^2)\, dt.$$

Continuing this process, we get a sequence of approximations $y_0(s), y_1(s), \ldots, y_n(s), \ldots$ where each term in the sequence is defined in terms of the previous one by the equation

$$y_{n+1}(s) = b + \int_a^s (y_n(t)^2 + t^2)\, dt.$$

(a) Show that y_n satisfies the initial condition $y_n(a) = b$ for all n.
(b) Using the initial condition $y(1) = 0$, start with the approximation $y_0(s) = 0$ and use a computer algebra system to find the next three approximations y_1, y_2, and y_3.
(c) Use a computer algebra system to find the solution y satisfying $y(1) = 0$, and sketch y, y_1, y_2, y_3 on the same axes. On what domain do the approximations appear to be accurate? [The solution y cannot be expressed in terms of elementary functions. If your computer algebra system cannot solve the equation exactly, use a numerical method such as Euler's method.]

60. Figure 11.98 shows the slope field for the differential equation[36]

$$\frac{dy}{dx} = \sqrt{1 - y^2}.$$

(a) Sketch the solution with $y(0) = 0$ for $-3 \le x \le 3$.

(b) Use a computer algebra system to find the solution in part (a).

(c) Compare the computer algebra system's solution with your sketch. Do they agree? If not, which one is right?

Figure 11.98

PROJECTS FOR CHAPTER ELEVEN

1. Medical Case Study: Anaphylaxis[37]

During surgery, a patient's blood pressure was observed to be dangerously low. One possible cause is a severe allergic reaction called *anaphylaxis*. A diagnosis of anaphylaxis is based in part on a blood test showing the elevation of the serum *tryptase*, a molecule released by allergic cells. In anaphylaxis, the concentration of tryptase in the blood rises rapidly and then decays back to baseline in a few hours.

However, low blood pressure from an entirely different cause (say from a heart problem) can also lead to an elevation in tryptase. Before diagnosing anaphylaxis, the medical team needs to make sure that the observed tryptase elevation is the result of an allergy problem, not a heart problem. To do this, they need to know the peak level reached by the serum tryptase. The normal range for the serum tryptase is 0–15 ng/ml (nanograms per milliliter). Mild to moderate elevations from low blood pressure are common, but if the peak were three times the normal maximum (that is, above 45 ng/ml), then a diagnosis of anaphylaxis would be made.

The surgeons who resuscitated this patient ran two blood tests to measure T_r, the serum tryptase concentration; the results are in Table 11.12. Use the test results to estimate the peak serum tryptase level at the time of surgery by making an assumption of *first-order kinetics*: the rate of tryptase decay, dT_r/dt, is proportional to the concentration of tryptase, T_r. Did this patient experience anaphylaxis?

Table 11.12   *Serum tryptase levels*

t, hours since surgery	4	19.5
T_r, concentration in ng/ml	37	13

The Spread of SARS

In the spring of 2003, SARS (Severe Acute Respiratory Syndrome) spread rapidly in several Asian countries and Canada. Predicting the course of the disease—how many people would be infected, how long it would last—was important to officials trying to minimize the impact of the disease.

2. SARS Predictions for Hong Kong

This project compares three predictions about the spread of SARS in Hong Kong. We measure time, t, in days since March 17, 2003, the date the World Health Organization (WHO) started to publish daily SARS reports.[38] Let P be the total number of cases reported in Hong Kong by day t. On March 17, Hong Kong reported 95 cases.

---

[36] Adapted from David Lomen and David Lovelock, *Differential Equations* (New York: John Wiley & Sons, Inc., 1999).

[37] From David E. Sloane, M.D., drawing from an actual episode in his clinic.

[38] www.who.int/csr/country/en, accessed July 13, 2003.

The constants in the three differential equations whose predictions are analyzed in this project were determined using WHO data available in March 2003. We compare predictions from the three models for June 12, 2003, the last day a new case was reported in Hong Kong.

(a) (i) *A Linear Model.* Suppose P satisfies

$$\frac{dP}{dt} = 30.2, \quad \text{with } P(0) = 95.$$

Solve the differential equation and use your solution to predict the number of cases of SARS in Hong Kong by June 12 ($t = 87$).

(ii) *An Exponential Model.* Suppose P satisfies

$$\frac{1}{P}\frac{dP}{dt} = 0.12, \quad \text{with } P(0) = 95.$$

Solve the differential equation and use your solution to predict the number of cases of SARS in Hong Kong by June 12 ($t = 87$).

(iii) *A Logistic Model.* Suppose P satisfies

$$\frac{1}{P}\frac{dP}{dt} = 0.19 - 0.0002P, \quad \text{with } P(0) = 95.$$

Solve the differential equation and use your solution to predict the number of cases of SARS in Hong Kong by June 12 ($t = 87$).

(b) (i) Comment on the June 12 predictions from the three models.

(ii) What do each of the three models in part (a) predict about the trend in the number of new cases each day?

(iii) In May 2003, *The Lancet* published[39] a graph like Figure 11.99. What trend do you see in the data? What does this trend suggest about which model fits the data best?

(c) Assume that the data follow a logistic model, which is the only one in part (a) to predict that the total number of cases will level off:

(i) Use your answer to part (a) (iii) to predict the maximum number of SARS cases.

(ii) Assume that the data follow a logistic model, but not necessarily with the parameters given in part (a) (iii). Use Figure 11.99 and the fact that there had been a total of 998 cases of SARS by April 10 to predict the maximum number of SARS cases.

(d) To see how well the three models worked in practice, plot the data in Table 11.13 and each of the three solution curves from part (a).

Table 11.13   *Total number of SARS cases reported in Hong Kong by day t (where $t = 0$ is March 17, 2003)*

t	P	t	P	t	P	t	P
0	95	26	1108	54	1674	75	1739
5	222	33	1358	61	1710	81	1750
12	470	40	1527	68	1724	87	1755
19	800	47	1621				

Figure 11.99: Daily increase in Hong Kong SARS cases

---

[39]"SARS, Lay Epidemiology and Fear," by O. Razum, H. Beecher, A. Kapuan, T. Junghauss, *The Lancet,* May 2, 2003.

3. An S-I-R Model for SARS

This project analyzes the spread of SARS through interaction between infected and susceptible people.

The variables are S, the number of susceptibles, I, the number of infecteds who can infect others, and R, the number removed (this group includes those in quarantine and those who die, as well as those who have recovered and acquired immunity). Time, t, is in days since March 17, 2003, the date the World Health Organization (WHO) started to publish daily SARS reports. On March 17, Hong Kong reported 95 cases. In this model

$$\frac{dS}{dt} = -aSI$$
$$\frac{dI}{dt} = aSI - bI,$$

and $S + I + R = 6.8$ million, the population of Hong Kong in 2003.[40] Estimates based on WHO data give $a = 1.25 \cdot 10^{-8}$.

(a) What are S_0 and I_0, the initial values of S and I?

(b) During March 2003, the value of b was about 0.06. Using a calculator or computer, sketch the slope field for this system of differential equations and the solution trajectory corresponding to the initial conditions. (Use $0 \leq S \leq 7 \cdot 10^6, 0 \leq I \leq 0.4 \cdot 10^6$.)

(c) What does your graph tell you about the total number of people infected over the course of the disease if $b = 0.06$? What is the threshold value? What does this value tell you?

(d) During April, as public health officials worked to get the disease under control, people who had been in contact with the disease were quarantined. Explain why quarantining has the effect of raising the value of b.

(e) Using the April value, $b = 0.24$, sketch the slope field. (Use the same value of a and the same window.)

(f) What is the threshold value for $b = 0.24$? What does this tell you? Comment on the quarantine policy.

(g) Comment on the effectiveness of each of the following policies intended to prevent an epidemic and protect a city from an outbreak of SARS in a nearby region.

    I Close off the city from contact with the infected region. Shut down roads, airports, trains, and other forms of direct contact.

    II Install a quarantine policy. Isolate anyone who has been in contact with a SARS patient or anyone who shows symptoms of SARS.

---

[40]www.census.gov, International Data Base (IDB), accessed June 8, 2004.

4. Pareto's Law

In analyzing a society, sociologists are often interested in how incomes are distributed through the society. Pareto's law asserts that each society has a constant k such that the average income of all people wealthier than you is k times your income ($k > 1$). If $p(x)$ is the number of people in the society with an income of x or above, we define $\Delta p = p(x + \Delta x) - p(x)$, for small Δx.

(a) Explain why the number of people with incomes between x and $x + \Delta x$ is represented by $-\Delta p$. Then show that the total amount of money earned by people with incomes between x and $x + \Delta x$ is approximated by $-x\Delta p$.

(b) Use Pareto's law to show that the total amount of money earned by people with incomes of x or above is $kxp(x)$. Then show that the total amount of money earned by people with incomes between x and $x + \Delta x$ is approximated by $-kp\Delta x - kx\Delta p$.

(c) Using your answers to parts (a) and (b), show that p satisfies the differential equation

$$(1 - k)xp' = kp.$$

(d) Solve this differential equation for $p(x)$.

(e) Sketch a graph of $p(x)$ for various values of k, some large and some near 1. How does the value of k alter the shape of the graph?

5. Vibrations in a Molecule

Suppose the force, F, between two atoms a distance r apart in a molecule is given by

$$F(r) = b\left(\frac{a^2}{r^3} - \frac{a}{r^2}\right)$$

where a and b are positive constants.

(a) Find the equilibrium distance, r, at which $F = 0$.

(b) Expand F in a series about the equilibrium position. Give the first two nonzero terms.

(c) Suppose one atom is fixed. Let x be the displacement of the other atom from the equilibrium position. Give the first two nonzero terms of the series for F in terms of x.

(d) Using Newton's Second Law of Motion, show that if x is small, the second atom oscillates about the equilibrium position. Find the period of the oscillation.

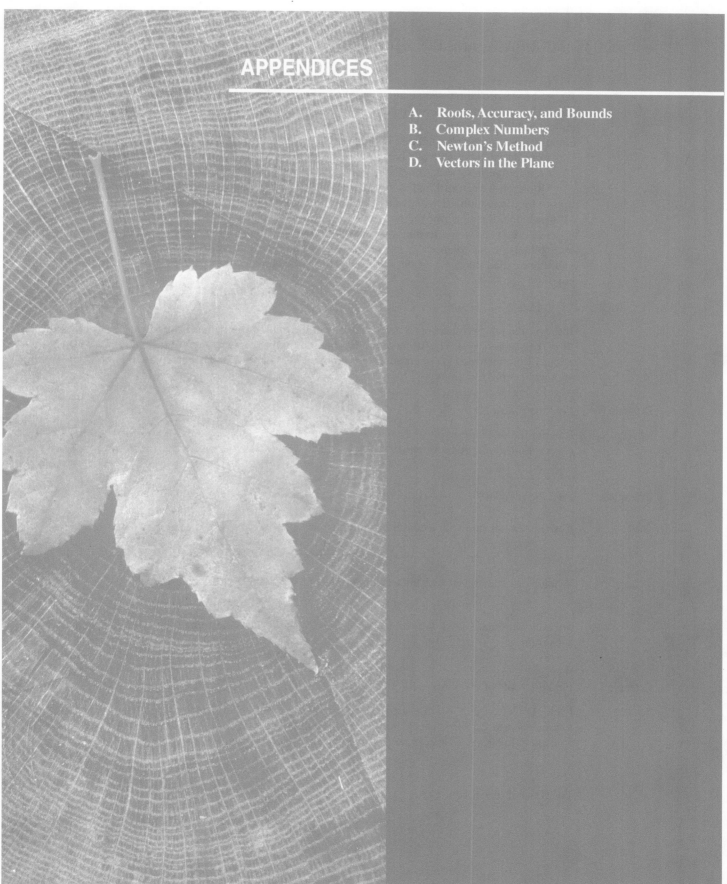

APPENDICES

A. Roots, Accuracy, and Bounds
B. Complex Numbers
C. Newton's Method
D. Vectors in the Plane

A   ROOTS, ACCURACY, AND BOUNDS

It is often necessary to find the zeros of a polynomial or the points of intersection of two curves. So far, you have probably used algebraic methods, such as the quadratic formula, to solve such problems. Unfortunately, however, mathematicians' search for similar solutions to more complicated equations has not been all that successful. The formulas for the solutions to third- and fourth-degree equations are so complicated that you'd never want to use them. Early in the nineteenth century, it was proved that there is no algebraic formula for the solutions to equations of degree 5 and higher. Most non-polynomial equations cannot be solved using a formula either.

However, we can still find roots of equations, provided we use approximation methods, not formulas. In this section we will discuss three ways to find roots: algebraic, graphical, and numerical. Of these, only the algebraic method gives exact solutions.

First, let's get some terminology straight. Given the equation $x^2 = 4$, we call $x = -2$ and $x = 2$ the *roots*, or *solutions of the equation*. If we are given the function $f(x) = x^2 - 4$, then -2 and 2 are called the *zeros of the function*; that is, the zeros of the function f are the roots of the equation $f(x) = 0$.

The Algebraic Viewpoint: Roots by Factoring

If the product of two numbers is zero, then one or the other or both must be zero, that is, if $AB = 0$, then $A = 0$ or $B = 0$. This observation lies behind finding roots by factoring. You may have spent a lot of time factoring polynomials. Here you will also factor expressions involving trigonometric and exponential functions.

Example 1   Find the roots of $x^2 - 7x = 8$.

Solution   Rewrite the equation as $x^2 - 7x - 8 = 0$. Then factor the left side: $(x + 1)(x - 8) = 0$. By our observation about products, either $x + 1 = 0$ or $x - 8 = 0$, so the roots are $x = -1$ and $x = 8$.

Example 2   Find the roots of $\dfrac{1}{x} - \dfrac{x}{(x + 2)} = 0$.

Solution   Rewrite the left side with a common denominator:

$$\frac{x + 2 - x^2}{x(x + 2)} = 0.$$

Whenever a fraction is zero, the numerator must be zero. Therefore we must have

$$x + 2 - x^2 = (-1)(x^2 - x - 2) = (-1)(x - 2)(x + 1) = 0.$$

We conclude that $x - 2 = 0$ or $x + 1 = 0$, so 2 and -1 are the roots. They can be checked by substitution.

Example 3   Find the roots of $e^{-x} \sin x - e^{-x} \cos x = 0$.

Solution   Factor the left side: $e^{-x}(\sin x - \cos x) = 0$. The factor e^{-x} is never zero; it is impossible to raise e to a power and get zero. Therefore, the only possibility is that $\sin x - \cos x = 0$. This equation is equivalent to $\sin x = \cos x$. If we divide both sides by $\cos x$, we get

$$\frac{\sin x}{\cos x} = \frac{\cos x}{\cos x} \quad \text{so} \quad \tan x = 1.$$

The roots of this equation are

$$\ldots, \frac{-7\pi}{4}, \frac{-3\pi}{4}, \frac{\pi}{4}, \frac{5\pi}{4}, \frac{9\pi}{4}, \frac{13\pi}{4}, \ldots.$$

Warning: Using factoring to solve an equation only works when one side of the equation is 0. It is not true that if, say, $AB = 7$ then $A = 7$ or $B = 7$. For example, you *cannot* solve $x^2 - 4x = 2$ by factoring $x(x - 4) = 2$ and then assuming that either x or $x - 4$ equals 2.

The problem with factoring is that factors are not easy to find. For example, the left side of the quadratic equation $x^2 - 4x - 2 = 0$ does not factor, at least not into "nice" factors with integer coefficients. For the general quadratic equation

$$ax^2 + bx + c = 0,$$

there is the quadratic formula for the roots:

$$x = \frac{-b \pm \sqrt{b^2 - 4ac}}{2a}.$$

Thus the roots of $x^2 - 4x - 2 = 0$ are $(4 \pm \sqrt{24})/2$, or $2 + \sqrt{6}$ and $2 - \sqrt{6}$.

Notice that in each of these examples, we have found the roots exactly.

The Graphical Viewpoint: Roots by Zooming

To find the roots of an equation $f(x) = 0$, it helps to draw the graph of f. The roots of the equation, that is the zeros of f, are *the values of x where the graph of f crosses the x-axis*. Even a very rough sketch of the graph can be useful in determining how many zeros there are and their approximate values. If you have a computer or graphing calculator, then finding solutions by graphing is the easiest method, especially if you use the zoom feature. However, a graph can never tell you the exact value of a root, only an approximate one.

Example 4   Find the roots of $x^3 - 4x - 2 = 0$.

Solution   Attempting to factor the left side with integer coefficients will convince you it cannot be done, so we cannot easily find the roots by algebra. We know the graph of $f(x) = x^3 - 4x - 2$ will have the usual cubic shape; see Figure A.1.

There are clearly three roots: one between $x = -2$ and $x = -1$, another between $x = -1$ and $x = 0$, and a third between $x = 2$ and $x = 3$. Zooming in on the largest root with a graphing calculator or computer shows that it lies in the following interval:

$$2.213 < x < 2.215.$$

Thus, the root is $x = 2.21$, accurate to two decimal places. Zooming in on the other two roots shows them to be $x = -1.68$ and $x = -0.54$, accurate to two decimal places.

Useful trick: Suppose you want to solve the equation $\sin x - \cos x = 0$ graphically. Instead of graphing $f(x) = \sin x - \cos x$ and looking for zeros, you may find it easier to rewrite the equation as $\sin x = \cos x$ and graph $g(x) = \sin x$ and $h(x) = \cos x$. (After all, you already know what these two graphs look like. See Figure A.2.) The roots of the original equation are then precisely the x coordinates of the points of intersection of the graphs of $g(x)$ and $h(x)$.

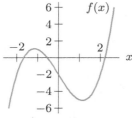

Figure A.1: The cubic
$f(x) = x^3 - 4x - 2$

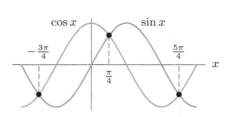

Figure A.2: Finding roots of
$\sin x - \cos x = 0$

Example 5   Find the roots of $2 \sin x - x = 0$.

Solution   Rewrite the equation as $2 \sin x = x$, and graph both sides. Since $g(x) = 2 \sin x$ is always between -2 and 2, there are no roots of $2 \sin x = x$ for $x > 2$ or for $x < -2$. We need only consider the graphs between -2 and 2 (or between $-\pi$ and π, which makes graphing the sine function easier). Figure A.3 shows the graphs. There are three points of intersection: one appears to be at $x = 0$, one between $x = \pi/2$ and $x = \pi$, and one between $x = -\pi/2$ and $x = -\pi$. You can tell that $x = 0$ is the exact value of one root because it satisfies the original equation exactly. Zooming in shows that there is a second root $x \approx 1.9$, and the third root is $x \approx -1.9$ by symmetry.

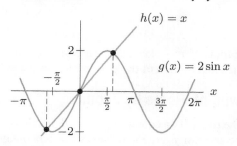

Figure A.3: Finding roots of $2 \sin x - x = 0$

The Numerical Viewpoint: Roots by Bisection

We now look at a numerical method of approximating the solutions to an equation. This method depends on the idea that if the value of a function $f(x)$ changes sign in an interval, and if we believe there is no break in the graph of the function there, then there is a root of the equation $f(x) = 0$ in that interval.

Let's go back to the problem of finding the root of $f(x) = x^3 - 4x - 2 = 0$ between 2 and 3. To locate the root, we close in on it by evaluating the function at the midpoint of the interval, $x = 2.5$. Since $f(2) = -2$, $f(2.5) = 3.625$, and $f(3) = 13$, the function changes sign between $x = 2$ and $x = 2.5$, so the root is between these points. Now we look at $x = 2.25$.

Since $f(2.25) = 0.39$, the function is negative at $x = 2$ and positive at $x = 2.25$, so there is a root between 2 and 2.25. Now we look at 2.125. We find $f(2.125) = -0.90$, so there is a root between 2.125 and 2.25, ... and so on. (You may want to round the decimals as you work.) See Figure A.4. The intervals containing the root are listed in Table A.1 and show that the root is $x = 2.21$ to two decimal places.

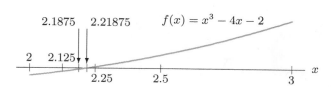

Figure A.4: Locating a root of $x^3 - 4x - 2 = 0$

Table A.1   *Intervals containing root of*
$x^3 - 4x - 2 = 0$ *(Note: $[2, 3]$ means $2 \leq x \leq 3$)*

$[2, 3]$
$[2, 2.5]$
$[2, 2.25]$
$[2.125, 2.25]$
$[2.1875, 2.25]$ So $x = 2.2$ rounded to one decimal place
$[2.1875, 2.21875]$
$[2.203125, 2.21875]$
$[2.2109375, 2.21875]$
$[2.2109375, 2.2148438]$ So $x = 2.21$ rounded to two decimal places

This method of estimating roots is called the **Bisection Method**:
- To solve an equation $f(x) = 0$ using the bisection method, we need two starting values for x, say, $x = a$ and $x = b$, such that $f(a)$ and $f(b)$ have opposite signs and f is continuous on $[a, b]$.
- Evaluate f at the midpoint of the interval $[a, b]$, and decide in which half-interval the root lies.
- Repeat, using the new half-interval instead of $[a, b]$.

There are some problems with the bisection method:
- The function may not change signs near the root. For example, $f(x) = x^2 - 2x + 1 = 0$ has a root at $x = 1$, but $f(x)$ is never negative because $f(x) = (x - 1)^2$, and a square cannot be negative. (See Figure A.5.)
- The function f must be continuous between the starting values $x = a$ and $x = b$.
- If there is more than one root between the starting values $x = a$ and $x = b$, the method will find only one of the roots. For example, if we had tried to solve $x^3 - 4x - 2 = 0$ starting at $x = -12$ and $x = 10$, the bisection method would zero in on the root between $x = -2$ and $x = -1$, not the root between $x = 2$ and $x = 3$ that we found earlier. (Try it! Then see what happens if you use $x = -10$ instead of $x = -12$.)
- The bisection method is slow and not very efficient. Applying bisection three times in a row only traps the root in an interval $(\frac{1}{2})^3 = \frac{1}{8}$ as large as the starting interval. Thus, if we initially know that a root is between, say, 2 and 3, then we would need to apply the bisection method at least four times to know the first digit after the decimal point.

There are much more powerful methods available for finding roots, such as Newton's method, which are more complicated but which avoid some of these difficulties.

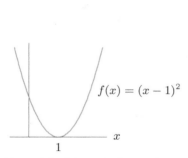

Figure A.5: f does not change sign at the root

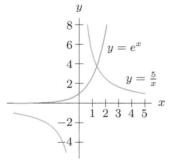

Figure A.6: Intersection of $y = e^x$ and $y = 5/x$

Table A.2 *Bisection method for* $f(x) = xe^x - 5 = 0$ *(Note that* $[1, 2]$ *means the interval* $1 \leq x \leq 2$*)*

Interval Containing Root
$[1, 2]$
$[1, 1.5]$
$[1.25, 1.5]$
$[1.25, 1.375]$
$[1.3125, 1.375]$
$[1.3125, 1.34375]$

Example 6   Find all the roots of $xe^x = 5$ to at least one decimal place.

Solution   If we rewrite the equation as $e^x = 5/x$ and graph both sides, as in Figure A.6, it is clear that there is exactly one root, and it is somewhere between 1 and 2. Table A.2 shows the intervals obtained by the bisection method. After five iterations, we have the root trapped between 1.3125 and 1.34375, so we can say the root is $x = 1.3$ to one decimal place.

Iteration

Both zooming in and bisection as discussed here are examples of *iterative* methods, in which a sequence of steps is repeated over and over again, using the results of one step as the input for the next. We can use such methods to locate a root to any degree of accuracy. In bisection, each iteration traps the root in an interval that is half the length of the previous one. Each time you zoom in on a calculator, you trap the root in a smaller interval; how much smaller depends on the settings on the calculator.

Accuracy and Error

In the previous discussion, we used the phrase "accurate to 2 decimal places." For an iterative process where we get closer and closer estimates of some quantity, we take a common-sense approach to accuracy: we watch the numbers carefully, and when a digit stays the same for several iterations, we assume it has stabilized and is correct, especially if the digits to the right of that digit also stay the same. For example, suppose 2.21429 and 2.21431 are two successive estimates for a zero of $f(x) = x^3 - 4x - 2$. Since these two estimates agree to the third digit after the decimal point, we probably have at least 3 decimal places correct.

There is a problem with this, however. Suppose we are estimating a root whose true value is 1, and the estimates are converging to the value from below—say, 0.985, 0.991, 0.997 and so on. In this case, not even the first decimal place is "correct," even though the difference between the estimates and the actual answer is very small—much less than 0.1. To avoid this difficulty, we say that an estimate a for some quantity r is *accurate to p decimal places* if the error, which is the absolute value of the difference between a and r, or $|r - a|$, is as follows:

Accuracy to p decimal places	means	Error less than
$p = 1$		0.05
2		0.005
3		0.0005
$\vdots$		$\vdots$
n		$0.\underbrace{000\ldots0}_{n}5$

This is the same as saying that r must lie in an interval of length twice the maximum error, centered on a. For example, if a is accurate to 1 decimal place, r must lie in the following interval:

$$a - 0.05 \qquad\qquad a \qquad\qquad a + 0.05$$

Since both the graphing calculator and the bisection method give us an interval in which the root is trapped, this definition of decimal accuracy is a natural one for these processes.

Example 7   Suppose the numbers $\sqrt{10}$, 22/7, and 3.14 are given as approximations to $\pi = 3.1415\ldots$. To how many decimal places is each approximation accurate?

Solution   Using $\sqrt{10} = 3.1622\ldots$,

$$|\sqrt{10} - \pi| = |3.1622\ldots - 3.1415\ldots| = 0.0206\ldots < 0.05,$$

so $\sqrt{10}$ is accurate to one decimal place. Similarly, using $22/7 = 3.1428\ldots$,

$$\left|\frac{22}{7} - \pi\right| = |3.1428\ldots - 3.1415\ldots| = 0.0013\ldots < 0.005,$$

so 22/7 is accurate to two decimal places. Finally,

$$|3.14 - 3.1415\ldots| = 0.0015\ldots < 0.005,$$

so 3.14 is accurate to two decimal places.

Warning:

- Saying that an approximation is accurate to, say, 2 decimal places does *not* guarantee that its first two decimal places are "correct," that is, that the two digits of the approximation are the same as the corresponding two digits in the true value. For example, an approximate value of 5.997 is accurate to 2 decimal places if the true value is 6.001, but neither of the 9s in the approximation agrees with the 0s in the true value (nor does the digit 5 agree with the digit 6).
- When finding a root r of an equation, the number of decimal places of accuracy refers to the number of digits that have stabilized in the root. It does *not* refer to the number of digits of $f(r)$ that are zero. For example, Table A.1 on page 668 shows that $x = 2.2$ is a root of $f(x) = x^3 - 4x - 2 = 0$, accurate to one decimal place. Yet, $f(2.2) = -0.152$, so $f(2.2)$ does not have one zero after the decimal point. Similarly, $x = 2.21$ is the root accurate to two decimal places, but $f(2.21) = -0.046$ does not have two zeros after the decimal point.

Example 8   Is $x = 2.2143$ a zero of $f(x) = x^3 - 4x - 2$ accurate to four decimal places?

Solution   We want to know whether r, the exact value of the zero, lies in the interval

$$2.2143 - 0.00005 < r < 2.2143 + 0.00005$$

which is the same as

$$2.21425 < r < 2.21435.$$

Since $f(2.21425) < 0$ and $f(2.21435) > 0$, the zero does lie in this interval, and so $r = 2.2143$ is accurate to four decimal places.

How to Write a Decimal Answer

The graphing calculator and bisection method naturally give an interval for a root or a zero. However, other numerical techniques do not give a pair of numbers bounding the true value, but rather a single number near the true value. What should you do if you want a single number, rather than an interval, for an answer? In general, averaging the endpoint of the interval is the best solution.

When giving a single number as an answer and interpreting it, be careful about giving rounded answers. For example, suppose you know a root lies in the interval between 0.81 and 0.87. Averaging gives 0.84 as a single number estimating the root. But it would be wrong to round 0.84 to 0.8 and say that the answer is 0.8 accurate to one decimal place; the true value could be 0.86, which is not within 0.05 of 0.8. The right thing to say is that the answer is 0.84 accurate to one decimal place. Similarly, to give an answer accurate to, say, 2 decimal places, you may have to show 3 decimal places in your answer.

Bounds of a Function

Knowing how big or how small a function gets can sometimes be useful, especially when you can't easily find exact values of the function. You can say, for example, that $\sin x$ always stays between -1 and 1 and that $2\sin x + 10$ always stays between 8 and 12. But 2^x is not confined between any two numbers, because 2^x will exceed any number you can name if x is large enough. We say that $\sin x$ and $2\sin x + 10$ are *bounded* functions, and that 2^x is an *unbounded* function.

A function f is **bounded** on an interval if there are numbers L and U such that

$$L \leq f(x) \leq U$$

for all x in the interval. Otherwise, f is **unbounded** on the interval.

We say that L is a **lower bound** for f on the interval, and that U is an **upper bound** for f on the interval.

Example 9   Use Figures A.7 and A.8 to decide which of the following functions are bounded.

(a) x^3 on $-\infty < x < \infty$; on $0 \leq x \leq 100$.
(b) $2/x$ on $0 < x < \infty$; on $1 \leq x < \infty$.

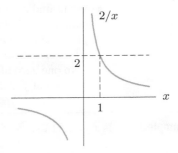

Figure A.7: Is x^3 bounded?   Figure A.8: Is $2/x$ bounded?

Solution   (a) The graph of x^3 in Figure A.7 shows that x^3 will exceed any number, no matter how large, if x is big enough, so x^3 does not have an upper bound on $-\infty < x < \infty$. Therefore, x^3 is unbounded on $-\infty < x < \infty$. But on the interval $0 \leq x \leq 100$, x^3 stays between 0 (a lower bound) and $100^3 = 1{,}000{,}000$ (an upper bound). Therefore, x^3 is bounded on the interval $0 \leq x \leq 100$. Notice that upper and lower bounds, when they exist, are not unique. For example, -100 is another lower bound and $2{,}000{,}000$ another upper bound for x^3 on $0 \leq x \leq 100$.

(b) $2/x$ is unbounded on $0 < x < \infty$, since it has no upper bound on that interval. But $0 \leq 2/x \leq 2$ for $1 \leq x < \infty$, so $2/x$ is bounded, with lower bound 0 and upper bound 2, on $1 \leq x < \infty$. (See Figure A.8.)

Best Possible Bounds

Consider a group of people whose height in feet, h, ranges from 5 feet to 6 feet. Then 5 feet is a lower bound for the people in the group and 6 feet is an upper bound:

$$5 \leq h \leq 6.$$

But the people in this group are also all between 4 feet and 7 feet, so it is also true that

$$4 \leq h \leq 7.$$

So, there are many lower bounds and many upper bounds. However, the 5 and the 6 are considered the best bounds because they are the closest together of all the possible pairs of bounds.

The **best possible bounds** for a function, f, over an interval are numbers A and B such that, for all x in the interval,

$$A \leq f(x) \leq B$$

and where A and B are as close together as possible. A is called the **greatest lower bound** and B is the **least upper bound**.

What Do Bounds Mean Graphically?

Upper and lower bounds can be represented on a graph by horizontal lines. See Figure A.9.

Figure A.9: Upper and lower bounds for the function f

Exercises for Appendix A

1. Use a calculator or computer graph of $f(x) = 13 - 20x - x^2 - 3x^4$ to determine:

   (a) The range of this function;
   (b) The number of zeros of this function.

For Problems 2–12, determine the roots or points of intersection to an accuracy of one decimal place.

2. (a) The root of $x^3 - 3x + 1 = 0$ between 0 and 1
   (b) The root of $x^3 - 3x + 1 = 0$ between 1 and 2
   (c) The smallest root of $x^3 - 3x + 1 = 0$

3. The root of $x^4 - 5x^3 + 2x - 5 = 0$ between -2 and -1

4. The root of $x^5 + x^2 - 9x - 3 = 0$ between -2 and -1

5. The largest real root of $2x^3 - 4x^2 - 3x + 1 = 0$

6. All real roots of $x^4 - x - 2 = 0$

7. All real roots of $x^5 - 2x^2 + 4 = 0$

8. The smallest positive root of $x \sin x - \cos x = 0$

9. The left-most point of intersection between $y = 2x$ and $y = \cos x$

10. The left-most point of intersection between $y = 1/2^x$ and $y = \sin x$

11. The point of intersection between $y = e^{-x}$ and $y = \ln x$

12. All roots of $\cos t = t^2$

13. Estimate all real zeros of the following polynomials, accurate to 2 decimal places:

    (a) $f(x) = x^3 - 2x^2 - x + 3$
    (b) $f(x) = x^3 - x^2 - 2x + 2$

14. Find the largest zero of

$$f(x) = 10xe^{-x} - 1$$

to two decimal places, using the bisection method. Make sure to demonstrate that your approximation is as good as you claim.

15. (a) Find the smallest positive value of x where the graphs of $f(x) = \sin x$ and $g(x) = 2^{-x}$ intersect.
    (b) Repeat with $f(x) = \sin 2x$ and $g(x) = 2^{-x}$.

16. Use a graphing calculator to sketch $y = 2\cos x$ and $y = x^3 + x^2 + 1$ on the same set of axes. Find the positive zero of $f(x) = 2\cos x - x^3 - x^2 - 1$. A friend claims there is one more real zero. Is your friend correct? Explain.

17. Use the table below to investigate the zeros of the function

$$f(\theta) = (\sin 3\theta)(\cos 4\theta) + 0.8$$

in the interval $0 \le \theta \le 1.8$.

θ	0	0.2	0.4	0.6	0.8	1.0	1.2	1.4	1.6	1.8
$f(\theta)$	0.80	1.19	0.77	0.08	0.13	0.71	0.76	0.12	-0.19	0.33

   (a) Decide how many zeros the function has in the interval $0 \le \theta \le 1.8$.
   (b) Locate each zero, or a small interval containing each zero.
   (c) Are you sure you have found all the zeros in the interval $0 \le \theta \le 1.8$? Graph the function on a calculator or computer to decide.

18. (a) Use Table A.3 to locate approximate solution(s) to

$$(\sin 3x)(\cos 4x) = \frac{x^3}{\pi^3}$$

in the interval $1.07 \leq x \leq 1.15$. Give an interval of length 0.01 in which each solution lies.

Table A.3

x	x^3/π^3	$(\sin 3x)(\cos 4x)$
1.07	0.0395	0.0286
1.08	0.0406	0.0376
1.09	0.0418	0.0442
1.10	0.0429	0.0485
1.11	0.0441	0.0504
1.12	0.0453	0.0499
1.13	0.0465	0.0470
1.14	0.0478	0.0417
1.15	0.0491	0.0340

(b) Make an estimate for each solution accurate to two decimal places.

19. (a) With your calculator in radian mode, take the arctangent of 1 and multiply that number by 4. Now, take the arctangent of the result and multiply it by 4. Continue this process 10 times or so and record each result as in the accompanying table. At each step, you get 4 times the arctangent of the result of the previous step.

1
3.14159...
5.05050...
5.50129...
$\vdots$

(b) Your table allows you to find a solution of the equation

$$4 \arctan x = x.$$

Why? What is that solution?

(c) What does your table in part (a) have to do with Figure A.10?
[Hint: The coordinates of P_0 are $(1, 1)$. Find the coordinates of P_1, P_2, P_3,...]

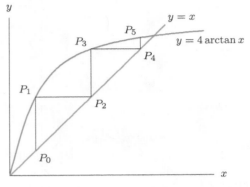

Figure A.10

(d) In part (a), what happens if you start with an initial guess of 10? Of -10? What types of behavior do you observe? (That is, for which initial guesses is the sequence increasing, and for which is it decreasing; does the sequence approach a limit?) Explain your answers graphically, as in part (c).

20. Using radians, apply the iteration method of Problem 19 to the equation

$$\cos x = x.$$

Represent your results graphically, as in Figure A.10.

For Problems 21–23, draw a graph to decide if the function is bounded on the interval given. Give the best possible upper and lower bounds for any function which is bounded.

21. $f(x) = 4x - x^2$ on $[-1, 4]$.

22. $h(\theta) = 5 + 3\sin\theta$ on $[-2\pi, 2\pi]$

23. $f(t) = \dfrac{\sin t}{t^2}$ on $[-10, 10]$

B COMPLEX NUMBERS

The quadratic equation

$$x^2 - 2x + 2 = 0$$

is not satisfied by any real number x. If you try applying the quadratic formula, you get

$$x = \frac{2 \pm \sqrt{4 - 8}}{2} = 1 \pm \frac{\sqrt{-4}}{2}.$$

Apparently, you need to take a square root of -4. But -4 does not have a square root, at least, not one which is a real number. Let's give it a square root.

We define the imaginary number i to be a number such that

$$i^2 = -1.$$

Using this i, we see that $(2i)^2 = -4$, so

$$x = 1 \pm \frac{\sqrt{-4}}{2} = 1 \pm \frac{2i}{2} = 1 \pm i.$$

This solves our quadratic equation. The numbers $1 + i$ and $1 - i$ are examples of complex numbers.

A **complex number** is defined as any number that can be written in the form

$$z = a + bi,$$

where a and b are real numbers and $i^2 = -1$, so we say $i = \sqrt{-1}$.
The *real part* of z is the number a; the *imaginary part* is the number b.

Calling the number i imaginary makes it sound as if i does not exist in the same way that real numbers exist. In some cases, it is useful to make such a distinction between real and imaginary numbers. For example, if we measure mass or position, we want our answers to be real numbers. But the imaginary numbers are just as legitimate mathematically as the real numbers are.

As an analogy, consider the distinction between positive and negative numbers. Originally, people thought of numbers only as tools to count with; their concept of "five" or "ten" was not far removed from "five arrows" or "ten stones." They were unaware that negative numbers existed at all. When negative numbers were introduced, they were viewed only as a device for solving equations like $x + 2 = 1$. They were considered "false numbers," or, in Latin, "negative numbers." Thus, even though people started to use negative numbers, they did not view them as existing in the same way that positive numbers did. An early mathematician might have reasoned: "The number 5 exists because I can have 5 dollars in my hand. But how can I have -5 dollars in my hand?" Today we have an answer: "I have -5 dollars" means I owe somebody 5 dollars. We have realized that negative numbers are just as useful as positive ones, and it turns out that complex numbers are useful too. For example, they are used in studying wave motion in electric circuits.

Algebra of Complex Numbers

Numbers such as 0, 1, $\frac{1}{2}$, π, and $\sqrt{2}$ are called *purely real* because they contain no imaginary components. Numbers such as i, $2i$, and $\sqrt{2}i$ are called *purely imaginary* because they contain only the number i multiplied by a nonzero real coefficient.

Two complex numbers are called *conjugates* if their real parts are equal and if their imaginary parts are opposites. The complex conjugate of the complex number $z = a + bi$ is denoted $\overline{z}$, so we have

$$\overline{z} = a - bi.$$

(Note that z is real if and only if $z = \overline{z}$.) Complex conjugates have the following remarkable property: if $f(x)$ is any polynomial with real coefficients ($x^3 + 1$, say) and $f(z) = 0$, then $f(\overline{z}) = 0$. This means that if z is the solution to a polynomial equation with real coefficients, then so is $\overline{z}$.

- Two complex numbers are equal if and only if their real parts are equal and their imaginary parts are equal. Consequently, if $a + bi = c + di$, then $a = c$ and $b = d$.

- Adding two complex numbers is done by adding real and imaginary parts separately:

$$(a + bi) + (c + di) = (a + c) + (b + d)i.$$

- Subtracting is similar:

$$(a + bi) - (c + di) = (a - c) + (b - d)i.$$

- Multiplication works just as for polynomials, using $i^2 = -1$:

$$(a + bi)(c + di) = a(c + di) + bi(c + di)$$
$$= ac + adi + bci + bdi^2$$
$$= ac + adi + bci - bd = (ac - bd) + (ad + bc)i.$$

- Powers of i: We know that $i^2 = -1$; then $i^3 = i \cdot i^2 = -i$, and $i^4 = (i^2)^2 = (-1)^2 = 1$. Then $i^5 = i \cdot i^4 = i$, and so on. Thus we have

$$i^n = \begin{cases} i & \text{for } n = 1, 5, 9, 13, \ldots \\ -1 & \text{for } n = 2, 6, 10, 14, \ldots \\ -i & \text{for } n = 3, 7, 11, 15, \ldots \\ 1 & \text{for } n = 0, 4, 8, 12, 16, \ldots \end{cases}$$

- The product of a number and its conjugate is always real and nonnegative:

$$z \cdot \bar{z} = (a + bi)(a - bi) = a^2 - abi + abi - b^2 i^2 = a^2 + b^2.$$

- Dividing by a nonzero complex number is done by multiplying the denominator by its conjugate, thereby making the denominator real:

$$\frac{a + bi}{c + di} = \frac{a + bi}{c + di} \cdot \frac{c - di}{c - di} = \frac{ac - adi + bci - bdi^2}{c^2 + d^2} = \frac{ac + bd}{c^2 + d^2} + \frac{bc - ad}{c^2 + d^2} i.$$

Example 1   Compute $(2 + 7i)(4 - 6i) - i$.

Solution $(2 + 7i)(4 - 6i) - i = 8 + 28i - 12i - 42i^2 - i = 8 + 15i + 42 = 50 + 15i.$

Example 2   Compute $\dfrac{2 + 7i}{4 - 6i}$.

Solution

$$\frac{2 + 7i}{4 - 6i} = \frac{2 + 7i}{4 - 6i} \cdot \frac{4 + 6i}{4 + 6i} = \frac{8 + 12i + 28i + 42i^2}{4^2 + 6^2} = \frac{-34 + 40i}{52} = \frac{-17}{26} + \frac{10}{13} i.$$

You can check by multiplying out that $(-17/26 + 10i/13)(4 - 6i) = 2 + 7i$.

The Complex Plane and Polar Coordinates

It is often useful to picture a complex number $z = x + iy$ in the plane, with x along the horizontal axis and y along the vertical. The xy-plane is then called the *complex plane*. Figure B.11 shows the complex numbers $-2i$, $1 + i$, and $-2 + 3i$.

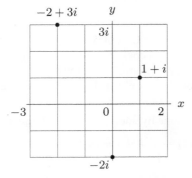

Figure B.11: Points in the complex plane

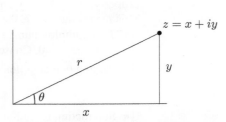

Figure B.12: The point $z = x + iy$ in the complex plane, showing polar coordinates

The triangle in Figure B.12 shows that a complex number can be written using polar coordinates as follows:

$$z = x + iy = r \cos \theta + ir \sin \theta.$$

Example 3   Express $z = -2i$ and $z = -2 + 3i$ using polar coordinates. (See Figure B.11.)

Solution   For $z = -2i$, the distance of z from the origin is 2, so $r = 2$. Also, one value for θ is $\theta = 3\pi/2$. Using polar coordinates, $-2i = 2\cos(3\pi/2) + i\,2(\sin 3\pi/2)$.

For $z = -2 + 3i$, we have $x = -2$, $y = 3$. So $r = \sqrt{(-2)^2 + 3^2} \approx 3.61$, and one solution of $\tan\theta = 3/(-2)$ with θ in quadrant II is $\theta \approx 2.16$. So $-2 + 3i \approx 3.61\cos(2.16) + i\,3.61\sin(2.16)$.

Example 4   Consider the point with polar coordinates $r = 5$ and $\theta = 3\pi/4$. What complex number does this point represent?

Solution   Since $x = r\cos\theta$ and $y = r\sin\theta$ we see that $x = 5\cos 3\pi/4 = -5/\sqrt{2}$, and $y = 5\sin 3\pi/4 = 5/\sqrt{2}$, so $z = -5/\sqrt{2} + i\,5/\sqrt{2}$.

Derivatives and Integrals of Complex-Valued Functions

Suppose $z(t) = x(t) + iy(t)$, where t is real, then we define $z'(t)$ and $\int z(t)\,dt$ by treating i like any other constant:

$$z'(t) = x'(t) + iy'(t)$$

$$\int z(t)\,dt = \int x(t)\,dt + i\int y(t)\,dt.$$

With these definitions, all the usual properties of differentiation and integration hold, such as

$$\int z'(t)\,dt = z(t) + C, \qquad \text{for } C \text{ is a complex constant.}$$

Euler's Formula

Consider the complex number z lying on the unit circle in Figure B.13. Writing z in polar coordinates, and using the fact that $r = 1$, we have

$$z = f(\theta) = \cos\theta + i\sin\theta.$$

It turns out that there is a particularly beautiful and compact way of rewriting $f(\theta)$ using complex exponentials. We take the derivative of f using the fact that $i^2 = -1$:

$$f'(\theta) = -\sin\theta + i\cos\theta = i\cos\theta + i^2\sin\theta.$$

Factoring out an i gives

$$f'(\theta) = i(\cos\theta + i\sin\theta) = i \cdot f(\theta).$$

As you know from Chapter 11, page 610, the only real-valued function whose derivative is proportional to the function itself is the exponential function. In other words, we know that if

$$g'(x) = k \cdot g(x), \quad \text{then} \quad g(x) = Ce^{kx}$$

Figure B.13: Complex number represented by a point on the unit circle for some constant C. If we assume that a similar result holds for complex-valued functions, then we have

$$f'(\theta) = i \cdot f(\theta), \quad \text{so} \quad f(\theta) = Ce^{i\theta}$$

for some constant C. To find C we substitute $\theta = 0$. Now $f(0) = Ce^{i \cdot 0} = C$, and since $f(0) = \cos 0 + i \sin 0 = 1$, we must have $C = 1$. Therefore $f(\theta) = e^{i\theta}$. Thus we have

---

Euler's formula

$$e^{i\theta} = \cos\theta + i\sin\theta.$$

This elegant and surprising relationship was discovered by the Swiss mathematician Leonhard Euler in the eighteenth century, and it is particularly useful in solving second-order differential equations. Another way of obtaining Euler's formula (using Taylor series) is given in Problem 46 on page 551. It allows us to write the complex number represented by the point with polar coordinates (r, θ) in the following form:

$$z = r(\cos\theta + i\sin\theta) = re^{i\theta}.$$

Similarly, since $\cos(-\theta) = \cos\theta$ and $\sin(-\theta) = -\sin\theta$, we have

$$re^{-i\theta} = r\left(\cos(-\theta) + i\sin(-\theta)\right) = r(\cos\theta - i\sin\theta).$$

Example 5   Evaluate $e^{i\pi}$.

Solution   Using Euler's formula, $e^{i\pi} = \cos\pi + i\sin\pi = -1$.

Example 6   Express the complex number represented by the point $r = 8$, $\theta = 3\pi/4$ in Cartesian form and polar form, $z = re^{i\theta}$.

Solution   Using Cartesian coordinates, the complex number is

$$z = 8\left(\cos\left(\frac{3\pi}{4}\right) + i\sin\left(\frac{3\pi}{4}\right)\right) = \frac{-8}{\sqrt{2}} + i\frac{8}{\sqrt{2}}.$$

Using polar coordinates, we have

$$z = 8e^{i\,3\pi/4}.$$

The polar form of complex numbers makes finding powers and roots of complex numbers much easier. Writing $z = re^{i\theta}$, we find any power of z as follows:

$$z^p = (re^{i\theta})^p = r^p e^{ip\theta}.$$

To find roots, we let p be a fraction, as in the following example.

Example 7   Find a cube root of the complex number represented by the point with polar coordinates $(8, 3\pi/4)$.

Solution   In Example 6, we saw that this complex number could be written as $z = 8e^{i3\pi/4}$. So,

$$\sqrt[3]{z} = \left(8e^{i\,3\pi/4}\right)^{1/3} = 8^{1/3}e^{i(3\pi/4)\cdot(1/3)} = 2e^{\pi i/4} = 2\left(\cos(\pi/4) + i\sin(\pi/4)\right)$$

$$= 2\left(1/\sqrt{2} + i/\sqrt{2}\right) = \sqrt{2}(1 + i).$$

You can check by multiplying out that $(\sqrt{2}(1 + i))^3 = -(8/\sqrt{2}) + i(8/\sqrt{2}) = z$.

Using Complex Exponentials

Euler's formula, together with the fact that exponential functions are simple to manipulate, allows us to obtain many results about trigonometric functions easily.

The following example uses the fact that for complex z, the function e^z has all the usual algebraic properties of exponents.

Example 8   Use Euler's formula to obtain the double-angle identities

$$\cos 2\theta = \cos^2 \theta - \sin^2 \theta \qquad \text{and} \qquad \sin 2\theta = 2 \cos \theta \sin \theta.$$

Solution   We use the fact that $e^{2i\theta} = e^{i\theta} \cdot e^{i\theta}$. This can be rewritten as

$$\cos 2\theta + i \sin 2\theta = (\cos \theta + i \sin \theta)^2.$$

Multiplying out $(\cos \theta + i \sin \theta)^2$, using the fact that $i^2 = -1$ gives

$$\cos 2\theta + i \sin 2\theta = \cos^2 \theta - \sin^2 \theta + i(2 \cos \theta \sin \theta).$$

Since two complex numbers are equal only if the real and imaginary parts are equal, we must have

$$\cos 2\theta = \cos^2 \theta - \sin^2 \theta \qquad \text{and} \qquad \sin 2\theta = 2 \cos \theta \sin \theta.$$

If we solve $e^{i\theta} = \cos \theta + i \sin \theta$ and $e^{-i\theta} = \cos \theta - i \sin \theta$ for $\sin \theta$ and $\cos \theta$, we obtain

$$\sin \theta = \frac{e^{i\theta} - e^{-i\theta}}{2i} \qquad \text{and} \qquad \cos \theta = \frac{e^{i\theta} + e^{-i\theta}}{2}.$$

By differentiating the formula $e^{ik\theta} = \cos(k\theta) + i \sin(k\theta)$, for θ real and k a real constant, it can be shown that

$$\frac{d}{d\theta}\left(e^{ik\theta}\right) = ike^{ik\theta} \qquad \text{and} \qquad \int e^{ik\theta}\, d\theta = \frac{1}{ik}e^{ik\theta} + C.$$

Thus complex exponentials are differentiated and integrated just like real exponentials.

Example 9   Use $\cos \theta = \left(e^{i\theta} + e^{-i\theta}\right)/2$ to obtain the derivative formula for $\cos \theta$.

Solution   Differentiating gives

$$\frac{d}{d\theta}(\cos \theta) = \frac{d}{d\theta}\left(\frac{e^{i\theta} + e^{-i\theta}}{2}\right) = \frac{ie^{i\theta} - ie^{-i\theta}}{2} = \frac{i(e^{i\theta} - e^{-i\theta})}{2}$$

$$= -\frac{e^{i\theta} - e^{-i\theta}}{2i} = -\sin \theta.$$

The facts that e^z has all the usual properties when z is complex leads to

$$\frac{d}{d\theta}(e^{(a+ib)\theta}) = (a + ib)e^{(a+ib)\theta} \qquad \text{and} \qquad \int e^{(a+ib)\theta}\, d\theta = \frac{1}{a + ib}e^{(a+ib)\theta} + C.$$

Example 10   Use the formula for $\int e^{(a+ib)\theta}\, d\theta$ to obtain formulas for $\int e^{ax}\cos bx\, dx$ and $\int e^{ax}\sin bx\, dx$.

Solution   The formula for $\int e^{(a+ib)\theta}\, d\theta$ allows us to write

$$\int e^{ax}e^{ibx}\, dx = \int e^{(a+ib)x}\, dx = \frac{1}{a+ib}e^{(a+ib)x} + C = \frac{a-ib}{a^2+b^2}e^{ax}e^{ibx} + C.$$

The left-hand side of this equation can be rewritten as

$$\int e^{ax}e^{ibx}\, dx = \int e^{ax}\cos bx\, dx + i\int e^{ax}\sin bx\, dx.$$

The right-hand side can be rewritten as

$$\frac{a-ib}{a^2+b^2}e^{ax}e^{ibx} = \frac{e^{ax}}{a^2+b^2}(a-ib)(\cos bx + i\sin bx),$$

$$= \frac{e^{ax}}{a^2+b^2}\left(a\cos bx + b\sin bx + i\left(a\sin bx - b\cos bx\right)\right).$$

Equating real parts gives

$$\int e^{ax}\cos bx\, dx = \frac{e^{ax}}{a^2+b^2}\left(a\cos bx + b\sin bx\right) + C,$$

and equating imaginary parts gives

$$\int e^{ax}\sin bx\, dx = \frac{e^{ax}}{a^2+b^2}\left(a\sin bx - b\cos bx\right) + C.$$

These two formulas are usually obtained by integrating by parts twice.

Example 11   Using complex exponentials, find a formula for $\int \sin 2x \sin 3x\, dx$.

Solution   Replacing $\sin 2x$ and $\sin 3x$ by their exponential form, we have

$$\int \sin 2x \sin 3x\, dx = \int \frac{\left(e^{2ix} - e^{-2ix}\right)}{2i}\frac{\left(e^{3ix} - e^{-3ix}\right)}{2i}\cdot dx$$

$$= \frac{1}{(2i)^2}\int \left(e^{5ix} - e^{-ix} - e^{ix} + e^{-5ix}\right)\, dx$$

$$= -\frac{1}{4}\left(\frac{1}{5i}e^{5ix} + \frac{1}{i}e^{-ix} - \frac{1}{i}e^{ix} - \frac{1}{5i}e^{-5ix}\right) + C$$

$$= -\frac{1}{4}\left(\frac{e^{5ix} - e^{-5ix}}{5i} - \frac{e^{ix} - e^{-ix}}{i}\right) + C$$

$$= -\frac{1}{4}\left(\frac{2}{5}\sin 5x - 2\sin x\right) + C$$

$$= -\frac{1}{10}\sin 5x + \frac{1}{2}\sin x + C.$$

This result is usually obtained by using a trigonometric identity.

Exercises for Appendix B

For Problems 1–8, express the given complex number in polar form, $z = re^{i\theta}$.

For Problems 9–18, perform the indicated calculations. Give your answer in Cartesian form, $z = x + iy$.

1. $2i$

2. -5

3. $1 + i$

4. $-3 - 4i$

9. $(2 + 3i) + (-5 - 7i)$

10. $(2 + 3i)(5 + 7i)$

5. 0

6. $-i$

7. $-1 + 3i$

8. $5 - 12i$

11. $(2 + 3i)^2$

12. $(1 + i)^2 + (1 + i)$

13. $(0.5 - i)(1 - i/4)$ **14.** $(2i)^3 - (2i)^2 + 2i - 1$

15. $(e^{i\pi/3})^2$ **16.** $\sqrt{e^{i\pi/3}}$

17. $(5e^{i7\pi/6})^3$ **18.** $\sqrt[4]{10e^{i\pi/2}}$

By writing the complex numbers in polar form, $z = re^{i\theta}$, find a value for the quantities in Problems 19–28. Give your answer in Cartesian form, $z = x + iy$.

19. $\sqrt{i}$ **20.** $\sqrt{-i}$ **21.** $\sqrt[3]{i}$

22. $\sqrt{7i}$ **23.** $(1+i)^{100}$ **24.** $(1+i)^{2/3}$

25. $(-4 + 4i)^{2/3}$ **26.** $(\sqrt{3} + i)^{1/2}$ **27.** $(\sqrt{3}+i)^{-1/2}$

28. $(\sqrt{5} + 2i)^{\sqrt{2}}$

29. Calculate i^n for $n = -1, -2, -3, -4$. What pattern do you observe? What is the value of i^{-36}? Of i^{-41}?

Solve the simultaneous equations in Problems 30–31 for A_1 and A_2.

30. $A_1 + A_2 = 2$
$(1 - i)A_1 + (1 + i)A_2 = 3$

31. $A_1 + A_2 = 2$
$(i - 1)A_1 + (1 + i)A_2 = 0$

32. **(a)** Calculate a and b if $\dfrac{3 - 4i}{1 + 2i} = a + bi$.
     (b) Check your answer by calculating $(1 + 2i)(a + bi)$.

33. Check that $z = \dfrac{ac + bd}{c^2 + d^2} + \dfrac{bc - ad}{c^2 + d^2}i$ is the quotient $\dfrac{a + bi}{c + di}$ by showing that the product $z \cdot (c + di)$ is $a + bi$.

34. Let $z_1 = -3 - i\sqrt{3}$ and $z_2 = -1 + i\sqrt{3}$.

     (a) Find $z_1 z_2$ and z_1/z_2. Give your answer in Cartesian form, $z = x + iy$.
     (b) Put z_1 and z_2 into polar form, $z = re^{i\theta}$. Find $z_1 z_2$ and z_1/z_2 using the polar form, and verify that you get the same answer as in part (a).

35. Let $z_1 = a_1 + b_1 i$ and $z_2 = a_2 + b_2 i$. Show that $\overline{z_1 z_2} = \bar{z}_1 \bar{z}_2$.

36. If the roots of the equation $x^2 + 2bx + c = 0$ are the complex numbers $p \pm iq$, find expressions for p and q in terms of b and c.

Are the statements in Problems 37–42 true or false? Explain your answer.

37. Every nonnegative real number has a real square root.

38. For any complex number z, the product $z \cdot \bar{z}$ is a real number.

39. The square of any complex number is a real number.

40. If f is a polynomial, and $f(z) = i$, then $f(\bar{z}) = i$.

41. Every nonzero complex number z can be written in the form $z = e^w$, where w is another complex number.

42. If $z = x + iy$, where x and y are positive, then $z^2 = a + ib$ has a and b positive.

For Problems 43–47, use Euler's formula to derive the following relationships. (Note that if a, b, c, d are real numbers, $a + bi = c + di$ means that $a = c$ and $b = d$.)

43. $\sin^2\theta + \cos^2\theta = 1$ **44.** $\sin 2\theta = 2\sin\theta\cos\theta$

45. $\cos 2\theta = \cos^2\theta - \sin^2\theta$ **46.** $\dfrac{d}{d\theta}\sin\theta = \cos\theta$

47. $\dfrac{d^2}{d\theta^2}\cos\theta = -\cos\theta$

48. Use complex exponentials to show that
$$\sin(-x) = -\sin x.$$

49. Use complex exponentials to show that
$$\sin(x + y) = \sin x \cos y + \cos x \sin y.$$

50. For real t, show that if $z_1(t) = x_1(t) + iy_1(t)$ and $z_2(t) = x_2(t) + iy_2(t)$ then
$$(z_1 + z_2)' = z_1' + z_2' \quad \text{and} \quad (z_1 z_2)' = z_1' z_2 + z_1 z_2'.$$

C   NEWTON'S METHOD

Many problems in mathematics involve finding the root of an equation. For example, we might have to locate the zeros of a polynomial, or determine the point of intersection of two curves. Here we will see a numerical method for approximating solutions which cannot be calculated exactly.

One such method, bisection, is described in Appendix A. Although it is very simple, the bisection method has two major drawbacks. First, it cannot locate a root where the curve is tangent to, but does not cross, the x-axis. Second, it is relatively slow in the sense that it requires a considerable number of iterations to achieve a desired level of accuracy. Although speed may not be important in solving a single equation, a practical problem may involve solving thousands of equations as a parameter changes. In such a case, any reduction in the number of steps can be important.

Using Newton's Method

We now consider a powerful root-finding method developed by Newton. Suppose we have a function $y = f(x)$. The equation $f(x) = 0$ has a root at $x = r$, as shown in Figure C.14. We begin with an initial estimate, x_0, for this root. (This can be a guess.) We will now obtain a better estimate x_1. To do this, construct the tangent line to the graph of f at the point $x = x_0$, and extend it until it crosses the x-axis, as shown in Figure C.14. The point where it crosses the axis is usually much closer to r, and we use that point as the next estimate, x_1. Having found x_1, we now repeat the process starting with x_1 instead of x_0. We construct a tangent line to the curve at $x = x_1$, extend it until it crosses the x-axis, use that x-intercept as the next approximation, x_2, and so on. The resulting sequence of x-intercepts usually converges rapidly to the root r.

Let's see how this looks algebraically. We know that the slope of the tangent line at the initial estimate x_0 is $f'(x_0)$, and so the equation of the tangent line is

$$y - f(x_0) = f'(x_0)(x - x_0).$$

At the point where this tangent line crosses the x-axis, we have $y = 0$ and $x = x_1$, so that

$$0 - f(x_0) = f'(x_0)(x_1 - x_0).$$

Solving for x_1, we obtain

$$x_1 = x_0 - \frac{f(x_0)}{f'(x_0)}$$

provided that $f'(x_0)$ is not zero. We now repeat this argument and find that the next approximation is

$$x_2 = x_1 - \frac{f(x_1)}{f'(x_1)}.$$

Summarizing, for any $n = 0, 1, 2, \ldots$, we obtain the following result.

Newton's Method to Solve the Equation $f(x) = 0$

Choose x_0 near a solution and compute the sequence $x_1, x_2, x_3 \ldots$ using the rule

$$x_{n+1} = x_n - \frac{f(x_n)}{f'(x_n)}$$

provided that $f'(x_n)$ is not zero. For large n, the solution is well approximated by x_n.

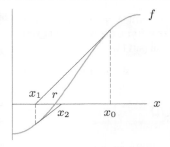

Figure C.14: Newton's method: successive approximations $x_0, x_1, x_2, \ldots$ to the root, r

---

Example 1   Use Newton's method to find the fifth root of 23. (By calculator, this is 1.872171231, correct to nine decimal places.)

Solution   To use Newton's method, we need an equation of the form $f(x) = 0$ having $23^{1/5}$ as a root. Since $23^{1/5}$ is a root of $x^5 = 23$ or $x^5 - 23 = 0$, we take $f(x) = x^5 - 23$. The root of this equation is between 1 and 2 (since $1^5 = 1$ and $2^5 = 32$), so we will choose $x_0 = 2$ as our initial estimate. Now $f'(x) = 5x^4$, so we can set up Newton's method as

$$x_{n+1} = x_n - \frac{x_n^5 - 23}{5x_n^4}.$$

In this case, we can simplify using a common denominator, to obtain

$$x_{n+1} = \frac{4x_n^5 + 23}{5x_n^4}.$$

Therefore, starting with $x_0 = 2$, we find that $x_1 = 1.8875$. This leads to $x_2 = 1.872418193$ and $x_3 = 1.872171296$. These values are in Table C.4. Since we have $f(1.872171231) > 0$ and $f(1.872171230) < 0$, the root lies between 1.872171230 and 1.872171231. Therefore, in just four iterations of Newton's method, we have achieved eight-decimal accuracy.

Table C.4   *Newton's method: $x_0 = 2$*

n	x_n	$f(x_n)$
0	2	9
1	1.8875	0.957130661
2	1.872418193	0.015173919
3	1.872171296	0.000004020
4	1.872171231	0.000000027

Table C.5   *Newton's method: $x_0 = 10$*

n	x_n	n	x_n
0	10	6	2.679422313
1	8.000460000	7	2.232784753
2	6.401419079	8	1.971312452
3	5.123931891	9	1.881654220
4	4.105818871	10	1.872266333
5	3.300841811	11	1.872171240

As a general guideline for Newton's method, once the first correct decimal place is found, each successive iteration approximately doubles the number of correct digits.

What happens if we select a very poor initial estimate? In the preceding example, suppose x_0 were 10 instead of 2. The results are in Table C.5. Notice that even with $x_0 = 10$, the sequence of values moves reasonably quickly toward the solution: We achieve six-decimal place accuracy by the eleventh iteration.

Example 2

Find the first point of intersection of the curves given by $f(x) = \sin x$ and $g(x) = e^{-x}$.

Solution

The graphs in Figure C.15 make it clear that there are an infinite number of points of intersection, all with $x > 0$. In order to find the first one numerically, we consider the function

$$F(x) = f(x) - g(x) = \sin x - e^{-x}$$

whose derivative is $F'(x) = \cos x + e^{-x}$. From the graph, we see that the point we want is fairly close to $x = 0$, so we start with $x_0 = 0$. The values in Table C.6 are approximations to the root. Since $F(0.588532744) > 0$ and $F(0.588532743) < 0$, the root lies between 0.588532743 and 0.588532744. (Remember, your calculator must be set in radians.)

Table C.6   *Successive approximations to root of $\sin x = e^{-x}$*

n	x_n
0	0
1	0.5
2	0.585643817
3	0.588529413
4	0.588532744
5	0.588532744

Figure C.15: Root of $\sin x = e^{-x}$

When Does Newton's Method Fail?

In most practical situations, Newton's method works well. Occasionally, however, the sequence x_0, x_1, x_2, ... fails to converge or fails to converge to the root you want. Sometimes, for example, the sequence can jump from one root to another. This is particularly likely to happen if the magnitude of the derivative $f'(x_n)$ is small for some x_n. In this case, the tangent line is nearly horizontal and so x_{n+1} will be far from x_n. (See Figure C.16.)

If the equation $f(x) = 0$ has *no* root, then the sequence will not converge. In fact, the sequence obtained by applying Newton's method to $f(x) = 1 + x^2$ is one of the best known examples of *chaotic behavior* and has attracted considerable research interest recently. (See Figure C.17.)

Figure C.16: Problems with Newton's method: Converges to wrong root

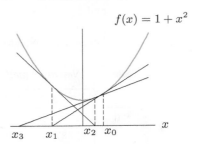

Figure C.17: Problems with Newton's method: Chaotic behavior

Exercises for Appendix C

1. Suppose you want to find a solution of the equation

$$x^3 + 3x^2 + 3x - 6 = 0.$$

Consider $f(x) = x^3 + 3x^2 + 3x - 6$.

(a) Find $f'(x)$, and use it to show that $f(x)$ increases everywhere.
(b) How many roots does the original equation have?
(c) For each root, find an interval which contains it.
(d) Find each root to two decimal places, using Newton's method.

For Problems 2–4, use Newton's method to find the given quantities to two decimal places:

2. $\sqrt[3]{50}$ 3. $\sqrt[4]{100}$ 4. $10^{-1/3}$

For Problems 5–8, solve each equation and give each answer to two decimal places:

5. $\sin x = 1 - x$ 6. $\cos x = x$

7. $e^{-x} = \ln x$

8. $e^x \cos x = 1$, for $0 < x < \pi$

9. Find, to two decimal places, all solutions of $\ln x = 1/x$.

10. How many zeros do the following functions have? For each zero, find an upper and a lower bound which differ by no more than 0.1.
    (a) $f(x) = x^3 + x - 1$ (b) $f(x) = \sin x - \frac{2}{3}x$
    (c) $f(x) = 10xe^{-x} - 1$

11. Find the largest zero of

$$f(x) = x^3 + x - 1$$

to six decimal places, using Newton's method. How do you know your approximation is as good as you claim?

12. For any positive number, a, the problem of calculating the square root, $\sqrt{a}$, is often done by applying Newton's method to the function $f(x) = x^2 - a$. Apply the method to obtain an expression for x_{n+1} in terms of x_n. Use this to approximate $\sqrt{a}$ for $a = 2, 10, 1000$, and π, correct to four decimal places, starting at $x_0 = a/2$ in each case.

D   VECTORS IN THE PLANE

Position Vectors

Consider a point (a, b) lying on a curve C in the plane (see Figure D.18). The arrow from the origin to the point (a, b) is called the *position vector* of the point, written $\vec{r}$. As the point moves

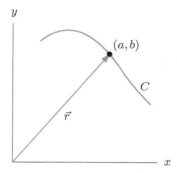

Figure D.18: A position vector $\vec{r}$

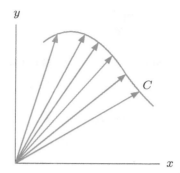

Figure D.19: Position vectors of points on curve C

along the curve, the position vector sweeps across the plane, the arrowhead touching the curve (see Figure D.19).

A position vector is defined by its magnitude (or length) and its direction. Figure D.20 shows two position vectors with the same magnitude but different directions. Figure D.21 shows two position vectors with the same direction but different magnitudes. An object that possesses both magnitude and direction is called a *vector*, and a position vector is one example. Other physical quantities (such as force, electric and magnetic fields, velocity and acceleration) that have both magnitude and direction can be represented by vectors. To distinguish them from vectors, real numbers (which have magnitude but no direction) are sometimes called *scalars*.

Vectors can be written in several ways. One is to write $\langle a, b \rangle$ for the position vector with tip at (a, b)— the use of the angle brackets signifies that we're talking about a vector, not a point. Another notation uses the special vectors $\vec{i}$ and $\vec{j}$ along the axes. The position vector $\vec{i}$ points to $(1, 0)$ and $\vec{j}$ points to $(0, 1)$; both have magnitude 1. The position vector $\vec{r}$ pointing to (a, b) can be written

$$\vec{r} = a\vec{i} + b\vec{j}.$$

The terms $a\vec{i}$ and $b\vec{j}$ are called the *components* of the vector.

Other special vectors include the zero vector, $\vec{0} = 0\vec{i} + 0\vec{j}$. Any vector with magnitude 1 is called a *unit vector*.

Figure D.20: Position vectors with same magnitude, different direction

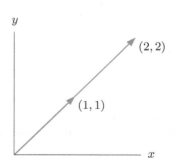

Figure D.21: Position vectors with same direction, different magnitude

Example 1   What are the components of the position vector in Figure D.22?

Solution   Since the vector points to $(3, -\sqrt{3})$, we have

$$\vec{r} = 3\vec{i} - \sqrt{3}\,\vec{j}.$$

Thus, the components of the vector are $3\vec{i}$ and $-\sqrt{3}\,\vec{j}$.

Figure D.22: Find the components
of this position vector

Magnitude and Direction

If $\vec{r}$ is the position vector $a\vec{i} + b\vec{j}$, then the Pythagorean Theorem gives the magnitude of $\vec{r}$, written $\|\vec{r}\|$. From Figure D.23, we see

$$\|\vec{r}\| = \|a\vec{i} + b\vec{j}\| = \sqrt{a^2 + b^2}.$$

The direction of a position vector $\vec{r} = a\vec{i} + b\vec{j}$ is given by the angle θ between the vector and the positive x-axis, measured counterclockwise. This angle satisfies

$$\tan\theta = \left(\frac{b}{a}\right).$$

Figure D.23: Magnitude $\|\vec{r}\|$ and
direction of the position vector $\vec{r}$

Figure D.24: Magnitude and direction of
the vector $3\vec{i} - \sqrt{3}\vec{j}$

Example 2   Find the magnitude and direction of the position vector $\vec{r} = 3\vec{i} - \sqrt{3}\vec{j}$ in Figure D.22.

Solution   The magnitude is $\|\vec{r}\| = \sqrt{3^2 + (-\sqrt{3})^2} = \sqrt{12} = 2\sqrt{3}$. For the direction, we find $\arctan(-\sqrt{3}/3) = -\pi/6$. Thus, the angle with the positive x-axis is $\theta = 2\pi - \pi/6 = 11\pi/6$. See Figure D.24.

Describing Motion with Position Vectors

The motion given by the parametric equations

$$x = f(t), y = g(t)$$

can be represented by a changing position vector

$$\vec{r}(t) = f(t)\vec{i} + g(t)\vec{j}.$$

For example, $\vec{r}(t) = \cos t\vec{i} + \sin t\vec{j}$ represents the motion $x = \cos t, y = \sin t$ around the unit circle.

Displacement Vectors

Position vectors are vectors that begin at the origin. More general vectors can start at any point in the plane. We view such an arrow as an instruction to move from one point to another and call it a displacement vector. Figure D.25 shows the same displacement vector starting at two different points; we say they are the same vector since they have the same direction and magnitude. Thus, a position vector $\vec{r}$ is a displacement vector beginning at the origin. The zero vector $\vec{0} = 0\vec{i} + 0\vec{j}$ represents no displacement at all.

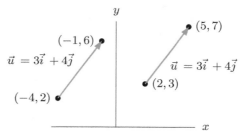

Figure D.25: Two equal displacement vectors:
Same magnitude and direction

Vector Operations

The sum $\vec{u}_1 + \vec{u}_2$ of two displacement vectors is the result of displacing an object first by $\vec{u}_1$ and then by $\vec{u}_2$; see Figure D.26. In terms of components:

If $\vec{u}_1 = a_1\vec{i} + b_1\vec{j}$ and $\vec{u}_2 = a_2\vec{i} + b_2\vec{j}$, then the sum is

$$\vec{u}_1 + \vec{u}_2 = (a_1 + a_2)\vec{i} + (b_1 + b_2)\vec{j}.$$

In other words, to add vectors, add their components separately.

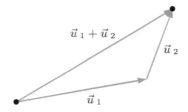

Figure D.26: Vector addition

Example 3   Find the sum of the following pairs of vectors:

(a) $3\vec{i} + 2\vec{j}$ and $-\vec{i} + \vec{j}$ (b) $\vec{i}$ and $3\vec{i} + \vec{j}$ (c) $\vec{i}$ and $\vec{j}$.

Solution   (a) $(3\vec{i} + 2\vec{j}) + (-\vec{i} + \vec{j}) = 2\vec{i} + 3\vec{j}$
            (b) $(\vec{i} + 0\vec{j}) + (3\vec{i} + \vec{j}) = 4\vec{i} + \vec{j}$
            (c) $(\vec{i} + 0\vec{j}) + (0\vec{i} + \vec{j}) = \vec{i} + \vec{j}$.

Vectors can be multiplied by a number. This operation is called scalar multiplication because it represents changing ("scaling") the magnitude of a vector while keeping its direction the same or reversing it. See Figure D.27.

If c is a real number and $\vec{u} = a\vec{i} + b\vec{j}$, then the *scalar multiple of* $\vec{u}$ *by* c, $c\vec{u}$, is

$$c\vec{u} = ca\vec{i} + cb\vec{j} .$$

In other words, to multiply a vector by a scalar c, multiply each component by c.

Figure D.27: Scalar multiplication

Example 4   If $\vec{u}_1 = 2\vec{i}$ and $\vec{u}_2 = \vec{i} + 3\vec{j}$, evaluate $6\vec{u}_2, (-2)\vec{u}_1$, and $2\vec{u}_1 + 5\vec{u}_2$.

Solution   We have

$$6\vec{u}_2 = 6\vec{i} + 18\vec{j} ,$$
$$(-2)\vec{u}_1 = -4\vec{i} ,$$
$$2\vec{u}_1 + 5\vec{u}_2 = (4\vec{i}) + (5\vec{i} + 15\vec{j}) = 9\vec{i} + 15\vec{j} .$$

Velocity Vectors

For a particle moving along a line with position $s(t)$, the instantaneous velocity is ds/dt. For a particle moving in the plane, the velocity is a vector. If the position vector is $\vec{r}(t) = x(t)\vec{i} + y(t)\vec{j}$, the particle's displacement during a time interval Δt is

$$\Delta\vec{r}(t) = \Delta x\vec{i} + \Delta y\vec{j} .$$

Dividing by Δt and letting $\Delta t \to 0$, we get the following result:

For motion in the plane with position vector $\vec{r}(t) = x(t)\vec{i} + y(t)\vec{j}$, the **velocity vector** is

$$\vec{v}(t) = \frac{dx}{dt}\vec{i} + \frac{dy}{dt}\vec{j}.$$

The direction of $\vec{v}(t)$ is tangent to the curve. The magnitude $\|\vec{v}(t)\|$ is the **speed**.

Notice the vector viewpoint agrees with the formulas for speed, v_x and v_y, given in Section 4.8, so we write

$$\vec{v}(t) = v_x\vec{i} + v_y\vec{j}.$$

Recall that for motion on a line, the acceleration is $a = dv/dt = d^2s/dt^2$. For motion in the plane, we have the following:

If the position vector is $\vec{r}(t) = x(t)\vec{i} + y(t)\vec{j}$, the **acceleration vector** is

$$\vec{a}(t) = \frac{d^2x}{dt^2}\vec{i} + \frac{d^2y}{dt^2}\vec{j}.$$

The acceleration measures both change in speed and change in direction of the velocity vector.

Example 5   Let $\vec{r}(t) = \cos(2t)\vec{i} + \sin(2t)\vec{j}$. Find the

(a) Velocity   (b) Speed   (c) Acceleration

Solution   (a) Differentiating $\vec{r}(t)$ gives the velocity vector

$$\text{Velocity} = \vec{v}(t) = -2\sin(2t)\vec{i} + 2\cos(2t)\vec{j}.$$

(b) Finding the magnitude of $\vec{v}(t)$, we have

$$\text{Speed} = \|\vec{v}(t)\| = \sqrt{(-2\sin(2t))^2 + (2\cos(2t))^2} = 2.$$

Notice that the speed is constant.

(c) Differentiating $\vec{v}(t)$ gives the acceleration vector

$$\text{Acceleration} = \vec{a}(t) = -4\cos(2t)\vec{i} - 4\sin(2t)\vec{j}.$$

Notice that even though the speed is constant, the acceleration vector is not $\vec{0}$, since the velocity vector is changing direction.

Exercises for Appendix D

Exercises

In Exercises 1–3, find the magnitude of the vector and the angle between the vector and the positive x-axis.

1. $3\vec{i}$ **2.** $2\vec{i} + \vec{j}$

3. $-\sqrt{2}\,\vec{i} + \sqrt{2}\,\vec{j}$

In Exercises 4–6, perform the indicated operations on the following vectors

$$\vec{u} = 2\vec{j} \qquad \vec{v} = \vec{i} + 2\vec{j} \qquad \vec{w} = -2\vec{i} + 3\vec{j}\,.$$

4. $\vec{v} + \vec{w}$ **5.** $2\vec{v} + \vec{w}$ **6.** $\vec{w} + (-2)\vec{u}$

Exercises 7–9 concern the following vectors:

$$3\vec{i} + 4\vec{j}, \quad \vec{i} + \vec{j}, \quad -5\vec{i}, \quad 5\vec{j}, \quad \sqrt{2}\vec{j}, \quad 2\vec{i} + 2\vec{j}, \quad -6\vec{j}$$

7. Which vectors have the same magnitude?

8. Which vectors have the same direction?

9. Which vectors have opposite direction?

10. If k is any real number and $\vec{r} = a\vec{i} + b\vec{j}$ is any vector, show that $\|k\vec{r}\| = |k|\|\vec{r}\|$.

11. Find a unit vector (that is, with magnitude 1) that is

    (a) In the same direction as the vector $-3\vec{i} + 4\vec{j}$.

    (b) In the direction opposite to the vector $-3\vec{i} + 4\vec{j}$.

In Exercises 12–15, express the vector in components.

12. The vector of magnitude 5 making an angle of $90°$ with the positive x-axis.

13. The vector in the same direction as $4\vec{i} - 3\vec{j}$ but with twice the magnitude.

14. The vector with the same magnitude as $4\vec{i} - 3\vec{j}$ and in the opposite direction.

15. The vector from $(3, 2)$ to $(4, 4)$.

In Exercises 16–19, determine whether the vectors are equal.

16. $6\vec{i} - 6\vec{j}$ and the vector from $(6, 6)$ to $(-6, -6)$.

17. The vector from $(7, 9)$ to $(9, 11)$ and the vector from $(8, 10)$ to $(10, 12)$.

18. $-\vec{i} + \vec{j}$ and the vector of length $\sqrt{2}$ making an angle of $\pi/4$ with the positive x-axis.

19. $5\vec{i} - 2\vec{j}$ and the vector from $(1, 12)$ to $(6, 10)$.

In Exercises 20–22, find the velocity vector and the speed, and acceleration.

20. $\vec{r}(t) = t\vec{i} + t^2\vec{j}, \quad t = 1$

21. $\vec{r}(t) = e^t\vec{i} + \ln(1 + t)\vec{j}, \quad t = 0$

22. $\vec{r}(t) = 5\cos t\,\vec{i} + 5\sin t\,\vec{j}, \quad t = \pi/2$

23. A particle is moving along the curve $\vec{r}(t) = \cos t\,\vec{i} + \sin t\,\vec{j}$. Find the particle's position and velocity vectors and its speed when $t = \pi/4$.

READY REFERENCE

This section contains a concise summary of the main definitions, theorems, and ideas presented throughout the book.

READY REFERENCE

A Library of Functions

Linear functions (p. 4) have the form $y = f(x) = b + mx$, where m is the **slope**, or rate of change of y with respect to x (p. 5) and b is the **vertical intercept**, or value of y when x is zero (p. 5). The slope is

$$m = \frac{\text{Rise}}{\text{Run}} = \frac{\Delta y}{\Delta x} = \frac{f(x_2) - f(x_1)}{x_2 - x_1} \quad \text{(p. 5).}$$

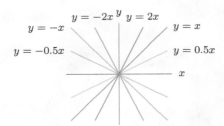

Figure R.1: The family $y = mx$ (with $b = 0$) (p. 6)

Figure R.2: The family $y = b + x$ (with $m = 1$) (p. 6)

Exponential functions have the form $P = P_0 a^t$ (p. 13) or $P = P_0 e^{kt}$ (p. 16), where P_0 is the initial quantity (p. 13), a is the growth (decay) factor per unit time (p. 13), $|k|$ is the continuous growth (decay) rate (pp. 16, 610), and $r = |a - 1|$ is the growth (decay) rate per unit time (p. 14).

Suppose $P_0 > 0$. If $a > 1$ or $k > 0$, we have **exponential growth**; if $0 < a < 1$ or $k < 0$, we have **exponential decay** (p. 15). The **doubling time** (for growth) is the time required for P to double (p. 14). The **half-life** (for decay) is the time required for P to be reduced by a factor of one half (p. 14). The continuous growth rate $k = \ln(1 + r)$ is slightly less than, but very close to, r, provided r is small (p. 611).

Figure R.3: Exponential growth: $P = a^t$, for $a > 1$ (p. 15)

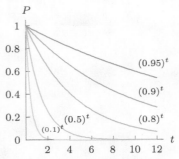

Figure R.4: Exponential decay: $P = a^t$, for $0 < a < 1$ (p. 15)

Common Logarithm and Natural Logarithm

$\log_{10} x = \log x =$ power of 10 that gives x (p. 29)
$\log_{10} x = c$ means $10^c = x$ (p. 29)
$\ln x =$ power of e that gives x (p. 29)
$\ln x = c$ means $e^c = x$ (p. 29)
$\log x$ and $\ln x$ are not defined if x is negative or 0 (p. 30).

Properties of Logarithms (p. 30)

1. $\log(AB) = \log A + \log B$ 4. $\log(10^x) = x$

2. $\log\left(\frac{A}{B}\right) = \log A - \log B$ 5. $10^{\log x} = x$

3. $\log(A^p) = p \log A$ 6. $\log 1 = 0$

The natural logarithm satisfies properties 1, 2, and 3, and $\ln e^x = x$, $e^{\ln x} = x$, $\ln 1 = 0$ (p. 30).

Trigonometric Functions The sine and cosine are defined in Figure R.5 (see also p. 37). The tangent is $\tan t = \frac{\sin t}{\cos t} =$ slope of the line through the origin $(0, 0)$ and P if $\cos t \neq 0$ (p. 40). The period of sin and cos is 2π (p. 37), the period of tan is π (p. 40).

Figure R.5: The definitions of $\sin t$ and $\cos t$ (p. 37)

A **sinusoidal function** (p. 38) has the form $y = C + A\sin(B(t + h))$ or $y = C + A\cos(B(t + h))$.

The **amplitude** is $|A|$, (p. 38), and the **period** is $2\pi/|B|$ (p. 38).

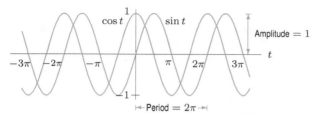

Figure R.6: Graphs of $\cos t$ and $\sin t$ (p. 37)

Trigonometric Identities

$$\sin^2 x + \cos^2 x = 1$$
$$\sin(2x) = 2\sin x \cos x$$
$$\cos(2x) = \cos^2 x - \sin^2 x = 2\cos^2 x - 1 = 1 - 2\sin^2 x$$
$$\cos(a+b) = \cos a \cos b - \sin a \sin b$$
$$\sin(a+b) = \sin a \cos b + \cos a \sin b$$

Inverse Trigonometric Functions: $\arcsin y = x$ means $\sin x = y$ with $-(\pi/2) \le x \le (\pi/2)$ (p. 41), $\arccos y = x$ means $\cos x = y$ with $0 \le x \le \pi$ (Problem 55, p. 44), $\arctan y = x$ means $\tan x = y$ with $-(\pi/2) < x < (\pi/2)$ (p. 41). The domain of arcsin and arccos is $[-1, 1]$ (p. 41), the domain of arctan is all numbers (p. 41). **Power Functions** have the form $f(x) = kx^p$ (p. 45). Graphs for positive powers:

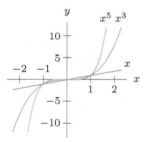

Figure R.7: Odd integer powers of x: "Seat" shaped for $k > 1$ (p. 46)

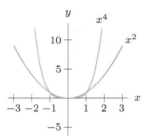

Figure R.8: Even integer powers of x: $\bigcup$-shaped (p. 46)

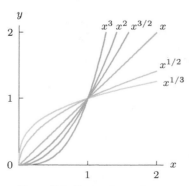

Figure R.9: Comparison of some fractional powers of x

Graphs for zero and negative powers:

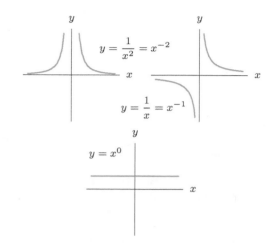

Figure R.10: Comparison of zero and negative powers of x

Polynomials have the form

$$f(x) = a_n x^n + a_{n-1}x^{n-1} + \cdots + a_1 x + a_0, \ a_n \ne 0 \ \text{(p. 46)}.$$

The **degree** is n (p. 47) and the **leading coefficient** is a_n (p. 47).

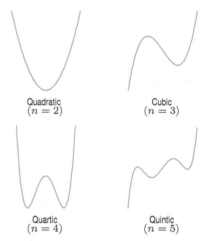

Figure R.11: Graphs of typical polynomials of degree n (p. 47)

Rational Functions have the form $f(x) = \dfrac{p(x)}{q(x)}$, where p and q are polynomials (p. 49). There is usually a vertical asymptote at $x = a$ if $q(a) = 0$ and a horizontal asymptote at $y = L$ if $\lim_{x \to \infty} f(x) = L$ or $\lim_{x \to -\infty} f(x) = L$ (p. 49).

Hyperbolic Functions:

$$\cosh x = \frac{e^x + e^{-x}}{2} \quad \sinh x = \frac{e^x - e^{-x}}{2} \quad \text{(p. 165)}.$$

Relative Growth Rates of Functions

Power Functions As $x \to \infty$, higher powers of x dominate, as $x \to 0$, smaller powers dominate.

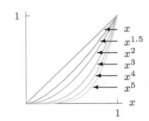

Figure R.12: For large x:
Large powers of x dominate

Figure R.13: For $0 \le x \le 1$:
Small powers of x dominate

Power Functions Versus Exponential Functions Every exponential growth function eventually dominates every power function (p. 46).

Figure R.14: Exponential function eventually dominates power function

Power Functions Versus Logarithm Functions The power function x^p dominates $A \log x$ for large x for all values of $p > 0$ and $A > 0$.

Figure R.15: Comparison of $x^{1/3}$ and $\log x$

Figure R.16: Comparison of $x^{1/3}$ and $100 \log x$

Numerical comparisons of growth rates:

Table R.1 *Comparison of $x^{0.001}$ and $1000 \log x$*

x	$x^{0.001}$	$1000 \log x$
10^{5000}	10^5	$5 \cdot 10^6$
10^{6000}	10^6	$6 \cdot 10^6$
10^{7000}	10^7	$7 \cdot 10^6$

Table R.2 *Comparison of x^{100} and 1.01^x*

x	x^{100}	1.01^x
10^4	10^{400}	$1.6 \cdot 10^{43}$
10^5	10^{500}	$1.4 \cdot 10^{432}$
10^6	10^{600}	$2.4 \cdot 10^{4321}$

Operations on Functions

Shifts, Stretches, and Composition Multiplying by a constant, c, stretches (if $c > 1$) or shrinks (if $0 < c < 1$) the graph vertically. A negative sign (if $c < 0$) reflects the graph about the x-axis, in addition to shrinking or stretching (p. 21). Replacing y by $(y - k)$ moves a graph up by k (down if k is negative) (p. 21). Replacing x by $(x - h)$ moves a graph to the right by h (to the left if h is negative) (p. 21). The composite of f and g is the function $f(g(x))$; f is the outside function, g the inside function (p. 21).

Symmetry We say f is an **even** function if $f(-x) = f(x)$ (p. 22) and f is an **odd** function if $f(-x) = -f(x)$ (p. 22).

Inverse Functions A function f has an inverse if (and only if) its graph intersects any horizontal line at most once (p. 24). If f has an inverse, it is written f^{-1}, and $f^{-1}(x) = y$ means $f(y) = x$ (p. 24). Provided the x and y scales are equal, the graph of f^{-1} is the reflection of the graph of f about the line $y = x$ (p. 25).

Proportionality We say y is proportional to x if $y = kx$ for k a nonzero constant. We say y is inversely proportional to x if $y = k(1/x)$ (p. 6).

Limits and Continuity

Idea of Limit (p. 58) If there is a number L such that $f(x)$ is as close to L as we please whenever x is sufficiently close to c (but $x \ne c$), then $\lim_{x \to c} f(x) = L$.

Definition of Limit (p. 59) If there is a number L such that for any $\epsilon > 0$, there exists a $\delta > 0$ such that if $|x - c| < \delta$ and $x \ne c$, then $|f(x) - L| < \epsilon$, then $\lim_{x \to c} f(x) = L$.

One-sided Limits (p. 61) If $f(x)$ approaches L as x approaches c through values greater than c, then $\lim_{x \to c^+} f(x) = L$. If $f(x)$ approaches L as x approaches c through values less than c, then $\lim_{x \to c^-} f(x) = L$.

Limits at Infinity (p. 63) If $f(x)$ gets as close to L as we please when x gets sufficiently large, then $\lim_{x \to \infty} f(x) = L$. Similarly, if $f(x)$ approaches L as x gets more and more negative, then $\lim_{x \to -\infty} f(x) = L$.

Theorem: Properties of Limits (p. 60) Assuming all the limits on the right-hand side exist:

1. If b is a constant, then $\lim_{x \to c} (bf(x)) = b \left(\lim_{x \to c} f(x) \right)$.
2. $\lim_{x \to c} (f(x) + g(x)) = \lim_{x \to c} f(x) + \lim_{x \to c} g(x)$.
3. $\lim_{x \to c} (f(x)g(x)) = \left(\lim_{x \to c} f(x) \right) \left(\lim_{x \to c} g(x) \right)$.
4. $\lim_{x \to c} \dfrac{f(x)}{g(x)} = \dfrac{\lim_{x \to c} f(x)}{\lim_{x \to c} g(x)}$, provided $\lim_{x \to c} g(x) \ne 0$.
5. For any constant k, $\lim_{x \to c} k = k$.
6. $\lim_{x \to c} x = c$.

Idea of Continuity (p. 53) A function is **continuous on an interval** if its graph has no breaks, jumps, or holes in that interval.

Definition of Continuity (p. 63) The function f is **continuous** at $x = c$ if f is defined at $x = c$ and

$$\lim_{x \to c} f(x) = f(c).$$

The function is **continuous on an interval** if it is continuous at every point in the interval.

Theorem: Continuity of Sums, Products, Quotients (p. 64) Suppose that f and g are continuous on an interval and that b is a constant. Then, on that same interval, the following functions are also continuous: $bf(x)$, $f(x) + g(x)$, $f(x)g(x)$. Further, $f(x)/g(x)$ is continuous provided $g(x) \neq 0$ on the interval.

Theorem: Continuity of Composite Functions (p. 64) Suppose f and g are continuous and $f(g(x))$ is defined on an interval. Then on that interval $f(g(x))$ is continuous.

Intermediate Value Theorem (p. 55) Suppose f is continuous on a closed interval $[a, b]$. If k is any number between $f(a)$ and $f(b)$, then there is at least one number c in $[a, b]$ such that $f(c) = k$.

The Extreme Value Theorem (p. 196) If f is continuous on the interval $[a, b]$, then f has a global maximum and a global minimum on that interval.

The Derivative

The slope of the secant line of $f(x)$ over an interval $[a, b]$ gives:

Average rate of change of f over $[a, b]$ $= \dfrac{f(b) - f(a)}{b - a}$ (p. 83).

Figure R.17: Visualizing the average rate of change of f (p. 84)

The **derivative** of f at a is the slope of the line tangent to the graph of f at the point $(a, f(a))$:

$$f'(a) = \lim_{h \to 0} \frac{f(a + h) - f(a)}{h},$$

and gives the **instantaneous rate of change** of f at a (p. 83). The function f is **differentiable** at a if this limit exists (p. 83). The **second derivative** of f, denoted f'', is the derivative of f' (p. 104).

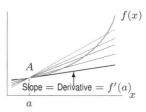

Figure R.18: Visualizing the instantaneous rate of change of f (p. 84)

The **units** of $f'(x)$ are: $\dfrac{\text{Units of } f(x)}{\text{Units of } x}$ (p. 99). If $f' > 0$ on an interval, then f is **increasing** over that interval (p. 92). If $f' < 0$ on an interval, then f is **decreasing** over that interval (p. 92). If $f'' > 0$ on an interval, then f is **concave up** over that interval (p. 104). If $f'' < 0$ on an interval, then f is **concave down** over that interval (p. 104).

The **tangent line** at $(a, f(a))$ is the graph of $y = f(a) + f'(a)(x - a)$ (p. 169). The **tangent line approximation** says that for values of x near a, $f(x) \approx f(a) + f'(a)(x - a)$. The expression $f(a) + f'(a)(x - a)$ is called the **local linearization** of f near $x = a$ (p. 169).

Derivatives of elementary functions

$\dfrac{d}{dx}(x^n) = nx^{n-1}$ (p. 126) $\dfrac{d}{dx}(e^x) = e^x$ (p. 133)

$\dfrac{d}{dx}(a^x) = (\ln a)a^x$ (p. 134) $\dfrac{d}{dx}(\ln x) = \dfrac{1}{x}$ (p. 156)

$\dfrac{d}{dx}(\sin x) = \cos x$ $\dfrac{d}{dx}(\cos x) = -\sin x$ (p. 151)

$\dfrac{d}{dx}(\arctan x) = \dfrac{1}{1 + x^2}$ (p. 157)

$\dfrac{d}{dx}(\arcsin x) = \dfrac{1}{\sqrt{1 - x^2}}$ (p. 158)

Derivatives of sums, differences, and constant multiples

$$\frac{d}{dx}[f(x) \pm g(x)] = f'(x) \pm g'(x) \quad \text{(p. 125)}$$

$$\frac{d}{dx}[cf(x)] = cf'(x) \quad \text{(p. 124)}$$

Product and quotient rules

$$(fg)' = f'g + fg' \quad \text{(p. 137)}$$

$$\left(\frac{f}{g}\right)' = \frac{f'g - fg'}{g^2} \quad \text{(p. 138)}$$

Chain rule

$$\frac{d}{dx}f(g(x)) = f'(g(x)) \cdot g'(x) \quad \text{(p. 143)}$$

Derivative of an inverse function (p. 158). If f has a differentiable inverse, f^{-1}, then

$$\frac{d}{dx}(f^{-1}(x)) = \frac{1}{f'(f^{-1}(x))}.$$

Implicit differentiation (p. 162) If y is implicitly defined as a function of x by an equation, then, to find dy/dx, differentiate the equation (remembering to apply the chain rule).

Applications of the Derivative

A function f has a **local maximum** at p if $f(p)$ is greater than or equal to the values of f at points near p, and a **local minimum** at p if $f(p)$ is less than or equal to the values of f at points near p (p. 187). It has a **global maximum** at p if $f(p)$ is greater than or equal to the value of f at any point in the interval, and a **global minimum** at p if $f(p)$ is less than or equal to the value of f at any point in the interval (p. 196).

A **critical point** of a function $f(x)$ is a point p in the domain of f where $f'(p) = 0$ or $f'(p)$ is undefined (p. 187).

Theorem: Local maxima and minima which do not occur at endpoints of the domain occur at critical points (pp. 188, 192).

The First-Derivative Test for Local Maxima and Minima (p. 188):

- If f' changes from negative to positive at p, then f has a local minimum at p.

- If f' changes from positive to negative at p, then f has a local maximum at p.

The Second-Derivative Test for Local Maxima and Minima (p. 189):

- If $f'(p) = 0$ and $f''(p) > 0$ then f has a local minimum at p.

- If $f'(p) = 0$ and $f''(p) < 0$ then f has a local maximum at p.

- If $f'(p) = 0$ and $f''(p) = 0$ then the test tells us nothing.

To find the **global maximum and minimum** of a function on an interval we compare values of f at all critical points in the interval and at the endpoints of the interval (or $\lim_{x \to \pm\infty} f(x)$ if the interval is unbounded) (p. 197).

An **inflection point** of f is a point at which the graph of f changes concavity (p. 190); f'' is zero or undefined at an inflection point (p. 190).

L'Hopital's rule (p. 243) If f and g are continuous, $f(a) = g(a) = 0$, and $g'(a) \neq 0$, then

$$\lim_{x \to a} \frac{f(x)}{g(x)} = \frac{f'(a)}{g'(a)}.$$

Parametric equations (p. 249) If a curve is given by the parametric equations $x = f(t)$, $y = g(t)$, the slope of the curve as a function of t is $dy/dx = (dy/dt)/(dx/dt)$.

Theorems About Derivatives

Theorem: Local Extrema and Critical Points (pp. 188, 192) Suppose f is defined on an interval and has a local maximum or minimum at the point $x = a$, which is not an endpoint of the interval. If f is differentiable at $x = a$, then $f'(a) = 0$.

The Mean Value Theorem (p. 175) If f is continuous on $[a, b]$ and differentiable on (a, b), then there exists a number c, with $a < c < b$, such that

$$f'(c) = \frac{f(b) - f(a)}{b - a}.$$

The Increasing Function Theorem (p. 176) Suppose that f is continuous on $[a, b]$ and differentiable on (a, b).

- If $f'(x) > 0$ on (a, b), then f is increasing on $[a, b]$.

- If $f'(x) \geq 0$ on (a, b), then f is nondecreasing on $[a, b]$.

The Constant Function Theorem (p. 177) Suppose that f is continuous on $[a, b]$ and differentiable on (a, b). If $f'(x) = 0$ on (a, b), then f is constant on $[a, b]$.

The Racetrack Principle (p. 177) Suppose that g and h are continuous on $[a, b]$ and differentiable on (a, b), and that $g'(x) \leq h'(x)$ for $a < x < b$.

- If $g(a) = h(a)$, then $g(x) \leq h(x)$ for $a \leq x \leq b$.

- If $g(b) = h(b)$, then $g(x) \geq h(x)$ for $a \leq x \leq b$.

Theorem: Differentiability and Local Linearity (p. 170) Suppose f is differentiable at $x = a$ and $E(x)$ is the error in the tangent line approximation, that is: $E(x) = f(x) - f(a) - f'(a)(x - a)$. Then $\lim_{x \to a} \dfrac{E(x)}{x - a} = 0$.

Theorem: A Differentiable Function Is Continuous (p. 113) If $f(x)$ is differentiable at a point $x = a$, then $f(x)$ is continuous at $x = a$.

The Definite Integral

The **definite integral of f from a to b** (p. 282), denoted $\int_a^b f(x)\,dx$, is the limit of the left and the right sums as the width of the rectangles is shrunk to 0, where

$$\textbf{Left-hand sum} = \sum_{i=0}^{n-1} f(x_i)\Delta x \quad \text{(p. 276)}$$

$$= f(x_0)\Delta x + f(x_1)\Delta x + \cdots + f(x_{n-1})\Delta x$$

$$\textbf{Right-hand sum} = \sum_{i=1}^{n} f(x_i)\Delta x \quad \text{(p. 281)}$$

$$= f(x_1)\Delta x + f(x_2)\Delta x + \cdots + f(x_n)\Delta x$$

Figure R.19: Left-hand sum (p. 276)

Figure R.20: Right-hand sum (p. 276)

If f is nonnegative, $\int_a^b f(x)\,dx$ represents the area under the curve between $x = a$ and $x = b$ (p. 283). If f has any sign, $\int_a^b f(x)\,dx$ is the sum of the areas above the x-axis, counted positively, and the areas below the x-axis, counted negatively (p. 284). If $F'(t)$ is the rate of change of some quantity $F(t)$, then $\int_a^b F'(t)\,dt$ is the **total change** in $F(t)$ between $t = a$ and $t = b$ (p. 291). The **average value** of f on the interval $[a, b]$ is given by $\dfrac{1}{b-a}\displaystyle\int_a^b f(x)\,dx$ (p. 304).

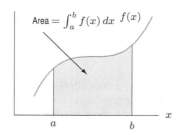

Figure R.21: The definite integral $\int_a^b f(x)\,dx$ (p. 283)

Figure R.22: Area and average value (p. 305)

The **units** of $\int_a^b f(x)\,dx$ are Units of $f(x) \times$ Units of x (p. 289).

The Fundamental Theorem of Calculus If f is continuous on $[a, b]$ and $f(x) = F'(x)$, then

$$\int_a^b f(x)\,dx = F(b) - F(a) \quad \text{(p. 290)}.$$

Properties of Definite Integrals (pp. 298, 300)
If a, b, and c are any numbers and f, g are continuous functions, then

$$\int_b^a f(x)\,dx = -\int_a^b f(x)\,dx$$

$$\int_a^b (f(x) \pm g(x))\,dx = \int_a^b f(x)\,dx \pm \int_a^b g(x)\,dx$$

$$\int_a^c f(x)\,dx + \int_c^b f(x)\,dx = \int_a^b f(x)\,dx$$

$$\int_a^b cf(x)\,dx = c\int_a^b f(x)\,dx$$

Antiderivatives

An **antiderivative** of a function $f(x)$ is a function $F(x)$ such that $F'(x) = f(x)$ (p. 320). There are infinitely many antiderivatives of f since $F(x) + C$ is an antiderivative of f for any constant C, provided $F'(x) = f(x)$ (p. 320). The **indefinite integral** of f is the family of antiderivatives $\int f(x)\,dx = F(x) + C$ (p. 326).

Construction Theorem (Second Fundamental Theorem of Calculus) If f is a continuous function on an interval and a is any number in that interval, then $F(x) = \int_a^x f(t)\,dt$ is an antiderivative of f (p. 340).

Properties of Indefinite Integrals (p. 329)

$$\int (f(x) \pm g(x))\,dx = \int f(x)\,dx \pm \int g(x)\,dx$$

$$\int cf(x)\,dx = c\int f(x)\,dx$$

Some antiderivatives:

$$\int k\,dx = kx + C \quad \text{(p. 327)}$$

$$\int x^n\,dx = \frac{x^{n+1}}{n+1} + C, \quad n \neq -1 \quad \text{(p. 327)}$$

$$\int \frac{1}{x}\,dx = \ln|x| + C \quad \text{(p. 328)}$$

$$\int e^x\,dx = e^x + C \quad \text{(p. 328)}$$

$$\int \cos x\,dx = \sin x + C \quad \text{(p. 328)}$$

$$\int \sin x\,dx = -\cos x + C \quad \text{(p. 328)}$$

$$\int \frac{dx}{1+x^2} = \arctan x + C \quad \text{(p. 382)}$$

$$\int \frac{dx}{\sqrt{1-x^2}} = \arcsin x + C \quad \text{(p. 380)}$$

Substitution (p. 354) For integrals of the form $\int f(g(x))g'(x)\,dx$, let $w = g(x)$. Choose w, find dw/dx and substitute for x and dx. Convert limits of integration for definite integrals.

Integration by Parts (p. 364) Used mainly for products; also for integrating $\ln x$, $\arctan x$, $\arcsin x$.

$$\int uv'\,dx = uv - \int u'v\,dx$$

Partial Fractions (p. 376) To integrate a rational function, $P(x)/Q(x)$, express as a sum of a polynomial and terms of the form $A/(x-c)^n$ and $(Ax+B)/q(x)$, where $q(x)$ is an unfactorable quadratic.

Trigonometric Substitutions (p. 380) To simplify $\sqrt{x^2-a^2}$, try $x=a\sin\theta$ (p. 380). To simplify a^2+x^2 or $\sqrt{a^2+x^2}$, try $x=a\tan\theta$ (p. 382).

Numerical Approximations for Definite Integrals (p. 387) Riemann sums (left, right, midpoint) (p. 387), trapezoid rule (p. 388), Simpson's rule (p. 391)

Approximation Errors (p. 389)
f concave up: midpoint underestimates, trapezoid overestimates (p. 389)
f concave down: trapezoid underestimates, midpoint overestimates (p. 389)

Evaluating Improper Integrals (p. 395)

- Infinite limit of integration: $\int_a^\infty f(x)\,dx = \lim_{b\to\infty}\int_a^b f(x)\,dx$ (p. 395)

- For $a<b$, if integrand is unbounded at $x=b$, then: $\int_a^b f(x)\,dx = \lim_{c\to b^-}\int_a^c f(x)\,dx$ (p. 398)

Testing Improper Integrals for Convergence by Comparison (p. 404):

- If $0\le f(x)\le g(x)$ and $\int_a^\infty g(x)\,dx$ converges, then $\int_a^\infty f(x)\,dx$ converges

- If $0\le g(x)\le f(x)$ and $\int_a^\infty g(x)\,dx$ diverges, then $\int_a^\infty f(x)\,dx$ diverges

Applications of Integration

Total quantities can be approximated by slicing them into small pieces and summing the pieces. The limit of this sum is a definite integral which gives the exact total quantity.

Applications to Geometry
To calculate the volume of a solid, slice the volume into pieces whose volumes you can estimate (pp. 414, 422). Use this method to calculate volumes of revolution (p. 422) and volumes of solids with known cross sectional area (p. 425). Curve $f(x)$ from $x=a$ to $x=b$ has

$$\text{Arc length} = \int_a^b \sqrt{1+(f'(x))^2}\,dx \quad \text{(p. 426)}.$$

Mass and Center of Mass from Density, δ

$$\text{Total mass} = \int_a^b \delta(x)\,dx \text{ (p. 440)}$$

$$\text{Center of mass} = \frac{\int_a^b x\delta(x)\,dx}{\int_a^b \delta(x)\,dx} \text{ (p. 444)}$$

To find the center of mass of two- and three-dimensional objects, use the formula separately on each coordinate (p. 445).

Applications to Physics

$$\text{Work done} = \text{Force} \times \text{Distance} \text{ (p. 449)}$$

$$\text{Pressure} = \text{Density} \times g \times \text{Depth} \text{ (p. 454)}$$

$$\text{Force} = \text{Pressure} \times \text{Area} \text{ (p. 454)}$$

Applications to Economics Present and future value of income stream, $P(t)$ (p. 459); consumer and producer surplus (p. 462).

$$\text{Present value} = \int_0^M P(t)e^{-rt}dt \text{ (p. 459)}$$

$$\text{Future value} = \int_0^M P(t)e^{r(M-t)}dt \text{ (p. 459)}$$

Applications to Probability Given a density function $p(x)$, the fraction of the population for which x is between a and b is the area under the graph of p between a and b (p. 469). The cumulative distribution function $P(t)$ is the fraction having values of x below t (p. 469). The median is the value T such that half the population has values of x less than or equal to T (p. 475). The mean (p. 477) is defined by

$$\text{Mean value} = \int_{-\infty}^\infty xp(x)dx.$$

Polar Coordinates

Figure R.23: Cartesian and polar coordinates for the point P

The **polar coordinates** (p. 432) of a point are related to its Cartesian coordinates by

- $x=r\cos\theta$ and $y=r\sin\theta$
- $r=\sqrt{x^2+y^2}$ and $\tan\theta=\dfrac{y}{x}$, $x\ne 0$

For a constant a, the equation $r=a$ gives a circle of radius a, and the equation $\theta=a$ gives a ray from the origin making an angle of θ with the positive x-axis. The equation $r=\theta$ gives an **Archimedean spiral** (p. 433).

Area in Polar Coordinates (p. 436)
For a curve $r=f(\theta)$, with $\alpha\le\theta\le\beta$, which does not cross itself,

$$\text{Area of region enclosed} = \frac{1}{2}\int_\alpha^\beta f(\theta)^2\,d\theta.$$

Slope and Arclength in Polar Coordinates (p. 437)

For a curve $r = f(\theta)$, we can express x and y in terms of θ as a parameter, giving

$$x = r\cos\theta = f(\theta)\cos\theta \quad \text{and} \quad y = r\sin\theta = f(\theta)\sin\theta.$$

Then

$$\text{Slope} = \frac{dy}{dx} = \frac{dy/d\theta}{dx/d\theta}$$

and

$$\text{Arc length} = \int_\alpha^\beta \sqrt{\left(\frac{dx}{d\theta}\right)^2 + \left(\frac{dy}{d\theta}\right)^2}\, d\theta.$$

Alternatively (p. 439),

$$\text{Arc length} = \int_\alpha^\beta \sqrt{(f'(\theta))^2 + (f(\theta))^2}\, d\theta.$$

Sequences and Series

A **sequence** $s_1, s_2, s_3, \ldots, s_n, \ldots$ has a **limit** L, written $\lim_{n\to\infty} s_n = L$, if we can make s_n as close to L as we please by choosing a sufficiently large n. The sequence **converges** if a limit exists, **diverges** if no limit exists (see p. 494). Limits of sequences satisfy the same properties as limits of functions stated in Theorem 1.2 (p. 60) and

$$\lim_{n\to\infty} x^n = 0 \quad \text{if } |x| < 1 \qquad \lim_{n\to\infty} 1/n = 0 \quad \text{(p. 494)}$$

A sequence s_n is **bounded** if there are constants K and M such that $K \le s_n \le M$ for all n (p. 494). A convergent sequence is bounded. A sequence is monotone if it is either increasing, that is $s_n < s_{n+1}$ for all n, or decreasing, that is $s_n > s_{n+1}$ for all n (p. 495).

Theorem: Convergence of a Monotone, Bounded Sequence (p. 495): If a sequence s_n is bounded and monotone, it converges.

A **series** is an infinite sum $\sum a_n = a_1 + a_2 + \cdots$. The nth **partial sum** is $S_n = a_1 + a_2 + \cdots + a_n$ (p. 505). If $S = \lim_{n\to\infty} S_n$ exists, then the series $\sum a_n$ **converges**, and its sum is S (p. 505). If a series does not converge, we say that it **diverges** (p. 505). The sum of a **finite geometric series** is (p. 500):

$$a + ax + ax^2 + \cdots + ax^{n-1} = \frac{a(1-x^n)}{1-x}, \qquad x \ne 1.$$

The sum of an **infinite geometric series** is (p. 501):

$$a + ax + ax^2 + \cdots + ax^n + \cdots = \frac{a}{1-x}, \qquad |x| < 1.$$

The p-**series** $\sum 1/n^p$ converges if $p > 1$ and diverges if $p \le 1$ (p. 509). The **harmonic series** $\sum 1/n$ diverges (p. 507), the **alternating harmonic series** $\sum (-1)^{n-1}(1/n)$ converges (p. 517). An **alternating series** can be absolutely or conditionally convergent (p. 518).

Convergence Tests

Theorem: Convergence Properties of Series (p. 507)

1. If $\sum a_n$ and $\sum b_n$ converge and if k is a constant, then
   - $\sum (a_n + b_n)$ converges to $\sum a_n + \sum b_n$.
   - $\sum k a_n$ converges to $k \sum a_n$.

2. Changing a finite number of terms in a series does not change whether or not it converges, although it may change the value of its sum if it does converge.

3. If $\lim_{n\to\infty} a_n \ne 0$ or $\lim_{n\to\infty} a_n$ does not exist, then $\sum a_n$ diverges.

4. If $\sum a_n$ diverges, then $\sum k a_n$ diverges if $k \ne 0$.

Theorem: Integral Test (p. 509) Suppose $c \ge 0$ and $f(x)$ is a decreasing positive function, defined for all $x \ge c$, with $a_n = f(n)$ for all n.

- If $\displaystyle\int_c^\infty f(x)\, dx$ converges, then $\sum a_n$ converges.

- If $\displaystyle\int_c^\infty f(x)\, dx$ diverges, then $\sum a_n$ diverges.

Theorem: Comparison Test (p. 512) Suppose $0 \le a_n \le b_n$ for all n.

- If $\sum b_n$ converges, then $\sum a_n$ converges.
- If $\sum a_n$ diverges, then $\sum b_n$ diverges.

Theorem: Limit Comparison Test (p. 514) Suppose $a_n > 0$ and $b_n > 0$ for all n. If

$$\lim_{n\to\infty} \frac{a_n}{b_n} = c \qquad \text{where } c > 0,$$

then the two series $\sum a_n$ and $\sum b_n$ either both converge or both diverge.

Theorem: Convergence of Absolute Values Implies Convergence (p. 515): If $\sum |a_n|$ converges, then so does $\sum a_n$.

We say $\sum a_n$ is **absolutely convergent** if $\sum a_n$ and $\sum |a_n|$ both converge and **conditionally convergent** if $\sum a_n$ converges but $\sum |a_n|$ diverges (p. 518).

Theorem: The Ratio Test (p. 515) For a series $\sum a_n$, suppose the sequence of ratios $|a_{n+1}|/|a_n|$ has a limit:

$$\lim_{n\to\infty} \frac{|a_{n+1}|}{|a_n|} = L.$$

- If $L < 1$, then $\sum a_n$ converges.
- If $L > 1$, or if L is infinite, then $\sum a_n$ diverges.
- If $L = 1$, the test does not tell us anything about the convergence of $\sum a_n$.

Theorem: Alternating Series Test (p. 517) A series of the form

$$\sum_{n=1}^\infty (-1)^{n-1} a_n = a_1 - a_2 + a_3 - a_4 + \cdots + (-1)^{n-1} a_n + \cdots$$

converges if $0 < a_{n+1} < a_n$ for all n and $\lim_{n\to\infty} a_n = 0$.

Theorem: Error Bounds for Alternating Series (p. 518) Let $S_n = \sum_{i=1}^{n} (-1)^{i-1} a_i$ be the nth partial sum of an alternating series and let $S = \lim_{n \to \infty} S_n$. Suppose that $0 < a_{n+1} < a_n$ for all n and $\lim_{n \to \infty} a_n = 0$. Then $|S - S_n| < a_{n+1}$.

Power Series

$$P(x) = C_0 + C_1(x-a) + C_2(x-a)^2 + \cdots$$
$$+ C_n(x-a)^n + \cdots$$
$$= \sum_{n=0}^{\infty} C_n(x-a)^n \quad \text{(p. 521)}.$$

The **radius of convergence** is 0 if the series converges only for $x = a$, ∞ if it converges for all x, and the positive number R if it converges for $|x - a| < R$ and diverges for $|x - a| > R$ (p. 523). The **interval of convergence** is the interval between $a - R$ and $a + R$, including any endpoint where the series converges (p. 523).

Theorem: Method for Computing Radius of Convergence (p. 524) To calculate the radius of convergence, R, for the power series $\sum_{n=0}^{\infty} C_n(x-a)^n$, use the ratio test with $a_n = C_n(x-a)^n$.

- If $\lim_{n \to \infty} |a_{n+1}|/|a_n|$ is infinite, then $R = 0$.
- If $\lim_{n \to \infty} |a_{n+1}|/|a_n| = 0$, then $R = \infty$.
- If $\lim_{n \to \infty} |a_{n+1}|/|a_n| = K|x - a|$, where K is finite and nonzero, then $R = 1/K$.

Approximations

The **Taylor polynomial of degree** n approximating $f(x)$ for x near a is:

$$P_n(x) = f(a) + f'(a)(x-a) + \frac{f''(a)}{2!}(x-a)^2 + \cdots\cdots$$
$$+ \frac{f^{(n)}(a)}{n!}(x-a)^n \quad \text{(p. 541)}$$

The **Taylor series** approximating $f(x)$ for x near a is:

$$f(x) = f(a) + f'(a)(x-a) + \frac{f''(a)}{2!}(x-a)^2 + \cdots$$
$$+ \frac{f^{(n)}(a)}{n!}(x-a)^n + \cdots \quad \text{(p. 547)}$$

Theorem: The Lagrange Error Bound for $P_n(x)$ (p. 560) Suppose f and all its derivatives are continuous. If $P_n(x)$ is the nth Taylor polynomial for to $f(x)$ about a, then

$$|E_n(x)| = |f(x) - P_n(x)| \le \frac{M}{(n+1)!}|x - a|^{n+1},$$

where $\max \left| f^{(n+1)} \right| \le M$ on the interval between a and x.

Taylor Series for $\sin x$, $\cos x$, e^x (p. 547):

$$\sin x = x - \frac{x^3}{3!} + \frac{x^5}{5!} - \frac{x^7}{7!} + \frac{x^9}{9!} - \cdots$$

$$\cos x = 1 - \frac{x^2}{2!} + \frac{x^4}{4!} - \frac{x^6}{6!} + \frac{x^8}{8!} - \cdots$$

$$e^x = 1 + x + \frac{x^2}{2!} + \frac{x^3}{3!} + \frac{x^4}{4!} + \cdots$$

Taylor Series for $\ln x$ about $x = 1$ converges for $0 < x \le 2$ (p. 548):

$$(x-1) - \frac{(x-1)^2}{2} + \frac{(x-1)^3}{3} - \frac{(x-1)^4}{4} + \cdots$$

The **Binomial Series** for $(1+x)^p$ converges for $-1 < x < 1$ (p. 549):

$$1 + px + \frac{p(p-1)}{2!}x^2 + \frac{p(p-1)(p-2)}{3!}x^3 + \cdots$$

The **Fourier Series** of $f(x)$ is (p. 568)

$$f(x) = a_0 + a_1 \cos x + a_2 \cos 2x + a_3 \cos 3x + \cdots$$
$$+ b_1 \sin x + b_2 \sin 2x + b_3 \sin 3x + \cdots,$$

where

$$a_0 = \frac{1}{2\pi} \int_{-\pi}^{\pi} f(x)\, dx,$$

$$a_k = \frac{1}{\pi} \int_{-\pi}^{\pi} f(x) \cos(kx)\, dx \quad \text{for } k \text{ a positive integer,}$$

$$b_k = \frac{1}{\pi} \int_{-\pi}^{\pi} f(x) \sin(kx)\, dx \quad \text{for } k \text{ a positive integer.}$$

Differential Equations

A **differential equation** for the function $y(x)$ is an equation involving x, y and the derivatives of y (p. 586). The **order** of a differential equation is the order of the highest-order derivative appearing in the equation (p. 588). A **solution** to a differential equation is any function y that satisfies the equation (p. 587). The **general solution** to a differential equation is the **family of functions** that satisfies the equation (p. 587). An **initial value problem** is a differential equation together with an **initial condition**; a solution to an initial value problem is called a **particular solution** (p. 587). An **equilibrium solution** to a differential equation is a particular solution where y is constant and $dy/dx = 0$ (p. 615).

First-order equations: methods of solution. A **slope field** corresponding to a differential equation is a plot in the xy-plane of small line segments with slope given by the differential equation (p. 591). **Euler's method** approximates the solution of an initial value problem with a string of small line segments (p. 599). Differential equations of the form $dy/dx = g(x)f(y)$ can be solved analytically by **separation of variables** (p. 604).

First-order equations: applications. The differential equation for **exponential growth and decay** is of the form

$$\frac{dP}{dt} = kP.$$

The **solution** is of the form $P = P_0 e^{kt}$, where P_0 is the initial value of P, and positive k represents growth while negative k represents decay (p. 610). Applications of growth and decay include **continuously compounded interest (p. 610)**, **population growth (p. 629)**, and **Newton's law of heating and cooling (p. 613)**. The **logistic equation** for population growth is of the form

$$\frac{dP}{dt} = kP\left(1 - \frac{P}{L}\right),$$

where L is the **carrying capacity** of the population (p. 629). The **solution to the logistic equation** is of the form $P = \dfrac{L}{1 + Ae^{-kt}}$, where $A = \dfrac{L - P_0}{P_0}$ (p. 630).

Systems of differential equations. Two interacting populations, w and r, can be modeled by two equations

$$\frac{dw}{dt} = aw - cwr \qquad \text{and} \qquad \frac{dr}{dt} = -br + kwr \quad \text{(p. 643)}.$$

Solutions can be visualized as **trajectories** in the wr-**phase plane** (p. 644). An **equilibrium point** is one at which $dw/dt = 0$ and $dr/dt = 0$ (p. 644). A **nullcline** is a curve along which $dw/dt = 0$ or $dr/dt = 0$ (p. 650).

Section 1.1

1 Pop 12 million in 2005

5 $y = (1/2)x + 2$

7 $y = 2x + 2$

9 Slope:$-12/7$
   Vertical intercept: $2/7$

11 Slope: 2
    Vertical intercept: $-2/3$

13 (a) (V)
   (b) (VI)
   (c) (I)
   (d) (IV)
   (e) (III)
   (f) (II)

15 $y - c = m(x - a)$

17 $y = -\frac{1}{5}x + \frac{7}{5}$

19 Parallel: $y = m(x - a) + b$
    Perpendicular:
    $y = (-1/m)(x - a) + b$

21 Domain: $1 \le x \le 5$
    Range: $1 \le y \le 6$

23 Domain: $0 \le x \le 5$
    Range: $0 \le y \le 4$

25 Domain: all x
    Range: $0 < y \le 1/2$

27 $V = kr^3$

29 $S = kh^2$

31 $N = k/l^2$

33 $f(0)$ meters

35 $f(0) = f(1) + 0.001$

37 V (thousand dollars)

41 (a) $C = 4.16 + 0.12w$
   (b) 0.12 $/gal
   (c) $4.16

43 (a) $C_1 = 40 + 0.15m$
        $C_2 = 50 + 0.10m$
   (b) C (cost in dollars)

   (c) For distances less than 200 miles, C_1 is
        cheaper.
        For distances more than 200 miles, C_2 is
        cheaper.

45 driving speed

47 distance from exit

49 (a) (i) $f(1985) = 13$
         (ii) $f(1990) = 99$
   (b) $(f(1990) - f(1985))/(1990 - 1985) =$
        17.2 billionaires/yr
   (c) $f(t) = 17.2t - 34{,}129$

51 (a) 2005–2007
   (b) 2004–2007

53 (a) 7.094 meters
   (b) 1958, 1883

55 (a) $\Delta w/\Delta h$ constant
   (b) $w = 5h - 174$; 5 lbs/in
   (c) $h = 0.2w + 34.8$; 0.2 in/lb

57 (a) $C = 10 + 0.2x$
   (c) Vertical intercept
        Slope of line

59 (a) $(-2, 4)$
   (b) $(-b, b^2)$

61 $y = 0.5 - 3x$ is decreasing

63 $y = 2x + 3$

65 False

67 False; $y = x + 1$ at points
    $(1, 2)$ and $(2, 3)$

69 (b), (c)

Section 1.2

1 Concave up

3 Neither

5 5; 7%

7 3.2; 3% (continuous)

9 $P = 15(1.2840)^t$; growth

11 $P = P_0(1.2214)^t$; growth

13 (a) 1.5
   (b) 50%

15 (a) $P = 1000 + 50t$
   (b) $P = 1000(1.05)^t$

17 (a) D to E, H to I
   (b) A to B, E to F
   (c) C to D, G to H
   (d) B to C, F to G

19 (a) $h(x) = 31 - 3x$
   (b) $g(x) = 36(1.5)^x$

21 Table D

23 (a) $P = 10^6(e^{0.02t})$
   (b)

25 (a) 125%
   (b) 9 times

27 (a) revenue

(b) temperature

29 (a) $g(x)$
   (b) $h(x)$
   (c) $f(x)$

31 $y = 3(2^x)$

33 $y = 2(3^x)$

35 $f(1) = 15, f(3) = 25, f(4) = 30$
    $g(1) = 10\sqrt{2}, g(3) = 20\sqrt{2}, g(4) = 40$

37 (a) 2.3 years

39 (a) $H, 2H, 3H$
   (b) t/H; $A = 325(1/2)^{t/H}$

41 30.268%

43 (a) 261 million gallons, 358 million gallons
   (b) consumption of
        biodiesel (mn gal)

45 (a) 16 trillion BTUs, 32 trillion BTUs
   (b) consumption of hydro.
        power (trillion BTU)

   (c) 2007, 13 trillion BTUs

47 (a) Increased: 2006, 2008; decreased: none
   (b) Yes

49 $y = 2x$ not concave up

51 $f(x) = 2(1.1)^x$

53 False

55 False

57 True; $f(x) = (0.5)^x$

59 True

Section 1.3

1 (a)

(b)

(c)

(d)

(e)

(f)

3
(a)

(b)

(c)

(d)

(e)

(f)

5

7

9 (a) $\sqrt{5}$
  (b) 5
  (c) $\sqrt{x^2 + 4}$
  (d) $x + 4$
  (e) $t^2\sqrt{t + 4}$

11 (a) $\dfrac{1}{7}$
   (b) 7
   (c) $\dfrac{1}{3x + 4}$
   (d) $\dfrac{3}{x} + 4$
   (e) $3 + \dfrac{4}{t}$

13 (a) $t^2 + 2t + 2$
   (b) $t^4 + 2t^2 + 2$
   (c) 5
   (d) $2t^2 + 2$
   (e) $t^4 + 2t^2 + 2$

15 $2zh + h^2$

17 $4hz$

21 (a) $y = 2x^2 + 1$

(b) $y = 2(x^2 + 1)$
(c) No

23 Not invertible

25 not invertible

27 Invertible

29 Neither

31 Neither

33 Even

35 Neither

37 $f(x) = x + 1$
   $g(x) = x^3$

39 $f(x) = e^x$
   $g(x) = 2x$

41 $y = (x - 2)^3 - 1$

43 $\{3, -7, 19, 4, 178, 2, 1\}$

45 Not invertible

47 Not invertible

49 $g(2r)$ ft^3

51 $f^{-1}(g^{-1}(10,000))$ min

53 18

55 Cannot be done

57 0.4

59 -0.9

61

63 (a) $f(15) \approx 48$
   (b) Yes
   (c) $f^{-1}(120) \approx 35$
      Rock is 35 millions yrs old at depth
      of 120 meters

65 $4000\pi/3 \text{ cm}^3$

67 Reflected about t-axis,
   shifted up S

69 Shift left

71 $f^{-1}(x) = x$

73 $f(x) = x^2 + 2$

75 $f(x) = 1.5x, g(x) = 1.5x + 3$

77 True

79 False

81 True

83 True; $f(x) = 0$

85 Impossible

87 Impossible

Section 1.4

1 $1/2$

3 $5A^2$

5 $-1 + \ln A + \ln B$

7 $(\log 11)/(\log 3) = 2.2$

9 $(\log(2/5))/(\log 1.04) = -23.4$

11 1.68

13 6.212

15 0.26

17 1

19 $(\log a)/(\log b)$

21 $(\log Q - \log Q_0)/(n \log a)$

23 $\ln(a/b)$

25 $P = 15e^{0.4055t}$

27 $P = 174e^{-0.1054t}$

29 $p^{-1}(t) \approx 58.708 \log t$

31 $f^{-1}(t) = e^{t-1}$

33 16 kg

35 (a) 2023
   (b) 338.65 million people

37 (a) $Q_0(1.0033)^x$
   (b) 210.391 microgm/cu m

39 (a) 10 mg
   (b) 18%
   (c) 3.04 mg
   (d) 11.60 hours

41 $C = 2, \alpha = -\ln 2 = -0.693, y(2) = 1/2$

43 (a) $B(t) = B_0 e^{0.067t}$
   (b) $P(t) = P_0 e^{0.033t}$
   (c) $t = 20.387$; in 2000

45 2023

47 (a) 0.00664
   (b) $t = 2.167$; March 2, 2013

49 6,301 yrs; 385,081 yrs

51 (a) 47.6%
   (b) 23.7%

53 2054

55 Yes

57 To the left

59 No effect

61 Function even

63 $f(x) = -x$

65 True

67 False

Section 1.5

1 Negative
  0
  Undefined

3 Positive
  Positive
  Positive

5 Positive
  Positive
  Positive

7 Positive
  Negative
  Negative

9 Negative
  Positive
  Negative

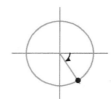

11 8π; 3

13 2; 0.1

15 $f(x) = 5\cos(x/3)$

17 $f(x) = -8\cos(x/10)$

19 $f(x) = 2\cos(5x)$

21 $f(x) = 3\sin(\pi x/9)$

23 $f(x) = 3 + 3\sin((\pi/4)x)$

25 0.588

27 $(\sin^{-1}(2/5))/3 \approx 0.1372$

29 $(\tan^{-1} 2)/5 = 0.221$

31 No solution

33 If $f(x) = \sin x$ and
   $g(x) = x^2$ then
   $\sin x^2 = f(g(x))$
   $\sin^2 x = g(f(x))$
   $\sin(\sin x) = f(f(x))$

35 (a)

   (b) $P = 800 - 100\cos(\pi t/6)$

37 (a) $f(t) = -0.5 + \sin t$
      $g(t) = 1.5 + \sin t$
      $h(t) = -1.5 + \sin t$
      $k(t) = 0.5 + \sin t$
   (b) $g(t) = 1 + k(t)$

39 (a) $\frac{1}{60}$ second
   (b) V_0 represents the amplitude of oscillation.
   (c)

41 $\theta = \pi/4; R = v_0^2/g$

$R = \frac{v_0^2}{g}\sin 2\theta$

43 (a) Average depth of water
   (b) $A = 7.5$
   (c) $B = 0.507$
   (d) The time of a high tide

45 0.3 seconds

47 27.3 days $\approx$ one month

49 $f(t)$ is C; $g(t)$ is B; $h(t)$ is A; $r(t)$ is D

51 (a) 2π

53 (a) 0.4 and 2.7
   (b) $\arcsin(0.4) \approx 0.4$
       $\pi - \arcsin(0.4) \approx 2.7$
   (c) -0.4 and -2.7.
   (d) $-0.4 \approx -\arcsin(0.4)$
       $-2.7 \approx \arcsin(0.4) - \pi$

55 (b)
$y = \arccos x$

(c) The domain of arccos and arcsin are the same because their inverses (sine and cosine) have the same range
(d) $[0, \pi]$
(e) On $[-\pi/2, \pi/2]$ sine is invertible but cosine is not

57 Max $y = A + C$

59 $400(\cos x) + 1600$.

61 False

63 False

65 False

67 True

69 True

71 True

Section 1.6

1 As $x \to \infty, y \to \infty$
   As $x \to -\infty, y \to -\infty$

3 $f(x) \to -\infty$ as $x \to +\infty$
   $f(x) \to -\infty$ as $x \to -\infty$

5 $f(x) \to +\infty$ as $x \to +\infty$
   $f(x) \to +\infty$ as $x \to -\infty$

7 $f(x) \to 3$ as $x \to +\infty$
   $f(x) \to 3$ as $x \to -\infty$

9 $f(x) \to 0$ as $x \to +\infty$
   $f(x) \to 0$ as $x \to -\infty$

11 $0.2x^5$

13 1.05^x

15 $25 - 40x^2 + x^3 + 3x^5$

17 (I) (a) 3 (b) Negative
   (II) (a) 4 (b) Positive
   (III) (a) 4 (b) Negative
   (IV) (a) 5 (b) Negative
   (V) (a) 5 (b) Positive

19 $y = -\frac{1}{2}(x+2)^2(x-2)$

21 $f(x) = kx(x+3)(x-4)$
   $(k < 0)$

23 $f(x) =$
   $k(x+2)(x-2)^2(x-5)$
   $(k < 0)$

25 r

27 1, 2, 3, 4, or 5 roots

(a) 5 roots

(b) 4 roots

(c) 3 roots

(d) 2 roots

(e) 1 root

29 $-10^5 \le x \le 10^5,\ -10^{15} \le y \le 10^{15}$

31 (a) $1.3\ \text{m}^2$
   (b) $86.8\ \text{kg}$
   (c) $h = 112.6s^{4/3}$

33 (a) $R = kr^4$
       (k is a constant)
   (b) $R = 4.938r^4$
   (c) $3086.42\ \text{cm}^3/\text{sec}$

35 (a) $S = 2\pi r^2 + 2V/r$
   (b) $S \to \infty$ as $r \to \infty$
   (c)

37 Horizontal: $y = 1$;
   Vertical: $x = -2, x = 2$

39 (a) 0
   (b) $t = 2v_0/g$
   (c) $t = v_0/g$
   (d) $(v_0)^2/(2g)$

41 (a) (i) $1 = a + b + c$
       (ii) $b = -2a$ and $c = 1 + a$
       (iii) $c = 6$
   (b) $y = 5x^2 - 10x + 6$

43 $(3/x) + 6/(x-2)$
   Horizontal asymptote: x-axis
   Vertical asymptote: $x = 0$ and $x = 2$

45 $h(t) = ab^t$
   $g(t) = kt^3$
   $f(t) = ct^2$

47 (a) $R(P) = kP(L - P)$
       $(k > 0)$
   (b)

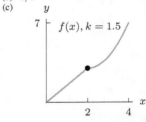

49 (a) $v = 3 \cdot 10^8$
   (b) $v < 1.5 \cdot 10^8$

51 $f(x) = (x^3 + 1)/x$ has no horizontal asymptote

53 $f(x) = 3x/(x-10)$

55 $f(x) = 1/(x + 7\pi)$

57 $f(x) = (x-1)/(x-2)$

59 True

Section 1.7

1 Yes

3 Yes

5 Yes

7 No

9 No

15 (a) Continuous
   (b) Not continuous

17 Velocity: Not continuous
   Distance: Continuous

19 $k = 5/3$

21 $k = 5/4$

23 (a)

(b) $3/2$
(c)

25 $k = -3$

27 $k = (\ln 3)/2$

29 $k = (e^6 - 1)/2$

31 No

33 $Q = \begin{cases} 1.2t & 0 \le t \le 0.5 \\ 0.6e^{0.001}e^{-.002t} & 0.5 < t \end{cases}$

35 Three zeros: one between 5 and 10, one between 10 and 12, the third either less than 5 or greater than 12

37 (a)

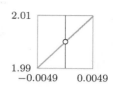

(b) No

39 Only for continuous function

41 $f(x) = \begin{cases} 1 & x \geq 15 \\ -1 & x < 15 \end{cases}$

43 $f(x) = \begin{cases} 1 & x \leq 2 \\ x & x > 2 \end{cases}$

45 False, $f(x) = \begin{cases} 1 & x \leq 3 \\ 2 & x > 3 \end{cases}$

47 False

Section 1.8

1 (a) 3
  (b) 7
  (c) Does not exist
  (d) 8

3 (a) 8
  (b) 6
  (c) 15
  (d) 4

5 Other answers are possible

7 Other answers are possible

9 Other answers are possible

11 $\lim_{x \to -\infty} f(x) = +\infty$;
   $\lim_{x \to +\infty} f(x) = -\infty$

13 $\lim_{x \to -\infty} f(x) = 3/5$;
   $\lim_{x \to +\infty} f(x) = 3/5$

15 $\lim_{x \to -\infty} f(x) = 0$;
   $\lim_{x \to +\infty} f(x) = +\infty$

17 0

19 2

21 $0.01745\ldots$

23 1

25 0.693

27 0

29 $\lim_{x \to 4^+} f(x) = 1$, $\lim_{x \to 4^-} f(x) = -1$, $\lim_{x \to 4} f(x)$ does not exist

31 $\lim_{x \to 3^+} f(x) = \lim_{x \to 3^-} f(x) = \lim_{x \to 3} f(x) = 7$

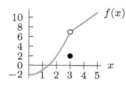

35 No. Limit does not exist at 0

37 No. $f(0) \neq$ limit at 0

39 $2.71828\ldots$

47 (b) -1
   (c)

-0.99

-1.01

-0.099   0.099

   (d) $-0.099 < x < 0.099$,
       $-1.01 < y < -0.99$

49 (b) 0
   (c)

0.01

-0.01

-0.0033   0.0033

   (d) $-0.0033 < x < 0.0033$,
       $-0.01 < y < 0.01$

51 (b) 3
   (c)

3.01

2.99

-0.047   0.047

   (d) $-0.047 < x < 0.047$,
       $2.99 < y < 3.01$

53 (b) 2
   (c)

2.01

1.99

-0.0049   0.0049

   (d) $-0.0049 < x < 0.0049$,
       $1.99 < y < 2.01$

55 $3/\pi$

57 $1/3$

59 $2/3$

61 $3/2$

63 $3/2$

65 5

67 $k \geq 2$

69 $k \geq 3$

71 $k \geq 0$

73 $0.46, 0.21, 0.09$

75 (a) $x = 1/(n\pi)$,
        $n = 1, 2, 3, \ldots$
   (b) $x = 2/(n\pi)$,
        $n = 1, 5, 9, \ldots$
   (c) $x = 2/(n\pi)$,
        $n = 3, 7, 11, \ldots$

77 (b) 0
   (c)

0.01

-0.01

-0.0029   0.0029

   (d) $-0.0029 < x < 0.0029$,
       $-0.01 < y < 0.01$

85 Limit does not exist

87 $f(x) = (x + 3)(x - 1)/(x - 1)$

89 True

91 True

93 False

95 True

97 False

99 False

101 (a) Follows
    (b) Does not follow (although true)
    (c) Follows
    (d) Does not follow

Chapter 1 Review

1 $y = 2x - 10$

3 $y = -3x^2 + 3$

5 $y = 2 + \sqrt{9 - (x + 1)^2}$

7 $y = -5x/(x - 2)$

9

heart
rate

administration
of drug

time

11 (a) $[0, 7]$
   (b) $[-2, 5]$
   (c) 5
   (d) $(1, 7)$
   (e) Concave up
   (f) 1
   (g) No

13 (a) Min gross income for \$100,000 loan
   (b) Size of loan for income of \$75,000

15 $t \approx 35.003$

17 $t = \log(12.01/5.02)/\log(1.04/1.03) = 90.283$

19 $P = 5.23e^{-1.6904t}$

21 $f(x) = x^3$
   $g(x) = \ln x$

23 Amplitude: 2
   Period: $2\pi/5$

25 (a) $f(x) \to \infty$
     as $x \to \infty$;
     $f(x) \to -\infty$
     as as $x \to -\infty$
   (b) $f(x) \to -\infty$
     as as $x \to \pm\infty$
   (c) $f(x) \to 0$ as $x \to \pm\infty$
   (d) $f(x) \to 6$ as $x \to \pm\infty$

27 $0.25\sqrt{x}$

29 $y = e^{0.4621x}$ or $y = (1.5874)^x$

31 $y = -k(x^2 + 5x)$
   $(k > 0)$

33 $z = 1 - \cos\theta$

35 $x = k(y^2 - 4y)$
   $(k > 0)$

37 $y = -(x + 5)(x + 1)(x - 3)^2$

39 Simplest is $y = 1 - e^{-x}$

41 $f(x) = \sin(2(\pi/5)x)$

43 Not continuous

45 $\lim_{x \to 3+} f(x) = 54$, $\lim_{x \to 3-} f(x) = -54$, $\lim_{x \to 3} f(x)$ does not exist

47 (b) 200 bushels
   (c) 80 lbs
   (d) $0 \le Y \le 550$
   (e) Decreasing
   (f) Concave down

49 (a) (i) $q = 320 - (2/5)p$
     (ii) $p = 800 - (5/2)q$
   (b)

51 (a) (i) Attractive force, pulling atoms together

(ii) Repulsive force, pushing atoms apart
   (b) Yes

53 2011

55 (a) Increased: 2009; decreased: 2006, 2007
   (b) False
   (c) True

57 Parabola opening downward

59 10 hours

61 About 14.21 years

63 (a) 81%
   (b) 32.9 hours
   (c)

65 One hour

67 US: 156 volts max, 60 cycles/sec
   Eur: 339 volts max, 50 cycles/sec

69 (a) (i) $V = 3\pi r^2$
     (ii) $V = \pi r^2 h$
   (b) (i) V

     (ii) V

71 (a)

73 (a) III
   (b) IV
   (c) I
   (d) II

75 $0.1, 0.05, 0.00007$

77 20

79 (a) $f(x) = (x - a)(x + a)(x + b)(x - c)$
   (b)

81 (a) $f(x) \to \infty$ as $x \to \infty$
     $f(x) \to 16$ as $x \to -\infty$
   (b) $(e^x + 1)(e^{2x} - 2)(e^x - 2)(e^{2x} + 2e^x + 4)$
     Two zeros
   (c) $(\ln 2)/2, \ln 2$
     One twice other

83 (a) $p(x) = x^2 + 3x + 9$
     $r(x) = -3, q(x) = x - 3$
   (b) $f(x) \approx -3/(x - 3)$ for x near 3
   (c) $f(x) \approx x^2 + 3x + 9$ as $x \to \pm\infty$

85 (a) $1 - 8\cos^2 x + 8\cos^4 x$
   (b) $1 - 8\sin^2 x + 8\sin^4 x$

Section 2.1

1 $265/3$ km/hr

3 -3 angstroms/sec

5 2 meters/sec

7 0 cm/sec

9 (a) (i) 0.04 m/sec
     (ii) 0.0004 m/sec
     (iii) 0.000004 m/sec
   (b) 0 m/sec

11

13

15 0

17 2.7

19 Positive: A and D
   Negative: C and F
   Most positive: A
   Most negative: F

21 $F < B < E < 0 < D < A < C$

23 $f(t)$

25 4

27 12

29 $|\text{velocity}| = \text{speed}$

33 $s(t) = t^2$

35 False

37 True

39 False

Section 2.2

1 12

3 (a) 70 \$/kg; 50 \$/kg
  (b) About 60 \$/kg

5 (b) 0.24
  (c) 0.22

7 negative

9 $f'(2) \approx 9.89$

11 $f'(d) = 0$, $f'(b) = 0.5$, $f'(c) = 2$,
  $f'(a) = -0.5$, $f'(e) = -2$

13 About 41

15 (a) $f(4)$
  (b) $f(2) - f(1)$
  (c) $(f(2) - f(1))/(2 - 1)$
  (d) $f'(1)$

17 $(4, 25)$; $(4.2, 25.3)$; $(3.9, 24.85)$

19

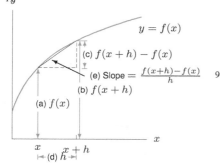

21 (a) $(f(b) - f(a))/(b - a)$
  (b) Slopes same
  (c) Yes

23 $g'(-4) = 5$

25 $y = 7x - 9$

27 $f'(2) \approx 6.77$

29 $f'(1) \approx -1.558$
  $f'(\frac{\pi}{4}) \approx -1$

31 8.84 million people/year
  9.28 million people/year

35 -6

37 -1

39 $1/4$

41 100

43 -1

45 $-1/4$

47 $y = 100x - 500$

49 $y = x$

51 $f'(0.5) > 0$

53 $f(x) = e^x$

55 True

57 True

Section 2.3

1 (a) 3
  (b) Positive: $0 < x < 4$
    Negative: $4 < x < 12$

3

5

7

9

11

13

15

17

19 $-1/x^2$

21 $4x$

23 (a)

  (b)

  (c)

  (d)

25 $f'(1) = 1$
  $f'(2) = 0.5$
  $f'(5) = 0.2$
  $f'(10) = 0.1$
  $f'(x) = \frac{1}{x}$

27 5.2

710

29

31

33

35

37

39

41 (a) $t = 3$
   (b) $t = 9$
   (c) $t = 14$
   (d)

43 (a) $x_1 < x < x_3$
   (b) $0 < x < x_1$; $x_3 < x < x_5$

45 (a) Periodic: period 1 year

(b) Max of 4500 on July 1st
   Min of 3500 on Jan 1st
(c) Growing fastest:
   around April 1st
   Decreasing fastest:
   around Oct 1st
(d) ≈ 0

47

49 0

53 Counterexample: e^{-x}

55 $f(t) = t(1 - t)$

57 True

59 False

Section 2.4

1 (a) Costs $1300 for 200 gallons
   (b) Costs about $6 for 201st gallon

3 (a) Positive
   (b) °F/min

5 (a) Quarts; dollars.
   (b) Quarts; dollars/quart

7 Dollars/percent; positive

9 Dollars/year; negative

11 (a) Investing the $1000 at 5%
   would yield about $1649 after 10 years
   (b) Extra percentage point would yield an increase of about $165; dollars/%

13 (b) Pounds/(Calories/day)

15

or

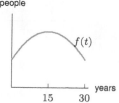

19 (a) 1986: pop. Mexico inc. 2 m. people/yr
   (b) Pop. 95.5 m. in 1996
   (c) 95.5 m.: about 0.46 yrs for pop. inc. of 1 m

21 (a) Depth 3 ft at $t = 5$ hrs
   (b) Depth increases 0.7 ft/hr
   (c) Time 7 hrs when depth 5 ft
   (d) Depth at 5 ft increases 1 ft in 1.2 hrs

23 Inches/year
   $g'(10) > 0$
   $g'(30) = 0$

25 Barrels/year; negative

27 (a) Gal/minute
   (b) (i) 0
   (ii) Negative
   (iii) 0

29 (a) 0.0851 people/sec
   (b) 12 seconds

31 Number of people 65.5–66.5 inches
   Units: People per inch
   $P'(66)$ between 17 and 34 million people/in
   $P'(x)$ is never negative

33 (a) $2.6 \cdot 10^{12}$; not compressible
   (b) $1.5 \cdot 10^{17}$; even less compressible

35 $r(t)$ is decreasing

39 True

41 False

43 (b), (d)

Section 2.5

1 (a) Increasing, concave up
   (b) Decreasing, concave down

3 B

5 (a)

(b)

(c)

(d)

7

9 $f'(x) < 0$
  $f''(x) = 0$

11 $f'(x) < 0$
  $f''(x) > 0$

13 $f'(x) < 0$
  $f''(x) < 0$

15 (a) Positive; negative
  (b) Neither; positive
  (c) Number of cars increasing at
     600,000 million cars per year in 2005

17 (a)

  (b)

  (c)

19

21

23

25 (a) utility

  (b) Derivative of utility is positive
     2nd derivative of utility is negative

29 (a) t_3, t_4, t_5
  (b) t_2, t_3
  (c) t_1, t_2, t_5
  (d) t_1, t_4, t_5
  (e) t_3, t_4

31 22 only possible value

33 It could be neither

35 $f(x) = b + ax, a \neq 0$

37 True

39 True

41 False

Section 2.6

1 (a) $x = 1$
  (b) $x = 1, 2, 3$

3 No

5 Yes

7 Yes

9 Yes

11 (a) Yes
  (b) Not at $t = 0$

13 (a) Yes
  (b) No

15 (a) Yes
  (b) No

17 Other cases are possible

19 $f(x) = |x - 2|$

21 $f(x) = (x^2 - 1)/(x^2 - 4)$

23 True; $f(x) = x^2$

25 True; $f(x) = \begin{cases} 1 & x \geq 0 \\ -1 & x < 0 \end{cases}$

27 (a) Not a counterexample
  (b) Counterexample
  (c) Not a counterexample
  (d) Not a counterexample

Chapter 2 Review

1 $72/7 = 10.286$ cm/sec

3 $(\ln 3)/2 = 0.549$ mm/sec

5 0 mm/sec

7 0 mm/sec

9 distance

11 (a)

  (b) Seven

(c) Increasing at $x = 1$
   Decreasing at $x = 4$
(d) $6 \leq x \leq 8$
(e) $x = -9$

13

15

17

19

21

23 $-1/x^2$

25 (a)   (i) C and D
     (ii) B and C
  (b) A and B,
     C and D

27 $10x$

29 $6x$

31 $2a$

33 $-2/a^3$

35 $-1/(2(\sqrt{a})^3)$

37 From smallest to largest:
   0, Vel at C, Vel at B, Av vel between A and B,
   1, Vel at A

39 (a) $A, C, F,$ and H.
  (b) Acceleration 0

41 (a) $f'(t) > 0$: depth increasing
     $f'(t) < 0$: depth decreasing
  (b) Depth increasing 20 cm/min
  (c) 12 meters/hr

43 (a) Thousand $ per $ per gallon
Rate change revenue with price/gal
(b) $ per gal/thousand $
Rate change price/gal with revenue

47 Concave up

49 (a)

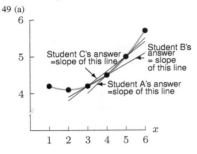

(b) Student C's
(c) $f'(x) = \dfrac{f(x+h) - f(x-h)}{2h}$

51 $x_1 = 0.9, x_2 = 1, x_3 = 1.1$
$y_1 = 2.8, y_2 = 3, y_3 = 3.2$

53 (a) Negative
(b) $dw/dt = 0$
(c) $|dw/dt|$ increases; dw/dt decreases

55 (a) Dose for 140 lbs is 120 mg
Dose increases by 3mg/lb
(b) About 135 mg

57 $P'(t) = 0.008P(t)$

59 (a) $f'(0.6) \approx 0.5$
$f'(0.5) \approx 2$
(b) $f''(0.6) \approx -15$
(c) Maximum: near $x = 0.8$
minimum: near $x = 0.3$

61 (a) At $(0, \sqrt{19})$: slope $= 0$
At $(\sqrt{19}, 0)$: slope is undefined
(b) slope $\approx 1/2$
(c) At $(-2, \sqrt{15})$: slope $\approx 1/2$
At $(-2, -\sqrt{15})$: slope $\approx -1/2$
At $(2, \sqrt{15})$: slope $\approx -1/2$

63 (a) Period 12 months

(b) Max of 4500 on June 1st
(c) Min of 3500 on Feb 1st
(d) Growing fastest:
April 1st
Decreasing fastest:
July 15 and Dec 15
(e) About 400 deer/month

65 (a) Concave down

(b) $120° < T < 140°$
(c) $135° < T < 140°$
(d) $45 < t < 50$

67 (a) $f'(0) = 1.00000$
$f'(0.3) = 1.04534$
$f'(0.7) = 1.25521$
$f'(1) = 1.54314$
(b) They are about the same

69 0, because $f(x)$ constant

71 (a) $-2a/e^{ax^2} + 4a^2x^2/e^{ax^2}$
(b)

$a = 1$

$a = 2$

$a = 3$

73 (a) $4x(x^2+1), 6x(x^2+1)^2, 8x(x^2+1)^3$
(b) $2nx(x^2+1)^{n-1}$

Section 3.1

3 Do not apply

5 $y' = \pi x^{\pi-1}$ (power rule)

7 $11x^{10}$

9 $-12x^{-13}$

11 $-3x^{-7/4}/4$

13 $3x^{-1/4}/4$

15 $3t^2 - 6t + 8$

17 $-5t^{-6}$

19 $-(7/2)r^{-9/2}$

21 $x^{-3/4}/4$

23 $-(3/2)x^{-5/2}$

25 $6x^{1/2} - \frac{5}{2}x^{-1/2}$

27 $17 + 12x^{-1/2}$

29 $20x^3 - 2/x^3$

31 $-12x^3 - 12x^2 - 6$

33 $6t - 6/t^{3/2} + 2/t^3$

35 $3t^{1/2} + 2t$

37 $(1/2)\theta^{-1/2} + \theta^{-2}$

39 $(z^2 - 1)/3z^2$

41 $1/(2\sqrt{\theta}) + 1/(2\theta^{3/2})$

43 $3x^2/a + 2ax/b - c$

45 a/c

47 $3ab^2$

49 $b/(2\sqrt{t})$

51 Rules of this section do not apply

53 $6x$
(power rule and sum rule)

55 $-2/3z^3$
(power rule and sum rule)

57 $y = 2x - 1$

59 $y = 7x - 9$

61 $y = 2x$ and $y = -6x$

63 $x > 1$

65 $f'(x) = 12x + 1$ and
$f''(x) = 12$

67 Proportional to r^2

69 (a) $v(t) = -32t$
$v \leq 0$ because the height is decreasing
(b) $a(t) = -32$
(c) $t = 8.84$ seconds
$v = -192.84$ mph

71 56 cm/sec^2

73 (a) $dg/dr = -2GM/r^3$
(b) dg/dr is rate of change of acceleration
g decreases with distance
(c) -3.05×10^{-6}
(d) Magnitude of dg/dr small; reasonable

75 (a) $dA/dr = 2\pi r$
(b) Circumference of a circle

79 $n = 1/13$

81 (a) $a = 4$
(b) No

83 $x^2 + a$

85 $f(x) = x^2, g(x) = 3x$

87 $f(x) = 3x^2$

89 False

91 True

Section 3.2

1 $2e^x + 2x$

3 $5\ln(a)a^{5x}$

5 $10x + (\ln 2)2^x$

7 $4(\ln 10)10^x - 3x^2$

9 $((\ln 3)3^x)/3 - (33x^{-3/2})/2$

11 $(\ln 4)^2 4^x$

13 $5 \cdot 5^t \ln 5 + 6 \cdot 6^t \ln 6$

15 ex^{e-1}

17 $(\ln \pi)\pi^x$

19 $(\ln k)k^x$

21 e^{t+2}

23 $a^x \ln a + ax^{a-1}$

25 $2 + 1/(3x^{4/3}) + 3^x \ln 3$

27 $2x + (\ln 2)2^x$

29 Rules do not apply

31 e^{x+5}

33 Rules do not apply

35 Rules do not apply

37 Rules do not apply

39 ≈ 7.95 cents/year

41 US, since $dU/dt > dM/dt$ at $t = 0$

43 (a) $f'(0) = -1$
 (b) $y = -x$
 (c) $y = x$

45 $g(x) = x^2/2 + x + 1$

47 e

49 $f'(x) = (\ln 2)2^x$

51 $f(x) = 0.5^x$

53 False; $f(x) = \ln x$

55 False; $f(x) = |x|$

Section 3.3

1 $5x^4 + 10x$

3 $e^x(x + 1)$

5 $2^x/(2\sqrt{x}) + \sqrt{x}(\ln 2)2^x$

7 $3^x[(\ln 3)(x^2 - x^{\frac{1}{2}}) + (2x - 1/(2\sqrt{x}))]$

9 $(1 - x)/e^x$

11 $(1 - (t + 1)\ln 2)/2^t$

13 $6/(5r + 2)^2$

15 $1/(5t + 2)^2$

17 $2e^t + 2te^t + 1/(2t^{3/2})$

19 $2y - 6$, $y \neq 0$

21 $\sqrt{z}(3 - z^{-2})/2$

23 $2r(r + 1)/(2r + 1)^2$

25 $17e^x(1 - \ln 2)/2^x$

27 1, $x \neq -1$

29 $6x\left(x^2 + 5\right)^2\left(3x^3 - 2\right)\left(6x^3 + 15x - 2\right)$

31 (a) 4

(b) Does not exist

(c) -4

33 (a) -2
 (b) Does not exist
 (c) 0

35 Approx 0.4

37 Approx 0.7

39 Approx -21.2

41 $f'(x) = 2e^{2x}$

43 $x > -2$

45 $y = 7x - 5$

47 (a) $\dfrac{d}{dx}\left(\dfrac{e^x}{x}\right) = \dfrac{e^x}{x} - \dfrac{e^x}{x^2}$

$\dfrac{d}{dx}\left(\dfrac{e^x}{x^2}\right) = \dfrac{e^x}{x^2} - \dfrac{2e^x}{x^3}$

$\dfrac{d}{dx}\left(\dfrac{e^x}{x^3}\right) = \dfrac{e^x}{x^3} - \dfrac{3e^x}{x^4}$

(b) $\dfrac{d}{dx}\left(\dfrac{e^x}{x^n}\right) = \dfrac{e^x}{x^n} - \dfrac{ne^x}{x^{n+1}}$

49 $4^x(\ln 4 \cdot f(x) + \ln 4 \cdot g(x) + f'(x) + g'(x))$

51 $(f'(x)g(x)h(x) + f(x)g'(x)h(x) - f(x)g(x)h'(x))/(h(x))^2$

53 (a) 19
 (b) -11

55 $f(x) = x^{10}e^x$

57 $r_2^2/(r_1 + r_2)^2$

59 (a) $g(v) = 1/f(v)$
 $g(80) = 20$ km/liter
 $g'(80) = -(1/5)$ km/liter for each
 1 km/hr increase in speed
 (b) $h(v) = v \cdot f(v)$
 $h(80) = 4$ liters/hr
 $h'(80) = 0.09$ liters/hr for
 each 1 km/hr inc. in speed

61 (a) $f'(x) = (x - 2) + (x - 1)$
 (b) $f'(x) = (x - 2)(x - 3) + (x - 1)(x - 3) + (x - 1)(x - 2)$
 (c) $f'(x) = (x - 2)(x - 3)(x - 4) + (x - 1)(x - 3)(x - 4) + (x - 1)(x - 2)(x - 4) + (x - 1)(x - 2)(x - 3)$

63 (a) $(FGH)' = F'GH + FG'H + FGH'$
 (c) $f_1'f_2f_3 \cdots f_n + f_1f_2'f_3 \cdots f_n + \cdots + f_1 \cdots f_{n-1}f_n'$

65 $f''(x)g(x) + 2f'(x)g'(x) + f(x)g''(x)$

67 Signs in numerator reversed

69 $f(x) = e^x \sin x$

71 False

73 False; $f(x) = x^2$, $g(x) = x^2 - 1$

Section 3.4

1 $99(x + 1)^{98}$

3 $56x(4x^2 + 1)^6$

5 $e^x/(2\sqrt{e^x + 1})$

7 $5(w^4 - 2w)^4(4w^3 - 2)$

9 $2r^3/\sqrt{r^4 + 1}$

11 $e^{2x}\left[2x^2 + 2x + (\ln 5 + 2)5^x\right]$

13 $\pi e^{\pi x}$

15 $-200xe^{-x^2}$

17 $(\ln \pi)\pi^{(x+2)}$

19 $e^{5-2t}(1 - 2t)$

21 $(2t - ct^2)e^{-ct}$

23 $(e^{\sqrt{s}})/(2\sqrt{s})$

25 $3s^2/(2\sqrt{s^3 + 1})$

27 $(e^{-z})/(2\sqrt{z}) - \sqrt{z}e^{-z}$

29 $5 \cdot \ln 2 \cdot 2^{5t-3}$

31 $-(\ln 10)(10^{\frac{5}{2} - \frac{y}{2}})/2$

33 $(1 - 2z \ln 2)/(2^{z+1}\sqrt{z})$

35 $\dfrac{\sqrt{x + 3}(x^2 + 6x - 9)}{2\sqrt{x^2 + 9}(x + 3)^2}$

37 $-(3e^{3x} + 2x)/(e^{3x} + x^2)^2$

39 $-1.5x^2(x^3 + 1)^{-1.5}$

41 $(2t + 3)(1 - e^{-2t}) + (t^2 + 3t)(2e^{-2t})$

43 $30e^{5x} - 2xe^{-x^2}$

45 $2we^w(5w^2 + 8)$

47 $-3te^{-3t^2}/\sqrt{e^{-3t^2} + 5}$

49 $2ye^{[e^{(y^2)} + y^2]}$

51 $6ax(ax^2 + b)^2$

53 $ae^{-bx} - abxe^{-bx}$

55 $abce^{-cx}e^{-be^{-cx}}$

57 (a) 2
 (b) Chain rule does not apply
 (c) -2

59 (a) Chain rule does not apply
 (b) Chain rule does not apply
 (c) Chain rule does not apply

61 $1/2$

63 -1

65 $y = 3x - 5$

67 $y = -16.464t + 87.810$

69 $x < 2$

71 (a) $13{,}394$ fish
 (b) 8037 fish/month

73 (a) 4
 (b) 2
 (c) $1/2$

75 $e^{(x^6)}/6$

77 (a) $g'(1) = 3/4$
 (b) $h'(1) = 3/2$

79 d; 0

81 Decreasing

83 Value of $h(x)$ decreases from d to $-d$

85 $P = 308.75e^{0.00923t}$

87 $f(5) = 6.3$ billion dollars; $f'(5) = 0.272$ billion dollars per year

89 (a) $P(1 + r/100)^t \ln(1 + r/100)$
 (b) $Pt(1 + r/100)^{t-1}/100$

91 (a) $dm/dv = m_0v/\left(c^2\sqrt{(1 - v^2/c^2)^3}\right)$
 (b) Rate of change of mass with respect to speed v

95 $f''(x)(g(x))^{-1} - 2f'(x)(g(x))^{-2}g'(x) + 2f(x)(g(x))^{-3}(g'(x))^2 - f(x)(g(x))^{-2}g''(x)$

97 $w'(x) = 2xe^{x^2}$

99 $f(x) = (x^2 + 1)^2$

101 False; $f(x) = 5x + 7, g(x) = x + 2$

Section 3.5

3 $\cos^2 \theta - \sin^2 \theta = \cos 2\theta$

5 $3\cos(3x)$

7 $-8\sin(2t)$

9 $3\pi \sin(\pi x)$

11 $3\pi \cos(\pi t)(2 + \sin(\pi t))^2$

13 $e^t \cos(e^t)$

15 $(\cos y)e^{\sin y}$

17 $3\cos(3\theta)e^{\sin(3\theta)}$

19 $2x/\cos^2(x^2)$

21 $4\cos(8x)(3 + \sin(8x))^{-0.5}$

23 $\cos x/\cos^2(\sin x)$

25 $2\sin(3x) + 6x\cos(3x)$

27 $e^{-2x}[\cos x - 2\sin x]$

29 $5\sin^4 \theta \cos \theta$

31 $-3e^{-3\theta}/\cos^2(e^{-3\theta})$

33 $-2e^{2x}\sin(e^{2x})$

35 $-\sin \alpha + 3\cos \alpha$

37 $3\theta^2 \cos \theta - \theta^3 \sin \theta$

39 $\cos(\cos x + \sin x) \cdot$
$(\cos x - \sin x)$

41 $(-t\sin t - 3\cos t)/t^4$

43 $\dfrac{\sqrt{1-\cos x}(1 - \cos x - \sin x)}{2\sqrt{1-\sin x}(1 - \cos x)^2}$

45 $(6\sin x \cos x)/(\cos^2 x + 1)^2$

47 $-ab\sin(bt + c)$

49 $y = 6t - 13.850$

51 $(\sin x + x \cos x)x \sin x$

53 $F(x) = -(1/4)\cos(4x)$

55 $2\sin(x^4) + 8x^4 \cos(x^4)$

57 (a) $v(t) = 2\pi \cos(2\pi t)$
   (b)

59 (a) $t = (\pi/2)(m/k)^{1/2};$
$t = 0;$
$t = (3\pi/2)(m/k)^{1/2}$
   (b) $T = 2\pi(m/k)^{1/2}$
   (c) $dT/dm = \pi/\sqrt{km};$
Positive sign means an increase in
mass causes the period to increase

61 (a) $0 \le t \le 2$
   (b) No, not at $t = 2$

63 At $x = 0$:
$y = x, \sin(\pi/6) \approx 0.524$
At $x = \pi/3$:
$y = x/2 + (3\sqrt{3} - \pi)/6,$
$\sin(\pi/6) \approx 0.604$

69 Cannot use product rule

71 $\sin x$

73 True

Section 3.6

1 $2t/(t^2 + 1)$

3 $10x/(5x^2 + 3)$

5 $1/\sqrt{1 - (x+1)^2}$

7 $(6x + 15)/(x^2 + 5x + 3)$

9 2

11 $e^{-x}/(1 - e^{-x})$

13 $e^x/(e^x + 1)$

15 $ae^{ax}/(e^{ax} + b)$

17 $3w^2 \ln(10w) + w^2$

19 e

21 $1/t$

23 $-1/(1 + (2-x)^2)$

25 $e^{\arctan(3t^2)}(6t)/(1 + 9t^4)$

27 $(\ln 2)z^{(\ln 2 - 1)}$

29 k

31 $-x/\sqrt{1 - x^2}$

33 $-1/z(\ln z)^2$

35 $3w^{-1/2} - 2w^{-3} + 5/w$

37 $(\cos x - \sin x)/(\sin x + \cos x)$

39 $1/(1 + 2u + 2u^2)$

41 $-(x+1)/(\sqrt{1 - (x+1)^2})$

43 $-1 < x < 1$

45 $\frac{d}{dx}(\log x) = \frac{1}{(\ln 10)x}$

47 $g(5000) = 32.189$ years
$g'(5000) = 0.004$ years per dollar

49 (a) $y = x - 1$
   (b) $0.1; 1$
   (c) Yes

51 (a) $f'(x) = 0$
   (b) f is a constant function

53 Any x with $25 < x < 50$

55 Any x with $75 < x < 100$

57 2.8

59 1.4

61 -0.12

63 (a) 12
   (b) $f^{-1}(x) = \sqrt[3]{x}$
   (c) $1/12$

65 $1/5$

67 (a) Pop is 296 m in 2005
   (b) 2005
   (c) Pop incr by 2.65 m/yr
   (d) 0.377 yr/million

69 $1/3$

71 (a) 1
   (b) 1
   (c) 1

73 (a) 1
   (c) e

75 $f'(x) = 1/(x \ln x)$

77 $f(x) = 2^x$

79 $y = \ln x$

81 False

Section 3.7

1 $dy/dx = -x/y$

3 $dy/dx = (y^2 - y - 2x)/(x - 3y^2 - 2xy)$

5 $-(1 + y)/(1 + x)$

7 $dy/dx = (y - 2xy^3)/(3x^2y^2 - x)$

9 $dy/dx = -\sqrt{y/x}$

11 $-3x/2y$

13 $-y/(2x)$

15 $dy/dx = (2 - y\cos(xy))/(x\cos(xy))$

17 $(y^2 + x^4y^4 - 2xy)/(x^2 - 2xy - 2x^5y^3)$

19 $(a - x)/y$

21 $(y + b\sin(bx))/$
$(a\cos(ay) - x)$

23 Slope is infinite

25 $-23/9$

27 $y = e^2 x$

29 $y = x/a$

31 (a) $(4 - 2x)/(2y + 7)$
   (b) Horizontal if $x = 2$,
Vertical if $y = -7/2$

33 $y = 2, y = -2$

35 (a) $dy/dx = (y^2 - 3x^2)/(3y^2 - 2xy)$
   (c) $y \approx 1.9945$
   (d) Horizontal:
$(1.1609, 2.0107)$
and
$(-0.8857, 1.5341)$
Vertical:
$(1.8039, 1.2026)$
and
$(\sqrt[3]{5}, 0)$

37 (a) $-(1/2P)f(1 - f^2)$

41 $(nb - V)/(P - n^2a/V^2 + 2n^3ab/V^3)$

43 Formula applies if point is on circle

45 $-x^2 + y^2 = 1$

Section 3.8

1 $3\cosh(3z + 5)$

3 $2\cosh t \cdot \sinh t$

5 $3t^2 \sinh t + t^3 \cosh t$

7 $\cosh x/(\cosh^2(3 + \sinh x))$

9 $\tanh(1 + \theta)$

11 0

15 $(t^2 + 1)/2t$

19 $\sinh(2x) = 2\sinh x \cosh x$

23 0

25 1

27 $|k| \le 3$

29 (a) $0.54\, T/w$

31 (a)

   (b) $A = 6.325$
(stretch factor)
$c = 0.458$
(horizontal shift)

33 (a) 0
(b) Positive for $x > 0$
   Negative for $x < 0$
   Zero for $x = 0$
(c) Increasing everywhere
(d) 1, −1

(e) Yes; derivative positive everywhere

35 $f'(x) = \sinh x$

37 $\tanh x \to 1$ as $x \to \infty$

39 $k = 0$

41 True

43 True

45 False

Section 3.9

1 $\sqrt{1 + x} \approx 1 + x/2$

3 $1/x \approx 2 - x$

5 $e^{x^2} \approx 2ex - e$

9 $|\text{Error}| < 0.2$
   Overestimate, $x > 0$
   Underestimate, $x < 0$

11 (a) $L(x) = 1 + x$
   (b) Positive for $x \neq 0$
   (c) 0.718

(d) $E(1)$ larger
(e) 0.005

13 (a) and (c)

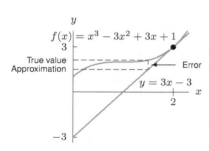

(b) $y = 3x - 3$

15 $a = 1; f(a) = 1$
   Underestimate
   $f(1.2) \approx 1.4$

17 0.1

19 (b) 0.1

21 (a)

(b) $y = (-9.69 \times 10^{-4})h + 30$
(c) $P = 30 - 0.001h$
(d) Both have P intercepts of 30, and slopes are almost the same
(e) Too small because it has a slightly smaller slope

23 (b) 1% increase

25 $f(1 + \Delta x) \geq f(1) + f'(1)\Delta x$

27 (a) 16,398 m
   (b) $16,398 + 682(\theta - 20)$ m
   (c) True: 17,070 m
   Approx: 17,080 m

29 (a) 1492 m
   (b) $1492 + 143(\theta - 20)$ m
   (c) True: 1638 m
   Approx: 1635 m

31 $f(x) \approx 1 + kx$
   $e^{0.3} \approx 1.3$

33 $E(x) = x^4 - (1 + 4(x - 1))$
   $k = 6; f''(1) = 12$
   $E(x) \approx 6(x - 1)^2$

35 $E(x) = e^x - (1 + x)$
   $k = 1/2; f''(0) = 1$
   $E(x) \approx (1/2)x^2$

37 $E(x) = \ln x - (x - 1)$
   $k = -1/2; f''(1) = -1$
   $E(x) \approx -(1/2)(x - 1)^2$

39 (c) 0

45 Only near $x = 0$

47 $f(x) = x^3 + 1, g(x) = x^4 + 1$

49 $f(x) = |x + 1|$

Section 3.10

1 False

3 False

5 True

7 No; no

9 No; no

11 $f'(c) = -0.5, f'(x_1) > -0.5,$
   $f'(x_2) < -0.5$

13 6 distinct zeros

19 Racetrack

21 Constant Function

23 $21 \leq f(2) \leq 25$

31 Not continuous

33 $1 \leq x \leq 2$

35 Possible answer: $f(x) = |x|$

37 Possible answer
$$f(x) = \begin{cases} x^2 & \text{if } 0 \leq x < 1 \\ 1/2 & \text{if } x = 1 \end{cases}$$

39 False

41 False

Chapter 3 Review

1 $200t(t^2 + 1)^{99}$

3 $(t^2 + 2t + 2)/(t + 1)^2$

5 $-8/(4 + t)^2$

7 $x^2 \ln x$

9 $\overline{(\cos \theta)}e^{\sin \theta}$

11 $-\tan(w - 1)$

13 $kx^{k-1} + k^x \ln k$

15 $3 \sin^2 \theta \cos \theta$

17 $6 \tan(2 + 3\alpha) \cos^{-2}(2 + 3\alpha)$

19 $(-e^{-t} - 1)/(e^{-t} - t)$

21 $1/\sin^2 \theta - 2\theta \cos \theta / \sin^3 \theta$

23 $-(2^w \ln 2 + e^w)/(2^w + e^w)^2$

25 $1/(\sqrt{\sin(2z)} \sqrt{\cos^3(2z)})$

27 $2^{-4z}[-4 \ln(2) \sin(\pi z) + \pi \cos(\pi z)]$

29 $e^{(e^\theta + e^{-\theta})}(e^\theta - e^{-\theta})$

31 $e^{\tan(\sin \alpha)} \cos \alpha / \cos^2(\sin \alpha)$

33 $e(\tan 2 + \tan r)^{e-1}/\cos^2 r$

35 $2e^{2x} \sin(3x)$
   $(\sin(3x) + 3\cos(3x))$

37 $2^{\sin x}\left((\ln 2)\cos^2 x - \sin x\right)$

39 $e^{\theta - 1}$

41 $(-cat^2 + 2at - bc)e^{-ct}$

43 $(\ln 5)5^x$

45 $(2abr - ar^4)/(b + r^3)^2$

47 $-2/(x^2 + 4)$

49 $20w/(a^2 - w^2)^3$

51 $ae^{au}/(a^2 + b^2)$

53 $\ln x/(1 + \ln x)^2$

55 $e^t \cos \sqrt{e^t + 1}/(2\sqrt{e^t + 1})$

57 $18x^2 + 8x - 2$

59 $(2 \ln 3)z + (\ln 4)e^z$

61 $3x^2 + 3^x \ln 3$

63 $-\frac{5}{2}\frac{\sin(5\theta)}{\sqrt{\cos(5\theta)}} + 12 \sin(6\theta) \cos(6\theta)$

65 $4s^3 - 1$

67 $ke^{kt}(\sin at + \cos bt) + e^{kt}(a \cos at - b \sin bt)$

69 $f'(t) = 4(\sin(2t) - \cos(3t))^3$
   $(2 \cos(2t) + 3 \sin(3t))$

71 $-16 - 12x + 48x^2 - 32x^3 + 28x^6 - 9x^8 + 20x^9$

73 $f'(z) = \frac{5}{2}(5z)^{-1/2} + \frac{5}{2}z^{-1/2} - \frac{5}{2}z^{-3/2} + \frac{\sqrt{5}}{2}z^{-3/2}$

75 $dy/dx = 0$

77 $dy/dx = -3$

79 $f'(t) = 6t^2 - 8t + 3$
   $f''(t) = 12t - 8$

81 $x = -1$ and $x = 5$

83 (a) −6
   (b) 0
   (c) −2

85 (a) 0
   (b) 4

716

87 (a) -10
   (b) 4

89 Approx 0.8

91 Approx -0.4

93 (a) $h(4) = 1$
   (b) $h'(4) = 2$
   (c) $h(4) = 3$
   (d) $h'(4) = 3$
   (e) $h'(4) = -5/16$
   (f) $h'(4) = 13$

95 (a) $f'(2) = 20$
   (b) $f'(2) = 11/9$
   (c) $f'(2) = -4$
   (d) $f'(2) = -24$
   (e) $f'(2) = \sin 3 - 8 \cos 3$
   (f) $f'(2) = 4 \ln 3 - 16/3$

97 These functions look like the line $y = 0$:
$$\sin x - \tan x, \quad \frac{x^2}{x^2 + 1}$$
$$x - \sin x, \quad \frac{1 - \cos x}{\cos x}$$
These functions look like the line $y = x$:
$$\arcsin x, \quad \frac{\sin x}{1 + \sin x}$$
$$\arctan x, \quad \frac{e^x - 1}{x}$$
$$\frac{x}{x + 1}, \quad \frac{x}{x^2 + 1}$$
These functions are undefined at the origin:
$$\frac{\sin x}{x} - 1, \quad -x \ln x$$
Defined at the origin but with a vertical tangent:
$$x^{10} + \sqrt[10]{x}$$

99 Perpendicular; $x = 0$ and $x = 1$

101 $y = x - e^b$

103 -2

105 (a) $y = 2 + (x - 4)/4$
    (b) 2.02485..., 2.025
    (c) True = 4, Approx = 5

107 (a) $f(t)$: linear
        $g(t)$: quadratic polynomial
        $h(t)$: exponential
    (b) $0.006°$C/yr; $0.0139°$C/yr; $0.00574°$C/yr
    (c) $0.78°$C; $1.807°$C; $0.746°$C
    (d) $0.78°$C; $0.793°$C; $0.728°$C
    (e) Linear
    (f) Quadratic

109 $-2GMm/r^3$

111 (a) $P'(t) = kP(t)$

113 (a) 1,000,000 people
    (b) No. Max number of people to fall sick in a day is 25,000

115 (c) -0.135%

117 $(f^{-1})'(5) \neq 1/f'(10)$

119 (b)

123 (a) $x(x + 1)^{x-1} + (x + 1)^x \ln(x + 1)$
       $x \cos x (\sin x)^{x-1} + (\sin x)^x \ln(\sin x)$
    (b) $x f'(x) (f(x))^{x-1} + (f(x))^x \ln(f(x))$
    (c) $(\ln x)^{x-1} + (\ln x)^x \ln(\ln x)$

125 (a) 0
    (b) 0
    (c) $2^{-2r} 4^r = 1$

Section 4.1

1

local max
local max
local min

3

Critical point
Not local max or min
Local min
x

5 Critical points: $x = 0$, $x = -\sqrt{6}$, $x = \sqrt{6}$
  Inflection points: $x = 0$, $x = -\sqrt{3}$, $x = \sqrt{3}$

7 Critical point: $x = 3/5$
  No inflection points

9 Critical points:
   $x = 0$ and $x = 1$
  Extrema:
   $f(1)$ local minimum
   $f(0)$ not a local extremum

11 Critical points:
   $x = 0$ and $x = 2$
  Extrema:
   $f(2)$ local minimum
   $f(0)$ not a local extremum.

13 Critical point: $x = 1/3$, local maximum

15 (a) Critical point $x \approx 0$;
     Inflection points between -1 and 0
     and between 0 and 1
   (b) Critical point at $x = 0$,
     Inflection points at $x = \pm 1/\sqrt{2}$

17 (a) Increasing for all x
   (b) No maxima or minima

19 (a) Incr: $-1 < x < 0$ and $x > 1$
     Decr: $x < -1$ and $0 < x < 1$

   (b) Local max: $f(0)$
     Local min: $f(-1)$ and $f(1)$

21 (a) $x = b$
   (b) Local minimum

23 $t = 0.5 \ln(V/U)$

25

x-values of these points give inflection points of f
$f'(x)$
x

27

y
$y' = 0$
$y'' = 0$ $y'' = 0$ $y' = 0$
$y = f(x)$
$y' > 0$ | $y' > 0$ | $y' > 0$ | $y' < 0$
$y'' < 0$ | $y'' > 0$ | $y'' < 0$ | $y'' < 0$
x
x_1 x_2 x_3

29
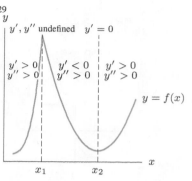
y
y', y'' undefined $y' = 0$
$y' > 0$ | $y' < 0$ | $y' > 0$
$y'' > 0$ | $y'' > 0$ | $y'' > 0$
$y = f(x)$
x_1 x_2 x

31 (a) $x \approx 2.5$ (or any $2 < x < 3$)
     $x \approx 6.5$ (or any $6 < x < 7$)
     $x \approx 9.5$ (or any $9 < x < 10$)
   (b) $x \approx 2.5$: local max;
     $x \approx 6.5$: local min;
     $x \approx 9.5$: local max

33

depth of water
Time at which water reaches corner of vase
time

35 $x = 0$: not max/min
    $x = 3/7$: local max
    $x = 1$: local min

37 (a) Yes, at 2000 rabbits

population of rabbits
2000
1500
1000
500
  10 20 30 40   years since 1774

   (b) 1787
     1000 rabbits

39 $a = -1/3$

41 Most: $x = 0, \pm 2\pi, \pm 4\pi, \pm 6\pi \ldots$
   Least: $x = \pm \pi, \pm 3\pi, \pm 5\pi \ldots$

43 $C = f$, $B = f'$, $A = f''$

45 I, III even; II odd
   I is f'', II is f', III is f

47 Incr: $-105 < x < 5$
   Decr: $x < -105$ and $x > 5$

49 (a) $x = \pm 2$
   (b) $x = 0, \pm \sqrt{5}$

51 (a) No critical points
   (b) Decreasing everywhere

53 Consider $f(x) = x^3$

55 $f(x) = x$

57 $f(x) = \cos x$ or $f(x) = \sin x$

59 True

61 False

63 True

65 False

67 $f(x) = x^2 + 1$

69 $f(x) = -x^2 - 1$

71 Impossible

73 (a), (c)

Section 4.2

1

Global and local max
Local min
Global and local min

3 (a)
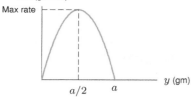

(b) $x = 4, y = 57$

5 Max: 9 at $x = -3$;
Min: -16 at $x = -2$

7 Max: 2 at $x = 1$;
Min: -2 at $x = -1, 8$

9 Max: 8 at $x = 4$;
Min: -1 at $x = -1, 1$

11 (a) $f(1)$ local minimum;
$f(0), f(2)$ local maxima
(b) $f(1)$ global minimum
$f(2)$ global maximum

13 (a) $f(2\pi/3)$ local maximum
$f(0)$ and $f(\pi)$ local minima
(b) $f(2\pi/3)$ global maximum
$f(0)$ global minimum

15 Global min $= 2$ at $x = 1$
No global max

17 Global min $= 1$ at $x = 1$
No global max

19 Global max $= 2$ at $t = 0, \pm 2\pi, \ldots$
Global min $= -2$ at $t = \pm\pi, \pm 3\pi, \ldots$

21 $0.91 < y \leq 1.00$

23 $0 \leq y \leq 2\pi$

25 $0 \leq y < 1.61$

27 $x = -b/2a$,
Max if $a < 0$, min if $a > 0$

29 $t = 2/b$

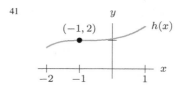

31 (a) Ordering: a/q
Storage: bq
(b) $\sqrt{a/b}$

33 (a) $0 \leq y \leq a$

rate (gm/sec)
Max rate
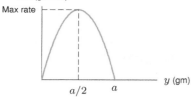
$a/2$ a y (gm)

(b) $y = a/2$

35 $r = 3B/(2A)$

37 (a) $k(\ln k - \ln S_0) - k + S_0 + I_0$
(b) Both

39
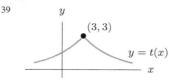
$(3, 3)$
$y = t(x)$

41
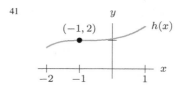
$(-1, 2)$ $h(x)$

43 $x = \left(\sum_{i=1}^{n} a_i\right)/n$

47 On $1 \leq x \leq 2$, global minimum at $x = 1$

49 $f(x) = 1 - x$

51 $\sqrt{2} \leq x \leq \sqrt{5}$

53 True

55 True

57 True

59 False

61 True

63 True

Section 4.3

1 2500

3 1536

5 1250 square feet

7 $x = 16^{1/3}$ cm, $h = 16^{1/3}/2$ cm

9 $r = h = (8/\pi)^{1/3}$ cm

11 0

13 Max: 0.552; Min: 0.358

15 $2000 - (1200/\sqrt{5})$

17 $w = 34.64$ cm, $h = 48.99$ cm

19 $1/\sqrt{2}$

21 (a) $xy + \pi y^2/4$
(b) $2x + \pi y$
(c) $x = 0, y = 100/\pi$

23 (a) Min at $x = \pi L/(4 + \pi)$
Max at $x = L$
(c) Yes

25 $5, \sqrt{125}$

27 $5\sqrt{5}, 25$

29 (a) $(9/4, \pm\sqrt{7}/4)$
(b) $(3, 0)$

31 Radius $= \sqrt{2/3}$
Height $= \sqrt{1/3}$

33 13.13 mi from first smokestack

35 Minimum: $x = -r_0/\sqrt{2}$
Maximum: $x = r_0/\sqrt{2}$

37 (a) $T^{2/3}/2^{1/3}$
(b) Increases by $\approx 58.74\%$

39 15 miles/hour

41 (a)
load
(number of worms)

Number of worms
time
P O

(b) 7 worms
(c) increases

43 (a) $E = 500e\left(\dfrac{2 - \cos\theta}{\sin\theta}\right) + 2000e$
$\left(\arctan\left(\dfrac{500}{2000}\right) \leq \theta \leq \pi/2\right)$
(b) $\theta = \pi/3$
(c) Independent of e, but dependent
on $\overline{AB}/\overline{AL}$

45 (a) $x = 1, P = (1, 1)$

47 (a) The arithmetic mean unless $a = b$,
in which case the two means are equal
(b) The arithmetic mean unless $a = b = c$,
in which case the two means are equal

49 (b) 2 hours
(c) Equal

51 (b) $f(v) = v \cdot a(v)$
(c) When $a(v) = f'(v)$
(d) $a(v)$

53 (a) $g(v) = f(v)/v$
(b) 220 mph
(c) 300 mph

55 Max V on $0 \leq h \leq 10$

57 9 cm by 1 cm

Section 4.4

1 (a)

small a large a

(b) Critical point moves right
(c) $x = a$

3 (a)

small a large a

(b) 2 critical points move closer to origin
(c) $x = \pm\sqrt{1/(3a)}$

5 (a)

large a small a

718

(b) Nonzero critical point moves down to the left
(c) $x = 0, 2/a$

7 (a) Larger $|A|$, steeper
  (b) Shifted horizontally by B
   Left for $B > 0$; right for $B < 0$
   Vertical asymptote $x = -B$
  (c)

9 A has $a = 1$, B has $a = 2$, C has $a = 5$

11 (a)

  (b)

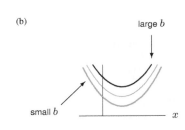

  (c) a moves critical point right;
   b moves critical point up
  (d) $x = a$

13 (a)

  (b)

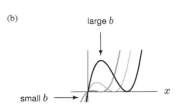

  (c) a moves one critical point up, does not move
   the other;
   b moves one critical point up to right, moves
   the other right
  (d) $x = b/3, b$

15 (a)

(b)

(c) a moves critical points to the right;
   b moves one critical point left, one up, one
   right

(d) $x = a, a \pm \sqrt{b}$

17 C has $a = 1$, B has $a = 2$, A has $a = 3$

19 (a)

  (b) $(1/b, 1/be)$

21 $Ax^3 + Cx$, Two

23 (a)

  (b) $-1 \le a \le 1$

25 Flatten out, raises min

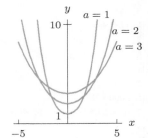

29 (a) $x = -1/b$
  (b) Local minimum

31 $k > 0$

33 $y = 3x^{-x^2/2}$

35 $y = 12/(1 + 2e^{-1.386x})$

37 $y = x^3 - 3x^2 + 6$

39 $y = (3/(2\pi)) \sin(\pi t^2/2)$

41 $y = e^{1-x} + x$

43 $y = 2t + 18/t$

45 (a) $x = e^a$
  (b) $a = -1$:

$a = 1$:

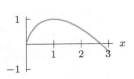

(c) Max at (e^{a-1}, e^{a-1}) for any a

49 (a) $x = 0$ and $x = \pm\sqrt{-a/2}$
  (b) For any a or b, $x = 0$ is crit pt.
   Only crit pt if $a \ge 0$
   Local minimum
  (c) If a is negative:
   $x = 0$ is local max,
   $x = \pm\sqrt{-a/2}$ are local min
  (d) No

51 (a) $b = 20°C, a = 180°C$
  (b) $k = (1/90)\text{min}^{-1}$

53

55 (a) Zero: $r = B/A$
   Vertical asymptote:
   $r = 0$
   Horizontal asymptote:
   $f(r) = 0$
  (b) Minimum:
   $\left(3B/(2A), -4A^3/(27B^2)\right)$
   Point of inflection:
   $\left(2B/A, -A^3/(8B^2)\right)$
  (c)

57 $f(x) = x^2 + 1$ has no zeros

59 $f(x) = kx(x - b)$

61 One possibility:
   $f(x) = ax^2, a \ne 0$

63 (a), (c)

Section 4.5

1 $5.5 < q < 12.5$ positive;
   $0 < q < 5.5$ and $q > 12.5$ negative;
   Maximum at $q \approx 9.5$

3 $5000, $2.40, $4

5 $C(q) = 35{,}000 + 10q$, $R(q) = 15q$,
   $\pi(q) = 5q - 35{,}000$.

7 $C(q) = 0.20q$, $R(q) = 0.25q$,
   $\pi(q) = 0.05q$

9 Global maximum of $6875 at $q = 75$

11 (a) $q = 2500$
   (b) $3 per unit
   (c) $3000

13 (a) Fixed costs
   (b) Decreases slowly, then increases

15 Increased

17 (a) No
   (b) Yes

19 $L = [\beta pcK^\alpha / w]^{1/(1-\beta)}$

21 (a) and (b)

Line through origin
is tangent here

$R(x)$

Optimal point on $r(x)$

$r(x)$

x

23 (a) $C(q) = 0.01q^3 - 0.6q^2 + 13q$
   (b) $1
   (c) $q = 30$, $a(30) = 4$
   (d) Marginal cost is 4

25 (a)

$x^2 + y^2 = 9$
$x^2 + y^2 = 4$
$x^2 + y^2 = 1$

$x + y = 4$

(c) 8

27 (a)

$C = 4$
$C = 3$
$C = 2$
$Q = x^{1/2}y^{1/2}$

(c) $2\sqrt{2}$

29 Maximum profit $\approx 13{,}000$ units

31

C

R

x

33 (a)

Section 4.6

1 $-0.32°\text{C/min}$; $-0.262°\text{C/min}$

3 $-81/R^2$

5 $-1°C$ minute

7 -4 newtons/sec

9 0.9 cm^2/min

11 (a) $-a/q^2$ dollars/cell phone
   (b) $-100a/q^2$ dollars/week; decreasing

13 24 meters^3/yr

15 (a) 1.19 meter^2
   (b) 0.0024 meter^2/year

17 1.8 cm/min

19 $1/16$ cm/min

21 (a) $CD - D^2$
   (b) $D < C$

23 (a) $2A/r^3 - 3B/r^4$; units of force/units of distance
   (b) $k(2A/r^3 - 3B/r^4)$; units of force/units of time

25 (a) 0.218 m/sec
   (b) 0.667 m/sec

27 0.038 meter/min

29 2513.3 cm^3/sec

31 (a) $-92.8V^{-2.4}$ atm/cm^3
   (b) Decreasing at 0.0529 atm/min

33 (a) 94.248 m^2/min
   (b) 0.0000267 m/min

35 (a) $80\pi = 251.327$ sec
   (b) $V = 3\pi h^3/25$ cm^3
   (c) 0.0207 cm/sec

37 $8/\pi$ meters/min

39 0.253 meters/second

41 (a) 0.04 gal/mile; 0.06 gal/mile
   (b) 25 mpg; 16.67 mpg
   (d) 1.4 gallons
   (e) 2.8 gal/hour; 1.8 gal/hour

43 (a) $k \approx 0.067$
   (b) $t \approx 10.3$ hours
   (c) Formula:
        $T(24) \approx 74.1°$F,
        rule of thumb: $73.6°$F

45 $2/\cos^2\theta$

47 $(1/V)dV/dt$

49 No

51 (b) (i) Brian's affection decreases
       (ii) Brian's affection increases
   (c) (i) Angela's affection increases
       (ii) Angela's affection decreases
   (d) Brian

53 $dD/dt = 2 \cdot dR/dt$

55 $y = f(x) = 2x + 1$ and $x = g(t) = 5t$

57 True

59 (c)

Section 4.7

1 $1/4$

3 1.5

5 0

7 0

9 0

11 $(1/3)a^{-2/3}$

13 $0.01x^3$

15 $e^{0.1x}$

17 Negative

19 Negative

21 0

23 0

25 ∞/∞, yes

27 none, no

29 none, no

31 $1/2$

33 1

35 2

37 Does not exist

39 ∞

41 e^3

43 ∞

45 0.909297

47 Does not exist

49 e^2

53 3

55 $\sqrt{15}$

57 0

59 $-1/6$

61 1

63 e^x dominates x^n for all positive integers n

65 $\lim_{x\to 0} \frac{x+1}{x+2}$

67 False

Section 4.8

1 The particle moves on straight lines from $(0, 1)$ to $(1, 0)$ to $(0, -1)$ to $(-1, 0)$ and back to $(0, 1)$

3 Two diamonds meeting at $(1, 0)$

5 $x = 3\cos t$, $y = -3\sin t$, $0 \le t \le 2\pi$

7 $x = 2 + 5\cos t$, $y = 1 + 5\sin t$,
   $0 \le t \le 2\pi$

9 $x = t$, $y = -4t + 7$

11 $x = -3\cos t$, $y = -7\sin t$,
    $0 \le t \le 2\pi$

13 Clockwise for all t

15 Clockwise: $-\sqrt{1/3} < t < \sqrt{1/3}$
    Counterclockwise: $t < -\sqrt{1/3}$ or $t > \sqrt{1/3}$

17 Clockwise: $2k\pi < t < (2k+1)\pi$
    Counterclockwise: $(2k-1)\pi < t < 2k\pi$

19 Line segment:
    $y + x = 4$, $1 \le x \le 3$

21 Line $y = (x - 13)/3$, left to right

23 Parabola $y = x^2 - 8x + 13$, left to right

25 Circle $x^2 + y^2 = 9$, counterclockwise

27 $(y - 4) = (4/11)(x - 6)$

29 $y = -(4/3)x$

31 Speed $= 2|t|$, stops at $t = 0$

33 Speed $= ((2t - 4)^2 + (3t^2 - 12)^2)^{1/2}$,
    Stops at $t = 2$

720

35

37 (a) The part of the line with
$x < 10$ and $y < 0$

(b) The line segment between
$(10, 0)$ and $(11, 2)$

39 (a) Both parameterize line
$y = 3x - 2$

(b) Slope $= 3$
y-intercept $= -2$

41 (a) $a = b = 0, k = 5$ or -5

(b) $a = 0, b = 5, k = 5$ or -5

(c) $a = 10, b = -10, k = \sqrt{200}$ or $-\sqrt{200}$

43 A straight line through the point $(3, 5)$

45 (a) $dy/dx = 4e^t$

(b) $y = 2x^2$

(c) $dy/dx = 4x$

47 (a) (i) $t = -0.25 \ln 3 = -0.275$

(ii) No vertical tangent

(b) $(3e^{2t} - e^{-2t})/(e^{2t} + e^{-2t})$

(c) 3

49 (a)

(b) $x(\pi/4) = 5$ and $y(\pi/4) = 0$;
$x'(\pi/4) = 0$ and $y'(\pi/4) = -8$

(c) Twice

(d) Parallel to y-axis, negative y direction

(e) 10

51 (a) No

(b) $k = 1$

(c) Particle B

53 (a) $y + \frac{1}{2} = -\frac{\sqrt{3}}{3}(x - \pi)$

(b) $t = \pi$

(c) 0.291, concave up

55 (a) $t = \pi/4$; at that time, speed $= \sqrt{9/2}$

(b) Yes, when $t = \pi/2$ or $t = 3\pi/2$

(c) Concave down everywhere

57

59

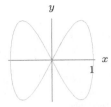

61 (b) For example:
$R = 12, t = \pi$

(c)

63 Gives circle centered at $(0, 0)$

65 $x = t, y = 2t, 0 \le t \le 1$

67 False

Chapter 4 Review

1

3 (a) $f'(x) = 3x(x - 2)$
$f''(x) = 6(x - 1)$

(b) $x = 0$
$x = 2$

(c) Inflection point: $x = 1$

(d) Endpoints:
$f(-1) = -4$ and $f(3) = 0$
Critical points:
$f(0) = 0$ and $f(2) = -4$
Global max:
$f(0) = 0$ and $f(3) = 0$
Global min:
$f(-1) = -4$ and $f(2) = -4$

(e) f increasing:
for $x < 0$ and $x > 2$
f decreasing:
for $0 < x < 2$
f concave up:
for $x > 1$
f concave down:
for $x < 1$

5 (a) $f'(x) =$
$- e^{-x} \sin x + e^{-x} \cos x$
$f''(x) = -2e^{-x} \cos x$

(b) Critical points:
$x = \pi/4$ and $5\pi/4$

(c) Inflection points:
$x = \pi/2$ and $3\pi/2$

(d) Endpoints:
$f(0) = 0$ and $f(2\pi) = 0$
Global max:
$f(\pi/4) = e^{-\pi/4}(\sqrt{2}/2)$
Global min:
$f(5\pi/4) = -e^{-5\pi/4}(\sqrt{2}/2)$

(e) f increasing:
$0 < x < \pi/4$ and
$5\pi/4 < x < 2\pi$
f decreasing:
$\pi/4 < x < 5\pi/4$
f concave down:
for $0 \le x < \pi/2$
and $3\pi/2 < x \le 2\pi$
f concave up:
for $\pi/2 < x < 3\pi/2$

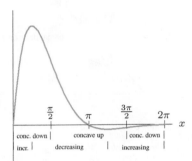

7 $\lim_{x \to \infty} f(x) = \infty$
$\lim_{x \to -\infty} f(x) = -\infty$

(a) $f'(x) = 6(x - 2)(x - 1)$
$f''(x) = 6(2x - 3)$

(b) $x = 1$ and $x = 2$

(c) $x = 3/2$

(d) Critical points:
$f(1) = 6, f(2) = 5$
Local max: $f(1) = 6$
Local min: $f(2) = 5$
Global max and min: none

(e) f increasing: $x < 1$ and $x > 2$
Decreasing: $1 < x < 2$
f concave up: $x > 3/2$
f concave down: $x < 3/2$

$f(x) = 2x^3 - 9x^2 + 12x + 1$

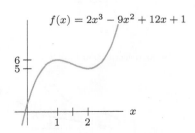

9 $\lim_{x \to -\infty} f(x) = -\infty$
$\lim_{x \to \infty} f(x) = 0$

(a) $f'(x) = (1 - x)e^{-x}$
$f''(x) = (x - 2)e^{-x}$
(b) Only critical point is at $x = 1$
(c) Inflection point: $f(2) = 2/e^2$
(d) Global max: $f(1) = 1/e$
Local and global min: none
(e) f increasing: $x < 1$
f decreasing: $x > 1$
f concave up: $x > 2$
f concave down: $x < 2$

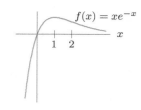

$f(x) = xe^{-x}$

11 Max: 22.141 at $x = \pi$;
Min: 2 at $x = 0$

13 Max: 1 at $x = 0$;
Min: Approx 0 at $x = 10$

15 Global max $= 1$ at $t = 0$
No global min

17 Local max: $f(-3) = 12$
Local min: $f(1) = -20$
Inflection pt: $x = -1$
Global max and min: none

$f(x) = x^3 + 3x^2 - 9x - 15$

19 Global and local min: $x = 2$
Global and local max: none
Inflection pts: none

$f(x) = x - \ln x$

21 Local max: $f(-2/5)$
Global and local min: $f(0)$
Inflection pts: $x = (-2 \pm \sqrt{2})/5$
Global max: none

$f(x) = x^2 e^{5x}$

-0.4

23 Max: $r = \frac{2}{3}a$; Min: $r = 0, a$

25 A has $a = 1$, B has $a = 2$, C has $a = 3$

27 (a) Critical points: $x = 0$, $x = \sqrt{a}$,
$x = -\sqrt{a}$
Inflection points: $x = \sqrt{a/3}$,
$x = -\sqrt{a/3}$
(b) $a = 4, b = 21$
(c) $x = \sqrt{4/3}, x = -\sqrt{4/3}$

29 Domain: All real numbers except $x = b$;
Critical points: $x = 0, x = 2b$

31 18

33 (a) $C(q) = 3 + 0.4q$ m
(b) $R(q) = 0.5q$ m
(c) $\pi(q) = 0.1q - 3$ m

35 2.5 gm/hr

37 Line $y = -2x + 9$, right to left

39 (a) x_3
(b) x_1, x_5
(c) x_2
(d) 0

41

$f'(x)$

f has a local min. f has crit. pt.
Neither max or min

43 $y = x^3 - 6x^2 + 9x + 5$

45 $y = 3x^{-1/2} \ln x$

47 $y = 2xe^{(1-x^2)/2}$

49 $x = \sqrt{8/3}$ cm, $h = \sqrt{2/3}$ cm

51 $r = h = \sqrt{8/3\pi}$ cm

53 $-4.81 \le f(x) \le 1.82$

55 Max: $m = -5k/(12j)$

57 (a) $t = 0$ and $t = 2/b$
(b) $b = 0.4$; $a = 3.547$
(c) Local min: $t = 0$; Local max: $t = 5$

59

$a = -2$
$a = 0$
$a = 2$
$a = 4$
$a = 6$
$y = -\frac{1}{2}x^3$

61 1.688 mm/sec away from lens

63 Minimum: -2 amps
Maximum: 2 amps

65 Max area $= 1$
$\left(\pm\frac{1}{\sqrt{2}}, 0\right)$; $\left(\pm\frac{1}{\sqrt{2}}, \frac{1}{\sqrt{2}}\right)$

67 $(0.59, 0.35)$

69 $r = \sqrt{2A/(4 + \pi)}$;
$h = \frac{A}{2} \cdot \frac{\sqrt{4+\pi}}{\sqrt{2A}} - \frac{\pi}{4} \cdot \frac{\sqrt{2A}}{\sqrt{4+\pi}}$

71 40 feet by 80 feet

73 (a) $\pi(q)$ max when
$R(q) > C(q)$ and R and Q are farthest apart

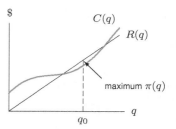

$C(q)$
$R(q)$
maximum $\pi(q)$
q_0

(b) $C'(q_0) = R'(q_0) = p$
(c)

$C'(q)$
p
q_0

75 About 331 meters, Maintain course

77 (a) $g(e)$ is a global maximum;
there is no minimum
(b) There are exactly two solutions
(c) $x = 5$ and $x \approx 1.75$

79 (a)

depth of water
$d(t)$
slope $= K$

(b)

depth of water
$d(t)$

81 -0.0545 m^3/min

83 $0/0$, yes

85 $-1/2$

87 $-1/6$

89 $1/\pi \approx 0.32\mu$m/day

91 (a) Angular velocity
(b) $v = a(d\theta/dt)$

93 $dM/dt = K(1 - 1/(1 + r))dr/dt$

95 Height: $0.3/(\pi h^2)$ meters/hour
Radius: $(0.3/\sqrt{3})/(\pi h^2)$ meters/hour

97 (a) Increasing
(b) Not changing
(c) Decreasing

99 398.103 mph

101 (a) Decreases
(b) -0.25 cm^3/min

722

103 (a)

$a = 0.5$

$a = 1$

$a = 2$

(b) Same graph all a

dy/dx

(c) dy/dx simplifies to $\sqrt{x}/(2x(1+x))$

105 (a) $1/\sqrt{x^2-1}$

107 (a) $dy/dx = \dfrac{\tan(x/2)}{2\sqrt{(1-\cos x)/(1+\cos x)}}$

(b) $dy/dx = 1/2$ on $0 < x < \pi$
$dy/dx = -1/2$ on $\pi < x < 2\pi$

Section 5.1

1 (a) Left sum
  (b) Upper estimate

(c) 6
(d) $\Delta t = 2$
(e) Upper estimate ≈ 24.4

3 (a) 408
  (b) 390

5 Between 140 and 150 meters

7 (a) Always same direction; speeding up, then slowing down
  (b) Overestimate $= 15$ cm; Underestimate $= 6$ cm

9 0 cm, no change in position

11 15 cm to the left

13 (a) 2; 15, 17, 19, 21, 23; 10, 13, 18, 20, 30
  (b) 122; 162
  (c) 4; 15, 19, 23; 10, 18, 30
  (d) 112; 192

15 (a) Lower estimate $= 5.25$ mi
      Upper estimate $= 5.75$ mi
  (b) Lower estimate $= 11.5$ mi
      Upper estimate $= 14.5$ mi
  (c) Every 30 seconds

17 1/5

19 0.0157

21 (a)

$v(t)$

(b) 3 sec, 144 feet
(c) 80 feet

23 (a) 14.73 minutes
      15.93 minutes
  (b) 0.60 minutes

25 (a) A: 8 hrs
      B: 4 hrs
  (b) 100 km/hr
  (c) A: 400 km
      B: 100 km

27 (a)

$v(t)$

(b) 125 feet
(c) 4 times as far

29 $v(t) = 32t$ ft/sec
    For $\Delta t = 1$:
      Right sum $= 320$ feet
      Left sum $= 192$ feet
      Precise dist $= 256$ feet

31 About 335 feet

33 If the acceleration is large the difference between the estimates can be large.

35 $f(x) = 10x, [a, b] = [0, 1]$

37 True

39 (a) $3 \le t \le 5, 9 \le t \le 10$
  (b) 3600 ft east
  (c) At $t = 8$ minutes
  (d) 30 seconds longer

Section 5.2

1 (a) Right
  (b) Upper
  (c) 3
  (d) 2

3 (a) Left; smaller

(b) 0, 2, 6, 1/3

5 28.5

7 1.4936

9 0.3103

11 $17,000, n = 4, \Delta x = 10$

13 543

15 60

17 -40

19 (a) 13
  (b) 1

21 (a) 16.25
  (b) 15.75
  (c) No

23 1

25 1.977

27 24.694

29 (a) 13
  (b) -2
  (c) 11
  (d) 15

31 (a) -2
  (b) $-A/2$

33 (a)

(b) 3.084
(c) 2.250

35 Positive

37 (a) $(\ln 1.5)0.5$

(b) $(\ln 1.5)0.5 + (ln2)0.5$

(c) Right: overestimate
    left: underestimate

39 (a) 78

(b) 46; underestimate

(c) 118; overestimate

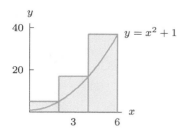

41 Left-hand sum $= 1.96875$
Right-hand sum $= 2.71875$
The most the estimate could be off is 0.375

43

45 (c) $n \geq 10^5$

47 Too many terms in sum

49 $f(x) = 2 - x$

51 False

53 False

55 False

57

Section 5.3

1 Dollars

3 Foot-pounds

5 Change in velocity; km/hr

7 Change in salinity; gm/liter

9 $\int_1^3 2t \, dt = 8$

11 $\int_1^5 1/t \, dt = \ln 5$

13 $\int_2^3 7 \ln(4) \cdot 4^t \, dt = 336$

15 (a) $3x^2 + 1$

(b) 10

17 (a) $\sin t \cos t$
(b)   (i) ≈ 0.056
   (ii) $\frac{1}{2}(\sin^2(0.4) - \sin^2(0.2))$

19 (a) Removal rate 500 kg/day on day 12
(b) Days, days, kilograms
(c) 4000 kg removed between day 5 and day 15

21 (a) $\int_0^2 R(t) \, dt$
(b)

(c) lower estimate: 2.81
upper estimate: 3.38

23 (a) $\int_0^5 f(t) \, dt$
(b) 177.270 billion barrels
(c) Lower estimate of year's oil consumption

25 (a) Upper estimate: 340 liters
Lower estimate: 240 liters
(b)

27 $2392.87

29 About $13,800

31 45.8°C.

33 $f(1) < f(0)$

35 12 newton · meters

37 (iii) < (ii) < (i) < (iv)

39 0.732 gals, 1.032 gals;
Better estimates possible

41 $\int_{2t_0}^{3t_0} r(t) \, dt \quad < \quad \int_{t_0}^{2t_0} r(t) \, dt \quad <$
$\int_0^{2t_0} r(t) \, dt$

43 0.14

45 1.53

47 0.5; cost of preparing is $0.5 million

49 $\int_2^4 r(t) \, dt > \int_0^2 r(t) \, dt$

51 $\int_0^8 r(t) \, dt < 64$ million

53 $\frac{d}{dx}(\sqrt{x}) \neq \sqrt{x}$

55

Section 5.4

1 10

3 9

5 $2c_1 + 12c_2^2$

7 2

9 2

11 (a) 8.5
(b) 1.7

13 4.389

15 0.083

17 7.799

19 0.172

21 (a) 2
(b) 12, 2
(c) 0, 0

23 (a) $\int_a^b 1 \, dx = b - a$
(b)   (i) $\int_2^5 1 \, dx = 3$
   (ii) $\int_{-3}^8 1 \, dx = 11$
   (iii) $\int_1^3 23 \, dx = 46$

25 $6080

27 30

29 0

31 14/3

33 (a) -4
(b) (ii)

35 (a) 140.508 million
(b) 142.743 million
(c) Graph below secant line

39

41

43 (viii) < (ii) < (iii) < (vi) < (i) <
(v) < (iv) < (vii)

45 (b) 0.64

47 Not enough information

49 5

51 25

53 (a)

(b) Largest to smallest:
$n = 1, n = 3,$
$n = 4,$ and $n = 2$

55

59 $\int_a^b (5 + 3f(x))\, dx = 5(b - a) + 3\int_a^b f(x)\, dx$

61 $f(x) = -1$

63 $(1/5)\int_0^5 v(t)\, dt$, where $v(t)$ miles/hr at t hours

65 False

67 True

69 True

71 False

73 True

75 False

77 True

79 (a) Does not follow
(b) Follows
(c) Follows

Chapter 5 Review

1 (a) Lower estimate = 122 ft
Upper estimate = 298 ft

(b)
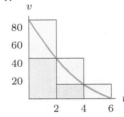

3 20

5 396

7 (a) Upper estimate = 34.16 m/sec
Lower estimate = 27.96 m/sec
(b) 31.06 m/sec;
It is too high

9 $\int_{-2}^1 (12t^3 - 15t^2 + 5)\, dt = -75$

11 36

13 1.142

15 13.457

17 $\int_{-1}^1 |x|\, dx = 1$

19 (a) 260 ft
(b) Every 0.5 sec

21 0.399 miles

23 (a) Emissions 1970–2000, m. metric tons
(b) 772.8 million metric tons

25 (a) Overestimate = 7 tons
Underestimate = 5 tons
(b) Overestimate = 74 tons
Underestimate = 59 tons
(c) Every 2 days

27 (a) $(1/5)\int_0^5 f(x)\, dx$
(b) $(1/5)(\int_0^2 f(x)\, dx - \int_2^5 f(x)\, dx)$

29 (a) $f(1), f(2)$
(b) 2, 2.31, 2.80, 2.77

31 (a) $F(0) = 0$
(b) F increases
(c) $F(1) \approx 0.7468$
$F(2) \approx 0.8821$
$F(3) \approx 0.8862$

33 4

35 3

37 3

39 (a) Odd integrand; areas cancel
(b) 0.4045
(c) -0.4049
(d) No. Different sized rectangles

41 (a) 21,000 megawatts; 189,525.284 megawatts
(b) 22%
(c) 76,602.402 megawatts

43 $\int_0^{0.5T} r(t)\, dt > \int_{0.5T}^T r(t)\, dt$

45 $\int_0^{T_h} r(t)\, dt < \int_0^{0.5T} r(t)\, dt$

47 30/7

49 V < IV < II < III < I
I, II, III positive
IV, V negative

51 2.5; ice 2.5 in thick at 4 am

53 (a) $2\int_0^2 f(x)\, dx$
(b) $\int_0^5 f(x)\, dx - \int_2^5 f(x)\, dx$
(c) $\int_{-2}^5 f(x)\, dx - \frac{1}{2}\int_{-2}^2 f(x)\, dx$

55 (a) At $t = 17, 23, 27$ seconds
(b) Right: $t = 10$ seconds
Left: $t = 40$ seconds
(c) Right: $t = 17$ seconds
Left: $t = 40$ seconds
(d) $t = 10$ to 17 seconds,
20 to 23 seconds, and
24 to 27 seconds
(e) At $t = 0$ and $t = 35$

57 About 48 feet

59 (a) 300 m³/sec
(b) 250 m³/sec
(c) 1996: 1250 m³/sec
1957: 3500 m³/sec
(d) 1996: 10 days
1957: 4 months
(e) 10^9 meter³
(f) $2 \cdot 10^{10}$ meter³

61 Overestimate

63 Overestimate

65 (a) $\int_0^T (f(t) - H_{\min})\, dt$
(b) $T \approx 11$ days

67 (a) $\sum_{i=1}^n i^4/n^5$
(b) $(6n^4 + 15n^3 + 10n^2 - 1)/30n^4$
(c) 1/5

69 (a) $\sum_{i=0}^{n-1} (n + i)/n^2$
(b) $3/2 - 1/(2n)$
(c) 3/2
(d) 3/2

71 (a) $\sum_{i=1}^n \sin(i\pi/n)\pi/n$
(b) $\pi\cos(\pi/2n)/n \sin(\pi/2n)$
(c) 2
(d) 2

73 (a) $-\ln(1 + a^2 b)/2b + \ln(1 + c^2 b)/2b$
(b) $\ln(1 + bx^2)/2b$

Section 6.1

1 (a) Increasing
(b) Concave up

3 $1, 0, -1/2, 0, 1$

5

7

9

11

13 128, 169, 217

15 Oscillates between $x = 5$ and $x = 15$

17
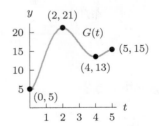

19 Critical points: $(0, 5), (2, 21), (4, 13), (5, 15)$

21

23 x_1 local max;
x_2 inflection pt;
x_3 local min

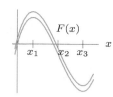

25 x_2, x_3 inflection pts

27 Maximum $= 6.17$ at $x = 1.77$

29 (a) 0; 3000; 12,000; 21,000; 27,000; 30,000
(b)

31 Statement has $f(x)$ and $F(x)$ reversed

33 $f(x) = 1 - x$

35 True

Section 6.2

1 $5x$

3 $x^3/3$

5 $2z^{3/2}/3$

7 $-1/t$

9 $-1/(2z^2)$

11 e^z

13 $2t^3/3 + 3t^4/4 + 4t^5/5$

15 $t^2/2 + \ln|t|$

17 $3t^2 + C$

19 $x^3/3 - 2x^2 + 7x + C$

21 $t^4/4 + 5t^2/2 - t + C$

23 $-\cos x + \sin x + C$

25 $2t^{1/2} + C$

27 $-5/(2x^2) + C$

29 $F(x) = 3x$
(only possibility)

31 $F(x) = -7x^2/2$
(only possibility)

33 $F(x) = x^2/8$
(only possibility)

35 $F(x) = (2/3)x^{3/2}$
(only possibility)

37 $(5/2)x^2 + 7x + C$

39 $2t + \sin t + C$

41 $3e^x - 2\cos x + C$

43 $(5/3)x^3 + (4/3)x^{3/2} + C$

45 $16\sqrt{x} + C$

47 $e^x + 5x + C$

49 $(2/5)x^{5/2} - 2\ln|x| + C$

51 36

53 $-(\sqrt{2}/2) + 1 = 0.293$

55 $3e^2 - 3 = 19.167$

57 $1 - \cos 1 \approx 0.460$

59 $16/3 \approx 5.333$

61 5.500 ft

63 (a) -60 revs/min^2
(b) 5.83 min
(c) 1020.83 revs

65 9

67 $\sqrt{3} - \pi/9$

69 (a) 253/12
(b) $-125/12$

71 8/3

73 1.257

75 $c = 3/4$

77 2

79 $-104/27$

81 (a) $x^x = (e^{\ln x})^x = e^{x\ln x}$
(b) $\frac{d}{dx}(x^x) = x^x(\ln x + 1)$
(c) $x^x + C$
(d) 3

83 5 to 1

85 All $n \neq -1$

87 $f(x) = -1$

89 True

91 False

93 True

95 False

Section 6.3

3 $y = x^2 + C$

5 $y = x^4/4 + x^5 + C$

7 $y = \sin x + C$

9 $y = x^3 + 5$

11 $y = e^x + 6$

13 80.624 ft/sec downward

15 10 sec

17 (a) $R(p) = 25p - p^2$
(b) Increasing for $p < 12.5$
Decreasing for $p > 12.5$

19 (a) $a(t) = -9.8$ m/sec^2
$v(t) = -9.8t + 40$ m/sec
$h(t) = -4.9t^2 + 40t + 25$ m
(b) 106.633 m; 4.082 sec
(c) 8.747 sec

21 (a) 32 ft/sec^2
(b) Constant rate of change
(c) 5 sec
(d) 10 sec
(e)
velocity (ft/sec)

(f) Height $= 400$ feet

(g) $v(t) = -32t + 160$
Height $= 400$ feet

23 5/6 miles

25 -33.56 ft/sec^2

27 (a) $y = -\cos x + 2x + C$

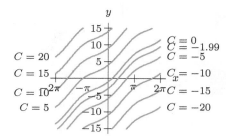

(b) $y = -\cos x + 2x - 1.99$

29 (a) 80 ft/sec
(b) 640 ft

31 128 ft/sec^2

33 10 ft; 4 sec

35 $v = -gt + v_0$
$s = -gt^2/2 + v_0 t + s_0$

37 (a) $t = s/(\frac{1}{2}v_{\max})$

39 (a) First second: $-g/2$
Second: $-3g/2$
Third: $-5g/2$
Fourth: $-7g/2$
(b) Galileo seems to have been correct

41 If $y = \cos(t^2)$, $dy/dt \neq -\sin(t^2)$

43 $dy/dx = 0$

45 $dy/dx = -5\sin(5x)$

47 True

49 False

51 True

53 True

Section 6.4

3 (a) Si(4) ≈ 1.76
Si(5) ≈ 1.55
(b) $(\sin x)/x$ is negative on that interval

5 $f(x) = 5 + \int_1^x (\sin t)/t \, dt$

7

9

11 $\cos(x^2)$

13 $(1 + x)^{200}$

15 $\arctan(x^2)$

17 Concave up $x < 0$, concave down $x > 0$

19 $F(0) = 0$
$F(0.5) = 0.041$
$F(1) = 0.310$
$F(1.5) = 0.778$
$F(2) = 0.805$
$F(2.5) = 0.431$

21 Max at $x = \sqrt{\pi}$;
$F(\sqrt{\pi}) = 0.895$

23 500

25 (a) 0
   (b)

   (c) $F(x) \geq 0$ everywhere
       $F(x) = 0$ only at integer multiples of π

27 (a) $R(0) = 0$, R is an odd function.
   (b) Increasing everywhere
   (c) Concave up for $x > 0$, concave down for
       $x < 0$.
   (d)

   (e) 1/2

29 2.747

31 1.99, overestimate; or 1.85, underestimate

33 $w'(0.4) = 3.9$; exact

35 $2x \ln(1 + x^4)$

37 $-2\sin(\sqrt{2t})$

39 $\mathrm{erf}(x) + (2/\sqrt{\pi})xe^{-x^2}$

41 $3x^2 e^{-x^6}$

43 $\frac{d}{dx}\int_0^5 t^2\, dt = 0$

45 Local min at $x = -1$ and $x = 3$

47 $G(x) = \int_7^x e^t\, dt$

49 True

51 False

53 True

Chapter 6 Review

3

5 (a) -19
   (b) 6

7 $x^4/4 + C$

9 $x^4/4 - 2x + C$

11 $-4/t + C$

13 $8w^{3/2}/3 + C$

15 $\sin\theta + C$

17 $x^2/2 + 2x^{1/2} + C$

19 $3\sin t + 2t^{3/2} + C$

21 $\tan x + C$

23 $(1/2)x^2 + x + \ln|x| + C$

25 $2^x / \ln 2 + C$

27 $2e^x - 8\sin x + C$

29 4

31 $x^4/4 + +2x^3 - 4x + 4.$

33 $e^x + 3$

35 $\sin x + 4$

39 $x^4/4 + 5x + C$

41 $8t^{3/2}/3 + C$

43 $2x^3 + 2x^2 - 14$

45 $-16t^2 + 100t + 50$

47 $-\cos(t^3)$

49 $(0, 1); (2, 3); (6, -4); (8, 0)$

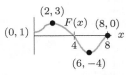

51 (a) $x = 1, x = 3$
   (b) Local min at $x = 1$, local max at $x = 3$
   (c)

53 (a) $f(x)$ is greatest at x_1
   (b) $f(x)$ is least at x_5
   (c) $f'(x)$ is greatest at x_3
   (d) $f'(x)$ is least at x_5
   (e) $f''(x)$ is greatest at x_1
   (f) $f''(x)$ is least at x_5

55 21

57 1/20

59 1/3

61 $4\sqrt{2}$

63 $2\sinh 1$

65 $c = 3$

67 $c = 6$

69 0.4

71 16/3

73 $3x^2\sin(x^6)$

75 $2e^{-x^4}$

77 (a) $f(t) = Q - \frac{Q}{A}t$
   (b) $Q/2$

79 (a) $t = 2, t = 5$
   (b) $f(2) \approx 55, f(5) \approx 40$
   (c) -10

81 (a) 14,000 revs/min^2
   (b) 180 revolutions

83 19.55 ft/sec^2

85 (b) Highest pt: $t = 2.5$ sec
       Hits ground: $t = 5$ sec
   (c) Left sum:
       136 ft (an overest.)
       Right sum:
       56 ft (an underest.)
   (d) 100 ft

87 $V(r) = (4/3)\pi r^3$

89 (b) $t = 6$ hours
   (c) $t = 11$ hrs

91 Increasing; concave down

93 (a) Zeros: $x = 0, 5$; Critical points: $x = 3$
   (b) Zeros: $x = 1$; Critical points: $x = 0, 5$

95 (a) $\Delta x = (b-a)/n$
       $x_i = a + i(b-a)/n$
   (b) $(b^4 - a^4)/4$

97 (a) $-(1/3)\cos(3x), -(1/4)\cos(4x),$
       $-(1/3)\cos(3x + 5)$
   (b) $-(1/a)\cos(ax + b)$

99 (a) $(1/2)(\ln|x - 3| - \ln|x - 1|),$
       $(1/3)(\ln|x - 4| - \ln|x - 1|),$
       $(1/4)(\ln|x + 3| - \ln|x - 1|)$
   (b) $(1/(b-a))(\ln|x - b| - \ln|x - a|)$

Section 7.1

1 (a) $(\ln 2)/2$
   (b) $(\ln 2)/2$

3 $(1/3)e^{3x} + C$

5 $-e^{-x} + C$

7 $-0.5\cos(2x) + C$

9 $\cos(3 - t) + C$

11 $(r + 1)^4/4 + C$

13 $(1/18)(1 + 2x^3)^3 + C$

15 $(1/6)(x^2 + 3)^3 + C$

17 $(1/5)y^5 + (1/2)y^4 + (1/3)y^3 + C$

19 $(1/3)e^{x^3 + 1} + C$

21 $-2\sqrt{4 - x} + C$

23 $-(1/8)(\cos\theta + 5)^8 + C$

25 $(1/7)\sin^7\theta + C$

27 $(1/35)\sin^7 5\theta + C$

29 $(1/3)(\ln z)^3 + C$

31 $t + 2\ln|t| - 1/t + C$

33 $(1/\sqrt{2})\arctan(\sqrt{2}x) + C$

35 $2\sin\sqrt{x} + C$

37 $2\sqrt{x + e^x} + C$

39 $(1/2)\ln(x^2 + 2x + 19) + C$

41 $\ln(e^x + e^{-x}) + C$

43 $(1/3)\cosh 3t + C$

45 $(1/2)\sinh(2w + 1) + C$

47 $\frac{1}{3}\cosh^3 x + C$

49 $(\pi/4)t^4 + 2t^2 + C$

51 $\sin x^2 + C$

53 $(1/5)\cos(2 - 5x) + C$

55 $(1/2)\ln(x^2 + 1) + C$

57 0

59 $1 - (1/e)$

61 $2e(e-1)$

63 $2(\sin 2 - \sin 1)$

65 40

67 $\ln 3$

69 14/3

71 $(2/5)(y+1)^{5/2} - (2/3)(y+1)^{3/2} + C$

73 $(2/5)(t+1)^{5/2} - (2/3)(t+1)^{3/2} + C$

75 $(2/7)(x-2)^{7/2} + (8/5)(x-2)^{5/2} +$
$(8/3)(x-2)^{3/2} + C$

77 $(2/3)(t+1)^{3/2} - 2(t+1)^{1/2} + C$

79 $y = 3x$

81 $w = e^z$

83 $1/(2\sqrt{w})$

85 Substitute $w = \sin x$

87 Substitute $w = \sin x, w = \arcsin x$

89 Substitute $w = x + 1, w = 1 + \sqrt{x}$

91 $e^{11} - e^7$

93 3

95 218/3

97 $(g(x))^5/5$

99 $-\cos g(x) + C$

101 $w = 1 - 4x^3, k = -1/12, n = 1/2$

103 $w = x^2 - 3, k = 1, n = -2$

105 $k = 1/\ln 2, n = -1, w_0 = 4, w_1 = 35$

107 $w = -x^2, k = -1/2$

109 $w = 0.5r, k = 2$

111 $w = 5t, k = 1/(5e^4)$

113 $a = 1, b = -1, A = -1/\pi, w = \cos(\pi t)$

115 (a) Yes; $-0.5\cos(x^2) + C$
   (b) No
   (c) No
   (d) Yes; $-1/(2(1+x^2)) + C$
   (e) No
   (f) Yes; $-\ln|2 + \cos x| + C$

117 $\ln 3$

119 $e^3(e^6 - 1)/3$

121 $3\ln 3 - 2$

123 $(1/2)\ln 3$

0.54931

$f(x) = \frac{1}{1+x}$

125 (a) 10
   (b) 5

127 (a) 0
   (b) 2/3

129 (a) $(\sin^2 \theta)/2 + C$
   (b) $-(\cos^2 \theta)/2 + C$
   (c) $-(\cos 2\theta)/4 + C$
   (d) Functions differ by a constant

131 $k = 1/2, w = \ln(x^2 + 1), a = \ln 5, b = \ln 26$

135 (a) I $C(t) = 1.3t + 311$
       II $C(t) = 0.5t + 0.015t^2 + 311$
      III $C(t) = 25e^{0.02t} + 286$

(b) I 402 ppm
    II 419.5 ppm
   III 387.380 ppm

137 (a) 6.9 billion, 7.8 billion
   (b) 6.5 billion

139 (a) $E(t) = 1.4e^{0.07t}$
   (b) $0.2(e^7 - 1) \approx 219$
       million megawatt-hours
   (c) 1972
   (d) Graph $E(t)$ and estimate t such that
       $E(t) = 219$

141 $(mg/k)t - (m^2g/k^2)(1 - e^{-kt/m}) + h_0$

143 (a) First case: 19,923
       Second case: 1.99 billion
   (b) In both cases, 6.47 yrs
   (c) 3.5 yrs

145 Integrand needs extra factor of $f'(x)$

147 Change limits of integration for substitution in definite integral

149 $\int \sin(x^3 - 3x)(x^2 - 1)\, dx$

151 False

Section 7.2

1 (a) $x^3 e^x/3 - (1/3)\int x^3 e^x \, dx$
   (b) $x^2 e^x - 2\int xe^x \, dx$

3 $-t\cos t + \sin t + C$

5 $\frac{1}{5}te^{5t} - \frac{1}{25}e^{5t} + C$

7 $-10pe^{(-0.1)p} - 100e^{(-0.1)p} + C$

9 $(1/2)x^2 \ln x - (1/4)x^2 + C$

11 $(1/6)q^6 \ln 5q - (1/36)q^6 + C$

13 $-(1/2)\sin\theta\cos\theta + \theta/2 + C$

15 $t(\ln t)^2 - 2t\ln t + 2t + C$

17 $(2/3)y(y+3)^{3/2} - (4/15)(y+3)^{5/2} + C$

19 $-(\theta+1)\cos(\theta+1) + \sin(\theta+1) + C$

21 $-x^{-1}\ln x - x^{-1} + C$

23 $-2t(5-t)^{1/2} - (4/3)(5-t)^{3/2} - 14(5-t)^{1/2} + C$

25 $r^2[(\ln r)^2 - \ln r + (1/2)]/2 + C$

27 $z\arctan 7z - \frac{1}{14}\ln(1+49z^2) + C$

29 $(1/2)x^2 e^{x^2} - (1/2)e^{x^2} + C$

31 $x\cosh x - \sinh x + C$

33 $5\ln 5 - 4 \approx 4.047$

35 $-11e^{-10} + 1 \approx 0.9995$

37 $\pi/4 - (1/2)\ln 2 \approx 0.439$

39 $\pi/2 - 1 \approx 0.571$

41 (a) Parts
   (b) Substitution
   (c) Substitution
   (d) Substitution
   (e) Substitution
   (f) Parts
   (g) Parts

43 $w = 5 - 3x, k = -2/3$

45 $w = \ln x, k = 3$

47 $2\arctan 2 - (\ln 5)/2$

49 $2\ln 2 - 1$

51 π

53 Integration by parts gives:
   $(1/2)\sin\theta\cos\theta + (1/2)\theta + C$
   The identity for $\cos^2\theta$ gives:
   $(1/2)\theta + (1/4)\sin 2\theta + C$

55 $(1/2)e^\theta(\sin\theta + \cos\theta) + C$

57 $(1/2)\theta e^\theta(\sin\theta + \cos\theta) - (1/2)e^\theta\sin\theta + C$

59 $xf'(x) - f(x) + C$

61 Integrate by parts choosing $u = x^n, v' = e^x$

63 Integrate by parts, choosing
   $u = x^n, v' = \sin ax$

65 (a) $A = a/(a^2 + b^2)$,
       $B = -b/(a^2 + b^2)$
   (b) $e^{ax}(b\sin bx + a\cos bx)/(a^2 + b^2) + C$

67 3

69 -5

71 45.71 (ng/ml)-hours

73 (a) $-(1/a)Te^{-aT} + (1/a^2)(1 - e^{-aT})$
   (b) $\lim_{T\to\infty} E = 1/a^2$

75 (a) $v = x, u' = (2/\sqrt{\pi})e^{-x^2} 1, v' = 1$
   (b) $w = -x^2, dw = -2x dx$
   (c) $x\,\mathrm{erf}(x) + (1/\sqrt{\pi})e^{-x^2} + C$

77 $u = \ln t, v' = t$

79 $\int f(x)\, dx = xf(x) - \int xf'(x)\, dx$

81 $\int x^3 e^x \, dx$

83 True

85 False

Section 7.3

1 $(1/6)x^6 \ln x - (1/36)x^6 + C$

3 $-(1/5)x^3 \cos 5x + (3/25)x^2 \sin 5x + (6/125)x\cos 5x - (6/625)\sin 5x + C$

5 $(1/7)x^7 + (5/2)x^4 + 25x + C$

7 $-(1/4)\sin^3 x\cos x - (3/8)\sin x\cos x + (3/8)x + C$

9 $((1/3)x^2 - (2/9)x + 2/27)e^{3x} + C$

11 $((1/3)x^4 - (4/9)x^3 + (4/9)x^2 - (8/27)x + (8/81))e^{3x} + C$

13 $(1/\sqrt{3})\arctan(y/\sqrt{3}) + C$

15 $(1/4)\arcsin(4x/5) + C$

17 $(5/16)\sin 3\theta\sin 5\theta + (3/16)\cos 3\theta\cos 5\theta + C$

19 $\frac{1}{2}\frac{\sin x}{\cos^2 x} + \frac{1}{4}\ln\left|\frac{\sin x+1}{\sin x-1}\right| + C$

21 $(1/34)e^{5x}(5\sin 3x - 3\cos 3x) + C$

23 $-(1/2)y^2\cos 2y + (1/2)y\sin 2y + (1/4)\cos 2y + C$

25 $\frac{1}{21}(\tan 7x/\cos^2 7x) + \frac{2}{21}\tan 7x + C$

27 $-\frac{1}{2\tan 2\theta} + C$

29 $\frac{1}{2}(\ln|x+1| - \ln|x+3|) + C$

31 $-(1/3)(\ln|z| - \ln|z-3|) + C$

33 $\arctan(z+2) + C$

35 $-\cos x + (1/3)\cos^3 x + C$

37 $\frac{1}{5}\cosh^5 x - \frac{1}{3}\cosh^3 x + C$

39 $-(1/9)(\cos^3 3\theta) + (1/15)(\cos^5 3\theta) + C$

41 $\frac{1}{3}(1 - \frac{\sqrt{2}}{2})$

43 $9/8 - 6\ln 2 = -3.034$

45 1/2

47 $\pi/12$

49 0.5398

51 $k = 0.5, w = 2x + 1, n = 3$

53 Form (i) with $a = -1/6, b = -1/4, c = 5$

55 Form (iii) with $a = 1, b = -5, c = 6, n = 7$

57 $a = 5, b = 4, \lambda = 2$

61 (a) 0
(b) $V_0/\sqrt{2}$
(c) 156 volts

63 Use V-26

65 $\frac{1}{4}e^{2x+1}(\sin(2x+1) - \cos(2x+1)) + C$

67 Table only has formulas for $\int p(x) \sin x \, dx$ where $p(x)$ polynomial

69 $\int 1/\sin^4 x \, dx$

71 False

73 True

Section 7.4

1 $(1/6)/(x) + (5/6)/(6+x)$

3 $1/(w-1) - 1/w - 1/w^2 - 1/w^3$

5 $-2/y + 1/(y-2) + 1/(y+2)$

7 $1/(2(s-1)) - 1/(2(s+1)) - 1/(s^2+1)$

9 $-2\ln|5-x| + 2\ln|5+x| + C$

11 $\ln|y-1| + \arctan y - \frac{1}{2}\ln|y^2+1| + C$

13 $\ln|s| - \ln|s+2| + C$

15 $\ln|x-2| + \ln|x+1| + \ln|x-3| + K$

17 $2\ln|x-5| - \ln|x^2+1| + K$

19 $x^3/3 + \ln|x+1| - \ln|x+2| + C$

21 $\arcsin(x-2) + C$

23 (a) Yes; $x = 3\sin\theta$
(b) No

25 $w = 3x^2 - x - 2, k = 2$

27 $a = -5/3, b = 4/5, c = -2/15, d = -3/5$

29 $A = 3.5, B = -1.5, w = e^x, dw = e^x dx, r = 1, s = 7$

31 $x = (\tan\theta) - 1$

33 $y = (\tan\theta) - 3/2$

35 $z = (\sin\theta) + 1$

37 $w = (t+2)^2 + 3$

39 $(\ln|x-5| - \ln|x-3|)/2 + C$

41 $(-\ln|x+7| + \ln|x-2|)/9 + C$

43 $\ln|z| - \ln|z+1| + C$

45 $(1/3)\ln|P/(1-P)| + C$

47 $(3/2)\ln|2y+1| - \ln|y+1| + C$

49 $\ln|x| + (2/x) - (1/2)\ln|1+x^2| + 2\arctan x + K$

51 $z/(4\sqrt{4-z^2}) + C$

53 $\arctan((x+2)/3)/3 + C$

55 $-(\sqrt{1+x^2})/x + C$

57 $-\sqrt{1-4x^2}/x - 2\arcsin(2x) + C$

59 $(1/6)\ln|(\sqrt{9-4x^2}-3)/(\sqrt{9-4x^2}+3)| + C$

61 $-(1/4)\sqrt{4-x^2}/x + C$

63 $(1/16)(x/\sqrt{16-x^2}) + C$

65 $5\ln 2$

67 $\pi/12 - \sqrt{3}/8$

69 $\ln(1+\sqrt{2})$

71 $(\ln|1+x| - \ln|1-x|)/2 + C$

73 $\ln|x| + \ln|x^2+1| + K$

75 (a) $(\ln|x-a| - \ln|x-b|)/(a-b) + C$
(b) $-1/(x-a) + C$

77 (a) $(\ln|x-\sqrt{a}| - \ln|x+\sqrt{a}|)/(2\sqrt{a}) + C$
(b) $-1/x + C$
(c) $(1/\sqrt{-a})\arctan(x/\sqrt{-a}) + C$

79 (a) $(k/(b-a))\ln|(2b-a)/b|$
(b) $T \to \infty$

81 $1/(x-1)$ term missing

83 $f(x) = 1/(1+x^2)$

85 $P(x) = x, Q(x) = x^2 + 1$

87 False

89 (e)

Section 7.5

1 (a) Underestimate

(b) Overestimate

(c) Overestimate

(d) Underestimate

3 (a) Underestimate

(b) Overestimate

(c) Underestimate

(d) Overestimate

5 (a) Underestimate

(b) Overestimate

(c) Overestimate

(d) Underestimate

7 (a) 27
  (b) 135
  (c) 81
  (d) 67.5
9 (a) MID(2)= 24;
     TRAP(2)= 28
  (b) MID(2) underestimate;
     TRAP(2) overestimate

11 −2.2
13 0.1703
15 (a)   (i) 0.8160
        (ii) 0.7535
       (iii) 0.7847
17 RIGHT < TRAP < Exact < MID < LEFT
19 RIGHT: over; LEFT: under
21 LEFT, TRAP: over; RIGHT, MID: under
23 (a) 16.392
  (b) $2(4^{3/2}) = 16$
  (c) −0.392
  (d) −0.00392
  (e) 16.00392

25 (a) TRAP(4); 1027.5
  (b) Underestimate
27 Large $|f'|$ gives large error
29 (a)

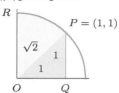

  (b) LEFT(5) ≈ 1.32350
       error ≈ −0.03810
       RIGHT(5) ≈ 1.24066
       error ≈ 0.04474
       TRAP(5) ≈ 1.28208
       error ≈ 0.00332
       MID(5) ≈ 1.28705
       error ≈ −0.001656
35 RIGHT(10) = 5.556
   TRAP(10) = 4.356
   LEFT(20) = 3.199
   RIGHT(20) = 4.399
   TRAP(20) = 3.799
39 TRAP(n) approaches value of definite integral, not 0
41 Total time grows exponentially with number of digits
43 $f(x) = e^x$
45 False
47 True
49 False
51 True
53 False
55 False

Section 7.6

1 (a)

  (b)

3 (a) 0.9596, 0.9995, 0.99999996
  (b) 1.0
5 Diverges
7 −1
9 Converges to 1/2
11 1
13 ln 2
15 4
17 Does not converge
19 $\pi/4$
21 Does not converge

23 Does not converge
25 0.01317
27 $1/\ln 3$
29 1/3
31 Does not converge
33 Does not converge
35 (a) 0.421
  (b) 0.500
37 The area is infinite
39 1/2
41 2/27
43 (b) $t = 2$
  (c) 4000 people
45 $\sqrt{b\pi}$
47 $\pi^4/120$
49 $f(x) = g(x) = 1/x$
51 $f(x) = 1/x$
53 True
55 False
57 True
59 True
61 True

Section 7.7

1 Converges; behaves like $1/x^2$
3 Diverges; behaves like $1/x$
5 Diverges; behaves like $1/x$
7 Converges; behaves like $5/x^3$
9 Converges; behaves like $1/x^2$
11 Does not converge
13 Converges
15 Does not converge
17 Converges
19 Converges
21 Converges
23 Converges
25 Does not converge
27 Converge
29 Converges for $p < 1$
   Diverges for $p \geq 1$
31 (a) e^t is concave up for all t
33 Converges
35 $f(x) = 1/x^2$
37 $f(x) = 3/(7x + 2)$
39 True

Chapter 7 Review

1 $(t + 1)^3/3$
3 $5^x/\ln 5$
5 $3w^2/2 + 7w + C$
7 $-\cos t + C$
9 $(1/5)e^{5z} + C$
11 $(-1/2)\cos 2\theta + C$
13 $2x^{5/2}/5 + 3x^{5/3}/5 + C$
15 $-e^{-z} + C$
17 $x^2/2 + \ln|x| - x^{-1} + C$
19 $(1/2)e^{t^2} + C$
21 $((1/2)x^2 - (1/2)x + 1/4)e^{2x} + C$

23 $(1/2)y^2 \ln y - (1/4)y^2 + C$

25 $x(\ln x)^2 - 2x \ln x + 2x + C$

27 $(1/3)\sin^3 \theta + C$

29 $(1/2)u^2 + 3u + 3\ln|u| - 1/u + C$

31 $\tan z + C$

33 $(1/12)t^{12} - (10/11)t^{11} + C$

35 $(1/3)(\ln x)^3 + C$

37 $(1/3)x^3 + x^2 + \ln|x| + C$

39 $(1/2)e^{t^2+1} + C$

41 $(1/10)\sin^2(5\theta) + C$ (other forms of answer are possible)

43 $\arctan z + C$

45 $-(1/8)\cos^4 2\theta + C$

47 $(-1/4)\cos^4 z + (1/6)\cos^6 z + C$

49 $(2/3)(1 + \sin\theta)^{3/2} + C$

51 $t^3 e^t - 3t^2 e^t + 6te^t - 6e^t + C$

53 $(3z + 5)^4/12 + C$

55 $\arctan(\sin w) + C$

57 $-\cos(\ln x) + C$

59 $y - (1/2)e^{-2y} + C$

61 $\ln|\ln x| + C$

63 $\sin\sqrt{x^2 + 1} + C$

65 $ue^{ku}/k - e^{ku}/k^2 + C$

67 $(1/\sqrt{2})e^{\sqrt{2}+3} + C$

69 $(u^3 \ln u)/3 - u^3/9 + C$

71 $-\cos(2x)/(4\sin^2(2x)) + \frac{1}{8}\ln\left|\frac{(\cos(2x)-1)}{(\cos(2x)+1)}\right| + C$

73 $-y^2 \cos(cy)/c + 2y\sin(cy)/c^2 + 2\cos(cy)/c^3 + C$

75 $\frac{1}{34}e^{5x}(5\cos(3x) + 3\sin(3x)) + C$

77 $(\sqrt{3}/4)(2x\sqrt{1 + 4x^2} + \ln|2x + \sqrt{1 + 4x^2}|) + C$

79 $x^2/2 - 3x - \ln|x + 1| + 8\ln|x + 2| + C$

81 $(1/b)(\ln|x| - \ln|x + b/a|) + C$

83 $(x^3/27) + 2x - (9/x) + C$

85 $-(1/\ln 10)10^{1-x} + C$

87 $\left((1/2)v^2 - 1/4\right)\arcsin v + (1/4)v\sqrt{1 - v^2} + K$

89 $z^3/3 + 5z^2/2 + 25z + 125\ln|z - 5| + C$

91 $(1/3)\ln|\sin(3\theta)| + C$

93 $(2/3)x^{3/2} + 2\sqrt{x} + C$

95 $(4/3)(\sqrt{x} + 1)^{3/2} + C$

97 $-1/(4(z^2 - 5)^2) + C$

99 $(1 + \tan x)^4/4 + C$

101 $e^{x^2+x} + C$

103 $-(2/9)(2 + 3\cos x)^{3/2} + C$

105 $\sin^3(2\theta)/6 - \sin^5(2\theta)/10 + C$

107 $(x + \sin x)^4/4 + C$

109 $\frac{1}{3}\sinh^3 x + C$

111 $49932\frac{1}{6}$

113 $201,760$

115 $3/2 + \ln 2$

117 $e - 2 \approx 0.71828$

119 $-11e^{-10} + 1$

121 $3(e^2 - e)$

123 0

125 $\frac{1}{2}\ln|x - 1| - \frac{1}{2}\ln|x + 1| + C$

127 $(\ln|x| - \ln|L - x|)/L + C$

129 $\arcsin(x/5) + C$

131 $(1/3)\arcsin(3x) + C$

133 $2\ln|x - 1| - \ln|x + 1| - \ln|x| + K$

135 $\arctan(x + 1) + C$

137 $(1/b)\arcsin(bx/a) + C$

139 $(1/2)(\ln|e^x - 1| - \ln|e^x + 1|) + C$

141 Does not converge

143 6

145 Does not converge

147 Does not converge

149 Converges to $\pi/8$

151 Converges to $2\sqrt{15}$

153 Does not converge

155 Converges to value between 0 and $\pi/2$

157 Does not converge

159 $e^9/3 - e^6/2 + 1/6$

161 Area $= 2\sqrt{2}$

163 $w = 3x^5 + 2, p = 1/2, k = 1/5$

165 $A = 2/5, B = -3/5$

167 $\int 0.5ue^u \, du;$
$k = 0.5, u = -x^2$

169 Substitute $w = x^2$ into second integral

171 Substitute $w = 1 - x^2, w = \ln x$

173 $w = 2x$

175 $5/6$

177 (a) 3.5
(b) 35

179 11/9

181 Wrong; improper integral treated as proper integral, integral diverges

183 $RT(5) < RT(10) < TR(10) < \text{Exact} < MID(10) < LF(10) < LF(5)$

185 (a) 4 places: 2 seconds
8 places: $\approx$ 6 hours
12 places: $\approx$ 6 years
20 places: $\approx$ 600 million years
(b) 4 places: 2 seconds
8 places: $\approx$ 3 minutes
12 places: $\approx$ 6 hours
20 places: $\approx$ 6 years

187 (a) $(k/L)\ln 3$
(b) $T \to \infty$

189 (a) 0.5 ml
(b) 99.95%

191 (a) 360 degree-days
(b)

(c) $T_2 = 36$

193 (a) $(\ln x)^2/2, (\ln x)^3/3, (\ln x)^4/4$
(b) $(\ln x)^{n+1}/(n + 1)$

195 (a) $(-9\cos x + \cos(3x))/12$
(b) $(3\sin x - \sin(3x))/4$

197 (a) $x + x/(2(1 + x^2)) - (3/2)\arctan x$
(b) $1 - (x^2/(1 + x^2)^2) - 1/(1 + x^2)$

Section 8.1

1 (a) $\sum 2x \, \Delta x$
(b) 9

3 (a) $\sum(3 - y/2) \, \Delta y$
(b) 9

5 15

7 15/2

9 $(5/2)\pi$

11 1/6

13 $\int_0^9 4\pi \, dx = 36\pi \text{ cm}^3$

15 $\int_0^5 (4\pi/25)y^2 \, dy = 20\pi/3 \text{ cm}^3$

17 $\int_0^5 \pi(5^2 - y^2) \, dy = 250\pi/3 \text{ mm}^3$

19 Triangle; $b, h = 1, 3$

21 Quarter circle $r = \sqrt{15}$

23

25 (a) $\int_0^4 ((12 - x) - 2x) \, dx = 24$
(b) $\int_8^8 (y/2) \, dy + \int_8^{12} (12 - y) \, dy = 16 + 8 = 24$

27 (a) $\int_0^3 2x \, dx + \int_3^5 6 \, dx = 9 + 12 = 21$
(b) $\int_0^6 (5 - (y/2)) \, dy = 21$

29 Cone, $h = 12, r = 4$

31 Hemisphere $r = 2$

33 $36\pi = 113.097 \text{ m}^3$

35 (a) $3\Delta x;$
$\int_0^4 3 \, dx = 12 \text{ cm}^3$

(b) $8(1 - h/3)\Delta h$;
$\int_0^3 8(1 - h/3)\, dh = 12\,\text{cm}^3$

37 $\int_0^{150} 1400(160 - h)\, dh = 1.785 \cdot 10^7\,\text{m}^3$

39 Change to $\int_{-10}^{10} \pi\left(10^2 - x^2\right)\, dx$

41 Region between positive x-axis, positive y-axis, and $y = 1 - x$

43 False

45 True

Section 8.2

1 (a) $4\pi \int_0^3 x^2\, dx$
  (b) 36π

3 (a) $(\pi/4) \int_0^6 (36 - y^2)\, dy$
  (b) 36π

5 $\pi/5$

7 $256\pi/15$

9 $\pi(e^2 - e^{-2})/2$

11 $\pi/2$

13 $2\pi/15$

15 2.958

17 2.302

19 π

21 $\sqrt{42}$

23 ≈ 24.6

25 $V = \int_0^2 [\pi(9 - y^3)^2 - \pi(9 - 4y)^2]\, dy$

27 $V = \int_0^9 [\pi(2 + \frac{1}{3}x)^2 - \pi 2^2]\, dx$

29 $V = \int_0^5 \pi((5x)^2 - (x^2)^2)\, dx$

31 $V = \int_0^5 \pi((4 + 5x)^2 - (4 + x^2)^2)\, dx$

33 3.820

35 (a) $16\pi/3$
  (b) 1.48

37 $V = (16/7)\pi \approx 7.18$

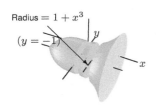

39 $V = (\pi^2/2) \approx 4.935$

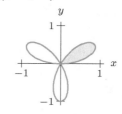

Radius $= \sin x$

41 $4\pi/5$

43 $8/15$

45 $\sqrt{3}/8$

47 $V \approx 42.42$

49 $V = (e^2 - 1)/2$

51 $g(x) = 2\sin x,\ -2\sin x$

53 2267.32 cubic feet

55 (a) Volume $\approx 152\,\text{in}^3$
  (b) About 15 apples

57 $40{,}000LH^{3/2}/(3\sqrt{a})$

59 (a) $dh/dt = -6/\pi$
  (b) $t = \pi/6$

61 (a) $4\int_0^r \sqrt{1 + (-x/y)^2}\, dx$
  (b) $2\pi r$

63 $\int_0^4 \sqrt{1 + (4 - 2x)^2}\, dx$

65 $\int_{-\sqrt{1/2}}^{\sqrt{1/2}} \sqrt{1 + 4x^2 e^{-2x^2}}\, dx$

67 4.624 meters

69 (c) $f(x) = \sqrt{3}x$

71 Change to $\int_0^5 \left(\pi(3x)^2 - \pi(2x)^2\right)\, dx$

73 Greater than 32

75 Region bounded by $y = 2x$, x-axis, $0 \leq x \leq 1$

77 $f(x) = x^2$

79 False

81 False

Section 8.3

1 $(-1/2, \sqrt{3}/2)$

3 $(3, -\sqrt{3})$

5 $(\sqrt{2}, \pi/4)$

7 $(2\sqrt{2}, -\pi/6)$

9 (b)

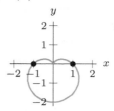

(c) Cartesian:
  $(\sqrt{3}/4, 1/4)$;
  $(-\sqrt{3}/4, 1/4)$ or polar:
  $r = 1/2, \theta = \pi/6$ or $5\pi/6$

(d)

11 Looks the same

13 Rotated by $90°$ clockwise

15 $\pi/4 \leq \theta \leq 5\pi/4$;
  $0 \leq \theta \leq \pi/4$ and $5\pi/4 \leq \theta \leq 2\pi$

17 $\sqrt{8} \leq r \leq \sqrt{18}$ and $\pi/4 \leq \theta \leq \pi/2$

19 $0 \leq \theta \leq \pi/2$ and $1 \leq r \leq 2/\cos\theta$

21 -1

23 $\sqrt{2}(e^\pi - e^{\pi/2})$

25

27 $4\pi^3$

29 (a) $r = 1/\cos\theta; r = 2$
  (b) $\frac{1}{2}\int_{-\pi/3}^{\pi/3}(2^2 - (1/\cos\theta)^2)\, d\theta$
  (c) $(4\pi/3) - \sqrt{3}$

31 $2\pi a$

33 $(5\pi/6) + 7\sqrt{3}/8$

35 (a)

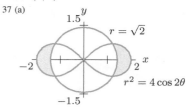

$r = 2\sin\theta$
$\theta = \pi/4$
$r = 2\cos\theta$

(b) $(\pi/2) - 1$

37 (a)

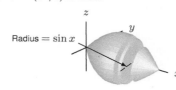

$r = \sqrt{2}$
$r^2 = 4\cos 2\theta$

(b) $2\sqrt{3} - 2\pi/3$

39 Horiz: $(\pm 1.633, \pm 2.309); (0, 0)$
  Vert: $(\pm 2.309, \pm 1.633); (0, 0)$

41 (a) $y = (2/\pi)x + (2/\pi)$
  (b) $y = 1$

43 21.256

47 2.828

49 Points are in quadrant IV

51

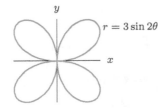

$r = 3\sin 2\theta$

53 $r = 100$

55 $r = 1 + \cos\theta$

Section 8.4

1 $1 - e^{-10}$ gm

3 (a) $\displaystyle\sum_{i=1}^{N}(2 + 6x_i)\Delta x$

  (b) 16 grams

5 (b) $\displaystyle\sum_{i=1}^{N}[600 + 300\sin(4\sqrt{x_i + 0.15})](20/N)$

  (c) ≈ 11513

7 2 cm to right of origin

9 45

11 186,925

13 1 gm

15 (a) 3 miles

  (b) 282,743

17 (a) $\displaystyle\int_0^5 2\pi r(0.115e^{-2r})\,dr$

  (b) 181 cubic meters

19 (a) $\pi r^2 l/2$

  (b) $2klr^3/3$

21 $\displaystyle\int_0^{60}(1/144)g(t)\,dt$ ft^3

23 $x = 2$

25 $\pi/2$

27 (a) Right

  (b) $2/(1 + 6e - e^2) \approx 0.2$

29 (a) 2/3 gm

  (b) Greater than 1/2

x^2

Δx

  (c) $\overline{x} = 3/4$ cm

33 $\overline{x} = (1 - 3e^{-2})/(2 - 2e^{-2}) \approx 0.343;$
   $\overline{y} = 0$

35 Density cannot be negative

37 $\delta(x) = x^2,$ for $-1 \le x \le 1$

39 $\delta(x) = \begin{cases} 5, & 0 \le x \le 1 \\ 1, & 1 < x < 5 \\ 4, & 5 \le x \le 10 \end{cases}$

41 $\delta(x) = 1$

43 False

45 True

47 True

Section 8.5

1 30 ft-lb

3 1.333 ft-lb

5 27/2 joules

7 $1.176 \cdot 10^7$ lb

9 20 ft-lb

11 $1.489 \cdot 10^{10}$ joules

13 3437.5 ft-lbs

15 6860 joules

17 784.14 ft-lb

19 1,058,591.1 ft-lbs

21 (a) 156,828 ft-lbs

  (b) 313,656 ft-lbs

  (c) 150,555 ft-lbs

23 27,788 ft-lbs

25 $0.366(k + 1.077)g\pi$ joules

27 (a) Force on dam
   $\approx \displaystyle\sum_{i=0}^{N-1} 1000(62.4h_i)\Delta h$

  (b) $\displaystyle\int_0^{50} = 1000(62.4h)\,dh = 78{,}000{,}000$ pounds

29 4,992,000 lbs

31 (a) $1.76 \cdot 10^6$ nt/m^2

  (b) $1.96 \cdot 10^7 \displaystyle\int_0^{180} h\,dh = 3.2 \cdot 10^{11}$ nt

33 (a) 780,000 lb/ft^2
   About 5400 lb/in^2

  (b) $124.8 \displaystyle\int_{-3}^{3}(12{,}500 - h)\sqrt{9 - h^2}\,dh$
   $= 2.2 \cdot 10^7$ lb

35 Potential
   $= 2\pi\sigma(\sqrt{R^2 + a^2} - R)$

37 15231 ergs

39 $\dfrac{GM_1M_2}{l_1l_2}\ln\left(\dfrac{(a + l_1)(a + l_2)}{a(a + l_1 + l_2)}\right)$

41 $(2GMmy/a^2)\left(y^{-1} - (a^2 + y^2)^{-1/2}\right)$

43 Less than twice as much

45 Book raised given vertical distance

47 False

49 False

51 False

Section 8.6

1 $C(1 + 0.03)^{25}$ dollars

3 $C/e^{0.03(5)}$ dollars

5 $\displaystyle\int_0^{15} C\,e^{0.02(15-t)}\,dt$ dollars

7 $\ln(25{,}000/C)/30$ per year

9 (a) Future value = \$6389.06
   Present value = \$864.66

  (b) 17.92 years

11 (a) \$43,645.71

  (b) \$20,000.00

  (c) \$23,645.71

13 4.621%/ yr

15 \$4000/ yr; \$21,034.18

17 \$1000/ yr; \$24,591.23

19 \$/year

t (years from present)

21 (a) \$5820 per year

  (b) \$36,787.94

23 Installments

25 3.641%/ yr

27 9.519%/ yr

29 (a) Option 1

  (b) Option 1: \$10.929 million;
   Option 2: \$10.530 million

31 In 10 years

33 (a) $\displaystyle\sum_{i=0}^{n-1}(2000 - 100t_i)e^{-0.1t_i}\Delta t$

  (b) $\displaystyle\int_0^{M} e^{-0.10t}(2000 - 100t)\,dt$

  (c) After 20 years
   \$11,353.35

35 \$85,750,000

39 (a) Less

  (b) Can't tell

  (c) Less

41 Future value more than \$20,000

43 PV requires integral

47 5%, \$4761.90

Section 8.7

1 (a)-(II), (b)-(I), (c)-(III)

3 % of population
   per dollar of income

income

% of population having
at least this income

income

5 pdf; 1/4

$P(x)$

1

$\frac{1}{4}$

x

7 cdf; 1

$P(x)$

1/5

5

x

9 cdf; 1/3

$\frac{1}{3}$

$\frac{1}{6}$

$p(x)$

2   4

x

11 For small Δx around 70, fraction of families with incomes in that interval about $0.05\Delta x$

13 A is 300 kelvins;
   B is 500 kelvins

15 (a) 0.9 m–1.1 m

19 (a) Cumulative distribution increasing
   (b) Vertical 0.2, horizontal 2

21 (a) 22.1%
   (b) 33.0%
   (c) 30.1%
   (d) $C(h) = 1 - e^{-0.4h}$

23 (b) About 3/4

25 Prob $0.02\Delta x$ in interval around 1

27 $\int_{-\infty}^{\infty} p(t)\, dt \neq 1$

29 $P(x)$ grows without bound as $x \to \infty$, instead of approaching 1

31 Cumulative distribution increasing

33 $P(t) = \begin{cases} 0, & t < 0 \\ t, & 0 \leq t \leq 1 \\ 1, & t > 1 \end{cases}$

35 $P(x) = (x-3)/4, 3 \leq x \leq 7$

37 False

Section 8.8

5 Mean 2/3; Median $2 - \sqrt{2} = 0.586$

7 (a) 0.684 : 1
   (b) 1.6 hours
   (c) 1.682 hours

9 (a) $P(t)$ = Fraction of population who survive up to t years after treatment
   (b) $S(t) = e^{-Ct}$
   (c) 0.178

11 (a) $p(x) = \frac{1}{15\sqrt{2\pi}} e^{-\frac{1}{2}\left(\frac{x-100}{15}\right)^2}$
   (b) 6.7% of the population

13 (c) μ represents the mean of the distribution, while σ is the standard deviation

15 (b)

17 (a) $p(r) = 4r^2 e^{-2r}$

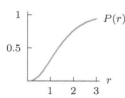

   (b) Mean: 1.5 Bohr radii
       Median: 1.33 Bohr radii
       Most likely:
       1 Bohr radius

19 Median cannot be 1 since all of the area is to the left of $x = 1$

21 $p(x) = \begin{cases} 0 & \text{for} & x < 0 \\ 1 & \text{for} & 0 \leq x \leq 1 \\ 0 & \text{for} & x > 1 \end{cases}$

23 True

25 False

Chapter 8 Review

1

3 $2\int_{-r}^{r} \sqrt{r^2 - x^2}\, dx = \pi r^2$

5 $3772\pi/15 = 790.006$

7 $\pi(1 - e^{-4})/4 = 0.771$

9 $27\pi = 84.823$

11 $V = \int_0^2 \pi(y^3)^2\, dy$

13 $V = \int_0^2 \left[\pi(10 - 4y)^2 - \pi(2)^2\right] dy$

15 $V = \int_0^2 \left[\pi(4y + 3)^2 - \pi(y^3 + 3)^2\right] dx$

17 $V = \pi$

19 $36\pi = 113.097$ m^3

21 $2\int_{-a}^{a} \sqrt{1 + b^2 x^2/(a^2(a^2 - x^2))}\, dx$

23 45.230

25 4.785

27 15.865

29 $\int_0^1 f(x)\, dx < 1/2$

31 $\int_0^1 f^{-1}(x)\, dx > 1/2$

33 $\int_0^1 \sqrt{1 + (f'(x))^2}\, dx > \sqrt{2}$

35

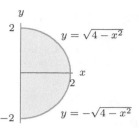

37 $V = \int_0^{25} \pi((8 - y/5)^2 - (8 - \sqrt{y})^2)\, dy$

39 (a) $V = 5\pi/6$
   (b) $V = 4\pi/5$

41 (a) $(1 - e^{-b})/b$
   (b) $\pi(1 - e^{-2b})/(2b)$

43 $736\pi/3 = 770.737$

45 $2\pi/3$

47 $\pi^2/2 - 2\pi/3 = 2.840$

49 $\pi/24$

51 Area under graph of f from $x = 0$ to $x = 3$

53 $e - e^{-1}$

55 (a) $a = b/l$
   (b) $(1/3)\pi b^2 l$

57 Volume $= 6\pi^2$

59 5π cubic inches/second

61 πa^2

63 (a) $(\sin^2\theta - \cos^2\theta)/(2\cos\theta\sin\theta)$
   (b) $\pi/4$

65 $\int_{-2}^{1} \pi\left((x-1)^2(x+2)\right)^2 dx$

67 (a) 2/3 gm
   (b) Less than 1/2

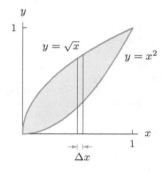

   (c) $\bar{x} = \bar{y} = 9/20$ cm

69 100 ft-lbs

71 1,404,000 ft-lbs

73 20,617 ft-lbs

75 21,600 ft-lbs

77 49 kg

79 $y = x^4$

81 B

83 $6.2828 billion

85 1.25 gallons

87 (a) $y = h + (2 - 2h)x^2$
   (b) Both events happen simultaneously

89 The hoop rotating about the cylindrical axis

91 (a) $\frac{1}{2}t\sqrt{1 + 4t^2} + \frac{1}{4}\text{arcsinh}\,(2t)$
   (b) t^2

93 (b) $(4\pi/3)(r^2 - a^2)^{3/2}$

Section 9.1

1. $0, 3, 2, 5, 4$
3. $2/3, 4/5, 6/7, 8/9, 10/11$
5. $1, -1/2, 1/4, -1/8, 1/16$
7. $s_n = 2^{n+1}$
9. $s_n = n^2 + 1$
11. $s_n = n/(2n+1)$
13. Diverges
15. Converges to 3
17. Diverges
19. Converges to 2
21. Diverges
23. Converges to 0
25. (a) (IV)
   (b) (III)
   (c) (II)
   (d) (I)
27. (a) (II)
   (b) (III)
   (c) (IV)
   (d) (I)
   (e) (V)
29. $1, 3, 6, 10, 15, 21$
31. $1, 5, 7, 17, 31, 65$
33. $13, 27, 50, 85$
35. $0.25, 0.00, 0.25, 1.00, 2.25, 4.00$
37. $0.841, 0.455, 0.047, -0.189, -0.192, -0.047$
39. $0, 0, 6, 6, 6, 0, 0 \ldots$ and
   $0, 2, 4, 6, 4, 2, \ldots$
41. $s_n = s_{n-1} + 2, s_1 = 1$
43. $s_n = 2s_{n-1} - 1, s_1 = 3$
45. $s_n = s_{n-1} + n, s_1 = 1$
51. Converges to 0.5671
53. Converges to 1
55. (a) $2, 4, 2^n$
   (b) 33 generations; overlap
57. (a) k rows; $a_n = n$
   (b) $T_n = T_{n-1} + n, n > 1; T_1 = 1$
61. For all $\epsilon > 0$, there is an N such
   that $|s_n - L| < \epsilon$ for all $n \geq N$
63. Converges to $3/7$
65. $s_n = -1/n$
67. False
69. True
71. False
73. True
75. (b)

Section 9.2

1. Sequence
3. Sequence
5. Series
7. Series
9. No
11. Yes, $a = 1$, ratio $= -1/2$
13. Yes, $a = 1$, ratio $= 2z$
15. Yes, $a = 1$, ratio $= -x$
17. Yes, $a = y^2$, ratio $= y$
19. 26 terms; 2.222
21. 9 terms; 0.0000222

23. 54
25. $80\sqrt{2}/(\sqrt{2} - 1) = 273.137$.
27. $1/(1 - 3x), -1/3 < x < 1/3$
29. $2/(1 + 2z), -1/2 < z < 1/2$
31. $4 + y/(1 - y/3), -3 < z < 3$
33. (a) $P_n =$
       $250(0.04) + 250(0.04)^2$
       $+ 250(0.04)^3 + \cdots$
       $+ 250(0.04)^{n-1}$
   (b) $P_n =$
       $250 \cdot 0.04(1 - (0.04)^{n-1})/(1 - 0.04)$
   (c) $\lim_{n \to \infty} P_n \approx 10.42$
       Difference between them is 250 mg
35.

q (quantity, mg)

37. (a) 14.916 years
   (b) 6.25 % annual reduction in consumption
39. (a) (i) \$16.43 million
      (ii) \$24.01 million
   (b) \$16.87 million
41. \$65,742.60
43. \$400 million
45. \$900 million
49. $|x| \geq 1$
51. $1 + (-1) + 1 + (-1) + \cdots$
53. $\sum_{n=0}^{\infty} 5(1/2)^n$

Section 9.3

1. $1, 3, 6, 10, 15$
3. $1/2, 2/3, 3/4, 4/5, 5/6$
5. Diverges
7. Converges
11. $f(x) = (-1)^x/x$ undefined
13. Diverges
15. Diverges
17. Converges
19. Converges
21. Converges
23. Diverges
25. Converges
27. Diverges
29. Diverges
31. Converges
35. (a) $\ln(n + 1)$
   (b) Diverges
37. (b) $S_3 = 1 - 1/4; S_{10} = 1 - 1/11; S_n = 1 - 1/(n + 1)$
49. (a) 1.596
   (b) 3.09
   (c) 1.635; 3.13
   (d) 0.05; 0.01
53. Terms approaching zero does not guarantee convergence
55. $\sum_{n=1}^{\infty} 1/n$
57. True

59. False
61. True
63. False
65. (d)

Section 9.4

5. Behaves like $\sum_{n=1}^{\infty} 1/n^2$; Converges
7. Behaves like $\sum_{n=1}^{\infty} 1/n^{1/2}$; Diverges
9. Converges
11. Converges
13. Diverges
15. Converges
17. Converges
19. Converges
21. Alternating
23. Not alternating
25. Converges
27. Converges
29. Absolutely convergent
31. Divergent
33. Conditionally convergent
35. Conditionally convergent
37. Absolutely convergent
39. Converges
41. Converges
43. Diverges
45. Diverges
47. Converges
49. Terms not positive
51. Limit of ratios is 1
53. $a_{n+1} > a_n$ or $\lim_{n \to \infty} a_n \neq 0$
55. $\lim_{n \to \infty} a_n \neq 0$
57. Does not converge
59. Converges to approximately 0.3679
61. Converges
63. Diverges
65. Diverges
67. Converges
69. Diverges
71. Diverges
73. Converges
75. Diverges
77. Converges
79. Converges if $a > 1$ and diverges if $a \leq 1$
81. Converges for $1/e < a < e$; diverges for $a \geq e$ and $0 < a \leq 1/e$
83. Converges
85. 12 or more terms
87. $\sum c_n$ converges, $\sum a_n$ diverges
95. Converges
97. Limit of ratios is 1, so ratio test inconclusive
99. $\sum_{n=1}^{\infty} (-1)^n/n$
101. $a_n = 3^n$
103. False
105. True
107. False
109. False

111 True

113 True

115 True

117 True

Section 9.5

1 Yes

3 No

5 $1 \cdot 3 \cdot 5 \cdots (2n-1)x^n/(2^n \cdot n!); n \geq 1$

7 $(-1)^k(x-1)^{2k}/(2k)!; k \geq 0$

9 $(x-a)^n/(2^{n-1} \cdot n!); n \geq 1$

11 1

13 1

15 2

17 2

19 1

21 1/4

23 1

25 (a) $R = 1$
(b) $-1 < x \leq 1$

27 $-3 < x < 3$

29 $-2 < x < 2$

31 $-\infty < x < \infty$

33 $-1/5 \leq x < 1/5$

35 $\sum_{n=0}^{\infty}(-2z)^n, -1/2 < z < 1/2$

37 $\sum_{n=0}^{\infty}3(z/2)^n, -2 < z < 2$

39 1

41 $5 \leq R \leq 7$

43 (a) False
(b) True
(c) False
(d) Cannot determine

45 (a) All real numbers
(b) $J(0) = 1$
(c) $S_4(x) = 1 - \frac{x^2}{4} + \frac{x^4}{64} - \frac{x^6}{2304} + \frac{x^8}{147,456}$
(d) 0.765
(e) 0.765

47 (a) Odd; $g(0) = 0$
(c) $\sin x$

49 Radius ∞, not 0

51 $\sum_{n=0}^{\infty}(x-2)^n/n$

53 $\sum x^n/n^2$

55 True

57 True

59 False

61 True

63 False

65 False

67 (d)

Chapter 9 Review

1 $3(2^{11}-1)/2^{10}$

3 619.235

5 $b^5(1-b^6)/(1-b)$ when $b \neq 1$;
6 when $b = 1$

7 $(3^{17}-1)/(2 \cdot 3^{20})$

9 36, 48, 52, 53.333;
$S_n = 36(1-(1/3)^n)/(1-1/3); S = 54$

11 $-810, -270, -630, -390$;
$S_n = -810(1-(-2/3)^n)/(1+2/3)$;

$S = -486$

13 Converges 4/7

15 Diverges

17 Converges

19 Converges

21 Converges

23 Diverges

25 Converges

27 Divergent

29 Divergent

33 Converges

35 Converges

37 Converges

39 Converges

41 Diverges

43 Diverges

45 Convergent

47 Converges

49 Converges

51 Diverges

53 Converges

55 Diverges

57 Diverges

59 ∞

61 1

63 $-3 < x < 7$

65 $-\infty < x < \infty$

67 $s_n = 2n + 3$

69 9, 15, 23

71 Converges if $r > 1$, diverges if $0 < r \leq 1$

73 (a) All real numbers
(b) Even

75 240 million tons

77 $926.40

79 (a) $124.50
(b) $125

81 £250

83 (a)　(i) $B_0 4^n$
(ii) $B_0 2^{n/10}$
(iii) $(2^{1.9})^n$
(b) 10.490 hours

85 5/6

87 $\sum(3/2)^n$, $\sum(1/2)^n$, other answers possible

89 Converges

91 Not enough information

93 Converges

95 (a) C_0 ————————
C_1 ——— ———
C_2 — —   — —
C_3 -- --   -- --

(b) $1/3 + 2/9 + 4/27 + \cdots + (1/3)(2/3)^{n-1}$
(c) 1

97 12

Section 10.1

1 $P_3(x) = 1 + x + x^2 + x^3$
$P_5(x) = 1 + x + x^2 + x^3$

$+ x^4 + x^5$
$P_7(x) = 1 + x + x^2 + x^3$
$+ x^4 + x^5 + x^6 + x^7$

3 $P_2(x) = 1 + (1/2)x - (1/8)x^2$
$P_3(x) = 1 + (1/2)x - (1/8)x^2 + (1/16)x^3$
$P_4(x) = 1 + (1/2)x - (1/8)x^2$
$+ (1/16)x^3 - (5/128)x^4$

5 $P_2(x) = 1 - x^2/2!$
$P_4(x) = 1 - x^2/2! + x^4/4!$
$P_6(x) = 1 - x^2/2! + x^4/4! - x^6/6!$

7 $P_3(x) = P_4(x) = x - (1/3)x^3$

9 $P_2(x) = 1 - (1/2)x + (3/8)x^2$
$P_3(x) = 1 - (1/2)x + (3/8)x^2$
$- (5/16)x^3$
$P_4(x) = 1 - (1/2)x + (3/8)x^2$
$- (5/16)x^3 + (35/128)x^4$

11 $P_3(x) = 1 - \frac{x}{2} - \frac{x^2}{8} - \frac{x^3}{16}$

13 $P_4(x) = \frac{1}{3}[1 - \frac{x-2}{3}$
$+ \frac{(x-2)^2}{3^2} - \frac{(x-2)^3}{3^3}$
$+ \frac{(x-2)^4}{3^4}]$

15 $P_3(x) = \frac{\sqrt{2}}{2}[-1 + (x + \frac{\pi}{4})$
$+ \frac{1}{2}(x + \frac{\pi}{4})^2 - \frac{1}{6}(x + \frac{\pi}{4})^3]$

17 $1 - x/3 + 5x^2/7 + 8x^3$

19 $P_2(x) = 4x^2 - 7x + 2$
$f(x) = P_2(x)$

21 (a) If $f(x)$ is a polynomial of degree n, then $P_n(x)$, the nth degree Taylor polynomial for $f(x)$ about $x = 0$, is $f(x)$ itself

23 $-3 + 5x - x^2 - x^4/24 + x^5/30$

25 $c < 0, b > 0, a > 0$

27 $a < 0, b > 0, c > 0$

31 (a) 1/2
(b) 1/6

33 (a) fs are Figure 10.9
gs are Figure 10.8
(b) $A = (0,1)$
$B = (0,2)$
(c) $f_1 = $ III, $f_2 = $ I, $f_3 = $ II
$g_1 = $ III, $g_2 = $ II, $g_3 = $ I

35 (a) $1 + 3x + 2x^2$
(b) $1 + 3x + 7x^2$
(c) No

37 (a) $P_4(x) = 1 + x^2 + (1/2)x^4$
(b) If we substitute x^2 for x in the Taylor polynomial for e^x of degree 2, we will get $P_4(x)$, the Taylor polynomial for e^{x^2} of degree 4
(c) $P_{20}(x) = 1 + x^2/1! + x^4/2!$
$+ \cdots + x^{20}/10!$
(d) $e^{-2x} \approx 1 - 2x + 2x^2$
$- (4/3)x^3 + (2/3)x^4 - (4/15)x^5$

39 (a) Infinitely many; 3
(b) That near $x = 0$
Taylor poly only accurate near 0

41 (b) 0, 0.2

43 $f'(0) = 1$

45 $p(x) = 1 + 3(x-1) + (x-1)^3$

47 False

49 False

51 False

53 True

Section 10.2

1 $f(x) = 1 + 3x/2 + 3x^2/8 - x^3/16 + \cdots$

3 $f(x) = -x + x^3/3! - x^5/5! + x^7/7! + \cdots$

5 $f(x) = 1 + x + x^2$
   $+ x^3 + \cdots$

7 $f(y) = 1 - y/3 - y^2/9$
   $- 5y^3/81 - \cdots$

9 $\cos\theta = \sqrt{2}/2 - (\sqrt{2}/2)(\theta - \pi/4)$
   $- (\sqrt{2}/4)(\theta - \pi/4)^2 \quad +$
   $(\sqrt{2}/12)(\theta - \pi/4)^3$
   $- \cdots$

11 $\sin\theta = -\sqrt{2}/2 + (\sqrt{2}/2)(\theta + \pi/4)$
   $+ (\sqrt{2}/4)(\theta + \pi/4)^2$
   $- (\sqrt{2}/12)(\theta + \pi/4)^3 + \cdots$

13 $1/x = 1 - (x - 1) +$
   $(x - 1)^2 - (x - 1)^3 + \cdots$

15 $\frac{1}{x} = -1 - (x + 1)$
   $- (x + 1)^2 - (x + 1)^3$
   $- \cdots$

17 $(-1)^n x^n; n \geq 0$

19 $(-1)^{n-1} x^n/n; n \geq 1$

21 $(-1)^k x^{2k+1}/(2k + 1); k \geq 0$

23 $(-1)^k x^{4k+2}/(2k)!; k \geq 0$

25 $-1 < x < 1$

27 (a) $-1 < x < 1$
   (b) 1

29 1

31 1

33 $\frac{d}{dx}(x^2 e^{x^2})|_{x=0} = 0$
   $\frac{d^6}{dx^6}(x^2 e^{x^2})|_{x=0} = \frac{6!}{2} = 360$

35 e^2

37 $4/3$

39 $\ln(3/2)$

41 e^3

43 $e^{-0.1}$

45 $e^{0.2} - 1$

47 Only converges for $-1 < x < 1$

49 $f(x) = \cos x$

51 False

53 True

55 True

Section 10.3

1 $e^{-x} = 1 - x + x^2/2!$
   $- x^3/3! + \cdots$

3 $\cos(\theta^2) = 1 - \theta^4/2! + \theta^8/4!$
   $- \theta^{12}/6! + \cdots$

5 $\arcsin x = x + (1/6)x^3$
   $+ (3/40)x^5 + (5/112)x^7 + \cdots$

7 $1/\sqrt{1 - z^2} = 1 + (1/2)z^2 + (3/8)z^4$
   $+ (5/16)z^6 + \cdots$

9 $\phi^3 \cos(\phi^2) = \phi^3 - \phi^7/2!$
   $+ \phi^{11}/4! - \phi^{15}/6! + \cdots$

11 $1 + 3x + 3x^2 + x^3$
   $0 \cdot x^n$ for $n \geq 4$

13 $1 + (1/2)y^2 + (3/8)y^4 + \cdots +$
   $((1/2)(3/2)\cdots(1/2 + n - 1)y^{2n})/n! +$
   $\cdots;$
   $n \geq 1$

15 $\sqrt{T + h} = \sqrt{T}(1 + (1/2)(h/T)$
   $- (1/8)(h/T)^2 + (1/16)(h/T)^3 + \cdots)$

17 $1/(a + r)^2 = (1/a^2)(1 - 2(r/a)$
   $+ 3(r/a)^2 - 4(r/a)^3 + \cdots)$

19 $a/\sqrt{a^2 + x^2} = 1 - (1/2)(x/a)^2 +$

$(3/8)(x/a)^4$
$- (5/16)(x/a)^6 + \cdots$

21 $e^t \cos t = 1 + t - t^3/3$
   $- t^4/6 + \cdots$

23 $1 + t + t^2/2 + t^3/3$

25 (a) $2x + x^3/3 + x^5/60 + \cdots$
   (b) $P_3(x) = 2x + x^3/3$

27 $1/(1 - x)^2$

29 $1 + \sin\theta \leq e^\theta \leq 1/\sqrt{1 - 2\theta}$

31 (a) I
   (b) IV
   (c) III
   (d) II

33 $f(x) = (1/3)x^3 - (1/42)x^7 +$
   $(1/1320)x^{11} - (1/75,600)x^{15} + \cdots$

35 1

37 $\sinh 2x = \sum_{m=0}^{\infty}(2x)^{2m+1}/(2m + 1)!$
   $\cosh 2x = \sum_{m=0}^{\infty}(2x)^{2m}/(2m)!$

39 (a) $f(x) = 1 + (a - b)x$
   $+ (b^2 - ab)x^2 + \cdots$
   (b) $a = 1/2, b = -1/2$

41 (a) If $M >> m$, then
   $\mu \approx mM/M = m$
   (b) $\mu = m[1 - m/M + (m/M)^2$
   $- (m/M)^3 + \cdots]$
   (c) -0.0545%

43 (a) $((l_1 + l_2)/c) \cdot$
   $(v^2/c^2 + (5/4)v^4/c^4)$
   (b) $v^2, (l_1 + l_2)/c^3$

45 (a) Set $dV/dr = 0$, solve for r. Check for max
   or min.
   (b) $V(r) = -V_0$
   $+ 72V_0 r_0^{-2} \cdot (r - r_0)^2(1/2)$
   $+ \cdots$
   (d) $F = 0$ when $r - r_0$

47 Right hand missing a factor of $1/2$

49 $\ln x$

51 True

53 False

55 False

57 (c)

Section 10.4

1 $|E_3| \leq 0.00000460, E_3 = 0.00000425$

3 $|E_3| \leq 0.000338, E_3 = 0.000336$

5 $|E_4| \leq 0.0156, E_3 = -0.0112$

7 $|E_3| \leq 16.5, E_3 = 0.224$

9 (c)

11 (a) 5
   (b) 1.06

13 (a) Overestimate:
   $0 < \theta \leq 1$
   Underestimate:
   $-1 \leq \theta < 0$
   (b) $|E_2| \leq 0.17$

15 (a) Underestimate
   (b) 1

17 (a) (i) 4, 0.2
   (ii) 1
   (b) $-4 \leq x \leq 4$

19 Four decimal places: $n = 7$
   Six decimal places: $n = 9$

23 (a) $\pi \approx 2.67$
   (b) $\pi \approx 2.33$
   (c) $|E_n| \leq 0.78$
   (d) Derivatives unbounded near $x = 1$

25 Cannot make $|f(x) - P_n(x)| < 1$ for all x
   simultaneously

27 $1 - (x - 1) + (x - 1)^2 - (x - 1)^3$

29 False

31 False

33 False

Section 10.5

1 Not a Fourier series

3 Fourier series

5 $F_1(x) = F_2(x) = (4/\pi)\sin x$
   $F_3(x) = (4/\pi)\sin x + (4/3\pi)\sin 3x$

$F_1(x) = F_2(x) = \frac{4}{\pi}\sin x$

$F_3(x) = \frac{4}{\pi}\sin x + \frac{4}{3\pi}\sin 3x$

7 99.942% of the total energy

9 $H_n(x) =$
   $\pi/4 + \sum_{i=1}^{n}((-1)^{i+1}\sin(ix))/i +$
   $\sum_{i=1}^{[n/2]}(-2/((2i - 1)^2\pi))\cos((2i - 1)x),$
   where $[n/2]$ denotes the biggest integer smaller
   than or equal to $n/2$

11 $a_0 = 1/2$

13 (b) $(1/7)\sin 7x$
   (c) $f(x) = 1$ for $2\pi \leq x < -\pi$
   $f(x) = -1$ for $-\pi \leq x < 0$
   $f(x) = 1$ for $0 \leq x < \pi$
   $f(x) = -1$ for $\pi \leq x < 2\pi\ldots$
   Not continuous

15 $F_4(x) = 1/2 - (2/\pi)\sin(2\pi x)$
   $- (1/\pi)\sin(4\pi x) - (2/3\pi)\sin(6\pi x)$
   $- (1/2\pi)\sin(8\pi x)$

17 52.93

23 (a) 6.3662%, 18.929%
  (b) $(4\sin^2(k/5))/(k^2\pi^2)$
  (c) 61.5255%
  (d) $F_5(x) =$
     $1/(5\pi) + (2\sin(1/5)/\pi)\cos x$
     $+ (\sin(2/5)/\pi)\cos 2x +$
     $(2\sin(3/5)/(3\pi))\cos 3x$
     $+ (\sin(4/5)/(2\pi))\cos 4x +$
     $(2\sin 1/(5\pi))\cos 5x$

25 The energy of the pulse train is spread out over more harmonics as c gets closer to 0

33 a_0 is average of $f(x)$ on interval of approximation

35 Any odd function with period 2π

37 (b)

Chapter 10 Review

1 $e^x \approx 1 + e(x-1) + (e/2)(x-1)^2$

3 $\sin x \approx -1/\sqrt{2} + (1/\sqrt{2})(x+\pi/4)$
   $+ (1/2\sqrt{2})(x+\pi/4)^2$

5 $P_3(x) = 4 + 12(x-1)$
   $+ 10(x-1)^2 + (x-1)^3$

7 $P_3(x) = \sqrt{2}[1 + (x-1)/4$
   $- (x-1)^2/32 + (x-1)^3/128]$

9 $P_7 = 3x - 9x^3 + (27/2)x^5 - (27/2)x^7$

11 $t^2 + t^3 + (1/2)t^4 + (1/6)t^5 + \cdots$

13 $\theta^2\cos\theta^2 =$
    $\theta^2 - \theta^6/2! + \theta^{10}/4! - \theta^{14}/6! + \cdots$

15 $t/(1+t) = t - t^2 + t^3$
    $- t^4 + \cdots$

17 $1/\sqrt{4-x} =$
    $1/2 + (1/8)x + (3/64)x^2 + (5/256)x^3 + \cdots$

19 $a/(a+b) = 1 - b/a + (b/a)^2 - (b/a)^3 \cdots$

21 $(B^2 + y^2)^{3/2} = B^3(1 + (3/2)(y/B)^2$
    $+ (3/8)(y/B)^4 - (1/16)(y/B)^6 + \cdots)$

23 1.45

25 3/4

27 $\sin 2$

29 (a) $7(1.02^{104} - 1)/$
       $(0.02(1.02)^{100})$
   (b) $7e^{0.01}$

31 Smallest to largest:
    $1 - \cos x,\ x\sqrt{1-x},$
    $\ln(1+x), \arctan x, \sin x,$
    $x,\ e^x - 1$

33 1/2

35 0.10008

37 0.9046

39 (a) $\arcsin x = x + (1/6)x^3 + (3/40)x^5 +$
       $(5/112)x^7 + (35/1152)x^9 + \cdots$
   (b) 1

41 (a)

(b)

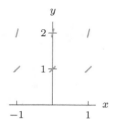

43 (a) $V(x) \approx V(0) + V''(0)x^2/2$
       $V''(0) > 0$
   (b) Force $\approx -V''(0)x$
       $V''(0) > 0$
       Toward origin

45 $x - x^2 + (3/2)x^3 - (8/3)x^4$

47 $P_3(t) = t + t^2/4 + (1/18)t^3$

49 (a) $F = GM/R^2 + Gm/(R+r)^2$
   (b) $F = GM/R^2$
       $+ (Gm/R^2)(1 - 2(r/R)$
       $+ 3(r/R)^2 - \cdots)$

51 (b) $F = mg(1 - 2h/R + 3h^2/R^2$
       $- 4h^3/R^3 + \cdots)$
   (c) 300 km

57 (b) If the amplitude of the kth harmonic of f is A_k, then the amplitude of the kth harmonic of f' is kA_k
   (c) The energy of the kth harmonic of f' is k^2 times the energy of the kth harmonic of f

61 (a) $P_7(x) = x - x^3/6 + x^5/120 - x^7/5040$
       $Q_7(x) = x - 2x^3/3 + 2x^5/15 - 4x^7/315$
   (b) For n odd, ratio of coefficients of x^n is 2^{n-1}

63 (a) $P_{10}(x) = 1 + x^2/12 - x^4/720 + x^6/30240 - x^8/1209600 + x^{10}/47900160$
   (b) All even powers
   (c) f even

Section 11.1

1 Yes

3 (a) Not a solution
  (b) Solution
  (c) Not a solution

9 12, 18, 27, 40.5

11 $x(t) = 5e^{3t}$

13 $y = \sqrt{2t+7}$

19 $k = 5$

21 (a) $C = 0$ and any n; $C \neq 0$ and $n = 3$
   (b) $C = 5$ and $n = 3$

23 (b) $A = k$

25 (a) (IV)
   (b) (III)
   (c) (III), (IV)
   (d) (II)

27 No

29 $Q = 6e^{4t}$ is particular solution, not general

31 $dy/dx = x/y$ and $y = 100$ when $x = 0$

33 $dy/dx = 2x$ with solutions $y = x^2$ and $y = x^2 + 5$

35 $dy/dx = 1/x$

37 $dy/dx = y - x^2$

39 False

41 False

43 False

45 True

47 False

Section 11.2

1 (a) $1; -1; 0; 3; -3; 0$
  (b)

3

5 Possible curves:

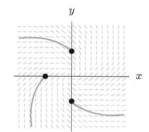

7 First graph

9 (a)

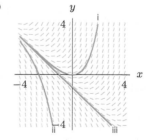

(b) $y = -x - 1$

11

13 (a)

P

$(-2, 12)$
$(-2, 10)$
$(1, 4)$
$(-5, 1)$ $(4, 1)$
$(0, 0)$

t

(b) Incr: $0 < P < 10$; decr: $P > 10$; P tends to 10

15 Slope field (b)

17 (a) (II)
(b) (I)
(c) (V)
(d) (III)
(e) (IV)

19 (e) $y' = 0.05y(y - 10)$

21 (b)

23 (a) IV
(b) I
(c) III
(d) V
(e) II
(f) VI

25 Graph of $y = x$ not tangent to slope field at $(1, 1)$

27 $dy/dx = x^2 + 1$

29

y

x

31 False

33 False

35 False

37 True

39 True

41 True

43 False

Section 11.3

3 1548, 1591.5917, 1630.860

5 (a) 24.39
(b) Concave up
(c) Underestimates

7 (a) $y(0.4) \approx 1.5282$
(b) $y(0.4) = -1.4$

9 (a)

11 (a) $y = 0.667$
(b) $y = 0.710$

13 Error in ten-step is half error ins five-step; $y = 0.753$

15 (a) $\Delta x = 0.5, y(1) \approx 1.5$
    $\Delta x = 0.25, y \approx 1.75$
(b) $y = x^2 + 1$, so $y(1) = 2$
(c) Yes

17 (a) $B \approx 1050$
(b) $B \approx 1050.63$
(c) $B \approx 1050.94$

19 For $dy/dx = k$, Euler's method gives exact solutions.

21 $dy/dx = 5$

23 False

Section 11.4

1 (a) Yes   (b) No   (c) Yes
(d) No   (e) Yes   (f) Yes
(g) No   (h) Yes   (i) No
(j) Yes   (k) Yes   (l) No

3 $P = 20e^{0.02t}$

5 $Q = 50e^{(1/5)t}$

7 $m = 5e^{3t-3}$

9 $z = 5e^{5t-5}$

11 $u = 1/(1 - (1/2)t)$

13 $y = 10e^{-x/3}$

15 $P = 104e^t - 4$

17 $Q = 400 - 350e^{0.3t}$

19 $R = 1 - 0.9e^{1-y}$

21 $y = (1/3)(3 + t)$

23 $y = 3x^5$

25 $z = 5e^{t+t^3/3}$

27 $w = -1/(\ln|\cos\psi| - 1/2)$

29 (a) $y = \sqrt[3]{6x^2 + B}$
(b) $y = \sqrt[3]{6x^2 + 1}$; $y = \sqrt[3]{6x^2 + 8}$; $y = \sqrt[3]{6x^2 + 27}$

31 (a) $y(t) = 100 - Ae^{-t}$
(b)

(c) $y(t) = 100 - 75e^{-t}$
    $y(t) = 100 + 10e^{-t}$
(d) $y(t) = 100 - 75e^{-t}$

33 (a)

y

$(0, 1)$
$(0, 0)$
x
$(0, -1)$

(b) One end asymptotic to $y = 0$, other end unbounded
(c) $y = -1/(x + C), x \neq -C$

35 $Q = Ae^{t/k}$

37 $Q = b - Ae^{-t}$

39 $R = -(b/a) + Ae^{at}$

41 $y = -1/\left(k(t + t^3/3) + C\right)$

43 $L = b + Ae^{k((1/2)x^2 + ax)}$

45 $x = e^{At}$

47 $y = 2(2^{-e^{-t}})$

49 (a) and (b)

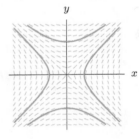

(c) $y^2 - x^2 = 2C$

53 Solution to $dP/dt = 0.2t$ is $P = 0.1t^2 + C$

55 $dy/dx = x + y$

57 $dy/dx = 2x$

59 True

61 True

Section 11.5

1 (a) (III)
(b) (IV)
(c) (I)
(d) (II)

3 (a) $y = 2$: stable; $y = -1$: unstable
(b)

5

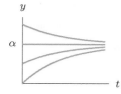

7 (a) $H = 200 - 180e^{-kt}$
   (b) $k \approx 0.027$ (if t is in minutes)

9 (a) $y = 0, y = 4, y = -2$
   (b) $y = 0$ stable, $y = 4$ and $y = -2$ unstable

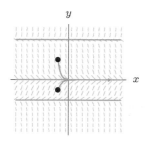

13 Longest: Lake Superior
   Shortest: Lake Erie
   The ratio is about 75

15 (a) $N =$ amount of nicotine in mg at time t;
       $t =$ number of hours since smoking a cigarette
   (b) $dN/dt = -0.347N$
   (c) $N = 0.4e^{-0.347t}$

17 (a) $G =$ size in acres of Grinnell Glacier in year t;
       $t =$ number of years since 2007
   (b) $dG/dt = -0.043G$
   (c) $G = 142e^{-0.043t}$

19 $dS/dt = -k(S - 65), k > 0$
   $S = 65 - 25e^{-kt}$

21 (a)

   (b) $dQ/dt = -0.0187Q$
   (c) 3 days

23 (a) 69,300 barrels/year
   (b) 25.9 years

25 About 2150 B.C.

27 (a) $dT/dt = -k(T - 10)$
   (b) $48°$F
       The pipes won't freeze

29 (a) $dH/dt = k(68 - H)$
   (b) $H = 68$, stable
   (c) $H = 68 - Ae^{-kt}$

(d) $57.8°$F

31 (a) $dB/dt = (r/100)B$
       Constant $= r/100$
   (b) $B = 0$, unstable
   (c) $B = Ae^{(r/100)t}$
   (d)

33 $y = x^2$ is not a constant solution

35 $dy/dt = -2y$

37

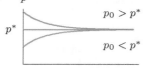

Section 11.6

1 (a) (III)
  (b) (V)
  (c) (I)
  (d) (II)
  (e) (IV)

3 $dB/dt = 0.037B + 5000$

5 $dB/dt = -0.065B - 50,000$

7 (a) $H' = k(H - 50); H(0) = 90$
  (b) $H(t) = 50 + 40e^{-0.05754t}$
  (c) 24 minutes

9 (a) $dB/dt = 0.08B - 2000$
  (b) $B = 25000$, unstable
  (c) $B = 25,000 + Ae^{0.08t}$
  (d) (i) $17,540.88
      (ii) $32,459.12

11 (a) Increasing; decreasing
   (b) Approach 50 metric tons

13 (a) $I = Ae^{-kl}$
   (b) 20 feet: 75%
       25 feet: 82.3%

15 (a) Mt. Whitney:
       17.50 inches
       Mt. Everest:
       10.23 inches
   (b) 18,661.5 feet

17 (b) $dQ/dt = -0.347Q + 2.5$
   (c) $Q = 7.2$ mg

19 $P = AV^k$

21 5.7 days, 126.32 liters

23 (a) $dp/dt = -k(p - p^*)$
   (b) $p = p^* + (p_0 - p^*)e^{-kt}$
   (c)

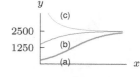

   (d) As $t \to \infty, p \to p^*$

---

25 (a) $Q = (r/\alpha)(1 - e^{-\alpha t})$
       $Q_\infty = r/\alpha$

   (b) Doubling r doubles Q_∞;
       Altering r does not alter the time it takes to reach $(1/2)Q_\infty$
   (c) Both Q_∞ and the time to reach $(1/2)Q_0$ are halved by doubling α

27 $t = 133.601$ min

29 $y = A\sqrt{x}$

31 (a) $dB/dt = 0.05B + 1200$
   (b) $B = 24,000(e^{0.05t} - 1)$
   (c) $6816.61

33 $dB/bt > 0$ when $B = 5000$

35 $dQ/dt = 50 - 0.08Q$

37 $dQ/dt = 0.5(1/Q)$

Section 11.7

1 (b) 1

3

5 dA/dt

7 dQ/dt

9 (a) $P = 0, P = 2000$
  (b) dP/dt positive; P increasing

11 (a) $k = 0.035$; gives relative growth rate when P is small
       $L = 6000$; gives limiting value on the size of P
   (b) $P = 3000$

13 $P = 2800/(1 + Ae^{-0.05t})$

15 $P = 4000/(1 + Ae^{-0.68t})$

17 $k = 10, L = 2, A = 3, P = 2/(1 + 3e^{-10t}), t = \ln(3)/10$

19 $k = 0.3, L = 100, A = 1/3, P = 100/(1 + e^{-0.3t}/3), t = -\ln(3)/0.3$

21 $P = 8500/(1 + 16e^{-0.8t})$

23 (a) 1
   (b) 2 people; 48 people

(c)

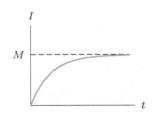

(d) About 15 hours; 30 hours
(e) When 200 people have heard the rumor

25 (a) 2500 fish
   (b) 2230 fish
   (c) 1500 fish

27 (a) 36 thousand; total number infected
   (b) $t \approx 16$, $n \approx 18$ thousand
   (c) Virus spreading fastest
   (d) Number infected half total

29 (a) 22.0 bn barrels/yr, 26.9 bn barrels/yr
   (b) 3.04% per year, 2.45% per year
   (c) $(1/P)(dP/dt) = 0.0418 - 0.0000157P$
   (d) 2662 billion barrels
   (e) $dP/dt = 0.0418P(1 - P/2662)$
       $P = 2662/(1 + 2.677e^{-0.0418t})$

31 (a)

(b)

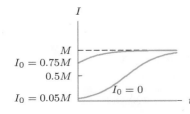

33 (a) 1426.603 bn barrels
   (b) 2066

35 (a) $dI/dt = k(M - I)$
       $(k > 0)$

(b) $dI/dt = kI(M - I)$
    $(k > 0)$

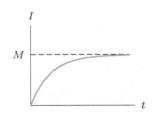

37 (a) logistically
   (b) $k \approx 0.045$
       $L \approx 5.8$

39 (a) $dp/dt = kp(B - p)$
       $(k > 0)$
   (b) Half of the tin

43 Occurs at $Q = 25$ not $t = 25$

45 Sales of a new product

47

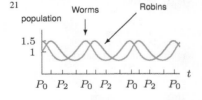

49 False

Section 11.8

1 x and y increase, about same rate

3 x decreases quickly while y increases more slowly

5 $(0, 0)$ and $(5, 3)$

7 $(0, 0)$ and $(-5, 3)$

9 (a) Both x and y are decreasing
   (b) x is increasing; y is decreasing

11 (a) Susceptibles: 1950, 1850, 1550, 1000, 750, 550, 350, 250, 200, 200, 200
       Infecteds: 20, 80, 240, 460, 500, 460, 320, 180, 100, 40, 20
   (b) Day 22, 500
   (c) 1800, 200

13 (a) a is negative; b is negative; c is positive
   (b) $a = -c$

17 $r = r_0 e^{-t}$, $w = w_0 e^t$

19 Worms decrease, robins increase. Long run: populations oscillate

21

23 Robins increase;
   Worms constant, then decrease;
   Both oscillate in long run

25 (a) Symbiosis
   (b) Both $\to \infty$ or both $\to 0$

27 (a) Predator-prey
   (b) x, y tend to ≈ 1

29 (a) $dy/dx = bx/ay$

31 (b) $dx/dt = -xy$, $dy/dt = -x$
   (c) $dy/dx = 1/y$
       soln: $y^2/2 = x + C$

(d) If $C > 0$, y wins
    If $C < 0$, x wins
    If $C = 0$, mutual annihilation
(e)

33 (a) $w = 0$, $r = 0$ and $w = b/k$, $r = a/c$
   (b) Worm equilibrium unchanged, robin equilibrium reduced

35 $dy/dx = (dy/dt)/(dx/dt)$

37 $dx/dt = 0.5x - 0.2xy$; $dy/dt = 0.1y - 0.3xy$

39 True

Section 11.9

1 $(4, 10)$

3

5 Tends towards point $(4, 10)$

7 (a) $dx/dt > 0$ and $dy/dt > 0$
   (b) $dx/dt < 0$ and $dy/dt = 0$
   (c) $dx/dt = 0$ and $dy/dt > 0$

9

11

13 Vertical nullclines:
$x = 0, x + y = 2$
Horizontal nullclines:
$y = 0, x + y = 1$
Equilibrium points:
$(0, 0), (0, 1), (2, 0)$

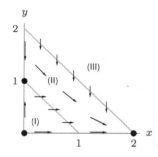

15 Horizontal nullclines;
$y = 0, y = 1 - 2x$
Vertical nullclines;
$x = 0, y = (1/2)(2 - x)$
Equilibrium points;
$(0, 0), (0, 1), (2, 0)$

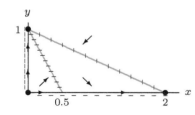

17 $dx/dt = 0$ when
$x = 0$ or $x + y/3 = 1$
$dy/dt = 0$ when
$y = 0$ or $y + x/2 = 1$
Equilibrium points:
$(0, 0), (0, 1), (1, 0), (4/5, 3/5)$

19 (a) $dS/dt = 0$ where $S = 0$ or $I = 0$
$dI/dt = 0$ where $I = 0$ or $S = 192$
(b) Where $S > 192$,
$dS/dt < 0$ and $dI/dt > 0$
Where $S < 192$,
$dS/dt < 0$ and $dI/dt < 0$
(c)

21 (a) In the absence of the other, each company
grows exponentially
The two companies restrain each other's
growth if they are both present
(b) $(0, 0)$ and $(1, 2)$
(c) In the long run, one of the companies will go
out of business

23 (a) $dP_1/dt = 0$ where $P = 0$ or
$P_1 + 3P_2 = 13$
$dP_2/dt = 0$ where $P = 0$ or
$P_2 + 0.4P_1 = 6$

25 $dx/dt \neq 0$

27

Chapter 11 Review

1 (I) satisfies equation (d)
(II) satisfies equation (c)

3 (a) (I)
(b) (IV)
(c) (III)

5 $y(x) = 40 + Ae^{0.2x}$

7 $H = Ae^{0.5t} - 20$

9 $P = 100Ae^{0.4t}/(1 + Ae^{0.4t})$

11 $P = (40000/3)(e^{0.03t} - 1)$

13 $y = \sqrt[3]{33 - 6\cos x}$

15 $\frac{1}{2}y - 4\ln|y| = 3\ln|x| - x$
$\quad + \frac{7}{2} - 4\ln 5$

17 $z(t) = 1/(1 - 0.9e^t)$

19 $20\ln|y| - y =$
$100\ln|x| - x + 20\ln 20 - 19$

21 $y = \ln(e^x + e - 1)$

23 $z = \sin(-e^{\cos\theta} + \pi/6 + e)$

25 $y = -\ln(\frac{\ln 2}{3}\sin^2 t\cos t$
$\quad + \frac{2\ln 2}{3}\cos t - \frac{2\ln 2}{3} + 1)/\ln 2$

27 (a) $y = 3$ and $y = -2$
(b) $y = 3$ unstable;
$y = -2$ stable

29 No

31 (a) $y(1) \approx 3.689$
(b) Overestimate

(c) $y = 5 - 4e^{-x}$
$y(1) = 5 - 4e^{-1} \approx$
3.528
(d) ≈ 3.61

33 (b) 2070

35 (a) $dM/dt = rM$
(b) $M = 2000e^{rt}$
(c)

742

37

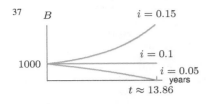

39 (a) $dB/dt = 0.05B - 12,000$
   (b) $B = (B_0 - 240,000)e^{0.05t} + 240,000$
   (c) $\$151,708.93$

41 $C(t) = 30e^{-100.33t}$

43 No, no

45 (a) $dx/dt = k(a - x)(b - x)$
   (b) $x = ab(e^{bkt} - e^{akt})/(be^{bkt} - ae^{akt})$

47 (a) $x \to \infty$ exponentially
       $y \to 0$ exponentially
   (b) Predator-prey

49 (a) $x \to \infty$ exponentially
       $y \to 0$ exponentially

   (b) y is helped by the presence of x

51 (a) $dy/dx = y(x + 3)/(x(y + 2))$
       $y^2 e^y = Ax^3 e^x$
   (d) $y^2 e^y = x^3 e^{x+4}$
   (e) $y = x = e^{-4} \approx 0.0183$
   (f) $y \approx e^{-13}$

53 (a) $x \to \infty$ if $y = 0$
       $y \to 0$ if $x = 0$
   (b) $(0, 0)$ and $(10, 000, 150)$
   (c) $dy/dx = y(-10 + 0.001x)/(x(3 - 0.02y))$
       $3 \ln y - 0.02y = -10 \ln x + 0.001x + 94.1$
   (f) $A \to B \to C \to D$
   (h) At points A and C:
       $dy/dx = 0$
       At points B and D:
       $dx/dy = 0$

55 P decreases to 0

57 P decreases towards $2L$

59 (c)

Appendix A

1 (a) $y \le 30$
   (b) two zeros

3 -1.05

5 2.5

7 $x = -1.1$

9 0.45

11 1.3

13 (a) $x = -1.15$
   (b) $x = 1, x = 1.41$,
       and $x = -1.41$

15 (a) $x \approx 0.7$
   (b) $x \approx 0.4$

17 (a) 4 zeros
   (b) $[0.65, 0.66], [0.72, 0.73]$,
       $[1.43, 1.44], [1.7, 1.71]$

19 (b) $x \approx 5.573$

21 Bounded $-5 \le f(x) \le 4$

23 Not bounded

Appendix B

1 $2e^{i\pi/2}$

3 $\sqrt{2}e^{i\pi/4}$

5 $0e^{i\theta}$, for any θ.

7 $\sqrt{10}e^{i(\arctan(-3)+\pi)}$

9 $-3 - 4i$

11 $-5 + 12i$

13 $1/4 - 9i/8$

15 $-1/2 + i\sqrt{3}/2$

17 $-125i$

19 $\sqrt{2}/2 + i\sqrt{2}/2$

21 $\sqrt{3}/2 + i/2$

23 -2^{50}

25 $2i\sqrt[3]{4}$

27 $(1/\sqrt{2})\cos(-\pi/12) + (i/\sqrt{2})\sin(-\pi/12)$

29 $-i, -1, i, 1$
   $i^{-36} = 1, i^{-41} = -i$

31 $A_1 = 1 + i$
   $A_2 = 1 - i$

37 True

39 False

41 True

Appendix C

1 (a) $f'(x) = 3x^2 + 6x + 3$
   (b) At most one
   (c) $[0, 1]$
   (d) $x \approx 0.913$

3 $\sqrt[4]{100} \approx 3.162$

5 $x \approx 0.511$

7 $x \approx 1.310$

9 $x \approx 1.763$

11 $x \approx 0.682328$

Appendix D

1 $3, 0$ radians

3 $2, 3\pi/4$ radians

5 $7\vec{j}$

7 $\|3\vec{i} + 4\vec{j}\| = \| -5\vec{i} \| = \|5\vec{j}\|, \|\vec{i} + \vec{j}\| = \|\sqrt{2}\vec{j}\|$

9 $5\vec{j}$ and $-6\vec{j}$; $\sqrt{2}\vec{j}$ and $-6\vec{j}$

11 (a) $(-3/5)\vec{i} + (4/5)\vec{j}$
   (b) $(3/5)\vec{i} + (-4/5)\vec{j}$

13 $8\vec{i} - 6\vec{j}$

15 $\vec{i} + 2\vec{j}$

17 Equal

19 Equal

21 $\vec{i} + \vec{j}, \sqrt{2}, \vec{i} - \vec{j}$

23 Pos: $(1/\sqrt{2})\vec{i} + (1/\sqrt{2})\vec{j}$
   Vel: $(-1/\sqrt{2})\vec{i} + (1/\sqrt{2})\vec{j}$
   Speed: 1

S-I-R model, 640
    SARS, 663
    threshold value, 642, 663
Δt, 276
Δ, Delta, notation, 5, 136
δ, delta, 59
ϵ, epsilon, 59
γ, Euler's constant, 511
$\int$, 326
$\int_a^b$, 282
μ, mean, 478
σ, standard deviation, 478
$\sum$, Sigma, notation, 281
$\rightarrow$, tends to, 49
d/dx notation, 99
e, the number, 15
    as limit, 161, 245, 533
    property of, 29
$f'(x)$ notation, 91
g, 334, 450
i, the number, 674
n factorial, 493
p-series, 509
r, θ, polar coordinates, 431

absolute growth rate, 609
absolute value function, 112
absolutely convergent, 518, 699
acceleration, 336
    average, 107
    instantaneous, 107
    vector, 689
acceleration due to gravity, 334
accuracy, 670
    to p decimal places, 671
addition of vectors, 687
air pressure, 173
alternating series, 517
    error bounds for, 518
    test, 517, 699
amplitude, 37
analytical solution
    of differential equation, 604
angular frequency, 572
antiderivative, 320, 697
    computing, 321, 327
    constructing with definite integral, 340
    Construction Theorem for, 340, 697
    differential equations and, 332
    family of, 320
    from graph, 321

Fundamental Theorem and, 321
    most general, 326
    of 0, 326
    of $1/x$, 328, 697
    of $\sin x$, $\cos x$, 697
    of $\sin x$, $\cos x$, 328
    of e^x, 328, 697
    of e^{-x^2}, 320, 340
    of x^n, 327, 697
    of constant function, 327
    of rational functions, 379
    of same function, 326
    of $\sin^m x \cos^n x$, 372
    properties of, 328
    reduction formulas, 369
        $x^n \cos ax$, 369
        $x^n \sin ax$, 369
        $x^n e^x$, 369
        $\cos^n x$, 369
    tables of, 371
    visualizing, 320
apple orchard yield, 350
approximation
    bisection, 668
    error in Taylor polynomial, 560, 700
    Euler's method, 600
    finite difference, 583
    Fourier polynomial, 566
    global vs. local, 568
    linear, 169, 538, 695
    Newton's method, 184, 669, 682
    of definite integral, 387
    Picard's method, 660
    quadratic, 539
    tangent line, 169, 538, 695
arc length, 425, 698
    circle, 36
    in polar coordinates, 437
    of hanging cable, 488
    of parametric curve, 427
arccosh, 266
arccosine function, 44, 693
Archimedean spiral, 433
Archimedes' Principle, 430
arcsine function, 41, 693
    derivative of, 158
    domain and range, 41, 693
    graph of, 41
arcsinh, 266
arctangent function, 41, 693
    derivative of, 157
    domain and range, 41, 693

    graph, 41
    Taylor series, 553
area
    between curves, 301
    definite integral and, 283, 291, 414
    finding by slicing, 414
    polar coordinates, 435
Aristotle (384-322 BC), 336
arithmetic mean, 214
Aswan Dam, 458
asymptote
    horizontal, 16, 49, 63, 693
    of rational functions, 49, 693
    vertical, 30, 49, 693
average cost, 231
average rate of change, 83, 695
average value of function, 304, 697
average velocity, 76, 308
    slope and, 79

bank deposits as series, 502
Barbra Streisand, 504
barometric pressure, 626
base
    of exponential function, 13
    of logarithm function, 29, 692
Bay of Fundy, 152
behaves like principle, 404
bell-shaped curve, 216, 308, 477
bending of light, 558
Bernoulli, Johann (1667-1748), 628
Bessel functions, 528
binomial series, 549, 700
bioavailability, 370
biodiesel fuel, 10, 20
bisection, method of, 669, 681
bladder, 324
Bohr radius, 480
Bohr, Niels (1885-1962), 480
Boltzmann constant, 489
bonds, 531
    trading at a discount, 504
    trading at a premium, 504
bound, 560
    above, 303
    below, 303
    best possible, 200, 672
    greatest lower, 672
    least upper, 672
    lower, 200, 672
    upper, 200, 672
bounded sequence, 494
Boyle's Law, 265

caffeine, 34, 626
calculators
        round-off error, 121, 133
Cantor Set, 532
carbon dioxide level, 363
carbon-14, 14, 618, 657
cardioid, 438, 439
carrying capacity, 52, 107, 629, 701
Cartesian coordinates, 431
catenary, 165, 168, 483
Cauchy, Augustin (1789-1857)
        formal definition of limit, 58
cdf, 470
center of mass, 442
        continuous mass density, 444
        moment, 442
        of point masses, 443
center of mass, 698
cephalexin, antibiotic, 531
chain rule, 143
        and units, 143
        applications, 156
        integration and, 354
chaos, 684
Chernobyl accident, 19
chlorofluorocarbons, 103, 111
circle
        parameterization of, 249
closed curves
        as trajectories in phase plane, 645
closed form of series, 499
closed interval, 2
CO_2
        in pond water, 292
coal production in US, 296
Cobb-Douglas
        function, 231
code-red computer virus, 636
common ratio, 500
comparison test
        for improper integrals, 404
        for series, 512, 699
competition, 647
Competitive Exclusion
        Principle of, 649
completing the square, 373, 383
complex number
        algebra of, 675
        complex plane, 676
        conjugates, 675
        definition, 675
        imaginary part, 675
        polar representation, 676
        powers of, 678
        real part, 675
        roots of, 678
complex plane, 676

polar coordinates, 676
compliance, 103
components of vector, 252, 685
composite functions, 21
        derivative of, 142
compound interest, 460, 621
        continuous, 610
        Rule of Seventy, 184
compressibility index, 103
concavity, 12
        downward, 12, 104, 695
        error in definite integrals and, 389
        Euler's method and, 600
        inflection point and, 190
        of parametric curve, 256
        power functions and, 128
        second derivative and, 104, 186
        upward, 12, 104, 695
concentration, 624
conditionally convergent, 518, 699
conjugates, 675
consols, 531
Constant Function Theorem, 177, 179,
        696
constant of proportionality, 6
Construction Theorem for Antideriva-
        tives, 340
consumer surplus
        definite integral for, 463
        definition, 463
continuity, 53
        at a point, 63
        definition, 63
        definition of, 694
        differentiability and, 113, 696
        extrema and, 196
        graphically, 53
        limits and, 55, 63
        numerically, 55
        of composite functions, 64
        of function, 54
        of sums, products, quotients of
                functions, 64, 695
        on an interval, 53, 63, 694, 695
continuous function, 53
continuous rate, 16
continuous variable, 2, 4
convergence
        of p-series, 509
        of alternating series, 517
        of geometric series, 501
        of improper integrals, 395, 399
        of partial sums, 505, 699
        of power series, 522
        of sequence, 494, 699
                bounded, monotone, 495
        of Taylor series, 548, 562

radius of, 525
coordinates
        Cartesian, 431
        polar, 431
        relation between Cartesian and po-
                lar, 432
Coroner's Rule of Thumb, 240
$\cosh x$, 165, 693
        Taylor polynomial, 558
cosine function, 37
        addition formula, 154
        derivative of, 149, 151
        graph of, 37, 693
        Taylor polynomial approximation,
                541
        Taylor series, 547
                convergence, 562
cost
        average, 231
        fixed, 11, 224, 331
        marginal, 100, 225, 331
                definition of, 226
        total, 224
        variable, 11
cost function, 224
coupon, 531
credit multiplier, 532
critical point, 187, 322, 696
        critical value, 187
        extrema and, 188, 696
cross-section, 425
cubic polynomial, 47, 693
cumulative distribution function, 469
        probability and, 473
        properties of, 470
curve
        length of, 427
        parameterization, 254

daylight hours
        as a function of latitude, 122
        Madrid, 120
decreasing, 5
decreasing function, 6
        derivative of, 92, 104, 186, 695
        integral of, 277
Decreasing Function Theorem, 179
definite integral, 281, 696
        odd and even functions, 302
        symmetry and, 302
        as antiderivative, 340
        as area, 283, 291, 414, 697
                in polar coordinates, 435
        as area above axis minus area be-
                low axis, 284
        as average, 304
        as total change, 291, 697
        by substitution, 358

changing limits of, 358
comparison of, 303
definition of, 282
for arc length, 426
   in polar coordinates, 437
   of parametric curve, 427
for average value, 304
for center of mass, 442
for consumer surplus, 463
for cumulative distribution function, 469
for electric potential, 458
for force, 454
for force of gravity, 458
for fraction of population, 469
for kinetic energy, 458
for mass, 440
for mean, 477
for present/future value, 462
for probability, 473
for producer surplus, 463
for surface area, 488
for volume, 415
for volume of revolution, 422
for work, 450
Fundamental Theorem of Calculus, 290, 294, 329, 697
interpretation, 283, 291
limits of integration, 298
notation for, 289
of density, 439
of density function, 469
of rate of change, 291
of sums and multiples, 300
properties of, 298, 697
units, 289
degree of a polynomial, 47
degree-days, 315, 412
Delta, Δ, notation, 5, 136
demand curve, 462
density, 439
   of earth, 448
   of water, 454
   probability, 468
   slicing and, 440
density function, 468, 698
   probability and, 473
   properties of, 469
dependent variable, 2, 4
depreciation, 9
derivative, 695
   e^x, 695
   n^{th}, 181
   of inverse function, 158
approximation of, 583
as a function, 90
   definition of, 91
   finding algebraically, 94

finding graphically, 91
finding numerically, 92
formulas for, 93
at a point, 83
chain rule, 143, 695
critical points, 187, 696
definition of, 83, 695
differentiability and, 112
estimating graphically, 91
estimating numerically, 85
graphical interpretation, 92
inflection point, 696
interpretation, 83, 99
Leibniz notation for, 99
local maxima/minima, 188
   test for, 188
of a^x, 134
of e^x, 133
of composite functions, 142, 695
of constant functions, 94
of constant multiples of a function, 124, 695
of cosine, 150, 695
of exponential functions, 132, 133, 157, 695
of hyperbolic functions, 167
of implicit functions, 162
of inverse trigonometric functions, 157, 695
of linear functions, 94
of ln x, 156, 695
of polynomials, 127
of positive integer powers, 125
of power functions, 126, 156, 695
of products of functions, 136, 695
of quotients of functions, 138, 695
of sine, 151, 152, 695
of sums and differences of functions, 124, 695
of tangent function, 151, 155
power rule, 95
product rule, 137, 695
quotient rule, 138, 695
second derivative, 104, 695
   concavity and, 104
   test, 189
slope of curve, 84
   in polar coordinates, 437
slope of tangent line, 84
units of, 99, 695
visualizing, 84, 591
visualizing, 695
derivative function, 91
Descartes, René (1596-1650), 336
difference quotient, 5, 83
differentiability
   continuity and, 113, 696

determining from graph, 111
   local linearity and, 170, 172, 696
differentiable, 83, 91, 111
   everywhere, 91
differential equations, 586, 700
   S-I-R model, 640
      SARS, 663
   account balance, 610
   analytical solution, 604
   antiderivatives and, 332
   arbitrary constants, 588
   compartmental analysis, 624
   concentration, 624
   decay, 609
   equilibrium solution, 616, 700
   Euler's method, 599
   existence of solutions, 593
   exponential decay, 604
   exponential growth, 604
      SARS, 662
   exponential growth and decay, 701
   first-order, 588
   general solution, 587, 700
      exponential equation, 604, 610
   growth, 609
   implicit functions and, 593
   initial conditions, 333, 587, 700
   initial value problem, 333, 587, 700
   logistic, 629, 631, 701
   Lotka-Volterra, 643
   net worth of a company, 621
   Newton's Law of Cooling (Heating), 613
   nullclines, 649, 650
   numerical solutions of first-order, 599
   oil prices, 629
   order of, 700
   particular solution, 333, 587, 700
   phase plane, 641
   Picard's method, 660
   pollution, 611
   population growth, 633
   predator-prey model, 643
   second-order, 588
   separation of variables, 604, 623
   slope field, 591, 700
   solution(s) to, 587, 700
   systems of, 639, 701
   thickness of ice, 620
   uniqueness of solutions, 593
differentiation
   implicit, 162
   of series, 553
dipole, 556
direction field, 351

direction of vector, 686
directly proportional, 6
discrete variable, 2, 4
disease, 639
disease incidence, 573
displacement, 442
displacement vector, 687
distance
    estimating from velocity, 272
    visualizing on velocity graph, 273
distribution function, 466
    cumulative, 469
    probability and, 473
distribution of resources, 350
divergence
    of geometric series, 501
    of harmonic series, 507
    of improper integrals, 396, 399
    of partial sums, 505, 699
    of sequence, 494, 699
diverging to infinity, 62, 396
domain, 2
    restricting, 3
dominance
    l'Hopital's rule and, 244
dominates, 46
double angle formulas, 362, 369, 679,
    693
double factorial, 512
doubling time, 14, 610, 692
drug dosage as series, 498, 503
Dubois formula, 51, 238

Ebbinghaus model, 627
economy of scale, 224
Einstein, Albert (1879-1955), 558
    Theory of Relativity, 148
electric charge, 149
electric circuits, 140
    resonance, 559
electric dipole, 556
electric potential, 580
    definite integral for, 458
electron wave function, 412
elementary functions, 354
end behavior of a function, 49
endocrinologist, 297
energy
    electrical, 363
    wind, 312
energy spectrum, 570
    musical instruments, 571, 576
energy theorem, 570
epidemic, 639, 642, 663
equation
    graphing in polar coordinates, 433
equations of motion, 334
equilibrium

stable, 70
equilibrium point, 650
    predator-prey model, 644
equilibrium price/quantity, 462
equilibrium solution
    of differential equation, 587
    of differential equation, 615, 621,
        700
    stable, 615, 616
    unstable, 615, 616
$erf(x)$, 121, 344, 370
error, 670
    alternating series bounds, 518
    concavity and, 389
    Euler's method, 601
    in approximating definite integral,
        698
    in approximating derivative, 583
    in linear approximation, 169
    in numerical integration, 389
    left and right rules, 390
    Riemann sum approximation, 277
    round-off, 89, 121, 133
    tangent line approximation, 170,
        171
        estimation of, 170
    Taylor polynomial, 560
    trapezoid vs. midpoint rule, 390
error bound, 560
    Lagrange, 560
error function, $erf(x)$, 121, 344, 370
escape velocity, 628
Ethanol fuel, 34
Euler's Constant, 511
Euler's formula, 678
Euler's method, 599, 700
    accuracy of, 601
    error, 601
Euler, Leonhard (1707-1783), 599, 678
Eulerian logarithmic integral, 370
even function, 22, 694
    definite integral of, 302
expansions, Taylor, 547
explicit function, 162
exponential decay, 13, 16, 692
    differential equation for, 609
    half-life, 14, 610, 692
    radioactive decay, 14
exponential function, 12, 13, 692
    y-intercept, 15
    population growth, 12
    as solution to differential equation,
        604
    base e, 15
    base of, 13
    compared to power functions, 46
    concavity, 12

derivative of, 132, 157
    domain, 14
    formula for, 13, 16, 692
    Padé approximant to, 558
    table of values, 12
    Taylor polynomial approximation,
        542
    Taylor series, 547
        convergence, 564
exponential growth, 12, 13, 16, 692
    annual, 611, 692
    continuous, 611, 692
    differential equation for, 609
    doubling time, 14, 610, 692
    growth factor, 12, 15
    rate
        absolute, 609
        annual, 611, 692
        continuous, 16, 611, 692
        continuous vs. annual, 611
        relative, 609
    SARS, 662
exponential growth and decay
    differential equation, 701
extrapolation, 4, 633
extrema, 196
    continuity and, 196
    critical point and, 188, 696
    local, 187
Extreme Value Theorem, 196, 695

factorial, 540
    double, 512
factoring, 666
family of functions, 5, 216
    antiderivatives, 320
    exponential, 15
        with limit, 218
    Gompertz growth, 223
    linear, 5
    logistic, 219
    motion due to gravity, 217
    normal density, 216
    power, 45
    sinusoidal, 38
    surge, 221
Fermat's Principle, 214
Fibonacci sequence, 497
finite difference approximation, 583
firebreaks, 268
first derivative
    inflection point and, 191
    test, 188, 696
First Fundamental Theorem of Calculus,
    290
fixed cost, 11, 224, 331
foot-pound, 454
force, 336, 453, 698

between atoms, 70
between molecules, 664
definite integral for, 454
from pressure, 454
of gravity
  definite integral for, 458
spring, 450
units, 449
force of gravity, 450
Four, Rule of, 2
Fourier coefficients
formulas for
  period 2π, 566
  period b, 572
justification of, 573, 577
Fourier polynomial, 566
square wave, 567
Fourier series, 565, 700
period 2π, 568
period b, 572
square wave, 568
Fourier, Joseph (1768–1830), 565
fraction of population
from cumulative distribution function, 470
from density function, 469
frequency
angular, 572
fuel consumption, 215
function, 2
absolute value, 112
average value of, 304, 697
bounded, 671
Cobb-Douglas, 231
composite, 21
concave (up or down), 12, 695
continuous, 53
cost, 224
cumulative distribution, 469
decreasing, 5, 6, 695
density, 468
distribution, 466
drug buildup, 16
elementary, 354
energy theorem, 570
even, 22
exponential, 12, 13, 692
family of, 217
Fourier series for, 568
gamma, 402
global approximation, 568
global behavior of, 46
graph of, 2
hyperbolic, 693
increasing, 4, 6, 695
input, 2
inverse, 23
inverse trigonometric, 40

invertible, 23
linear, 4, 5, 692
local approximation, 568
local behavior of, 46
logarithm, 29
logistic, 631
monotonic, 6
odd, 22
output, 2
periodic, 37, 565
piecewise linear, 112
polynomial, 46, 693
power, 45
probability density, 468, 473
profit, 225
pulse train, 569
rational, 49, 693
reflection about x-axis, 21
representation, 2
revenue, 224
shift and stretch, 21
sinusoidal, 38, 692
surge, 221
table, 2
Taylor series for, 547
trigonometric, 36
  cosine, 37
  sine, 37
  tangent, 40
unbounded, 671
zeros of, 47, 666
fundamental harmonic, 569
Fundamental Theorem of Calculus, 290, 294, 321, 329, 340, 697
future value, 698
annual compounding, 460
continuous compounding, 460
definite integral for, 462
definition, 459
of income stream, 461

G. H. Hardy, 1847 − 1947, 511
Galilei, Galileo (1564-1642), 11, 339, 619
Dialogues Concerning Two New Sciences, 336
gamma function, 402
Gause yeast population model, 638, 654
general solution of differential equation, 332
general term, 547
general term of a series, 505
geometric mean, 214
geometric series, 498, 500, 699
as binomial series, 550
common ratio, 500
convergence of, 501
divergence of, 501

finite, sum of, 500, 699
infinite, 500
infinite, sum of, 501, 699
partial sum of, 500
geometry
definite integral and, 422
Gini's index of inequality, 350
global behavior of a function, 46, 48
global maxima/minima, 196, 696
Golden Gate Bridge, 488
golden ratio, 497
Gompertz equation, 598
Gompertz growth, 223
Grand Canyon flooding, 314
Grand Coulee Dam, 421
graph
in polar coordinates, 433
gravitational constant, 339
gravitational field, 580
gravity
acceleration due to, 131, 174, 183, 334, 336, 338, 628
force of, 183, 237, 339, 458, 581
Great Lakes, 611, 617
Great Pyramid of Egypt, 418, 453
greatest lower bound, 672
Greenland Ice Sheet, 102
Gregory, James (1638–1675), 553
Grinnell Glacier, 618
growth
continuous, 16
growth factor, 12, 15
growth of children, 297
growth rate
absolute, 609
annual, 611
continuous, 611
relative, 609
guess-and-check, 354

half-life, 14, 610, 692
hanging cable, 590
arc length, 488
harmonic series, 507
harmonics, 569
height velocity graph, 297
histogram, 466, 468
Hooke's Law, 450
Hoover Dam, 455
l'Hopital, Marquis de (1661–1704), 266, 628
l'Hopital's rule, 243, 696
horizontal asymptote, 16, 49
horizontal line, 5
horizontal line test, 24
Hubbert, M. King (1903–1989), 629
hybrid cars, 280, 314
hydroelectric power, 10, 20

hydrogen, reduced mass of, 559
hyperbola, 166
hyperbolic
        cosine, 165, 693
        identities, 166
        sine, 165, 693
        tangent, 167
hyperbolic functions
        derivative of, 167
hyperbolic tangent
        inverse, 580
hyperinflation, 35

identities, 693
imaginary numbers, 674, 675
imaginary part of complex number, 675
implicit differentiation, 162, 695
implicit function
        as solution to differential equation,
            593
        derivative of, 162
improper integral, 395, 698
        comparing, 403, 404
            with $1/x^p$, 404
            with e^{-ax}, 404
        comparison test, 404, 698
        convergence/divergence, 395, 399
        energy and, 397
        infinite integrand, 398
income stream, 461
increasing function, 4, 6, 176
        derivative of, 92, 104, 186, 695
        integral of, 277
Increasing Function Theorem, 176, 696
indefinite integral, 326, 697
        computing, 327
        properties of, 328, 697
        visualizing, 320
independent variable, 2, 4
index in power series, 547
index in Taylor series, 547
inertia, principle of, 336
infinite series
        geometric, 500
        sum of, 498
inflection point, 190, 322, 696
        first derivative and, 191
initial condition, 333
initial value problem, 333, 587, 700
input into a function, 2
instantaneous
        velocity, 79
        growth rate, 611
        rate of change, 83, 695
        speed, 252
        velocity, 78
integral
        definite vs. indefinite, 326

definite see definite integral, 281
equation, 660
improper see improper integral,
    395
indefinite see indefinite integral,
    326
integral test for series, 509
integrand, 282
    infinite, 398
    sums and multiples, 300
integration
    applications, 698
    limits of, 282, 298
    numerical methods, 387
        error, 389
        LEFT(n), 387
        left-hand sum, 282
        MID(n), 387
        midpoint rule, 387
        Riemann sums, 282, 387
        RIGHT(n), 387
        right-hand sum, 282
        SIMP(n), 391
        TRAP(n), 388
    of series, 553
    reduction formulas, 369, 371
    techniques
        by parts, 364, 365, 697
        completing the square, 373, 383
        factoring, 373
        guess-and-check, 354
        long division, 373
        partial fractions, 376, 697
        reduction formulas, 371
        sine substitution, 380
        substitution, 354, 355, 358, 697
        tangent substitution, 382
        trigonometric substitutions, 380
        using table, 371
intercept
    factored form and, 47
    vertical, 4, 5, 692
interest, 621
    compound, 460
    continuously compounded, 610
    Rule of Seventy, 184
Intermediate Value Theorem, 53, 54,
    695
interval notation, 2
interval of convergence, 523, 700
inverse
    hyperbolic tangent function, 580
inverse function, 23
    definition, 24
    derivative of, 158
    domain and range, 23
    for exponential function, 32

formulas for, 24
    graphs of, 25
inverse square law, 339
inverse trigonometric functions, 40
    arccosine, 44, 693
    arcsine, 41, 693
    arctangent, 41, 693
    derivative of, 157
inversely proportional, 6
invertible function, 23
isotopes, 35
iteration, 670, 681
Iwo Jima, Battle of, 648

joule, 449

Keeling Curve, 148
kinetic energy, 485
    definite integral for, 458

l'Hopital's rule, 243, 696
    $0 \cdot \infty$, 245
    and e, 245
    limits involving ∞, 244
l'Hopital, Marquis de (1661–1704),
    266, 628
Lagrange error bound, 560, 700
Lagrange, Joseph-Louis (1736–1813),
    560
Lake Mead, 421
Lambert function, 580
Lanchester, F.W. (1868–1946)
    differential equations, 648
    square law, 648
lapse rate, 102
leading coefficient, 46
leaf decomposition, 626
least upper bound, 672
left rule, LEFT(n), 387
    error in approximation, 390
LEFT(n), 387
left-hand limit, 61
left-hand sum, 696
Leibniz, Wilhelm Gottfried (1646-
    1716), 99, 607
lemniscate, 439
Lennard-Jones model, 223
Leonardo di Pisa, 497
light
    reflection, 214
light, bending of, 558
limaçon, 434
limit, 57, 694
    ϵ, δ definition, 694
    ϵ, δ definition, 59
    at infinity, 63, 66, 694
    continuity and, 55, 63
    definite integral and, 281

definition, 58, 694
instantaneous acceleration and, 107
instantaneous velocity and, 78
left-hand, 61
   definition, 66
local linearity and, 242
meaning of, 58
notation, 58
of $(1 + h)^{1/h}$, 133, 161, 533
of x^n/n, 563
of $(\sin h)/h$, 150
of a constant function, 60
of a constant multiple, 60
of a product, 60
of a quotient, 60
of a sum, 60
of improper integrals, 395
of sequence, 494
of sum, 125
one-sided, 61, 694
properties of, 60, 67, 694
right-hand, 61
   definition, 66
round-off error and, 133
two-sided, 61
limit comparison test, 514, 699
limits of integration, 282, 298
   substitution and, 358
line
   best fitting, 268
   equation of, 5, 692
   parametric equation, 251
   tangent, 84
linear approximation, 169, 538, 695
linear function, 4, 5, 692
   derivative of, 94
   intercept of, 5, 692
   slope of, 5, 692
   table of, 5
linearization, 169
Lissajous figure, 255, 259
Liu Hui, 488
loading curve, 213
local behavior of a function, 46, 48
local extrema, 187
local linearity, 170, 242, 696
   differentiability and, 170
local linearization, 169, 695
local maxima/minima, 187, 696
   tests for, 187
logarithm function, 29
   derivative of, 156
   domain, 30, 692
   graph, 30
   intercept, 30
   Taylor polynomial approximation, 543

Taylor series, 548
   vertical asymptote, 30
logarithms, 29
   base e (natural), 29
   base ten (common), 29, 692
   definition of, 29
   properties, 30
   rules of manipulation, 30, 692
   solving equations, 31
logistic equation, 629
logistic function, 631
logistic model, 106, 219, 266, 411, 629, 701
   analytic solution to, 631
   carrying capacity, 107, 629
   equation, 634
   peak oil, 629
   qualitative solution to, 630
   SARS, 662
   spread of information, 637
long division, 373, 379
Lotka-Volterra equations, 643
lottery winnings, 464
lower bound, 200, 672
lung, 103

Machin's formula for π, 583
magnitude of vector, 686
marginal, 224, 225
   costs/revenues, 100, 225, 331
Marquis de l'Hopital (1661–1704), 266, 628
mass
   center of, 442
   from density, 440
   of earth, 448
   relativistic, 559
   vs weight, 454
Mass Action, Law of, 386
mass vs weight, 450
Massachusetts Turnpike, 440
Mauna Loa Observatory, 44, 148
maxima/minima
   concavity and, 189
   global, 196, 696
      continuity and, 196
      on (a, b), 197
      on $[a, b]$, 197
   local, 187, 229, 696
      first derivative test, 188, 696
      second derivative test, 189, 696
Maxwell distribution, 489
mean, 476
   arithmetic vs. geometric, 214
   definite integral for, 477
   of normal distribution, 478
Mean Value Inequality, 179
Mean Value Theorem, 175, 204, 696

measles, 573
median, 475
meteorology, 102
Michelson-Morley experiment, 559
MID(n), 387
midpoint rule, MID(n), 387
   error in approximation, 389, 391
modeling, 205
   and differential equations, 586, 620
   compartmental analysis, 624
   competitive exclusion, 649
   epidemic, 639
   growth and decay, 609
   logistic
      peak oil, 629
   optimization, 206
   predator-prey, 643
   US population, 633
moment, 442
monotone sequence, 495
monotonic function, 6, 104, 111, 186
Montgolfier brothers, 314
morphine, 627
motion
   xy-plane, 253
   parametric equations, 249
   position vectors and, 687
Mt. Shasta, 484
murder, 613, 619

natural logarithm, 29
   derivative of, 156
   graph of, 30
Nelson, Admiral Horatio, 659
newton, 449, 454
Newton's law of gravity, 339
Newton's method, 669, 682
   chaos, 684
   failure, 684
   initial estimate, 184, 683
Newton, Isaac (1642-1727)
   Law of Cooling (Heating), 148, 613
   Law of Gravity, 45
   laws of motion, 336
      First Law, 336
      Second Law, 336, 623
Nicotine, 618
nondecreasing function, 176
nondifferentiability, examples, 112
normal distribution, 216, 308, 477, 478
   standard, 478
normal line, 135
nullclines, 649, 650
numerical methods
   accuracy, 670
   bisection, 669, 681

decimal answer, 671
differential equations, 599
error, 670
    left and right rules, 390
    trapezoid and midpoint rules, 390
Euler's method, 599
finding derivative, 92
integration, 387, 698
    error, 389
    left rule, 387
    midpoint rule, 387
    right rule, 387
    Simpson's rule, 391
    trapezoid rule, 388
iterative, 184, 670, 682
Newton's method, 184, 682
Picard's method, 660

odd function, 22, 694
    definite integral of, 302
oil prices, 629
oil production
    worldwide, 637
Olympic pole vault, 4
one-sided limit, 61
open interval, 2
optimization, 196, 205
    constrained, 232
    maximizing/minimizing averages, 209
optimal values, 196
output of a function, 2
ozone, 111
ozone depleting gas index, 103

Padé approximants, 558
parabola, 47
parallel lines, 7
parameter, 6, 216
    change of, 250
parameterization
    length of a curve and, 427
    of circle, 249
    of curve, 254
        changing, 250
    of graph of function, 254
    of line, 251
    speed and, 252
    tangent lines and, 253
    velocity, 252
        components, 252
parametric curve
    concavity of, 256
    slope of, 255
parametric equations, 249
parasite drag, 215
Pareto's Law, 664

partial fractions, 376, 697
    method of, 697
partial sum, 505, 699
    of geometric series, 500
particular solution, 333
parts
    integration by, 364, 697
pascal, 454
pdf, 469
peak oil, 629
    US, 633
pendulum, 131, 237
    differential equation for, 546
period, 37, 693
    angular frequency and, 572
periodic function, 37, 565
perpendicular lines, 7
pH, 160
phase difference, 38
phase plane, 641, 644
    equilibrium point, 650
    nullclines, 650
    trajectories, 641, 645, 652
phase shift (angle), 38
phyllotaxis, 497
Picard's method, 660
piecewise linear function, 113
Pisa, Tower of, 336
Planck, Max (1858-1947)
    radiation law, 263, 407
plutonium, 35
Poiseuille's Law, 51, 485
polar coordinates, 431
    Archimedean spiral, 433
    area, 435
    cardioid, 438
    circle, 433
    graphing equations, 433
    lemniscate, 439
    limaçon, 434
    negative r, 434
    roses, 434
    slope, 437
polynomial, 46, 693
    cubic, 47, 693
    degree of, 47
    derivative of, 127
    double zero, 48
    factoring, 666
    Fourier, 566
    intercepts, 47
    leading coefficient, 50
    quadratic, 47, 693
    quartic, 47, 693
    quintic, 47, 693
    zeros, 48
population

of Burkina Faso, 12, 31
of China, 34
of Hungary, 183
of India, 34, 618
of Mexico, 135, 307
of US, 33, 122, 135, 148, 633
of world, 18, 34, 134, 148, 183, 237, 294, 363, 497, 626
population growth, 633
    equilibrium population, 644
    exponential, 12
    logistic, 633
    predator-prey model, 643
position vector, 684
    motion and, 687
potential energy, 559
power function, 45, 693
    compared to exponential functions, 46
    concavity of, 128
    derivative of, 125, 156
    formula for, 45
    long-term behavior, 694
power rule, 95, 126
power series, 521, 700
    convergence of, 522
    interval of convergence, 523, 700
    radius of convergence, 523
    ratio test, 524, 700
    Taylor, 547
predator-prey model, 643
    equilibrium values, 644
prednisone, immunosuppressant, 534
present value, 504, 698
    annual compounding, 460
    continuous compounding, 460
    definite integral for, 461
    definition, 459
    of income stream, 461
pressure, 453, 698
    air, 173
    barometric, 626
    definite integral of, 454
    units, 454
principal, 531
Principle of Competitive Exclusion, 649
probability, 473
    cumulative distribution function, 473
    definite integral for, 473
    density function and, 473
    histogram, 466
probability density function, 468
producer surplus, 463
    definite integral for, 463
product rule, 137
    three dimensional, 141

production
and price of raw materials, 231
production function
Cobb-Douglas, 231
profit, 225
maximizing, 227, 228
projectile
motion of, 174
proportional
directly, 6
inversely, 6
pulmonologist, 103
pulse train, 569, 577
Pyramid of Egypt, 418, 453

Quabbin Reservoir, 325
quadratic approximation, 539
quadratic formula, 667
quadratic polynomial, 47, 693
quarantine, 663
quartic polynomial, 47, 693
quintic polynomial, 47, 693
quotient rule, 138

Racetrack Principle, 177, 179, 696
radians, 36
conversion to degrees, 36
vs degrees for calculus, 85
radius of convergence, 523
and ratio test, 525
range, 2
rate of change, 233
absolute, 184
average, 83, 695
instantaneous, 83, 695
related, 234
relative, 184
ratio test
finding radius of convergence, 525
power series, 524, 700
series of constants, 515, 699
rational functions, 49, 693
asymptotes, 49, 693
end behavior, 49
intercepts, 49
real part of complex number, 675
recurrence relations, 494
reduction formulas
$p(x)\cos x$, 371
$p(x)\sin x$, 371
$p(x)e^x$, 371
$x^n \ln x$, 371
$\cos^n x$, 371
$\sin^n x$, 371
reflection coefficient, 154
reflection of light, 214
reflection, Law of, 214
related rate, 233, 234

relative growth rate, 609
relative rate of change, 184
relativistic mass, 559
Relativity, Theory of, 148, 559
rent controls, 466
resistance, wind, 363
resonance, 559
revenue
marginal, 225
definition of, 226
total, 224
revenue function, 224
Richardson arms race model, 654, 660
Riemann sum, 282, 285
area, 414
in polar coordinates, 435
density, 439
for arc length, 425
for center of mass, 442
for consumer surplus, 463
for force, 454
for mass, 440
for mean, 476
for present/future value, 461
for producer surplus, 463
for volume of revolution, 422
for work, 450
slicing and, 415
right rule, **RIGHT**(n), 387
error in approximation, 390
RIGHT(n), 387, 394
right-hand limit, 61
right-hand sum, 696
rise, 5, 692
Rolle's Theorem, 176, 204
root mean square, 376
root test, 520
roots, 666
by bisection method, 668
by factoring, 666
by Newton's method, 184, 682
by numerical methods, 668
by zooming, 667
roses, 434
round-off error, 133
Rule of Four, 2
Rule of Seventy, 184
run, 5, 692

Saint Louis arch, 168
sample a signal, 496
SARS, 661
satellite power, 317
saturation level, 16, 218
scalar, 685
scalar multiplication, 688
second derivative, 104
concavity and, 104, 186

inflection point and, 190
interpretation, 106
maxima/minima, 189
test, 189, 696
Second Fundamental Theorem of Calculus, 340
sensitivity of a drug, 202
separation of variables, 604, 623, 700
exponential growth equation, 604
justification, 606
sequence, 492, 494
bounded, 494
bounded, monotone
convergence of, 495
Calkin-Wilf-Newman, 497
convergence of, 494, 699
defined recursively, 493
divergence of, 494, 699
Fibonacci, 497
general term, 492
limit of, 494
monotone, 495
of partial sums, 505
smoothing, 496
series, 498
p-series, 509
general term, 547
alternating, 517
harmonic, 517
alternating series test, 517
binomial, 549, 700
closed form, 499
comparison test, 512, 699
convergence, 505
absolute vs conditional, 518, 699
convergence properties, 507, 699
divergence, 505
Fourier, 565, 568, 700
period b, 572
general term, 505
geometric, 498, 500, 699
as binomial series, 550
harmonic, 507
alternating, 517
infinite, 498
integral test, 509, 699
limit comparison test, 514, 699
of constants, 699
partial sum of, 505, 699
power, 521, 700
ratio test, 515, 699
root test, 520
sum of, 498
Taylor, 547, 700
terms in, 498
Si(x), 342

Sigma, $\sum$, notation, 281
sigmoid curve, 630
signal, 496
SIMP(n), 391
Simpson's rule
    approximating by quadratic, 394
Simpson's rule, SIMP(n), 391
sine function, 37
    addition formula, 154
    derivative of, 149, 151
    graph of, 37, 693
    Taylor polynomial approximation, 541
    Taylor series, 547
        convergence, 564
sine-integral, Si(x), 342, 343, 351
sinh x, 165, 693
    Taylor polynomial, 558
sinusoidal functions, 38, 692
slicing, 415, 440
slope, 5
    of curve, 78, 84
    of line, 5, 692
    of parametric curve, 255
    parallel lines, 7
    perpendicular lines, 7
    polar coordinates, 437
    units of, 5
    velocity and, 79
slope field, 351, 591, 700
smooth a sequence, 496
Snow tree cricket, 2
solar panels, 10
solar photovoltaic installations, 618
solar power, 43
solid of revolution, 422
    surface area, 489
solution curve, 592
Soviet-German pipeline, 465
speed, 76, 427, 689
    instantaneous, 252
    parameterized curve, 253
    vs. velocity, 76
speed of sound, 173
spiral, Archimedean, 433
spring, 154
square wave, 566
    Fourier polynomial, 567
    Fourier series, 568
Srinivasa Ramanujan, 1887 – 1920, 511
stable equilibrium, 70, 615
standard deviation of normal distribution, 478
Statue of Liberty, 213
Streisand, Barbra, 504
strontium-90, 19, 71
substitution, 697
    into definite integrals, 358

into indefinite integrals, 355
into Taylor series, 552
sum
    left-hand, 276
    of infinite series, 498
    overestimate vs. underestimate, 276
    Riemann, 282, 285
    right-hand, 276
    visualizing left- and right-hand, 276, 277
sum formulas for sin/cos, 693
summation notation, 281
supply curve, 462
surface area, 488
surge function, 199, 221
surplus, consumer and producer, 462
survival time, 479
symbiosis, 643, 647
symmetry, 22
    definite integral and, 302
Syracuse snowfall, 2
systems of differential equations, 639, 701

table, 2
    exponential function, and, 12
    linear function, and, 5
table of integrals, 371
tangent field, 351
tangent function, 40
    asymptotes, 40
    derivative of, 151, 155
    domain, 40
    graph, 40
    period, 40
tangent line, 84, 695
    approximation, 169, 538, 695
        error, 169–171, 175, 696
    for parametric curves, 253
    slope of, 84
tanh x, 167
tax cut, 504
Taylor expansions, 547
Taylor polynomial
    for ln x near $x = 1$, 543
    about $x = 0$, 541
    about $x = a$, 543
    accuracy, 544
    degree n, 541, 700
    degree one, 538
    degree two, 539
    error, 560
        bound, 560, 700
    for $1/(1 - x)$, 542
    for cos x, 541
    for cosh x, 558
    for sinh x, 558

for sin x, 541
for e^x, 542
inequalities, 412
linear approximation and, 171
Taylor series, 546, 700
    $(1 + x)^p$, 549
    cos x, 547, 700
    sin x, 547, 700
    e^x, 547, 700
    e^{-x^2}, 552
    general term, 547
    about $x = 0$, 547
    about $x = a$, 547
    arctan x, 553
    comparing, 555
    condition for, 547
    convergence of, 548, 561
        e^x, 564
        cos x, 561, 562
        $\ln(1 + x)$, 548
        sin x, 564
    differentiation of, 553
    general, 547
    integration of, 553
    $\ln(1 + x)$, 548
    manipulations of, 552
    multiplying, 554
    substitution, 552, 554
terminal velocity, 102, 218, 623
terms in series, 498
theorem
    Antiderivative Construction, 340
    Constant Function, 177
    Extreme Value, 196
    Fundamental, of Calculus, 290, 340
    Increasing Function, 176
    Lagrange Error Bound, 560
    Mean Value, 175
Theory of Relativity, 148, 559
Three Gorges Dam, 458
threshold value, 642, 663
tin pest, 638
Titanic, 454, 458
Torricelli's Law, 484
total cost, 224
total quantity
    from density, 440
total revenue, 224
total utility, 110
Trafalgar, Battle of, 659
trajectories
    phase plane, 641, 645, 652
transmission coefficient, 154
TRAP(n), 388, 394
trapezoid rule, TRAP(n), 388
    error in approximation, 389, 391

trapezoid, area of, 388
triangular wave, 566
trigonometric functions, 36
    amplitude, 37, 693
    cosine, 37
    derivatives of, 149, 154
    inverse, 40
    period, 37, 693
    phase difference, 38
    sine, 37
    tangent, 40
trigonometric identity, 37, 693
    addition formula, 681
    double angle, 362, 369, 679
trigonometric substitutions, 380
    method of, 380
two-sided limit, 61

unbounded function, 671
unit circle, 36, 37, 692
units
    force, 449, 454
    pressure, 454
    work, 449
unstable equilibrium, 615
upper bound, 200, 672
urologist, 324

Van der Waal's equation, 165, 559
variable
    continuous, 2
    dependent, 2, 4

discrete, 2
    discrete vs. continuous, 4
    independent, 2, 4
variable cost, 11
vector, 684
    acceleration, 689
    addition, 687
    components, 685
    direction, 686
    displacement, 687
    magnitude, 686
    position, 684
    scalar multiplication, 688
    unit, 685
    velocity, 689
velocity
    xy-plane, 253
    as derivative, 83
    average, 76, 308
    escape, 628
    instantaneous, 78, 107
    of a falling body, 622
    parameterized curve, 253
    slope and, 79
    speed, 427
    terminal, 102, 623
    vector, 689
    visualizing from distance graph, 78
    vs. speed, 76
velocity vector, 252

Verhulst, P. F. (1804–1849), 629
Vermeer (1632–1675), 35
vertical asymptote, 30, 49
voltage, 43, 376
volume
    definite integral for, 415
    finding by slicing, 415
    from cross-sections, 425
    of revolution, 422
        surface area, 488

warfarin, anticoagulant, 618
water clock, 484
water, density of, 454
weight, 450
weight vs mass, 454
wind power, 20
wind resistance, 363
winning probability, 534
work, 449, 698
    definite integral for, 450
    definition, 449
    units, 449

Zeno, 76
zeros, 666
zeros of a function, 47
    continuity and, 53
    double, 48
    multiplicity m, 149
zooming, 667

Lines

Slope of line through (x_1, y_1) and (x_2, y_2):

$$m = \frac{y_2 - y_1}{x_2 - x_1}$$

Point-slope equation of line through (x_1, y_1) with slope m:

$$y - y_1 = m(x - x_1)$$

Slope-intercept equation of line with slope m and y-intercept b:

$$y = b + mx$$

Rules of Exponents

$$a^x a^t = a^{x+t}$$
$$\frac{a^x}{a^t} = a^{x-t}$$
$$(a^x)^t = a^{xt}$$

Definition of Natural Log

$y = \ln x \quad$ means $\quad e^y = x$

ex: $\ln 1 = 0$ since $e^0 = 1$

Identities

$$\ln e^x = x$$
$$e^{\ln x} = x$$

Rules of Natural Logarithms

$$\ln(AB) = \ln A + \ln B$$
$$\ln \left(\frac{A}{B} \right) = \ln A - \ln B$$
$$\ln A^p = p \ln A$$

Distance and Midpoint Formulas

Distance D between (x_1, y_1) and (x_2, y_2):

$$D = \sqrt{(x_2 - x_1)^2 + (y_2 - y_1)^2}$$

Midpoint of (x_1, y_1) and (x_2, y_2):

$$\left(\frac{x_1 + x_2}{2}, \frac{y_1 + y_2}{2} \right)$$

Quadratic Formula

If $ax^2 + bx + c = 0$, then

$$x = \frac{-b \pm \sqrt{b^2 - 4ac}}{2a}$$

Factoring Special Polynomials

$$x^2 - y^2 = (x + y)(x - y)$$
$$x^3 + y^3 = (x + y)(x^2 - xy + y^2)$$
$$x^3 - y^3 = (x - y)(x^2 + xy + y^2)$$

Circles

Center (h, k) and radius r:

$$(x - h)^2 + (y - k)^2 = r^2$$

Ellipse

$$\frac{x^2}{a^2} + \frac{y^2}{b^2} = 1$$

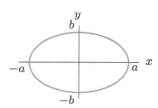

Hyperbola

$$\frac{x^2}{a^2} - \frac{y^2}{b^2} = 1$$

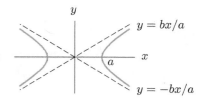

Geometric Formulas

Conversion Between Radians and Degrees: π radians $= 180°$

Triangle

$A = \frac{1}{2}bh$

$\quad = \frac{1}{2}ab\sin\theta$

Circle

$A = \pi r^2$

$C = 2\pi r$

Sector of Circle

$A = \frac{1}{2}r^2\theta \quad (\theta \text{ in radians})$

$s = r\theta \quad (\theta \text{ in radians})$

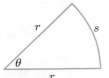

Sphere

$V = \frac{4}{3}\pi r^3 \quad A = 4\pi r^2$

Cylinder

$V = \pi r^2 h$

Cone

$V = \frac{1}{3}\pi r^2 h$

Trigonometric Functions

$\sin\theta = \dfrac{y}{r}$

$\cos\theta = \dfrac{x}{r}$

$\tan\theta = \dfrac{y}{x}$

$\tan\theta = \dfrac{\sin\theta}{\cos\theta}$

$\cos^2\theta + \sin^2\theta = 1$

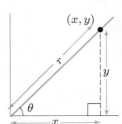

$\sin(A\pm B) = \sin A\cos B \pm \cos A\sin B$

$\cos(A\pm B) = \cos A\cos B \mp \sin A\sin B$

$\sin(2A) = 2\sin A\cos A$

$\cos(2A) = 2\cos^2 A - 1 = 1 - 2\sin^2 A$

The Binomial Theorem

$(x+y)^n = x^n + nx^{n-1}y + \dfrac{n(n-1)}{1\cdot 2}x^{n-2}y^2 + \dfrac{n(n-1)(n-2)}{1\cdot 2\cdot 3}x^{n-3}y^3 + \cdots + nxy^{n-1} + y^n$

$(x-y)^n = x^n - nx^{n-1}y + \dfrac{n(n-1)}{1\cdot 2}x^{n-2}y^2 - \dfrac{n(n-1)(n-2)}{1\cdot 2\cdot 3}x^{n-3}y^3 + \cdots \pm nxy^{n-1} \mp y^n$

Differentiation Formulas

1. $(f(x) \pm g(x))' = f'(x) \pm g'(x)$

2. $(kf(x))' = kf'(x)$

3. $(f(x)g(x))' = f'(x)g(x) + f(x)g'(x)$

4. $\left(\dfrac{f(x)}{g(x)}\right)' = \dfrac{f'(x)g(x) - f(x)g'(x)}{(g(x))^2}$

5. $(f(g(x)))' = f'(g(x)) \cdot g'(x)$

6. $\dfrac{d}{dx}(x^n) = nx^{n-1}$

7. $\dfrac{d}{dx}(e^x) = e^x$

8. $\dfrac{d}{dx}(a^x) = a^x \ln a \quad (a > 0)$

9. $\dfrac{d}{dx}(\ln x) = \dfrac{1}{x}$

10. $\dfrac{d}{dx}(\sin x) = \cos x$

11. $\dfrac{d}{dx}(\cos x) = -\sin x$

12. $\dfrac{d}{dx}(\tan x) = \dfrac{1}{\cos^2 x}$

13. $\dfrac{d}{dx}(\arcsin x) = \dfrac{1}{\sqrt{1-x^2}}$

14. $\dfrac{d}{dx}(\arctan x) = \dfrac{1}{1+x^2}$

A Short Table of Indefinite Integrals

I. Basic Functions

1. $\displaystyle\int x^n \, dx = \dfrac{1}{n+1}x^{n+1} + C, \quad n \neq -1$

5. $\displaystyle\int \sin x \, dx = -\cos x + C$

2. $\displaystyle\int \dfrac{1}{x} \, dx = \ln|x| + C$

6. $\displaystyle\int \cos x \, dx = \sin x + C$

3. $\displaystyle\int a^x \, dx = \dfrac{1}{\ln a}a^x + C, \quad a > 0$

7. $\displaystyle\int \tan x \, dx = -\ln|\cos x| + C$

4. $\displaystyle\int \ln x \, dx = x \ln x - x + C$

II. Products of e^x, $\cos x$, and $\sin x$

8. $\displaystyle\int e^{ax} \sin(bx) \, dx = \dfrac{1}{a^2 + b^2}e^{ax}[a \sin(bx) - b \cos(bx)] + C$

9. $\displaystyle\int e^{ax} \cos(bx) \, dx = \dfrac{1}{a^2 + b^2}e^{ax}[a \cos(bx) + b \sin(bx)] + C$

10. $\displaystyle\int \sin(ax) \sin(bx) \, dx = \dfrac{1}{b^2 - a^2}[a \cos(ax) \sin(bx) - b \sin(ax) \cos(bx)] + C, \quad a \neq b$

11. $\displaystyle\int \cos(ax) \cos(bx) \, dx = \dfrac{1}{b^2 - a^2}[b \cos(ax) \sin(bx) - a \sin(ax) \cos(bx)] + C, \quad a \neq b$

12. $\displaystyle\int \sin(ax) \cos(bx) \, dx = \dfrac{1}{b^2 - a^2}[b \sin(ax) \sin(bx) + a \cos(ax) \cos(bx)] + C, \quad a \neq b$

III. Product of Polynomial $p(x)$ with $\ln x$, e^x, $\cos x$, $\sin x$

13. $\displaystyle\int x^n \ln x \, dx = \dfrac{1}{n+1}x^{n+1} \ln x - \dfrac{1}{(n+1)^2}x^{n+1} + C, \quad n \neq -1$

14. $\displaystyle\int p(x)e^{ax} \, dx = \dfrac{1}{a}p(x)e^{ax} - \dfrac{1}{a}\int p'(x)e^{ax} \, dx$

$$= \dfrac{1}{a}p(x)e^{ax} - \dfrac{1}{a^2}p'(x)e^{ax} + \dfrac{1}{a^3}p''(x)e^{ax} - \cdots$$

$(+ - + - \ldots)$

(signs alternate)

15. $\displaystyle\int p(x)\sin ax\,dx = -\frac{1}{a}p(x)\cos ax + \frac{1}{a}\int p'(x)\cos ax\,dx$

$\displaystyle\qquad = -\frac{1}{a}p(x)\cos ax + \frac{1}{a^2}p'(x)\sin ax + \frac{1}{a^3}p''(x)\cos ax - \cdots$

$\qquad (-++--++\ldots)$

(signs alternate in pairs after first term)

16. $\displaystyle\int p(x)\cos ax\,dx = \frac{1}{a}p(x)\sin ax - \frac{1}{a}\int p'(x)\sin ax\,dx$

$\displaystyle\qquad = \frac{1}{a}p(x)\sin ax + \frac{1}{a^2}p'(x)\cos ax - \frac{1}{a^3}p''(x)\sin ax - \cdots$

$\qquad (++--++--\ldots)$ (signs alternate in pairs)

IV. Integer Powers of sin x and cos x

17. $\displaystyle\int \sin^n x\,dx = -\frac{1}{n}\sin^{n-1} x\cos x + \frac{n-1}{n}\int \sin^{n-2} x\,dx, \quad n \text{ positive}$

18. $\displaystyle\int \cos^n x\,dx = \frac{1}{n}\cos^{n-1} x\sin x + \frac{n-1}{n}\int \cos^{n-2} x\,dx, \quad n \text{ positive}$

19. $\displaystyle\int \frac{1}{\sin^m x}\,dx = \frac{-1}{m-1}\frac{\cos x}{\sin^{m-1} x} + \frac{m-2}{m-1}\int \frac{1}{\sin^{m-2} x}\,dx, \quad m \neq 1, m \text{ positive}$

20. $\displaystyle\int \frac{1}{\sin x}\,dx = \frac{1}{2}\ln\left|\frac{(\cos x)-1}{(\cos x)+1}\right| + C$

21. $\displaystyle\int \frac{1}{\cos^m x}\,dx = \frac{1}{m-1}\frac{\sin x}{\cos^{m-1} x} + \frac{m-2}{m-1}\int \frac{1}{\cos^{m-2} x}\,dx, \quad m \neq 1, m \text{ positive}$

22. $\displaystyle\int \frac{1}{\cos x}\,dx = \frac{1}{2}\ln\left|\frac{(\sin x)+1}{(\sin x)-1}\right| + C$

23. $\displaystyle\int \sin^m x\cos^n x\,dx$: If m is odd, let $w = \cos x$. If n is odd, let $w = \sin x$. If both m and n are even and positive, convert all to $\sin x$ or all to $\cos x$ (using $\sin^2 x + \cos^2 x = 1$), and use IV-17 or IV-18. If m and n are even and one of them is negative, convert to whichever function is in the denominator and use IV-19 or IV-21. If both m and n are even and negative, substitute $w = \tan x$, which converts the integrand to a rational function that can be integrated by the method of partial fractions.

V. Quadratic in the Denominator

24. $\displaystyle\int \frac{1}{x^2 + a^2}\,dx = \frac{1}{a}\arctan\frac{x}{a} + C, \quad a \neq 0$

25. $\displaystyle\int \frac{bx+c}{x^2+a^2}\,dx = \frac{b}{2}\ln|x^2+a^2| + \frac{c}{a}\arctan\frac{x}{a} + C, \quad a \neq 0$

26. $\displaystyle\int \frac{1}{(x-a)(x-b)}\,dx = \frac{1}{a-b}(\ln|x-a| - \ln|x-b|) + C, \quad a \neq b$

27. $\displaystyle\int \frac{cx+d}{(x-a)(x-b)}\,dx = \frac{1}{a-b}[(ac+d)\ln|x-a| - (bc+d)\ln|x-b|] + C, \quad a \neq b$

VI. Integrands Involving $\sqrt{a^2+x^2}$, $\sqrt{a^2-x^2}$, $\sqrt{x^2-a^2}$, $\quad a > 0$

28. $\displaystyle\int \frac{1}{\sqrt{a^2-x^2}}\,dx = \arcsin\frac{x}{a} + C$

29. $\displaystyle\int \frac{1}{\sqrt{x^2 \pm a^2}}\,dx = \ln\left|x + \sqrt{x^2 \pm a^2}\right| + C$

30. $\displaystyle\int \sqrt{a^2 \pm x^2}\,dx = \frac{1}{2}\left(x\sqrt{a^2 \pm x^2} + a^2\int \frac{1}{\sqrt{a^2 \pm x^2}}\,dx\right) + C$

31. $\displaystyle\int \sqrt{x^2 - a^2}\,dx = \frac{1}{2}\left(x\sqrt{x^2 - a^2} - a^2\int \frac{1}{\sqrt{x^2 - a^2}}\,dx\right) + C$

FUNCTIONS MODELING CHANGE:
A Preparation for Calculus

Produced by the Calculus Consortium and initially funded by a National Science Foundation Grant.

Eric Connally
Harvard University Extension

Deborah Hughes-Hallett
University of Arizona

Andrew M. Gleason
Harvard University

Philip Cheifetz
Nassau Community College

Ann Davidian
Gen. Douglas MacArthur HS

Daniel E. Flath
Macalester College

Brigitte Lahme
Sonoma State University

Patti Frazer Lock
St. Lawrence University

Jerry Morris
Sonoma State University

Karen Rhea
University of Michigan

Ellen Schmierer
Nassau Community College

Pat Shure
University of Michigan

Carl Swenson
Seattle University

Katherine Yoshiwara
Los Angeles Pierce College

Elliot J. Marks

with the assistance of
Frank Avenoso
Nassau Community College

John Wiley & Sons, Inc.

Dedicated to Maria, Ben, Jonah, and Isabel

PUBLISHER	Laurie Rosatone
SENIOR ACQUISITIONS EDITOR	Angela Y. Battle
MARKETING MANAGER	Amy Sell
FREELANCE DEVELOPMENTAL EDITOR	Anne Scanlan-Rohrer
SENIOR PRODUCTION EDITOR	Ken Santor
ASSISTANT EDITOR	Shannon Corliss
MARKETING ASSISTANT	Tara Martinho©

This book was set in Times Roman by the Consortium using TeX, Mathematica, and the package AsTeX, which was written by Alex Kasman. It was printed and bound by Von Hoffmann Press. The cover was printed by Von Hoffmann Press. The process was managed by Elliot Marks.

This material is based upon work supported by the National Science Foundation under Grant No. DUE-9352905. Opinions expressed are those of the authors and not necessarily those of the Foundation.

ISBN-13 978-0-471-. 4- 51*3

Printed in the United States of America

APPENDICES

Many of the skills you need for this book were covered in previous courses. However, it may have been a long time since you systematically practiced these skills. This appendix is designed as a review of some basic rules and definitions. As you work through the problems of the appendix, try to make both the vocabulary and the manipulations second nature so that you can use them quickly and appropriately.

A EXPONENTS

Positive Integer Exponents

Repeated addition leads to multiplication. For example,

$$\underbrace{2 + 2 + 2 + 2 + 2}_{\text{5 terms in sum}} = 5 \times 2.$$

Similarly, repeated multiplication leads to *exponentiation*. For example,

$$\underbrace{2 \times 2 \times 2 \times 2 \times 2}_{\text{5 factors in product}} = 2^5.$$

Here, 5 is the *exponent* of 2, and 2 is called the *base*. Notice that 2^5 is not the same as 5^2, because $2^5 = 32$ and $5^2 = 25$.

In general, if a is a real number and n is a positive integer, then we define exponentiation as an abbreviation for multiplication:

$$\underbrace{a \cdot a \cdot a \cdots a}_{n \text{ factors}} = a^n.$$

It's worth noticing that $a^1 = a$, because here we have only 1 factor of a.

Exponent Rules

There are five basic facts, called exponent rules, which follow as a direct consequence of the definition of exponents. These rules are summarized in the following box.

Exponent Rules

If a and b are real numbers and m and n are positive integers,

1. $a^n \cdot a^m = a^{n+m}$
2. $\dfrac{a^n}{a^m} = a^{n-m}$
3. $(a^m)^n = a^{m \cdot n}$

4. $(ab)^n = a^n b^n$
5. $\left(\dfrac{a}{b}\right)^n = \dfrac{a^n}{b^n}$

The explanation of all five rules are very straightforward. If you forget one of the rules, you should be able to immediately rederive it using the following logic.

For exponent rule 1, we have

$$a^n \cdot a^m = \underbrace{a \cdot a \cdot a \cdots a}_{n \text{ factors}} \underbrace{a \cdot a \cdot a \cdots a}_{m \text{ factors}} = \underbrace{a \cdot a \cdot a \cdots a}_{n + m \text{ factors}} = a^{n+m}.$$

For example, $2^3 \cdot 2^5 = (2 \cdot 2 \cdot 2) \cdot (2 \cdot 2 \cdot 2 \cdot 2 \cdot 2) = 2^8$, and $8 = 3 + 5$.

For exponent rule 2, suppose n and m are positive integers and $n > m$. Then the m factors of a in the denominator cancel with some of the n factors of a in the numerator, leaving only $n - m$ factors of a:

$$\frac{a^n}{a^m} = \frac{\overbrace{a \cdot a \cdot a \cdot a \cdots a}^{n \text{ factors of } a}}{\underbrace{a \cdot a \cdots a}_{m \text{ factors of } a}} = \frac{\overbrace{\not{a} \cdot \not{a} \cdots \not{a}}^{m \text{ factors of } a \text{ cancel}} \cdot \overbrace{a \cdots a}^{\substack{n - m \text{ factors} \\ \text{of } a \text{ are left} \\ \text{after cancelling}}}}{\underbrace{\not{a} \cdot \not{a} \cdots \not{a}}_{\substack{m \text{ factors} \\ \text{of } a \text{ cancel}}}} = \underbrace{a \cdot a \cdot a \cdots a}_{n - m \text{ factors}} = a^{n-m}$$

For example,

$$\frac{4^5}{4^3} = \frac{4 \cdot 4 \cdot 4 \cdot 4 \cdot 4}{4 \cdot 4 \cdot 4} = \frac{\cancel{4} \cdot \cancel{4} \cdot \cancel{4} \cdot 4 \cdot 4}{\cancel{4} \cdot \cancel{4} \cdot \cancel{4}} = 4 \cdot 4 = 4^2 = 4^{5-3},$$

For exponent rule 3,

$$(a^m)^n = \underbrace{(a \cdot a \cdot a \cdots a)}_{m \text{ factors of } a}{}^n = \overbrace{\underbrace{(a \cdot a \cdot a \cdots a)}_{m \text{ factors of } a}\underbrace{(a \cdot a \cdot a \cdots a)}_{m \text{ factors of } a} \cdots \underbrace{(a \cdot a \cdot a \cdots a)}_{m \text{ factors of } a}}^{\substack{\text{The } m \text{ factors of } a \text{ are multiplied } n \text{ times,} \\ \text{giving a total of } m \cdot n \text{ factors of } a}} = a^{m \cdot n}.$$

For example,

$$(a^2)^3 = (\underbrace{a \cdot a}_{2 \text{ factors of } a})^3 = \underbrace{(a \cdot a)(a \cdot a)(a \cdot a)}_{3 \text{ times 2 factors of } a} = a^6.$$

An alternative explanation for rule 3 uses rule 1:

$$(a^m)^n = \underbrace{a^m \cdot a^m \cdots a^m}_{n \text{ factors of } a^m} = a^{\overbrace{m + m + \cdots + m}^{n \text{ terms in sum}}} = a^{m \cdot n}.$$

For example, $(2^5)^3 = 2^5 \cdot 2^5 \cdot 2^5 = 2^{5+5+5} = 2^{15}$, and $15 = 5 \cdot 3$.

To justify exponent rule 4, we use the commutative property of multiplication, which states that the order in which numbers are multiplied together does not affect the result. For example, $2 \cdot 9 \cdot 13 = 13 \cdot 2 \cdot 9 = 9 \cdot 13 \cdot 2 = 234$.

$$(a \cdot b)^n = \underbrace{(a \cdot b)(a \cdot b)(a \cdot b) \cdots (a \cdot b)}_{n \text{ factors of } (a \cdot b)} = \underbrace{\overbrace{(a \cdot a \cdot a \cdots a)}^{n \text{ factors of } a} \cdot \overbrace{(b \cdot b \cdot b \cdots b)}^{n \text{ factors of } b}}_{\substack{\text{Since we can rearrange the order using the} \\ \text{commutative property of multiplication}}} = a^n \cdot b^n.$$

For example, $(5 \cdot 8)^2 = (5 \cdot 8)(5 \cdot 8) = (5 \cdot 5)(8 \cdot 8) = 5^2 \cdot 8^2 = 1600$.

For exponent rule 5,

$$\left(\frac{a}{b}\right)^n = \underbrace{\left(\frac{a}{b}\right) \cdot \left(\frac{a}{b}\right) \cdot \left(\frac{a}{b}\right) \cdots \left(\frac{a}{b}\right)}_{n \text{ factors of } a/b} = \frac{\overbrace{a \cdot a \cdot a \cdots a}^{n \text{ factors of } a}}{\underbrace{b \cdot b \cdot b \cdots b}_{n \text{ factors of } b}} = \frac{a^n}{b^n}.$$

For example, $\left(\frac{2}{7}\right)^3 = \left(\frac{2}{7}\right) \cdot \left(\frac{2}{7}\right) \cdot \left(\frac{2}{7}\right) = \frac{2 \cdot 2 \cdot 2}{7 \cdot 7 \cdot 7} = \frac{2^3}{7^3} = \frac{8}{343}$.

Be aware of the following notational conventions:

$$ab^n = a(b^n), \qquad \text{but } ab^n \neq (ab)^n,$$
$$-b^n = -(b^n), \qquad \text{but } -b^n \neq (-b)^n,$$
$$-ab^n = (-a)(b^n).$$

For example, $-2^4 = -(2^4) = -16$, but $(-2)^4 = (-2)(-2)(-2)(-2) = +16$. Also, be sure to realize that for values of n other than 0 and 1,

$$(a + b)^n \neq a^n + b^n \qquad \text{Power of a sum} \neq \text{Sum of powers.}$$

Rational Exponents

The natural definition for exponentiation as an abbreviation for multiplication holds for positive integers only. For example, 4^5 means 4 multiplied times itself 5 times, but we cannot use the same definition for 4^0 or 4^{-1} or $4^{1/2}$. We must choose a definition for exponents which are not positive integers.

The five exponent rules follow from the definition of positive integer exponents. Therefore, it makes sense to choose a definition for exponents like $0, -1, 1/2$ which is consistent with the five exponent rules. The definitions are summarized in the following box. After the box, explanations are given for these choices of definition.

Definitions For Exponentiation

If a is a real number and m and n are positive integers:[1]

- $a^0 = 1$ (for $a \neq 0$)
- $a^{-n} = \frac{1}{a^n}$ (for $a \neq 0$)
- $a^{1/n} = \sqrt[n]{a}$ (if n is even, then we assume $a \geq 0$.)
- $a^{m/n} = \sqrt[n]{a^m} = (\sqrt[n]{a})^m$ (if n is even, then we assume $a^m \geq 0$.)

To understand the definition of a^0, consider the following example. If we apply exponent rule 1 when one of the exponents is $m = 0$, and $a \neq 0$, then

$$a^n \cdot a^m = a^n \cdot a^0 = a^{n+0} = a^n,$$

so

$$a^n \cdot a^0 = a^n.$$

Notice that if we divide both sides of the equation by a^n, we get $a^0 = 1$. Therefore, if we want exponent rule 1 to hold for any exponent, including $m = 0$, we must define $a^0 = 1$, for $a \neq 0$. (We leave 0^0 undefined.)

Next we define a^{-n}, where n is a positive integer. Consider the following example. By the definition of a^2 and a^5,

$$\frac{a^2}{a^5} = \frac{a \cdot a}{a \cdot a \cdot a \cdot a \cdot a} = \frac{\cancel{a} \cdot \cancel{a}}{\cancel{a} \cdot \cancel{a} \cdot a \cdot a \cdot a} = \frac{1}{a^3}.$$

Alternatively, if we apply exponent rule 2, we see that the result is a negative exponent:

$$\frac{a^2}{a^5} = a^{2-5} = a^{-3}.$$

Therefore, if we want exponent rule 2 to hold for any exponent, including negative numbers, we must define $a^{-3} = \frac{1}{a^3}$. In general, $a^{-n} = \frac{1}{a^n}$. Notice that, in particular, $a^{-1} = \frac{1}{a}$.

Example 1   Use the rules of exponents to simplify the following:

(a) $3b(2b)^3(b^{-1})$

(b) $\dfrac{y^4(x^3y^{-2})^2}{2x^{-1}}$

(c) $\left(\dfrac{2^{-3}}{L}\right)^{-2}$

(d) $\dfrac{5(2s+1)^4(s+3)^{-2}}{2s+1}$

(e) $-2^2p^0(-3q)^4$

(f) $(-z)^{-n}$

---

[1]When we write a fractional power, we assume that the base is restricted to the values for which the power is defined.

Solution   (a) $3b(2b)^3 \left(b^{-1}\right) = 3b^1(2^3b^3)b^{-1} = 3 \cdot 8 \cdot b^1b^3b^{-1} = 3 \cdot 8 \cdot b^{3+(-1)+1} = 24b^3$

(b) $\dfrac{y^4 \left(x^3 y^{-2}\right)^2}{2x^{-1}} = \dfrac{y^4 x^6 y^{-4}}{2x^{-1}} = \dfrac{y^{(4-4)} x^{(6-(-1))}}{2} = \dfrac{y^0 x^7}{2} = \dfrac{x^7}{2}$

(c) $\left(\dfrac{2^{-3}}{L}\right)^{-2} = \dfrac{2^{(-3)(-2)}}{L^{-2}} = \dfrac{2^6}{L^{-2}} = 64L^2$ (Note that $\dfrac{1}{L^{-2}} = \dfrac{L^0}{L^{-2}} = L^{0-(-2)} = L^2$.)

(d) $\dfrac{5(2s+1)^4(s+3)^{-2}}{(2s+1)} = \dfrac{5(2s+1)^{4-1}}{(s+3)^2} = \dfrac{5(2s+1)^3}{(s+3)^2}$

(e) $-2^2 p^0(-3q)^4 = -4 \cdot 1(-3)^4 q^4 = -4(81)q^4 = -324q^4.$

(f) $(-z)^{-n} = \dfrac{1}{(-z)^n} = \dfrac{(-1)^n}{z^n}.$

Before explaining the definitions for fractional exponents, we review some notation:

Let n be an integer greater than 1:
- For $a \geq 0$,

  $\sqrt{a}$ is the positive number whose square is a.
  $\sqrt[n]{a}$ is the positive number whose n^{th} power is a.

- For $a < 0$,

  If n is even, $\sqrt[n]{a}$ is not a real number.
  If n is odd, $\sqrt[n]{a}$ is the negative number whose n^{th} power is a.

We say that $\sqrt[n]{a}$ is the nth **root of a**.

For example, $\sqrt{49} = 7$ because $7^2 = 49$. Likewise, $\sqrt[3]{125} = 5$ because $5^3 = 125$, and $\sqrt[5]{32} = 2$ because $2^5 = 32$. Similarly, $\sqrt[3]{-27} = -3$ because $(-3)^3 = -27$, and $\sqrt{-9}$ is not a real number, because the square of no real number is negative. When $\sqrt[n]{a}$ and $\sqrt[n]{b}$ are real numbers with $b \neq 0$, the rules for radicals are as follows:

$$\sqrt[n]{ab} = \sqrt[n]{a}\,\sqrt[n]{b}, \qquad \sqrt[n]{\dfrac{a}{b}} = \dfrac{\sqrt[n]{a}}{\sqrt[n]{b}}$$

Example 2   Simplify the following radicals:

(a) $\sqrt{36}$ (b) $\sqrt[3]{-8x^6}$ (c) $\sqrt{\dfrac{16R^8}{25}}$ (d) $\sqrt[4]{16u^8 w^{12}}$

Solution   (a) $\sqrt{36} = +6$ (Notice that the answer is the positive root, not ± 6.)

(b) $\sqrt[3]{-8x^6} = \sqrt[3]{-8} \cdot \sqrt[3]{x^6} = -2x^2$

(c) $\sqrt{\dfrac{16R^8}{25}} = \dfrac{\sqrt{16R^8}}{\sqrt{25}} = \dfrac{\sqrt{16}\sqrt{R^8}}{\sqrt{25}} = \dfrac{4R^4}{5}$

(d) $\sqrt[4]{16u^8 w^{12}} = \sqrt[4]{16}\sqrt[4]{u^8}\sqrt[4]{w^{12}} = 2u^2 w^3$, because $2^4 = 16$, $(u^2)^4 = u^8$, and $(w^3)^4 = w^{12}$.

> **Special case: n-th root of a^n**
>
> If n is odd,
> $$\sqrt[n]{a^n} = a \qquad \text{by definition.}$$
>
> If n is even,
> $$\sqrt[n]{a^n} = |a| = \begin{cases} a & \text{if } a \geq 0 \\ -a & \text{if } a < 0 \end{cases}.$$

Example 3   Simplify:

(a) $\sqrt[4]{(-1)^4}$

(b) $\sqrt{9x^2}$

Solution   (a) $\sqrt[4]{(-1)^4} = \sqrt[4]{1} = 1$ (Notice that in this case $\sqrt[n]{a^n} \neq a$.)

(b) $\sqrt{9x^2} = 3|x|$ (since x can be either positive or negative).

To see why fractional exponents are defined in the way they are, we again consider the consequences of the exponent rules. Suppose we evaluate an expression with a fractional exponent, such as $(a^{1/2})^2$, for $a \geq 0$. If we apply exponent rule 3, we get

$$(a^{1/2})^2 = a^{(1/2) \cdot 2} = a^1 = a, \quad \text{so} \quad (a^{1/2})^2 = a.$$

Taking the square root of both sides results in $a^{1/2} = \sqrt{a}$. Therefore, if we want exponent rule 3 to hold for any exponent, including fractions, we must define $a^{1/2} = \sqrt{a}$. In general, $a^{1/n} = \sqrt[n]{a}$. Note that when n is even, then a must be non-negative, and $a^{1/n} \geq 0$.

We can extend this explanation to an expression such as $(a^{1/3})^2$. Since $a^{1/3} = \sqrt[3]{a}$, we must have $(a^{1/3})^2 = (\sqrt[3]{a})^2$. Exponent rule 3 gives

$$(a^{1/3})^2 = a^{(1/3) \cdot 2} = a^{2/3}.$$

Therefore, if we want exponent rule 3 to hold for any exponent, including fractions, we must define $a^{2/3} = (\sqrt[3]{a})^2$. In general, $a^{m/n} = (\sqrt[n]{a})^m$. Because multiplication is commutative, we have

$$a^{m/n} = a^{m \cdot (1/n)} = a^{(1/n) \cdot m}$$
$$= (a^m)^{1/n} = (a^{1/n})^m$$
$$\text{so} \quad a^{m/n} = \sqrt[n]{a^m} = (\sqrt[n]{a})^m.$$

We have chosen these definitions so that exponent rules hold for any rational exponent.

Example 4   Find $(27)^{2/3}$.

Solution $(27)^{2/3} = \sqrt[3]{27^2} = \sqrt[3]{729} = 9$, or, equivalently, $(27)^{2/3} = \left(27^{\frac{1}{3}}\right)^2 = \left(\sqrt[3]{27}\right)^2 = 3^2 = 9$.

Example 5   Simplify:

(a) $\left(\dfrac{M^{1/5}}{3N^{-1/2}}\right)^2$

(b) $\dfrac{3u^2\sqrt{uw}}{w^{1/3}}$

Solution   (a) $\left(\dfrac{M^{1/5}}{3N^{-1/2}}\right)^2 = \dfrac{\left(M^{1/5}\right)^2}{\left(3N^{-1/2}\right)^2} = \dfrac{M^{2/5}}{3^2 N^{-1}} = \dfrac{M^{2/5}N}{9}$

(b) $\dfrac{3u^2\sqrt{uw}}{w^{1/3}} = \dfrac{3u^2 u^{1/2}w}{w^{1/3}} = 3u^{(2+1/2)}w^{(1-1/3)} = 3u^{5/2}w^{2/3}$

Calculator Note: Some calculators will not compute $a^{m/n}$ for $m \neq 1$ when a is negative, even if n is odd. For example, though $(-1)^{2/3}$ is well defined, a calculator may display "error."

Example 6   Evaluate, if possible:

(a) $(-2197)^{2/3}$

(b) $(-256)^{3/4}$

Solution   (a) To find $(-2197)^{2/3}$ on a calculator, we can first evaluate $(-2197)^{1/3}$, and then square the result. This gives 169.

(b) $(-256)^{3/4}$ is not a real number since $(-256)^{1/4}$ is not real.

Irrational and Variable Exponents

The rules for exponents given for integer and fractional exponents apply also when the exponent is an irrational number, as in $x^{\sqrt{3}}$, or a variable, as in 5^x.

Example 7   Simplify:

(a) $p^{\sqrt{2}} \cdot p^{\sqrt{8}}$

(b) $\sqrt{\dfrac{x^{3\pi}}{x^{\pi}}}$

Solution   (a) $p^{\sqrt{2}} \cdot p^{\sqrt{8}} = p^{(\sqrt{2}+\sqrt{8})} = p^{(\sqrt{2}+2\sqrt{2})} = p^{3\sqrt{2}}$

(b) $\sqrt{\dfrac{x^{3\pi}}{x^{\pi}}} = \left(\dfrac{x^{3\pi}}{x^{\pi}}\right)^{1/2} = \left(x^{3\pi-\pi}\right)^{1/2} = \left(x^{2\pi}\right)^{1/2} = x^{2\pi(1/2)} = x^{\pi}$

Example 8   Simplify:

(a) $-3^x \cdot 3^{-x}$

(b) $\dfrac{4^p}{2^p}$

(c) $\dfrac{a^{2/3}(a^k)(a^k)}{a}$

(d) $\dfrac{f^{2y}g^y}{f^{3y}}$

Solution   (a) $-3^x \cdot 3^{-x} = -(3^x)(3^{-x}) = -(3^{x-x}) = -(3^0) = -1$

(b) $\dfrac{4^p}{2^p} = \left(\dfrac{4}{2}\right)^p = 2^p$

(c) $\dfrac{a^{2/3}(a^k)(a^k)}{a} = a^{2/3}(a^k)(a^k)(a^{-1}) = a^{((2/3)+k+k-1)} = a^{2k-1/3}$

(d) $\dfrac{f^{2y}g^y}{f^{3y}} = \left(\dfrac{f^2 g}{f^3}\right)^y = \left(\dfrac{g}{f}\right)^y$

Problems for Section A

For Problems 1–16, evaluate without a calculator.

1. 4^3

2. $(-5)^2$

3. 11^2

4. 10^4

5. $(-1)^{12}$

6. $(-1)^{13}$

7. $\dfrac{5^3}{5^2}$

8. $\dfrac{5^3}{5}$

9. $\dfrac{10^8}{10^5}$

10. $\dfrac{6^4}{6^4}$

11. 8^0

12. $\sqrt{4}$

13. $\sqrt{4^2}$

14. $\sqrt{4^3}$

15. $\sqrt{4^4}$

16. $\sqrt{(-4)^2}$

For Problems 17–44, simplify the following expressions.

17. $\sqrt{x^4}$

18. $\sqrt{y^8}$

19. $\sqrt{w^8 z^4}$

20. $\sqrt{x^5 y^4}$

21. $\sqrt{16x^3}$

22. $\sqrt{49w^9}$

23. $\sqrt{25x^3 z^4}$

24. $\sqrt{r^2}$

25. $\sqrt{r^3}$

26. $\sqrt{r^4}$

27. $\sqrt{36t^2}$

28. $\sqrt{64s^7}$

29. $\sqrt{50x^4 y^6}$

30. $\sqrt{48u^{10} v^{12} y^5}$

31. $\sqrt{8m}\sqrt{2m^3}$

32. $\sqrt{6s^2 t^3 v^5}\sqrt{6st^5 v^3}$

33. $(32)^{1/5}$

34. $(16)^{1/2}$

35. $16^{1/4}$

36. $16^{3/4}$

37. $16^{5/4}$

38. $16^{5/2}$

39. 3^{-1}

40. 3^{-2}

41. $3^{-(3/2)}$

42. 25^{-1}

43. 25^{-2}

44. $25^{-(3/2)}$

Evaluate the quantities in Problems 45–59 mentally.

45. $\dfrac{1}{7^{-2}}$

46. $\dfrac{2^7}{2^3}$

47. $(-1)^{445}$

48. -11^2

49. $(-2)(3^2)$

50. $(5^0)^3$

51. $2.1(10^3)$

52. $\sqrt[3]{-125}$

53. $\sqrt{(-4)^2}$

54. $(-1)^3 \sqrt{36}$

55. $(0.04)^{1/2}$

56. $(-8)^{2/3}$

57. $(1/27)^{-1/3}$

58. $(0.125)^{1/3}$

59. $100^{5/2}$

Simplify the expressions in Problems 60–77 and leave without radicals.

60. $(0.1)^2 (4xy^2)^2$

61. $3(3^{x/2})^2$

62. $(4L^{2/3}P)^{3/2}(P)^{-3/2}$

63. $7(5w^{1/2})(2w^{1/3})$

64. $(S\sqrt{16xt^2})^2$

65. $\sqrt{e^{2x}}$

66. $(3AB)^{-1}(A^2 B^{-1})^2$

67. $e^{kt} \cdot e^3 \cdot e$

68. $\sqrt{M+2}(2+M)^{3/2}$

69. $(3x\sqrt{x^3})^2$

70. $x^e (x^e)^2$

71. $(y^{-2} e^y)^2$

72. $\dfrac{4x^{(3\pi+1)}}{x^2}$

73. $\dfrac{4A^{-3}}{(2A)^{-4}}$

74. $\dfrac{a^{n+1} 3^{n+1}}{a^n 3^n}$

75. $\dfrac{12u^3}{3(uv^2 w^4)^{-1}}$

76. $(a^{-1} + b^{-1})^{-1}$

77. $\left(\dfrac{35(2b+1)^9}{7(2b+1)^{-1}}\right)^2$

(Do not expand $(2b+1)^9$.)

If possible, evaluate the quantities in Problems 78–86. Check your answers with a calculator.

78. $(-32)^{3/5}$

79. $-32^{3/5}$

80. $-625^{3/4}$

81. $(-625)^{3/4}$

82. $(-1728)^{4/3}$

83. $64^{-3/2}$

84. $-64^{3/2}$

85. $(-64)^{3/2}$

86. $81^{5/4}$

Determine whether the statements in Problems 87–96 are true or false.

87. $t^3 t^4 = t^{12}$

88. $(u+v)^{-1} = \dfrac{1}{u} + \dfrac{1}{v}$

89. $-4w^2 - 3w^3 = -w^2(4 + 3w)$

90. $5z^{-4} = \dfrac{1}{5z^4}$

91. $x^2 y^5 = (xy)^{10}$ 92. $(p^3)^8 = p^{11}$

93. $\sqrt[3]{-64b^3 c^6} = -4bc^2$ 94. $\dfrac{m^8}{2m^2} = \dfrac{1}{2}m^4$

95. $5u^2 + 5u^3 = 10u^5$ 96. $(3r)^2 9s^2 = 81r^2 s^2$

B MULTIPLYING ALGEBRAIC EXPRESSIONS

The *distributive property* for real numbers a, b, and c tells us that

$$a(b + c) = ab + ac,$$

and

$$(b + c)a = ba + ca.$$

We use the distributive property and the rules of exponents to multiply algebraic expressions involving parentheses. This process is sometimes referred to as *expanding* the expression.

Example 1   Multiply the following expressions and simplify.

(a) $3x^2 \left(x + \dfrac{1}{6}x^{-3} \right)$ (b) $\left((2t)^2 - 5 \right) \sqrt{t}$ (c) $2^x (3^x + 2^{x-1})$

Solution   (a) $3x^2 \left(x + \dfrac{1}{6}x^{-3} \right) = (3x^2)(x) + (3x^2)\left(\dfrac{1}{6}x^{-3} \right) = 3x^3 + \dfrac{1}{2}x^{-1}$

(b) $\left((2t)^2 - 5 \right) \sqrt{t} = (2t)^2(\sqrt{t}) - 5\sqrt{t} = (4t^2)\left(t^{1/2} \right) - 5t^{1/2} = 4t^{5/2} - 5t^{1/2}$

(c) $2^x \left(3^x + 2^{x-1} \right) = (2^x)(3^x) + (2^x)\left(2^{x-1} \right) = (2 \cdot 3)^x + 2^{x+x-1} = 6^x + 2^{2x-1}$

If there are two terms in each factor, then there are four terms in the product:

$$(a + b)(c + d) = a(c + d) + b(c + d) = ac + ad + bc + bd.$$

The following special cases of the above product occur frequently. Learning to recognize their forms aids in factoring.

$$(a + b)(a - b) = a^2 - b^2$$
$$(a + b)^2 = a^2 + 2ab + b^2$$
$$(a - b)^2 = a^2 - 2ab + b^2$$

Example 2   Expand the following and simplify by gathering like terms.

(a) $(5x^2 + 2)(x - 4)$ (b) $(2\sqrt{r} + 2)(4\sqrt{r} - 3)$

(c) $(e^x + 1)(2x + e^{-x})$ (d) $\left(3 - \dfrac{1}{2}x \right)^2$

Solution   (a) $\left(5x^2 + 2 \right)(x - 4) = \left(5x^2 \right)(x) + \left(5x^2 \right)(-4) + (2)(x) + (2)(-4) = 5x^3 - 20x^2 + 2x - 8$

(b) $(2\sqrt{r} + 2)(4\sqrt{r} - 3) = (2)(4)(\sqrt{r})^2 + (2)(-3)(\sqrt{r}) + (2)(4)(\sqrt{r}) + (2)(-3) = 8r + 2\sqrt{r} - 6$

(c) $(e^x + 1)\left(2x + e^{-x} \right) = (e^x)(2x) + (e^x)\left(e^{-x} \right) + (1)(2x) + (1)(e^{-x})$

$$= 2xe^x + e^{x-x} + 2x + e^{-x}$$
$$= 2xe^x + 1 + 2x + e^{-x}$$

(d) $\left(3 - \dfrac{1}{2}x \right)^2 = 3^2 - 2(3)\left(\dfrac{1}{2}x \right) + \left(-\dfrac{1}{2}x \right)^2 = 9 - 3x + \dfrac{1}{4}x^2$

Problems for Section B

Simplify the expressions in Problems 1–2.

1. $-(x-3) - 2(5-x)$

2. $(x-5)6 - 5(1 - (2-x))$

For Problems 3–20, expand each of the following products.

3. $3(x+2)$

4. $5(x-3)$

5. $2(3x-7)$

6. $-4(y+6)$

7. $12(x+y)$

8. $-7(5x-8y)$

9. $x(2x+5)$

10. $3z(2x-9z)$

11. $-10r(5r+6rs)$

12. $x(3x-8) + 2(3x-8)$

13. $5z(x-2) - 3(x-2)$

14. $(x+1)(x+3)$

15. $(x-2)(x+6)$

16. $(5x-1)(2x-3)$

17. $(x+2)(3x-8)$

18. $(y+1)(z+3)$

19. $(12y-5)(8w+7)$

20. $(5z-3)(x-2)$

Multiply and write the expressions in Problems 21–30 without parentheses. Gather like terms.

21. $\left(3x - 2x^2\right)(4) + (5+4x)(3x-4)$

22. $\left(t^2+1\right)(50t) - \left(25t^2 + 125\right)(2t)$

23. $P(p-3q)^2$

24. $\left(A^2 - B^2\right)^2$

25. $4(x-3)^2 + 7$

26. $-\left(\sqrt{2x}+1\right)^2$

27. $u\left(u^{-1} + 2^u\right)2^u$

28. $K(R-r)r^2$

29. $(x+3)\left(\dfrac{24}{x} + 2\right)$

30. $\left(\dfrac{e^x + e^{-x}}{2}\right)^2$

C FACTORING ALGEBRAIC EXPRESSIONS

To write an expanded expression in factored form, we "un-multiply" the expression. Some techniques for factoring are given in this section. We can check factoring by remultiplying.

Removing a Common Factor

It is sometimes useful to factor out the same factor from each of the terms in an expression. This is basically the distributive law in reverse:

$$ab + ac = a(b+c).$$

One special case is removing a factor of -1, which gives

$$\boxed{-a - b = -(a+b)}$$

Another special case is

$$\boxed{(a-b) = -(b-a)}$$

Example 1 Factor the following:

(a) $\dfrac{2}{3}x^2 y + \dfrac{4}{3}xy$
(b) $e^{2x} + xe^x$
(c) $(2p+1)p^3 - 3p(2p+1)$
(d) $-\dfrac{s^2 t}{8w} - \dfrac{st^2}{16w}$

Solution (a) $\dfrac{2}{3}x^2 y + \dfrac{4}{3}xy = \dfrac{2}{3}xy(x+2)$

(b) $e^{2x} + xe^x = e^x \cdot e^x + xe^x = e^x(e^x + x)$

(c) $(2p+1)p^3 - 3p(2p+1) = (p^3 - 3p)(2p+1) = p(p^2 - 3)(2p+1)$
(Note that the expression $(2p+1)$ was one of the factors common to both terms.)

(d) $-\dfrac{s^2 t}{8w} - \dfrac{st^2}{16w} = -\dfrac{st}{8w}\left(s + \dfrac{t}{2}\right).$

Grouping Terms

Even though all the terms may not have a common factor, we can sometimes factor by first grouping the terms and then removing a common factor.

Example 2   Factor $x^2 - hx - x + h$.

Solution $x^2 - hx - x + h = (x^2 - hx) - (x - h) = x(x - h) - (x - h) = (x - h)(x - 1)$

Factoring Quadratics

One way to factor quadratics is to mentally multiply out the possibilities.

Example 3   Factor $t^2 - 4t - 12$.

Solution   If the quadratic factors, it will be of the form

$$t^2 - 4t - 12 = (t + ?)(t + ?).$$

We are looking for two numbers whose product is -12 and whose sum is -4. By trying combinations, we find

$$t^2 - 4t - 12 = (t - 6)(t + 2).$$

Example 4   Factor $4 - 2M - 6M^2$.

Solution $4 - 2M - 6M^2 = (2 - 3M)(2 + 2M)$

Perfect Squares and the Difference of Squares

Recognition of the special products $(x + y)^2$, $(x - y)^2$ and $(x + y)(x - y)$ in expanded form is useful in factoring. Reversing the results in the last section, we have

$$a^2 + 2ab + b^2 = (a + b)^2,$$
$$a^2 - 2ab + b^2 = (a - b)^2,$$
$$a^2 - b^2 = (a - b)(a + b).$$

When we can see that terms in an expression we want to factor are squares, it often makes sense to look for one of these forms. The difference of squares identity (the third one listed above) is especially useful.

Example 5   Factor: (a) $16y^2 - 24y + 9$ (b) $25S^2R^4 - T^6$ (b) $x^2(x - 2) + 16(2 - x)$

Solution   (a) $16y^2 - 24y + 9 = (4y - 3)^2$
      (b) $25S^2R^4 - T^6 = (5SR^2)^2 - (T^3)^2 = (5SR^2 - T^3)(5SR^2 + T^3)$
      (c) $x^2(x - 2) + 16(2 - x) = x^2(x - 2) - 16(x - 2) = (x - 2)(x^2 - 16) = (x - 2)(x - 4)(x + 4)$

Example 6   Factor $z^{2/3} - z^{1/3} - 6$.

Solution   Notice that $z^{2/3} - z^{1/3} - 6$ is a quadratic. It is helpful to substitute $u = z^{1/3}$. Then

$$z^{2/3} - z^{1/3} - 6 = u^2 - u - 6$$
$$= (u - 3)(u + 2)$$

Now undo the substitution, that is, let $u = z^{1/3}$. Therefore,

$$z^{2/3} - z^{1/3} - 6 = (z^{1/3} - 3)(z^{1/3} + 2).$$

Problems for Section C

For Problems 1–42, factor completely if possible.

1. $2x + 6$
2. $3y + 15$
3. $5z - 30$
4. $4t - 6$
5. $10w - 25$
6. $u^2 - 2u$
7. $3u^4 - 4u^3$
8. $3u^7 + 12u^2$
9. $12x^3y^2 - 18x$
10. $14r^4s^2 - 21rst$
11. $x^2 + 3x + 2$
12. $x^2 + 3x - 2$
13. $x^2 - 3x + 2$
14. $x^2 - 3x - 2$
15. $x^2 + 2x + 3$
16. $x^2 - 2x - 3$
17. $x^2 - 2x + 3$
18. $x^2 + 2x - 3$
19. $2x^2 + 5x + 2$
20. $3x^2 - x - 4$
21. $2x^2 - 10x + 12$
22. $x^2 + 3x - 28$
23. $x^3 - 2x^2 - 3x$
24. $x^3 + 2x^2 - 3x$
25. $x^2 - 1.4x - 3.92$
26. $a^2x^2 - b^2$
27. $\pi r^2 + 2\pi rh$
28. $B^2 - 10B + 24$
29. $c^2 + x^2 - 2cx$
30. $x^2 + y^2$
31. $a^4 - a^2 - 12$
32. $(t + 3)^2 - 16$
33. $hx^2 + 12 - 4hx - 3x$
34. $r(r - s) - 2(s - r)$
35. $y^2 - 3xy + 2x^2$
36. $x^2e^{-3x} + 2xe^{-3x}$
37. $t^2e^{5t} + 3te^{5t} + 2e^{5t}$
38. $(s + 2t)^2 - 4p^2$
39. $P(1 + r)^2 + P(1 + r)^2r$
40. $x \sin x - \sin x$
41. $\cos^2 x - 2\cos x + 1$
42. $e^{2x} + 2e^x + 1$

D WORKING WITH FRACTIONS

Algebraic fractions are combined in the same manner as numeric fractions–that is, according to the following rules:

$$\frac{a}{c} + \frac{b}{c} = \frac{a + b}{c} \qquad \text{add numerators when denominators are equal, or}$$

$$\frac{a}{b} + \frac{c}{d} = \frac{a(d)}{b(d)} + \frac{(b)c}{(b)d} = \frac{ad + bc}{bd} \qquad \text{find a common denominator}$$

$$\frac{a}{b} \cdot \frac{c}{d} = \frac{ac}{bd} \qquad \text{multiply numerators and denominators for a product}$$

$$\frac{a/b}{c/d} = \frac{a}{b} \cdot \frac{d}{c} = \frac{ad}{bc} \qquad \text{to divide by a fraction, multiply by its reciprocal}$$

(We assume that no denominators are zero.)

To expand the last case, where either the numerator or denominator of a fraction is itself a fraction, remember that

$$\frac{\frac{a}{b}}{c} = \frac{\frac{a}{b}}{\frac{c}{1}} = \frac{a}{b} \cdot \frac{1}{c} = \frac{a}{bc} \qquad \text{and} \qquad \frac{a}{\frac{b}{c}} = \frac{\frac{a}{1}}{\frac{b}{c}} = \frac{a}{1} \cdot \frac{c}{b} = \frac{ac}{b}.$$

In all cases, we cannot divide by zero; that is, $(a/0)$ is not defined. Also the sign of a fraction is changed by changing the sign of the numerator or the denominator (but not both):

$$-\frac{a}{b} = \frac{-a}{b} = \frac{a}{-b}.$$

Example 1   Perform the indicated operations and express the answers as a single fraction.

(a) $\dfrac{4}{x^2+1} - \dfrac{1-x}{x^2+1}$

(b) $\dfrac{M}{M^2-2M-3} + \dfrac{1}{M^2-2M-3}$

(c) $\dfrac{-H^2P}{17} \cdot \dfrac{\left(PH^{1/3}\right)^2}{K^{-1}}$

(d) $\dfrac{2z/w}{w(w-3z)}$

Solution   (a) $\dfrac{4}{x^2+1} - \dfrac{1-x}{x^2+1} = \dfrac{4-(1-x)}{x^2+1} = \dfrac{3+x}{x^2+1}$

(b) $\dfrac{M}{M^2-2M-3} + \dfrac{1}{M^2-2M-3} = \dfrac{M+1}{(M^2-2M-3)} = \dfrac{M+1}{(M+1)(M-3)} = \dfrac{1}{M-3}$

(c) $\dfrac{-H^2P}{17} \cdot \dfrac{\left(PH^{1/3}\right)^2}{K^{-1}} = \dfrac{-H^2P\left(P^2H^{2/3}\right)}{17K^{-1}} = -\dfrac{H^{8/3}P^3K}{17}$

(d) $\dfrac{2z/w}{w(w-3z)} = \dfrac{2z}{w} \cdot \dfrac{1}{w(w-3z)} = \dfrac{2z}{w^2(w-3z)}$

Example 2   Simplify the following expressions:

(a) $2x^{-1/2} + \dfrac{\sqrt{x}}{3}$

(b) $2\sqrt{t+3} + \dfrac{1-2t}{\sqrt{t+3}}$

Solution   (a) $2x^{-1/2} + \dfrac{\sqrt{x}}{3} = \dfrac{2}{\sqrt{x}} + \dfrac{\sqrt{x}}{3} = \dfrac{2 \cdot 3 + \sqrt{x}\sqrt{x}}{3\sqrt{x}} = \dfrac{6+x}{3\sqrt{x}} = \dfrac{6+x}{3x^{1/2}}$

(b) $2\sqrt{t+3} + \dfrac{1-2t}{\sqrt{t+3}} = \dfrac{2\sqrt{t+3}}{1} + \dfrac{1-2t}{\sqrt{t+3}}$

$\qquad = \dfrac{2\sqrt{t+3}\sqrt{t+3} + 1 - 2t}{\sqrt{t+3}}$

$\qquad = \dfrac{2(t+3) + 1 - 2t}{\sqrt{t+3}}$

$\qquad = \dfrac{7}{\sqrt{t+3}} = \dfrac{7}{(t+3)^{1/2}}$

Finding a Common Denominator

We can multiply (or divide) both the numerator and denominator of a fraction by the same non-zero number without changing the fraction's value. This is equivalent to multiplying by a factor of $+1$. We are using this rule when we add or subtract fractions with different denominators. For example, to add $\dfrac{x}{3a} + \dfrac{1}{a}$, we multiply $\dfrac{1}{a} \cdot \dfrac{3}{3} = \dfrac{3}{3a}$. Then

$$\frac{x}{3a} + \frac{1}{a} = \frac{x}{3a} + \frac{3}{3a} = \frac{x+3}{3a}.$$

Example 3 Perform the indicated operations:

(a) $3 - \dfrac{1}{x-1}$

(b) $\dfrac{2}{x^2+x} + \dfrac{x}{x+1}$

Solution (a) $3 - \dfrac{1}{x-1} = 3\dfrac{(x-1)}{(x-1)} - \dfrac{1}{x-1} = \dfrac{3(x-1)-1}{x-1} = \dfrac{3x-3-1}{x-1} = \dfrac{3x-4}{x-1}$

(b) $\dfrac{2}{x^2+x} + \dfrac{x}{x+1} = \dfrac{2}{x(x+1)} + \dfrac{x}{x+1} = \dfrac{2}{x(x+1)} + \dfrac{x(x)}{(x+1)(x)} = \dfrac{2+x^2}{x(x+1)}$

Note: We can multiply (or divide) the numerator and denominator by the same non-zero number because this is the same as multiplying by a factor of $+1$, and multiplying by a factor of 1 does not change the value of the expression. However, we cannot perform any other operation that would change the value of the expression. For example, we cannot *add* the same number to the numerator and denominator of a fraction *nor* can we square both, take the logarithm of both, etc., without changing the fraction.

Reducing Fractions: Canceling

We can reduce a fraction when we have the same (non-zero) factor in both the numerator and the denominator. For example,

$$\frac{ac}{bc} = \frac{a}{b} \cdot \frac{c}{c} = \frac{a}{b} \cdot 1 = \frac{a}{b}.$$

Example 4 Reduce the following fractions (if possible).

(a) $\dfrac{2x}{4y}$

(b) $\dfrac{2+x}{2+y}$

(c) $\dfrac{5n-5}{1-n}$

(d) $\dfrac{x^2(4-2x)-(4x-x^2)(2x)}{x^4}$

Solution (a) $\dfrac{2x}{4y} = \dfrac{2}{2} \cdot \dfrac{x}{2y} = \dfrac{x}{2y}$

(b) $\dfrac{2+x}{2+y}$ cannot be reduced further.

(c) $\dfrac{5n-5}{1-n} = \dfrac{5(n-1)}{(-1)(n-1)} = -5$

(d) $\dfrac{x^2(4-2x)-(4x-x^2)(2x)}{x^4} = \dfrac{x^2(4-2x)-(4-x)(2x^2)}{x^4}$

$= \dfrac{[(4-2x)-2(4-x)]}{x^2}\left(\dfrac{x^2}{x^2}\right)$

$= \dfrac{4-2x-8+2x}{x^2} = \dfrac{-4}{x^2}$

Complex Fractions

A *complex fraction* is a fraction whose numerator or denominator (or both) contains one or more fractions. To simplify a complex fraction, we change the numerator and denominator to single fractions and then divide.

Example 5 Write the following as simple fractions in reduced form.

(a) $\dfrac{\dfrac{1}{x+h} - \dfrac{1}{x}}{h}$

(b) $\dfrac{a+b}{a^{-2}-b^{-2}}$

Solution   (a) $\dfrac{\dfrac{1}{x+h} - \dfrac{1}{x}}{h} = \dfrac{\dfrac{x - (x+h)}{x(x+h)}}{h} = \dfrac{\dfrac{-h}{x(x+h)}}{\dfrac{h}{1}} = \dfrac{-h}{x(x+h)} \cdot \dfrac{1}{h} = \dfrac{-1}{x(x+h)} \dfrac{(h)}{(h)} = \dfrac{-1}{x(x+h)}$

(b) $\dfrac{a+b}{a^{-2} - b^{-2}} = \dfrac{a+b}{\dfrac{1}{a^2} - \dfrac{1}{b^2}} = \dfrac{a+b}{\dfrac{b^2 - a^2}{a^2 b^2}} = \dfrac{a+b}{1} \cdot \dfrac{a^2 b^2}{b^2 - a^2} = \dfrac{(a+b)(a^2 b^2)}{(b+a)(b-a)} = \dfrac{a^2 b^2}{b-a}$

Splitting Expressions

We can reverse the rule for adding fractions to split up an expression into two fractions,

$$\frac{a+b}{c} = \frac{a}{c} + \frac{b}{c}.$$

Example 6   Split $\dfrac{3x^2 + 2}{x^3}$ into two reduced fractions.

Solution $\dfrac{3x^2 + 2}{x^3} = \dfrac{3x^2}{x^3} + \dfrac{2}{x^3} = \dfrac{3}{x} + \dfrac{2}{x^3}$

Sometimes we can alter the form of the fraction even further if we can create a duplicate of the denominator within the numerator. This technique is useful when graphing some rational functions. For example, we may rewrite the fraction $\dfrac{x+3}{x-1}$ by creating a factor of $(x-1)$ within the numerator. To do this, we write

$$\frac{x+3}{x-1} = \frac{x - 1 + 1 + 3}{x-1}$$

which can be written as

$$\frac{(x-1) + 4}{x-1}.$$

Then, splitting this fraction, we have

$$\frac{x+3}{x-1} = \frac{x-1}{x-1} + \frac{4}{x-1} = 1 + \frac{4}{x-1}.$$

Problems for Section D

For Problems 1–23, perform the following operations. Express answers in reduced form.

1. $\dfrac{3}{5} + \dfrac{4}{7}$

2. $\dfrac{7}{10} - \dfrac{2}{15}$

3. $\dfrac{1}{2x} - \dfrac{2}{3}$

4. $\dfrac{6}{7y} + \dfrac{9}{y}$

5. $\dfrac{-2}{yz} + \dfrac{4}{z}$

6. $\dfrac{-2z}{y} + \dfrac{4}{y}$

7. $\dfrac{2}{x^2} - \dfrac{3}{x}$

8. $\dfrac{6}{y} + \dfrac{7}{y^3}$

9. $\dfrac{\frac{3}{4}}{\frac{7}{20}}$

10. $\dfrac{\frac{5}{6}}{15}$

11. $\dfrac{\frac{3}{x}}{\frac{x^2}{6}}$

12. $\dfrac{\frac{3}{x}}{\frac{6}{x^2}}$

13. $\dfrac{13}{x-1} + \dfrac{14}{2x-2}$

14. $\dfrac{14}{x-1} + \dfrac{13}{2x-2}$

15. $\dfrac{4z}{x^2 y} - \dfrac{3w}{xy^4}$

16. $\dfrac{10}{y-2} + \dfrac{3}{2-y}$

17. $\dfrac{8y}{y-4} + \dfrac{32}{y-4}$

18. $\dfrac{8y}{y-4} + \dfrac{32}{4-y}$

19. $\dfrac{\dfrac{1}{x} - \dfrac{2}{x^2}}{\dfrac{2x-4}{x^5}}$

20. $\dfrac{9}{x^2 + 5x + 6} + \dfrac{12}{x+3}$

21. $\dfrac{8}{3x^2 - x - 4} - \dfrac{9}{x+1}$

22. $\dfrac{5}{(x-2)^2(x+1)} - \dfrac{18}{(x-2)}$

23. $\dfrac{15}{(x-3)^2(x+5)} + \dfrac{7}{(x-3)(x+5)^2}$

In Problems 24–35, perform the specified operations. Express answers in reduced form.

24. $\dfrac{3}{x-4} - \dfrac{2}{x+4}$

25. $\dfrac{x^2}{x-1} - \dfrac{1}{1-x}$

26. $\dfrac{1}{2r+3} + \dfrac{3}{4r^2 + 6r}$

27. $u + a + \dfrac{u}{u+a}$

28. $\dfrac{1}{\sqrt{x}} - \dfrac{1}{(\sqrt{x})^3}$

29. $\dfrac{1}{e^{2x}} + \dfrac{1}{e^x}$

30. $\dfrac{a+b}{2} \cdot \dfrac{8x+2}{b^2 - a^2}$

31. $\dfrac{0.07}{M} + \dfrac{3}{4}M^2$

32. $\dfrac{1}{r_1} + \dfrac{1}{r_2} + \dfrac{1}{r_3}$

33. $\dfrac{8y}{y-4} - \dfrac{32}{y-4}$

34. $\dfrac{a}{a^2 - 9} + \dfrac{1}{a-3}$

35. $\dfrac{x^3}{x-4} \Big/ \dfrac{x^2}{x^2 - 2x - 8}$

In Problems 36–49, simplify, if possible.

36. $\dfrac{\frac{1}{x+y}}{x+y}$

37. $\dfrac{\frac{w+2}{2}}{w+2}$

38. $\dfrac{\dfrac{1}{(x+h)^2} - \dfrac{1}{x^2}}{h}$

39. $\dfrac{a^{-2} + b^{-2}}{a^2 + b^2}$

40. $\dfrac{a^2 - b^2}{a^2 + b^2}$

41. $\dfrac{[4 - (x+h)^2] - [4 - x^2]}{h}$

42. $\dfrac{b^{-1}(b - b^{-1})}{b+1}.$

43. $\dfrac{1 - a^{-2}}{1 + a^{-1}}.$

44. $\dfrac{x^{-1} + x^{-2}}{1 - x^{-2}}.$

45. $p - \dfrac{q}{\dfrac{p}{q} + \dfrac{q}{p}}$

46. $\dfrac{\dfrac{3}{xy} - \dfrac{5}{x^2 y}}{\dfrac{6x^2 - 7x - 5}{x^4 y^2}}$

47. $\dfrac{\frac{1}{x}(3x^2) - (\ln x)(6x)}{(3x^2)^2}$

48. $\dfrac{2x(x^3 + 1)^2 - x^2(2)(x^3 + 1)(3x^2)}{[(x^3 + 1)^2]^2}$

49. $\dfrac{\frac{1}{2}(2x - 1)^{-1/2}(2) - (2x - 1)^{1/2}(2x)}{(x^2)^2}$

In Problems 50–55, split into a sum or difference of reduced fractions.

50. $\dfrac{26x + 1}{2x^3}$

51. $\dfrac{\sqrt{x} + 3}{3\sqrt{x}}$

52. $\dfrac{6l^2 + 3l - 4}{3l^4}$

53. $\dfrac{7 + p}{p^2 + 11}$

54. $\dfrac{\frac{1}{3}x - \frac{1}{2}}{2x}$

55. $\dfrac{t^{-1/2} + t^{1/2}}{t^2}$

In Problems 56–61, rewrite in the form $1 + (A/B)$.

56. $\dfrac{x-2}{x+5}$

57. $\dfrac{q-1}{q-4}$

58. $\dfrac{R+1}{R}$

59. $\dfrac{3 + 2u}{2u + 1}$

60. $\dfrac{\cos x + \sin x}{\cos x}$

61. $\dfrac{1 + e^x}{e^x}$

Determine whether the statements in Problems 62–67 are true or false.

62. $\dfrac{a+c}{a} = 1 + c$

63. $\dfrac{rs - s}{s} = r - 1$

64. $\dfrac{y}{y+z} = 1 + \dfrac{y}{z}$

65. $\dfrac{2u^2 - w}{u^2 - w} = 2$

66. $\dfrac{x^2 yz}{2x^2 y} = \dfrac{z}{2}$

67. $x^{5/3} - 3x^{2/3} = \dfrac{x^2 - 3x}{x^{1/3}}$

E CHANGING THE FORM OF EXPRESSIONS

Rearranging Coefficients and Exponents

Changing the form of an expression can often be useful. Manipulations like the following occur frequently:

- $\dfrac{x}{2} = \left(\dfrac{1}{2}\right) x$

- $\dfrac{3}{4(2r+1)^{10}} = \dfrac{3}{4}(2r+1)^{-10}$

- $2^{-n} = \left(\dfrac{1}{2}\right)^{n}$

- $2^{x+3} = 2^{x} \cdot 2^{3} = 8(2^{x})$

- $\dfrac{3x + \sqrt{2x}}{\sqrt{x}} = \dfrac{3x}{\sqrt{x}} + \dfrac{\sqrt{2x}}{\sqrt{x}} = \dfrac{3x}{\sqrt{x}} + \dfrac{\sqrt{2}\sqrt{x}}{\sqrt{x}} = 3x^{(1-1/2)} + \sqrt{2} = 3x^{1/2} + \sqrt{2}$

Completing the Square

Another example of changing the form of an expression is the conversion of $ax^2 + bx + c$ into the form $a(x-h)^2 + k$. We make this conversion by *completing the square*, a method for producing a perfect square within a quadratic expression. A perfect square is an expression of the form:

$$(x+n)^2 = x^2 + 2nx + n^2$$

for some number n.

In order to complete the square in a given expression, we must find that number n. Observe that when a perfect square is multiplied out, the coefficient of x is 2 times the number n. Therefore, we can find n by dividing the coefficient of the x term by 2. Once we know n, then we know that the constant term in the perfect square must be n^2. In summary:

To complete the square in the expression $x^2 + bx + c$, divide the coefficient of x by 2, giving $b/2$. Then add and subtract $(b/2)^2 = b^2/4$ and factor the perfect square:

$$x^2 + bx + c = \left(x + \frac{b}{2}\right)^2 - \frac{b^2}{4} + c.$$

To complete the square in the expression $ax^2 + bx + c$, factor out a first.

Example 1 Rewrite $x^2 - 10x + 4$ in the form $a(x-h)^2 + k$.

Solution Notice that half of the coefficient of x is $\frac{1}{2}(-10) = -5$. Squaring -5 gives 25. We have

$$\begin{aligned}
x^2 - 10x + 4 &= x^2 - 10x + (25 - 25) + 4 \\
&= (x^2 - 10x + 25) - 25 + 4 \\
&= (x-5)^2 - 21.
\end{aligned}$$

Thus, $a = +1$, $h = +5$, and $k = -21$.

Example 2   Complete the square in the formula $h(x) = 5x^2 + 30x - 10$.

Solution   We first factor out 5:

$$h(x) = 5(x^2 + 6x - 2).$$

Now we complete the square in the expression $x^2 + 6x - 2$.

Step 1: Divide the coefficient of x by 2, giving 3.
Step 2: Square the result: $3^2 = 9$.
Step 3: Add the result after the x term, then subtract it:

$$h(x) = 5(\underbrace{x^2 + 6x + 9}_{\text{Perfect square}} -9 - 2).$$

Step 4: Factor the perfect square and simplify the rest:

$$h(x) = 5\left((x + 3)^2 - 11\right).$$

Now that we have completed the square, we can multiply by the 5:

$$h(x) = 5(x + 3)^2 - 55.$$

The Quadratic Formula

We derive a general formula for the zeros of $q(x) = ax^2 + bx + c$, with $a \neq 0$, by completing the square. To find the zeros, set $q(x) = 0$:

$$ax^2 + bx + c = 0.$$

Before we complete the square, we factor out the coefficient of x^2:

$$a\left(x^2 + \frac{b}{a}x + \frac{c}{a}\right) = 0.$$

Since $a \neq 0$, we can divide both sides by a:

$$x^2 + \frac{b}{a}x + \frac{c}{a} = 0.$$

To complete the square, we add and then subtract $\left((b/a)/2\right)^2 = b^2/(4a^2)$:

$$\underbrace{x^2 + \frac{b}{a}x + \frac{b^2}{4a^2}}_{\text{Perfect square}} - \frac{b^2}{4a^2} + \frac{c}{a} = 0.$$

We factor the perfect square and simplify the constant term, giving:

$$\left(x + \frac{b}{2a}\right)^2 - \left(\frac{b^2 - 4ac}{4a^2}\right) = 0 \qquad \text{since } \frac{-b^2}{4a^2} + \frac{c}{a} = \frac{-b^2}{4a^2} + \frac{4ac}{4a^2} = -\left(\frac{b^2 - 4ac}{4a^2}\right)$$

$$\left(x + \frac{b}{2a}\right)^2 = \frac{b^2 - 4ac}{4a^2} \qquad \text{adding } \frac{b^2 - 4ac}{4a^2} \text{ to both sides}$$

$$x + \frac{b}{2a} = \pm\sqrt{\frac{b^2 - 4ac}{4a^2}} = \frac{\pm\sqrt{b^2 - 4ac}}{2a} \qquad \text{taking the square root}$$

$$x = \frac{-b}{2a} \pm \frac{\sqrt{b^2 - 4ac}}{2a} \qquad \text{subtracting } b/2a$$

$$x = \frac{-b \pm \sqrt{b^2 - 4ac}}{2a}.$$

Problems for Section E

In Problems 1–12, rewrite each expression as a sum of powers of the variable.

1. $3x^2\left(x^{-1}\right) + \dfrac{1}{2x} + x^2 + \dfrac{1}{5}$

2. $10\left(3q^2 - 1\right)(6q)$

3. $\left(y - 3y^{-2}\right)^2$

4. $x(x + x^{-1})^2$

5. $2P^2(P) + (9P)^{1/2}$

6. $\dfrac{(1 + 3\sqrt{t})^2}{2}$

7. $\dfrac{18 + x^2 - 3x}{-6}$

8. $\left(\dfrac{1}{N} - N\right)^2$

9. $\dfrac{-3(4x - x^2)}{7x}$

10. $\dfrac{x^4 + 2x + 1}{2\sqrt{x}}$

11. $\dfrac{ax^2 + bx + c}{x}$

12. $\sqrt{1 + p^2} \cdot (1 + p^2)^{3/2}$

In Problems 13–18, rewrite each expression in the form $a(bx + c)^n$.

13. $\dfrac{12}{\sqrt{3x + 1}}$

14. $\dfrac{250\sqrt[3]{10 - s}}{0.25}$

15. $0.7(x - 1)^3(1 - x)$

16. $\dfrac{1}{2(x^2 + 1)^3}$

17. $4(6R + 2)^3(6)$

18. $\sqrt{\dfrac{28x^2 - 4\pi x}{x}}$

In Problems 19–30, rewrite each expression in the form ab^x or ab^t.

19. $\dfrac{1^x}{2^x}$

20. $\dfrac{1}{2^x}$

21. $10{,}000(1 - 0.24)^t$

22. e^{2x+1}

23. $2 \cdot 3^{-x}$

24. $2^x \cdot 3^{x-1}$

25. $16^{t/2}$

26. $\dfrac{e^3}{e^{-x+4}}$

27. $\dfrac{5^x}{-3^x}$

28. $\dfrac{e \cdot e^x}{0.2}$

29. $\left(10e^t\right)^2$

30. $\dfrac{e^{kt}}{1/A}$

For Problems 31–36, rewrite each expression as a sum of positive powers of the variable.

31. $x^2 + x^{-3}$

32. $\dfrac{5}{x^{-2}} + x + 1$

33. $(2y^2 - 5)3y$

34. $y^3(y + 1)^2$

35. $z^4(1 + z^{-2})^2$

36. $z^5(z^{-3}) - 2z^{-1} + 6$

For Problems 37–42, complete the square for each expression.

37. $x^2 + 8x$

38. $y^2 - 12y$

39. $w^2 + 7w$

40. $2r^2 + 20r$

41. $s^2 + 6s - 8$

42. $3t^2 + 24t - 13$

In Problems 43–46, rewrite each expression in the form $a(x - h)^2 + k$.

43. $x^2 - 2x - 3$

44. $10 - 6x + x^2$

45. $-x^2 + 6x - 2$

46. $3x^2 - 12x + 13$

In Problems 47–52, simplify and rewrite using only positive exponents .

47. $-3\left(x^2 + 7\right)^{-4}(2x)$

48. $-2(1 + 3^x)^{-3}(\ln 2)(2^x)$

49. $-(\sin(\pi t))^{-1}(-\cos(\pi t))\pi$

50. $-(\tan z)^{-2}\left(\dfrac{1}{\cos^2 z}\right)$

51. $\dfrac{-e^x\left(x^2\right) - e^{-x}2x}{\left(x^2\right)^2}$

52. $-x^{-2}(\ln x) + x^{-1}\left(\dfrac{1}{x}\right)$

In Problems 53–60, simplify and rewrite in radical form.

53. $(5x)^{1/2}$

54. $(3x - 2)^{-(1/2)}$

55. $6y(4z - 5)^{1/3}$

56. $(27z)^{5/3}(3w - 1)^{-(1/2)}$

57. $\frac{1}{2}(x^2 + 16)^{-1/2}(2x)$

58. $\frac{1}{2}(x^2 + 10x + 1)^{-1/2}(2x + 10)$

59. $\frac{1}{2}(\sin(2x))^{-1/2}(2)\cos(2x)$

60. $\frac{2}{3}\left(x^2 - e^{3x}\right)^{-5/3}\left(3x^2 - e^{3x}(3)\right)$

F SOLVING EQUATIONS

Solving in Your Head

When we first look at an equation, we see if we can guess the answer by mentally trying numbers. Consider the following equations and mental solutions.

$\sqrt{x} - 4 = 0$	*"I'm looking for a number whose square root is 4."*	$\sqrt{16} - 4 = 0$
$2x - 3 = 0$	*"What value can I use for x that will give $2x = 3$?"*	$2\left(\frac{3}{2}\right) - 3 = 0$
$\frac{3}{x} + 1 = 0$	*"Three divided by what number gives -1?"*	$\frac{3}{(-3)} + 1 = 0$
$e^x = 1$	*"What exponent can I use with the base e to get 1?"*	$e^{(0)} = 1$
$x^2(x + 2) = 0$	*"What number makes each factor zero?"*	$0^2 = 0$ and $(-2) + 2 = 0$
$\frac{(x + 1)(3 - x)}{(1 - x)^2} = 0$	*"What numbers make the numerator equal to 0?"*	$(-1) + 1 = 0$ and $3 - (3) = 0$
$1 - \sin x = 0$	*"What numbers make the sine value equal 1?"*	$1 - \sin\left(\frac{\pi}{2}\right) = 0$

Notice that the last equation, $\sin x = 1$, has many other solutions as well.

Solving Exactly Versus Solving Approximately

Some equations can be solved exactly, often by using algebra. For example, the equation $7x - 1 = 0$ has the exact solution $x = 1/7$. Other equations can be hard or even impossible to solve exactly. However, it is often possible, and sometimes easier, to find an approximate solution to an equation by using a graph or a numerical method on a calculator. The equation $7x - 1 = 0$ has the approximate solution $x \approx 0.14$ (since $1/7 = 0.142857\ldots$). We use the sign $\approx$, meaning approximately equal, when we want to emphasize that we are making an approximation.

Example 1   Give exact and approximate solutions to $x^2 = 3$.

Solution   The exact solutions are $x = \pm\sqrt{3}$; approximate ones are $x \approx \pm 1.73$, or $x \approx \pm 1.732$, or $x \approx \pm 1.73205$. (since $\sqrt{3} = 1.732050808\ldots$). Notice that the equation $x^2 = 3$ has only two exact solutions, but many possible approximate solutions, depending on how much accuracy is required.

Operations on Equations

For more complicated equations, additional steps may be needed in order to find a solution.

Linear Equations

To solve a linear equation, we clear any parentheses and then isolate the variable.

Example 2   Solve $3 - [5.4 + 2(4.3 - x)] = 2 - (0.3x - 0.8)$ for x.

Solution   We begin by clearing the innermost parentheses on each side. This gives

$$3 - [5.4 + 8.6 - 2x] = 2 - 0.3x + 0.8.$$

Then

$$3 - 14 + 2x = 2 - 0.3x + 0.8$$
$$2.3x = 13.8,$$
$$x = 6.$$

Example 3   Solve for q if $p^2q + r(-q - 1) = 4(p + r)$.

Solution

$$p^2q - rq - r = 4p + 4r$$
$$p^2q - rq = 4p + 5r$$
$$q(p^2 - r) = 4p + 5r$$
$$q = \frac{4p + 5r}{p^2 - r}$$

Solving by Factoring

Some equations can be put into factored form such that the product of the factors is zero. Then we solve by using the fact that if $a \cdot b = 0$, then either a or b (or both) is zero.

Example 4   Solve $(x + 1)(x + 3) = 15$ for x.

Solution   Do not make the mistake of setting $x + 1 = 15$ and $x + 3 = 15$. It is not true that $a \cdot b = 15$ means that $a = 15$ or $b = 15$ (or both). (Although it is true that if $a \cdot b = 0$, then $a = 0$ or $b = 0$, or both.) So, we must expand the left-hand side and set the equation equal to zero:

$$x^2 + 4x + 3 = 15,$$
$$x^2 + 4x - 12 = 0.$$

Then, factoring gives

$$(x - 2)(x + 6) = 0.$$

Thus $x = 2$ and $x = -6$ are solutions.

Example 5   Solve $2(x + 3)^2 = 5(x + 3)$.

Solution   You might be tempted to divide both sides by $(x + 3)$. However, if you do this you will overlook one of the solutions. Instead, write

$$2(x + 3)^2 - 5(x + 3) = 0$$
$$(x + 3)\left(2(x + 3) - 5\right) = 0$$
$$(x + 3)(2x + 6 - 5) = 0$$
$$(x + 3)(2x + 1) = 0.$$

Thus, $x = -\frac{1}{2}$ and $x = -3$ are solutions.

Example 6   Solve $e^x + xe^x = 0$.

Solution   Factoring gives $e^x(1 + x) = 0$. Since e^x is never zero, $x = -1$ is the only solution.

Using the Quadratic Formula

If an equation is in the form $ax^2 + bx + c = 0$, we can use the quadratic formula to find the solutions,

$$x = \frac{-b + \sqrt{b^2 - 4ac}}{2a} \quad \text{or} \quad x = \frac{-b - \sqrt{b^2 - 4ac}}{2a}.$$

provided that $\sqrt{b^2 - 4ac}$ is a real number.

Example 7   Solve $11 + 2x = x^2$.

Solution   The equation is

$$-x^2 + 2x + 11 = 0.$$

The expression on the left does not factor using integers, so we use

$$x = \frac{-2 + \sqrt{4 - 4(-1)(11)}}{2(-1)} = \frac{-2 + \sqrt{48}}{-2} = \frac{-2 + \sqrt{16 \cdot 3}}{-2} = \frac{-2 + 4\sqrt{3}}{-2} = 1 - 2\sqrt{3},$$

$$x = \frac{-2 - \sqrt{4 - 4(-1)(11)}}{2(-1)} = \frac{-2 - \sqrt{48}}{-2} = \frac{-2 - \sqrt{16 \cdot 3}}{-2} = \frac{-2 - 4\sqrt{3}}{-2} = 1 + 2\sqrt{3}.$$

The exact solutions are $x = 1 - 2\sqrt{3}$ and $x = 1 + 2\sqrt{3}$.

The decimal approximations to these numbers $x = 1 - 2\sqrt{3} = -2.46$ and $x = 1 + 2\sqrt{3} = 4.46$ are approximate solutions to this equation. The approximate solutions could be found directly from a graph or calculator.

Fractional Equations

If an equation involves fractions, we can eliminate the fractions by multiplying both sides of the equation by the least common denominator and then solving as before. However, we must check for extraneous solutions at the end.

Example 8   Solve $\dfrac{2x}{x + 1} - 3 = \dfrac{2}{x^2 + x}$ for x.

Solution   To look for a common denominator, factor $x^2 + x$. Then we have

$$\frac{2x}{x + 1} - 3 = \frac{2}{x(x + 1)}.$$

Multiplying both sides by $x(x + 1)$ gives

$$x(x + 1)\left(\frac{2x}{x + 1} - 3\right) = 2$$
$$2x^2 - 3x(x + 1) = 2$$
$$2x^2 - 3x^2 - 3x = 2$$
$$-x^2 - 3x - 2 = 0,$$

or

$$x^2 + 3x + 2 = 0.$$

Factoring, we have

$$(x + 2)(x + 1) = 0,$$

so $x = -2$ and $x = -1$ are potential solutions. However, the original equation is not defined for $x = -1$, so $x = -1$ is extraneous. The only solution is $x = -2$.

Example 9   Solve for P_2 if $\dfrac{1}{P_1} + \dfrac{1}{P_2} = \dfrac{1}{P_3}$.

Solution   Multiplying by $P_1 P_2 P_3$ gives

$$P_2 P_3 + P_1 P_3 = P_1 P_2.$$

We are solving for P_2, so we move all P_2 terms to one side

$$P_2 P_3 - P_1 P_2 = -P_1 P_3.$$

Factoring out P_2 gives

$$P_2(P_3 - P_1) = -P_1 P_3$$
$$P_2 = \frac{-P_1 P_3}{P_3 - P_1} = \frac{P_1 P_3}{P_1 - P_3}.$$

Note that we assume that none of P_1, P_2, or $P_3 = 0$. Also, we assume $P_3 \neq P_1$, or else the denominator of the solution is 0.

Radical Equations

We solve radical equations by raising both sides of the equation to the same power. The principle is that if $a = b$, then $a^r = b^r$. Again, we must check for extraneous solutions.

Example 10   Solve $2\sqrt{x} = x - 3$.

Solution   Squaring both sides gives

$$(2\sqrt{x})^2 = (x - 3)^2$$
$$4x = x^2 - 6x + 9.$$

Then

$$x^2 - 10x + 9 = 0$$
$$(x - 1)(x - 9) = 0,$$

so $x = 1$ and $x = 9$ are potential solutions. Since $x = 1$ is not a solution of the original equation, the only solution is $x = 9$.

Example 11   Solve $4 = x^{-1/2}$.

Solution   Taking both sides to the -2 power:

$$(4)^{-2} = (x^{-1/2})^{-2}$$
$$(4)^{-2} = x,$$
$$x = \frac{1}{16}.$$

Exponential Equations

When the variable we want to solve for is in the exponent, we again "do the same thing" to both sides of the equation. This time we take logarithms using the property that if $a = b$ then $\log a = \log b$, (provided $a, b > 0$). Note that we could also use the natural logarithm. The logarithm rule that $\log(m^x) = x \log m$ enables us to solve the equation.

Example 12   Solve $10^{2x+1} = 3$ for x.

Solution   Taking logs,

$$\log 10^{2x+1} = \log 3$$
$$2x + 1 = \log 3, \qquad \text{Since } \log 10^P = P$$
$$x = \frac{(\log 3) - 1}{2}.$$

The solution $x = ((\log 3) - 1)/2$ is exact; converting the solution to $x \approx -0.2614$ gives an approximate solution.

Example 13   Solve $2e^x = 12$.

Solution   We have

$$e^x = 6 \qquad \text{Dividing both sides by 2}$$
$$\ln e^x = \ln 6 \qquad \text{Taking the natural log of both sides}$$
$$x = \ln 6 \qquad \text{Since } \ln e^P = P.$$

Example 14   Solve $1.07 = 4^{-x}$.

Solution   Taking natural logs of both sides

$$\ln 1.07 = \ln(4^{-x})$$
$$\ln 1.07 = (-x)(\ln 4)$$
$$x = -\frac{\ln 1.07}{\ln 4}$$

When applying the logarithm function to both sides of an equation, we may use log base 10 or log base e (the natural log). In Example 12, log base 10 is most convenient, as is the natural log for Example 13. The answers $x = ((\log 3) - 1)/2$ and $x = \ln 6$ are *exact* solutions. In order to compare answers in different forms or use these solutions in a numerical computation, we use a calculator to find a decimal approximation.

Example 15   Solve for x in Examples 13 and 14 by taking the logarithm base 10 (rather than the natural logarithm) of both sides of the equations. Determine decimal approximations (to the accuracy of your calculator) for the solutions you find and for the solutions given in Examples 13 and 14. Do the answers agree?

Solution   In Example 13, we have

$$2e^x = 12$$
$$e^x = 6$$
$$\log e^x = \log 6$$
$$x \log e = \log 6$$
$$x = \frac{\log 6}{\log e} \approx 1.791759469.$$

The exact answer $x = \ln 6$ given in Example 13 is in a simpler form, but $\ln 6 \approx 1.791759469$, an approximate solution. Yes, the answers agree (to at least nine decimal places)

In Example 14,

$$1.07 = 4^{-x}$$

$$\log 1.07 = \log 4^{-x}$$

$$\log 1.07 = -x \log 4$$

$$x = -\frac{\log 1.07}{\log 4} \approx -0.0488053983.$$

This agrees with the exact solution $x = -\dfrac{\ln 1.07}{\ln 4} \approx -0.0488053983.$

The solutions $-\log 1.07 / \log 4$ and $-\ln 1.07 / \ln 4$ are two different ways of writing the exact solution, while -0.0488053983 is an approximate solution.

Example 16 Solve for t in the equation $P = P_0 e^{kt}$.

Solution Dividing both sides by P_0, we have

$$\frac{P}{P_0} = e^{kt},$$

so

$$\ln\left(\frac{P}{P_0}\right) = \ln e^{kt},$$

$$\ln\left(\frac{P}{P_0}\right) = kt.$$

Thus, $t = \dfrac{1}{k} \ln\left(\dfrac{P}{P_0}\right).$

Problems for Section F

For Problems 1–23, solve each of the following equations for the variable.

1. $3x = 15$
2. $-2y = 12$
3. $4z = 22$
4. $x + 3 = 10$
5. $y - 5 = 21$
6. $w - 23 = -34$
7. $2x - 5 = 13$
8. $7 - 3y = -14$
9. $13t + 2 = 47$
10. $2x - 5 = 4x - 9$
11. $17 - 28y = 13y + 24$
12. $x^2 + 7x + 6 = 0$
13. $y^2 - 5y - 6 = 0$
14. $2w^2 + w - 10 = 0$
15. $4s^2 + 3s - 15 = 0$
16. $\dfrac{2}{x} + \dfrac{3}{2x} = 8$
17. $\dfrac{3}{x - 1} + 1 = 5$
18. $\sqrt{y - 1} = 13$
19. $\sqrt{5y + 3} = 7$
20. $\sqrt{2x - 1} + 3 = 9$
21. $\dfrac{21}{z - 5} - \dfrac{13}{z^2 - 5z} = 3$
22. $-16t^2 + 96t + 12 = 60$
23. $2(r + 5) - 3 = 3(r - 8) + 21$

For Problems 24–35, solve each of the following equations for the specified variable.

24. $A = l \cdot w$, for l.
25. $C = 2\pi r$, for r.
26. $I = Prt$, for P.
27. $C = \dfrac{5}{9}(F - 32)$, for F.
28. $e^{kt} = 1.0573$, for k.
29. $0.079 = \ln B$, for B.
30. $3xy + 1 = 2y - 5x$, for y.
31. $\dfrac{At - B}{C - B(1 - 2t)} = 3$, for t.
32. $\dfrac{a - cx}{b + dx} + a = 0$, for x.
33. $Ab^5 = C$, for b.
34. $|2x + 1| = 7$, for x.
35. $P = Qe^{kt} - P$, for t.

Solve the equations in Problems 36–58.

36. $B - 4[B - 3(1 - B)] = 42$ 37. $1.06s - 0.01(248.4 - s) = 22.67s$

38. $\dfrac{5}{3}(y + 2) = \dfrac{1}{2} - y$ 39. $3t - \dfrac{2(t - 1)}{3} = 4$ 40. $8 + 2x - 3x^2 = 0$

41. $2p^3 + p^2 - 18p - 9 = 0$ 42. $N^2 - 2N - 3 = 2N(N - 3)$ 43. $\dfrac{1}{64}t^3 = t$

44. $x^2 - 1 = 2x$ 45. $4x^2 - 13x - 12 = 0$ 46. $60 = -16t^2 + 96t + 12$

47. $y^2 + 4y - 2 = 0$ 48. $\dfrac{2}{z - 3} + \dfrac{7}{z^2 - 3z} = 0$ 49. $\dfrac{x^2 + 1 - 2x^2}{(x^2 + 1)^2} = 0$

50. $4 - \dfrac{1}{L^2} = 0$ 51. $2 + \dfrac{1}{q + 1} - \dfrac{1}{q - 1} = 0$ 52. $\sqrt{r^2 + 24} = 7$

53. $\dfrac{1}{\sqrt[3]{x}} = -2$ 54. $3\sqrt{x} = \dfrac{1}{2}x$ 55. $10 = \sqrt{\dfrac{v}{7\pi}}$

56. $\dfrac{(3x + 4)(x - 2)}{(x - 5)(x - 1)} = 0$ 57. $5^{2x} - 5^x - 6 = 0$ 58. $2 \cdot 16^x - 5 \cdot 4^x = 12$

For Problems 59–62, express answers in exact form and give a decimal approximation (to two decimal places).

59. $5000 = 2500(0.97)^t$ 60. $280 = 40 + 30e^{2t}$

61. $\dfrac{1}{2}(2^x) = 16$ 62. $1 + 10^{-x} = 4.3$

In Problems 63–76, solve for the indicated variable.

63. $\left(\dfrac{1}{2}\right)^{t/1000} = e^{kt}$.   Solve for k (to six decimal places).

64. $\dfrac{1}{2}P_0 = P_0(0.8)^x$.   Solve for x (to three decimal places).

65. $T = 2\pi\sqrt{\dfrac{l}{g}}$. Solve for l.

66. $y'y^2 + 2xyy' = 4y$. Solve for y'.

67. $l = l_0 + \dfrac{k}{2}w$. Solve for w.

68. $2x - (xy' + yy') + 2yy' = 0$. Solve for y'.

69. $by - d = ay + c$. Solve for y.

70. $u(v + 2) + w(v - 3) = z(v - 1)$. Solve for v.

71. $S = \dfrac{rL - a}{r - 1}$. Solve for r.

72. $h = v_0t + \dfrac{1}{2}at^2$. Solve for a.

73. $K = \dfrac{MA(y - z)}{N}$. Solve for z.

74. $R = \dfrac{eb + de}{e + f}$. Solve for e.

75. $x + z = \dfrac{y + z}{y} + w$. Solve for z.

76. $\dfrac{3s - t}{2s} = 4 - \dfrac{v}{w}$. Solve for s.

77. Solve for x by completing the square: $8x^2 - 1 = 2x$.

78. Solve for x:

$$\dfrac{x^2 - 5mx + 4m^2}{x - m} = 0.$$

G SYSTEMS OF EQUATIONS

To solve for two unknowns, we must have two equations— that is, two relationships between the unknowns. Similarly, three unknowns require three equations, and n unknowns (n an integer) require n equations. The group of equations is known as a *system* of equations. To solve the system, we find the *simultaneous* solutions to all equations in the system.

Example 1   Solve for x and y in the following system of equations.

$$\begin{cases} y + \dfrac{x}{2} = 3 \\ 2(x + y) = 1 - y \end{cases}$$

Solution   Solving the first equation for y, we write $y = 3 - x/2$. Substituting for y in the second equation gives

$$2\left(x + \left(3 - \frac{x}{2}\right)\right) = 1 - \left(3 - \frac{x}{2}\right).$$

Then

$$2x + 6 - x = -2 + \frac{x}{2}$$
$$x + 6 = -2 + \frac{x}{2}$$
$$2x + 12 = -4 + x$$
$$x = -16.$$

Using $x = -16$ in the first equation to find the corresponding y, we have

$$y - \frac{16}{2} = 3$$
$$y = 3 + 8 = 11.$$

Thus, the solution that simultaneously solves both equations is $x = -16$, $y = 11$.

Example 2   Solve for x and y in the following system.

$$\begin{cases} y = x - 1 \\ x^2 + y^2 = 5 \end{cases}$$

Solution   We substitute the expression $(x - 1)$ for y in the second equation. Then

$$x^2 + (x - 1)^2 = 5$$
$$x^2 + x^2 - 2x + 1 = 5$$
$$2x^2 - 2x - 4 = 0$$
$$x^2 - x - 2 = 0.$$

Factoring gives $(x - 2)(x + 1) = 0$, so $x = 2$ or $x = -1$.

We then find the y-values which correspond to each x. If $x = 2$, then $y = (2) - 1 = 1$. If $x = -1$, then $y = (-1) - 1 = -2$. The solutions to the system are $x = 2$ and $y = 1$ or $x = -1$ and $y = -2$. Notice that $x = 2$ and $y = -2$ is *not* a solution; nor is $x = -1$ and $y = 1$.

Example 3   Solve for Q_0 and a in the system

$$\begin{cases} 90.7 = Q_0 a^{10} \\ 91 = Q_0 a^{13}. \end{cases}$$

Solution   Taking ratios,

$$\frac{Q_0 a^{13}}{Q_0 a^{10}} = \frac{91}{90.7}$$
$$a^3 = \frac{91}{90.7},$$
$$a = \sqrt[3]{\frac{91}{90.7}} \approx 1.0011.$$

To find Q_0,

$$90.7 = Q_0(1.0011)^{10},$$
$$Q_0 = 89.7083.$$

The simultaneous solution is $a \approx 1.0011$ and $Q_0 \approx 89.7083$.

Graphically, the simultaneous solutions to a system of equations give us the coordinates of the point (or points) of intersection for the graphs of the equations in the system. For example, the solutions to Example 2 give the coordinates of the points where the line $y = x - 1$ intersects the circle centered at the origin with radius $\sqrt{5}$.

Example 4   Find the points of intersection for the graphs in Figure G.1.

Solution   We can solve $y = x^2 - 1$ and $y = x + 1$ simultaneously by setting the y-values equal to one another. Then

$$x^2 - 1 = x + 1$$
$$x^2 - x - 2 = 0$$
$$(x + 1)(x - 2) = 0,$$

so $x = -1$ and $x = 2$ are solutions. To get the corresponding y-values, we use either equation to find $x = -1$ gives $y = 0$, and $x = 2$ gives $y = 3$. The graphs intersect at the points $(-1, 0)$ and $(2, 3)$.

For some systems of equations, it is impossible to find the simultaneous solution(s) using algebra. In this case, the only choice is to find the solution(s) by approximating the point(s) of intersection graphically.

Figure G.1

Figure G.2: The graphs reveal two intersection points

Example 5   Solve the system:

$$\begin{cases} y = x + 1 \\ y = 3^{x-1} \end{cases}$$

Solution   We are looking for the point or points of intersection of the line $y = x + 1$ and the exponential equation $y = 3^{x-1}$. Setting the expressions for y equal to one another gives

$$x + 1 = 3^{x-1}.$$

We cannot use the algebraic techniques of the previous section to solve this equation. We might try to guess a solution. Note that

$$2 + 1 = 3^{2-1}$$
$$3 = 3,$$

so $x = 2$, $y = 3$ is a solution to the system. If you were not able to guess this solution, you would be able to approximate it from the graph.

However, the graphs of the equations in Figure G.2 reveal that the system has two solutions. There is also a value of x such that $-1 < x < 0$ where the two graphs intersect. By tracing along the graph, we find

$$x \approx -0.8721, \, y \approx 0.1279.$$

Thus, the solutions to the system are $x = 2$ and $y = 3$ or $x \approx -0.8721$ and $y \approx 0.1279$.

Simultaneous solutions to a system of equations in two variables can always be approximated by graphing, whereas it is only sometimes possible to find exact solutions using algebra.

Problems for Section G

Solve the systems of equations in Problems 1–12 for x and y.

1. $\begin{cases} x + y = 3 \\ x - y = 5 \end{cases}$

   2. $\begin{cases} 2x - y = 10 \\ x + 2y = 15 \end{cases}$

   3. $\begin{cases} 3x - 2y = 6 \\ y = 2x - 5 \end{cases}$

4. $\begin{cases} x = 7y - 9 \\ 4x - 15y = 26 \end{cases}$

   5. $\begin{cases} x^2 + y^2 = 36 \\ y = x - 3 \end{cases}$

   6. $\begin{cases} 2x + 3y = 7 \\ y = -\frac{3}{5}x + 6 \end{cases}$

7. $\begin{cases} y = 2x - x^2 \\ y = -3 \end{cases}$

   8. $\begin{cases} y = 4 - x^2 \\ y - 2x = 1 \end{cases}$

   9. $\begin{cases} y = 1/x \\ y = 4x \end{cases}$

10. $\begin{cases} 2(x + y) = 3 \\ x = y + 3(x - 5) \end{cases}$

    11. $\begin{cases} y = x^3 - 1 \\ y = e^x \end{cases}$

    12. $\begin{cases} ax + y = 2a \\ x + ay = 1 + a^2 \end{cases}$

13. Let ℓ be the line of slope 3 passing through the origin. Find the points of intersection of the line ℓ and the parabola whose equation is $y = x^2$. Sketch the line and the parabola, and label the points of intersection.

Determine the points of intersection for Problems 14–16.

14.

15.

16.

H INEQUALITIES

Just as we can solve some simple equations mentally, we can solve some inequalities mentally. Consider the following examples.

To solve:	We think:	The solution is:
$x - 1 > 0$	*"If x is larger than +1, the left hand side is positive."*	$x > 1$
$x + 4 < 10$	*"As long as x stays smaller than +6, the left hand side will be less than the right hand side."*	$x < 6$
$3 - x < 0$	*"When x gets larger than +3, the left hand side will be negative."*	$x > 3$
$x - 2 \geq 0$	*"If x = 2 then x − 2 is 0. When x is larger than 2, then x − 2 is positive."*	$x \geq 2$
$x^2(x + 5) > 0$	*"The value of x^2 is always positive, so x + 5 needs to be positive."*	$x > -5$

We solve inequalities using some of the techniques used in solving equations. However, there are some important differences in the application of these techniques to inequalities.

For a, b, and c real numbers, if $a < b$, then

$$a + c < b + c$$
$$a \cdot c < b \cdot c \qquad \text{if } c > 0$$
$$a \cdot c > b \cdot c \qquad \text{if } c < 0 \qquad \text{(Inequality reverses direction)}.$$

For a and b positive, when $a < b$, then

$$a^2 < b^2 \quad \text{, and} \quad \frac{1}{a} > \frac{1}{b} \qquad \text{(Inequality reverses direction)}.$$

Linear Inequalities

We solve linear inequalities with the techniques we use to solve linear equations; however, the inequality is reversed when we multiply or divide both sides of the inequality by a negative number.

Example 1   Solve for x:

$$1 - \frac{3}{2}x \leq 16.$$

Solution   We have

$$1 - \frac{3}{2}x - 1 \leq 16 - 1$$
$$-\frac{3}{2}x \leq 15$$
$$\left(-\frac{2}{3}\right)\left(-\frac{3}{2}x\right) \geq \left(-\frac{2}{3}\right)15$$
$$x \geq -10.$$

Example 2   Solve for x:

$$-6 < 4x - 7 < 5.$$

Solution   The solutions to this double inequality is all values of x such that $4x - 7$ is between -6 and 5. We can operate on all three sections of the inequality at once (if we're careful). We start by adding 7 to each part which gives

$$-6 + 7 < 4x - 7 + 7 < 5 + 7.$$
$$1 < 4x < 12$$
$$\frac{1}{4} < x < 3.$$

The solution is all numbers between 1/4 and 3.

Checking the Sign of an Expression

When an expression is a product or a quotient, we can determine the sign of the expression on an interval by looking at the sign of each factor over the interval.

Example 3   Determine the values of x which make the expression $(4 - x)^2 e^{-x}$ positive, negative, and zero respectively.

Solution   The expression e^{-x} is always positive, and $(4 - x)^2$ is positive for any value of x except $x = 4$, where it equals zero. Therefore, $(4 - x)^2 e^{-x} > 0$ for $x \neq 4$, and $(4 - x)^2 e^{-x} = 0$ if $x = 4$.

Example 4   Determine the values of x which make the expression $(x + 1)(x - 7)$ positive, negative, and zero respectively.

Solution   The expression is zero if $x = -1$ or $x = +7$. The product can change sign at $x = -1$ or $x = +7$. We check the sign of the expression by looking at the sign of each factor over the intervals established by dividing the number line at $x = -1$ and $x = +7$. The expression is positive when both factors have the same sign.

$$
\begin{array}{ccccc}
(-)(-) & & (+)(-) & & (+)(+) \\
\hline
\text{Positive} & -1 & \text{Negative} & 7 & \text{Positive}
\end{array} \quad x
$$

Thus,

$$(x + 1)(x - 7) = 0 \quad \text{for } x = -1 \text{ or } x = 7,$$
$$(x + 1)(x - 7) < 0 \quad \text{for } -1 < x < 7,$$
$$(x + 1)(x - 7) > 0 \quad \text{for } x < -1 \text{ or } x > 7.$$

Example 5   Determine the values of r for which the expression $\dfrac{2r + 5}{(r - 1)(r - 3)}$ is zero, positive, negative, or undefined.

Solution   A fraction is equal to 0 if the numerator is 0, so this expression equals 0 if $r = -\frac{5}{2}$. The values $r = 1$ and $r = 3$ make the expression undefined because the denominator is zero there. We divide the number line by marking $-\frac{5}{2}$, 1, and 3, and we check the sign of each each factor on each interval. This gives

$$
\begin{array}{ccccccc}
\dfrac{(-)}{(-)(-)} & & \dfrac{(+)}{(-)(-)} & & \dfrac{(+)}{(+)(-)} & & \dfrac{(+)}{(+)(+)} \\
\hline
\text{Negative} & -\frac{5}{2} & \text{Positive} & 1 & \text{Negative} & 3 & \text{Positive}
\end{array} \quad r
$$

Therefore,

$$\frac{2r + 5}{(r - 1)(r - 3)} \quad \text{is not defined for } r = 1 \text{ or } r = 3.$$
$$\frac{2r + 5}{(r - 1)(r - 3)} = 0 \quad \text{for } r = -\frac{5}{2},$$
$$\frac{2r + 5}{(r - 1)(r - 3)} > 0 \quad \text{for } -\frac{5}{2} < r < 1 \text{ or } r > 3,$$
$$\frac{2r + 5}{(r - 1)(r - 3)} < 0 \quad \text{for } r < -\frac{5}{2} \text{ or } 1 < r < 3,$$

Example 6   Determine y-values which make the expression $\dfrac{\sqrt{y+2}}{y^3}$ positive, negative, zero, or undefined.

Solution   The expression is zero if $y = -2$. It is not defined if y is less than -2 because we cannot take the square root of a negative number. Furthermore, the quotient is not defined if $y = 0$ because that puts a zero in the denominator. The radical is always positive (where defined), so the numerator is positive. Because the cube of a negative number is negative, we can visualize signs in each interval.

So

$$\dfrac{\sqrt{y+2}}{y^3} \quad \text{is undefined for } y < -2 \text{ or } y = 0,$$

$$\dfrac{\sqrt{y+2}}{y^3} = 0 \quad \text{for } y = -2,$$

$$\dfrac{\sqrt{y+2}}{y^3} > 0 \quad \text{for } y > 0.$$

$$\dfrac{\sqrt{y+2}}{y^3} < 0 \quad \text{for } -2 < y < 0,$$

Solving Nonlinear Inequalities by Factoring and Checking Signs

We can often solve polynomial and rational inequalities by starting out the same way we would with an equation and then using a number line to find the intervals on which the inequality holds.

Example 7   Solve for x if

$$2x^2 + x^3 \leq 3x.$$

Solution   We first set the inequality so that zero is on one side. Then

$$x^3 + 2x^2 - 3x \leq 0,$$
$$x(x^2 + 2x - 3) \leq 0,$$
$$x(x + 3)(x - 1) \leq 0.$$

The left hand side equals 0 for $x = 0$, $x = -3$, and $x = 1$. To solve the inequality we want to select the x-values for which the left hand side is negative. We check signs over the four intervals created by marking $x = 0, -3, +1$.

$$
\begin{array}{ccccccc}
(-)(-)(-) & & (-)(+)(-) & & (+)(+)(-) & (+)(+)(+) & \\
\hline
\text{Negative} & -3 & \text{Positive} & & 0 \quad \text{Negative} & 1 \quad \text{Positive} & x
\end{array}
$$

So $x^3 + 2x^2 - 3x < 0$ for $x < -3$ or $0 < x < 1$ and $x^3 + 2x^2 - 3x = 0$ at $x = 0$, $x = -3$, and $x = 1$. Therefore, $2x^2 + x^3 \leq 3x$ for $x \leq -3$ or $0 \leq x \leq 1$.

Example 8   Solve for q: $\quad \dfrac{1}{2 - q} > q.$

Solution   First, put 0 on the right, then combine the fractions on the left.

$$\frac{1}{2-q} - q > 0,$$

$$\frac{1}{2-q} - q\frac{(2-q)}{(2-q)} > 0,$$

$$\frac{1 - q(2-q)}{2-q} > 0,$$

$$\frac{1 - 2q + q^2}{2-q} > 0.$$

We want this quotient to be positive, so the numerator and denominator must have the same sign. Notice that $q \neq 2$. Factoring the numerator, we have $\dfrac{(1-q)^2}{2-q} > 0$. The numerator is never negative, and the denominator is positive if $2 - q > 0$ which gives $q < 2$. However, $(1-q)^2 = 0$ if $q = 1$, so $q = 1$ must be excluded in order to preserve the inequality. Therefore, $\dfrac{1}{2-q} > q$ for $q < 2$ and $q \neq 1$.

Radical inequalities

We can eliminate radicals by raising both sides of an equation to the same power. However, we must check our answers for extraneous roots.

Example 9   Solve for x: $\sqrt{x - 6} < 2$.

Solution   The expression $\sqrt{x - 6}$ is not defined unless $x \geq 6$, so we can restrict the x-values we consider to $x \geq 6$. Also, $\sqrt{x - 6} \geq 0$, so we can square both sides giving

$$(\sqrt{x - 6})^2 < 2^2,$$

$$x - 6 < 4,$$

$$x < 10.$$

However, we are only considering x-values which are 6 or larger, so $\sqrt{x - 6} < 4$ for $6 \leq x < 10$.

Example 10   Solve for x: $\sqrt{2 - x} > 3$.

Solution   Squaring both sides gives

$$(\sqrt{2 - x})^2 > 3^2,$$

$$2 - x > 9,$$

$$-x > 7,$$

$$x < -7.$$

In this case, the fact that the radical is only defined for $x \leq 2$ does not affect our solution because any number which is less than -7 is also less than 2.

Inequalities and Interval Notation

Inequalities can be used to describe sets of numbers. For instance $x \leq 5$ represents the set of all real numbers less than or equal to 5. Likewise, $x \geq -2$ represents the set of all real numbers greater than or equal to -2. Graphically, we represent the set of real numbers less than or equal to 5 as

5

The dot at 5 shows that the number 5 is included. Alternatively, this set of real numbers can be represented using interval notation. For example, $x \leq 5$ can be written as $(-\infty, 5]$, where $-\infty$ means that we consider arbitrarily large negative numbers.

Example 11   Represent the intervals (a) $-2 \leq y \leq 5$ (b) $-2 < y < 5$ graphically and using interval notation.

Solution   (a)

and $[-2, 5]$.

(b)

and $(-2, 5)$.

Notice that the endpoint of an interval is included if the dot on a number line is filled in, or if square brackets, [,], are used in interval notation. If the dot is not filled in or parentheses, (,), are used in the interval notation, the endpoint of the intervals is not included.

Example 12   Use interval notation to represent the following intervals of real numbers:

(a) $-2 \leq x < 3$ (b) $r < 0$ (c) $10 < t \leq 17.5$

(d) $\dfrac{1}{2} \leq w \leq \dfrac{9}{2}$ (e) $-12 < r$ (f) $|x| < 9$

Solution   (a) $[-2, 3)$ (b) $(-\infty, 0)$ (c) $(10, 17.5]$ (d) $[1/2, 9/2]$ (e) $(-12, \infty)$ (f) $(-9, 9)$

Problems for Section H

Solve the inequalities in Problems 1–15 mentally.

1. $2(x - 7) \geq 0$ 2. $\sqrt{x} > 4$ 3. $x^2 < 25$
4. $x - 3 > 2$ 5. $1 + \sqrt{x + 4} > 0$ 6. $|t| < 5$
7. $x^2 \geq 16$ 8. $1 + x^2 > 0$ 9. $5 - x < 0$
10. $2^{-x} > 0$ 11. $|\theta| - 1 \leq 7$ 12. $2x^2 + 1 < 0$
13. $\dfrac{x - 5}{x^2 + 1} > 0$ 14. $e^t(t + 3) < 0$ 15. $\dfrac{2 + z}{5 + z^4} < 0$

Write the statements in Problem 16–21 as inequalities.

16. The x-values which are less than 0.001   17. The y-values between -1 and 1
18. All p-values except 5   19. All the positive values of k
20. All the r-values which are not negative   21. The t-values during or after the year 1995

For Problems 22–35, solve the following inequalities and graph the solutions on a number line.

22. $x - 3 > 1$ 23. $3x - 5 > 1$ 24. $-2x > 8$ 25. $-4x + 7 < 13$

26. $x^2 - 5x + 6 > 0$ 27. $x^2 - 7x < 8$ 28. $\dfrac{1}{x - 3} > 0$ 29. $\dfrac{2}{x - 5} > 3$

30. $|x| > 2$ 31. $|y - 2| > 4$ 32. $|3w - 2| - 4 < 0$ 33. $|2z - 7| < 8$
34. $|r| \geq 0$ 35. $|r| < 0$

In Problems 36–47, determine the real number values of the variable (if any) which will make each expression (a) undefined, (b) zero, (c) positive, (d) negative.

36. $3x^2 + 6x$

37. $(2x)e^x + x^2 e^x$

38. 2^{-x}

39. $6t^2 - 30t + 36$

40. $\frac{1}{3}x^{-2/3}$

41. $\frac{-24}{p^3}$

42. $\frac{1}{2\sqrt{x^2 + 1}}(2x)$

43. $\frac{\ln x}{x}$

44. $\frac{t - 3}{t^2 + 10}$

45. $\frac{x - 1}{x - 2}$

46. $\frac{1 - 3u^2}{(u^2 + 1)^3}$

47. $-\frac{2x - 1}{\left(x(x - 1)\right)^2}$

Solve the inequalities in Problems 48–59.

48. $4 - x^2 > 0$

49. $-1 \leq 4x - 3 \leq 1$

50. $0 \leq \frac{1}{2} - n < 11$

51. $\sqrt{3l} - \frac{1}{4} > 0$

52. $t^2 - 3t - 4 \geq 0$

53. $2(x-1)(x+4)+(x-1)^2 > 0$

54. $\frac{5x}{3} - \frac{3}{2} \leq \frac{8x}{5}$

55. $\frac{1}{x} < \frac{1}{2}$

56. $2 + \frac{r}{r - 3} > 0$

57. $\frac{1}{x} > \frac{1}{x + 1}$

58. $\frac{2x^2 - (2x + 1)(2x)}{x^4} < 0$

59. $\frac{3(x + 2)^2 - 6x(x + 2)}{(x + 2)^4} > 0$

9 92

11 1600

13 $16n^2$

15 (a) $1, n$

   (b) $n, n(n+1)/2$

17 (b) $c_n = 300 + \frac{1}{2}(n-1)(3n-46)$
    $c_{12} = 245, c_{50} = 2848$

   (c) 19

Section 11.2

1 Yes, $a = 2$, ratio $= 1/2$.

3 No. Ratio between successive terms is not constant

5 Yes, $a = 1$, ratio $= -x$.

7 Yes, $a = y^2$, ratio $= y$.

9 $1/(1+x), |x| < 1$

11 $\sum_{n=0}^{4} 4^n$

13 $\sum_{n=0}^{6} 2(5^n)$

15 889

17 5.997

19 3,985,805

21 1/54

23 8184

25 (a) $0.23 + 0.23(0.01) + +0.23(0.01)^2 + \cdots$

   (b) $0.23/(1 - 0.01) = 23/99$

27 613/99

29 431/900

31 3781/4950

33 $Q_3 = 260.40$
    $Q_{40} = 260.417$
    Approaches 260.417 mg

37 \$25,503

39 \$1081.11

Section 11.3

1 $y = 3x - 5$

3 $y = 2x^2 + 1$

5 $y = (x+4)^2$

7 $y = x^{3/2}$

9 $y = (2/3) \ln x, x > 0$

11 $(x-3)^2 + (y-2)^2 = 1$

13 Lines from $(0,1)$ to $(1,0)$ to $(0,-1)$ to $(-1,0)$ to $(0,1)$

15 Lines from $(-1,1)$ to $(1,1)$ to $(-1,-1)$ to $(1,-1)$ to $(-1,1)$

17 (a) $x = t, y = t^2$
    $x = t+1, y = (t+1)^2$

   (b) $x = t, y = (t+2)^2 + 1$
    $x = t+1, y = (t+3)^2 + 1$

19 Clockwise for all t

21 Counterclockwise: $t > 0$

23 (a) Right of $(2,4)$

   (b) $(-1,-3)$ to $(2,4)$

   (c) $t < -2/3$

25 (a) Line $y = x$

   (b) Circle, with starting point $(1,0)$ and period 2π

   (c) Ellipse, with starting point $(1,0)$ and period 2π

27 $x = t, y = -4t + 7$

35 (a) $x = t, y = -16t^2 + 48t + 6$

   (c) 6 feet

   (d) 3 seconds

   (e) 42 feet

Section 11.4

1 (a) Center $(2, -4)$, radius $\sqrt{20}$

   (b) Center $(-1, 2)$, radius $\sqrt{11}$

3 (a) Center $(-5, 2)$; Vertices $(-5 \pm \sqrt{6}, 2)$; Asymptotes $y = \pm(2/\sqrt{6})(x+5) + 2$

   (b) Center $(-1, -2)$; Vertices $(-1 \pm \sqrt{14}, -2)$; Asymptotes $y = \pm(x+1) - 2$

5 Ellipse, centered $(-1, 1)$ horizontal axis of length 8 vertical axis of length 4

7 Hyperbola, centered $(-1, -3)$ width of rectangle: 2 length: 6

9 $(x-2)^2 + (y-3)^2 = 36$

11 $\frac{(y-4)^2}{16} - \frac{(x+2)^2}{16} = 1$

13 $\frac{(x+4)^2}{4} + \frac{(y+2)^2}{16} = 1$

15 $x = 2 + 5\cos t, y = 1 + 5\sin t,$ $0 \le t \le 2\pi$

17 $(4 + 4\cos(t - \pi/2), 4 + 4\sin(t - \pi/2))$

19 $x = -3\cos t, y = -7\sin t,$ $0 \le t \le 2\pi$

21 Parabola:
    $y = (x-2)^2, 1 \le x \le 3$

23 Implicit: $xy = 1, x > 0$
    Explicit: $y = \frac{1}{x}, x > 0$
    Parametric: $x = t, y = \frac{1}{t}, t > 0$

25 Implicit:
    $x^2 - 2x + y^2 = 0, y < 0,$
    Explicit:
    $y = -\sqrt{-x^2 + 2x},$
    Parametric:
    $x = 1 + \cos t, y = \sin t,$
    with $\pi \le t \le 2\pi$

27 (a) $a = b = 0, k = 5$ or -5

   (b) $a = 0, b = 5, k = 5$ or -5

   (c) $a = 10, b = -10, k = \sqrt{200}$ or $-\sqrt{200}$

Section 11.5

1 $2e^{i\pi/2}$

3 $5e^{i4.069}$

5 $e^{i3\pi/2}$

7 $-3 - 4i$

9 $-5 + 12i$

11 $3 - 6i$

13 $\frac{\sqrt{3}}{2} + \frac{i}{2}$

15 $\sqrt{2} + i\sqrt{2}$

17 $\frac{\sqrt{3}}{2} + \frac{i}{2}$

19 $\sqrt[3]{2} \cdot \frac{\sqrt{3}}{2} + i\sqrt[3]{2} \cdot \frac{1}{2}$

21 $\frac{1}{\sqrt{2}} \cos(\frac{-\pi}{12}) + i\frac{1}{\sqrt{2}} \sin(\frac{-\pi}{12})$

23 $A_1 = 1 - i, A_2 = 1 + i$

25 (a) $z_1 z_2 = 6 - i2\sqrt{3}$
    $\frac{z_1}{z_2} = i\sqrt{3}$

   (b) $z_1 = 2\sqrt{3} e^{i7\pi/6},$
    $z_2 = 2 e^{i2\pi/3}$

27 True

29 False

31 True

Section 11.6

3 $\sinh x \to (e^x)/2$ as $x \to \infty$
   $\sinh x \to -(e^{-x})/2$ as $x \to -\infty$

5 $\cosh 2x = \cosh^2 x + \sinh^2 x$

9 $\sin(ix) = i \sinh x$

Chapter 11 Review

1 $\sum_{n=0}^{10}(100 - 10n)$

3 603, 59

5 Yes, $a = 1$, ratio $= 2z$.

7 $1/(1 - 2z), |z| < 1/2$

9 (a) $h_n = 10(3/4)^n$

   (b) $D_1 = 10$ feet
    $D_2 = h_0 + 2h_1 = 25$ feet
    $D_3 = h_0 + 2h_1 + 2h_2 = 36.25$ feet
    $D_4 = h_0 + 2h_1 + 2h_2 + 2h_3 \approx 44.69$ feet

   (c) $D_n = 10 + 60\left(1 - (3/4)^{n-1}\right)$

11 (a) \$1250

   (b) 12.50

13 $x = t, y = 5$

15 $(2\cos(t + \pi/2), 2\sin(t + \pi/2))$

17 Equation of curve is
    $x = 1 - 2y^2, -1 \le y \le 1$

19 (a) $(x, y) = (t, 1)$

   (b) $(x, y) = (t + \cos t, 1 - \sin t)$

21 $13e^{i - 1.176}$

23 $-125i$

25 $8i\sqrt[3]{2}$

Appendix A

1 64

2 25

3 121

4 10,000

5 1

6 -1

7 5

8 25

9 1,000

10 1

11 1

12 2

13 4

14 8

15 16

16 4

17 x^2

18 y^4

19 $w^4 z^2$

20   $x^{5/2}y^2$
21   $4x^{3/2}$
22   $7w^{9/2}$
23   $5x^{3/2}z^2$
24   r
25   $r^{3/2}$
26   r^2
27   $6t$
28   $8s^{7/2}$
29   $5\sqrt{2}x^2y^3$
30   $4\sqrt{3}u^5v^6y^{5/2}$
31   $4m^2$
32   $6s^{3/2}t^4v^4$
33   2
34   4
35   2
36   8
37   32
38   1024
39   1/3
40   1/9
41   $1/(3\sqrt{3})$
42   1/25
43   1/625
44   1/125
45   49
46   16
47   -1
48   -121
49   -18
50   1
51   2100
52   -5
53   4
54   -6
55   0.2
56   4
57   3
58   0.5
59   100,000
60   $0.16x^2y^4$
61   3^{x+1}
62   $8L$
63   $70w^{5/6}$
64   $16S^2xt^2$
65   e^x
66   $A^3/\left(3B^3\right)$
67   e^{kt+4}
68   $(M+2)^2$
69   $9x^5$
70   x^{3e}
71   e^{2y}/y^4
72   $4x^{(3\pi-1)}$
73   $64A$
74   $3a$
75   $4u^4v^2w^4$
76   $ab/(b+a)$
77   $25(2b+1)^{20}$
78   -8
79   -8
80   -125

81   Not a real number
82   20,736
83   1/512
84   -512
85   Not a real number
86   243
87   False
88   False
89   True
90   False
91   False
92   False
93   True
94   False
95   False
96   True

Appendix B

1   $x-7$
2   $x-25$
3   $3x+6$
4   $5x-15$
5   $6x-14$
6   $-4y-24$
7   $12x+12y$
8   $-35x+56y$
9   $2x^2+5x$
10   $6xz-27z^2$
11   $-50r^2-60r^2s$
12   $3x^2-2x-16$
13   $5xz-10z-3x+6$
14   x^2+4x+3
15   $x^2+4x-12$
16   $10x^2-17x+3$
17   $3x^2-2x-16$
18   $yz+3y+z+3$
19   $96wy+84y-40w-35$
20   $5xz-10z-3x+6$
21   $4x^2+11x-20$
22   $-200t$
23   $Pp^2-6Ppq+9Pq^2$
24   $A^4-2A^2B^2+B^4$
25   $4x^2-24x+43$
26   $-2x-2\sqrt{2x}-1$
27   2^u+u2^{2u}
28   KRr^2-Kr^3
29   $30+72/x+2x$
30   $(e^{2x}+2+e^{-2x})/4$

Appendix C

1   $2(x+3)$
2   $3(y+5)$
3   $5(z-6)$
4   $2(2t-3)$
5   $5(2w-5)$
6   $u(u-2)$
7   $u^3(3u-4)$
8   $3u^2(u^5+4)$
9   $6x(2x^2y^2-3)$
10   $7rs(2r^3s-3t)$
11   $(x+2)(x+1)$
12   Cannot be factored

13   $(x-2)(x-1)$
14   Cannot be factored
15   Cannot be factored
16   $(x-3)(x+1)$
17   Cannot be factored
18   $(x+3)(x-1)$
19   $(2x+1)(x+2)$
20   $(3x-4)(x+1)$
21   $2(x-3)(x-2)$
22   $(x+7)(x-4)$
23   $x(x-3)(x+1)$
24   $x(x+3)(x-1)$
25   $(x+1.4)(x-2.8)$
26   $(ax-b)(ax+b)$
27   $\pi r(r+2h)$
28   $(B-6)(B-4)$
29   $(x-c)^2$
30   Cannot be factored.
31   $(a-2)(a+2)(a^2+3)$
32   $(t-1)(t+7)$
33   $(hx-3)(x-4)$
34   $(r+2)(r-s)$
35   $(y-2x)(y-x)$
36   $xe^{-3x}(x+2)$
37   $e^{5t}(t+1)(t+2)$
38   $(s+2t+2p)(s+2t-2p)$
39   $P(1+r)^3$
40   $\sin x(x-1)$
41   $(\cos x-1)^2$
42   $(e^x+1)^2$

Appendix D

1   41/35
2   17/30
3   $(3-4x)/6x$
4   $69/7y$
5   $-2(1-2y)/yz$
6   $-2(z-4)/y$
7   $(2-3x)/x^2$
8   $(6y^2+7)/y^3$
9   15/7
10   1/18
11   $18/x^3$
12   $x/2$
13   $20/(x-1)$
14   $41/(2(x-1))$
15   $(4y^3z-3wx)/(x^2y^4)$
16   $7/(y-2)$
17   $(8(y+4))/(y-4)$
18   8
19   $x^3/2$
20   $3(4x+11)/((x+3)(x+2))$
21   $(-27x+44)/((x+1)(3x-4))$
22   $(-18x^2+18x+41)/((x-2)^2(x+1))$
23   $2(11x+27)/((x-3)^2(x+5)^2)$
24   $(x+20)/(x^2-16)$
25   $(x^2+1)/(x-1)$
26   $1/2r$
27   $\left((u+a)^2+u\right)/(u+a)$
28   $(x-1)/(\sqrt{x})^3 = x\sqrt{x}-\sqrt{x}/x^2$
29   $(1+e^x)/e^{2x}$

30 $(4x + 1)/(b - a)$
31 $(0.28 + 3M^3)/(4M)$

32 $(r_2r_3 + r_1r_3 + r_1r_2)/(r_1r_2r_3)$
33 8
34 $(2a + 3)/((a + 3)(a - 3))$
35 $x(x + 2)$
36 $1/(x + y)^2$
37 $1/2$
38 $(-2x - h)/\left(x^2(x + h)^2\right)$
39 $1/(a^2b^2)$
40 Cannot be simplified further
41 $-2x - h$
42 $(b - 1)/b^2$
43 $1 - (1/a)$
44 $1/(x - 1)$
45 $p^3/(p^2 + q^2)$
46 $x^2y/(2x + 1)$
47 $(1 - 2\ln x)/\left(3x^3\right)$
48 $(2x - 4x^4)/(x^3 + 1)^3$
49 $(-4x^2 + 2x + 1)/(x^4\sqrt{2x - 1})$
50 $13/x^2 + 1/(2x^3)$
51 $1/3 + 1/\sqrt{x}$
52 $(2/l^2) + (1/l^3) - 4/(3l^4)$
53 $7/(p^2 + 11) + p/(p^2 + 11)$
54 $1/6 - 1/(4x)$
55 $1/t^{5/2} + 1/t^{3/2}$
56 $1 - 7/(x + 5)$
57 $1 + 3/(q - 4)$
58 $1 + 1/R$
59 $1 + 2/(2u + 1)$
60 $1 + \sin x/\cos x$
61 $1 + 1/e^x$
62 False
63 True
64 False
65 False
66 True
67 True

Appendix E

1 $3x + (1/2)x^{-1} + x^2 + 1/5$
2 $180q^3 - 60q$
3 $y^2 - 6y^{-1} + 9y^{-4}$
4 $x^3 + 2x + x^{-1}$
5 $2P^3 + 3P^{1/2}$
6 $1/2 + 3t^{1/2} + (9/2)t$
7 $-3 - (1/6)x^2 + (1/2)x$
8 $N^{-2} - 2 + N^2$
9 $-12/7 + (3/7)x$
10 $(1/2)x^{7/2} + x^{1/2} + (1/2)x^{-1/2}$
11 $ax + b + cx^{-1}$
12 $1 + 2p^2 + p^4$
13 $12(3x + 1)^{-1/2}$
14 $1000(10 - s)^{1/3}$
15 $-0.7(x - 1)^4$
16 $(1/2)(x^2 + 1)^{-3}$
17 $24(6R + 2)^3$
18 $2(7x - \pi)^{1/2}$
19 $(1/2)^x$
20 $(1/2)^x$

21 $10{,}000(0.76)^t$
22 $e\left(e^2\right)^x$
23 $2(1/3)^x$
24 $(1/3)6^x$
25 4^t
26 $(1/e)e^x$
27 $-(5/3)^x$
28 $5e(e^x)$
29 $100(e^2)^t$
30 $A(e^k)^t$
31 $x^2 + (1/x^3)$
32 $5x^2 + x + 1$
33 $6y^3 - 15y$
34 $y^5 + 2y^4 + y^3$
35 $z^4 + 2z^2 + 1$
36 $z^2 - (2/z) + 6$
37 $(x + 4)^2 - 16$
38 $(y - 6)^2 - 36$
39 $(w + (7/2))^2 - (7/2)^2$
40 $2(r + 5)^2 - 50$
41 $(s + 3)^2 - 17$
42 $3(t + 4)^2 - 61$
43 $(x - 1)^2 - 4$
44 $(x - 3)^2 + 1$
45 $-(x - 3)^2 + 7$
46 $3(x - 2)^2 + 1$
47 $-6x/(x^2 + 7)^4$
48 $(-2^{x+1}\ln 2)/(1 + 3^x)^3$
49 $\pi\cos(\pi t)/\sin(\pi t)$
50 $-1/\sin^2 z$
51 $-\left(xe^{2x} + 2\right)/x^3e^x$
52 $(1 - \ln x)/x^2$
53 $\sqrt{5x}$
54 $1/\sqrt{3x - 2}$
55 $6y\sqrt[3]{4z - 5}$
56 $(3^5z^{5/3})/\sqrt{3w - 1}$
57 $x/\sqrt{x^2 + 16}$
58 $(x + 5)/\sqrt{x^2 + 10x + 1}$
59 $\cos(2x)/\sqrt{\sin(2x)}$
60 $2/\left(\sqrt[3]{x^2 - e^{3x}}\right)^2$

Appendix F

1 $x = 5$
2 $y = -6$
3 $z = (11/2)$
4 $x = 7$
5 $y = 26$
6 $w = -11$
7 $x = 9$
8 $y = 7$
9 $t = 45/13$
10 $x = 2$
11 $y = -(7/41)$
12 $x = -6$ or $x = -1$
13 $y = -1$ or $y = 6$
14 $w = (-5/2)$ or $w = 2$
15 $x = (-3 \pm \sqrt{249})/8$
16 $x = (7/16)$

17 $x = 7/4$
18 $y = 170$
19 $y = (46/5)$
20 $x = (37/2)$
21 $(18 \pm \sqrt{285})/3$
22 $t = 3 \pm 2\sqrt{3}$
23 $r = 10$
24 $l = A/w$
25 $r = (C/2\pi)$
26 $P = (I/rt)$
27 $F = (9/5)C + 32$
28 $k = (\ln 1.0573/t)$
29 $B = e^{0.079}$
30 $y = (-5x - 1)/(3x - 2)$
31 $t = (3C - 2B)/(A - 6B)$
32 $x = -a(b + 1)/(ad - c)$
33 $b = \sqrt[5]{C/A}$
34 $x = 3, x = -4$
35 $t = \ln\sqrt[k]{2P/Q}$
36 $B = -2$
37 $s = -0.115$
38 $y = -17/16$
39 $t = 10/7$
40 $x = 2, x = -4/3$
41 $p = 3, p = -3, p = -1/2$
42 $N = 3, N = 1$
43 $t = 0, t = \pm 8$
44 $x = 1 \pm \sqrt{2}$
45 $x = 4, x = -3/4$
46 $t = 3 \pm \sqrt{6}$
47 $y = -2 \pm \sqrt{6}$
48 $z = -7/2$
49 $x = \pm 1$
50 $L = \pm 1/2$
51 $q = \pm\sqrt{2}$
52 $r = \pm 5$
53 $x = -1/8$
54 $x = 0, x = 36$
55 $v = 700\pi$
56 $x = -4/3, x = 2$
57 $x = 0.6826$
58 $x = 1$
59 $t = \ln 2/\ln 0.97 \approx -22.76$
60 $t = \ln 8/2 \approx 1.04$
61 $x = 5$
62 $x = -\log 3.3 \approx -0.52$
63 $k = \ln(1/2)/1000 \approx -0.000693$
64 $x = \ln(0.5)/\ln(0.8) \approx 3.106$
65 $l = gT^2/4\pi^2$
66 $y' = 4/(y + 2x)$
67 $w = (2/k)(l - l_0)$
68 $y' = 2x/(x - y)$
69 $y = (c + d)/(b - a)$
70 $v = (3w - 2u - z)/(u + w - z)$
71 $r = (S + a)/(S - L)$
72 $a = 2(h - v_0t)/t^2$
73 $z = y - (NK)/(MA)$
74 $e = (Rf)/(b + d - R)$
75 $z = (y + wy - xy)/(y - 1)$
76 $s = (tw)/(2v - 5w)$
77 $x = 1/2, -1/4$

78    $x = 4m$

Appendix G

1    $x = 4,\ y = -1$
2    $x = 7,\ y = 4$
3    $x = 4,\ y = 3$
4    $x = (317/13),\ y = (62/13)$
5    $x = (3 \pm \sqrt{63})/2,$
     $y = (-3 \pm \sqrt{63})/2$
6    $x = -55,\ y = 39$
7    $x = 3$ and $y = -3$, or $x = -1$ and
     $y = -3$
8    $x = -3$ and $y = -5$, or $x = 1$ and
     $y = 3$
9    $x = 1/2$ and $y = 2$, or $x = -1/2$
     and $y = -2$
10    $x = 13.5;\ y = -12$
11    $x = 2.081,\ y = 8.013$
      $x = 4.504,\ y = 90.348$
12    $x = 1,\ y = a$
13    $(0,0)$ and $(3,9)$
14    $(3/2, 3/2)$
15    $(4,3),\ (-3,-4)$
16    $(2,4)$, or $(4,16),\ (-0.7667, 0.5878)$

Appendix H

1    $x \geq 7$
2    $x > 16$
3    $-5 < x < 5$
4    $x > 5$
5    $x \geq -4$
6    $-5 < t < 5$
7    $x \leq -4$ or $x \geq 4$
8   All real numbers
9    $x > 5$
10   All real numbers
11    $-8 \leq \theta \leq 8$
12   No solution
13    $x > 5$
14    $t < -3$
15    $z < -2$
16    $x < 0.001$

17    $-1 < y < 1$
18    $p \neq 5$
19    $k > 0$
20    $r \geq 0$
21    $t \geq 1995$
22    $x > 4$
23    $x > 2$
24    $x < -4$
25    $x > -(6/4)$
26    $x < 2$, or $x > 3$
27    $-1 < x < 8$
28    $x > 3$
29    $5 < x < (17/3)$
30    $x < -2$ or $x > 2$
31    $y < -2$ or $y > 6$
32    $-(2/3) < w < 2$
33    $-(1/2) < z < (15/2)$
34   All real numbers
35   No values
36   (a)   None
      (b) $x = 0, x = -2$
      (c) $x > 0, x < -2$
      (d) $-2 < x < 0$
37   (a)   None
      (b) $x = 0, x = -2$
      (c) $x > 0, x < -2$
      (d) $-2 < x < 0$
38   (a)   None
      (b)   None
      (c)   All real numbers
      (d)   None
39   (a)   None
      (b) $t = 2, t = 3$
      (c) $t < 2, t > 3$
      (d) $2 < t < 3$
40   (a) $x = 0$
      (b)   None
      (c) $x \neq 0$
      (d)   None
41   (a) $p = 0$
      (b)   None

      (c) $p < 0$
      (d) $p > 0$
42   (a)   None
      (b) $x = 0$
      (c) $x > 0$
      (d) $x < 0$
43   (a) $x \leq 0$
      (b) $x = 1$
      (c) $x > 1$
      (d) $0 < x < 1$
44   (a)   None
      (b) $t = 3$
      (c) $t > 3$
      (d) $t < 3$
45   (a) $x = 2$
      (b) $x = 1$
      (c) $x < 1$ or $x > 2$
      (d) $1 < x < 2$
46   (a)   None
      (b) $u = 1/\sqrt{3}, u = -1/\sqrt{3}$
      (c) $-1/\sqrt{3} < u < 1/\sqrt{3}$
      (d) $u < -1/\sqrt{3}, u > 1/\sqrt{3}$
47   (a) $x = 0, x = 1$
      (b) $x = 1/2$
      (c) $x < 1/2$ and $x \neq 0$
      (d) $x > 1/2$ and $x \neq 1$
48    $-2 < x < 2$
49    $1/2 \leq x \leq 1$
50    $1/2 \geq n > -21/2$
51    $l > 1/48$
52    $t \leq -1, t \geq 4$
53    $x < -7/3, x > 1$
54    $x \leq \dfrac{45}{2}$
55    $x < 0$ or $2 < x$
56    $r < 2, r > 3$
57    $x < -1, x > 0$
58    $x < -1, x > 0$
59    $-2 < x < 2$

NOTES